WARMAN'S
ANTIQUES
AND THEIR PRICES

19th Edition

---

*The Standard Price Reference for antiques
and collectibles, for collectors, dealers
and professionals in the trade.*

Edited by
Harry L. Rinker

**Completely illustrated
and authenticated**

**Warman Publishing Co., Inc.
Elkins Park, PA 19117**

ISBN: 0-911594-06-X
ISSN: 0196-2272
Library of Congress Catalog Card No. 82-643542
Printed in the United States of America

Additional copies of this book may be obtained from your bookstore or directly from the publisher, Warman Publishing Co., P.O. Box 26742, Dept. 19, Elkins Park, PA 19117. Enclose $10.95 plus $1.50 for postage and handling. Pennsylvania residents please add 66¢ state sales tax.

EDITORIAL STAFF, 19TH EDITION

John B. Darrow
50 Orchard Rd.
Akron, OH 44313
(216) 836-4458
Cameras

Robert Dellaposta
Candy Containers
Collectors of America
P. O. Box 184
Lucerne Mines, PA
15724
(412) 479-9692
Candy Containers

Lee and Rally Dennis
The Game Preserve
Spring Rd.
Peterborough, NH
03458
(603) 924-6710
Games

Craig Dinner
P. O. Box 455
Valley Stream, NY
11582
(516) 825-0145
Doorstops

Robert A. Doyle
East Coast Casino
Antiques
98 Main St.
Fishkill, NY 12524
(914) 896-9492
Razors

Caroline E. Edleman
653 S. Fifth Ave.
Royersford, PA 19468
(215) 948-9128
Nodders

Regis and Mary Ferson
122 Arden Rd.
Pittsburgh, PA 15216
(412) 563-1964
Milk Glass

Mildred Fishman
37 Canaan Close
New Haven, CT 06840
(203) 966-0748
*Goss and Crested
Wares*

Doug Flynn and Al
Bolton
Holloway House
P. O. Box 210
Lititz, PA 17543
*British Royalty
Commemoratives*

Ron Fox
Fox-Terry Steins, Inc.
416 Throop St.
N. Babylon, NY 11704
(516) 669-7232
Mettlach, Steins

Walter Glenn
Geode Ltd.
3393 Peachtree Rd.
Atlanta, GA 30326
(404) 261-9346
Frankart

Dan Golden
1030 Robin Hill Dr.
San Marcos, CA 92069
(619) 744-9393
Telephones

Ted Hake
Hake's Americana &
Collectibles
P. O. Box 1444
York, PA 17405
(717) 843-3731
*Disneyana, Political
Items*

David and Betty Hallam
P. O. Box 175
Monmouth, IL 61462
(309) 734-4933
Old Sleepy Eye

Bruce and Lorry Hanes
51 Washington St.
Winchester, MA 01890
(617) 729-3223
Food Molds

John High
415 E. 52nd St.
New York, NY 10022
(212) 758-1692
Stevensgraphs

Joanne Hull
1376 Nevada
Huron, SD 57350
(605) 352-1685
Hull Pottery

David and Sue Irons
Irons Antiques
R. D. #4, Box 101
Northampton, PA
18067
(215) 262-9335
Irons

Kip and Linda Jones
America The Beautiful
P. O. Box 28
Ridgefield, CT 06877
(203) 438-5113
Stoneware

Judy Knauer
1224 Spring Valley
Lane
West Chester, PA
19380
(215) 431-3477
Toothpicks

Glenn M. Kramer
20E Taylor Lane
Fishkill, NY 12524
(914) 896-6390
Musical Instruments

Gail Krause
The Krause's
994 Jefferson Ave.
Washington, PA 15301
(412) 228-5033
Duncan Miller

Herb and Joyce
Krueger
Mostly Majolica
P. O. Box 225
Newport, MI 48166
(313) 242-0939
Majolica

Ron Lieberman
The Family Album
R. D. #1
Glen Rock, PA 17327
(717) 235-2134
*Almanacs; Books,
Modern American
First Editions*

Elyce Litts
P. O. Box 394
Morris Plains, NJ
07950
(201) 361-4087
Geisha Girl

Pamela A. Luttig
Blue Boar Ltd.
215 West Main St.
Grand Ledge, MI 48837
(517) 627-5291
Tiles

Clarence and Betty
Maier
The Burmese Cruet
P. O. Box 432
Montgomeryville, PA
18936
(215) 855-5388
*Burmese Glass, Crown
Milano, Royal Flemish*

Donal Markey
179 Palmer Hill Rd.
Stamford, CT 06902
Banks, Still Metal

James S. Maxwell, Jr.
Box 5039
Neffsville, PA 17601
(717) 569-7717 or 569-
0719
Banks, Mechanical

Dori Miles
Box 20
Crown Point, NY
12928
(518) 597-3432
Pattern Glass

Lois Misiewicz
2062 Trevino St.
Oceanside, CA 92056
(619) 757-2062
Willow Ware

Bea Morgan
Lakeview Terr.
Sandy Hook, CT 06482
(203) 426-5425
*Salt and Pepper
Shakers*

Scott H. Nelson
270 Spanglers Mill Rd.
New Cumberland, PA
17070
(717) 774-6019
Van Briggle

Joan Oates
5912 Kingsfield Dr.
W. Bloomfield, MI
48033
(313) 661-2335
Phoenix Bird Pattern

John D. Querry
R. D. 2
Martinsburg, PA 16662
(814) 793-3185
Gaudy Dutch

Richard and Joan
Randles
From The Cutter's
Wheel
P. O. Box 285
Webster, NY 14580
(716) 671-3760
Cut Glass

Benjamin Rapaport
5101 Willowmeade Dr.
Fairfax, VA 22030
(703) 830-8584
Pipes

Roy C. Repsher
256 N. Chestnut St.
Bath, PA 18014
(215) 837-0138
Pocket Knives

Ferill J. Rice
302 Pheasant Run
Kaukauna, WI 54130
(414) 766-9176
Fenton

Charles H. Rosaco
P. O. Box 1270
Pensacola, FL 32596
(904) 432-8100
Corkscrews

Ralph U. Saarinen
705 Grove St.
Worcester, MA 01605
   Mt. Washington,
   Smith Bros.

Paul Sebastian
Sebastian Exchange
P. O. Box 4905
Lancaster, PA 17604
(717) 569-2631
   Sebastians

Allan B. and Helen B.
Smith
The Country House
15 Thomas Ave.
Topsham, ME 04086
(207) 729-8941
   Salts

Carolyn Sunstein
P. O. Box 26734
Elkins Park, PA 19117
(215) 884-6171
   Miniatures

Mark Supnick
8524 NW 2nd St.
Coral Springs, FL
33065
(305) 755-3449
   Shawnee Pottery

George Theofiles
Miscellaneous Man
Box 1776
New Freedom, PA
17349
(717) 235-4766
   Posters

Margaret L. Tyrrell
117 North 40th St.
Allentown, PA 18104
(215) 395-9364
   Children's Books

Ben Weber
1160 East 8th St.
Brooklyn, NY 11230
(212) 338-7904
   Scientific Instruments

Bill Wheeler
The Oarhouse
P. O. Box 3434
Clearwater Beach, FL
33515
(813) 441-8288
   Nautical, Scrimshaw,
   Whaling

Kathy Wojciechowski
R. D. #2, Box 81
Peotone, IL 60468
(312) 258-6105
   Nippon

INTRODUCTION

"The Tradition Continues"

Warman's always has been the leader in the antiques price guide field. This 19th Edition heralds the evolution of our publication into a newer, more modern form of price guide. No longer must the collector and dealer settle for a mere price list. The publications of the 1980's will guide the collector and dealer not only to prices, but also to histories, reference books, periodicals, collectors' clubs, and museums. It also will provide useful buying and collecting hints.

The new format of our 19th Edition is in direct response to an extensive survey of our users. We thank all who participated.

ORGANIZATION

Listings: Objects are listed alphabetically by category, beginning with ABC Plates and ending with Zsolnay Pottery. If you have trouble identifying the category in which your object falls, use the extensive index in the back of the book. It is designed to guide you to the proper category.

In past editions, Pattern Glass was listed as a separate section. It is now found alphabetically under the "P's." In addition to relocating Pattern Glass, we have combined our three previous sections [clear, colored, and opalescent] into one alphabetical listing of patterns. The new format gives a clearer and more concise listing of pattern glass and will be much easier to use. More than thirty pattern glass dealers have helped us in redesigning this section.

We have attempted to make the listings descriptive enough so that specific objects can be identified. We also have placed emphasis on those items which are actively being sold in the marketplace. Nevertheless, some harder-to-find objects are included in order to demonstrate the market spread.

Each year as the market changes, we carefully consider which categories to include, which to drop, and which to add. **Warman's** is a direct response to the developing trends in the marketplace. To further help collectors and dealers, **Warman** has published *Warman's Americana & Collectibles.* It is an excellent source for information and prices on collectibles and items of nostalgia.

History: Every collector should know something about the history of his object. We have presented a capsule background for each category. In many cases the background contains collecting hints or tips to spot reproductions.

References: Special references are listed for each category to help collectors learn more about their objects. Included are author, title, publisher [if published by a small firm or individual, we have indicated "privately printed"], and date of publication or most recent edition.

Finding these books may present a problem. The antiques and collectibles field is blessed with a dedicated core of book dealers who stock these specialized publications. You may find them at flea markets, antiques shows, and advertised in leading publications in the field. Many dealers publish annual or semi-annual catalogs. Ask to be put on their mailing lists. Books go out-of-print quickly, yet many books printed over twenty-five years ago remain the standard work in a field. Used book dealers can often turn up many of these valuable reference materials.

Periodicals: Generally, the newsletter or bulletin of a collectors' club focuses on the specific publication needs within a category. However, there are other publications, not associated with collectors' clubs, of which the collector and dealer should be aware. These are covered under specific categories.

In addition, there are general interest newspapers and magazines which deserve to be brought to our user's attention. These are:

Antique Monthly, P.O. Drawer 2, Tuscaloosa, Al 35402

Antique Showcase, Amis Gibbs Publications, Ltd., Canfield, Ontario, Canada, N0A 1C0

Antique Trader Weekly, P. O. Box 1050, Dubuque, IA 52001

Antique Week - Tri-State Trader, P. O. Box 90, Knightstown, IN 46148

Antiques (The Magazine Antiques), 551 Fifth Avenue, New York, NY 10017

Collector News, Box 156, Grundy Center, IA 50638

Hobbies, 1006 S. Michigan Ave., Chicago, IL 60605

Maine Antique Digest, P. O. Box 358, Waldoboro, ME 04572

Ohio Antique Review, P. O. Box 538, Worthington, OH 43085

Southern Antiques & Southeast Trader, P. O. Box 1550, Lake City, FL 32055

West Coast Peddler, P. O. Box 5134, Whittier, CA 90607

It is impossible to list all the national and regional publications in the antiques and collectibles field. The above is merely a sampling. A check with your local library will bring many other publications to your attention.

Collectors' Clubs: The large number of collectors' clubs adds vitality to the antiques and collectibles fields. Their publications and conventions produce knowledge which often cannot be found anywhere else. Many of these clubs are short-lived; others are so strong that they have regional and local chapters.

Museums: The best way to study a specific field is to see as many documented examples as possible. For this reason, we have listed museums where significant collections in that category are on display. Special attention must be directed to the complex of museums which make up the Smithsonian Institution in Washington, D.C.

Reproductions: Reproductions are a major concern to all collectors and dealers. Most reproductions are unmarked; the newness of their appearance is often the best clue to uncovering them. Specific objects known to be reproduced are marked within the listings with an asterisk (*).

Index: A great deal of effort has been expended to make our index useful. Always try to find the most specific reference. For example, if you have a piece of china, look first for the maker's name and second for the type. The key is to ask the right questions of yourself.

Photographs: You may encounter a piece you cannot identify well enough to use the index. Consult the photographs and marks. If you own the last several editions of **Warman's,** you have assembled a valuable photographic reference to the antiques and collectibles field.

PRICE NOTES

In assigning prices we assume the object is in very good condition. If otherwise, we note this in our description. It would be ideal to suggest that mint, or unused, examples of all objects do exist. The reality is that objects from the past were used, whether they be glass, china, dolls, or toys. Because of this, some normal wear must be expected. In fact, if an object such as furniture does not show wear, its origins may be more suspect than if it does show wear.

Whenever possible, we have tried to provide a broad listing of prices within a category so you have a "feel" for the market. We emphasize the middle range of prices within a category, while also listing some objects of high and low value to show the market spread.

We do not use ranges because they tend to confuse rather than help the collector and dealer. How do you determine if your object is at the high or low end of the range? There is a high degree of flexibility in pricing in the antiques field. If you want to set ranges, add or subtract 10% from our prices.

One of the hardest variants with which to deal is the regional fluctuations of prices. Victorian furniture brings widely differing prices in New York, Chicago, New Orleans, or San Francisco. We have tried to strike a balance. Know your region and subject before investing heavily. If the best prices for cameo glass are in Montreal or Toronto, then be prepared to go there if you want to save money or add choice pieces to your collection. Research and patience are key factors to building a collection of merit.

Another factor that affects prices is a sale by a leading dealer or private collector. We have tempered both dealer and auction house figures.

PRICE RESEARCH

Everyone asks—where do we get our prices? They come from many sources.

First, we rely on auctions. Auction houses and auctioneers do not always command the highest prices. If they did, why do so many dealers buy from them? The key to understanding auction prices is to know when a price is high or low in the range. We think we do this and do it well.

Second, we work closely with dealers. We screen our contacts to make certain they have a full knowledge of the market. Dealers make their living from selling antiques; they cannot afford to have a price guide which is not in touch with the market.

Over thirty antiques magazines, newspapers, and journals come into our office regularly. They are excellent barometers of what is moving and what is not. We don't hesitate to call an advertiser and ask if their listed merchandise sold.

When the editorial staff is doing field work, we identify ourselves. Our conversations with dealers and collectors around the country have enhanced this book. Teams from **Warman's** are in the field at antiques shows, flea markets, and auctions recording prices and taking photographs.

Collectors work closely with us. They are specialists whose devotion to research and accurate information is inspiring. Generally, they are not dealers. Whenever we have asked them for help, they have responded willingly and admirably.

BOARD OF ADVISORS

Our Board of Advisors are specialists, both dealers and collectors, who feel a commitment to accurate information. You'll find their names listed in the front of the book. Several have authored a major reference work on their subject.

Members of the Board of Advisors file lists of prices in their categories for which they are responsible. They help select and often supply the photographs used. If you wish to buy or sell an object in their field of expertise, drop them a note. If time or interest permits, they will respond.

BUYER'S GUIDE, NOT SELLER'S GUIDE

Warman's is designed to be a buyer's guide to what you would have to pay to purchase an object on the open market from a dealer or collector. **It is not a seller's guide to prices.** People frequently make this mistake. In doing so, they deceive themselves. If you have an object listed in this book and wish to sell it to a dealer, you should expect to receive approximately fifty percent (50%) of the listed value. If the object is not anticipated to be resold quickly, expect to receive even less.

A private collector may pay more, perhaps seventy to eighty percent of our list price. Your object will have to be something needed for his or her collection. If you have an extremely rare object or an object of exceptionally high value, these guidelines do not apply.

Examine your piece as objectively as possible. As an antiques appraiser, I spend a great deal of time telling people their treasures are not "gold" at all, but items readily available in the marketplace.

In respect to buying and selling, a simple philosophy is that a good purchase occurs when the buyer and seller are happy with the price. Don't look back. Hindsight has little value in the antiques field. Given time, things tend to balance out.

COMMENTS INVITED

Warman's Antiques and Their Prices continues to be the leader in the antiques and collectibles price guide field because we listen to our readers. Readers are encouraged to send their comments and suggestions to our Editorial Office, P. O. Box 265, Zionsville, PA 18092.

ACKNOWLEDGEMENTS

Doris Ford and Ellen Schroy committed themselves totally to making certain that our new format maintained and surpassed the high standards of the past.

They met deadlines cheerfully and did much to make working on this book a most pleasant and rewarding experience.

Connie A. Moore, my wife, continued to provide support at all levels. She has assisted on field trips, and organized and reviewed copy.

V.I.P. Color Labs, Bethlehem, PA, has continued to be the source of the high level of quality for the photographs in this book.

Finally, I cannot emphasize enough the cooperation I received from everyone in the field during my travels this past year. I hope that they can see the results of their suggestions and time in this book. They have contributed so much.

Editorial Office
Warman Publishing Co., Inc.
P. O. Box 265
Zionsville, PA 18092
February, 1985

HARRY L. RINKER
Editor-in-Chief

STATE OF THE MARKET

Recovery was the key word for the 1983 market. A feeling of optimism was being expressed at all levels of the antiques and collectibles field. In 1984 that momentum slowed considerably, especially in the middle and low end of the market. Dealers complained about the lack of sales in the last three months of 1984. Caution now is the watchword. 1985 promises to be a pivotal year and potentially has the ability to set the trend for prices in the last half of the 1980's.

High quality items in all categories of antiques and collectibles have continued their upward trend. The setting of record prices was not restricted to the large New York auction houses, but worked its way down to the regional houses and in a few instances to country auctions. Sotheby's realized $308,000 for a card table attributed to Samuel McIntire and $33,000 for a Chinese Export, 16″, oval platter in the Fitzhugh pattern with the Order of Cincinnati insignia. A needlework picture of a shepherdess scene, Boston School, circa 1750, brought $69,300 at Robert W. Skinner Galleries. A Lancaster County (PA) tall case clock with sulphur inlay sold for over $45,000 at a Pennsylvania country auction.

The broadening of price ranges within each category of antiques and collectibles is leading to confusion among collectors and dealers in respect to pricing an object. If a category ranges from $50 to $75,000 for a piece, what constitutes a $100, $500, $2,500, $10,000, $20,000, or $50,000 example? The current situation is that within many categories, the bulk of the objects fall in the lower third of the price spread with a few quality objects occupying the top price levels. The middle is not yet clearly established, primarily because spending $25,000 for a middle level object is something most collectors cannot yet accept. The problem becomes more acute when the range goes to $300,000 plus, as it has in several furniture categories.

As these ranges spread, what happens to the beginning collector? It now requires a capitalization of $10,000 plus to enter the top end of the market in many categories. The beginning collector is being forced to turn more and more to the collectibles field or to out-of-fashion china, glass, and furniture in order to find something within his budget. The result is that the antiques and collectibles field is moving at a number of complex levels. Understanding the trends is no longer as simple as it once was.

One obvious trend in 1984 was the return of the monied collector to the blue chip sector of the market. Early American furniture, oil paintings, historical Staffordshire, early American glass, Chinese Export porcelains, silver, and autographs were highly favored.

It is almost as though we are returning full cycle to the collecting interests of the 1920's and 1930's. Is this the result of the conservative mood which currently grips the country? Are there Republican and Democrat antiques and collectibles styles?

One difference from the earlier period is the entrance into the blue chip sector of a number of "prestige" collectibles. Tin toys, mechanical banks, and dolls now are found in the "very best" collections.

A dangerous trend noted in 1984 was the return of the speculator to the marketplace. Perhaps the new-found buoyancy of the market, the publicity surrounding so many record prices, and the general economic recovery indicated to the speculators that antiques and collectibles again have become an acceptable inflation hedge. These speculators are advised to remember the shake-out of the late 1970's.

Two major collecting areas demonstrated that they have entered a period of long-term price stability. The first is American folk art, especially the 20th century variety. The first signs were noticed as the American Bicentennial cooled. The crass exploitation of modern folk artists by a few select authors and dealers has caused a saturation of the market. Within the next few years many of the pieces bought in the late 1970's and early 1980's will be entering the resale market for the first time. It will be a key test of the present stability.

The American country look is waning. We can thank the interior decorators for causing both the rise and end of this trend. It is time to move on to something else.

Merchandise was selling in all categories, although slower in some areas than in others. Those categories which showed unusual strength or weakness at the end of 1984 were:

Gaining	*Declining*
Architectural Elements	Autumn Leaf
Christmas Items	Bohemian Glass
Depression Glass	Country Antiques
Games	Lustre Wares
Kitchen Collectibles	Pennsylvania
Rhinestone Jewelry	German Items
Tools	Norman Rockwell
Victorian Furniture	Stock and Bond
	Certificates
	Tall Case Clocks

An important market trend is the collecting of material associated with the 1950's and 1960's. Within the past three years, several key museum exhibitions have concentrated on the work of furniture and industrial designers of the mid-twentieth century. If we now accept material from these decades as collectible and perhaps the finest designs as antiques, what has become of the standard definition of antiques as objects dating from 1900 or earlier?

Within the next few years the market will be examining again the furniture and other products of the 1900 to 1940 period. What was formerly considered "second-hand" material may be viewed in a new context. A quality, factory made, Governor Winthrop, cherry secretary from the 1920's now can command $750 to $1,250, hardly the price of second-hand merchandise.

Each year we point out the problems of reproductions, the vast majority of which are unmarked. Resist them, fight them, and complain about them to any dealer, show promoter, or government official who will listen. Question everything you see! If you don't, you are bound to get stung.

There is no substitute for buying quality. Push yourself to acquire that elusive piece you want. Better to own one $250 object than five $50 objects. Most of all, buy your antiques because you want to live with them. Over an extended period of time, you will gain both from the pleasure they bring as well as a rise in their value.

AUCTION HOUSES

The following auction houses cooperated with Warman Publishing Co. by providing catalogues of their auctions and price lists. In addition, Bourne, Butterfield's, Oliver, Rinsland, Roan and Theriault's provided photographs for our use. This effort is most appreciated.

W. Graham Arader III
1000 Boxwood Court
King of Prussia, PA
19406
(215) 825-6570

Ark Antiques
Box 3133
New Haven, CT 06515
(203) 387-3754

Robert F. Batchelder
1 West Butler Avenue
Ambler, PA 19002
(215) 643-1430

Richard A. Bourne,
Co., Inc.
Corporation St. (P. O.
Box 141)
Hyannis, MA 02647
(617) 775-0797

Butterfield's
1244 Sutter Street
San Francisco, CA
94109
(415) 673-1362

Christie's
502 Park Avenue
New York, NY 10022
(212) 546-1000

Christie's East
219 E. 67th Street
New York, NY 10021
(212) 546-1000

Marvin Cohen Auctions
Box 425, Routes 20 &
22
New Lebanon, NY
12125
(518) 794-7477

Robert A. Doyle
98 Main Street
Fishkill, NY 12524
(914) 896-9492

William Doyle
Galleries, Inc.
175 E. 87th Street
New York, NY 10028
(212) 427-2730

Early Auction Co.
123 Main Street
Milford, OH 45150
(513) 831-4833

Ron Fox
F. T. S. Inc.
416 Throop Street
N. Babylon, NY 11704
(516) 669-7232

Garth's Auction, Inc.
2690 Stratford Road
P. O. Box 369
Delaware, OH 43015
(614) 362-4771 or 369-
5085

Hake's Americana and
Collectibles
P. O. Box 1444
York, PA 17405
(717) 848-1333

Harris Auction
Galleries, Inc.
873-875 N. Howard
Street
Baltimore, MD 21201
(301) 728-7040

Richard Opfer
Auctioneering, Inc.
1919 Green Spring
Drive
Timonium, MD 21093
(301) 252-5035

Phillips
876 Madison Avenue
New York, NY 10021
(212) 570-4830

Lloyd Ralston Toys
447 Stratfield Road
Fairfield, CT 06432
(203) 366-3399 or 335-
4054

Rinsland's Americana
Mail Auction
P. O. Box 265
Zionsville, PA 18092
(215) 966-3939

Roan Bros. Auction
Gallery
R.D. 3, Box 118
Cogan Station, PA
17728
(717) 494-0170

Robert W. Skinner Inc.
Bolton Gallery
Route 117
Bolton, MA 01740
(617) 779-5528

Sotheby's
1334 York Avenue
New York, NY 10021
(212) 472-8424

Swann Galleries, Inc.
104 E. 25th Street
New York, NY 10010
(212) 254-4710

Theriault's
P. O. Box 151
Annapolis, MD 21404
(301) 269-0680

Waverlys Auctions
7649 Old Georgetown
Road
Bethesda, MD 20814
(301) 951-0919

Wolf's Auction Gallery
13015 Larchmere Blvd.
Shaker Heights, OH
44120
(216) 231-3888

Woody Auction
Douglass, KS 67039
(316) 746-2694

ABC PLATES

History: The majority of early ABC plates were manufactured in England, imported into the United States, and achieved their greatest popularity from 1780 to 1860. Since a formal education was limited in the early 19th century, the ABC plate was a method of educating the poor for a few pennies.

ABC plates are found in glass, pewter, porcelain, pottery, and tin. Porcelain plates range in diameter from 4⅜ to slightly over 9½ inches. The rim usually contains the alphabet and/or numbers with animals, great men, maxims, or nursery rhymes in the center.

Reference: Mildred L. and Joseph P. Chalala, *A Collector's Guide to ABC Plates, Mugs and Things,* Pridemark Press, 1980.

Tin, Liberty, 5½", $70.00.

GLASS

Bulldog, aqua.	55.00
Child's head, 6", frosted	45.00
Clock, ABC's and numbers, yellow. . . .	25.00
Dog, standing, 6", clear.	30.00
Elephant, 6¼", clear.	30.00
Garfield, frosted portrait, c1885	40.00
Hen and chicks, 6", clear	25.00
Mary Had A Little Lamb, clear.	45.00
Milk glass, 7", beaded edge, plain center	35.00
New Pony	62.00
Old Independence Hall, 7", clear	65.00
Rover, 6".	35.00
Stork, carnival	68.00
Village Blacksmith	60.00

PORCELAIN OR POTTERY

April, boy in center, 7", red, green and brown.	45.00
Behold Him Rising From the Grave, 5½", imp Meakin.	75.00
F, letter, 7"	45.00
Franklin Maxim, 6¾", black transfer, For Age and Want Save While You May-No Morning Sun Lasts All Day	65.00
Goat boy, horn, dog, polychrome, Staffordshire	75.00
Harry Baiting His Line For to Fish He Doth Incline, 5½", imp Elsmore	58.00
Harvest Home, 5½", polychrome, Meakin.	58.00
Hunter with dogs, 1860.	38.00
Little Jack Horner, 7⁵⁄₁₆", Tunstall England, 1887	45.00
Old Mother Hubbard, 7"	48.00
Old Woman, Old Woman, D. M. McNicol	38.00
Ploughing, 4¼", c1850	58.00
Rabbits, four, 6"	35.00
Red Riding Hood Starting, 7¼", c1890.	38.00
Robinson Crusoe & Family at Dinner, 6", green transfer.	60.00
Robinson Crusoe Finding Footprints. . .	50.00
Soldier on horse attacking foot soldier, 7½", polychrome.	55.00
The Baker, 7¼", black transfer	55.00
The Candle Fish, 7½", 2 Indians in canoe fishing with rake, Staffordshire	55.00
The Drive, couple in buggy, c1840. . . .	40.00
Thoroughbreds, sheep in pasture by woods, 6¼", brown, gold letter border	40.00
Three Blind Mice/See How They Run, 7¾", blue transfer	52.00
Who Killed Cock Robin, 7¾"	38.00

TIN

Boy and girl rolling hoops, 3"	50.00
Girl in swing, 3½".	40.00
Hey, Diddle, Diddle, 9"	42.00
Jumbo, 6¼".	65.00
Kittens, 2 playing with yarn, 6"	32.00
Liberty, 5½".	50.00
Tom Thumb, 3"	30.00
Victoria and Albert, 6¼"	50.00
Washington, 6".	95.00
Who Killed Cock Robin, 8", c1880. . . .	75.00

ADAMS ROSE

History: Adams Rose, made c1820–40 by Adams and Son in the Staffordshire district of England, is decorated with brilliant red roses and green leaves on a white ground.

G. Jones and Son, England, made a variant known as "Late Adams Rose." The colors are not as brilliant and the ground is a "dirty" white. It commands less than the price of the early pattern.

Bowls
6″, early		300.00
6″, late		100.00

Creamers
Early		325.00
Late		100.00

Cup and Saucer, saucer 6″, $75.00.

Cup and Saucer, scalloped edge, handleless, early	225.00
Pitcher, 7″, late	125.00

Plates
7¼″, early	145.00
7½″, late	35.00
8½″, early	185.00
8½″, late	45.00
9″, early	210.00
9½″, late	68.00
10½″, soup, early	225.00
10½″, soup, late	125.00
Platter, 15″, oval, early	300.00
Sugar, cov, late	150.00

Teapots
Early	600.00
Late	210.00
Vegetable Dish, cov, 12⅝″, c1850	500.00
Wash Bowl and Pitcher, early	1,000.00

ADVERTISING

History: Before the days of mass media, advertisers relied on colorful product labels and advertising giveaways to promote their products. Containers were made to appeal to the buyer by the use of stylish lithographs and bright colors. Many of the illustrations used the product in the advertisement so that even an illiterate buyer could identify a product.

Advertisements were put on almost every household object imaginable and were constant reminders to use the product or visit a certain establishment.

References: Jim Cope, *Old Advertising*, Great American Publishing Co., 1980; Ray Klug *Antique Advertising Encyclopedia*, L-W Promotions, 1978.

Collectors' Clubs: The Ephermera Society of America, 124 Elm Street, Bennington, VT 05021. Dues: $20.00; National Association of Paper and Advertising Collectibles, P. O. Box 471, Columbia, PA 17512. Dues: $10.00; Tin Container Collectors Association, 11650 Riverside Drive, North Hollywood, CA 91602. Dues: $20.00.

Additional Listings: See *Warman's Americana & Collectibles* for more examples.

Ashtray, Jewel Stoves & Ranges, cast iron, horseshoe shape	15.00
Beater Jar, Farmer's Elevator, Peterson, IA, stoneware, brown stripes	35.00

Blotters
Columbian Stoves and Ranges, multicolored celluloid button, 3 x 7½″	3.00
Old Reliable Peanut Butter, country black saying "Some Butter" as ram sneaks up behind	10.00
Booklet, Piso Patent Medicine, sailing ships and steamers, 9 color litho	35.00
Bookmark, Hoskin Social and Business Stationery, Philadelphia, celluloid, peep coming out of eggshell at top, 1½ x 5″	15.00

Dispenser, 6 x 5¾ x 13½″, tin, litho, A.M.D. Co., $395.00.

Bottle Opener, For Home Brew Use, B-Wise Malt, designed like touring car, brass, 3″ 10.00

Box, Fairy Soap, Fairbanks, wooden, Christmas scene of girl on lid, multi-colored label, 1898, 16 x 16 x 9″ ... 125.00

Boxing Gloves, Esso, Tony The Tiger . . 10.00

Buttons (Pinbacks)

Allentown Duck Farm, C. W. B. Gernerd Prop., white duck on black ground, 1¼″, c1901 .... 20.00

Artic Rainbow Ice Cream Cones, cello, multicolored, ⅞″, c1910 .... 10.00

Fleischmann's Yeast, In Storm, In Sunshine, Rain Or Sleet, You See Our Wagons On The Street, multi-colored, 1¾″ 65.00

Gold Dust Washing Powder, multi-colored, c1896. .... 40.00

Cabinet, Putnam Dyes, wood and tin . . 175.00

Calendar, F. D. Stauffer Cigar Box Factory, Yorkana, PA, cardboard, full color illus of woman surrounded by flowers and trees, 8 x 12″ 30.00

Change Receiver, Baby Ruth, tin and glass 85.00

Charms

Nipper, diecut, celluloid, c1930 ..... 5.00

Zimmerman Mfg Co., Auburn, IN, 1″ diecut brass. 50.00

Cigar Box, John P. Dunn's Paris Kid Glove Cigar, wood, brass hinges, hook, 3 x 5 x 10″, c1900 .... 25.00

Clickers

Endicott-Johnson Shoes, Shoes For The Entire Family, olive letters on orange ground. 10.00

Mrs. Schlorer's French Dressing, tin, multicolored litho 20.00

Clip, Anheuser Busch, brass clip on leather strap, c1900 .... 25.00

Clock, Golden Girl Cola, bottle of pop and girl sitting in a coffee cup, "Refreshing As A Cup of Coffee". 75.00

Cracker Box, Robinson Bro's Bakery, wooden, paper label with birds feeding on branches, 23½ x 14 x 13″ 50.00

Cuff Links, Lucky Strike, miniature cigarette packs, c1930. .... 35.00

Dice Game, Lewis 66 Rye, 5 dice under glass, mirror on reverse 20.00

Display Figures

Dentyne, lady with tassel, tin 25.00

Heinz Aristocrat Tomato Man, composition, colorful 1939 World's Fair Heinz exhibit brochure in hand ... 40.00

Philip Morris Johnny, wooden, holding cigarettes in hand 75.00

Display Stands

Baby Ruth 1¢ Candy, cheerleaders, 1936. .... 30.00

Everready Flashlight Batteries and Mazda Lamps 100.00

German's Sweet Choc. Walter Baker Co., 1906 .... 15.00

Teaberry Gum, milk glass globe 30.00

Door Push, Vicks Vapor Rub, porcelain 65.00

Door Push, 3½ x 6¾″, tin, litho, red, white, and blue, $50.00.

Fans

Drink Moxie, celluloid, white, slogan cut out on each section, white ribbon, c1900 .... 75.00

Victrola, cardboard, 8″ d, black, white, red, and brown, wooden handle, one side shows woman holding record. 30.00

Hat, Lebels Dairy, beenie style 15.00

Jar, glass, Listerated Pepsin Gum, emb 125.00

Lamp, Budweiser, hanging, revolving, Clydesdales on sides. 600.00

Letter Opener, Phillips Milk of Magnesia, magnifying glass on top, metal 20.00

Lighter, Winston Cigarettes, red, white and gold, c1960 .... 5.00

Match Holders

Dorkash Stove Factory, Scranton, Pa., wall type, black, brown, and gold, 3½ x 5″. 20.00

Dr. Pepper, green, 10-2-4 logo 40.00

Mephisto Cigars, D. Hirsch & Co., New York, brass plated copper, hinged lid, depicting winged devil standing atop world, striker on side, c1900 . 50.00

Tadcaster Ale, Worcester, Mass., multicolored, celluloid 50.00

Mirrors, hand held

A. B. White, Humbaldt, Iowa, woman in car 15.00

Emerson-Brantingham Implement Co., Rockford, IL, brass, name surrounds scroll initials "EBI Co", deeply emb, 3″ d, 6″ l 65.00

Merode Knit Underwear, woman
dressing **20.00**

Mugs

Drink Hires, It Is Pure, stoneware . . . **45.00**

Golden Knight Shaving Soap, glass,
emb **10.00**

Oats Box, Mother's Crushed Oats, The
Quaker Oats Co., mother feeding
child, litho label on cardboard. **25.00**

Paper Clip, Parisian Novelty Co., 22nd &
La Salle St., Chicago, 1¾" celluloid
button on horizontal metal clip,
1930 . . . . **30.00**

Paperweights

Deal Saw Mills Company, Tuscaloosa,
Ala., Yellow Pine Lumber, black,
white, and red, 2½ x 4", glass . . . **15.00**

The Wolf Co., Chambersburg, PA,
shows roller machines on ¾" cel-
luloid disc, metal rim **20.00**

Pencil Clip, Rub No More, black and
white, celluloid, depicts mother elephant giving baby a shower, c1900. . **20.00**

Pin, Harley Davidson, plastic cycle
shape, gold with yellow wheels, name
on gas tank, c1940 . . . . **15.00**

Pin Holder, Worcester Brand Salt, oval,
cardboard, black and white **5.00**

Pocket Mirrors

Friedman's Shoes **40.00**

Red Cross Stoves **25.00**

Schaefer's Pianos, oval **35.00**

Poster, John Deere, Model D Tractor, full
color, 1931 . . . . **165.00**

Puzzles

McKesson Drugs, "Our Gang", jigsaw,
c1932 . . . . **60.00**

Westinghouse Electric, wooden
blocks, MIB, 1926 . . . . **15.00**

Rolling Pins

Jos. Blink Gen Merchandise, Rhodes,
IA, stoneware **145.00**

Kelvinator, white china. **60.00**

Sharpeners

Hypodermic Needle, Everhart Physi-
cians-Surgeons-Hospital Supplies,
Atlanta, GA, red, white, and blue
celluloid on one side, sharpener on
other, c1930 . . . . **75.00**

Knife, The Sterling Grinding Wheel
Co., black, white, and blue, celluloid
pin, sharpener on reverse. **15.00**

Shot Glass, Jack Daniels, emb **15.00**

Sidewalk Marker, Enjoy Grapette, Walk
Safely, 4" solid brass, 2" pin in center
back. **10.00**

Signs

Bichhoff Furniture, tin, shows 5 pcs of
Victorian furniture, c1880 . . . . **100.00**

Budweiser, Custer's Last Fight, 1952 **125.00**

Crescent Drink, emb tin, pretty lady
holding bottle, c1920 . . . . **85.00**

Dr. Pepper, tin, 11 x 30" **85.00**

Sign, 22⅛ x 28⅛", tin, litho, Charles W.
Shoreh Co., $1,200.00.

Doctor Radcliffe's Great Remedy, tin,
bottle shape, c1895 . . . . **85.00**

Early Times Whiskey, plaster, shows
distillery. **400.00**

Emmoline Skin Food, emb tin, shows
jar, c1905 . . . . **115.00**

Evinrude Outboard Motors, tin, 2 men
with fishing poles in boat riding into
sunset. **175.00**

Fleischmann's Yeast, emb tin, shows
package, 1934. . . . . **85.00**

Froelich's Sausage & Hams, tin, full
color, table laden with meats **145.00**

Globe Weinicke Bookcases, tin, picture of man and woman filling
bookcase **325.00**

Grapette, countertop **25.00**

Green River Whiskey, tin **125.00**

Hires, cardboard, Soda Jerk, 1915 . . **125.00**

Hoagland Jewelry & Optician, Shel-
don, IL, cardboard, apple shape
with lady on front. **65.00**

Moxie, tin, horse and rider in Rolls-
Royce rolling down highway in front
of billboard **475.00**

Odo Ro No, cardboard, bottle
shaped **45.00**

Seal of North Carolina Tobacco, cardboard, pictures man and woman,
1900 . . . . **100.00**

Thomas Wilson Cigars, litho tin by Se-
tenne & Green, 3 men, box of ci-
gars, matches, oak frame, c1900 . **325.00**

Walk Over Shoes, litho tin, pretty lady
stepping over highbutton shoes,
wood frame. **200.00**

Whitemores Shoe Polishes, tin,
mother polishing daughter's shoes,
c1920 . . . . **135.00**

Soda Glass, Moxie	20.00
Spoon, Horn & Hardart Automat	10.00

Stickpins
Atkins Saws, saw shape, brass	15.00
Niagara Buffalo Wheel Co., scrolling letter N, brass	45.00
Shoot Winchester, shell shape, brass, red letters	75.00
Stud, Bear In Mind Our Trademark—Pettijohn's Breakfast Food, diecut bear shape, brass, c1900	25.00

Syrup Dispensers
Wards Orange Crush	275.00
Welch-Ade, milk glass, 1917	110.00

Tape Measures
Dixie Tailoring Co., Made To Measure Clothes, red, white, and blue celluloid, photo of Statue of Liberty	35.00
Frigidaire, brown, yellow	15.00
J. R. Clausen & Son, Sole Selling Agents For Schuylkill Valley Clay Mfg Co., 2000 Market St., Philadelphia, black and white celluloid, 1¾", c1900	25.00
North American Life and Casualty Co., For Confident Living, gold and green tape, picture of family on one side	10.00
Tape Moistener, Baby Ruth, porcelain, 2 pc	40.00

Thermometers
Camel's Cigarettes, raised back	40.00
Dad's Root Beer	45.00
Doctor Scholl's, porcelain, hand pointing to foot, "Let Us Take Care of Your Foot Troubles", 1916	125.00
St. Paul Milk Co.—Baby's Guardian, celluloid, beige, black and red letters on white, color scene of pilgrim couple at top, Pat 1923 by Parisian Novelty Co., Chicago, 2 x 6"	35.00
Stetheson Union Suits, porcelain, 1 man in long johns, another holding up shirt, 1916	245.00
Throat Atomizer, Rexall Drugs "Defender" knight on horseback emb on glass, rubber bulb	15.00

Tins
Baking Powder, Buttermilk and Soda Baking Powder, girl with Jersey cow, paper label	25.00

Candy
Lummis Krisp Krunch	20.00
Mary Had A Little Lamb	35.00
Whitman's Salmagundi, litho tin, multicolored, Art Nouveau design, 3 x 4 x 7½"	20.00

Coffee
Riechelieu Coffee	30.00
Vetran Coffee	25.00
Cookies, Golden Bear	30.00
Peanut Butter, Sweetheart Pure Peanut Butter	40.00

Peanuts
Pansies	95.00
St. Laurent Peanuts	25.00

Talcum
Cloverine	150.00
Oakley's Corylopis	60.00
Teriff's	250.00
Tire Talc, Oneida, picture of family in Model T, early dome top	35.00

Tobacco
Blue Boar	45.00
Brown Beauty	45.00
Camel	40.00
Curve Cut	15.00
Golden Sceptre, pocket	150.00
Good Cheer	70.00
Lafayette	30.00
Monopol	40.00
Postmaster	30.00
Raptco	25.00
Rice's Agent	45.00
Satisfied Customer, roly poly	450.00
Sterling	75.00
Sure Shot	120.00
Train Master	45.00
Vanco	40.00
War Eagle	50.00
White Ash	25.00
World's Navy	35.00
Yankee Boy, pocket, upright, blonde baseball player	175.00
Tobacco Pouch, soft, Dixie Queen	100.00
Top, Derby Petroleum, celluloid, red, white, and blue, 1930	10.00

Tray, 16½ x 13½", tin, litho, Standard Adv. Co., 1909, $1,200.00.

Trays
Carnation Milk — Contented Cows, litho tin, oval, 6 black and white cows in green meadow, snow capped mountain in background, "Compliments of Pacific Coast Condensed Milk Co., General Offices, Seattle," 5½"	65.00

Chero Cola, tin, shows bottle, "There's None So Good 5¢", 1905. . . . . **165.00**

Fan Tan Gum, tin **75.00**

Fraternal Life & Accident Insurance, Home of the Brotherhood of American Yoeman, Des Moines, dark blue edge, full color center, 3½ x 5". **45.00**

Strohs Beer, Charles Shonk litho, Chicago. **85.00**

Watch Fobs

American Bottlers of Carbonated Beverages, diecut silvered brass with triangle in blue. **35.00**

Bull Durham 5¢ Cigar—Not Made By The Trust—A Bully Good Smoke—Hettermann Brothers Co., Louisville, KY, silvered brass **75.00**

Flood & Conklin Co., Varnish Makers, Newark, NJ, can shaped. **50.00**

O'Halloran & Jacobs Slate, Pittsburgh, silvered brass, raised image of slate worker's tools **85.00**

Wet Paint Sign, Dutch Boy Paints, Dutch Boy giving warning with raised hand, cardboard, c1940 . . . . **10.00**

ADVERTISING TRADE CARDS

History: Advertising trade cards are small, thin cardboard cards made to advertise the merits of a product and usually bear the name and address of a merchant.

With the invention of lithography, colorful trade cards became a popular advertising media in the late 19th and early 20th century. They were made especially to appeal to children, Young and old alike collected and treasured them in albums and scrapbooks. Very few are dated; 1880 to 1893 were the prime years for trade cards; 1810 to 1850 cards can be found, but rarely. By 1900 trade cards were rapidly lossing their popularity. By 1910 they had all but vanished.

References: Kit Barry, *The Advertising Trade Card*, privately printed, 1981; John and Margaret Kaduck, *Advertising Trade Cards*, privately printed.

Additional Listings: See *Warman's Americana & Collectibles* for more examples.

CANDY & GUM

Chocolat L'Aiglon, Reine Astrid, Nov. 1905, shows Princess of Denmark . . **2.50**

Kis-Me-Gum Co., little tailor sewing, cat beside him, "As with my shears, I cut my fabric stout, so Kis-Me Gum cuts all her rivals out". **4.00**

CLOTHING

Black Cat Hosiery, diecut of black cat, 3 x 6". **10.00**

Furniture, Mexican Hammock, 5⅜ x 3⅜", $5.00.

M. Hopkins & Co., Dry Goods, Cloaks, Suits and Notions, Utica, NY, 5 small blacks having their picture taken by another black **5.00**

Nicoll The Tailor, 617 Pennsylvania Ave., Washington, Jack and Jill falling down the hill **3.00**

Reed's Fine Boot & Shoe Store, "Handmade work a Specialty", bird, colorful flowers in corner **5.00**

COFFEE

Lion Coffee Co., scene of pioneers, children in covered wagon, woman cooking, cattle, reverse "The Woolson Spice Co. Midsummer Greeting". . . . **5.00**

McLaughlin's XXXX Coffee, picture of young girl in picture hat, pink band, flower, dress, holding yellow bird in one hand, white, gray cat in other hand, copyrighted 1891 . . . . **15.00**

Sarica Coffee, picture of pretty girl in waitress costume, "I drink Sarica Coffee, Thank You" **4.00**

FARM MACHINERY

Eclipse Halter, ad for Montrose, PA, dealer in harnesses, 1884 Pat, 3 x 5" **5.00**

Gehho Ball and Plow Co, Canton, OH, "The Princess Plow—Queen of the Turf and Pride of the Farm". **8.00**

FOOD

Allen's Root Beer Extract, 5 x 3½" . . . **4.00**

Bovine Beef Extract **12.00**

Drink Geyser Table Water, "Returning Home in the Evening", picture of man and lady in riding habits on horseback, artist sgd Harry Payne, reverse advertisement for Geyser water, bottled at geysers in California **15.00**

E. W. Gillett M'fg, Chicago, Magic Yeast Cakes, diecut in shape of sailboat, 2 boys on boat, green sea, flowers . . . **10.00**

Great Atlantic & Pacific Tea Co., two children dressed like court jestors, one pouring tea into oversized cup, the other smoking cigar **5.00**

Unrivaled Baking Powder, children playing 3 x 5″ **2.50**

W. K. Kellogg, two children, one sad, other happy **10.00**

MEDICINE

American Star, "Soft capsules, castor oil and other nauseous medicines taken without taste or smell", silhouette of 4 boys with soldier hats, sword, flag, small dog, garden background **10.00**

Burdock Blood Bitters, cat giving a bill to another cat **10.00**

Dalley's Magical Pain Extractor, "The Great Family Ointment," picture of lady in riding habit riding horse side saddle, male rider in background, hunting dog running **5.00**

Maltese, nude cherub in wheat field holding large bottle of product **8.00**

Lydia E. Pinkham's Vegetable Compound, winter scene, 3 x 5″ **3.00**

Quaker Bitters, portrait of Grover Cleveland **12.00**

Uncle Sam's Nerve and Bone Liniment, two farmers talking **4.00**

Medicine, Hires Cough Cure, 3 x 5″, 8.00.

MISCELLANEOUS

Collinder Billiard Tables, diecut in shape of easel **10.00**

Indian Queen Perfume, Indian maiden with quiver and bow gathering nector from flowers, Philadelphia store address and program on back for Philadelphia bicentennial events, 1882, 3 x 4½″ **15.00**

Light Running Jackson Wagon, balloon ascension by Prof. Hogan, his airship lifting Jackson wagon in 1884 . . . . . **20.00**

New York Life Insurance Co., celluloid, 1931 calendar on reverse **10.00**

Spencer Mfg Co., Rev. Turtle expressing joy over discovery of celluloid tortoise shell eyeglass frames **15.00**

SOAPS AND CLEANERS

Banner Soap, flag of Egypt, one of a series **5.00**

Bell Soap, white buffalo pulling children on soap box, card 6 of series **5.00**

California Soap Plant, black boy stealing watermelons "How can I leave thee?" **8.00**

Gillett's 100% Lye, birds, 3 x 5″ **3.00**

Swift's Washing Powder, dwarfs doing their wash and dishes **12.00**

THREAD AND SEWING

Brainerd and Armstrong Silk Thread . . . **8.00**

Clark's O.N.T. Spool Cotton, figural, girl in pinafore surrounded by spools of thread **5.00**

Davis Vertical Feed Sewing Machine . . **5.00**

TRANSPORTATION

E. J. Pedder, Carriage Propietor, Lynton, card adv. train excursions, photograph of Lynmouth **15.00**

United States Mail Steamers, "*Arizona*—Fastest Steamer Afloat," 3 x 5″ **45.00**

AGATA GLASS

History: Agata glass was invented in 1887 by Joseph Locke of the New England Glass Company, Cambridge, Massachusetts.

Agata glass was produced by using a piece of peachblow glass, coating it with metallic stain, spattering the surface with alcohol, and firing. The result was a high gloss, mottled appearance of oil droplets floating on a watery surface. Shading usually ranged from opaque pink to dark rose. A few pieces have been found in a satin finish.

Bowl, 5″ d, crimped **900.00**

Creamer and Sugar, 2½″ h, 5″ d, bulbous **1,300.00**

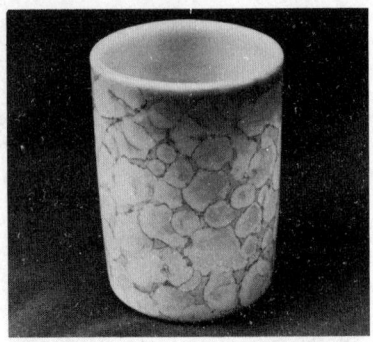

Whiskey Taster, 2⅝″, $575.00.

Finger Bowl, 2⅝″ h, 5¼″ d, crushed
  raspberry to creamy pink shading, all
  over gold oily mottling, bits of blue
  mottling **1,000.00**
Mustard, metal top, deep raspberry
  color, mottling, gold tracery at base . **1,300.00**
Pitcher, milk, 6″, sq mouth **1,200.00**
Punch Cup. **350.00**
Toothpick, 2½″ h, pinched in tricorn
  top. **600.00**
Tumbler. **600.00**
Vases
  4½″, sq shape, pinched sides, ruffled
    four scallope rim **550.00**
  8″, lily. **1,150.00**
  8¼″, stick. **375.00**

ALMANACS

History: Collectible 18th and 19th century American alamanacs contain astronomical data carefully calculated to the area of publication, weather forecasts and agricultural information, and political, social, and moral commentary. They are a combination of the most "down to earth" aspects of rural life and the mystical, showing the dualistic concerns of early Americans.

As important documents of early printing in America, their value increases when they contain woodcuts such as the astrological man, ships, exotic animals (elephants, tigers, etc.), and genre scenes. The Pennsylvania almanacs were among the first to label Washington as "Father" of his country and hence, are eagerly sought after by collectors.

By the mid-19th century alamancs became a compendia of useful information - stage coach routes, court schedules, business listings, humourous stories and jokes, health information, and feature articles. Their emphasis became strongly rural-agricultural. Businesses also began to issue almanacs to help advertise and promote their products.

Condition is a prime consideration in acquiring and pricing almanacs. All pages should be present, including covers if applicable. Frayed edges and soil detract somewhat from the price; but, almanacs were heavily used, so mint examples are rare. Almanacs with woodcuts are most desirable; but, cuts should be clean and clearly defined. Many 20th century almanacs are printed on poor quality paper and become brittle with age.

References: Milton Drake, *Almanacs Of The U. S.*, 2 vols., 1962; George Lyman Kittredge, *The Old Farmer And His Almanac*, Cambridge, 1920; Robb Sagendorph, *American and Her Almanacs, 1639–1970*, Dublin, NH, 1970.

Note: Mint (really crisp) examples may realize 50% more than the prices listed below.

1714, Angelus Brittanicus: An Ephemeris, London, printed by E. Janeway
  for the Company of Stationers, 48
  pgs **65.00**
1750, Nathanial Ames, An Astronomical
  Diary: Or, Almanack . . . Calculated For
  The   Meridian   of   Boston
  . . . , Boston, printed by J. Draper, 16
  pgs **60.00**
1760, Roger Sherman's An Astronomical Diary, Or, An Almanack . . . Calculated For The Meridian of Boston .
  . . , Boston, printed for Henchman, Edwards, Dennis, Winter, Leverett and
  Webb, 18 pgs. **50.00**
1775, Nathanial Ames. An Astronomical
  Diary; Or, An Almanack . . . Calculated

1888, The Diamond Dye Almanac and Household Guide, published by Wells, Richardson & Co, Burlington, VT, 84 pgs, $25.00.

For The Meridian Of Boston . . . , Boston, printed at Draper's, Edes & Gills, and T. & J. Fleets, 20 pgs **70.00**

1775, John Anderson's, Almanack And Ephemeris . . . Calculated For Newport, Rhode Island . . . , Newport, printed by Solomon Southwick, 28 pgs **80.00**

1779, Bickerstaff's, New England Almanack . . . Referred To The Horizon of 41 Degrees, 35 Minutes, North Latitude and A Meridian of 4 Hours, 30 Minutes West . . . , Norwich, printed by J. Trumbull, 22 pgs **65.00**

1780, Nathanial Low, An Astronomical Diary: Or Almanack . . . Calculated For The Meridian of Boston . . . , Boston, printed by John Gill and T. and J. Fleet, 20 pgs . . . . ● **45.00**

1781, George's Almanack . . . Calculated For The Meridian of Boston . . . , Newbury-Port, printed by Johy Mycall, woodcut of elephant on title page with an interesting four-page related account, 18 pgs **80.00**

1782, Thomas's Massachusetts, Connecticut, Rhode Island, New Hampshire, and Vermont Almanack for . . . 1782, woodcut of astrological man, 36 pgs **45.00**

1783, Benjamin West, The North-American Calendar: Or The Rhode-Island Almanack . . . Calculated For the Meridian of Providence . . . , Providence, printed by Bennett Wheeler, reference to Treaty of Alliance with France, 24 pgs **55.00**

1783, Nathaniel Low, An Astronomical Diary: Or Almanack . . . Calculated For The Meridian of Boston . . . Boston, printed by T. and J. Fleet and Gill and Willis, 22 pgs **45.00**

1788, Nathaniel Low, An Astronomical Diary: Or Almanack . . . Calculated For The Meridian of Boston . . . Boston, printed by T. & J. Fleet, 20 pgs **40.00**

1796, Poor Will's Almanack for . . . 1796, Philadelphia, printed and sold by Joseph Crukshank, woodcut of the astrological man, 40 pgs **35.00**

1805, Webster's Calendar of the Albany Almanack for . . . 1805, Albany, printed by Charles R. & George Webster, illus of astrological woman, 36 pgs **35.00**

1807, Daniel Sewall, An Astronomical Diary of Almanac for . . . 1807, Portsmouth, New Hampshire, 24 pgs **20.00**

1807, The Farmer's Calendar or Utica Almanack for the Western District of the State of New York for . . . 1807, Utica, Andrew Beers, printed by Asahel Seward **20.00**

1808, Robert B. Thomas, The Farmer's

Almanack for . . . 1808, Boston, printed for John West, 42 pgs **22.00**

1810, Mathew Carey, Franklin Almanac, For The Year 1810 . . . Calculated by Abraham Shoemaker . . . Philadelphia, printed for Mathew Carey by Lydia R. Bailey, 56 pgs **20.00**

1818, Robert B. Thomas, The Farmer's Almanack **20.00**

1821, Issac Bickerstaff, Rhode Island Almanack, printed at Providence, Rhode Island **20.00**

1822, David Young, Poor Richard's Almanac . . . New York, printed by S. Marks for Daniel D. Smith, 36 pgs . . **20.00**

1824, Bailey, Washington Almanac . . . Calculated By Joshua Sharp, Philadelphia, printed by Lydia R. Bailey, 34 pgs **25.00**

1847, American Anti-Slavery Almanac for 1847, American Anti-Slavery Society, 48 pgs, no page numbers variation **25.00**

1857, The Lady's Almanac, Boston, hardbound **20.00**

1875, The Boston Almanac, hardbound with business directory **40.00**

1888, Diamond Dye Almanac and Household Guide, Wells, Richardson & Co. Burlington, Vermont, 84 pgs . . **25.00**

1900, Barkber's Illus. Farmer's Guide & Household Cook Book with cartoons **25.00**

1909, International Harvester Almanac **25.00**

1918, Dr. Miles New Weather Almanac **9.00**

1926, Dr. Kilmer & Co., Binghamton, New York, Swamp-Root, 32 pgs **8.00**

1927, Rawleigh's Good Health Guide Almanac Cook Book **10.00**

1938, Kellog's Housewife's Almanac . . **6.50**

AMBERINA GLASS

History: Joseph Locke developed Amberina glass in 1883 for the New England Glass Works. "Amberina," a trade name, describes a transparent glass which shades from deep ruby to amber color. It was made by adding powdered gold to the ingredients for an amber glass batch. A portion of the glass was reheated later to produce the shading effect. Usually it was the bottom which was reheated to form the deep red; however, reverse examples have been found.

Most early Amberina is of flint quality glass, blown or pattern molded. Patterns include diamond quilted, daisy and button, Venetian diamond, diamond and star, and thumbprint.

In addition to the New England Glass Works, the Mt. Washington Glass Company of New Bedford, Massachusetts, copied the glass in the 1880s and sold it at first under the Amberina trade name and later as "Rose Amber." It is difficult to distinguish pieces from these two New England factories. Boston and Sandwich Glass Works never produced the glass.

Amberina glass also was made in the 1890s by several Midwest factories, among which was Hobbs, Brockunier & Co. Trade names included "Ruby Amber Ware" and "Watermelon." The Midwest glass shaded from cranberry to amber and resulted from a thin flashing of cranberry applied to the reheated portion. This created a sharp demarkation between the two colors. This less expensive version caused the death knell for the New England variety.

In 1884 Edward D. Libbey was assigned the trade name "Amberina" by the New England Glass Works. Production occured in 1900, but ceased shortly thereafter. In the 1920s Edward Libbey renewed production at his Toledo, Ohio, plant for a short period. The glass was of high quality. Amberina from this era is marked "Libbey" in script on the pontil.

Reproductions abound.

Bowl, 3¾" d, DQ, polished pontil, $225.00.

NEW ENGLAND

Bowls
3¾", handkerchief top	375.00
9", sq, berry, Daisy & Button	230.00
10", canoe shape, Daisy & Button . .	550.00
10", 5¾ h, IVT, 3 applied amber feet, tricorn top, fancy amber applied edging, heavy gold flowers and leaves decor	400.00

Bride's Basket, ribbed, ruffled, sp holder 650.00
Butter Tub, cov, Daisy & Button. 475.00
Carafe, 8¼", DQ, Sandwich. 175.00
Castor Set, 6 bottles, silver holder, bottles etched, one stopper missing . . . 925.00
Champagne, 4", hollow stem, New England Glass Co. 200.00
Cologne Bottle, 6", Daisy & Button, orig stopper. 2,200.00

Compote, 4⅛", fuchsia shading, sgd Libbey 575.00
Creamer, 5½", IVT 275.00
Cruets
6", bulbous, 3 petal top, DQ, amber applied handle, amber cut faceted stopper 295.00
6¾", Reverse Thumbprint, applied amber handle, orig faceted stopper 245.00
Finger Bowls
Bowl, IVT 225.00
Bowl, underplate, fuchsia to red, sgd Libbey, 1917 . . . . 550.00
Ice Cream Dish, sq, Daisy & Button . . . 100.00
Jug, 5¾", IVT, applied amber reeded handle, Mt. Washington 350.00
Lamp, hanging, DQ, brass font 1,500.00
Lemonade, DQ. 275.00
Pickle Castor, hobnail, ornate SP frame, marked Acme Silverplate Co., Boston. 450.00
Pitchers
7", 4⅛" d, tankard, round mouth, DQ, applied amber handle. 325.00
7½", IVT, applied amber reeded handle, decor 425.00
8¼", DQ. 375.00
Punch Cup, IVT 110.00
Ramekin, bowl, 2¾" d, 2¼" h, underplate, 4¼" d, slightly ribbed 195.00
Spooners
Daisy & Button 325.00
DQ, square top 300.00
Sugar, cov, 4¾", IVT 325.00
Toothpick, 2", DQ, tricorn fold over top 225.00
Tumblers
DQ. 100.00
Ribbed 70.00
Vases
7", lily, ribbed, sgd Libbey 250.00
11¾", 5⅛" d, amber applied ruffled top, blue, pink, white and green enameled paisley designs, florals, applied amber feet, pr 475.00
Whiskey, 2⅝", DQ. 145.00
Wine, IVT 125.00

MID-WESTERN

Bowl, 4½" d, DQ, 3 applied feet 110.00
Celery, Inverted Coinspot 60.00
Decanter, 11" h, 4" d, orig amber bubble stopper. 145.00
Finger Bowl, Coin Spot 120.00
Juice, 4¼", flared top 55.00
Pickle Castor, IVT, 2⅞" d 150.00
Pitchers
7½", 5" d, bulbous, IVT, amber applied handle. 195.00
8½", melon ribbed, plain amber applied strap handle 190.00
8½", swirl, amber handle 180.00

Salt Shaker, reverse, Inverted Baby
  Thumbprint, pewter top **165.00**
Spooner, reverse, DQ **100.00**
Sugar, 4½″ h, 5¼″ d, 2 handle, Thumb-
  print, ribbed, quatrefoil top **160.00**
Tumbler, swirled, bulbous base, heavy
  enamel floral decor **80.00**
Vases
  8⅛″, fan top, amber edging, swirl, ap-
    plied amber wishbone feet **135.00**
  9⅞″, Jack-in-the-pulpit, heavy gold
    flowers, blue enamel decor **225.00**
  10⅛″, swirl, amber rigaree applied
    around top edge **175.00**
Water Bottle, Inverted Coin Spot **70.00**

AMBERINA GLASS—PLATED

History: The New England Glass Company,
Cambridge, Massachusetts, first made Plated Amberina in 1886; Edward Libbey patented the process for the company in 1889.

Plated Amberina was made by taking a gather
of chartreuse or cream opalescent glass, dipping
it in Amberina and working the two, often utilizing
a mold. The finished product had a deep amber to
deep ruby red shading, a fiery opalescent lining,
and often vertical ribbing for enhancement. Designs
ranged from simple forms to complex pieces with
collars, feet, gilding, and etching.

A cased Wheeling glass of similar appearance
has an opaque white lining, but is not opalescent
and the body is not ribbed.

Bowl, 5½″ h, 3⅜″ d, fluted edge **3,500.00**
Celery **2,600.00**
Creamer, squatty **3,000.00**
Cruet, faceted amber stopper **3,100.00**

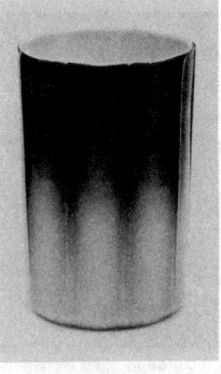

Tumbler, 3¾″ h, $2,250.00.

Pitcher, milk, amber applied handle, orig
  Aurora label, New England Glass Co.,
  patent dates on label. **7,000.00**
Salt Shaker, orig top **1,000.00**
Syrup, orig sp lid and underplate **6,000.00**
Toothpick. **3,500.00**
Vases
  3¼″, bulbous **2,300.00**
  7″, tricorn lily, translucent saffron
    foot. **2,750.00**

AMPHORA

History: The Amphora Porcelain Works was one
of several pottery companies located in the Teplitz-
Turn region of Bohemia in the late 19th and early
20th centuries. It is best known for art pottery, especially Art Deco pieces.

Several markings were used, including the name
and location of the pottery and the Imperial mark
which included a crown. Prior to WWI Bohemia was
part of the Austro-Hungarian Empire so the word
"Austria" may appear as part of the mark; after
WWI the word "Czechoslovakia" may be part of
the mark.

Additional Listings: Teplitz.

Baskets
  7½″ h, double handles, flower puffs
    dec, sgd **50.00**
  12″ h, bearded man, imp "Imperial
    Amphora" **165.00**
Bowl, 8″ d, beige, raised apples, vines,
  and leaves, ftd **150.00**
Bust, woman, 16″ h, low cut dress, ruf-
  fled neckline, mkd "Turn Teplitz-Boh-
  emia and Amphora, Austria, RS&K" . **275.00**
Centerpiece, 13½″ d, molded water lil-
  ies, applied blackberries. **145.00**
Compote, double handle, applied blackberries, Imperial mark **200.00**
Ewers
  9″ h, hp mosaic panels on sides, mkd
    "Amphora-Teplitz" **70.00**
  15″, pear shape, root applied handle,
    green ground, purple and cream
    flowers **100.00**
  17″, gold and pink dragonfly in relief,
    matte green ground, mkd "Turn Te-
    plitz-Bohemia and Amphora, Aus-
    tria, RS&K" **120.00**
Pitcher, 10½″ h, cat, whimsical, red rib-
  bon, mkd "Amphora, Austria". **150.00**
Vases
  6″ h, floral design, artist sgd **200.00**

Vase, 11½", stylized floral dec, polychrome, sgd Amphora, Austria, $200.00.

6", green and gold scenic design, mkd "Turn-Teplitz, Amphora, Austria" . . **150.00**

6¾", handled, mottled beige satin ground, cobalt blue top and base, emb enamel parrots, multicolored, artist sgd, Campina Art Deco, mkd Amphora. **165.00**

7½", bulbous, pinched, blown out cobalt floral top, mottled green and brown, large red and green leaves, flowing leaf handle, imp crown mark. **155.00**

7¾", cobalt, irid greens, spider webs, jewels, butterflies, and fishnet **250.00**

9", green, irid reds, ducks in flight, tall leafy grass, moon **220.00**

9⅛", matte gray ground, large stylized raised flowers, blue, rose, white, and gold, small band of flowers at base, cobalt blue glossy top band, mkd **175.00**

11½", green, irid, leaf design, gold buds at neck **235.00**

13¼", two children on side pulling on doll in middle, Imperial mark **425.00**

16½", cream emb basketweave ground, deep green top and bottom borders, applied blackberries, leaves on front, rope handle, sgd . **450.00**

ART DECO

History: The Art Deco period was named for an exhibition, "L'Exposition Internationale des Arts Decoratifs," held in Paris in 1927. It is a later period than Art Nouveau; but sometimes the two periods cross since they were closely related in time.

The designs of Art Deco are angular and of simple lines. This was the period of skyscrapers, movie idols, and the cubists works of Picasso and Legras. It was used for every conceivable object being produced in the 1920s and 1930s, including ceramics, furniture, glass, and metals, not only in Europe, but in America as well.

Reference: Victor Arwas, *Glass: Art Nouveau To Art Deco*, Rizzoli, 1977; Bryan Catley, *Art Deco And Other Figures*, Antique Collectors' Club.

Additional Listings: Furniture and Jewelry. Also check glass, pottery, and metal categories.

Ashtray, 5½", sq. bronze, ftd base, kneeling Egyptian woman. **100.00**

Billards Table, 48 x 96 x 30", wooden, inlaid pewter, metal tag imp "Proust/ Les Billards De Haute Precision/120 rue de Tolbaic/Paris" **1,650.00**

Bookends, 5¾" l, cold painted bronze, ivory, and marble, 2 seated medival court figures, sgd engraved Roland Paris **1,400.00**

Candlesticks, pr, 4" h, SS, sockets on reeded band, slightly domed foot, Presner **200.00**

Cigar Box, 9⅜", rect, incised with parallel and perpendicular lines enclosing monogram "MEG", lined in cedar with removable dividers, c1927 . . . . **675.00**

Cigarette Box, 7¼ x 3½ x 3", painted brass, red ground, black highlights, ashtray inserts in interior, $65.00.

Cigarette Box, 6 x 3½", Coquille d'oeuf and black lacquer **120.00**

Cigarette Case, 4⅛" l, Coquille d'oeuf and enamel, diagonal geometric band and brick red enamel. **200.00**

Cigarette Case and matching lighter, rect, silver gilt enamel zigzags enclosing eggshell triangles, parallelogram cartouche, monogrammed, mkd Dunhill, c1928. . . . . **500.00**

Cigarette Lighter, chrome and enamel, Ronson **50.00**

Cocktail Service, 11" h shaker, 8 glasses, ashtray, black bakelite handles **400.00**

Cocktail Shaker, cov, amethyst glass, chrome lid **50.00**

Coffee Service, 10" h coffee pot, creamer, cov sugar, oval 17¼" l tray, Georg Jensen style, ivory handles set at right angles, ivory ball finials, mkd Woodside Sterling Co. NY, c1915. . . . . . . **1,600.00**

Cup and Saucer, demitasse, blue, pink, green, and lavender design, mkd Clarice Cliff Fantasque Bizarre **45.00**

Decanters
9½", figural, ceramic, monkey, light green and blue glazes, Germany . . **45.00**
11½", sq, clear glass body engraved with figure of Diana with arms upraised holding a bow, animals at her feet, inscribed Orefors, numbered, c1940. . . . . **300.00**

Door, 32 x 71", etched glass, stylized foliage design, metal frame **300.00**

Dresser Box, cov, 9½ x 13⅝", porcelain, lady, full figure, blue short skirt, blue and yellow clown hat. **200.00**

Dresser Sets
5 pc, SS, pyramid pattern, mirror, 2 brushes, nail file, shoe horn, designed by Harold Nielsen, #134 and #134A, Georg Jensen, Copenhagen, c1935 . . . . **950.00**
16 pc, traveling, SS, 2 brushes, shoe horn, pr fingernail scissors, pr toenail scissors, nail file, button hook, pr powder canisters, shaving brush cov, pr vials, soap box, safety razor with 2 blades by Gillette, each engraved "CS" in oval cartouche with simulated rivets, hammered surface, monogramed green leather fitted case, c1930. . . . . **550.00**

Ewer, 8 x 4½", pottery, cream ringed ground, emb rust, gold, and green flowers, tan branch handles, green trim inside top, mkd Clarice Cliff. . . . **85.00**

Figures
9 x 4 x 5½", lady, satin finish, blue dress, green trim, green hat, mkd Royal Dux, pink triangle mark **300.00**
12½", patinated metal, female hoop

dancer, stepped black marble base, cast after model by Fayral **375.00**

Flower Frog, 7", glass, nude **60.00**

Furniture
Buffet, 5'5½" l, 35" h, walnut burr, black painted pulls accented in aluminum, side doors painted black, Donald Deskey style, c1935 . . . . . **900.00**
Chairs, pr, Barcelona, chromed steel, upholstered in buttoned black leather, designed by Mies van der Rohe, 1929 . . . . **700.00**
Firescreen, 48" l, gilt metal, 2 concentric circles, American, c1940 . . **550.00**
Hall Stand, 78" h, wrought iron fronted planter with pate-de-verre tilted back, flanked by rounded cupboards and open shelves inlaid with a medallion of fruit in MOP, topped by a panel painted by A. Levy, marquetry signature of Louis Majorelle **3,500.00**

Figure, 14½" h, Goldschneider, Dakon artist, mkd 7195/374/2, $1,300.00.

Settee, 68", tubular metal, upholstered in tan vinyl, designed by Gilbert Rohde for Troy Sunshade Co., c1935 . . . . **950.00**
Table, 27⅛" h, SS, baluster form on spreading circular foot, 4 applied strapwork feet, circular wooden top mounted with gallery, fitted glass roundel engraved in center with starburst, rim, shoulder and foot engraved with geometric strapwork, mkd Merrill Shops, NY, c1925. . . . **2,750.00**

Table and Barstool, 20" w, 25" h stand, 23" h stool, tubular metal with black bakelite top, rounded edges, tubular metal barstool with foot continuing to form seat rail, upholstered in red vinyl, attributed to Wolfgang Hoffman, Howell Co., c1935 . . . . . **350.00**

Inkstand, 9½" l, rect, openwork rail, bracket supports, engraved with foliage and reed design, inlaid triads of coral, 2 hinged cov wells, single globular spirit burner, cabochon coral finials, mkd Cartier, Paris, c1925 . . . . . **2,650.00**

Jam Jar, 4½ x 3¾", pottery, gold and green with blue and pink flowers, SP top, rim and handle, mkd Clarice Cliff Bizarre **120.00**

Jewelry

Brooch, 1¾", circular, convex surface molded with a profusion of daisy blossoms, set against golden foil ground, gilt metal mount, stamped Lalique **825.00**

Necklace, 42" l, 18 deep aqua green molded ivy leaves strong on green silk cord, one inscribed R. Lalique, c1930 . . . . **1,100.00**

Lamp, Oriental man seated, glass shade, gold crackle, Ronson label. **100.00**

Mirror, wall, 24" h, inverted teardrop form with scrolling bronze and geometric wrought iron support **400.00**

Panel, 49 x 34", commissioned for the Grand Salon of the *S. S. Normandie*, designed by Jean Dupas, done by Chamigneulle, gilt horsehead rising from frothing wave in pale blue and white, c1934 . . . . **5,500.00**

Sugar Shaker, 3¼" d, 5½" h, mottled gold and tan, raised brightly colored flowers around base, mkd "My Garden", sgd Clarice Cliff Pottery **120.00**

Torcheres, pr, 5½" x 4" h, silvered conical light socket raised on black fluted standard, c1935 . . . . **1,050.00**

Travel Suitcase, 3 bottles, comb, brush, mirror **75.00**

Tray, 29" l, rect, mahogany, gilt metal panel inset molded with a design of a female and fish **40.00**

Vanity Mirror, 22" h, tripartite, tops with geometric pattern in black glass **75.00**

Vases

6¾", SS, sculptured mermaid, porcelain lining. **350.00**

8 x 5¾", pottery, cream ground, orange, yellow, and green flowers, emb blue and orange leaves, brown and green branches, green interior, mkd Clarice Cliff **125.00**

11½", ivory, 2 nudes in relief, blue interior **85.00**

Wall Pocket, 6¼ x 8½", pottery, woman mask, light gray. **165.00**

ART NOUVEAU

History: Art Nouveau is the French term for the "new art" which had its beginning in the early 1890s and continued for the next 40 years. The flowing and sensuous female forms used in this period were popular in Europe and America. Among the most recognized artists of this period were Galle, Lalique, and Tiffany.

Art Nouveau can be identified by its flowing, sensuous lines, floral forms, insects, and the feminine form. These designs were incorporated on almost everything produced at that time, from art glass to furniture, silver, and personal objects.

References: Victor Arwas, *Glass: Art Nouveau To Art Deco*, Rizzoli, 1977; Don Fredgant, *Collecting Art Nouveau: Identification And Values*, Books Americana; Albert Christian Revi, *American Art Nouveau Glass*, Schiffer Publishing, reprint.

Additional Listings: Furniture and Jewelry. Also check glass, pottery, and metal categories.

Jewelry Box, 4⅞ x 3 x 4 ", pink satin interior, bronze finish, mkd, $45.00.

Andirons, 27" h, bronze and patinated metal, figural terminals of woman's head, flowers in flowing hair, French, c1900. . . . . **2,000.00**

Ashtray, 26½", standing, bronzed pot metal, nude female with round dish ashtray in one uplighted hand, other hand at side with fingers pointing out, chin lifted up towards dish **125.00**

Basket, centerpiece, 15" h, parcel-gilt silver, vase form on sq base with 4 bracket feet, applied high upright handle, 4 cartouches etched with chrysanthemums, 14K gold trim, mkd Sweetser Co. NY, c1910 . . . . **725.00**

Boxes

4¼", rect, SS, hinged lid enameled with seated nude holding a fan, gilt interior, designed by Wiener Werkstatte, Vienna **3,575.00**

12½" l, rect silver mounted wood, Athenic style, applied corner brackets, flowing tendrils extending from top to front, monogrammed cartouche, mkd Gorham Co., c1898. . . . . **725.00**

Bowl, 9½ x 2½″, green lustre, portrait center of Victorian lady in lavender dress, heavy gold border and trim, mkd E. S. Prov. Saxe **265.00**

Centerpiece Bowl, 13″ d, SS, lobed circular section, wide rim and spreading pedestal foot with applied irises, Reed & Barton, c1900 . . . . **675.00**

Creamer, 4″, silver gilt, inverted pear shape, openwork of flowers, scrolling foliage, cartouches, and gadrooned shoulder, emb and chased under scrolling foliate rim, double S-scroll foliate handle, emerald green enamel interior, circular ribbed foot, Gorham, 1892 . . . . **275.00**

Desk Set, silver on bronze, inkwell, calendar, pen tray, stamp box, letter rack, and paper knife, c1910 . . . . **100.00**

Dresser Set, SS, 9 pc, mirror, comb, cov cut glass jar, hair brush, clothes brush, 2 rect brushes, pr tweezers, shoe horn, emb and chased with undulating strapwork and flowering foliage, monogrammed "AN," mkd R. Blackinton & Co., North Attleboro, Mass. 1897/1898/1900 . . . . **550.00**

Ewer, 12¾″, pewter, 2 "C" scroll handles cast as leafy vines, tapering cylindrical form, molded in medium relief with cupid holding a hand mirror before a nude woman in a wooded landscape, inscribed F. Massuch, stamped Etain Garanti/Pur **425.00**

Figures
5″, porcelain, nude bathing beauty emerging from center of waterlily, German. **120.00**

8¾″, polychromed bronze, woman in long flowered skirt, polka dotted bodice holding ivory dove to her breast, hands and head of ivory, gilt, green, and brown patinas, onyx base, inscribed I. Gallo, c1925 . . . **1,600.00**

9″, glazed stoneware, bird, grinning with paunch, talonned, webbed feet, finished in tan, blue, and green glaze, incised R. W. Martin & Bros., London & Southall, 1902 . . . . **2,100.00**

19¾″, bronze, dancer, elaborate beaded costume with short bolero and cloche hat, dancing with both hands and one leg raised, ivory head and hands, green, silvered, and gilt patinas, red marble base, incised D. Chiparus, c1925 . . . . . . **7,700.00**

23″, Nature as standing female raising silvered cloak from her head and shoulders, scarab holding giltbronze robes below her breast, in-

scribed E. Barrias, imp circular foundry mark "Susse Freres Editeurs Paris" **4,200.00**

Furniture
Armoire, 80″ l, 90″ h, pale burled wood, central mirrored door, mkd Ecole de Nancy, c1900 . . . . **825.00**

Cabinet, 67″ l, 65″ h, silvered metal mounted mahogany, 3 doors, interior fitted with adjustable shelving, metal tag printed Mercier/Freres/PARIS, c1925 . . . . **3,750.00**

Desk, 27″ l, 37″ h, inlaid walnut, upper surface edged in light wood and ivory, legs banded in ivory, door opens to reveal 3 frieze drawers, sliding writing surface, French, c1925. . . . . **1,050.00**

Table, 2 tiers, 34″ l, 31″ h, fruitwood with bronze mounts, rect top inlaid with mistletoe blossoms and berries and "au gui l'an neuf," lower tier inlaid with mistletoe and set with 2 gilt bronze handles, sgd in marquetry Majorelle, c1900 . . . . **1,650.00**

Tables, nest of 4, 24½″ l, 30½″ h, fruitwood, inlaid marquetry of different blossoming branches **1,250.00**

Tea Cart, 28″ l, 30″ h, shaped fruitwood top with bronze handles, inlaid leafage, 4 hinged sides inlaid with foraging mice, sgd in marquetry, L. Majorelle. **2,000.00**

Inkwell, 4¾″ h, lobed pear shaped glass bottle, cut foliage designs, bulbous SS lid reposse and chased with canterbury bells, leaves, gilt interior, on repousse and chased SS stand with 4 tucked in pad feet, mkd The Gorham Co., Martele, 1898, retailed by Theodore B. Starr, NY **2,000.00**

Jewelry
Brooch, 1″ d, circular, modeled in medium relief with helmeted warrior framed by foliage, titled "Gaule", side stamped V. Prouve **1,000.00**

Pendant, 13¼″ l, triangular, head of maiden framed by leaves and circular devices, cream, yellow, and green enamel against a pale yellow and mauve plique-a-jour enamel ground, set with sapphire and round pearl drop, gold link chain, stamped L. Gautrait. **14,500.00**

Lamps
17¼″ h, wrought iron and mottled glass, figural, parrot on a perch, pierced wrought iron body enclosing mottled glass shading from deep sapphire blue to emerald green, lemon-yellow, and orange, circular studded base, inscribed E. Chapelle/Nancy, c1925 . . . . **5,000.00**

18″, moss agate shade, vase shape, marble rect base, 2 bronze nudes kneeling on either side of shade . . **1,850.00**

Letter Opener, SS, knife shape, ornate handle **50.00**

Mirrors

10⅛″, SS mounted, handle in form of maiden with arms outstretched, back emb and chased with vines of roses, hovering cupid, monogrammed "AKS", c1900 . . . . **330.00**

20″, pewter, upright, rect, crest cast with pierced foliage, woman seated beside a peacock on base, easel support imp Wurttenbergische Metallwarenfabrik, c1900 . . . . **1,600.00**

Panel, 42 x 47″, incised and painted with a peacock on a pebble-strewn ground, oriental leafage, pale green and blues, heightened in silver on gilt ground, incised William Fuller Curtis, A.D. MDCCCCVII **2,325.00**

Pitchers, water

8¼″, SS, baluster form, repousse and chased with stems of marigolds, stamped 800, Sterling, 3 stars within a triangle **825.00**

10¾″, silver mounted cut glass, bulbous body cut with daffodils, leaves, stems, mount emb and chased with narcissus and leaves, harp shaped handle, Gorham Co., 1871 . . . . . . **2,500.00**

Salt and Pepper Shakers, pr, SS, 2⅛″, ftd **250.00**

Shelf, 21½″ l, curved fruitwood shelf and bracket support, demilune panel of gray glass overlaid in shades of puce and cut with idyllic river landscape, glass sgd in cameo Jacques/Gruber, c1900 . . . . **1,150.00**

Soap Dish, 5½ x 6½″, bronze, female, upper body, holding bunch of grapes over head, drape over one shoulder flows into dish base **375.00**

Tazza, 8½″ l, SS, undulating rim, emb and chased with flowers, leaves, tendrils, conforming ribbed and domed foot with 4 tucked in scroll supports, mkd Gorham Co. Martele, 1908 . . . . **950.00**

Tea Tray, 14″ l, fruitwood inlaid with branch of thistles and croix de Lorraine, galleried silver apron raised on 4 ball feet, sgd Galle, mounts sgd Marret, c1900 . . . . **600.00**

Tray, 7¾″, figure of girl in mid-Eastern dress with hinged skirt, dished marble base, cold painted bronze, imp France Bergman, Nam Greg, Austrian, c1910 . . . . **450.00**

Vases

7½″, satin glass, green, enameled silver head of lady with long flowing hair **400.00**

8⅛″, cameo, slender cylindrical neck with notched lip continuing to a bulbous thick walled clear glass foot, acid etched sides enameled with sprays of wildflowers and leaves in shades of yellow, ochre, lavender, dusty rose, and turquoise, egg and dart border base, sgd in gilt Miesenthal/B/S/& Co. within a stylized thistle **575.00**

15¾″, teardrop form on cushion base, enameled in blue and orange with fruiting branches, incised Le Verre Francais **350.00**

16″, silver mounted cut glass, elongated body cut with panels of starbursts and intersecting rays, mounted rim of applied lilies and foliage, Gorham Co., 1906 . . . . **950.00**

18¼″, SS, elongated pear shaped body, emb and chased with budding iris and leaves, dec spreading domed foot, monogrammed "HSK", mkd Gorham Co., Providence, RI, c1900 . . . . **825.00**

21½″, gilt metal mounted pottery, shouldered ovoid, drip glaze of deep brown over pale celadon, whiplash handles, French, c1900 . . . . **275.00**

ART PEWTER

History: Pewter objects produced during the Art Nouveau, Arts and Crafts, and Art Deco periods are gaining in popularity. These mostly utilitarian objects, e.g., tea sets, trays, and bowls, were elaborately decorated and produced in the Jugendstil manner by German firms, such as Kayserzinn, and Austrian companies, such as Orivit. In England, Liberty and Company marketed Tudric Pewter, which often had a hammered surface and was embellished with enameling or semi-precious stones. Most pieces of art pewter contain the maker's mark.

KAYSERZINN

Bowl, 10″ d, 3 lobsters	**100.00**
Chamberstick, 9½″ h, emb poppies . . .	**125.00**
Ice Bucket, 9″, 3 handles, floral design	**130.00**
Lamp, table, Aladdin, Art Nouveau design, berries	**150.00**
Plate, 10½″, Art Nouveau	**75.00**
Platter, 20″ l, fish, crab among water lilies on rim	**200.00**
Tray, 8½″, Art Nouveau	**45.00**
Tureen, cov, 12″ h, floral dec	**50.00**

ORIVIT

Creamer, individual, floral dec	**20.00**
Inkwell, double, orig undertray, Art Nouveau flowers	**110.00**

Kayserzinn, bowl, cov, 7½″ d, sunflowers, handled, ftd, bulbous sides, mkd 4038, $125.00.

Pitcher, 10½″ h, emb grapes and leaves	**125.00**
Dresser Tray, 6″, Art Nouveau	**35.00**
Vase, 7″, 3 cut out handles, gilding . . .	**85.00**

TUDRIC

Bowl, 6″, hammered finish	**25.00**
Jug, 6″, stylized foliage, rattan handle .	**70.00**
Money clip, Art Nouveau	**25.00**
Teapot, hammered finish, wood handle	**75.00**

ART POTTERY (GENERAL)

History: The period of art pottery reached its zenith in the late 19th and early 20th century. Over a hundred companies produced individually designed and often decorated wares which served a utilitarian as well as an aesthetic purpose. Artists moved about from company to company, some forming their own firms.

Quality of design, beauty in glazes, and condition are the keys in buying art pottery. This category covers companies not found elsewhere in the guide.

References: Paul Evans, *Art Pottery of the United States,* Everybodys Press, Inc., 1974; Ralph and Terry Kovel, *The Kovels' Collector's Guide To American Art Pottery,* Crown Publishers, Inc., 1974.

Additional Listings: See Cambridge, Clewell, Clifton, Cowan, Dedham, Fulper, Grueby, Jugtown, Marblehead, Moorcroft, Newcomb, Ohr, Owens, Paul Revere, Peters and Reed, Rookwood, Roseville, Van Briggle, Weller, and Zanesville.

Arc-En-Ciel Pottery (1903–05), Zanesville, OH	
Vase, 7″, swirling stems, flowers, gilt glaze	**200.00**
Arequipa Pottery (1913–18), Fairfax, CA	
Vase, 4½″, purple glaze	**350.00**

California Faience Co. (1916–30), Berkeley, CA	
Bowl, 12″, Chinese shape, 3 colors .	**275.00**
Figurine, Oriental man with washtub, 5 colors, artist sgd	**240.00**
Vase, 4″, blue, high glaze	**100.00**
Cincinnati Art Pottery (1880–91), Cincinnati, OH	
Vase, 8 x 8½″, pocket shape, black ground, applied flowers, in white, high glaze	**100.00**
Kenton Hills, (1939–42), Erlanger, KY	
Vase, 8¼″, white ground, portrait of lion in shades of brown, blue band at top, imp mark, sgd "Unica Kenton Hills Porcelain, D. Seyler"	**350.00**
Vase, 12½″, white ground, pink, blue, gray, and brown floral dec, high glaze, sgd "Hentschel"	**300.00**
Merrimac Ceramic Company (1897–08), Newburyport, MA	
Vase, 7″, yellow drip over matte white glaze, paper label	**250.00**
Middle Lane Pottery (1894–32), East Hampton and Westhampton, NY	
Vase, 4 x 3″, green fire paint glaze . .	**600.00**
Norse (1903–13), Edgerton, WI, and Rockford, IL	
Vase, 4½″, ftd, applied dragon, matte black with green highlights	**85.00**
Overbeck Pottery (1911–55), Cambridge City, IN	
Vase, 3¾ x 2½″, brown, incised dec of stylized trees, green color behind trees in 2 panels, Overbeck logo and artist sgd "EH"	**350.00**
Pewabic Pottery (1903–61), Detroit, MI	
Cup and Saucer, irid	**200.00**

Walrath, nude, 4¾″, mustard color on greenish base, impressed "Walrath/1912," $450.00.

Tea Tile	**45.00**
Vase, 8″, purple lustre glaze	**450.00**

Pisgah Forest (1913–Present), Mt. Pisgah, NC

Creamer, 3½″, red and white, high glaze.	**35.00**
Pitcher, 5″, aqua, 1938	**25.00**
Vase, 5¾″, oriental shape, pale blue crystalline glaze over buff, sgd, dated 1940	**250.00**
Vase, 5¾″, turquoise to purple, crystalline, sgd "Stephen", dated 1949	**75.00**
Vase, 6″, maroon, 1950.	**25.00**
Vase, 6½″, gray-green crystalline glaze, sgd, dated 1939	**125.00**

Roblin Art Pottery (1898–06), San Francisco, CA

Tile, 3″ sq, bird and 2 cabins in blue, brown, and white, high glaze, corner chip, mkd Roblin, sgd "AWR" on back, artist sgd on front	**600.00**
Vase, 4½″, multifaceted dark green high glaze, mkd "Roblin"	**400.00**

School of Mines, University of North Dakota (1892–Present)

Rose Bowl, 3 x 4½″, beige, matte glaze, inscribed "North Dakota/North Dakota Wheat".	**350.00**
Tile, scenic, carved, 6 colors, 1928, sgd "Mattson".	**450.00**
Vase, 3″, Art Deco multicolored floral design, dark blue high glaze	**200.00**
Vase, 3½ x 4½″, Black Indian type design, Bentonite glaze	**375.00**
Vase, 6½ x 7″, incised leaves	**250.00**
Vase, 9″, carved Indian on horseback, sgd "Mattson".	**375.00**

Schrimer, Phoebe (1900), Baltimore Academy of Art

Vase, 5″, light green with dark green Art Deco design, sgd "PS".	**45.00**

Stockton Art Pottery (1890–95, 1896–1900), Stockton, CA

Vase, 8″, floral dec	**100.00**
Wallpocket	**75.00**

Swastika Keramos

Vase, 8″, red flowers and green leaves, gilt trim, mkd	**200.00**
Vase, 8″, variegated gold and green mkd	**225.00**

Teco (1886–30), Terra Cotta, IL

Vase, 5″ matte green	**100.00**

Vance/Avon Pottery (1892–08), Tiltonville, OH and Wheeling, WV

Pitcher, 5″, red tulips, white interior, dark blue high glaze, sgd	**150.00**
Vase, 5″, fine flower and leaf artwork, standard glaze	**300.00**

Walrath Pottery, Rochester, NY

Paperweight, 3 x 1″, scarab, matte green glaze	**150.00**

Wheatley, T. J. & Co. (1880–82), Cincinnati, OH

Overbeck, vase, 5¾″, thrown by Elizabeth, decor by Mary F., beige ground, pale green, $850.00.

Vase, 10″, floral artwork, sgd "Hickman", drilled for lamp base.	**200.00**
Vase, 12 x 10″, black with orange flower, blue drip, mkd "Sept 28, 1880", foot chip.	**175.00**

ARTS AND CRAFTS MOVEMENT

History: The Arts and Crafts Movement in American decorative arts took place between 1895 and 1920. Leading proponents of the movement were Elbert Hubbard and his Roycrofters, the brothers Stickley, Frank Lloyd Wright, Charles and Henry Greene, George Niedecken, and Lucia and Arthur Mathews.

The movement was marked by individualistic design (although the movement was national in scope) and re-emphasis on handcraftsmanship and appearance. A reform of industrial society was part of the long range goal. Most pieces of furniture favored a rectilinear approach and were made of oak.

In 1982 a series of landmark sales were held: Skinner's Arts and Craft Sale in March, the estate of Leopold Stickley in Fayetteville, New York, in May, and Sotheby's in May and November. The sales marked an end to the rash speculation in the Arts and Crafts material and brought some stability to the market.

References: David M. Cathers, *Furniture Of The American Arts and Crafts Movement*, New American Library, c1981; David A. Hanks, *The Decorative Designs Of Frank Lloyd Wright*, E. P. Dutton, 1979;

Coy L. Ludwig, *The Arts and Crafts Movement In New York State, 1890s–1920s*, Gallery Association of New York State, 1983.

Periodical: *Tiller*, c/o Artsman, P. O. Box 508, Bryn Mawr, PA 19010. Subscription: $125.00 (bimonthly).

Museum: Museum of Modern Art, New York, NY.

Additional Listings: Roycroft Items and art pottery categories.

Catalog, *The Craftsman Workshops, Syracuse, NY, Hand Wrought Metal Work*	400.00
Chandelier, brass, slag glass, silk fringe	150.00
Fireplace Surround, polished black marble, upper shelf raised on 2 columnar supports, designed by Kem Weber, c1930.	3,000.00
Jardiniere, 28 x 36″, hammered metal repousse plaques with geometric devices pendant from blue beads, early 20th C	275.00
Lamp, 11″ h, 16″ d shade, pottery base made from vase, pink, blue, and white iris dec, fitted leaded shade of white and green opal, base sgd "K" and "BFK"	100.00
Pitcher, 10″, incised birds, sgd "Martin Bros"	200.00

Tankard, 14″ h, copper and brass, pewter lined, possibly English, $285.00.

Pool Tables
55 x 92½ x 28″, oak, rails inlaid at intervals with bone lozenges, turned sharply tapering supports, labeled "August Jungblat Co. 833 Filmore St., S.F., Serial No. 66864"...... **1,500.00**
60 x 110″, MOP inlay, ebonized string-

ing, tag emb "Fast/G. Gorreale & Sons/349 West Side Ave/Jersey City, NJ/Cushions," c1910 ...... **1,200.00**
Sconces, 13″, pr, sq section set with mottled green and pale pink glass tiles on opal white ground, turned stained wood supports, designed by Orlando Giannini, executed by Giannini and Hilgart, c1902................... **4,300.00**
Screens
19¼ x 72″, 3 fold, each section stained oak frame, leaded glass panels with stylized tree rising from sq pot, opaque, irid and clear glass panes in yellow, amber, and green, plaque on center panel inscribed "The Art & Craft of the Machine/A Lecture By Frank Lloyd Wright/Hull House Chicago, March 6, 1901/The Chicago Arts & Crafts Society", small metal plaque at bottom imp "Niedecken," designed by Frank Lloyd Wright, executed by Giannini and Hilgart **5,500.00**
30 x 52″, giltwood, painted leather and embroidered silk, panel dec in Japanese manner, c1880......... **625.00**
Tables
18½ x 22¼″, circular, sq legs, branded "Limbert's Arts & Crafts Furniture/Made In Grand Rapids & Holland" **110.00**
50 x 18¼″, stained oak, octagonal top, inset with leaded irid stained glass panel with overlapping circles and arcs in purple, blue, gold, green, magenta, brown, and milky white, lighted from below, octagonal pedestal base, stenciled "Plycraft" and "Frank Lloyd Wright Design" within rect in black **2,750.00**
54 x 28½″, library, oak, round, stretcher holds 2nd round surface, mkd "Limbert"............. **1,875.00**
Vases
5″, incised flowers, sgd "Martin Bros" **110.00**
7½″, gourd shape, raised white dots on green ground, sgd "Martin Bros. London & Southall" **500.00**
Wine Cabinet, oak, shelf top over 2 glass doors, 1 int. shelf, locking base, mkd "Art Crafters of Cincinnati," c1915, minor veneer loss.............. **1,225.00**

AUSTRIAN WARE

History: Over a hundred potteries were located in the Austro-Hungarian Empire in the late 19th and early 20th centuries. Although Carlsbad was the center of the industry, the factories spread as far as modern day Czechoslovakia.

Many of the factories were either owned or supported by Americans; hence, their wares were produced mainly for export to the United States. Responding to the 1891 law that imported products must be marked as to country of origin, many wares do not have a factory mark, but only the word "Austrian."

Additional Listings: Amphora, Carlsbad, Royal Dux, and Royal Vienna.

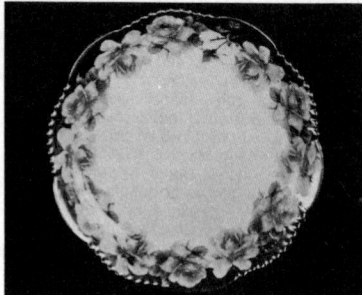

Plate, 9¾" d, rose dec, scalloped and beaded edge, gold border, mkd crown/B/&/Würtemberg, $40.00.

Basket, pink rose, and lavender flowers, gold trim, artist sgd, mkd M.Z. and Austria 40.00
Biscuit Jar, classical portrait, cobalt, gold trim, beehive mark 80.00
Bowls
 7½" d, ftd, hydrangea dec in pink, white, and greens 20.00
 13¼", shallow, pierced for hanging, center portrait of dancing maidens, semi-nude cupid playing lyre, green and red, gold trim 120.00
Butter Dish, cov, insert, 7½" d, yellow flowers, green vines, gold trim, hp .. 30.00
Celery Tray, pink floral center, blue and gold border, mkd Royal 20.00
Cheese Dish, cov, gold florals, leaves, red and blue berries, cream ground, beehive mark 100.00
Chocolate Pot, 9¾" h, small pink roses, green leaves, gold bands and trim, white ground, mkd M.Z. and Austria . 70.00
Compote, Greek key and leaf border, hp, mkd M.Z. and Austria 50.00
Cookie Jar, 6½" d, melon shape, pink roses, green leaves, gold trim, white ground, mkd M.Z. and Austria 90.00
Creamer and Sugar, cov, yellow flowers, pale green ground, heavy gold handles and trim, mkd Royal Austria ... 85.00
Fish Set, platter, 12 plates, lavender flowers, pale blue ground, gold trim . 275.00

Jug, 8½" h, red, green, cream, and gray dec, gold trim, mkd Alhambra 135.00
Mayonnaise Set, 5" bowl, attached underplate, ladle, hp violets on interior and exterior, mkd Imperial 40.00
Plates
 6", hp, grapes and foliage 80.00
 9½", pink and yellow roses, green leaves in center and border, gold scalloped rim, mkd M.Z. and Austria, set of 6. .... 75.00
Ramekin, underplate, fluted, white, set of 6 .... 30.00
Ring Tree, hp, pink and green flowers, gold center, mkd M.Z. and Austria .. 35.00
Salt and Pepper Shakers, hp, yellow roses, coin gold trim 20.00
Sauce Dish, pink roses, gold trim, mkd M.Z. 10.00
Soup Tureen, cov, floral dec, mkd Royal 45.00
Sugar Shaker, yellow flowers, green leaves, pale yellow ground, gold metal top 40.00
Teapot, 4½" h, 8¼" w spout to handle, geometric greens and reds, gold scroll dec, handle, spout, and finial, Alhambra mark in red, Vienna, Austria 60.00
Vases
 5½", roses, handle 50.00
 5¾", irid purple, blue and gold, pinched in sides 65.00
 6", handles, woman in portrait medallion. 65.00
 11", Art Deco, cylindrical, all around design of brown trees reflected in water, yellow ground, shiny pearlized glaze, mkd M.Z. and Austria . 70.00
 13", jug shape, lavender pansies on matte tan ground 85.00

AUTOGRAPHS

History: Autographs occur in a wide variety of formats—letters, documents, photographs, books, and cards, etc. Most collectors focus on a particular person, country, or category, e.g. signers of Declaration of Independence.

The condition and content of letters and documents bears significantly on value. Collectors should know their source since forgeries abound, and copy machines compound the problem. Further, some signatures of recent presidents and movie stars are done by machine rather than by the person themselves. A good dealer or advanced collector can help one spot the differences.

The leading auction sources for autographs are Swann Galleries, Sotheby's, Christie's, and Phillips, all located in New York City.

References: Charles Hamilton, *American Autographs*, University of Oklahoma Press, 1983; William Rodger, *The Official Price Guide to Old Books and Autographs*, House of Collectibles, 1979, 2nd ed.

Collectors' Club: Universal Autograph Collectors Club, P. O. Box 467 Rockville Center, NY 11571.

Additional Listings: See *Warman's Americana & Collectibles* for more examples.

The following abbreviations denote type of autograph material and their sizes.

ADS	Autograph Document Signed
ALS	Autograph Letter Signed
AQS	Autograph Quotation Signed
CS	Card Signed
DS	Document Signed
LS	Letter Signed
PS	Photograph Signed
TLS	Typed Letter Signed

Sizes (approximate):

Folio	12 x 16 inches
4to	8 x 10 inches
8vo	5 x 7 inches
12mo	3 x 5 inches

COLONIAL AMERICA

Adams, Samuel, ALS, "Saml Adams", 1 pg, small 4to, Philadelphia, Feb. 3, 1781, to James Bowdoin in Boston, browned, stained, thanking Bowdoin for group of pamplets **675.00**

Chase, Samuel, ALS, 1 pg, small 4to, Baltimore, Dec. 4, 1796, silk reinforced at right and left hand margins **1,900.00**

Franklin, Benjamin, ALS, 1 pg, small folio, Philadelphia, Sept. 19, 1785, to Jane Mecom, re recent trip and return, lightly browned, 2 small holes at intersection of folds **4,675.00**

Hall, Layman, Governor of Georgia, 1 pg, folio, Georgia, April 7, 1786, to Captain Elnathan, Wallingford, CT, slightly browned, repair to seal tear, letter from Hall as Governor of Georgia giving insight to planter's life **2,750.00**

Heyward, Thomas, Jr., ALS, 3 pgs, 4to, White Hall, SC, March 13, 1790, slightly browned, neatly mended at center fold, re attempts to settle family estate. **3,575.00**

Livingston, Philip, ALS, 1 pg, 4 to, New York, Oct. 16, 1775 to John Alsop, scattered foxing, endorsed on integral blank, re shipping **1,225.00**

Morris, Robert, ALS, 1 pg, 4 to, Philadelphia, Dec. 2, 1797, to Richard Carson, re failed 3rd party payment. . . . **200.00**

EUROPEAN

Charles II, King of England, DS, 1 pg, folio, Windsor, July 30, 1674, King Charles II Order For The Acceptance Of The Dutch Surrender of New York. **32,000.00**

Churchill, Sir Winston Spencer, TLS, 1 pg, 4to, 28 Hyde Park Gate, Dec. 12, 1957, personal letter to daughter Sarah, re Lady Churchill's health, autographed salutation and conclusion **2,000.00**

George III, King of England, DS, 1 pg, folio, parchment, April 1, 1776, paper seal, paper stamp, wear at folds, re Sir Henry Clinton's commission as "General in America only". **5,000.00**

Mussolini, Benito, DS, 2½ pgs, 4to, Rome, Nov. 21, 1923, as Prime Minister, selling property owned by Italian embassy in Washington, DC. **350.00**

Windsor, Edward, Duke, formerly King Edward VIII, TLS, 1 pg, 4to, St. James' Palace, Jan. 19, 1921, to Viscount Burnham, re gift for development of Boy Scouts, autographed salutation and conclusion, sgd as Prince of Wales, Edward P. **225.00**

GENERAL

Audubon, John James, ALS, 1 pg, 4to, Edinburgh, Oct 7, 1843 to John Cabert in Leeds. **825.00**

Barnum, Phineas T, DS, 1 pg, 8vo, Waldemere, Bridgeport, June 30, 1896, testimonial to Abraham Lincoln. **900.00**

Bell, Alexander Graham, LS, 1 pg, folio, 1331 Connecticut Ave, Jan. 20, 1898, form letter to Honorable Russell A. Alger, re memorial meeting of National Geographical Society. **300.00**

Edison, Thomas Alva, LS, 1 pg, 4to, Orange, NJ, July 26, 1913, to Simon Goldstein, New York, regarding dietary regime **775.00**

Fulton, Robert, ALS, 1 pg, 4to, New York, April 21, 1813, to Allan McLane, Wilmington, re work on torpedo boats **1,100.00**

Green, Henrietta, H.R. "Hetty", DS, 1 pg, oblong small 4to, New York, June 29, 1898, receipt from estate of Thomas Lyman **350.00**

Key, Francis Scott, ALS, 1 pg, folio, Washington, July 21, 1874 to Blair & Gantt of St. Louis, re royalties **350.00**

Lindbergh, Charles A., ALS, 4 pgs, 4to, Sevenoaks, Oct. 30, 1936, to Martin, concerning park in Minnesota to be named in his father's memory, holograph. **1,250.00**

Pinkerton, William A, TLS, 1 pg, 8 vo, Sept 7, 1907, to Oliver Fessenden, thank you letter for sympathy on the death of brother Robert **150.00**

LITERATURE

Greenaway, Catherine, "Kate", ALS, 4 pgs, 8vo, Hempstead, Jan. 16, 1891, to friend Lily **225.00**

Hawthorne, Nathaniel, ALS, 1 pg, 8 vo, Concord, June 27, 1853, letter to Mr. George H. Forster **200.00**

Huges, Langston, 1 pg, 4to, typescript of poem "Peace Conference in American Town", boldly inscribed and sgd in blue ink, 4 other unsigned typescripts of poem attached **200.00**

Norris, Kathleen, AQS, 1 pg, 12 mo, March, 1918, "Who loseth his life shall gain it" **25.00**

Verne, Jules, ALS, 1 pg, 8vo, Paris, Aug. 18, 1874, to Mr. Farrington, thank you in French **350.00**

MUSIC

Bartok, Bela, Hungarian composer, ALS, Denver, CO, Jan. 20, 1928, 11 lines on message portion of postcard, good musical content, in Hungarian **450.00**

Blake, Eubie, ALS, 1 p, 4to Brooklyn, NY, June 29, 1978, to Mr. & Mrs. Britton, comments on writing of "I'm Just Wild About Harry" **120.00**

Offenbach, Jacques, autograph musical manuscript, 2 pgs (front and back of large folio sheet), over 100 bars of music **400.00**

Sousa, John Phillip, AQS, musical, April 1901, small white card, five bars of music **250.00**

Stokowski, Leopold, TLS, 1 p, 4to, New York, June 27, 1963, to Summy Birchard Co. requesting Bloch score . . . **45.00**

Walter, Bruno, TLS, 1 p, 4to, Beverly Hills, Dec. 29, 1956, to Paul Nettl thanking him for material sent **25.00**

PRESIDENTIAL, AMERICAN

Adams, John, ALS, 3 pgs, 4to, Quincy, Dec. 5, 1812, repair to center fold, small hole on last pg, letter to son-in-law Col. William Stephens Smith on Smith's standing for election to Congress as federalist **10,000.00**

Buchanan, James, ALS, 2 pgs, 4to, Senate Chamber, Jan. 13, 1842, to John C. Plume in Pennsylvania, endorsing candidacy of Judge Rogers for reappointment to the state bench **2,475.00**

Carter, Jimmy, first day cover, World Peace Through Law, franked Washington, D.C., Sept. 29, 1975, First Day of Issue, sgd by Jimmy Carter, Menachim Begin, and Anwar Sadat (twice once in Arabic and once in English) **1,200.00**

Coolidge, Calvin, ALS, 1 pgs, 4to, Washington, to officers of his savings bank in Northampton, MA, on stationery of the Vice President **1,650.00**

Harrison, William Henry, ALS, 1 pg, long 12 mo, Greenville, July 31, 1795, note to commissory for provisions for the Delawares **500.00**

Hayes, Rutherford B. ALS, 1 pg, 8vo, Washington, Feb. 21, 1881, to Edw. F. Gladwin of Brooklyn, Executive Mansion stationery, mounted with portrait of Hayes **550.00**

Jackson, Andrew, DS, 1 pg, 4to, Murfeesborough, May 13, 1814, copy of account between U.S. government and Dr. J. Roane, in amount of $22.00 . . . . **500.00**

Jefferson, Thomas, ALS, 1½ pgs, 4to, Williamsburg, July 17, 1779, to Richard Henry Lee at Chantilly in Westmoreland County, Virginia, browned, integral address leaf endorsed by Lee, Jefferson's plans for Virginia's naval defense **6,100.00**

Lincoln, Abraham, DS, 1 pg, folio, Washington, March 17, 1863, Godfrey Weitzel's commission as Brigadier General of Volunteers, countersigned by Edwin M. Stanton, Secretary of War **1,650.00**

Monroe, James, DS, affidavit of appointment, 1 pg, 4to, Washington, Dec. 20, 1815, seal of Secretary of State center left **250.00**

Roosevelt, Franklin D., TLS, 1 og, 8vo, White House stationery, Hyde Park, Aug. 22, 1933, note re Glass-Steagall Act **750.00**

SHOW BUSINESS

Barrymore, Lionel, DS, 4 pgs, 4to, April 26, 1946, Metro-Goldwyn Mayer letterhead, re contract **75.00**

Crosby, Bing, CS, postcard from Don the Beachcomber restaurant, 1955, to Charles Graves of London, pencil . . . **30.00**

Garbo, Greta, DS, 1 pg, 4to, Santa Monica, California, Aug, 9, 1944, "Statement of Identity for Title Insurance", lists place of birth as "Sweden", age "over 21" and occupation "Actress" **600.00**

Kelly, Emmet, postcard sgd, glossy, in hobo costume **50.00**

Rodgers, Richard, PS, 4to, Rogers standing by piano **45.00**

Russell, Lillian, ALS, 5 pgs, small folio, 8vo, New York, Dec. 5, 1911, to Theodore Mitchell, Colonial Theatre, Boston **100.00**

SPORTS

Boston Celtics, autographs on program of MA High School Tech Tourney, March 1964, Most, Auerbach, Lostcutoff, Lovelette and Havlicek **35.00**
Gehrig, Lou, PS, sepia glossy, 5 x 7″, Gehrig wearing windbreaker, shadowy figure of ballplayer in background, may have been taken at spring training camp **350.00**

Aaron, Hank, baseball, $18.00.

Foxx, Jimmie, CS 3 x 5″ **25.00**
Notre Dame, *Look* magazine article, Dec. 12, 1945, sgd by Frank Leahy . **10.00**
Phillies, 1980 World Champions in baseball, autographed baseball, all 31 signatures **95.00**

STATESMEN, AMERICAN

Bayard, James A., ALS, 1 pg, 4to, Ghent, Dec. 9, 1814, to Sylvanus Bourne, re message from Secretary of State . . . **150.00**
Clay, Henry, ALS, 1 pg, folio, Washington, Dec. 14, 1813, to Mr. Simmons, accountant at War Dept, cover letter for papers re Col. Allen's widow **200.00**
Conkling, Roscoe, ALS, 3 pgs, 8vo, May 12, 1866, Congressional stationery, to George C. Bingdow, re attack by James G. Blaine **100.00**
Houston, Samuel, ALS, 1 pg, 8vo, Washington, Feb. 12, 1858 to John Burt of Bellvale, New York **800.00**
King, Martin Luther, first day postal cover, franked, for Lincoln Sesquicentennial Series, Washington, May 30, 1959 . . . . **600.00**

Lee, Robert E, ALS, 1 pg, 4to, Headquarters, Army of Northern Virginia, May 14, 1863, to Lieut. Gen. James Longstreet, Lee prods Longstreet to action **3,025.00**
Lodge, Henry Cabot, ALS, 2 pgs, 8vo, U. S. Senate, Jan. 3, 1898, re book *Hero Tales From American History* . . **100.00**
Webster, Daniel, ALS, 1 pg, 4to, Boston, Nov. 3, 1840, reports on voting of 1840 election **235.00**

AUTOMOBILES

History: Automobiles can be classified into several categories. In 1947 the Antique Automobile Club of America devised a system whereby any motor vehicle (car, bus, motorcycle, etc.) made prior to 1930 is an "antique" car. The Classic Car Club of America expanded the list focusing on luxury models from 1925 to 1948. The Milestone Car Society developed a list for cars in the 1948 to 1964 period.

Some states, such as Pennsylvania, have devised a dual registration system for older cars - antique and classic. Models from the 1960s and 1970s, especially convertibles and limited production models, fall into the "classic" designation depending how they are used.

Reference: Dean V. Kruse, *The Official Price To Collector Cars*, House Of Collectibles, 1983, 4th edition.

Periodicals: *Hemmings Motor News*, Box 100, Bennington, VT 05201. Subscription: $15.50; *Old Cars Price Guide*, 700 E. State Street, Iola, WI 54990. Subscription: $7.00.

Collectors' Clubs: Antique Automobile Club of America, 501 W. Governor Road, Hershey, PA 17033; Classic Car Club of America, P. O. Box 443, Madison, NJ 07940; Milestone Car Society, P. O. Box 50850, Indianapolis, IN 46250.

Note: The prices below are based upon a car in running condition, with a high percentage of original parts, and somewhere between 60 and 80% restored. *Prices can vary by as much as 30% in either direction.*

Many older cars, especially if restored, now exceed $15,000.00. Their limited availability makes them difficult to price. Auctions, more than any other source, are the true determinant of value at this level. Especially helpful are the catalogs and sale bills of Kruse Auctioneers, Inc., Auburn, Indiana, 46706.

A. C. (Buckland), 1949, 4 passenger roadster, "Ace," 2 litre OHC six with three carbs, all aluminum body, only 85 built **11,500.00**
Alvis, 1959, TD-21, convertible, V8, left drive **10,500.00**
Auburn, 1932, Model 8-100A, brougham, 2 door, 8 cyl, custom dual ratio **13,000.00**

Auburn, 1935, Model 8-851, phaeton, 8 cyl, custom dual ratio **40,000.00**

Austin-Healey, 1961, 3000 Mark I, 6 cyl, 124 hp **5,000.00**

Bentley, 1929, Vanden Plas, touring, 4.5 litre **35,000.00**

Berkeley, 1958, Model SE492, roadster **2,750.00**

Brewster, 1922, town car, full collapsible, dual side mounts, owned by Sec. of State under FDR **25,000.00**

Buick, 1910, Model 14, roadster, 2 cyl. **8,500.00**

Buick, 1940, Special Series 40, convertible, 4 door, 8 cyl **10,500.00**

Buick, 1955, Special Series 40, sedan, 2 door, V8 . . . . **4,000.00**

Cadillac, 1909, Model 30, touring, 4 cyl **10,000.00**

Cadillac, 1937, Series 90, limousine, V16 . . . . **46,500.00**

Cadillac, 1949, Series 62, sedan, V8 . . **4,750.00**

Cadillac, 1956, Series 62, Eldorado, convertible, V8 . . . . **14,000.00**

Cadillac, 1976, Eldorado, convertible, V8 . . . . **11,000.00**

Chevrolet, 1924, Superior, roadster, 4 cyl **9,500.00**

Chevrolet, 1928, Model AB, sedan, 2 door, 4 cyl **4,500.00**

Chevrolet, 1931, Model AE, deluxe phaeton, 4 door, 6 cyl **16,000.00**

Chevrolet, 1940, Special Deluxe, sedan, 2 door, 4 cyl **3,000.00**

Chevrolet, 1948, Fleetmaster, woody station wagon, 6 cyl **7,500.00**

Chevrolet, 1954, Bel Air, sports coupe, 6 cyl **5,000.00**

Chevrolet, 1957, Model 210, sedan, 2 door, V8 . . . . **4,000.00**

Chevrolet, 1958, Corvette, hardtop . . . **16,000.00**

Chevrolet, 1965, Impala Super Sport, convertible, V8 . . . . **5,500.00**

Chevrolet, 1968, Corvair, series 500, 2 door, 6 cyl **1,750.00**

Chrysler, 1932, Model CH, Imperial Series, Standard Line, rumble seat coupe, 8 cyl **21,750.00**

Chrysler, 1947, Town & Country, sedan, 4 door **9,250.00**

Chrysler, 1964, 300 Series, hardtop, 2 door, silver edition **2,500.00**

Citroen, 1949, sedan, 2CV **3,750.00**

Cord, 1936, Model 810, Beverly, sedan, V8 . . . . **32,500.00**

Crosley, 1949, Hot Shot, roadster, 4 cyl **2,850.00**

Daimler, 1955, one of 12 built for royal family, Hooper body **18,000.00**

Delage, 1914, roadster **13,000.00**

DeSoto, 1930, Model CK, business coupe, 6 cyl **3,750.00**

DeSoto, 1936, Airflow III S-2, sedan, 6 cyl **5,750.00**

DeSoto, 1955, Firedome, convertible, V8 . . . . **6,000.00**

Dodge, 1915, touring, 4 cyl **6,500.00**

Dodge, 1928, Victory Series, touring, 6 cyl **10,750.00**

Dodge, 1939, Special Series, 4 door, 6 cyl **2,500.00**

Dodge, 1946, Custom Series, D24, club coupe, 6 cyl **2,250.00**

Dodge, 1953, Series D44, Coronet, sedan, 4 door, V8 . . . . **3,750.00**

Durant, 1929, Model 55, sedan, 6 cyl. . **6,500.00**

Edsel, 1959, Ranger Series, sedan, 2 door, V8 . . . . **4,500.00**

Essex, 1928, coupe, rumble seat, 6 cyl **4,750.00**

Excalibur, 1965, Series I, roadster **15,000.00**

Ferrari, 1969, Model 365, Gran Turismo 2 + 2, V12 . . . . **19,500.00**

Ford Thunderbird, 1956, $13,000.00.

Ford, 1915, Model T, touring, 4 cyl . . . **12,000.00**

Ford, 1924, Model T, coupe, 4 cyl **4,000.00**

Ford, 1928, Model A, Tudor sedan **5,500.00**

Ford, 1930, Model A, deluxe roadster . . **9,750.00**

Ford, 1931, Model A, sedan, A-400 convertible, 4 cyl **23,000.00**

Ford, 1938, Model 81A, Standard, sedan, 4 door **4,250.00**

Ford, 1946, Super Deluxe, convertible, V8 . . . . **8,500.00**

Ford, 1949, Custom, woody station wagon, V8 . . . . **7,500.00**

Ford, 1951, Deluxe, sedan, 2 door, V8. **1,500.00**

Ford, 1956, Thunderbird, convertible, 302 V8 . . . . **16,000.00**

Ford, 1957, Sky Hardtop Convertible, 8 cyl **8,000.00**

Ford, 1963, Falcon Futura, sedan, 2 door, 6 cyl **1,800.00**

Ford, 1967, Mustang, convertible, 6 cyl **5,750.00**

Franklin, 1926, doctor's coupe, 6 cyl . . **12,500.00**

Gardner, 1927, Model 90, roadster, 8 cyl **6,000.00**

Graham, 1939, Model 97, Supercharged, sedan, 4 door, 6 cyl **5,500.00**

Henry J, 1951, Deluxe, sedan, 2 door, 6 cyl **2,500.00**

Hillman, 1923, drop head coupe, 4 cyl. **3,500.00**

Hudson, 1937, Custom Eight, Series 75,
Terraplane sedan, 8 cyl **4,500.00**
Hudson, 1952, Wasp, Series 5B, sedan,
4 door, 6 cyl **2,500.00**
Hupmobile, 1927, Model E, sedan, 6
cyl **8,000.00**
Isotta-Fraschini, 1929, Model 8A, phae-
ton, 8 cyl **90,000.00**
Jaguar, 1952, Model XK-120, roadster,
6 cyl **14,000.00**
Jensen, 1974, Interceptor, convertible,
V8 . . . . **17,500.00**
Jordan, 1930, Series T, roadster, 8 cyl **17,000.00**
Kaiser, 1953, Manhatten, sedan, 4 door,
6 cyl **2,600.00**
Kissel, 1923, Model 45, phaeton **12,000.00**
Laucia, 1911, touring **10,750.00**
LaSalle, 1929, Series 328, sedan, 4
door, V8 . . . . **20,000.00**
Lincoln, 1930, Model L, Standard Line,
sport phaeton, V8 . . . . **45,000.00**
Lincoln, 1949, Cosmopolitan, sports se-
dan, V8 . . . . **3,500.00**
Lincoln, 1956, Continental Mark II, hard-
top, V8 . . . . **12,000.00**
Lincoln, 1967, Continental, convertible,
4 door, V8 . . . . **5,575.00**
Lotus, 1963, Elan S1, roadster **9,500.00**
Marmon, 1925, Model D-74, open tour-
ing car phaeton. **30,000.00**
Maxwell, 1911, Model AB, runabout . . . **8,750.00**
Mercedes-Benz, Model 190-SL, 300
convertible **24,000.00**
Mercedes-Benz, Model 220S, sedan, 6
cyl **5,750.00**
Mercury, 1941, Series 09A, convertible,
V8 . . . . **17,500.00**
Mercury, 1950, Series OCM, coupe, V8 **5,000.00**
Mercury, 1963, Comet, convertible, 6
cyl **2,850.00**
MG, 1949, Model TC, roadster. **10,000.00**
Milburn, 1915, electric, coupe **7,500.00**
Nash, 1960, Metropolitan, Series 1500,
convertible, 4 cyl. **2,800.00**
Oakland, 1920, sport touring **6,500.00**
Oldsmobile, 1940, Series 90, sedan, 4
door, 8 cyl **4,500.00**
Oldsmobile, 1969, F-85, Cutlass-S, con-
vertible, V8 . . . . **3,000.00**
Opel, 1969, GT, 1.9 litre **1,500.00**
Overland, 1926, touring, 4 door **5,200.00**
Packard, 1929, Model 626, Standard
Eight, convertible, 8 cyl **40,000.00**
Packard, 1932, Model 902, convertible,
roadster **30,000.00**
Packard, 1948, Super 8, limousine **5,750.00**
Packard, 1952, 200 Std, convertible. . . **6,800.00**
Pierce-Arrow, 1931, Model 41, dual cowl
phaeton, 8 cyl **45,000.00**
Plymouth, 1930, Model U, sedan, 4 cyl **4,500.00**
Plymouth, 1954, Model P25-3, Belved-
ere, convertible, 6 cyl **3,650.00**
Plymouth, 1960, Fury, convertible, V8. . **2,200.00**

Pontiac, 1931, Model 401, sports coupe,
6 cyl. **9,250.00**
Pontiac, 1947, Streamliner, sedan, 8
cyl **2,750.00**
Pontiac, 1960, Bonneville Safari, station
wagon, 4 door, 8 cyl **1,500.00**
Porche, 1974, Model 911, coupe, 6 cyl **9,750.00**
Rambler, 1965, Marlin, V8 . . . . **3,000.00**
Renault, 1907, Model B2, limousine, 4
cyl **20,000.00**
Reo, 1910, 1 cyl. **12,000.00**
Reo, 1929, sedan, 4 door **4,250.00**
Rolls-Royce, 1927, Model PI, Spring-
field, convertible, 4 door **45,000.00**
Rolls-Royce, 1961, Cloud II, V8 . . . . . . **11,500.00**
Sayers & Scoville, 1926, Washington
Casket Coach **7,500.00**
Schacht, 1905, 2 passenger **9,500.00**
Singer, 1952, roadster, 6 cyl **3,650.00**
Star, 1926, sedan, 4 door, 4 cyl. **5,750.00**
Stoddard Dayton, 1911, touring, 30 hp. **20,000.00**
Studebaker, 1941, Model 7C, President,
sedan, 8 cyl **4,500.00**
Studebaker, 1950, Champion Starlite,
coupe, 6 cyl **3,750.00**
Studebaker, 1963, Avanti, hardtop, V8. **12,000.00**
Triumph, 1967, GT6 . . . . **3,250.00**
Volkeswagon, 1954, DeLuxe, sedan, 2
door, 4 cyl **3,500.00**
Volvo, 1972, P-1800ES. **5,750.00**
Willy-Knight, 1927, Model 70, sedan, 4
door. **5,750.00**

MISCELLANEOUS

Fire Engines
Ahrens Fox, 1928, NS4, pumper. . . . **8,000.00**
American-LaFrance, 1951, Series
700, 350 gpm, pumper **3,500.00**
Chevrolet, 1936, pumper **850.00**
Mack, 1946, Type 45, 500 gpm,
pumper **4,200.00**
Monarch, 1926, pumper, Buda 6 cyl
engine. **4,750.00**
Seagrave, 1944, aerial ladder, 65',
Pierce V12 . . . . **3,000.00**
Seagrave, 1954, pumper, V12 . . . . . **5,000.00**
Stoughton, 1916, pumper. **4,000.00**
Motorcycles
Ariel, square four, 1958 . . . . **3,500.00**
BSA, 1948, B33, 500 single **1,350.00**
Excelsior, 1914 . . . . **2,500.00**
Harley,1942,Police Special, ULH,80 ci **4,000.00**
Indian, 1938, Junior Scout **4,000.00**
Nimbus, 1948 . . . . **2,800.00**
Smith, 1916, motor wheel on bicycle. **1,800.00**
Trucks
Chevrolet, 1931, 1½ ton panel **6,500.00**
Dodge, 1952, Big 6, 1½ ton, tow . . . **6,500.00**
Ford, 1922, Model TT **5,000.00**
Ford, 1926, Model T stake. **6,700.00**
Ford, 1930, Model A, popcorn
wagon. **18,000.00**

Chevrolet Huckster truck, 1932, $4,500.00.

Ford, 1947, Deluxe Sedan, delivery, 8	9,000.00
International, 1941, pick-up, grain box	1,500.00
Moreland, 1925, F02, flatbed, stake sides	3,000.00
Plymouth, 1941, pick-up	3,750.00
Reo, 1948, 1½ ton stake	1,650.00
Willys, 1951, M-38 military Jeep	4,500.00

AUTOMOBILIA

History: The amount of items related to the automobile is endless. Collectors seem to fit into three groups - those collecting parts to restore a car, those collecting information about a company or certain model for research purposes, and those trying to use automobile items for decorative purposes. Most material changes hands at the hundreds of swap meets and auto shows around the country.

Periodical: *Hemmings Motor News*, Box 100, Bennington, VT 05201. Subscription: $15.50.

Advertising	
Card, showroom, Studebaker, 1954	3.00
Poster, showroom, Willys, 1957, all Jeep models, color	35.00
Sign, Ford, dealer's, neon	750.00
Ashtray, 1933, Chrysler, Corp., World's Fair, copper	12.50
Bottle Opener, Chevrolet, 1957, Smooth and Sassy	20.00
Buttons, pinback	
Buick, "Looking Fine for 39"	45.00
Chevrolet, 1932, Queen of the Shows	15.00
Carburetors	
Chevrolet, 1929-31, Carter brass bowl, rebuilt	120.00
Holley, 1907-08, updraft	175.00
International Harvester, brass	50.00
Locomobile, 1915-23, bronze and aluminum	350.00
Oldsmobile, 1949-60, 2 barrel	115.00
Clock, Ford, 1937	50.00

Employee's Badges, metal	
Chevrolet, Janesville	30.00
Ford, Rouge, Buffalo Stamping, and Highland Park	15.00
Engines	
Cadillac, 1915–18, V8	1,500.00
Maxwell, 1914	250.00
Gearshift Knob, blue and white glass swirl, no insert	15.00
Grilles	
Mercedes 300SL	1,850.00
Packard, 1941	125.00
Horn, Pierce-Arrow, outside, Bosch	100.00
Lamps	
Auteroche, French, taxi, nickel-plated, sidelamps, pr.	150.00
J. Carriere, metal, self-generating, headlamp	75.00
Dietz, Regal, right, bail, sidelamp	100.00
Ducellier, metal, self-generating, headlamp	75.00
E & J, black/brass, 3-lens, tail lamp	50.00
Nirona #600, bullet, headlamps, pr.	300.00
License Plates	
Enameled, each	10–25.00
Porcelain, each	35–100.00
Literature	
ABC Automobiles, 1908-10, non-color catalog, 6 x 8½", 24 pgs	125.00
Chevrolet, 1930, Salesman's non-color catalog, 5 x 7½", 169 pgs	100.00
Chevrolet, 1964, Dealer's large part-color catalog, "Spotlight"	14.00
Durant, 1929, non-color folder, Specs and prices, 4 & 6-60	16.00
Ford, 1957, Thunderbird, large color catalog, folded, #7706	55.00
Holsman, 1909, part-color folder, 17 x 11½"	60.00
Nash, 1949, Prestige, color catalog	25.00

Advertising Sign, 27⅞ x 9⅝", tin litho, H. L. Moore Co., Cochranton, PA, $55.00.

Pierce-Arrow, 1920, owner's manual	60.00
Stanley, 1908, non-color catalog, 9 x 6", 24 pgs	100.00
Magazines	
Chevrolet Friends, June 1952	5.00
Ford Times, May 1932	25.00
Road and Track, August 1951 to Dec. 1960, 94 issues	200.00
Medallions, brass	
Chevrolet, Ready for Winter	10.00

Chrysler, 1934, A Century Of Progress In A Decade	25.00
Cyrus McCormick Centennial Of Reaper	12.00

Ornaments, Hood

Bulldog	75.00
Bugatti	150.00
DeSoto, 1941	40.00
Lincoln, 1953	50.00
Packard, 1926–31	160.00
Packard, 1935-38, part #304766	50.00

Ornaments, Radiator, Pontiac, 1928, Indian head	150.00
Pencil, mechanical, wooden bat shape, "Chevrolet You're Up"	30.00
Plate, Buick, dinner, stoneware, Odd Fellows lodge emblem on top, Buick in blue script logo on bottom	45.00

Postcards

Apperson, 1922, plus advertising letter	18.00
Buick, 1939, King & Queen Of England, convertible	25.00
Ford, 1930s, tri-motor plane	8.00

Radios

Buick, Skylark, 1970-72, AM-FM	35.00
Ford, Thunderbird, 1962, AM	50.00
Stewart-Warner, 1931-33, large model, steering column dial	300.00

Radiator Shells

Buick, 1911–13	550.00
Ford, English, 1965	15.00
Mercury, 1953	75.00
Reo, diamond, chrome	75.00

Record, 1965, Oldsmobile, Promotional, popular songs	12.00
Record Jacket, 1963, LP, Buick Riviera on cover	15.00
Shoe Shine Cloth, Kaiser-Frazer, 1940s	10.00
Speedometer, Dodge, 1935	25.00
Starter, Pierce-Arrow, 1915-21, 48 hp.	200.00

Toys

Champion Motorcycle, driver, side car, 6"	125.00
Fire Engine, Buddy L, unrestored, no rust	225.00
Gas Station, Texaco, Keystone, 1940s	100.00
Plymouth, Dinky #278, taxi, 1970s	10.00
Pontiac, 1954, 2 door, red, 10", friction, India	45.00

BACCARAT GLASS

History: The Sainte-Anne glassworks at Baccarat in the Voges, France, was founded in 1764

and produced utilitarian soda glass. In 1816 Aime-Gabriel d'Artiques purchased the glassworks; and, a Royal Warrant was issued in 1817 for the opening of Verrerie de Vonêche à Baccarat. The firm concentrated on lead crystal glass products. In 1824 a limited company was created.

From 1823 to 1857 Baccarat and Saint-Louis glassworks had a commercial agreement and used the same outlets. No merger occurred. Baccarat began the production of paperweights in 1846. In the late 19th century the firm achieved an international reputation for cut glass table services, chandeliers, display vases and centerpieces, and sculptures. Products eventually included all forms of glass ware. The firm still is active today.

Additional Listing: Paperweights.

Perfume Atomizer, 6", Amberina, $60.00.

Biscuit Jar, 6", etched ground, cranberry flowers, leaves, and vines, sgd inside lid	400.00

Bowls

4½" d, Rose Teinte, swirl, sgd	50.00
5½", cameo, clear etched leaf ground, chartreuse floral dec	60.00

Candy Dish, 8½" h, 5¼" d, pastel pink and yellow ground, hp roses, gold handle, artist sgd, 1916	35.00
Champagne, nude on clear stem	45.00

Cologne Bottles, orig stoppers

6¾" h, 2½" d, Rose Teinte, emb swirl pattern	70.00
7" h, 3" d, Rose Teinte, emb alternating diamond point swirl and plain panels, pr	150.00
7¾" h, faceted, gilt classical scene, mkd Houbigand, Baccarat, France	70.00
8" h, 3" d, Rose Teinte, emb swirl pattern	90.00

Decanter, 9¾" h, Rose Teinte, matching stopper	110.00

Dresser Tray, 12″ d, Rose Teinte.	**85.00**
Epergnes	
12½″ h, bronze base, upper bowl supported by two bronze cherubs. . . .	**200.00**
15″ h, 10″ d, scalloped edges, Rose Teinte Swirl, 3 vases	**450.00**
Fairy Lamps	
3¾″ h, Rose Teinte, emb sunburst, matching saucer	**200.00**
4½″, amberina	**225.00**
Figures, pr, pelicans, 6½″, crystal	**225.00**
Finger Bowl, 4¾″ d, underplate, 6¼″ d, ruby, gold dec, medallions and florals.	**325.00**
Goblet	
Green to clear, sgd	**90.00**
Rose Teinte, 4½″ h, emb swirl	**55.00**
Perfume Bottles, orig stoppers	
3″, Buddha shape	**65.00**
1½″ w, 3″ d, 4½″ h, clear glass, rectangular, roof like top overhang, ground glass stopper with open triangle finial.	**45.00**
5¾″ h, Rose Teinte, emb swirl	**70.00**
Plate, 7″, amberina, swirl.	**55.00**
Ring Tree, 3″ h, sq base, swirl.	**60.00**
Rose Bowl, 3″ h, cranberry, lace enamel dec	**150.00**
Sugar, cov, 4¾″ h, 4½″ d, Rose Teinte, emb swirl	**95.00**
Toothpick, 2½″ h, scalloped top, Rose Teinte, ovals.	**100.00**
Tray, 11¼″ d, round, scalloped edge, Rose Teinte, emb swirl	**90.00**
Tumbler, 4″, green octagonal panels with jewels, gold trim	**70.00**
Tumble-Up, Rose Teinte, swirl.	**150.00**
Vases	
7″, teardrop, sgd	**50.00**
14⅜″ h, 6½″ d, trumpet shape, scalloped top, Rose Teinte swirl, fancy ormolu base	**225.00**
16″, cameo, clear, etched with cranberry flowers	**300.00**
Wash Bowl and Pitcher, Rose Teinte, swirl, sgd	**550.00**
Water Set, Thumbprint, amberina, 7″ pitcher, six 4″ glasses	**300.00**
Wine, Perfection pattern	**45.00**

BANKS, MECHANICAL

History: Banks which display some form of action while utilizing a coin are considered mechanical banks. Although mechanical banks are known which date back to ancient Greece and Rome, the majority of collectors center their interests in those made between 1867 and 1928 in Germany, England, and the United States. Recently there has been an upsurge of interest in later types, some of which date into the 1970s.

Initial research suggested that approximately 250 to 300 different or variant designs of banks were made in the early period. Today that number has been revised to 2,000–3,000 types and varieties. The field remains ripe for discovery and research.

Over 80% of all cast iron mechanical banks produced between 1869 and 1928 were made by J.E. Stevens Co., Cromwell, CT. Tin banks tend to be German in origin.

Reproductions, fakes, and forgeries exist of many banks. Forgeries of some mechanical banks were made as early as 1937, so age alone is not a guarantee of authenticity. In our listing two "**" indicate banks for which serious forgeries exist and one "*" banks for which casual reproductions have been made.

While rarity is a factor in value, appeal of design, action, quality or manufacture, country of origin, and history of collector interest also are important. Radical price fluctuations may occur with an imbalance of these factors. Rare banks may sell for a few hundred dollars while one of more common design with greater appeal will sell in the thousands.

While a few mechanical banks have dropped in value, far more have risen dramatically this past year. The most important event ever to take place in mechanical bank collecting circles, the dispersal of the Edwin Mosler Collection at an individually priced outright sale, occurred in 1983. The Mosler collection was the most comprehensive of all known mechanical bank collections. On Mosler's death, rumors swept the field of a possible upcoming collapse in mechanical bank prices due to the large number of banks that would appear in the market. In reality, several million dollars' worth of banks were absorbed readily within a few days; and, there was an upward surge in the market stimulated by the supply.

The prices on our list represented fairly what a bank sells for in the specialized collectors market. Some banks are hard to find and establishing a price outside auction is difficult.

The prices listed are for original old mechanical banks with no repaired, missing, or replaced parts, in sound operating condition, and with the vast majority of the original paint intact.

Reference: Bill Norman, *The Bank Book: The Encyclopedia of Mechanical Bank Collecting,* Collectors' Showcase, 1984.

Advisor: James S. Maxwell, Jr.

**Afghanistan, iron	**1,450.00**
African Native, tin	**420.00**
Alligator, pot metal, spring jawed	**400.00**
Artillery Bank, eight sided block house, cannon shoots	**575.00**
Aunt Dinah and the Good Fairy	**RARE**
Automatic Coin Savings, iron	**1,800.00**
Baby Elephant Unlocks at 10 o'clock, lead and wood	**5,750.00**
Bamboula, iron	**575.00**
Bank Teller, iron, tall man behind three sided lattice work grill	**8,000.00**

**Acrobats, iron, $1,000.00.

Bear, tin.	900.00
**Bear & Tree Stump, iron	675.00
**Bill E. Grin, iron.	750.00
**Bird on Roof, iron	975.00
Blacksmith, lead.	2,875.00
Bow-ery, iron, wooden works.	15,000.00
Bowling Alley, wood and iron, ball knocks down wooden pins and rings bell	18,000.00
**Boy and Bull Dog, brass	650.00
**Boy Robbing Bird's Nest, iron.	1,350.00
Boy Scout with Tray, tin	950.00
Breadwinners, iron	5,500.00
**Bucking Mule, iron.	1,000.00
**Bull and Bear, brass	3,000.00
Bulldog, tin, English type.	550.00
**Bulldog Standing, coin on tongue	575.00
**Bull with Movable Horns, iron.	335.00
Bureau, iron, Ideal	750.00
Bureau, wood, Lewando's toy savings	1,050.00
Bureau, wood, Serrill patent.	975.00
**Butting Goat, tree stump	650.00
*Cabin, iron	275.00
Called Out, brass pattern	3,250.00
**Called Out, iron, painted	6,000.00
Calumet with Calumet Kid, cardboard and tin can.	150.00
Calumet with Sailor, cardboard and tin can	300.00
Calumet with Soldier, cardboard and tin can	300.00
**Camera, iron.	2,400.00
Carnival, iron	1,125.00
**Cat & Mouse, iron, cat stands on hands.	940.00
Cat, pot metal, spring jawed	300.00
**Chief Big Moon, iron	845.00
Chinaman, coin on tongue.	405.00
Chinaman in Boat, lead.	10,000.00
Chinaman with Queue, tin	1,750.00
Circus, iron	4,450.00
Clever Dick, tin.	1,200.00

Clown, tin, white faced	475.00
Clown Bust with Acorn Shaped Hat, iron	1,900.00
Clown on Lattice Base, tin clown with tray on iron base, does flip.	8,000.00
Coasting, iron.	7,500.00
Columbian Magic Savings, iron	215.00
*Creedmoor, iron	445.00
Crossed Legged Minstrel, tin	675.00
Cupola, iron, man in circular building	1,800.00
*Darktown Battery, iron.	925.00
Darky Fisherman, lead	14,000.00
Dinah, iron.	300.00
Ding Dong Bell, tin, wind-up	8,000.00
Dog on Turntable, iron	400.00
Dog Standing, tin, nods head	2,000.00
Droste's, tin	360.00
*Eagle and Eaglettes, iron.	575.00
**Elephant, iron, Hannibal.	540.00
Elephant, iron, made in Canada, trunk moves	625.00
**Elephant, iron, three stars	335.00
**Elephant, iron, tusks on wheels	1,800.00
Elephant, tin, safe deposit.	5,000.00
*Elephant and Three Clowns.	950.00
**Elephant with Howdah, iron, pull tail	240.00
Feed the Goose, pot metal	280.00
Feed the Kitty, pot metal.	650.00
**Ferris Wheel, iron and tin, no markings (smaller then Bowen's Pat. model)	1,500.00
Five Cent Adding, iron	945.00
**Football, iron, boy and shed.	1,900.00
Fortune Wheel, tin	875.00
Freedman, wood, pewter, cloth, etc., man sitting at desk	RARE
**Frogs, iron, two.	475.00
Frogs on Rock, iron	270.00
**Gem, iron.	400.00
Giant in Tower, iron	5,500.00
*Girl Skipping Rope, iron.	6,000.00
**Glutton, iron, lifts turkey.	725.00
**Goat, Frog, and Old Man, iron	2,000.00
Grenadier, iron.	540.00
Guessing, lead and iron, woman's figure	10,000.00
Hall's Excelsior, iron and wood, monkey figure	335.00
Hall's Lilliput, Type I	700.00
Hall's Lilliput, Type III	350.00
Hall's Yankee Notion, iron.	2,700.00
Hardwig and Vogel Candy Dispenser, tin	660.00
Hen and Chick, iron	1,125.00
**Hindu, iron	1,450.00
**Hold the Fort, iron, seven holes	1,900.00
Home, tin.	240.00
Hoop-la, iron	725.00
**Horse Race, iron with tin horses, straight base.	1,650.00
Horse Race Savings Bank, tin, Pat. Oct. 5, 1897	5,000.00
Huntley and Palmers Biscuit Tin, drawer pulls out.	710.00

I Always Did 'Spise A Mule, iron, jockey 540.00
***Indian and Bear, iron, brown bear ... 750.00
Indian Chief, aluminum, bust, black face with headress .... **RARE**
Japanese Ball Tosser, tin, wind-up. ... **RARE**
John Bull's Money Box, iron 8,000.00
**Jolly Nigger, aluminum, bar and screw side 165.00
**Jolly Nigger, aluminum, moves ears, high hat 250.00
**Jolly Nigger, aluminum, with fez 400.00
**Jolly Nigger, iron, butterfly tie 190.00
**Jolly Nigger, iron, fixed eyes. 240.00
*Jonah and Whale, iron, rectangular base 925.00
**Jumbo, iron, elephant on wheels 1,125.00
Key, iron, Golden Gate Exposition 625.00
Kilte, iron. 850.00
Lehmann London Tower, tin 2,200.00
Lighthouse, pot metal 600.00
Lion, tin. 1,150.00
**Lion and Two Monkeys, iron 575.00
Little Jack Horner, tin, wind-up. ...... **RARE**
Little Joe, iron 205.00
**Lost Dog, iron. 725.00
**Magic Man, iron 750.00
Magic Safe, tin. 450.00
Magie, tin. 1,400.00
**Mama Katzenjammer, iron, 1905–08, dark blue dress painted to neck 2,750.00
Mammy and Child, iron 1,100.00
Man in Chair with Dog near Feet, wood 2,300.00
Man standing wearing Top Hat, wood . 835.00
Memorial Liberty Bell, iron. 640.00
**Merry-Go-Round, iron, semi-mechanical version 400.00
Mickey Mouse with Accordian, tin 4,000.00
**Milking Cow, iron. 1,800.00

Model Railroad Drink Dispenser, tin ... 2,200.00
Model Railroad Ticket Dispenser, tin .. 2,200.00
**Monkey, iron, drop coin in stomach . 1,800.00
Monkey Face. 1,125.00
Moody and Sanky, iron and paper 700.00
Moonface, tin. 1,000.00
Motor, iron, trolley car. 5,000.00
Musical, tin 875.00
Musical Savings, wood and tin, Regina music box. 4,000.00
Musical Savings, wood base 2,075.00
National, iron 1,000.00
New, iron, lever on side 500.00
North Pole, iron 5,500.00
Novelty, iron, Johnson's Pat. 400.00
Old Woman in Shoe, iron .... **RARE**
*Organ, iron, boy and girl 575.00
*Organ, iron, medium 625.00
Owl, iron, slot in book. 370.00
*Owl, iron, turns head. 270.00
Panorama, iron. 2,000.00
Patronize the Blind Man, iron. 1,900.00
**Pelican with Arab, iron. 900.00
**Pelican with man thumbing Nose, iron 1,125.00
**Perfection Registering, iron, girl at blackboard 3,850.00
**Piano, iron, modern conversion to musical. 1,000.00
Picture Gallery Bank. 2,250.00
Pistol, cast iron 1,000.00
Popeye Knockout, tin 375.00
Preacher in Pulpit, iron .... **RARE**
Preston, iron and sheet metal, 1930s house. 525.00
Presto, iron, small building with drawer 205.00
Professor Pug Frog, iron. 2,700.00
Punch and Judy, cast iron front, tin back. 1,550.00
Punch and Judy, tin, beach scene 300.00
Puss and Boots, iron 20,000.00
Queen Victoria, brass, bust 5,000.00
Rabbit, iron, small. 475.00
Registering Dime Savings 425.00
Robot, aluminum 3,000.00
**Rooster, iron. 305.00
Sailor Face, tin. 775.00
Sambo, iron 625.00
**Santa Claus, iron. 780.00
Savo, tin, rectangular with lines 210.00
Savo, tin, rectangular with soldiers. ... 275.00
Schley Bottling Up Cervera, iron 6,000.00
Seek Him Frisk, iron, dog chases cat up tree 30,000.00
Sentry, tin, raises bugle. 1,000.00
Shoot That Hat, iron. 12,000.00
Shoot the Chute, iron. 6,500.00
**Smyth X-Ray, iron. 2,150.00
**Snap It, iron 270.00
Springing Cat, lead. 6,000.00
Squirrel, lead 285.00
Starkies Aeroplane .... **RARE**
Stollwerk, tin, Vending. 200.00

*Stump Speaker	875.00
**Tabby, iron	540.00
Tank and Cannon, iron	595.00
Target Building, iron	750.00
*Teddy and the Bear, iron	840.00
Thrifty Animal, tin	420.00
Tid-Bits Automatic Money Box, tin	1,250.00
Time Is Money, iron, embossing of man bent over	5,000.00
Toad on Stump, iron	440.00
Tommy iron	2,915.00
*Trick Dog, iron, six part base	540.00
**Trick Donkey, iron	605.00
Trick Savings, wood, end drawer	285.00
**Tricky Pig, iron, risque	1,000.00
**Turtle, iron	10,000.00
Twentieth Century Savings Bank	1,250.00
U. S., iron	1,675.00
Uncle Sam, iron, standing figure	1,000.00
**Uncle Tom, iron, no star	540.00
Uncle Tom, iron, no lapels	510.00
Village School Master, tin, wind-up	RARE
Watch, tin, dime disappears, several varieties	1,100.00
Watch Dog Savings, wood	950.00
*William Tell, iron	540.00
Winner Savings, tin and glass, horse race	5,750.00
Wishbone, iron	12,500.00
Woodchopper, iron	810.00
Woodpecker, tin, 1940s	300.00
World's Fair, iron	965.00

BANKS, STILL

History: Banks with no mechanical action are known as still banks. Many of these banks were made in the United States with leading manufacturers being Arcade Mfg. Co., J. Chein & Co., Hubley, Kenton Hardware Mfg. Co., J. & E. Stevens, and A. C. Williams.

Banks can be found in all forms, e.g., animals, buildings, character figures, safes, etc. Although the early cast iron banks are most popular, collectors also focus on aluminum, glass, plastic, pottery, and tin examples. Banks with advertising features are eagerly sought.

References: Andy and Susan Moore, *The Penny Bank Book-Collecting Still Banks*, Schiffer Publishing Ltd, 1984; Earnest and Ida Long and Jane Pitman, *Dictionary of Still Banks*, privately printed, 1980; Robert L. McCumber, *Toy Bank Reproductions and Fakes*, privately printed, 1970; Hurbert B. Whitman, *Old Iron Still Banks*, 1968, out-of-print.

Collectors' Club: Still Bank Collectors Club of America, P.O. Box 356, Bradford, VT 05033.

GLASS STILL BANKS

Baseball, Mobil Gas, plastic base	65.00
Boy On Drum, 4¼", painted, tin closure	25.00
Bulldog, 4½", sitting, tin closure	30.00
Clock, 3¾", mantel, painted, tin closure	20.00
Happy Fats, Boy On Drum, painted, tin closure	30.00
House, 3" w, clear, Pittsburgh Paint House	30.00
Independence Hall, 7¼", clear, tin closure	225.00
Kewpie and Barrel, 3¼", painted	15.00
Liberty Bells	
4¼", blue glass	20.00
4¼", milk glass, orig label, Liberty Bell, Robinson & Loeble's Wine Jelly, tin closure	30.00
Monkey, Jocko	20.00
Owl, 7", carnival glass, marigold	22.00
Pig, 4¼" l, painted, gold	20.00
Radio, clear	25.00
World Globe, 4½", clear	50.00

METAL STILL BANKS

Animals

Bear, 6¼", standing upright	225.00
Bird On Stump, 4¾", painted	165.00
Buffalo, 5", painted, Amherst Stove	100.00
Camel, 7¼", painted	125.00
Cat, 3⅞", painted, black with red bow, "Cutie Bank"	48.00
Cow, 5" l, painted	150.00
Deer, 6", with antlers	45.00
Dogs	
Dog on tub, 4", painted	60.00
Dog with pack, 5½"	35.00
Fido, 4¾", painted	50.00
Scotty, 3¼", painted	100.00
Spitz, 4¼", painted, gold	100.00
Donkey, 7 x 7", painted	95.00
Ducks	
4", painted	225.00
5½", duck on tub wearing top hat, "Save For A Rainy Day"	100.00
Elephant, 4", trunk in air, "G.O.P."	45.00
Goose, painted, gold	115.00
Horse, prancing, 7½", oblong base, painted	55.00
Lion, sitting on tub, 5½"	110.00
Pig, 7" l, "A Christmas Roast"	85.00
Polar Bear, sitting up, 5¼", c1930	25.00
Rabbit, standing, 6¾", painted	100.00
Squirrel, eating nut, 4", painted	500.00
Turkey, 3¾", painted	75.00

Other

Barrel, dime registering, 4", japanned	35.00
Baseball player	85.00
Basket, harvest type, side handles, registering, 3", electroplated	30.00
Battle Ship Oregon, 4" h, 5" l, no paint	250.00
Billiken, seated, 4¼", painted, gold, red trim	35.00

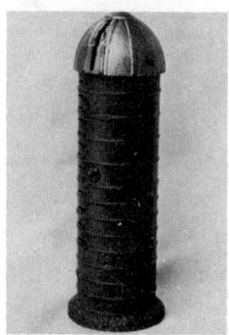

Cast Iron, 5½″, "A Marietta Silo Saves You Money," gray, silver top, $475.00.

Boy Scout, standing, holding tall stick in right hand, 6″, painted, gold . . .	65.00
Buildings	
Church, 7½″, painted, die cast . . .	150.00
House, 11″, painted, cardboard dividers inside, no lock	425.00
State Bank, 8½″, japanned	200.00
Buster Brown, Tige, horse, and horseshoe	100.00
Campbell Kids, 3¼″	90.00
Captain Kid, beside tree trunk, 6″ . . .	120.00
Chest, combination lock, 6¼″ w, emb swirl, ftd. electroplated	65.00
Clock, 3¾″, "A Money Saver"	65.00
Clown with crooked hat, standing, 6¾″, painted	500.00
Crosley Radio, 4¼″, painted, cast iron and pressed steel, Kenton	25.00
Devil, 2 faced, 4¼″, painted, black . .	265.00
Elephant Clown, seated, 4″, painted	125.00
Gas Pump, 5¾″, painted	225.00
Golliwog, standing, 6¼″, gray, aluminum	35.00
Graf Zeppelin, 6½″, painted, silver . .	125.00
Kitchen Sink with Pump, 6″ w, painted	40.00
Mail Box, 5½″, painted, green, "US Mail," die cast	35.00
Mammy, black, right arm holds basket, 5½″, painted	90.00
Mary and Little Lamb, painted	225.00
Money Box, handle, 4½″, electroplated	25.00
Moody and Sankey Hold the Fort, 5″, painted	375.00
Old Negro Head, double faced, 4¼″ h, 3″ d	150.00
Palace, 8″ h to top of cupola	325.00
Parlor Stove, 7″, nickel plated	275.00
Phonograph, 5″, "Save For Your Brunswick," electroplated, die cast	50.00

Policeman, 5½″, painted, Arcade . . .	175.00
Rumplestiltskin, seated, 6″, painted .	200.00
Safes	
Mascot Safe, 5″, litho and pressed steel	100.00
Security Safe Deposit, 8½″, drawers inside	145.00
Soldier's Hat, 2″ h, WWI style, pressed steel	55.00
Statue of Liberty, 6″	60.00
Tank, 6″ l, painted, gold, "Tank Bank, USA, 1918".	110.00
Trolley, 4½″	190.00
Trunk, 2½″, painted.	25.00
Washington Bust, 8″, painted	600.00
Yellow Cab, 3½″ l, painted.	750.00

POTTERY STILL BANKS

Accordion, 3¼″ w	200.00
Acorn, 3″, brown	125.00
Bear in Wheelchair, 4″ h	825.00
Beehive, 4½″	300.00
Buffalo, reclining, 6″l, glazed, brown. . .	35.00
Cat, sitting, 3¼″	95.00
Dog's Head, 4″, mottled	445.00
Happy Hooligan in Barrel, 4½″, glazed	35.00
Hat, 3″, glazed	45.00
House, 3½″ l, two chimneys	65.00
Jug, 4½″ h.	40.00
Lincoln's Log Cabin, 3¾″, Austria, Van Dyke Texas	200.00
Owl on Tree Stump, 7″, painted.	45.00
Pig, sitting, 6″ l, glazed	35.00
Ram's Head, 3″	125.00

Pottery, 2¾″ sq., ochre, $35.00.

Santa Claus, standing, pack on back, oval base, 6¾″	700.00
Shoe, man's high top, 5½″	125.00
Soldier, emerging from tank, 4″ h, "Where's That Blinking Kaiser"	350.00
Teapot, 3¼″, basketweave base, brown.	65.00

BARBER BOTTLES

History: Barber bottles, colorful glass bottles found on the shelves and counters in barber shops, held the liquids barbers used daily. A specific liquid was kept in a specific bottle which the barber knew by color, design, or lettering. The bulk liquids were kept in utilitarian containers under the counter or in a storage room. The attractive bottles held the place of honor.

Barber bottles are found in many types of glass: art glass with varied decoration, pattern glass, and commercially prepared and labeled bottles.

References: Hugh Cleveland, *Bottle Pricing Guide,* Collector Books, 1980; Ralph & Terry Kovel, *The Kovel's Bottle Price List,* Crown Publishers, Inc., 1982, 6th ed.

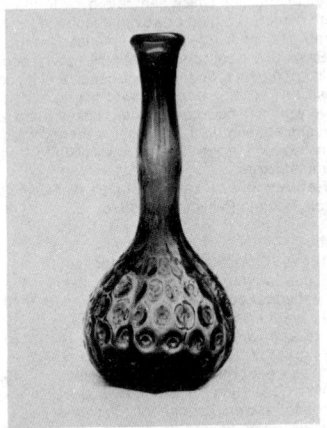

Teal, 8¾", I.V.T., made in South NJ, $100.00.

Blown
Amethyst

Enamel floral dec, gilt trim	100.00
Enamel floral dec, lady's leg stopper	175.00
Cobalt blue, enamel floral dec	150.00
Ruby, cut design	125.00
Sapphire blue, IVT	110.00
Clambroth, pr, red letters, one "Witch Hazel," other "Water"	75.00
Cut Glass, Brilliant period, orig top	135.00
Cranberry, IVT, orig white porcelain stopper	125.00
Hobnail	
Amber, orig top	90.00
Cranberry, orig top	100.00
Mary Gregory type, cobalt, boy playing tennis	175.00

Milk Glass, adv "Silkodono for Hair and Scalp"	75.00
Opalescent	
Amber, Honeycomb pattern	145.00
Blue, Stars & Stripes pattern, orig top	200.00
Cranberry, raised coral design, 6⅞" .	150.00
White	
Swirl pattern, orig pewter top	145.00
Windows pattern, polished pontil . .	125.00
Opaline, "Herkel Bros., K.C., MO, Hair Tonic" in gold letters, enameled flowers	80.00
Porcelain, hp roses, "Bay Rum" in gold	75.00
Satin, azure, silver overlay in Art Nouveau flowers	200.00
Spatter, blue and white	125.00

BAROMETERS

History: A barometer is an instrument which measures atmospheric pressure which, in turn, aids weather forecasting. Low pressure indicates the coming of rain, snow, or storm; high pressure signifies fair weather.

Most barometers use an evacuated and graduated glass tube which contains a column of mercury and are classified by the shape of the case. An aneroid barometer has no liquid and works by a needle connected to the top of a metal box in which a partial vacuum is maintained. The movement of the top moves the needle.

Aneroid	
6½" d, hand carved oak frame	55.00
13" dial, wood case	50.00
Banjo	
35½" h, mahogany, thermometer, architectural cresting	300.00
38", mahogany, satinwood inlay, George III, sgd A. Lolca, c1800 . . .	400.00
38½", mahogany, inlaid case, thermometer and silvered dial, sgd "Pastorelli, Bowling St., Westminster," Victorian	600.00
44", mahogany, clock, barometer, level, hygrometer, mercury thermometer, sgd "J. Vassalli, Scarborough," late 18th C	1,200.00
Desk Top, gilt metal, clock, barometer, and thermometer, light house shape, 21" h	775.00
Gimbal	
36½" h, stick, carved mahogany, arched glass panel, gilt surround, engraved ivory weather indicator inscribed "Fair, Change, Rain, Stormy" below "S. Willard, Boston," adjustable brass gimbal	5,000.00
39½", cherry, replaced pendant, mercury missing, sgd "C. Wilder, Peterboro, N.H."	450.00

Stick
35¼", walnut, turned bulb cover, white
metal face **700.00**
37¼", curly walnut case, white metal
plated brass face plate engraved
"Charles Wilder, Aterboro, N.H.",
mercury tube intact **675.00**
38", mahogany, gabled top, thermom-
eter, ivory scales, sgd Cary, London,
late Victorian **650.00**
38", walnut, sgd "John M. Merrick &
Co., Worcester, MA, Timky's Patent
No. 3, 1857" **400.00**
39", mahogany, George III, thermom-
eter,sgd "A. Crioli, Fecit," late 18th C **750.00**
39¼", marine, silvered scales, thermometer, maker's name (Cary) en-
graved on brass plaque **1,000.00**
43", walnut, Queen Anne, urn top and
bottom, c1790 . . . . **2,000.00**

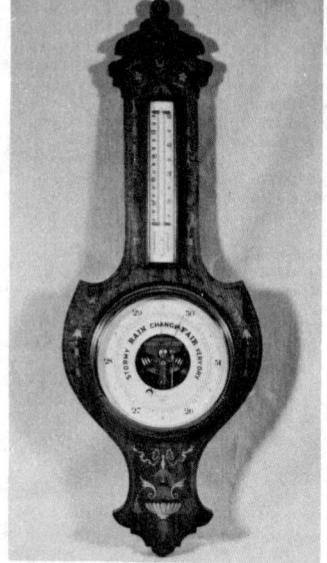

**Banjo, 33½" h, mahogany, mkd "Short
& Mason, London, TYCOS #2468,
$1,250.00.**

Wheel
38" h, mahogany, case inset with thermometer and hydrometer, S.
Crocker, Kingston **300.00**
41", walnut, 9½" silvered register,
sgd "J. Casartelli, Manchester,"
restored **350.00**

43½", rosewood, mercury wheel, inlaid with brass foliage, mid 19th C **450.00**
44¾", rosewood, 11½" silvered dial,
cast inlaid with cut MOP, mounted
with bow front thermometer, sgd "J.
Amadio, 6 Shorters Court, Throg-
morton Str, City" **1,650.00**

BASKETS

History: Baskets were invented when man first
required containers to gather, store, and transport
goods. Today's collector, influenced by the country
look, focuses on baskets made of splint, rye straw,
or willow. Emphasis is placed on handmade examples. Nails or staples, wide splints which are thin
and evenly cut, and a wire bail handle denote factory construction which can date back to the mid-
19th century. Painted or woven decorated baskets
rarely are handmade, unless American Indian.

Baskets are collected by (a) type - berry, egg, or
field, (b) region - Nantucket or Shaker, and (c) composition - splint, rye, or willow. Stick to examples
in very good condition; damaged baskets are a poor
investment even at a low price. Modern reproductions abound, from the craft revivalists to foreign
manufacturers.

Reference: Lew Larson, *The Basket Collectors
Book,* Scorpio Publications, 1978.

Berry
10" w, 10½" d, 6" h plus wooden handle, woven splint, buttocks, good
age and color **70.00**
10¾ x 11½ x 5½" plus wooden han-
dle, woven splint, buttocks **135.00**
Drying, 11 x 15 x 6¼", woven splint,
open work bottom, open rim handles **45.00**
Feather Gathering, 14" d, 18" h, Shaker,
painted brown, permanently fastened
cover slides up and down, 19th C. . . **550.00**
Food Storage
12½ x 18 x 13", woven splint, cover,
potato print design in faded red,
blue, and green **150.00**
27" h, woven splint, cover, bentwood
handles **60.00**
Garden, 9" d, 7" h, woven splint, wooden
handle, sgd in pencil "D. S. & R. L.
Pierce" **75.00**
Gathering
11¾ x 16¼ x 6¾" plus wooden handle, woven splint, buttocks, 2
wooden strengthening battens in
bottom, minor wear **125.00**
12½ x 13½ x 6" plus wooden handle,
woven splint, well made, good cond,
early 20th C **85.00**
17 x 23 x 7¾", woven splint, oblong,
built up rim handles, good age and
color, minor rim wear **75.00**
18 x 9 x 13", woven splint, well shaped

Field, 23 x 15″, fruit, oak splint, damaged, $85.00.

bentwood handles, faded red and
blue design, minor wear 85.00
18″ d, 12½″ h, woven splint, bentwood
rim handles, minor wear 105.00
Hanging Loom, 5 x 7 x 9″, woven splint,
several shades of brown in woven de-
sign, minor wear 110.00
Kitchen
7¼″ d, 4″ h, woven splint, curlicues
around sides, minor wear 35.00
12 x 14 x 6½″, plus handle, woven
splint, buttocks, woven in 3 shades
of splint.   155.00
Laundry, 19 x 31 x 13½″ h, Shaker,
woven splint, bentwood rim handles.   110.00
Miniature
3″ d, 2¼″ h plus splint handle, woven
splint, natural with green stripe . . .   30.00
3½″ d, woven grass, brown and
natural 35.00
Nantucket
6¼″ d, 2¾″ h, tightly woven splint and
cane, wood bottom 100.00
10″ d, 6¼″ h, willow and ash, tightly
woven, round wood board base,
center swing handle on brass ears,
sgd on base "Lightship Basket
Made By A. T. Williams, Nantucket,
Mass, 1917" 635.00
6½ x 9 ⅛ x 4″, plus wooden handle,
tightly woven, stationary handle,
oval 450.00
13″ d, 6″ h, willow and ash, tightly
woven, turned wood board base,
center swing handle on metal ears,
sgd "Mitchie Ray, 1903, Nantucket
Lightship" 725.00
Rye Straw
5½″ d, 3¼″ h, bentwood rim handles
with chip carved detail 275.00
15″ d, 7½″ h, rim handles, minor
wear 145.00
Scrimshaw, 3¾″ d, woven entirely of bal-

een, whale ivory center in bottom, walrus ivory polar bear's head finial on
cover, Nantucket shape 700.00
Sewing
6½″ d, 4¼″ h, woven splint, pink cloth
lining, 3 various sized pillow
pincushions 65.00
8¼ x 8½ x 3¼″, plus handle, finely
woven splint, bands of curlicues and
bands of woven grass, interior has
attached small oval basket and pin
cushion 45.00
Sower's
12 x 14½ x 7″ plus wooden handle,
woven splint, minor wear 55.00
12 x 16½ x 8″ plus handle, woven
splint, minor damage 65.00
14 x 15 x 7″ plus wooden handle, mi-
nor wear and stains 75.00

BATTERSEA ENAMELS

History: Battersea enamel originally referred
only to the painted enamels on metal made in the
Battersea area of England. Stephen J. Janssen first
demonstrated a method of transferring prints from
engraved copper plates onto enameled surfaces in
the early 1750s at York House, Battersea. In 1756
financial difficulties forced him to sell his copper
plates and materials, much of which was purchased
by firms in the Staffordshire district. Eventually the
term "Battersea enamel" was broadened to refer
to enamel products made throughout England in
18th and 19th centuries.

Boxes, Patch
Florals
1½″ d, 1″ h, hinged lid, mottled
green base, lid with white ground,
brown spread wing eagle, cross
standards, green laurel wreath,
crown top. 225.00
2″ d, circular, pale blue ground,
scattered floral sprays. 300.00
2¾″ d, circular, basket of flowers on
hinged lid, green trellis pattern
ground, scroll and foliage within
pink border, sides of base panels
of flower sprays, pink ground. . .   365.00
Inscriptions
"A Trifle From Philadelphia," blue
and white, clasped hands, 1″ d .   350.00
"And Tighter The Knot, The Farther
Apart," heart shaped, yellow
ground. 550.00
"Love Is Thine," flowers, 2¾″ d . .   625.00
"May Nature Paint The Cheek and
Virtue The Mind," white base,
portrait in center, 1⅞″ oval 425.00
"Take This For A Kiss," pair of love-
birds on lift off cover, mirror inside
lid, c1770, 2″ d. 500.00

Boxes, Snuff

Bird shape, floral sprig on bottom, left
wing with small retouching of en-
amel, 1⅝" h **725.00**

Inscribed

"Friendship Shall Ever Be Sacred
Between My Worthy Friend and
Me," blue base, black letters,
1¾" d oval. **300.00**

"I Will Never Change," bird shape,
inscribed on bottom, 1⅝" h **975.00**

Snuff, 1¼" d, yellow, floral top, $225.00.

Necessaire, 2¾" h, implements
missing. **700.00**

Salts, round, 3 pad feet, white ground,
gold borders, gold rural scene,
2½" d, pr **550.00**

Scent Bottle, bunch of purple fruit and
leaves, fitted with dolphin stopper attached by chain, 3" h **750.00**

BAVARIAN CHINA

History: Bavaria, Germany, was an important
porcelain production center, similar to the Staffordshire district in England. The name Bavarian China
refers to companies operating in Bavaria, among
which were Hutschenreuther, Schuman, Thomas,
and Zeh, Scherzer & Co. (Z. S. & Co.). Very little
of the production from this area was imported into
the United States prior to 1870.

Biscuit Jar, cov, 2 handles, Roman key
borders. **45.00**

Bowls

4½" d, 2" h, cov, pink pansies dec on
lid, sides, mkd R.C. **30.00**

7" d, 2½" h, 4 feet, transfer swans on
lake, blue ground, gold scalloped
trim, mkd with crossed swords and
JPVS **50.00**

8" d, pedestal base, Dresden type
dec, Schumann **80.00**

Cake Plate, large roses, hp, crown
mark **50.00**

Cake Set, large cake plate, six serving
plates, pink apple blossoms dec, gold
trim **95.00**

Celery Tray, hp parrots on white
ground **25.00**

Chocolate Set, cov chocolate pot, six
cups and saucers, lavender bands on
pearlized ground **100.00**

Dish, 5¾", leaf shape, pink flowers . . . **7.50**

Dresser Set, pagoda shape, pink powder
dish, 2 covered perfumes. **25.00**

Hair Receiver, pink roses, green leaves,
gold trim, mkd Z.S. & Co.. . . . . **25.00**

Jam Jar, underplate, hp, purple grapes,
green leaves and stems, pale yellow
ground, gold finial, handles, Hutschenreuther. **70.00**

Mug, 6", gold dragon shaped handle, hp
grape clusters, green leaves **65.00**

Plates

6", geranimums dec, Z. S. & Co. . . . **15.00**

8", set of 6, fruit dec, gold rim **30.00**

8¼", reticulated rim, hp flowers, gold
trim, Schumann **30.00**

9", octagon, bird of paradise on blossoming branch, wide green border,
gold rim. **35.00**

12", flowers and cut peaches dec, art-
ist sgd DuPont. **50.00**

12", portrait, beautiful women, veiled
with roses, heavy gold, wide border,
hp. **100.00**

13", portait, Hortensia, transfer decal,
floral border, Thomas. **40.00**

13", yellow and red roses **55.00**

Powder Jar, cov, pearlized, hp, sgd Es-
ther Gardner. **25.00**

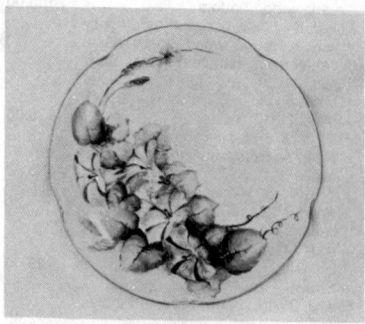

**Plate, 8¾", hp pink, blue, purple Morn-
ing Glories, sgd E. H. Koeher, Stamped
Louise, Bavaria, $14.00.**

Salt, individual, gold trim, white ground — **15.00**

Salt and Pepper Shakers, hp, pink roses, square, Victorian **25.00**

Tea Set, cov teapot, creamer, cov sugar, 6 sided, pink roses, gold trim, Z. S. & Co. **95.00**

Vase, 4¾" h, 4½" d, green and cream ground, scene of Psyche kneeling at edge of water, reverse with scene of lady sitting by water, gold trim, mkd Royal Crown **125.00**

BELLEEK

History: Belleek, a thin, ivory colored, almost iridescent-type porcelain, was first made in 1857 in county Ferman, Ireland. Production continued until World War I, was discontinued for a period of time, and then resumed. The Shamrock pattern is most familiar; but, many patterns were made, including Limpet, Tridacna, and Grasses.

Irish Belleek has several identifying marks, e.g., the Harp and Hound (1865–80) and Harp, Hound, and Castle (1863–91). After 1891 the word "Ireland" or "Erie" was added. Some pieces are marked "Belleek Co., Fermanagh."

There is an Irish saying: If a newly married couple receives a gift of Belleek, their marriage will be blessed with lasting happiness.

Several American firms made a Belleek-type porcelain. The first was Ott and Brewer Co., Trenton, New Jersey, in 1884, followed by Willets. Other firms included The Ceramic Art Co. (1889), American Art China Works (1892), Columbian Art Co. (1893), and Lenox, Inc. (1904).

Reference: Mary Frank Gaston, *American Belleek*, Collector Books, 1984.

Additional Listings: Lenox.

Abbreviations: 1BM = 1st Black Mark; 2BM = 2nd Black Mark; 3BM = 3rd Black Mark.

AMERICAN

Bowl, 8" d, 1½" h, ruffled heavy gold rim, 2 handles, floral painting, artist H.B., Willets, brown mark **145.00**

Chocolate Pot, green and cream ground, gold floral dec, dragon spout, Ott and Brewer **1,100.00**

Cup and Saucer, creamy ivory, pearlized, gold trim, Ott and Brewer **145.00**

Ewer, bulbous, melon ribbed, thistle, Ott and Brewer **900.00**

Mug, 4½", floral dec, twig handle, Willets **200.00**

Pitchers

4", gold ground, gold paste dec, Rittenhouse and Evans, Trenton **500.00**

13½", 7" d, Indian in full headdress, Lenox Ceramic Art **420.00**

Plates

8", Ott and Brewer, pastel, scenic, boy fishing, tree, house, burgundy border **900.00**

8", Willets, all-over tiny roses with gold **95.00**

Sculpture, Morning Glory, 6" h, 7" d, Ott and Brewer **800.00**

Tankards

14¼", handle, large white, yellow, and red roses, turquoise jeweling, Lenox **335.00**

16", artist's dog, dragon handle, artist sgd Houghton, Willets **700.00**

Vases

7½", ovoid body, reticulated neck, scroll handles, low relief naked child wearing rabbit skin hat and playing with 3 bunnies in tall grass, The Ceramic Art Company, Trenton, NJ, sgd K.B. Sears, c1890 . . . . **5,775.00**

Vase, 13¾", pastel, mkd "Belleek/Willets," $295.00.

10", yellow, Ott and Brewer **700.00**

12", pink cabbage roses, green ground, Willets **420.00**

12", pink and white orchid, mottled green, Ott and Brewer **450.00**

12", 9" d, urn shape, gold baroque handles, enameled flowers, gold int., Lenox **400.00**

13", cylinder, lovebird dec, Willets . . **225.00**

14", floral, artist sgd Houghton, Willets **425.00**

15", large cabbage roses, butterscotch ground, sgd Morley, Lenox. **700.00**

IRISH

Baskets

4½ d, 4″ h, heart shape, 4 strand, 3 pads, Belleek Co. Fermanagh, Ireland **165.00**

12⅝″ d, Henshalls, pierced, applied floral and leaf dec, applied banner mark with imp Belleek, Ireland ... **275.00**

Bowls

5½″ d, 3″ h, Neptune pattern, pink trim, 2BM **145.00**

12¼″, cov, pierced, applied floral and leaf dec, crabstock handles, applied banner mark with imp Belleek, Ireland **350.00**

Bread Plate, Grasses, D743, 1BM **250.00**

Cake Plate, 8¾″, round edge, pierced, basketweave center, imp Belleek, Ireland **125.00**

Candlestick, 7″, Thorn, D344, 2BM ... **200.00**

Centerpiece, 11½″ h, trumpet shape, applied floral and leaf dec, pale yellow details, 3GM **210.00**

Compote, 10″ d, Greek pattern, gilted, 2BM **750.00**

Condiment Set, 4½″ h, 6½″ d, open salt, cov mustard pot and pepper shaker, Shamrock pattern, green trim harp, 2BM **550.00**

Creamer, Celtic pattern, red and gilted, 3BM **200.00**

Creamers and Sugars

2½″ h, 4″ d, open sugar, 3¼ h, 3½″ d, creamer, Echinus, pink trim, 2BM **325.00**

High Lily, green trim **160.00**

Shamrock, basketweave, 3BM **90.00**

Cups and Saucers

Hawthorne, pink flowers, gold trim, 1BM **135.00**

Hexagon, white and green, 2BM.... **85.00**

High Lily, white and green, 2BM **85.00**

Limpet, demitasse, 3BM.......... **60.00**

Egg Cup Holder with 6 egg cups, 5½″ h, 6¾″ d, basketweave, ring handle, lease #957, 1BM............ **850.00**

Figurines

Leprechaun sitting on mushroom, 5¼″ h, 3″ d, yellow lustre trim, 2BM **500.00**

Pig, sitting, 2⅞″ h, 2″ w, 4″ l, 2BM .. **375.00**

Flower Pot, ruffled rim, applied flowers and leaves, 3BM.................... **200.00**

Honey Jar, beehive shape, Shamrock pattern, 2BM.................... **385.00**

Jam Pot, Ribbon pattern, D496, 1BM .. **265.00**

Kettle, large, Echinus, pink and gilt trim, D345, 1BM.................... **345.00**

Muffin Dish, 4½″ h, 8½″ d, cov, shells and green trim, imp registry mark, 1BM.................... **550.00**

Mustache Cup, ring handle gilt trim, 1BM.................... **225.00**

Pitchers

6″, tulip shape, green handle and trim, 2BM **250.00**

7″, light pink leaves, rope handle, 1BM **175.00**

7½″, Harp Handle pattern, gold trim, 1BM **300.00**

Plates

5″, Grasses, D740, 1BM **65.00**

6″, Lily, green trim, D542, 2BM..... **50.00**

8″, New Shell, pink trim, 3BM...... **40.00**

Salt Stand, 4″ h, 3″ d, 5″ l, turquoise seahorse, pink trim shell, gold trim, lease 824, 1BM.................... **550.00**

Spill Vase, 4″ l, cylindrical, Cleary pattern, 1BM.................... **300.00**

Spoon Rest, 4″, Boat, 1BM........ **275.00**

Teapots

4″ h, 4¾″ d, Tridacna pattern, pink trim and handle, 1BM **200.00**

7″ h, 6¼″ d, Grasses, color trim, 1BM . **600.00**

Tea Set, teapot, sugar, creamer, 2 cups and saucers, Cone pattern, green trim, D432-435, 2BM............... **750.00**

Vases

4⅜″, 2¾″ x 4½″, flying fish, pink trim, 2BM **500.00**

5½″, frog, D181, 1BM **575.00**

6″, Aberdeen, handled, applied floral and leaf dec, 3BM **250.00**

9″, Princess, handled, applied floral and leaf dec, 3BM **275.00**

13″, 5½″, d, Vine pattern, 2BM..... **500.00**

Wall Pocket, 9″ h, Swan, gilted, 1BM.. **1,650.00**

BELLS

History: Bells have been used for centuries for many different purposes. They have been traced as far back as 2697 B.C., though at that time they did not have any true tone. One of the oldest bells is the "crotal," a tiny sphere with small holes and a ball or stone or metal inside. This type now appears as sleigh bells.

True bell making began when bronze, the mixing of tin and copper, was discovered. There are now many types of materials of which bells are made - almost as many materials as there are uses for them.

Bells of the late 19th century show a high degree of workmanship and artistic style. Glass bells from this period are sometimes an example of the glass blower's talent and the glass manufacturer's product.

Collectors' Club: American Bell Association, Rt. 1, Box 286, Natronia Heights, PA 15065. Dues $12.00. *The Bell Tower* newsletter.

Additional Listings: See *Warman's Americana & Collectibles* for more examples.

Animal

Cow, 8″ h, sheet iron. **15.00**

Horse, harness bells, brass straps, 4
bells, 13¾" 1 . . . .   35.00
Sheep, brass, 4" h 30.00
Turkey, brass 35.00
China
Limoges, 4", cow shape, pale blue,
pink roses, gilded handle 35.00
Royal Bayreuth, Sand Babies 300.00
Staffordshire
5¼" h, girl, full skirt 65.00
6" h, girl, blue, white and gold. . . .   85.00
Souvenir and Commemorative, El
Camino Real, San Diego, Los An-
geles, San Francisco, 1769-1915,
base emb "Mission Bell Guide Post
Marking El Camino Real, The King's
Highway," 6½" h 50.00
Desk, 7" h, 5½" d, brass, face in top
center of fancy work, operating gonger
on each side. 125.00
Figural, Brass
Bear and shield, 7⅞" h, 4¾" d, brass,
figures around sides. 175.00
Elizabeth I, 7" 90.00
Gourd and leaf, ftd, base with man
holding bracket and striker 22.50
Lady in hoopskirt, 3¾", carries um-
brella, feet form clapper 40.00
Lady in powdered wig, hoop skirt, 5¾"   70.00
Monk, 5", carries umbrella and
basket.   75.00
Nun, 4¾" 60.00
Old Lady, 4¼" 60.00
Old Woman carrying pot, 5" h, feet
form clapper 75.00
Pomade Seller, nodding head, 4" h,
old man crying his wares, head fas-
tened to clapper 200.00
Turtle, bell bracket and striker on
shell 27.50
Victory, 5¼" h, 4⅝" d, emb heads of
Churchill, Stalin and Roosevelt on
sides, V on handle, made from Ger-
man aircraft shot down over Britain,
WWII. 60.00
Glass
Amberina, Daisy & Button 200.00
Amethyst, 12" h, 5" d, applied
threading. 375.00
Bristol, 11½". 100.00
Cased, 6", blue, white lining, applied
dec. 75.00
Cranberry, 11½", IVT. 135.00
Crystal, 6", Dorflinger's Kalana Lily,
etched 85.00
Custard, Smocking pattern. 65.00
Fenton, 7", Rosaline 30.00
Venetian, 4¼", latticino 150.00
Hand
4" h, 3" d, brass, fancy, tutonic heads
emb on each side 75.00
6½" h, 5¼" d, brass, raised Assyrian
figures around sides. 110.00

Sleigh, $275.00.

Locomotive, brass, emb "E.M.D.", cast
iron ball clapper, mounted in steel tri-
pod, 12" d 275.00
School
Brass, oak handle 50.00
Metal, 10⅜" h, turned curly maple
handle.   45.00
Servant Calling, 4¾" h, 3⅝" d, three
painted medallions under glass, Eiffel
Tower, scenes, brass bunches of
grapes, bird perched on top, alabaster
base 125.00
Ship's, bronze, 140 lbs, 20" d, base, from
U. S. Lighthouse Engineers Vessel,
Crocus 325.00
Sleigh, 4 brass bells, 15½" 1 leather
strap 65.00

J. NORTON
BENNINGTON
VT.

BENNINGTON AND
BENNINGTON-TYPE POTTERY

History: In 1845 Christopher Webber Fenton
joined Julius Norton, his brother-in-law, in the manufacturing of stoneware pottery in Bennington, Vermont. Fenton sought to expand the company's
products and glazes; Norton wanted to concentrate
solely on stoneware. In 1847 Fenton broke away
and established his own factory.

Fenton introduced the famous Rockingham
glaze, developed in England and named after the
Marquis of Rockingham, to America. In 1849 he
patented a flint enamel glaze, "Fenton's Enamel,"
which added flecks, spots, or streaks of color (usually blues, greens, yellows, and oranges) to the
brown Rockingham glaze. Forms included candlesticks, coachman bottles, cow creamers, poodles,
sugar bowls, and toby pitchers.

Fenton produced the little known scroddled

ware, commonly called lava or agate ware. Scroddled ware is composed of different colored clays, mixed with cream colored clay, molded, turned on a potter's wheel, coated with feldspar and flint, and fired. It was not produced in quantity, as there was little demand for it.

Fenton also introduced Parian ware to America. Parian was developed in England in 1842 and known as "Statuary ware." Parian is a translucent porcelain which has no glaze and resembles marble. Bennington made the blue and white variety in the form of vases, cologne bottles, and trinkets.

Five different marks were used, with many variations. Only about twenty percent of the pieces carried any mark; some forms were almost always marked, others never. Marks: (a) 1849 mark (4 variations) for flint enamel and Rockingham; (b) E. Fenton's Works, 1845–47, on Parian and occasionally on scroddled ware; (c) U. S. Pottery Co., ribbon mark, 1852–58, on Parian and blue and white porcelain; (d) U. S. Pottery Co., lozenge mark, 1852–58, on Parian; and (e) U. S. Pottery, oval mark, 1853–58, mainly on scroddled ware.

The hound handled pitcher is probably the best known Bennington piece. Hound handled pitchers also were made by some 30 potteries in over 55 different variations. Rockingham glaze was used by over 150 potteries in 11 states, mainly the Mid-West, between 1830 and 1900.

References: Richard Carter Barret, *Bennington Pottery and Porcelain,* Bonanza Books, out-of-print; Richard Carter Barret, *How To Identify Bennington Pottery,* Stephen Greene Press, 1964; Laura Woodside Watkins, *Early New England Potters And Their Wares,* Harvard University Press, 1950.

Museums: Bennington Museum, Bennington, VT; East Liverpool Museum of Ceramics, East Liverpool, OH.

Additional Listings: Stoneware.

Advisor: Charles and Barbara Adams.

Creamer, light brown, $425.00.

BENNINGTON POTTERY

Book Flasks
5⅞" h, "Battle of Bennington," flint enamel glaze, greens, yellows, and blues, 1849 mark 900.00

6", "Departed Spirits", flint enamel glaze, yellow and brown glaze. . . . 600.00
6", "Life of Kossuth", flint enamel glaze. 750.00
Candlesticks
6⅞" h, sngl, flint enamel glaze, strong greens 475.00
8⅛", pr, columnar, Rockingham glaze. 1,000.00
9⅛" Pair, flint enamel glaze, greens, yellows, blue 1,400.00
Single, flint enamel glaze, blues, greens, yellow 575.00
9¼", Rockingham glaze. 375.00
Chamberstick, 4⅞" d, 3¼" h, ring handle (rare), flint enamel glaze, blues, greens, and yellows, base imp "J" . . 900.00
Frame, 10¾", oval, Rockingham glaze 450.00
Goblet, ftd, 4½" h, Rockingham glaze . 275.00
Inhalator (croup kettle), 6½" h, inset spout, Rockingham glaze 575.00
Mantel Ornament, Poodle, 8½" h, holding a basket of colored fruit in its mouth, applied "coleslaw" mane and ears, gray-green and yellow-brown glaze 1,500.00
Milk Pan, 13" d, 4" h, Rockingham glaze, 1849 mark 400.00
Paperweight, 2¾" h, spaniel reclining on cushion, yellow and brown Rockingham glaze, 1849 mark. 675.00
Pipkin, 7¼" h, Alternate Rib, flint enamel glaze, 1849 mark 550.00
Pitchers
5⅛" h, barrel shape, Rockingham glaze. 250.00
8¾", 2 qt, Bennington hound handle, Rockingham glaze 700.00
10½", Alternate Rib, flint enamel glaze, 1849 mark 550.00
11", Diamond pattern, flint enamel glaze. 400.00
Snuff Jar, Toby, 4¼" h, hat, flint enamel glaze, 1849 mark 550.00
Sugar Bowls
7½" h, Alternate Rib, flint enamel glaze, 1849 mark 700.00
9¾", cov, flint enamel glaze, 1849 mark. 900.00
Tobacco Jar, cov, 10½" h, applied handles, Gothic Arches, Rockingham glaze 300.00
Toby Bottles
10½" h, Rockingham glaze,1849 mark 600.00
10¾", flint enamel glaze, holding bottle, tassels, mustache, 1849 mark, rare. 900.00
Vases
8½", Parian, American Eagle, blue and white, c1850 . . . . 200.00
9", Tulip, flint enamel glaze 650.00
9¾", Tulip, scroddled, variegated brown clays. 1,500.00

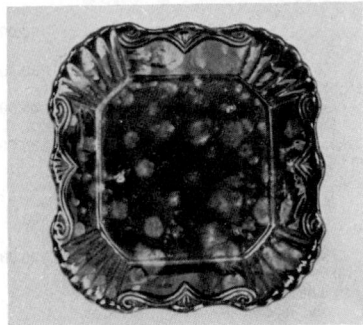

Serving Plate, 8¾", $375.00.

Wash Bowl and Pitcher, Diamond Pattern, flint enamel glaze, brightly colored oranges, yellows, and greens, 1849 mark, bowl 13" d, 4⅜" h, pitcher 10½" h. 950.00

BENNINGTON-TYPE

Bowl, 14¼" d, 5¼" h, mixing, Rockingham glaze 185.00

Cake Mold, 9½" d, 4" h, Rockingham glaze 150.00

Mug, 4⅛" h, handled, mottled Rockingham glaze 125.00

Pie Plate, 10", Rockingham glaze 130.00

Pitcher, 10" h, Tulip design, Rockingham glaze 225.00

Plate, 9" sq, emb design, Rockingham glaze 285.00

Soap Dish, round, 4" d, 2½" h, Rockingham glaze 95.00

BISCUIT JARS

History: The biscuit or cracker jar was the forerunner of the cookie jar. They were made of various materials by leading glassworks and potteries of the late 19th and early 20th centuries.

Note: All items listed have silver plated mountings unless otherwise noted.

Bristol Glass, 7¼" h, 5" d, blue, multicolored enamel flowers, green leaves 120.00

Cased, pink ground, prunus flowers outlined in gold, emb florals 160.00

Crown Milano, Burmese coloring, acorns and leaves outlined in gold 425.00

Doulton, Burslem, 7¾" h, 6" d, cream ground, ribbed, turquoise band with animals and birds, sgd. 175.00

English, pottery

6¾" h, 5½" d, pink to cream ground, purple orchids, green leaves, mkd Carlton Ware 90.00

7¼" h, 5½" d, soft green ground, shaded pink roses, green leaves, gold trim 70.00

German, 7", bulbous, 3 round panels, cherub or floral designs, front panel has Elizabethan lady with crown, 3 oval panels with cherub portraits on cov 85.00

Jasperware, 5" h, 5" d, blue, Wedgwood/Made in England, $225.00.

Jasperware, 6½" h, 5" d, deep blue, white classical ladies, mkd Wedgwood Only. 150.00

Porcelain

6½" h, 4¾" d, hp, scenic all around, Arabian man on camel, river, palm trees 90.00

Melon shape, green, large gold flowers, leaves, mkd P.M.C. 225.00

Royal Worcester, 6¼" h, 4¾" d, satin finish, beige shaded to aqua, gold trim, sgd, date mk 1897 . . . . 220.00

Satin Glass

6½", pink, shell pat, enamel dec . . . 200.00

7", white, molded floral dec 175.00

Smith Bros., sq, swirl rib, daisy spray, leaves, rampant lion mk. 700.00

Wave Crest, 8", puffy mold, creamy ivory, enameled beading and floral dec 400.00

BISQUE

History: Bisque or biscuit china is the name given to wares that have been fired once and are not glazed.

Bisque figurines and busts were popular during the Victorian era, being used on fireplace mantels, dining room buffets, and end tables. Manufacturing was centered in the United States and Europe. By the mid-20th century the Japanese were the principal source of bisque items, especially character related items.

Piano Baby, light blue dress, brown hair, $255.00.

Bank, 3", fox head, wearing glasses . .	375.00
Busts	
7¼" h, 3½" d, boy and girl wearing hats, boy: white with blue and gold trim, girl: blue, pink, and white with florals, tan bases, pr.	200.00
15", Abraham Lincoln, polychrome enamel and gilt, detachable socle, Japanese, late 19th C	1,500.00
Bowl, cov, 3", ftd, emb lavender flowers, cov bust of Victorian lady.	35.00
Cigarette Holder, 4½" h, 3" d, figural, elf dressed in yellow and green, holes in head to hold matches, head lifts to expose cigarette holder	100.00
Figurines	
7¾", girl in dress, apron, and bonnet holding up foot, mouse peeking out	125.00
10⅛" h, 3¾" d, girl with pitchfork, white blouse, blue bodice, cream apron and bonnet	135.00
15⅜" h, 5¼" d, lady, blonde hair, long flowing blue dress, holding blue stole over head, bare feet, Robinson and Leadbeater.	400.00
21½", pr, couple, 18th C dress, she in pink bonnet, pink bodice, flowered skirt, holds finger to lips, he with flower in hat, gray jacket, flowered waistcoat, presents pansy, floral encrusted scrolled circular base	425.00

Match Holders	
5½", girl holding doll	50.00
6", girl lying on stomach, mkd Germany.	150.00
Night Light, 3½", cat head, shades of gray, blue collar, green eyes	145.00
Nodder, 4¾", poodle and bulldog on oval base	135.00
Piano Babies	
4" lying on back, left foot in air, white gown, blue trim, sunburst mark, Heubach	100.00
5", crawling, right foot up, white gown, sunburst mark, Heubach.	135.00
7" h, 5½" d, sitting, one leg crossed over other, holds large pink, blue and yellow ball, yellow gown, eyelet trim, gold beading, white stockings, pink shoes, intaglio eyes, unmarked Heubach	225.00
Plate, 6¼", baby angel in relief	10.00
Shoe, 6¼", white love birds on top, 3 blue birds on sides	70.00
Trinket Box, cov, 5 x 4¼ x 3", pale mauve, applied flowers on cov	25.00
Toothbrush Holder, 4", Three Little Pigs, standing, yellow back holds 2 toothbrushes, mkd Made In Japan, Walt Disney	75.00
Vases	
8¼" h, 5" d, girl standing by vase, shaded blue dress and hat with raised dots	110.00
11⅜" h, 5½" d, light green ground, girl in green, white and gold standing in front, flowers and leaves, dark green trim	165.00

BITTERS BOTTLES

History: Bitters, a "remedy" made from natural herbs and other mixtures with an alcohol base, often was viewed as the universal cure-all. The names given to various bitter mixtures were imaginative, though the bitters seldom cured what their makers claimed.

The manufacturers of bitters needed a way to sell and advertise their products. They designed bottles in many shapes, sizes, and colors to attract the buyer. Many forms of advertising, including trade cards, billboards, signs, almanacs, and novelties proclaimed the virtues of a specific bitter.

During the Civil War a tax was levied on alcoholic beverages. Since bitters were identified as medicines, they were exempt from this tax. The alcohol content was never mentioned. In 1907 when the Pure Foods Regulations went into effect, "an honest statement of content on every label" put most of the manufacturers out of business.

References: Carlyn Ring, *For Bitters Only*, 1980; J. H. Thompson, *Bitters Bottles*, Century House,

1947; Richard Watson, *Bitters Bottles*, Thomas Nelson and Sons, 1965.

Periodicals: *Old Bottle Magazine*, Maverick Publications, P. O. Box 243, Bend, OR 97701. Subscription: $10.00.

America's Suffolk Bitters Life Preserver, pig shape, amber, 9½″ l 30.00
Atwood's Quinine Tonic Bitters, rect, aqua 145.00
Ayer, Dr. M. C., Restorative Bitters, Boston, rect, aqua 170.00
Baxter's, Dr., Mandrake Bitters, Lord Bros., Burlington, VT, 12 sided, clear 35.00
Beggs Dandelion Bitters, Chicago, sq, amber 145.00
Berlin Magen Bitters, emb S. B. Rothenberg, sq, milk glass 135.00
Brophy's Bitters, Nokomis, IL, sq, aqua, ornate crescent and star trademark . 185.00
Burdock Blood Bitters, rect, aqua. 18.00
California Fig and Herb Bitters, San Francisco, sq, amber. 125.00
Caroni Bitters, round, green. 135.00
Dandelion Bitters, Utica, NY, rect, strap flask, clear 75.00
Electric Brand Bitters, H. E. Bucklen & Co., Chicago, sq, amber. 35.00
Fenner's, Dr. M. M., Capitol Bitters, Fredonia, NY, rect, aqua. 100.00
Fisch's, Dr., Bitters, figural, amber 200.00
Gates Life of Man Bitters, rect, aqua . . 110.00
Gentiana Root and Herb Bitters, Seth C. Clapp, Boston, sq, aqua. 225.00
Hall's Bitters, figural barrel, yellow-amber 165.00
Home Bitters, Jas A. Jackson & Co., St. Louis, sq, amber 75.00

Green, label front and back, $75.00.

Iron Bitters, Brown Chemical Co., Baltimore, sq, amber 35.00
Johnson's Calisaya Bitters, Burlington, VT, sq, amber. 125.00
Kaiser Wilhelm Bitters Co., Sandusky, OH, round, amber 100.00
Kaufmann's, Dr., Sulpher Bitters, orig label, oval, aqua 30.00
Kennedy's East India Bitters, Iler & Co., Omaha, sq, clear. 115.00
Lash's Bitters, sq, amber. 25.00
Litthauer Stomach Bitters Invented 1864 by Joseph Loewenthal, Berlin, sq, case gin, milk glass. 175.00
Malt Bitters Co., Boston, round, green . 30.00
Marshall's Bitters, The Best Laxative and Blood Purifer, sq, amber 65.00
Old Dr. Warner's Quaker Bitters, Flint & Co., Providence, RI, rect, aqua. 75.00
Old Sachem Bitters and Wigwam Tonic, figural barrel, golden amber 280.00
O'Leary's 20th Century Bitters, sq, amber 265.00
Oswego Bitters, emb 25¢, oval, amber
Paines Celery Compound, amber. 20.00
Peruvian Bitters, sq, bright orange-amber 85.00
Peychaud's American Aromatic Bitter Cordial, New Orleans, round, amber
Pineapple, figural, amber. 150.00
Plantation Bitters, S. T. Drakes, log cabin shape, golden amber, 1860, 10¼″ h. 125.00
Pond's Kidney and Liver Bitters, an Unexcelled Laxative, sq, orange-amber 55.00
Rising Sun Bitters, John C. Hurst, Phila., sq, amber. 165.00
Robacks, Dr., Cincinnati, brown 145.00
Royal Amaranth Bitters, Alfred Savigear & Co., round, aqua, double collar . . . 500.00
Ryder's, Dr., Clover Bitters, rect, amber 145.00
Sarasina Stomach Bitters, sq, amber . . 100.00
Sarsaparilla and Tomato Bitters, F. Brown, Boston, oval, aqua 225.00
Sun Kidney and Liver Bitters, Vegetable Laxative Bowel Regulator and Blood Purifier, sq, amber. 150.00
Tonic Bitter, J. T. Higby, Milford, CT, sq, amber 150.00
Tonola Bitters, Phila., ornate trademark of Phoenix, sq, aqua 155.00
Vermo Stomach Bitters, Tonic and Appetizer, sq, clear 100.00
Von Hopf's, Dr., Curacoa Bitters, Chamberlain and Co., Des Moines, IA, rect, amber 140.00
Wheat Bitters, rect, amber. 120.00
Whitcomb's, Faith, Bitters, Boston, rect, aqua 145.00
Yerba Buena Bitters, San Francisco, rect, straped flask shape 165.00
Zu Zu Bitters, sq, aqua 175.00

BLOWN THREE MOLD

History: The Jamestown colony in Virginia introduced glass making into America. The artisans used a "free blown" method.

Blowing molten glass into molds was not introduced into America until the early 1800s. Blown three mold glass used a pre-designed mold that consisted of two, three, or more hinged parts. The glass maker placed a quantity of molten glass on the tip of a rod or tube, inserted it into the mold, blew air into the tube, waited until the glass cooled, and removed the finish product. The three part mold is the most common and lends its name to this entire category.

The impressed decorations on blown mold glass usually are reversed, i.e., what is raised or convex on the outside will be concave on the inside. This is a useful in identifying the blown form.

By 1850 American made glassware was in relatively common usage. The increased demand led to large factories and the creation of a technology which eliminated the smaller companies.

Reference: George S. and Helen McKearin, *American Glass,* Crown Publishers, 1941, 1948.

Advisor: David and Linda Arman.

Beaver Hat, purple blue rayed base, (Type IV), G-III-23, $450.00.

Bottles
Bar, 7¾", aqua, globular, Kent, minor int. sickness, McKearin G-II-6, ex-collection McKearin and Jim and Eileen Courtney **1,450.00**
Vinegar, cobalt blue, matching stopper, Sandwich, McKearin G-I-7, type 4 . . . . **350.00**
Bowls
4" d, 1¾" h, ftd, clear, McKearin G-I-5, ex-collection McKearin **200.00**
5⅞" d, 4¼" h, light grass green, applied foot, folded over rim, Kent Glass Works (Park Edmunds & Park), McKearin G-II-6, ex-collection Jim and Eileen Courtney . . **11,750.00**
7¼" d, 3⅛" h, olive-yellow, folded over rim, McKearin G-II-6 . . . . **7,500.00**
Carafe, 8½", quart plus, deep aqua/ green, star crack in neck that was fire polished closed in making, slight deposit, McKearin G-I-29 . . . . **325.00**
Creamers
3½", clear, tooled rim, ringed base, McKearin G-III-26 . . . .
3¾", clear, circular pedestal foot, applied cobalt blue rim, McKearin G-II-12, ex-collection McKearin . . . **550.00**
Decanters
7⅛", pint, olive-amber, Keene, NH, McKearin G-III-16 . . . . **250.00**
7½" plus stopper, yellow-green, stopper made from two fragments found at Kent excavation, minor int. sick-

ness, McKearin G-II-6, ex-collection Jim and Eileen Courtney **1,250.00**
7⅝", light green, Mantua, small star bruise in shoulder, McKearin G-II-33, one of two known, ex-collection Jim and Eileen Courtney **4,500.00**
10¼" to stopper, quart, clear, matching stopper, McKearin G-III-19 . . . . **170.00**
11¾", clear, baroque, stopper perfect fit, but may not be orig, McKearin G-V-17 . . . . **325.00**
Dishes
Deep
4¼" d, clear, rayed base, McKearin G-II-12, D-5, ex-collection McKearin **90.00**
5" d, clear, rayed base, McKearin G-III-20, D-5, ex-collection McKearin **135.00**
Shallow
4" d, clear, McKearin G-III-23, D-2, unlisted small size, ex-collection McKearin **125.00**
6" d, clear, McKearin G-III-24 . . . . **90.00**
Flips
4⅞", clear, McKearin G-III-22 . . . . . . **200.00**
5½", 4⅝" d, clear, 18 diamond base, McKearin G-II-18 . . . . **100.00**
5⅞", clear, rayed base, McKearin G-III-22, ex-collection McKearin. . . **195.00**
7½", giant, clear, McKearin G-II-34 . . **250.00**
Hats, Beaver
2", 4¼" d, green, tooled from an inkwell mold, plain base, scarred pontil, American, probably New England, McKearin G-II-15 . . . . . . **1,800.00**
2¼", clear, McKearin G-II-18 . . . . . . **70.00**
2⅜", clear, McKearin G-III-6 . . . . . . **60.00**
Inkwell, 1½" h, 2⅜" d, dark golden amber, ringed base, large unbroken bubble around opening under surface, McKearin G-II-18 . . . . **80.00**

Mug, 2¾", clear, strap handle, unrecorded pattern 125.00
Pitchers
  5", cream, baroque, clear, applied handle, McKearin G-V-14 . . . . 450.00
  6¼", clear, baroque, check and small flake at base of handle, shallow broken blister on one rib, McKearin G-V-6, ex-collection Jim and Eileen Courtney 375.00
  8", clear, no example in McKearin but similar to parts of G-V-20,21, and 22 550.00
Salts, individual
  1¾", cobalt blue, Sandwich Glass, McKearin G-III-25. . . . . 350.00
  2⅛", 3¼" d, clear, McKearin G-III-6 . 1,250.00
  2⅛", cobalt blue, McKearin G-III-21 . 235.00
  *2¼", amethyst, sliver out of rim, McKearin G-II-18, MUTZER FAKE 185.00
  2⅝", clear, McKearin G-III-13, S-10 . 135.00
Salt, master, 2½" h, 2¾" d, clear, circular, ftd, McKearin G-III-21 . . . . 170.00
Sugar Bowl, 6", clear, applied foot, folded rim on lid, probably Sandwich, McKearin G-II-18, illus. *Antiques* (June 1967, pg 747), ex-collection Jim and Eileen Courtney. 3,150.00
Tumblers
  2⅝", aqua, inkwell mold, McKearin G-II-15, illus. *Antiques* (June 1967, pg 747), ex-collection Jim and Eileen Courtney 625.00
  3⅜", clear, barrel shape, McKearin G-I-16 . . . . 160.00
  3½", clear, barrel shape, McKearin G-II-21 . . . . 95.00
Whiskeys
  2½", clear, barrel shape, McKearin G-II-18 . . . . 225.00
  2⅞", clear, McKearin G-I-20. . . . . . . 110.00

BOHEMIAN GLASS

History: The once independent country of Bohemia, now a part of Czechoslovakia, produced a variety of fine glassware: etched, cut, overlay, and colored. Their glasswares were first imported into America in the early 1820s and continue today.

Bohemia is known for its "flashed" glass that was produced in the familiar ruby color, and also in amber, green, blue, and black. Common patterns include "Deer and Castle," "Deer and Pine Tree," and "Vintage."

Most of the Bohemian glass encountered in today's market is of the 1875–1900 period. A Bohemian type glass also was made in England, Switzerland, and Germany.

Beakers
  5½", amber flashed, engraved, animals and building, C scroll panels, flared foot, c1860. . . . . 75.00

6½", armorial, engraved shield with coat of arms, flower sprays, bands of stylized flowers, dated Anno 1791. . . . . 185.00
Bowls
  6¾", blue cut to milky ground in 2 oval panels, painted figures, 19th C . . . 75.00
  7", gilt crystal and ruby overlay. 200.00
Castor Set, 5 bottles, ruby flash, cut to clear, SP holder 250.00
Champagne Glass, ruby, Vintage 90.00
Cologne Bottle, 7⅜" h, 2½" d, ruby, frosted, ruby circles and medallion with etched scene of deer, cut scalloped base, ruby cut stopper 135.00
Compote, 10¾", cov, scalloped edge, clear and pale ruby, ribbed, pedestal base, faceted knop, c1860. . . . . 125.00
Cruet, stopper, 6", ruby flashed, cut to clear, etched Vintage. 65.00
Decanters
  11½", ruby, ribbed, mid 19th C 100.00
  11¾", ruby, etched, blown stopper, Vintage 85.00
  13", ruby flashed, engraved to clear. 90.00
  Amber, cut and frosted monkeys and pheasants among flowers and foliage, faceted cut stopper. 175.00

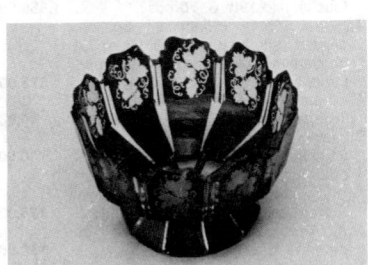

Bowl, 2" h, 3⅛" d, ftd, 10 paneled, $45.00.

Dish, 4" d, 2½" h, green, Deer and Castle pattern. 45.00
Garniture, 3 pcs, oblong compote, 2 lustres, 10¼", white overlay cut to green, painted florals, long cut prisms 230.00
Goblets
  5", yellow overlay, carved animal cartouches 100.00
  6", amethyst, gilt lip, etched blossoms, late 19th C 85.00
  7", octagon, crystal, etched, 2 deer feeding in woodland scene 140.00
  7½", red overlay, carved stag and fox seeking hare, clear stem 150.00

Mug, 5″, ruby, frosted, etched vintage, frosted geometric band around base, applied handle **35.00**

Mustard Jar, ruby, Deer and Castle pattern **50.00**

Paperweight, 2⅜″, faceted, concentric millefiori **235.00**

Perfume Bottles
6½″, ruby, Deer and Castle pattern. . **65.00**
8½″, ruby, birds and flowers. **62.00**

Pitcher, 11″, ruby, engraved forest scene, clear applied handle **100.00**

Pokals
12″, cov, amethyst, copper wheel engraved. **175.00**
15½″, cov, ruby, engraved floral panels. **125.00**

Salts, set of 6, 5⅛″, shell shape, ruby, etched mythological landscape, faceted, hexagonal foot, c1860. . . . . . . **1,050.00**

Sherberts, 4¼″, clear ruby, long ribbed stem, c1860, set of 14. . . . . **800.00**

Sherry Glass, 5¼″, ribbed, clear ruby, mid 19th C **75.00**

Sugar Shaker, ruby, Deer and Castle pattern, SP top **55.00**

Table Service, armorial, clear, fluted glasses, coat of arms in oval cartouche, mid 19th C, 70 pcs **1,550.00**

Tankard, 5¾″, cylindrical, opaline, painted scroll cartouche, bust of gentleman, flower sprays, red trellis band, c1750 . . . . **675.00**

Toothpick Holder, ruby, Deer and Pine Tree pattern, c1900. . . . . **40.00**

Tumblers
5″, ribbed, pale ruby, clear, mid 19th C **50.00**
5¼″, flared, pink ground, white overlay, painted bouquets, cut ogival medallions, gilded, c1850 . . . . **125.00**

Urn, 14″ cov, ruby, Deer and Pine Tree pattern **150.00**

Vases
4½″, floral design **35.00**
8″, ftd, amber, etched, Deer and Castle pattern, c1860. . . . . **50.00**
11″, lily shape, ruby flash, engraved to clear **100.00**
11¼″, urn shape, cov, 2 rib scroll handles, sq foot, amber flashed, roundels with sportsman and hound, sporting trophy, zigzag band on cov and foot, 19th C **235.00**
11¾″, pedestal base, etched flowers and leaves, etched flowers in oval ruby panels, reserved on alternate yellow and clear ground, gold trim, 19th C **475.00**
13″, white overlay cut to cranberry, maiden in oval panel, gilt, late 19th C **225.00**
24″, pr, 2 part, flared necks, overlay white cut to clear, stylized motifs, late 19th C **1,800.00**

BOOKS, MODERN FIRST EDITIONS

History: Collecting first editions is almost as old as the printing of books. First edition collectors always have constituted the "blue-chip" aspect of the book collecting market.

Collecting modern first editions can be very financially and aesthetically rewarding. Speculators are cautioned about the volatility of the market.

Modern first editions must be in fine condition and complete with dust jacket (dj) to be of value. The dust jacket is very important; books without it are worth substantially less. Most collectors will automatically reject book club editions.

The following prices are for books in fine condition. Hints are given to help identify first editions. These are called "points" by collectors.

References: Jacob Blanck, *Bibliography Of American Literature;* Van Allen Bradley, *The Book Collector's Handbook Of Values;* Larry Dingman, *Bibliography Of Limited & Signed Editions In Literature: 20th Century American Authors;* Marjorie M. and Donald L. Hinds, *How To Make Money Buying & Selling Old Books,* The Messenger Book Press, 1974; Katherine and Daniel Leab (eds.), *American Book Prices Current;* Jack Tannen, *How To Identify & Collect American First Editions;* Lyle H. Wright, *American Fiction/1744–1900.*

Advisor: Ron Lieberman

Adams, Ansel, *Born Free And Equal,* NY:1944, wraps. **80.00**

Adams, Ansel, *My Camera In The National Parks,* Yosemite & Boston:1950, 30 photos inset on glass paper, spiral bound boards, 4to **300.00**

Adams, Richard, *Watership Down,* London:1972, illus, dj
American First Edition **22.50**
English First Edition. **200.00**

Agee, James, *Let Us Now Praise Famous Men,* Boston:1941, illus with 31 photos by Walker Evans, cloth, 4to. . **75.00**

Albee, Edward, *A Delicate Balance,* NY:1966, dj. **25.00**

Atget, Eugene, *A Vision Of Paris,* NY:1963, photos by Atget, text by Marcel Proust, half leather, 4to **80.00**

Avedon, Richard, *Nothing Personal,* NY:1964, photos by Avedon, text by James Baldwin **90.00**

Baldwin, James, *Going To Meet The Man,* NY:1965, dj **10.00**

Barnes, Djunia, *Night Among The Horses,* 1929 . . . . **50.00**

Barth, John, *Chimera,* NY:1972, boxed, one of 300 sgd **100.00**

Bellow, S., *Humbolt's Gift,* NY:1975 . . . **20.00**

Bradbury, Ray, *Dark Carnival,* Sauk City, WI:1947, one of only 300 copies, dj . **200.00**

Bradbury, Ray, *Fahrenheit 451,*

NY:Ballantine Books:[1953]
First Edition, dj 200.00
First Edition, one of 200 bound in
asbestos 1,250.00
Bradbury, Ray, *Martian Chronicles*, Garden City, NY:1951, dj, sgd by author   275.00
Burroughs, William S. *Exterminator*, NY:1973, sgd by author, dj 35.00
Caldwell, Erskine, *Journeyman*, NY:1935, one of 1,475 numbered copies, box 30.00
Capote, Truman, *A Christmas Memory*, NY:[1966], orig slipcase. 25.00
Cather, Willa, *Sapphira And The Slave Girl*, NY:1940, one of 520 copies sgd by author 75.00
Cheever, John, *Bullet Park*, NY:1969 . .   15.00
Cheever, John, *The National Pastime*, Los Angeles:1982, one of 330 copies sgd by author 60.00
Clarke, Arthur C., *Against The Fall Of The Night*, NY:Gnome Press:[1953], dj. 60.00
Clarke, Arthur C., *Expedition To Earth*, NY:Ballantine Books:[1953], dj 160.00
Faulkner, William, *A Fable*, NY:[1954], one of 1,000 copies 300.00
Faulkner, William, *Light In August*, NY:[1932], dj 200.00
Faulkner, William, *Mosquitoes*, NY:1927, dj. 140.00
Faulkner, William, *The Sound And The Fury*,NY:[1929], dj 160.00
Fitzgerald, F. Scott, *The Great Gatsby*, NY:1925 . . . .   85.00
Forester, C. S., *To The Indies*, NY:1940 . . . .   20.00
Forester, C. S., *The Sky And The Forest*, London:1948, dj 18.00
Goldman, William, *Boys And Girls Together*, NY:[1964], dj 10.00
Gorey, Edward, *The Unstrung Harp*, NY:[1953], illus, dj 75.00
Greene, G., *Honorary Consul*, NY:1973   15.00
Hailey, Arthur, *Airport*, Garden City, NY:1968, dj. 9.00
Harris, Joel Chandler, *The Tar-Baby & Other Rhymes*, NY:1904, illus. 80.00
Harris, Joel Chandler, *Uncle Remus: His Songs And Sayings*, NY:1881, illus . .   80.00
Heinlein, Robert, *Between Planets*, NY:Scribner's:1951, dj 120.00
Heinlein, Robert, *Farnham's Freehold*, NY:Putnam:[1964], dj. 240.00
Heinlein, Robert, *Stranger In A Strange Land*, NY:Putnam:[1961], dj 200.00
Hemingway, Ernest, *Death In The Afternoon*, NY:1932, illus, dj 130.00
Hemingway, Ernest, *A Farewell To Arms*, NY:1929, first issue without legal disclaimer, dj.   120.00
Hemingway, Ernest, *For Whom The Bell Tolls*, NY:1940, dj 110.00

Hilton, James, *So Well Remembered*, Boston: 1945, dj 14.00
Hunter, E., The Blackboard Jungle, NY: 1954, dj 45.00
Huxley, A., *The Olive Tree*, London: 1936, dj 25.00
Irving, John, *The Hotel New Hampshire*, NY:[1981], dj 18.00
Jones, James, *A Tough Of Danger*, Garden City, NY:1973, dj. 14.00
Lawrence, D. H., *Lady Chaterly's Lover*, [Florence]:1928, one of 1,000 copies sgd by author, bds, 4to 550.00
LeCarre, J., *Tinker, Tailor, Soldier, Spy*, London:1974. . . . .   15.00
Maugham, W. Somerset, *A Writer's Notebook*, NY:1949, one of 1,000 sgd by author, cracked box 100.00
Milne, A. A., *The House At Pooh Corner*, London:1928, illus by E. H. Shepard, dj. 200.00
Milne, A. A., *Now We Are Six*, London:1927, illus by E. H. Shepard, dj .   60.00
Milne, A. A., *Winnie-The-Pooh*, London:1926, illus by E. H. Shepard, dj .   200.00
Nabokov, V., *Invitation To A Beheading*, NY:1959.   20.00
Nabokov, V., *Quartet*, 1966, dj. 30.00
Naipaul, V. S., *A Congo Diary*, Los Angeles:1980, one of 330 copies sgd by author, dj 50.00
O'Neill, *Iceman Cometh*, 1946, dj. 35.00
Salinger, J. D., *Franny and Zooey*, Boston:[1961], dj 30.00
Stein, Gertrude, *The Autobiography Of Alice B. Toklas*, NY:[1933], dj. 80.00
Stein, Gertrude, *Ida*, 1941, dj. 50.00
Steinbeck, John, *Grapes Of Wrath*, NY:[1939], first issue, dj. 220.00
Steinbeck, John, *Of Mice And Men*, NY:[1937], first issue, dj. 165.00
Steinbeck, John, *The Pastures Of Heaven*, NY:1932, first issue, dj 85.00
Theroux, Paul, *Mosquito Coast*, 1982, sgd by author 20.00
Theroux, Paul, *Picture Palace*, Boston:1978, first printing, dj 8.00
Vonnegut, K., *Palm Sunday*, NY:1981. .   9.00
White, Elwyn Brooks, Charlotte's Web, NY:[1952], dj 40.00
Woolf, Virginia, *Jacob's Room*, London:Hogarth Press:1922. . . . .   110.00
Woolf, Virginia, *The Waves*, London:1931, dj 75.00

BOOTJACKS

History: Bootjacks are metal or wooden objects which facilitate the removal of boots. Bootjacks are used by placing the heel of the boot in the "U" shaped opening, putting a foot on the back of the bootjack, and pulling the front boot off the foot.

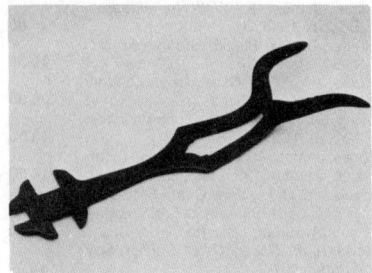

Cast Iron, 13½", "Boot Jack" on prongs, $40.00.

Cast Iron
Cricket, 9¼" l	45.00
Lee Rider advertisement, child's. . . .	10.00
Musselman's Plug Tobacco advertisement	130.00
Intertwining scrolls form letter "M" on pointed end, 11½" l	25.00
Naughty Nellie, 9" l	45.00
Openwork design, heart, 12½".	110.00
Pittsburgh Novelty Works, opposite end is buggy wrench	60.00
Revolver, folding, "The American Bull Dog Boot Jack", 8¼" l	75.00
"Try Me"	40.00

Wooden
Mahogany, folding, c1860	35.00
Pine, chip carved horseshoe, "C", 15¼" l	25.00
Pine, rose head nails, pierced for hanging, 24" l	40.00
Walnut, cast iron frame, carpeted top	50.00
Walnut, heart and diamond openwork, 22" l	40.00

BOTTLES, GENERAL

History: Cosmetic bottles held special creams, oils, and cosmetics, designed to enhance the beauty of the user. Some also claimed, especially on their colorful labels, to cure or provide relief from common ailments.

A number of household items, e.g., cleaning fluids and polishes, required glass storage containers. Many are collected for their fine lithograph labels.

Mineral water bottles contained water from a natural spring. Spring water was favored by health conscious people between the 1850s and 1900s.

Nursing bottles, used to feed the young and sickly, were a great help to the housewife because of graduated measures, replaceable nipples, ease of cleaning, sterilizing, and reuse.

References: Hugh Cleveland, *Bottle Pricing Guide*, Collector Books, 1980; Ralph & Terry Kovel, *The Kovels' Bottle Price List*, Crown Publishers, Inc., 1982, 6th ed.; Carlo & Dot Sellari, *The Illustrated Price Guide To Antique Bottles*, Country Beautiful Corp, 1975.

Periodicals: *Antique Bottle World*, 5003 West Berwyn, Chicago, IL 60630; *Old Bottle Magazine*, P. O. Box 243, Bend, OR 97701. Subscription: $10.00.

Additional Listings: Barber Bottles, Bitter Bottles, Figural Bottles, Food Bottles, Ink Bottles, Medicine Bottles, Poison Bottles, Sarsaparilla Bottles, Snuff Bottles, and Whiskey Bottles (Collectors' Special Editions). Also see the bottle categories in *Warman's Americana & Collectibles* for more examples.

COSMETICS

Creme Simon, J.S., 80 on bottom, milk glass, 2½"	10.00
Gouraud's Oriental Cream, NY, name emb on one side, "London" on other, machine made, 4¼"	5.00
Ingrams Shaving Cream, screw top, round, milk glass, 2¼".	5.00
Mineralava Face Finish, NY, Scotts Face Finish label on back, clear, 5¼" . . .	10.00
Pompeian Massage Cream, amethyst, 2¾"	8.00
Violet Dulce Vanishing Cream, 8 panels, 2½"	12.00

HOUSEHOLD

Alma Polish, emb shoulder, M & Co. on base, aqua, 5"	5.00
Bull Dog Brand Liquid Glue, crude ring collar, aqua, 3½".	10.00
Clorox, machine made, 9 part mold, amber, 8"	8.00
E. Z. Stove Polish, #14, aqua, 6"	10.00
Jennings Blueing, blob top, aqua, 7" . .	5.00

MINERAL OR SPRING WATER

Aetna Spouting Spring, Saratoga, NY, horseshoe lettering in center, A and E in block letters, aqua, pint	50.00
Chamberlain, W. C., Mineral Water, Lancaster, PA, green, iron pontil	30.00
Clark & White, emb in horseshoe, back emb Mineral Water, olive green, 9½"	15.00
Crook, Albert, Saratoga Co., NY, emb in circle, center emb "Paradise Spring", tapered top, 6 rings, green, pint	75.00
Dobbs Ferry Mineral Water Co., Dobbs Ferry, NY, aqua, 6½".	10.00
Jubille Spring Water Co., 101 on bottom, aqua, 11½".	25.00
Pablo & Co., "Mineral Water Factory" on back, aqua, 7½"	20.00

Saxlehner's Bitterquell, Hunyade Janos,
olive green, 9½" **5.00**
Tweddles Celebrated Soda Or Mineral
Water, back reads "Courtland Street,
#38, NY", graphite pontil, cobalt,
7½" **75.00**
Wasino Spring Water, bale, porcelain
stopper, aqua, 12", ½ gallon **15.00**

**Mineral Water, 7⅛", graphite, Twitchel,
Phila, $40.00.**

NURSING

American Feeding Bottle, turtle, light
aqua **15.00**
Blown, 7⅞", fifteen diamonds, Mantua,
pictured in Harry Wite's *The Story of
Mantua Glass and Antiques* (Nov.
1935), pinpoint lip flakes and minor
ext. wear **375.00**
Cala Nurser Baby Bottle, emb on circular
slug plate, ounces on back, clear,
7⅛" **8.00**
Empire Nursing Bottle, one flat side,
neck tapered, amethyst, 5¼" **5.00**
Nonpareil Nurser, aqua, 5½" **20.00**
Sunshine Dairy, picture of baby, orig cap,
nipple, 8 oz. **5.00**

BRASS

History: Brass is a durable, malleable, and ductile metal alloy consisting mainly of copper and zinc.
It achieved its greatest popularity for utilitarian and
decorative art items in the eighteenth and nineteenth centuries.

Many modern reproductions are being made of
earlier brass forms, especially in the areas of buckets, fireplace equipment, and kettles.

Reference: Peter, Nancy, and Herbert Schiffer,
The Brass Book, Schiffer Publishing, Ltd, 1978.

Additional Listings: Bells, Candlesticks, Fireplace Equipment, and Scientific Instruments.

Andirons
20" h, double lemon top, ring-turned
mid-band over columnar standard,
spurred arched legs on ball feet,
1800–1820 . . . .   **675.00**
25" h, twisted flame detail with double
finial and matching log stops, ball
and claw feet, 18th C. **300.00**
Ashtray, emb hunting scene **50.00**
Bed Warmers
42½", engraved floral lid, turned
wooden handle with brushed brown
graining **375.00**
44", engraved scroll lid, turned
wooden handle **265.00**
Bell, school, 6¾", turned wooden
handle **40.00**
Boxes
7½", cast ball and claw feet, lion's
head ring handles, tooled geometric
and foliage designs, polished,
c1890 . . . .   **125.00**
11¾" h, 11" w, hanging, sheet brass,
hinged lid, floral emb crest,
polished **90.00**
Braizer, 8½" l, small, turned wooden
handle **120.00**
Buckets
11¾" d, 8¼" h, iron bale handle . . .   **125.00**
18½" d, iron bale handle **250.00**
Calipers, 3" l, shaped like legs. **75.00**
Candle Snuffer, 7¼", scissors-type . . .   **40.00**
Candlesticks
5½", capistan, large cylindrical base,
polished **650.00**
5¾", pr, molded nozzle, circular can-
dlecup over baluster and ring-turned
stem, octagonal dish base, c1700
6¼", George II, flared cylindrical candlecup, baluster turned stem,
domed circular foot, early 18th C. .   **165.00**
10", pr, Empire, acanthus dec sockets,
fluted tapering columns, grape leaf
dec, circular foot, French, early
19th C **245.00**
11", pr, Empire, vase shape candle-
cup, swag dec flared rim, geometric
dec over fluted columnar standard,
acanthus leaf dec foot, French,
c1820 . . . .   **300.00**
Chafing Dish, 7¼" h, 7" d, George III,
cylindrical, 3 pierced panels of winged
figures and foliage, dish held by 3 scalloped uprights continuing to form feet,
dated 1775. . . . . **1,210.00**

Chamberstick, 2⅞" h, wide cup base, c1900........................ **100.00**

Chandelier, 23½" d, circular, flame finial above flaring shaft with foliate pendant, 6 anthemia, 6 swan shaped candlearms, 3 with figures of angels, French, 19th C................ **3,520.00**

Charger, 16" d, central medallion with Temptation scene, Nuremburg, 17th C.......................... **400.00**

Chestnut Roaster, 18½" l, oval sheet brass pan, cast handle.......... **125.00**

Cigar Box, 9½ x 5½ x 3½"......... **200.00**

Coal Hod, 16" sq, slanting sides, Neo-classical, ring handles, ball feet, urn shape finial, inner liner, Edwardian.. **120.00**

Dipper, 17½" l, brass bowl, wrought iron handle..................... **100.00**

Door Handles, pr, 9¼", shaped plate mounted with molded D-shaped handle, oval shaped thumb grip, English, 18th C..................... **175.00**

Ewer and Basin, 12" h pear shaped ewer, shaped rim, scroll handle, molded foot, 15" d circular basin, broad rim, 18th C.............. **1,550.00**

Figure, dachshund, 1½" h, 2½" w, 5" l, running position, black finish, oval base, c1900................... **150.00**

Fireplace Fenders
46" w, 10" h, D-shape, 2 bands of pierced guilloche over coved base molding, cast paw feet, English, early 19th C............... **200.00**
54" w, 10" h, reticulated leaf design, ribbed feet................. **375.00**

Grate, 32½" h, 28¼" w, 16½" d, shaped Cl crest with scrolling terminals, brass

Bed Warmer, 46" l, pine handles, $325.00.

run shape finials, scroll pierced brass skirt with urn finials, inverted scrolled legs, ring feet, 1810–1830........ **950.00**

Ice Tongs..................... **40.00**

Jar, 3¼" baluster, double ear handles, dovetailed construction.......... **50.00**

Kettle Shelf, 14 x 6 x 5½" pierced rectangular, 4 shaped legs.......... **95.00**

Kettles
5½", cylindrical, engraved floral dec, gooseneck spout, shaped swing handle, 19th C.............. **500.00**
6¼", heavy, cast, 2 animal head spouts, figural handle ears, wrought iron bale handle, animal head finial..................... **2,525.00**
8¼", straight spout, shaped, swing, turned wooden handle, small ball feet....................... **100.00**

Lamps, whale oil, pr, 10½", Gardon burners, early 19th C........... **300.00**

Lantern, 9½", cylindrical, engraved mounts at corners, strap handle with scrolled and incised mounts, molded base, 19th C................. **550.00**

Letter Rack, fish in relief on each side....................... **35.00**

Matchholders
3¾", cast brass horse on semicircular wooden base with matchbook holder, c1900.............. **45.00**
4¾" h, chimney with emb bricks.... **80.00**

Mortar and Pestle, 3" h, polished..... **65.00**

Mug, 6½", late 18th C........... **95.00**

Pans
Sauce, 8" d, heavy, copper rivets, wrought iron handle........... **175.00**
Spider, 6¼" d, 9" wrought handle, 3 legs, spun brass............ **65.00**

Pastry Cutter, 4¼" l, copper rivets, tooling, initialed "BM,"............ **75.00**

Pill Box, figural turtle, nickle plated brass....................... **65.00**

Pipe Tamper, figural powder horn, c1910...................... **25.00**

Rim Lock, 4" w, 5⅛" l, rectangular, cove molded edge, iron spindle with 2 ball turned knobs and petal shaped escutcheon, marked I. George, 18th C **175.00**

Sconce, wall, candle, 8", hand made, c1900..................... **60.00**

Scoop, 13" l, cylindrical, cast handle.. **65.00**

Septre, church, 9¼" l,............ **50.00**

Sewing Bird, 5" l, emb, bird has white underbelly, red and green stripes, olive velvet pincushion........... **135.00**

Skimmers
15⅞", wrought iron handle stamped F. B. S. Canton, O. Pat. June 26, '86 **100.00**
23½", well shaped wrought iron handle................... **150.00**

Spoon, tasting, 14¼", sold brass bowl, plated handle............... **70.00**

Trays
  7″ w, 13″ l, 3″ h, almond shape,
  reticulate sides **125.00**
  12¼″ d, circular, lightly hammered
  sides, imp WIENER/WERK/
  STATTE, JH, 1903–1921 . . . . **550.00**
Tobacco Boxes
  5¾″ l, 1″ h, oval, hinged lid, reeded
  molding, engraved with figures and
  inscriptions top and bottom, Dutch,
  18th C **220.00**
  6″ l, hanging, emb, tooled, sheet
  brass, polished **95.00**
Vases
  8″, pr, sq, flared sides, ridged flared
  foot, polished, imp WIENER/
  WERK/STATTE, reg trademark,
  JH, 1903–1931 . . . . **2,000.00**
  14½″, pr, cornucopia shape, beaded
  acanthus dec rim on rectangular
  phinth with garlands and butterflies,
  19th C **1,250.00**
Wine Cooler, 8½″ d, 6½″ h, ring handles,
  c1900. . . . . **120.00**

BREAD PLATES

History: Beginning in the mid-1880s, special trays or platters were made for serving bread and rolls. Designated by collectors as "bread plates," these small trays or platters can be found in porcelain, glass (especially pattern glass), and metals.

Bread plates often were part of a china or glass set. However, many glass companies made special plates which honored national heroes, commemorated historical or special events, offered a moral maxim, or supported a religious attitude. The theme on the plate could be either in a horizontal or vertical format. The favorite shape for these plates is oval, with a common length being ten inches.

Additional Listings: Pattern Glass.

Aluminum, hand wrought
  Chrysanthemum, Continental, bail
  handle. **10.00**
  Pine cone decor **8.00**
Bakelite, 18″, free-form, 2 handles, red-
  dish brown **16.00**
Bavarian China, 14 x 7″, spring scene,
  pastel colors, gold band, hp, artist
  sgd **80.00**
Lenox, 14 x 7″, flower chain decor, hp
  handles **135.00**
Limoges, 14 x 9½″, forget-me-nots, gold
  handles **40.00**
Majolica, 13″ l, "Eat Thy Bread With
  Thankfulness". **120.00**
Milk Glass, lattice edge. **30.00**
Onion Meissen, 12″ l, oval **65.00**
Pattern Glass
  Actress, "Give Us Our Daily Bread,"
  Pinafore **75.00**

American, 10½″, Fostoria.	**35.00**
Barley, oval.	**45.00**
Beaded Grape, 10″	**45.00**
Canadian	**45.00**
Columbus.	**40.00**
Deer and Pine Tree, 13″	**45.00**
Diagonal Band, 11½ x 9″, "Eureka"	**36.00**
Egg In Sand	**25.00**
Egyptian, Cleopatra	**45.00**
Frosted Lion.	**45.00**
Frosted Ribbon.	**35.00**

Venus and Psyche, 11 x 7½″, $45.00.

Garden of Eden, motto	**30.00**
Grape, "It Is Pleasant To Labor For Those We Love"	**65.00**
Horseshoe	**35.00**
Iowa City, "Be Industrious"	**75.00**
Loops and Fans	**25.00**
Maple Leaf, vaseline	**40.00**
Minerva, "Give Us Our Daily Bread"	**55.00**
Oak Leaf, amber.	**45.00**
One Hundred One, "Give Us Our Daily Bread"	**55.00**
Peerless, oval, handled	**20.00**
Polar Bear, frosted, artic scene	**110.00**
Rock of Ages, clear, milk glass insert.	**175.00**
Rose in Snow	**40.00**
Scalloped Tape, "Bread Is The Staff of Life".	**40.00**
Scroll With Flowers	**30.00**
Stippled Star, "Mother"	**40.00**
Star Rosette, "Mother"	**40.00**
Three Presidents.	**145.00**
Tree of Life, oval.	**35.00**
Transcontinental Railroad.	**75.00**
U. S. Coin, dated 1892 on one coin .	**75.00**
Valencia Waffle, amber	**45.00**
R. S. Germany, 14″, green luster, pink roses, shadow leaves, gold scal-loped rim.	**55.00**
White Patterned Ironstone, 15″, leaf design.	**15.00**

BRIDE'S BASKETS

History: A ruffled edge, glass bowl in a metal holder was a popular wedding gift in the 1880–1910 era, hence, the name of "bride's basket." The glass bowls can be found in most glass types of the period. The metal holder was generally silver plated with a bail handle, thus enhancing the basket image.

Over the years bowls and bases became separated; and, married pieces resulted. Reproductions exist, especially the glass bowls.

Note: Items listed have silver plated holder unless otherwise noted.

Pairpoint, 8¾" d, peppermint stick rim to frosted bowl, SP frame, 6 medallions of busts, 4 feet, $140.00.

Burmese, 12½", gold leaves, pink flowers, painted Burmese colored ext., yellow-green int., attr. to Pairpoint Glass Co.. . . . . 450.00
Cased
   10", deep pink int., white ext., applied amber rim 150.00
   10¾", blue int., enameled gold scrolls, blue forget-me-nots, pink roses, lacy foilage, white ext.. . . . . 300.00
   11" d, 6" h, white ext., shaded pink int., crimped, fluted, applied clear amber rim 175.00
   11" d, 12" h, yellow ext., tomato red int., clear rim, Middletown SP frame 395.00
Cranberry
   8", ruffled rim 135.00
   10½", shaded cranberry to white, raised orange and white enamel decor 225.00
Custard, shaded to ruby 200.00
Hobnail, 10¼", red, enameled blue and yellow floral decor, ruffled rim with enameled yellow scroll and applied clear edge 275.00
Mt. Washington, 9", ruffled top, ribbed base, bowl only. 150.00

Opalescent
   11½", white stripes, shaded, crimped, fluted, bowl only. 65.00
   11¾" d, 17 ¾" h, light green to pink, DQ, ruffled, fancy pewter frame. . . 195.00
   Blue, lattice design, crimped, fluted. . 165.00
Satin
   10½", pink, maroon flowers, green, yellow, and lavender leaves, gold trim, ruffled frosted edge, white ext.. . . . . 245.00
   10½", shell shape, orange ribbed int., cream ext.. . . . . 155.00
   Blue, MOP, DQ 100.00
Stevens and Williams, blue satin swirl int., white ext., birds in flight. 200.00
Webb, 11" d, 7½" h, pleated, coral-pink shading to creamy white, clear cased with thin clear border, figural Kate Greenaway Hartford SP holder 695.00

BRISTOL GLASS

History: Bristol glass is a designation given to a semi-opaque glass, usually decorated with enamel and cased with another color. Initially the term referred only to glass made in Bristol, England, in the 17th and 18th centuries. By the Victorian era firms on the Continent and in America were copying the glass and its forms.

Biscuit Jars
   7¼" h, 5" d, opaque blue, enameled multicolored florals, green leaves, SP bail and cover 120.00
   7½", jewel and floral decor, metal bail and lid 150.00
Bottles
   3⅞" h, 2½" d, perfume, turquoise blue, gold scrolls, small white florals, applied red jewels, gold decor stopper 100.00
   11½", green, satin finish 65.00

Vases, 11⅛", pedestal foot, pr, $55.00.

Perfume, blue neck, hp blue bird in center medallion, gilt, teardrop stopper 100.00

Box, 2½" h, 5⅝" d, hinged, opaque white, hp green and gold leaves, lid with boy and girl sledding in reserve 145.00

Bride's Basket, 10½", pink to rose, ruffled edge, delicate flowers inside, bowl only 95.00

Cake Stand, 6½", celadon, pair enameled herons in flight, gold trim 100.00

Ewer, 9", cherub decor 90.00

Honey Pot, 4", pale gray, enamel floral decor, metal lid and bail handle 60.00

Lamps
9½", hand, blue decor, orig chimney 135.00
10⅝" h, 4¼" d, miniature, pink, enameled floral decor, white, green, gray, tan, and brown, gold trim, orig brass burner, holder, and chimney 650.00

Mantel Lusters, pr, 10¾" h, 5" d, glossy and satin finish, 8 crystal spear point cut prisms, gold decor 300.00

Parfaits, yellow, engraved flowers and fruit, sgd, set of 8 . . . . 320.00

Sweetmeat Jar, 5" h, 3" d, pink ground, enameled blue and white florals, green foliage, colored ducks in flight 100.00

Tobacco Jar, hp, SP top with pipe 125.00

Vases
6" h, 4½" d, oval, scenic, boy playing horn, 2 tiny dolls dancing, reverse of hp horn, blue and white tambourine with strands of green leaves 125.00
9½", pedestal base, opaque frosted ground, hp and enameled orange and white poppies, green leaves, gilt decor, pr 145.00
9½" h, 4" d, pink, white cased, white Mary Gregory type boy with hoop . 165.00
10¾", bulbous, rust to beige, enameled brown leaves, blue birds, white and gold trim 95.00
11", blue satin ground, gold and white grape and leaf decor, pedestal base 80.00
11", frosted blue, enameled flowers, pedestal base 65.00
12", pink, floral decor, white cased, pr 150.00
15" h, 5" d, pink overlay, all over blue and white enameled flowers, white heron in marsh outlined in blue dots, scalloped cut top, gold trim, pedestal base 200.00

BRITISH ROYALTY COMMEMORATIVES

History: British commemorative china, souvenirs to commemorate coronations and other royal events, dates from the 1600s, with the early pieces being rather crude in design and form. The development of transfer printing, c1780, led to a much closer likeness of the reigning monarch on the ware.

King George IV's coronation was the first royal occasion at which children received municipal gifts. Victoria's Jubilee expanded the practice. The Royal Wedding of Prince Charles to Lady Diana Spencer and the subsequent births of their sons, Prince William Philip Louis [heir to the throne] and Prince Henry Charles Albert David, heralded a new wave of commemoratives.

Some British Royalty commemoratives are easily recognized by their portraits of past or present monarchs. Some may be in silhouette profile. Other royal symbols include crowns, dragons, royal coats of arms, national flowers, swords, sceptres, dates, messages, and initials.

On August 25, 1984, Phillips in New York conducted the first American auction to feature a majority of British Royalty commemoratives.

References: John May, *Victoria Remembered, A Royal History 1817–1861,* London, 1983: John and Jennifer May, *Commemorative Pottery 1780–1900, A Guide for Collectors,* Charles Scribner's Sons, 1972; Josephine Jackson, *Fired For Royalty,* Heaton Moor, 1977; David Rogers, *Coronation Souvenirs and Commemoratives,* Latimer New Dimensions, Ltd., 1975; Sussex Commemorative Ware Centre, *200 Commemoratives,* Metra Print Enterprises, 1979; Geoffrey Warren, *Royal Souvenirs,* Orbis, 1977.

Collectors' Club: Royalty Collectors Association of North America, 30 East 60th Street, Suite #803, New York, NY 10022.

Additional Listings: See *Warman's Americana & Collectibles* for more examples.

Advisor: Doug Flynn and Al Bolton.

Beaker, 4" h, 1937, Coronation, Minton, limited edition of 2,000, $245.00.

Beakers
Elizabeth II, 1977 Jubilee, gold lion head handles, 4½″ h, Caverswall . . 40.00
George VI/Elizabeth, 1937 Coronation, 4¼″, Wedgwood & Co., Ltd . . 55.00
George V/Mary and Prince of Wales [later Edward VIII], 1911 Coronation, enamel on tin, 3¾″ h, unmarked 45.00
Edward VII/Alexandra, 1902 Coronation, 3¾″ h, Foley China 50.00

Bowls
Elizabeth II, 1977 Jubilee, ftd, 5½″ d, Aynsley 32.50
Edward VIII, 1937 Coronation, 6¼″ d, Grindley 50.00
George V/Mary, 1911 Coronation, 7⅝″ d, unmarked 40.00
Edward VII/Alexandra, 1902 Coronation [correct date—August 9, 1902], 5″ d, unmarked 100.00

Boxes
Elizabeth II, 1972, 25th Wedding Anniversary, heart shaped, cov, 4″ d, Aynsley 45.00
Charles/Diana, 1981 Wedding, cov, raised gold silhouettes, 4″ d, Coalport 27.50
Prince William of Wales, 1982 Birth, locking top, 3″ d, Coalport, limited edition of 2,000 . . . . 45.00

Bust, Parian, Elizabeth II, 1953 Coronation, maroon glazed base, 5½″ h, Foley 60.00
Compact, Edward VIII, 1937 Coronation, large color portrait and date, 2⅝″ sq 35.00

Cups and Saucers
Elizabeth II, 1953 Coronation, Aynsley 75.00
Elizabeth/Margaret, child's play set, c1936, foreign 52.50
George VI/Elizabeth, Wartime series, "There'll Always Be An England," Roslyn 90.00
George V/Mary, 1911 Coronation, portraits and battleships, Aynsley . 70.00
Horse Brass, George V/Mary, 1911 Coronation, 3¾ x 3″ 18.00

Jugs
George VI/Elizabeth, 1937 Coronation, 4¾″ h, Aynsley 60.00
Edward VIII, 1937 Coronation
Art Deco design, 5½″, unmarked . . 40.00
Musical, shape of king's head, plays "God Save The King," 8″ h, Bretby 200.00
Victoria, 1887 Jubilee, large pastel portrait of the Queen, 8″ h, Empress 200.00

Lithophanes
Cup, Mary, Prince of Wales feathers, 2¾″ h 150.00
Cups, pr, Edward VII/Alexandra,

"1902" on each cup, crown and cypher, 3″ h 225.00
Mug, Edward VII, "1902" on mug, crown and cypher, 3¾″ h 90.00

Loving Cups (measured handle to handle)
Elizabeth II, 1953 Coronation, 5½″, John Wadsworth design, Minton . . 200.00
George VI/Elizabeth, 1937 Coronation, 5¾″, Royal Crown Derby 325.00
George V, 1936 Memorial, 7½″, Royal Doulton 245.00
George V/Mary
1935 Jubilee, colored flower handles, 6″, Paragon 160.00
1911 Coronation, 3 handled, 4¾″, unmarked 65.00

Mugs
Elizabeth II
1977, Jubilee, "kneeling mug," 4¼″ h, Carlton Ware 25.00
1953, Coronation, 4¼″ h, Eric Ravilious design, Wedgwood 160.00
Anne/Mark, 1973 Wedding, ftd, 4½″ h, Crown Staffordshire 45.00
George V/Mary, 1935 Jubilee, 3⅞″, G. W. S. Longton 40.00

Invitation, Coronation Dinner, July 5, 1902, Edward VII/Alexandra, 12½ x 10½″, $45.00.

Edward VII/Alexandra, 1902 Coronation, 3¼″ h, unmarked 50.00
Alexandra, 1902 Coronation, 2″ h, Made in Germany 40.00
Victoria, 1897 Jubilee, young and old portraits of Queen, 3″ h, Empire Works 85.00
Orb, Elizabeth II, 1953 Coronation, 5″ h, Wedgwood & Co. Ltd. 65.00

Pepper Shaker, Mary, 1911 Coronation, champagne bottle shape, 4" h, unmarked **30.00**

Plates

Elizabeth II

1977 Jubilee, 7½" d, Crown Staffordshire, limited edition of 10,000 . . . . **50.00**

1953 Coronation, "Royal Souvenir," black and white portraits on glass, 9¾" d **40.00**

c1928, baby's plate, Marcus Adams portrait, 8¼ x 5¾", Paragon . . . **240.00**

Charles/Diana, 1981 Wedding, 10½" d, Aynsley, limited edition of 10,000 . . . . **235.00**

Elizabeth, the Queen Mother, 1980 [80 birthday], 10½" d, Coalport, limited edition of 2,000 . . . . **95.00**

Edward VII/Alexandra

1901 Accession, 8¼" d, unmarked **115.00**

1888 Silver Wedding Anniversary, 7" d, Rd. No. 9144 . . . . **115.00**

Pitcher, musical, George VI/Elizabeth, 1937 Coronation, Elizabeth/Margaret portraits on reverse, plays "Here's A Health Unto His Majesty," 7¼", Shelley **240.00**

Pot Lid, Edward VII/Alexandra, Marriage, color portrait, 4" d, Prattware . **155.00**

Printed Matter

Books

Princess Margaret's 20th Birthday Book, Anne Packard [story], Pitkins **9.00**

The Queen Mother, 75 Glorius Years, Angus Hall **5.00**

The Royal Children's Birthday Book, 1952, Pitkins **8.00**

Newspaper, *Picture Post*, special Coronation souvenir number, 6/13/53 **7.00**

Print, "His Majesty King Edward The Eighth," black and white, from portrait by Bertram Park, 14 x 19" . . . **25.00**

Program, *Coronation Of King Edward VIII And Queen Alexandra,* official program of procession, Friday, June 27, 1902 . . . . **16.00**

Reverse Painting On Glass, Albert, 2½" d **155.00**

Shaving Mugs

Charles/Diana, 1981 Wedding, 6¾" across, Keystone **35.00**

Edward VII/Alexandra, 1902 Coronation, color portraits, 5½" across, unmarked **95.00**

Spoons, SS

Elizabeth II, 1977 Jubilee, 5⅜" l **45.00**

George VI/Elizabeth, 1937 Coronation, 4½" l, orig box **45.00**

Edward VIII, 1937 Coronation, profile in army uniform, date in bowl, 3¾" l **37.50**

Victoria, 1897 Jubilee, gold wash, heavily dec bowl, 4¾" l **65.00**

Teapots

Elizabeth II, 1953 Coronation, aluminum, 3½" h, Swan-Cromalin **35.00**

George V/Mary, 1911 Coronation, 4" h, unmarked **90.00**

Edward VII/Alexandra, 1902 Coronation, 4" h **135.00**

Victoria, 1897, Jubilee, 6" h, Aynsley **220.00**

Teapots, with Sugar and Creamer

Elizabeth/Margaret, child's play set, c1936, foreign **160.00**

Margaret, Birth, parakeets, roses, marguerites, and heather, Paragon **325.00**

Tins

Elizabeth II, 1953 Coronation, Oxo Ltd **12.00**

Charles/Diana, 1981 Wedding, money box, shape of post box, 4¼" h . . . **8.00**

George VI/Elizabeth, 1937 Coronation, 10" d, round, A. S. Wilkin . . . **52.50**

Edward VIII, 1937 Coronation, Windsor Castle on sides, 5¾" h **40.00**

George V/Mary, 1935 Jubilee, water color box, 7½" l, Reeves **50.00**

Princess Mary, 1922 Marriage, 3 color portraits, 6" h **65.00**

Edward VII/Alexandra, 1902 Coronation, color portraits, Cadbury **30.00**

Victoria, 1897 Jubilee, black and white portraits of Queen and late Prince Consort, and two more generations [Edward/Alexandra and George/ Mary], 7" h, Coleman's Mustard . . **135.00**

BRONZE

History: Bronze is an alloy of copper, tin, and traces of other metals. It has been used since Biblical times not only for art objects, but also for utilitarian purposes. After a slump in the Middle Ages, bronze was revived in the 17th century and continued in popularity until the early 20th century.

Notes: Do not confuse a "bronzed" object with a true bronze. A bronzed object usually is made of white metal and then coated with a reddish-brown material to give it a bronze appearance.

A signed bronze commands a higher market price than an unsigned one. There also are "signed" reproductions in the market. It is very important to know the history of the mold and the background of the foundry.

Animals

Bird of paradise, walking, extended feathers, black marble base, 20th C, 26" **650.00**

Bull, rearing, A. Barye, late 19th C, 10¾" **1,100.00**

Cat, black patina, L. Riche, c1890, 10" **500.00**

Plaque, 8½″, Marat, $250.00.

Deer, golden brown patina, marble base, A. Barye, 19th C, 6½″ **800.00**

Eagle perched on rockwork, gilt eyes and beak, Japanese, 19th C, 10¼″ **400.00**

Dog, seated, brown patina, P. Mene, c1900, 6½″ **450.00**

Elephant, striding, ivory tusks, A. panse, late 19th C, 13½″ **620.00**

Hen and rooster, pr, polychrome, Austrian, Geschutz, c1880, 4¾″ **500.00**

Horse, reared on hind legs, "Portugese Bull Fighter", Herbert Haseltine, 1922, 11¼″ h, 10½″ 1 . . . . . **700.00**

Irish setter, reclining, red brown patina, W. Habisch, late 19th C, 7¾″ **500.00**

Lion, roaring, marble base, T. Cartier, 1909, 24″ **1,000.00**

Lion walking, dark red brown patina, A. Barye, 19th C, 15½″ **1,500.00**

Panther, stalking, dark patina, stepped black marble base, A. Lapointe, 1920s, 5¾″ **900.00**

Pigs, 2, oval mud-molded base, green marble stand, I. Bonheur, late 19th C, 8¾″ **900.00**

Pointer, red brown patina, P. Mene, mid 19th C, 5¼″ **550.00**

Raccoon with ear of corn, 3 x 4½ x 2¾″ **125.00**

Sparrow, fallen, shot by careless hunter, Commalera, 4″ h, 2″ 1 . . . . **325.00**

Tiger, green and brown patina, Jewetterlund, c1900, 15¼″ **900.00**

Ashtray, wild boar, green onyx dish, Art Deco, French, 1920s, 4″ **120.00**

Bookends, pr, woman, seated, reading book, brown patina, L. Baer, 1913, 6¾″ **650.00**

Bowls

Chrysanthemums, molded, pierced, cov, Japanese, c1850, 9″ d **450.00**

Snails and branches, c1900, 5″ d . . . **175.00**

Boxes

Oval, scroll handles, pin tray base,

painted panels, gilt, French, c1910, 9¼″ **225.00**

Rectangular, Favrile pine needle pattern, gilt, ball feet, Tiffany, c1900, 6½″ **150.00**

Busts

Christ, 19th C, 27″ h **550.00**

Queen Victoria, C. F. Ball, English, 1848, 17″ h **775.00**

Brush Holder, shape of gnarled segment of bamboo, 2 leafy sprigs form handles, late 17th C, ¼″ **675.00**

Candle Snuffer, heart and cross design, late 17th C, 6½″ 1 . . . . **120.00**

Candelabras, prs

3-light, spray of lilies, bow at stems, cast, European, 18th C, 6″ h. **650.00**

4-light, scroll molded stems and bases, foliate branches, gilt, Louis XV, late 19th C, 19¾″ h **800.00**

8-light, lion masks, pierced stem, foliate scrolled branches, gilt, late 19th C, 24″ h. **900.00**

Candlesticks, pr, circular, molded base, multi-ring turned stem, late 17th C, 9″ **220.00**

Car Mascot, Indian warrior with spear, stylized, gilt, F. Bazin, 1920s, 6″ **275.00**

Chandeliers, pr, 6-light, baluster stem, grapevine arms, grapes, fox heads, gilt, late 19th C, 44″ h **1,700.00**

Cup, circular, pierced stem, T'ang, 3¼″ **500.00**

Desk Calendar, emb scroll, 8″ h, 7″ w . **150.00**

Dish, sq, inscribed in center, low relief dragons on base, Ming Dynasty, 5⅜″ **225.00**

Figures

Arab maiden, seated, upswept hair, diaphanous skirt, N. Greb, c1900, 11¼″ **600.00**

Dancer, gypsy, green brown patina, L. Delapchiez, 19th C, 16½″ **1,100.00**

Diana, red brown patina, marble base, P. Kowalczewski, late 19th C, 12″ **700.00**

Dignitary, standing, hands clasped, short jacket with billowing sleeves over long robe tied low, gilded, Ming Dynasty, 6½″. **600.00**

Girl, clown costume, gilt, ivory, D. Chiparus, c1925, 8⅜″ **500.00**

Girl, windswept, clutching hooded cloak with school bag underneath, ivory face, round marble base, D. Chiparus, 7″ **425.00**

Jockey, standing, saddle draped over arm, circular base, late 19th C, 14″ **750.00**

Miner, hanging lantern and pick, French, c1900, 9″ **350.00**

Nymph, seated, golden brown patina, Moreau, late 19th C, 19″ **1,600.00**

Roman warrior, standing, helmut, shield, c1920, 8″ **250.00**

Viking, horned helmut, horn at hips, spear, loin cloth, 20th C, 12¾″ . . . **620.00**

Woman, classical dress, rocky col-

umn, gilt, marble base, F. Barbe-
dienne, c1900, 14".......... **500.00**
Frame, rectangular, pine needle dec,
beaded border, green Favrile glass,
Tiffany, early 20th C, 7½"........ **150.00**
Humidor, rectangular, hinged cov, all
over floral repousse dec, stamped E.
F. Caldwell & Co, New York, 10½ x
13¾ x 4"................... **675.00**
Incense Burner, flared sided, ftd, handles, olive brown, gold splashed,
pierced wood cov, 18th C, 5⅜" h... **1,025.00**
Inkwells, pr, cut crystal inkwells mounted
on leaf shape base, 19th C, 3¼"... **200.00**
Lamp, cylindrical, flaring cylindrical
etched glass shade, column turned
shaft, sq base, brass label "W. Car-
leton, Boston", electrified, early 19th
C, 17¾"................... **350.00**
Medallion, octagonal, maiden, flowers,
P, Turin, 1925, 2¼' d........... **150.00**
Mirror, circular, barbed rim, ship and
dragon, 4-character seal in relief,
Koryo, 6¾".................. **420.00**
Mortar, cylindrical, tapered flared rim,
molded foot, banding, English, 17th C, 4" **175.00**
Stamp Box, Zodiac dec, gilt finish, Tif-
fany Studios................. **175.00**
Tray, rectangular, handles molded with
Japanese beetle, branches, gilt, L.
Levee, late 19th C, 6" 1......... **250.00**
Urn, large bird in tree and fox, high relief,
E. Sanglan.................. **420.00**
Vases
Nude girl and water nymph seated on
shell, fish on base, F. Mage, late
19th C, 15"................ **700.00**
Putto sitting on branch, baluster
shape, applied handles, A. Moreau,
late 19th C, 11¾"........... **300.00**
Woven basketwork overlay, knotted at
collar, Japanese, 19th C, 12".... **325.00**
Wall Sconces, pr, 2-light, merman, head
supporting foliate and fluted scones,
gilt, late 19th C, 21"........... **800.00**

DELDARE WARE
UNDERGLAZE

BUFFALO POTTERY

History: Buffalo Pottery Co., Buffalo, New York,
was chartered in 1901. The first kiln was fired in

October 1903. Larkin Soap Company conceived
Buffalo Pottery to produce premiums for its extensive mail order business. Wares also were sold to
the public by better department and jewelry stores.
Elbert Hubbard and Frank L. Wright, who designed
the Larkin Administration Building in Buffalo in
1904, were two prominent names associated with
the Larkin Company.

Early production consisted mainly of dinner sets
of semi-vitreous china. Buffalo was the first pottery
in the United States to produce successfully the
Blue Willow pattern, marked "First Old Willow Ware
Mfg. in America." Buffalo also made a line of hand
decorated, multicolored willow ware, called Gaudy
Willow. Other early items include a series of game,
fowl, and fish sets, pitchers, jugs, and a line of
commemorative, historical, and advertising plates
and mugs.

In 1908-09 and 1921-23, Buffalo Pottery produced the line for which it is most famous, Deldare
Ware, The earliest of this olive green, semi-vitreous
china depicts hand decorated scenes from the English artist Cecil Aldin's *Fallowfield Hunt*. Hunt
scenes only were done in 1908-09. English village
scenes also were characteristic and found throughout the series. Most are artist signed.

In 1911 Buffalo Pottery produced Emerald Deldare, which used scenes from Goldsmith's *The
Three Tours of Dr. Syntax* and an Art Nouveau type
border. Completely decorated Art Nouveau pieces
also were made.

In 1912 Abino was born. Abino was done on
Deldare bodies and showed sailing, windmill, and
seascape scenes. The main color was rust. All
pieces are artist signed and numbered.

In 1915 the pottery was modernized, giving it the
ability to produce vitrified china. Consequently, hotel and institutional ware became their main production, with hand decorated ware de-emphasized.
Buffalo china became a leader in producing and
designing the most famous railroad, hotel, and restaurant patterns. These wares, especially railroad
items, are eagerly sought by collectors.

In the early 1920s fine china was made for home
use, e.g., the Bluebird pattern. In 1950 Buffalo
made their first Christmas plate. They were given
away to customers and employees from 1950-60.
Hample Equipment Co. ordered some in 1962. The
Christmas plates are very scarce.

The name Buffalo Pottery and Buffalo China are
synonomous. The difference being one is semi-vitreous ware and the other vitrified. In 1956 the company was reorganized and Buffalo China became
the corporate name. Today Buffalo China is owned
by Oneida Silver Company. The Larkin family no
longer is involved.

Reference: Seymour and Violet Altman, *The
Book Of Buffalo Pottery*, Crown Publishers, 1969.
Updated price guide available from author.

Note: Numbers in parenthesis refer to plates in
the Altman's book.

Advisor: Seymour & Violet Altman.

Saucer, 4⅜", Wanamaker Store Jubilee Year 1861–1911, Buffalo mark, green and white, $60.00.

ABINO WARE

Plaques
12", desert scene (239)	**1,750.00**
12¼", sailing ships (241)	**1,000.00**
13½", In The Pastures (244)	**2,500.00**
Plate, 6½", bread and butter, windmill scene (243)	**250.00**
Sugar, cov, nautical scene (249)	**550.00**
Vase, 6¾", windmill scene (258)	**850.00**

BLUE AND GAUDY WILLOW

Blue Willow
Chicago Jug, 1 pint, 6½ oz (103)	**110.00**
Creamer, double lip, 2½ oz (30)	**12.50**
Cup and Saucer (26)	**35.00**
Plate, 9¼" (75)	**20.00**
Sugar and Creamer (26)	**90.00**

Gaudy Willow
Cup and Saucer (26)	**125.00**
Plate, 9", dinner (26)	**100.00**
Platter, 8½ x 10½" (40)	**175.00**

CHRISTMAS PLATES

1951 (261)	**50.00**
1956 (266)	**45.00**
1960 (270)	**50.00**

COMMERCIAL SERVICES

Cup and Saucer, Genesee Hotel (302)	**50.00**
Plate, 7¼", Jack Dempsey's Restaurant (289)	**100.00**

Plates, serving
9½", Barclay Hotel (292)	**100.00**
10½", Mont Clair Hotel (293)	**100.00**
11", Hotel Pere Marquette (297)	**150.00**

DELDARE

Bowl, 9", The Fallowfield Hunt, The Death (125)	**475.00**

Cake Plate, 10", Ye Village Gossips (148)	**375.00**
Calling Card Tray, Ye Lion Inn (173)	**300.00**

Chocolate
Cup and Saucer (163)	**250.00**
Pot, 9" (163)	**1,500.00**
Hair Receiver, cov, Ye Village Street (143)	**295.00**
Humidor, 7", octagon shape, Ye Lion Inn (174)	**650.00**
Match Box Holder and Ashtray (combination), Scenes Of Village Life In Ye Olden Days (155)	**400.00**

Mugs
2½", Scenes Of Village Life In Ye Olden Days (122)	**250.00**
4¼", At The Three Pigeons (122)	**250.00**
Nut Bowl, 8", Ye Lion Inn (175)	**475.00**

Pitchers
6", Their Manner Of Telling Stories (165)	**400.00**
10", The Fallowfield Hunt, Breaking Cover (127)	**650.00**
Plaque, wall, 12", Fallowfield Hunt, Breakfast At The Three Pigeons (120)	**500.00**

Plates
8½", Fallowfield Hunt, The Death (123)	**125.00**
14", chop, Fallowfield Hunt, The Start	**550.00**
Powder Jar, cov, Ye Village Street (143)	**295.00**
Punch Bowl, 14¾ x 9¼", Fallowfield Hunt scenes	**5,000.00**
Relish Tray, Ye Olden Times (151)	**350.00**
Tankard, 6¾", white lining, Ye Lion Inn (177)	**725.00**
Tea Tile, 6", Traveling In Ye Olden Days (140)	**300.00**
Teapot, 5¾", Scenes Of Village Life In Ye Olden Days	**375.00**

Vase, 8″, untitled, fashionable men and
women (162). **675.00**
Vegetable Server, open, Ye Olden Times
(149) **375.00**

DELDARE SPECIALS

Mug, 4½″, Indian scene (231) **475.00**
Plaque, 13½″, Lost, sheep in winter
scene (220) **2,000.00**

EMERALD DELDARE

Candlestick, 9″, bayberry motif (192) . .   **800.00**
Fern Dish, 8″, butterflies and flowers
(186) **700.00**
Fruit Bowl, octagon shaped, matching
tray, Art Nouveau decor (183) **3,500.00**
Inkwell, set, covers, Art Nouveau decor
(196) **5,000.00**
Plaques
12″, Dr. Syntax Sketching The Lake
(208). **1,000.00**
16½″, The Garden Trio (211) **3,500.00**
Vase, 8″, kingfisher, dragonflies, iris, and
waterlilies (188). **850.00**

GAME SETS

Plaque, 9″, The Gunner (70) **75.00**
Plates, 9″
Fish, Rainbow Trout (59) **50.00**
Fish, Striped Bass (60) **50.00**
Fowl, American Woodcock (65) **60.00**
Fowl, Mallard Duck (63). **60.00**
Platter, rect, 11 x 14″, The Buffalo
Hunt. **175.00**

HISTORICAL, COMMEMORATIVE, AND ADVERTISING ITEMS

Mug, 4½″, Masonic (110) **75.00**
Plates, Commemorative
7½″, Erie Tribe, Improved Order of
Redmen (91). **75.00**
7½″, Hudson Terminal Buildings (89)   **85.00**
7½″, Protective Order of Elks (93) . .   **65.00**
8″, Theodore Roosevelt (87) **200.00**
Plates, Historical, 10″
Independence Hall, Philadelphia, PA
(82). **50.00**
White House, Washington, D.C. (80)   **50.00**

MISCELLANEOUS

Cowboy Hat (354) **25.00**
Dinner Sets, 100 pcs
Bonrea (319). **550.00**
Kenmore (315) **500.00**
Tea Rose (314). **400.00**
Feeding Dishes
Bluebird (321). **35.00**
Campbell Kids, without alphabet
(329). **175.00**

Medallion, oval, 6 x 7½″, John Larkin
(342) **250.00**
Tea Set, child's, violets, 22 pcs (315). .   **250.00**
Teapot, teaball, Argyle (336) **175.00**
Toilet Sets, 11 pieces
Cairo (325) **400.00**
White and Gold (325) **400.00**
Turkey Platter (340) **150.00**
Vase, Portland, 1946 series (341) **600.00**

PITCHERS AND JUGS

Jugs
Landing of Roger Williams (36). **525.00**
Rip Van Winkle (31) **475.00**
Pitchers
Nautical (34). **500.00**
Roosevelt Bears (42). **1,500.00**

BURMESE GLASS

History: Burmese glass is a translucent art glass
originated by Frederick Shirley and manufactured
by the Mt. Washington Glass Co., New Bedford,
Massachusetts, from 1885 to c1891. Burmese
glass shades from a soft lemon to a salmon pink.
Uranium was used to attain the yellow color and
gold was added to the batch so that upon reheating
one end turned pink. Upon reheating again, the
edges would revert to the yellow coloring. The
blending of the colors was so gradual that it was
difficult to determine where one color ended and
the other began.

Although some of the glass has a surface that
is glossy, most of it is acid finished. The majority
of the items were free blown, but some were blown
molded in a ribbed, hobnail, or diamond quilted design.

American-made Burmese is quite thin, fragile,
and brittle. The only factory licensed to make Burmese was Thos. Webb & Sons in England. Out of
deference to Queen Victoria, they called their
wares "Queen's Burmese."

Note: Reproductions abound in almost every
form. Since uranium can no longer be used, some
of the reproductions are easy to spot. In the 1950s
Gunderson produced many pieces in imitation of
Burmese.

MW = Mount Washington

Wb = Webb

a.f. = acid finish

s.f. = shiny finish

Advisor: Clarence and Betty Maier.

Biscuit Jar, 6″ h to top of SP bail, Wb,
a.f., prunus blossoms dec **1,450.00**
Bowls
4″ d, 3″ h, MW, a.f., pie crust crimped
edge, good color, paper label **375.00**
4″ d, 2¼″ h, MW, s.f., tricorn bowl,
three applied feet. **285.00**

5″ d, MW, a.f., exquisite Queen's design dec **945.00**
Finger Bowl, MW, a.f., ruffled top . . . **250.00**
Condiment set, MW, a.f., melon shaped cruet, two barrel shaped salt and pepper shakers, and a barrel shaped mustard pot, SP holder **1,400.00**
Cruet, 6½″, MW, melon ribbed, mushroom stopper, delicate color
A.f.. . . . . **965.00**
S.f.. . . . . **900.00**
Demitasse, MW, s.f., very thin glass, good color **335.00**
Fairy Lamps, 6″ h, Wb, a.f.
Decorated, prunus blossoms on sq base with fold-in sides, prunus blossoms on dome, excellent Burmese color, clear glass candle cup. **1,450.00**
Undecorated, good color to base and dome, clear glass candle cup **600.00**
Muffineers, MW, a.f.
Ball shaped, enamel floral dec, SP top **585.00**
Egg shaped, enamel forget-me-not dec. **675.00**
Pitchers, tankard shape, 10″, MW, good color
A.f.. . . . . **850.00**
S.f.. . . . . **725.00**
Plate, 10″, MW, a.f., enamel pansies dec, great color **585.00**
Sugar and Creamer Set, creamer 3¼″ h, sugar 2⅛″ h, MW, a.f., excellent color **585.00**
Syrup, 6″, MW, a.f., enamel pansies dec, excellent cond **1,950.00**
Toothpick Holders
2½″, MW, a.f., hat shaped, crimped brim
Rigaree collar, Heacock's #5, good color **450.00**
Without rigaree collar **375.00**
2½″, MW, s.f., square top, opitic DQ **200.00**
2⅞″, MW, a.f., barrel shape, autumn leaves dec, Heacock's #27 . . . . . **285.00**
Tumbler, 3¾″, MW, good color
A.f.. . . . . **185.00**
S.f.. . . . . **150.00**
Vases
2¼″, Wb, a.f., florals in three tone gold, colorful enamel butterfly **285.00**
3¾″, Wb, a.f., petal top
Ivory leaves dec, unsigned **300.00**
Undecorated, very little color, sgd **185.00**
4¾″, MW, a.f., bell shaped, applied crimped base, great color **350.00**
9″, MW, a.f., egg shaped, daisy-like blossoms (not Queen's design) . . . **685.00**
9½″, MW, a.f., fish swimming behind a net. **3,000.00**
11″, MW, a.f.
Enamel daisies and verse by James Montgomery, bulblous, shape . . **1,950.00**

GUBA ducks, slight crack in one of two applied handles **2,500.00**
12″, MW, a.f.
Enamel dec. of two sacred Ibis in flight over desert scene, marvelous color **3,9500.00**
Jack-in-Pulpit, excellent color **845.00**
14″, MW, a.f., tapered, Garden of Allah scene, masterpiece **6,500.00**

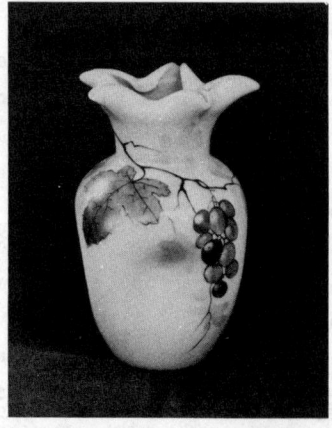

Vase, 4⅝″, hp, Thomas Webb, relief mark on base, reg. 67648, $650.00.

BUSTS

History: The portrait bust has its origins in pagan and Christian tradition. Greek and Roman heroes, and later images of Christian saints, dominate the early examples. Busts of the "ordinary man" first appeared in the Renaissance.

Busts of the nobility, poets, and other notable persons dominated the 18th and 19th century, especially those designed for use in a home library. Because of the large number of these library busts, excellent examples can be found at reasonable prices, depending on artist, subject, and material.

Additional Listings: Ivory, Parian Ware, Soapstone, and Wedgwood.

Bisque, maiden, voluptuous, blue gown, blonde curls, emerging from center of yellow flower, waisted socle, fluted column base, German, late 19th C, 30¾″ **1,320.00**
Bronze
Boy and girl, pr, each wearing military headdress, boy with military jerkin, green-black patina, inscribed Don-

ato, wooden plinths, French, late
19th C, 21¾″ **1,870.00**
Diana, looking over right shoulder,
strap of horn over right shoulder,
French, c1900, 24½″ **550.00**
Erodiade, upswept hair, elaborate
headband, inscribed George Coud-
ray, imp CH. GAUTIFA BRONIER,
late 19th C, 24¼″ **1,100.00**
Lincoln, dark patina, gilded, plinth
mark, 8″ **65.00**
Maiden, dust cap, low cut gown with
rose, sgd E. Laurent, France,
19¾″ **700.00**
Mercury, gazing to right, mustard pa-
tina, bronze mounted red marble
base, French, c1875, 19½″ **750.00**
Woman, Charlotte Corday, solemn
expression, cap, long hair, brown
patina, bronze socle, inscribed J.
Chesinger Rome, 1858/F. Barbe-
dienne Fondeur, late 19th C, 28″ . **1,2100.00**
Woman, upswept hair, long curl on
each side, brown patina, gray marble plinth set with plaque of putti at
musical pursuits, inscribed H. Du-
maige, late 19th C, 30″ **1,450.00**
Chalkware, gentleman, hollow mold,
19th C, 9¾″ **750.00**

**Bronze, 8½″, "Wm. Penn," sgd Greil,
$325.00.**

Marble
Napoleon, carved, marble socle, Con-
tinental, late 19th C, 20½″ **500.00**
Young lady, Victorian bonnet, short
hair, sq neck dress, 13½″ **200.00**
Parian
Clytie, imp "Art Union of London-
1863-C. Delpech," N & 76 red T
around base, 14″ **600.00**
Homer, 13″ h, 8″ base. **90.00**
Shakespeare, T and R Boote, c1890,
8″ **100.00**
Tennyson **65.00**
Sandstone, Indian red, god, Suryea,
wearing high cylindrical mitre, remnants of orig 2 lotus at his shoulders,
backed by circular prabha, old damage, black wood base, c9th/10th C,
16″ **540.00**
Staffordshire, Rev. John Wesley, white
curly hair, green robe, white collar, sq
base, Enoch Wood, c1791, 12½″ . . . **625.00**

BUTTER PRINTS

History: Butter prints divide into two categories:
butter molds and butter stamps. Butter molds are
generally of three piece construction—the design,
the screw-in handle, and the case. Molds both mold
and stamp the butter at the same time. Butter
stamps are of one piece construction, sometimes
two pieces if the handle is from a separate piece
of wood. Stamps decorate the top of butter after it
is molded.

The earliest prints were one piece and hand
carved, often thick and deeply carved. Later prints
were factory made with the design forced into the
wood by a metal die.

Some of the most common designs are sheaves
of wheat, leaves, flowers, and pineapples. Animal
designs and Germanic tulips are difficult to find.
Rare prints include unusual shapes, such as half-
rounded and lollipop, and those with designs on
both sides.

MOLDS

Cherries, almond shaped, removable
hinged frame, 10½″ l **125.00**
Cow, rectangular, removable hinged
frame, 6″ h, 9½″ l **300.00**
Leaves and flowers, double, 4¾″ l **70.00**
Pomegrantes, floral branches on reverse
side, almond shape, hand carved,
6¾″ l, 3¾″ h **325.00**
Swan, minor age cracks, 4½″ d **75.00**

STAMPS

Acorn and Oak Leaves, round, inserted
turned handle, 4½″ d **95.00**

Stamp, 3½" d, 2⅝" h, scallop, $80.00.

Compass Star, chip carved edge, lollipop shape, 8" l	**300.00**
Deer, hand carved, bell shaped, knob handle, 5⅛" d, 4⅜" h	**265.00**
Eagle, turned handle, deeply carved, 3⅝" d	**150.00**
Floral, stylized, primitively carved, round, one piece, large turned handle, 4⅞" d, 5⅛" h	**115.00**
Lamb with cross and banner, (Christian symbol), minor age cracks, 3¼" d	**200.00**
Pineapple and Leaves, half round, 3½" d, 7" l	**200.00**
Rose, buds and leaves, hand carved, 3½" d	**250.00**
Sheaf, round, one piece with turned handle, age cracks, 4¼" d	**85.00**
Starflower, deeply cut design, round, primitive carving, 5" d	**125.00**
Tulips, deeply carved, chip carved edge, round, turned inserted handle, 4⅛" d	**215.00**

CALENDAR PLATES

History: Calendar plates were first made in England in the late 1880s. They became popular in the United States after 1900, the peak years being 1909 to 1915. The majority of the advertising plates were made of porcelain or pottery with a calendar, the name of a store or business, and either a scene, portrait, animal, or flowers. Some also were made of glass or tin.

Additional Listings: See *Warman's Americana & Collectibles* for more examples.

1908, 7¼", crossed American flags, Oyster Bay, NY	**32.00**
1908, 9¾", hunting dog, Pittston, Pa.	**35.00**
1909, 8", red breasted bird, scenes of seasons	**25.00**
1909, 8", bird, Souvenir of Andover, Maine	**20.00**
1909, 8½", flower girl, Souvenir of Abrams, Wisc.	**37.00**
1909, 9", Mediterranean woman, John Kemper, Harness Maker, Butler, Pa.	**24.00**
1909, 9¼", house with lady feeding ducks	**30.00**
1910, 7½", boxer dog, Somerville, NJ	**35.00**
1910, 7½", Wayne State Bank, Kansas	**25.00**
1910, 8", 2 cherubs ring in New Year, Swem Jewelers, NY	**35.00**
1910, 8", Gibson girl, bust	**45.00**
1910, 8½", Gibson girl, flower cluster border	**28.00**
1911, 8", moon over water	**35.00**
1911, 8", red open touring car, Buffalo Pottery	**35.00**
1912, airplane, fruit and floral border	**28.00**
1912, cherubs and fruit	**26.00**
1912, 8¼", scenic, White River Tavern, Hartford, Vt.	**32.00**
1913, 8¼", Christmas bells, holly, blue forget-me-nots, and robin, Easton, Pa.	**35.00**
1913, 8¼", sweet peas, pink and lavender	**45.00**
1914, 9¼", Washington's Tomb, A. Smith, Milford, Del.	**30.00**
1915, 8", Panama Canal	**25.00**

1912, 8⁷⁄₁₆", Richfield Springs, NY, Dresden, $22.50.

1916, 8¼", eagle with shield and American flag	**30.00**
1916, Indian maid, bust	**30.00**
1919, 8¼", American flag, John J. Rutgers Co., Holland, Mich.	**35.00**
1929, 6¼", octagon shape, clematis flowers, red and blue, Langley's Store, Springview, Neb.	**45.00**

CALLING CARD CASES AND RECEIVERS

History: Calling cards, usually carried in specially designed cases, played an important social role in the United States from the period of the Civil War until the end of World War I. When making a formal visit, a caller left their card in a receiver (card dish) in the front hall. Strict rules of etiquette developed. For example, the lady in a family was expected to make calls of congratulations, visits to the ill, and condolence.

The cards themselves were small, embossed or engraved with the caller's name, and often carried a floral design. Many hand done examples, especially in Spencerian script, can be found. The cards themselves are considered collectible and range in price from a few cents to several dollars.

Note: Don't confuse a calling card case with a match safe.

CALLING CARD CASES

Chinese Export, silver, pierced design of
   chrysanthemums and birds. 450.00
Ivory
   Carved scene, French, c1880. . . . . .   250.00
   Inlaid, hundreds of small pieces of
     ivory, silver, malachite in geometric
     quilt-like design 55.00
Leather and ivory, 2 pockets 65.00
Mother-Of-Pearl, carved scene of girls
   dancing, $2^{7}/_{8}$ x $3^{7}/_{8}''$ 45.00
Sterling Silver
   Bright cut dec, hinged lid, chain han-
     dle, $3^{1}/_{2}''$ h, $2^{1}/_{2}''$ w plus handle . . .   125.00
   Engraved dec, chain handle, mkd Gor-
     ham 1878 . . . .   65.00
   Molded flowers, scrolls, monogram. .   80.00

CALLING CARD RECEIVERS

China
   Bavaria, $9^{3}/_{4}''$ sq, double handles,
     flowers 30.00
   Hand Painted
     Flowers, double handles, $12''$ l,
       $8''$ w 35.00
     Scenic, $6''$ l, $3''$ w. 65.00
   Nippon, $7^{1}/_{2}''$ l, rolled edges, cobalt
     ground, white and pink flowers,
     green leaves, gold tracery, blue
     mark. 165.00
   R. S. Prussia, $11^{1}/_{2}''$ l, pink roses, gold
     trim, stippled floral mold border. . .   265.00
Silver Plated
   Alvin, rectangular, $6''$ l, $2^{1}/_{4}''$ w, scroll
     border.   120.00
   Meriden, dish of engraved leaf shape,
     small bird perched on edge, $6''$ fi-
     gural vase holder shaped like run-
     ning Greek boy, crystal bud vase, 4

     small pad feet, mkd Meriden Silver
     Plate Co. 195.00
   Southington, leaf shape, $7''$, engraved
     pedestal base, large bird with out-
     spread wings perched on coiled
     stem handle 150.00

Receiver, $10^{1}/_{2}''$ w, $7^{1}/_{4}''$ l, $1^{1}/_{2}''$ h, #3031, $485.00.

CAMBRIDGE GLASS

History: Cambridge Glass Company, Cambridge, Ohio, was incorporated in 1901. Initially the company made clear tableware, later expanding into colored, etched, and engraved glass. Over 40 different hues were produced in blown and pressed glass.

Five different marks were employed during the production years, but not every piece was marked.

The plant closed in 1954. Some of the molds were later sold to the Imperial Glass Company, Bellaire, Ohio.

References: National Cambridge Collectors, Inc., *The Cambridge Glass Co., Cambridge, Ohio* (reprint of 1930 catalog and supplements through 1934), Collector Books, 1976; National Cambridge Collectors, Inc., *The Cambridge Glass Co., Cambridge, Ohio, 1949 Thru 1953* (catalog reprint), Collector Books, 1976; National Cambridge Collectors, Inc., *Colors In Cambridge Glass*, Collector Books, 1984.

Collectors' Club: National Cambridge Collectors, Inc., P. O. Box 416, Cambridge, OH 43725. Dues: $10.00 *Crystal Ball* (monthly).

Advisor: Joyce C. Clement.

Ashtrays
   Caprice, triangle 12.00
   Crown Tuscan, bowling ball 65.00
Baskets
   $6''$, Ebony. 38.00
   $6''$, Rose Point, 2 handled 50.00
Bonbons
   $6''$, Decagon, 2 handled, pink. 12.50
   $6''$, Martha, 2 handled 12.00

7", Wildflower, gold encrusted 30.00
Bookends, Scotty, pr 115.00
Bowls
    7", Cascade, 2 handled, crystal 10.00
    7½", Rose Point 14.00
    8¼", Tally Ho, amber 10.00
    8½", Cleo, 2 handled, blue. 20.00
    13", Everglades, rolled, crystal 70.00
    Centerpiece, Crown Tuscan, nude . . 200.00
Candlesticks
    7½", Ramshead, pillar stem,
       amethyst 25.00
    9", Doric Column, ivory 65.00
    9½", Dolphin with bobeche, crystal. . 95.00
    10", Caprice, 3 light, crystal, pr. 70.00
    Diane, 2 light, pr 50.00
    Rosepoint, keyhole, with prisms, pr. . 135.00
Candy Dishes
    Farberware, lady holder, amethyst
       insert 55.00
    Gaudroon, cov, crystal. 48.00
Celery, 11", Rose Point. 40.00
Champagne, Chantilly 15.00
Cocktail Shaker, Wildflower 95.00
Cocktails
    Crown Tuscan, yellow bowl, nude
       stem 135.00
    Nude, black 60.00
    Rose Point 35.00
    Wildflower. 28.00

Compote, 8⅜" d, 3¾" h, ftd, Honeycomb, etched cut floral, rubina, $135.00.

Compotes
    4", Crown Tuscan, dolphin ftd 50.00
    8", Crown Tuscan, nude shell. 175.00
Creamers and Sugars
    Chantilly, individual 38.00
    Rose Point 40.00
    Shell, crystal. 35.00
Cruet, 6 oz, Rose Point. 95.00
Cups and Saucers
    Apple Blossom, yellow. 18.50
    Caprice, blue 14.50
    Decagon, pink. 8.00
    Mt. Vernon 7.00

Decanters
    Nautilus, red 38.00
    Pristine, crystal 22.00
    Tally Ho, 6 handled mugs 95.00
Flower Block, 4¾", Caprice, blue. 50.00
Flower Figures (Frogs)
    Draped Lady
       8", Moonlight, satin 300.00
       8½", amber 175.00
       8½", green 145.00
       8½", pink 140.00
       13", pink, frosted 250.00
       13½", green, frosted 170.00
    Heron, 9" 70.00
    Seagull, 9", crystal 45.00
Goblets
    Chantilly, crystal 20.00
    Diane 20.00
    Elaine. 22.00
    Marjorie 15.00
    Mt. Vernon, crystal 8.00
    Portia 20.00
    Roselyn 27.50
    Tally Ho, hunt scene 45.00
Hat, Tally Ho, amber. 125.00
Ice Buckets
    Cascade, crystal 27.50
    Cleo, green. 60.00
    Decagon, pink. 30.00
    Tally Ho, cobalt. 65.00
    Wildflower, tongs. 60.00
Ivy Ball, Crown Tuscan, keyhole 42.50
Jelly Dish, 5", Caprice, crystal 7.50
Lamp, 10", hurricane, Rose Point. 250.00
Mayonnaise Sets
    Cleo, pink, 2 piece 35.00
    Rose Point, 2 piece 28.00
    Tally Ho, crystal, 4 piece 50.00
Plates
    6", Caprice, crystal 5.00
    8", Decagon, etched, yellow. 12.00
    8", Mt. Vernon, crystal 8.00
    8", Rosepoint 13.00
    9½", Decagon, amber 20.00
    12½", Blossom Time 36.00
    16", Caprice, blue 55.00
    16", Everglades, flowered, dark
       green 75.00
Relish Dishes
    2 part, Roslyn 11.00
    3 part, Apple Blossom, amber 45.00
    3 part, Blossom Time, crystal 28.00
    3 part, Diane. 25.00
    3 part, Rose Point. 45.00
    4 part, Alpine, blue 45.00
Rose Bowl, Crown Tuscan, Rosepoint . 80.00
Salt and Pepper Shakers
    Daffodil 35.00
    Diane 22.00
    Rose Point 50.00
    Tally Ho, amethyst 40.00
Sugar Shaker, Decagon, floral cutting,
    emerald green. 55.00

Sherbets
5 oz, Caprice, blue	30.00
6 oz, Carmen, tall, red	15.00
7 oz, Elaine, tall	12.00
8 oz, Farberware, cobalt, set of 8 . . .	90.00
Mt. Vernon, crystal	7.00

Swans
3″, Crown Tuscan	32.00
3½″, crystal	20.00
3½″, green	25.00
3½″, pink	35.00
5½″, crystal	35.00

Tumblers
4 oz, Decagon, ftd, green	8.00
10 oz, Apple Blossom, cry	7.50
10 oz, Cleo, amber	20.00
12 oz, Farberware, royal blue, set of 6	90.00
12 oz, Mt. Vernon, amber	20.00
13 oz, Optic	14.00
Rose Point, water, ftd	27.50
Wildflower, barrel	26.50

Vases
10″, Cornucopia, black	65.00
10″, Cornucopia, Caprice, crystal . . .	22.50
10″, Keyhole, amber	35.00
11″, Everglades, ftd	45.00
12″, Keyhole, Rose Point	70.00

Wines
Portia	24.50
Pristine, trumpet	15.00

CAMBRIDGE

CAMBRIDGE POTTERY

History: The Cambridge Art Pottery was incorporated in Ohio in 1900. Between 1901 and 1909 the firm produced the usual line of jardinieres, tankards, and vases with underglazed slip decorations and glazes similar to other Ohio potteries. Line names included Terrhea, Oakwood, Otoe, and others.

In 1904 the company introduced Guernsey kitchenwares. It was so well received that it became the plant's primary product; and, in 1909 the company's name was changed to Guernsey Earthenware Company.

All wares were marked.

Bowls
8″, berry motif, glossy brown glaze . .	75.00
8″, brown glaze, mkd Terrhea	85.00

Vase, 6½″, green, acorn mark, $75.00.

Candlesticks, pr, 4″, standard brown glaze, mkd Terrhea	50.00
Ewer, underglaze slip painted dec, standard shaded brown glaze, mkd Terrhea	250.00
Inkwell, acorn stopper, mkd Terrhea . .	100.00
Mug, 4¼″, two cherries and leaf, artist initials "AL", acorn mark, mold #204	125.00
Pitcher, 6″ h, 3 ftd, handle, dark brown ground, honeysuckle dec, sgd "DL," mkd Cambridge and CAP	200.00
Tankard, 16½″, two ears of corn, incised sgd, mold #263	700.00

Vases
5½″, underglaze slip painted floral dec, mkd Terrhea	225.00
7¼″, bud, brown streaked, molded flowers, mkd Oakwood	75.00
8″, high glaze, handle, saucer base, extended body, yellow, green, brown, mkd Oakwood, mold #235	150.00
8″, Otoe	85.00
9″, dog portrait, brown glaze, sgd "AV Lewis"	675.00
9″, saucer bottom with extended (concave) neck, nasturiums and leaves, brown ground, mkd Terrhea	300.00

CAMEO GLASS

History: Cameo glass is a form of cased glass. A shell of glass was prepared; then one or more layers of glass of a different color(s) was faced to the first. A design was then cut through the outer layer(s) leaving the inner layer(s) exposed.

This type of art glass originated in Alexandria, Egypt, 100-200 A.D. The oldest and most famous example of cameo glass is the Barberini or Portland vase which was found near Rome in 1582. It contained the ashes of Emperor Alexander Serverus who was assasinated in 235 A.D.

Emile Galle is probably one of the best known artists of cameo glass. He established a factory at Nancy, France, in 1884. Although much of the glass bears his signature, he was primarily the designer. On many pieces assistants did the actual work, even to signing his name. Glass made after his death in 1904 has a star before the name Galle. Other makers of French cameo glass include D'Argental, Daum Nancy, LeGras, and Delatte.

English cameo does not have as many layers of glass (colors) and cuttings as do French pieces. The outer layer is usually white, and cuttings are very fine and delicate. Most pieces are not signed. The best known makers are Thomas Webb & Sons and Stevens and Williams.

Reference: Victor Arwas, *Glass Art Nouveau to Art Deco*, Rizzoli International Publications, Inc., 1977; Albert C. Revi, *Nineteenth Century Glass*, Schiffer Publishing, reprint.

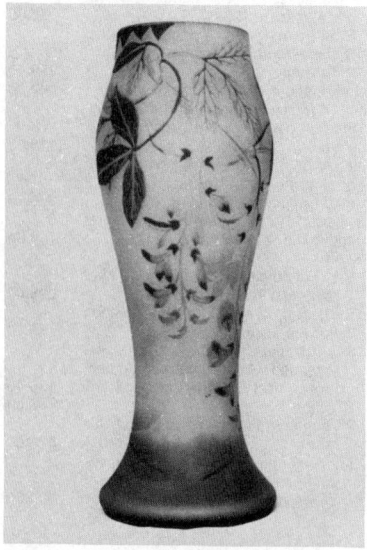

Vase, 12½″ h, Richard, chartreuse ground, amber deco, French, $950.00.

AMERICAN

Tiffany
  Vases
    5¼″ h, spherical, finely carved nasturtium blossoms, leaves in Chinese red and apple green on translucent white sides, int. washed in amber irid, inscribed "L. C. Tiffany Favrile 4914C", c1908 . . . . **3,250.00**
    8½″, ovoid, calla lilies, leaves, and insects in white and lime green on pearly irid body, inscribed "L.C.T. X1175", c1892–1928 . . . . **5,500.00**
    13¼″, floriform, finely cut leaves continuing into slender rod standard, inverted pyriform bowl overlaid in white and lime green, clear glass circular domed foot further dec with green striated feathers, inscribed "L.C.T. X6812", c1905 **8,750.00**

ENGLISH

Stevens & Williams
  Perfume Bottle, 4″, bulbous, trailing white fuchsia on red ground, hinged silvered metal spherical cap, c1900 . . . . **350.00**
  Vases
    4¼″, ovoid, white anemone blossoms and leaves on cornflower-blue ground, c1900 . . . . **500.00**
    4¾″, ovoid, white blossoming magnolia on cornflower-blue ground, flaring lip, c1895 . . . . **500.00**
Unknown Makers
  Spoon, serving, 7⅞″ l, white flowers and vine pattern on amber ground on handle, silver gilt finished ladle with small porcelain medallion in center **500.00**
  Vases
    5″ h, large fern leaves in cut on frosty blue ground **800.00**
    7¼″, white poppies on Burmese ground cut to ivory **1,400.00**
Thomas Webb & Sons
  Bowl, 3½″ d, underplate, 4⅝″ d, pr, white flowers and butterflies on deep blue to deep red ground. . . . **2,600.00**
  Biscuit Jar, 5¼″ d, cov, carved on one side with white leaves on deep red, mounted SP lip, hinged handle, circular SP cov, classical finial, c1900 . . . . **550.00**
  Cologne Bottles
    5″ h, white fruit, blossoms, and butterfly on ground, SS collar and screw top **750.00**
    7⅝″, white pattern of grapes and leaves on raspberry red drapery like ground, matching stopper . . **4,100.00**
  Decanter, 9″ h, pattern of pink and white flowers on frosty amber ground, repose silver and spring hinged stopper. **3,000.00**
  Flower Holder, 7¼″ h, pear shape, 6

various panels of white florals surrounded by white prunus blossoms on frosty green ground, stem handle, repairs to handle **3,000.00**

Scent Bottles

1¾", white dogwood blossoms and leaves on deep red ground **500.00**

2½", white floral pattern on deep red ground, SS screw top and collar with English hallmarks **600.00**

3¾", white floral pattern with butterfly on deep raspberry red ground, SS collar, repousse screw top, made for Theodore B. Starr & Co. **600.00**

Vases

6⅛" h, daisies, lily of the valley, other flowers including 7 colorful flowers in red, white, blue, yellow, and green, white flowers, green leaves on frosty medium blue ground **6,000.00**

6½", h, 7" d, cut in repeated floral pattern in white on soft pink ground **8,500.00**

7", white spray of flowers cut to lavender on frosty electric blue ground **1,700.00**

7½", overall design of chrysanthemums in white on frosty pink ground, key pattern in upper border, arched leaf design in white around base **7,000.00**

8¼", ovoid, short neck, waisted foot, carved white and pink Ganymede being carried off by Zeus in the form of an eagle, neck with flowers and leaves on brilliant azure ground, foot with twisted chain dec, acid stamped "Webb" within quatrefoil and "Ganymede" within ribbon,c1890 . . . **15,400.00**

8⅝", white calla lilies, tulips and other flowers on soft frosty pink ground **6,250.00**

FRENCH

Burgun & Schverer, c1895, pieces mkd in gilt "Verrerie D'Art/De Lorraine/B/S/&/Co/depose" with croix de Lorraine and thistle

Vases

5½", baluster, carved with pinwheels and cherry blossoms and leaves in pale dusty rose and green on pale amber martele sides, int. streaked in oxblood red, gilded base **3,850.00**

8", baluster, pinwheels and 5 petaled dusty rose and white blossoms, green leaves on pale green

sides, int. streaked with shaded oxblood red whiplash tendrils, martele sides, foot and neck with applied foliate silver gilt mounts, c1895 . . . . **4,500.00**

D'Argental, pieces sgd "D'Argental" in cameo

Sealing Wax Light, 7¼" h, pink flowers with brown leaves, stems on light peach tinted ground, complete with wicks, cap, dec metal top in gold bronze **550.00**

Vases

5½", pyriform, trumpet blossoms in apricot and leafy branches in avocado on yellow ground **800.00**

13¾", swollen cylindrical, scene of medieval ruins high above a gorge and waterfall in pink and ochre on pale yellow glass, c1920 . . . . **1,550.00**

Daum Nancy, pieces sgd in gilt intaglio "Daum/Nancy" with croix de Lorraine

Bowls

3¾" h, oval, floral layers in dark blue on mossy green ground with autumn colored leaves **250.00**

6" d, daisies, leaves, applied stamens in dusty rose, white, green, and cranberry with yellow inclusions on mottled gray and mustard sides, c1910 . . . . **1,000.00**

Box, cov, 6" d, 4¼" h, round, flowers and leaves in dark green on brilliant mottled ground of pinks and yellows **750.00**

Dish, 5¾" l, sq, rounded corners, cut with oak leaves in rust, applied acorn and 2 beetles in white, red, and green on mottled rust, brown and gray sides **800.00**

Ewer, 16½" h, slender waisted cylindrical body with flat shoulder, straight neck, elongated spout, lily blossoms and leaves in deep purple shading to brilliant royal blue on tooled martele ground streaked with burgundy, applied angular handles, c1900 . . . . **9,500.00**

Jar, cov, 4½" h, cylindrical, wheel carved with primrose blossoms and leaves in spring green on pale pink and green ground, partially fire polished, neck set with band of hammered silver, circular star incised on hammered silver cov with angular handle. **500.00**

Lamp, 17" h, 6½" d, triangular sloping shade, paneled baluster base in gray glass mottled with olive green, overlaid in deep purple and cut with river scene, shade and base sgd in cameo, c1920 . . . . **2,325.00**

Vase, 5¾", Gallé, peach to light olive frosted ground, pilgram flask form, French, $1,250.00.

Snuff Bottle, 2" h, landscape of trees against river in apricot and brown on butterscotch ground. **100.00**

Vases
   5", swelling cylindrical, enameled red and green wildflowers and leaves on frosted lemon-yellow and plum sides, c1910 . . . . **375.00**
   6½", irregular baluster, branches of prunus blossoms and leaves in white on pale lavender ground, white circular foot, c1900 . . . . . **1,325.00**
   11¼", bulging baluster contour, landscape of stately leafy trees in shades of green splashed with yellow and violet on mottled green and red sides, c1900 . . . . **2,250.00**
   19¾", baluster, nasturtium blossoms and undulating leaves in Chinese red and slate green on mottled mustard body, sgd in cameo, c1920 . . . . **1,000.00**

Andre Delatte, Nancy, pieces sgd in cameo "A Delatte/Nancy" with croix de Lorraine
   Automobile Urn, 7", pinkish amber roses, leaves, and stem on rich honey amber ground **350.00**
   Vases
      6¾", spherical, trumpet flower blossoms, leaves in maroon on gray body shading to maroon, c1920 **550.00**
      13¼", spherical with short bulging neck, sprays of magnolia blossoms and leaves in purple on mottled gray and maroon sides, c1920 . . . . **1,325.00**

Desire Christian Meisenthal
   Vase, 14⅜" h, elongated baluster, circular domed foot, finely wheel carved with upright branch supporting venus flytrap blossoms and

leaves in cranberry reds partially martele frosted gray glass sides splashed with cranberry red, lower section and foot intaglio carved with grasses and leaves, sgd in intaglio "D. Christian Meisenthal-Loth", c1895 . . . . **3,000.00**

de Vez, pieces sgd "de Vez" in cameo, c1920
   Vases
      4½", slender neck, bulging waist, cylindrical body, cut with mountainous river landscape, leafy trees in foreground in deep red and blue on pale yellow glass shaded with red **600.00**
      8", baluster, northern lakescape with spruce trees, birds, water, mountains in brown on pink, amber, and frosted clear ground. . . **850.00**
      12⅜", swelling ovoid, landscape of village nestled in mountain cove, sailing boats and trees in background in salmon and green on pale blue ground. **700.00**

Emile Gallé, pieces sgd "Gallé" in cameo
   Bowls
      4¼", conical, notched rim in clear glass, wheel carved with prunus blossoms, leaves and vines in dusty rose and lavender on clear glass martele surface, fire polished, c1900 . . . . **4,750.00**
      12½" d, high relief of sea shells cut with sea grasses in rust and sea green, opal olive green walls, c1920 . . . . **6,600.00**
   Box, cov, 6¾" d, round, cut with maple buds and leaves in shades of green and white, pale gray sides shaded with peach, sgd in cameo "Galle" after a star, remnants of orig paper label, c1904–1910 . . . . **550.00**
   Cup, 4¼" h, conical, cut upright overlapping leaves in lime green on gray glass body, raised on short slender olive green stem, circular foot, sgd "Galle" in intaglio **1,000.00**
   Lamp, 9½" h, 5½" d, domical shade and pyriform base, cut bird perched on a branch and dragonflies on shade, base with cut butterfly in blue-gray on pale orange glass, c1900 . . . . **6,325.00**
   Liqueur, 3" h, ftd, spherical bowl, nasturtium blossoms and leaves in dusty rose on clear glass bowl, raised on short cylindrical standard and avocado green circular foot, fire polished, c1900 . . . . **2,000.00**
   Perfume Bottles
      5¼", lobed, cut with poppies and

leaves in pale lavender on gray
body streaked with pale lavender,
stopper in form of floret, fire pol-
ished, c1900 . . . .   **880.00**
5½″ h, rect, cut in amber on obverse
with kneeling figure and bear, reverse of figure on horseback on
pale gray walls splashed with oxblood red, cut and enameled in
blue, white, and rust with Persian
florets and strap work, sgd in enamel "Emile Gallé á Nancy/
déposé", c1900 . . . .   **600.00**
Tumbler, 2½″ h, tapering cylindrical,
cut with branch of flowering leaves,
in deep green on gray sides
splashed with olive green, c1900. .   **200.00**
Vases
3″, oval, cut and enameled blossoms and leaves, 3 beetles in
tones of azure, rust, pink, green,
and brown on pale green glass,
gilt details, c1900 . . . .   **1,320.00**
5″, horn shaped, brown berries and
leaves on butterscotch-yellow
ground. **225.00**
5½″, pyriform, fuchsia blossoms
and leaves enameled and cut in
shades of amber, mustard, oxblood red, pale green, and deep
brown reserved on acid etched
pale amber ground, gilt, c1900. .   **2,000.00**
6″, stick type, oval, elongated neck,
gold and brown dragonfly over
pinkish water filled with brown lily
pads, gold blossoms **550.00**
9″, waisted neck and flattened
ovoid body, pine boughs covered
with cones in ochre brown on ice
blue glass, neck with applied silver lip and pendant of molded
pine branch, silver ring on foot,
c1900 . . . .   **3,425.00**
9¾″, ovoid, molded with branches
of rosehips in shades of violet on
yellow glass, raised on a spread-
ing pale violet foot, c1925 . . . . .   **2,000.00**
11″, bulbous, molded and cut with
rhododendron blossoms, buds,
and leaves in shades of fuchsia
on gray and yellow sides, c1925   **4,125.00**
18½″, expanding cylindrical form,
landscape of mountains and alpine lake, tall conifers in blue and
violet on shaded yellow and gray
sides, c1900. . . . .   **2,150.00**
19″, pyriform, cut with continuous
scene of Rio de Janeiro with Su-
garloaf in the distance in blue and
violet on pale yellow ground, titled
in cameo "Rio/de/Janeiro",
c1900 . . . .   **5,500.00**

Gruber, pieces sgd "Jacques/Gruber" in
cameo
Tray, 20½″, rect, cut with river bend
and pines on both shores, hazy
mountain ranges in the distance in
shades of plum on gray glass panel,
oak surround with 2 pierced demi-
lune handles, c1900. . . . .   **1,450.00**
Wall Shelf, 21½″ l, demilune gray
glass panel overlaid in shades of
coffee and cut with lazy river landscape, shaped fruitwood frame and
shelf **1,225.00**
Legras
Vases
11½″, swollen cylindrical form, cut
and enameled with scene of 2
swans in lake, trees in white,
green and brown against shaded
green and apricot ground, gray
acid etched walls, sgd "Legras"
in enamel, c1900 . . . .   **300.00**
15¾″, swollen cylindrical contour,
enameled in shades of green,
brown, and yellow with a lake with
trees and mountains in the background on frosted gray sides, sgd
in cameo "Legras", c1920. . . . .   **800.00**
Muller Freres
Bowl, 6″ h, avocado undulating blossoms and leaves on avocado and
dusty rose sides, sgd in intaglio "H
Muller/Croismere/près   Nancy",
c1920 . . . .   **825.00**
Vases
8¾″ h, baluster, cut with berry and
flower laden leafy branches in
ochre, lavender, sienna, and
white on tomato red walls shading
to white and lavender at waisted
base, sgd in cameo "Muller Fres/
Luneville", c1920 . . . .   **2,200.00**
10½″, shouldered baluster contour,
sprays of poppy blossoms and
leaves in vanilla on pale turquoise
sides, fire polished, sgd in gilt intaglio   "Muller/Croismere/près
Nancy" around a butterfly mark,
c1910 . . . .   **1,000.00**
15½″, slender cylindrical neck,
bulging body, cut with berry laden
leafy branches at base and neck
in Chinese red, lime green, ochre,
and sienna on gray glass shaded
with maroon, sgd in cameo
"Muller Fres/Luneville", c1920 .   **3,100.00**

CAMERAS

History: The collecting of cameras, except in
isolated instances, started about 1970. Although
photography generally is considered to have had

its beginning in 1839, it is very unusual to find a camera made before 1880. These cameras and other made before 1925 are considered to be antique cameras. Most cameras made after 1925, and no longer made, are considered to be classic cameras. American, German, and Japanese cameras are found most often.

Value of cameras is affected by both exterior and mechanical conditions. Particular attention must be given to the condition of the bellows if cameras have them.

References: John F. Maloney, *An Identification And Value Guide To Vintage Cameras And Images*, Books Americana, 1981; J. M. and J. C. McKeown, *Official Dealer Blue Book of Cameras*, Centennial Photo Service, 1982, 1st edition; J. M. and J. C. McKeown, *Price Guide To Antique and Classic Still Cameras*, Centennial Photo Service, 1983, 4th edition; David Sharbrough, *American Premium Guide To Olde Cameras*, Books Americana, 1983; M. Wolf, *Blue Book Illustrated Price Guide to Collectible Cameras*, Photographic Memorabilia, 1982.

Collectors' Clubs: American Photographic Historical Society, P. O. Box 1775, Grand Central Station, New York, NY 10163. Dues: $22.50. *Photographica;* Leica Historical Society of America, 2314 W. 53rd Street., Minneapolis, MN 55410. Dues: $20.00; National Steroscopic Association, P. O. Box 14801, Columbus, OH 43214. Dues: $20.00. *Stereo World* (bimonthly).

Museum: Smithsonian Institution, Washington, DC.

Additional Listings: See *Warman's Americana & Collectibles* for more examples.

Advisor: John B. Darrow.

Ansco (Binghamton, NY)

Automatic Reflex, twin lens reflex, later models with flash sync, 6 x 6 cm on 120 film, f3.5 Anastigmat 83 mm lens, 1947-49	125.00
Photo Vanity, gray, 1926	1,100.00

Argus (Ann Arbor, MI)

Argoflex E, twin lens reflex.	25.00
Model C4, f2.8/150 mm, Cintar coupled rangefinder, 1951	35.00
Baldinette, folding 35 mm, f2.9/50, Schneider Radionar, Balda-Werke (Dresden, Germany), 1950	45.00
Blair No. 7, box, 3½ x 5¼ rollfilm, 1897, Weno Hawk-Eye, (Boston, MA).	25.00
Canon 7, 1961–64, (Tokyo, Japan).	175.00
Century Grand, 5 x 7″, (Rochester, NY)	100.00
Ciro 35, 35 mm, 1949, (Delaware, OH)	25.00
Clarus MS-35, rangefinder, 35 mm, f2.8/ 50 mm Wollensak Velostigmat lens, (Minneapolis, MN)	45.00
Compass, rangefinder 35 mm, aluminum body, f3.5/50 mm lens, (London, England).	800.00
Coronet, "3-D" Stereo Camera, plastic, 4 stereo pairs or 8 single exp. 4.5 x	

4.5 cm on 127 film, meniscus lenses, (Birmingham, England).	25.00
Detrola Model HW, 127 film with meter, (Detroit, MI)	20.00

Eastman Kodak (Rochester, NY)

Beau Brownie, 120 film, 2 tone case, 1930.	75.00
Chevron, 2¼ x 2½ on 620 Kodak Ektar, f3.5/78 mm, 1955	175.00
Kodak 35, with rangefinder, 1940	25.00

Box Camera, #7 Weno Hawk-Eye, Eastman Kodak Co., $25.00.

Kodak Reflex II, twin-lens reflex	50.00
No. 2, Bull's Eye, box, leather cov wood, 3½ x 3½ exp on 103 rollfilm.	30.00
No. 3A, Autographic Kodak Special, 3¼ x 5½ on 122, 1974.	60.00
No. 4, Kodak Jr, 60 exp 3½ x 4¼ rollfilm, B & L Universal lens, c1890.	400.00
Retina IIa, single window view/ rangefinder, Xenon f2.	65.00
Super Kodak Six-20, coupled electric-eye for automatic exposure setting, 2½ x 3¼ exp on 620 film, Kodak Anastigmat Special lens, f4.5	1,000.00
Exakta VX-IIA, Ihagee Kamerawerk, (Dresden, Germany)	85.00
Fotron III, Triad Corp., (Encino, CA)	35.00
Goerz Asnchutz, 9 x 12 cm, folding, 1890, (Berlin, Germany).	125.00
Graflex RB Super D, 3¼ x 4¼″, (Rochester, NY)	200.00
Ingento, 3A Folding, Burke & James, (Chicago, IL)	30.00
Kombi, 4 oz seamless metal box, oxidized silver finish, 25 exp 1⅛″ sq on rollfilm, A. C. Kemper, (Chicago, IL)	175.00
Lecia IIIa (G), full frame 24 x 36 mm exp, 1/1000 sec shutter speed, f3.5/50 Elmar, 1953, E. Leitz, (Wetzlar, Germany).	150.00

Polaroid 110B, Polaroid, (Cambridge, MA) **75.00**
Revere Stereo 33, Amaton f3.5/35 mm, shutter 2-200, MFX sync, rangefinder, Revere, (Chicago, IL) **150.00**
Rexo, 31 Folding, Burke & James, (Chicago, IL) **20.00**
Robot II, Otto Berning, (Duesseldorf, Germany) **95.00**
Rochester Optical Co. (Rochester, NY)
  Cyclone Senior, 4 x 5″, box **30.00**
  Premo, long focus, 5 x 7″, folding, 1900 . . . . **135.00**
Seneca Chautauqua, 4 x 5″, folding, Wollensak lens, Seneca Uno shutter, (Rochester, NY) **50.00**
Stereo Relist, f3.5 1950, David White Co., (Milwaukee, WI) **125.00**
Tom Thumb Camera Radio, 1948, Automatic Radio Mfg. Co., (Boston, MA) **110.00**
Univex Model A, Universal Camera Corp. black plastic, 00 rollfilm, 1936, (New York, NY) **15.00**
View-Master Personal Stereo, Sawyers, Inc., Anast. f3.5/25 mm, 1960, (Portland, OR) **110.00**
Zeiss, Contax IIa, colored shutter-speed dial, (Stuttgart, Germany) **250.00**

CAMPHOR GLASS

History: Camphor glass derives its name from its color. Most have a cloudy white appearance, similar to gum camphor; the remainder has a pale colored tint. Camphor glass is made by treating the glass with hydrofluoric acid vapors.

Vase, 8″ h, max width 10″, frosted, clear leaf deco, $80.00.

Biscuit Jar, brass bail, cov **65.00**
Bookends, pr, Grecian columns **90.00**
Candlestick, 8″ h, 4⅛″ d, figural seated female nude, arms raised, clusters of grapes, leaves at top and base **60.00**
Candy Dish, cov, ftd, pink **40.00**
Creamer, Wild Rose & Bowknot, pink roses, green leaves **30.00**
Elephant, enamel decor and "G.O.P." on side **40.00**
Perfume Bottle, 6″, florals and scrolls, fan shaped stopper **40.00**
Pitcher, enamel dec of violets **45.00**
Powder Jars, cov, figural finial
  Elephant, pink **35.00**
  Flapper, pink **25.00**
  Parrots **20.00**
Rolling Pin **60.00**
Sugar, open, 2 handles, Wild Rose & Bowknot, pink roses, green leaves . . **30.00**
Sugar Shakers
  Leaf mold **85.00**
  Swirl **75.00**
Syrup, metal lid, enamel dec, Wild Rose & Bowknot **110.00**
Toothpick, egg shape, blue ribbon and floral wreath dec **85.00**
Vases 7″, bud, green **15.00**

CANDLESTICKS

History: The domestic use of candlesticks is traced to the 14th century. The earliest was a picket type, named for the sharp point to hold the candle. The socket type was established by the mid-1660s.

By the late 17th century, a baluster stem was introduced, replacing the earlier Doric or clustered column stem. After 1730 candlesticks reflected rococo ornateness. Neo-classic styles followed in the 1760s. Candlestick design continues to mirror furniture design to modern times.

Reference: Margaret and Douglas Archer, *The Collector's Encyclopedia Of Glass Candlesticks*, Collector Books, 1983.

Bell Metal, 10¾″, urn shaped candle cup, fluted column, sq base, gadrooned molding, George III, late 18th C **165.00**
Brass
  6¼″, fluted, sq base, pushup, Adam's period, English, late 18th C **120.00**
  7¼″, cylindrical, molded base, side handle ejector, early 19th C **185.00**
  9½″, Queen of Diamonds, cylindrical, cone shape base, English, c1820, pr **190.00**
  10″, cylindrical, 4 feet, heavy, English, 18th C **300.00**
  10″, cylindrical, large mid drip pan, molded dome foot, English, late 17th C **400.00**

Noritake, 6⅜", yellow ground, black band, purple flower, $38.00.

Glass
  Canary, 6¾", round bases, hexagonal
    stems, petal sockets, pr **200.00**
  Flint, 9⅝", hexagonal, clear, pewter in-
    serts, Pittsburgh, pr **110.00**
  Fry, 10½", Foval, fiery opalescent with
    blue wafers, Delft blue spiral stems,
    pr **250.00**
  Opalescent, 9½", crucifix, fiery, pr . .   **225.00**
  Sandwich, 6¾", loop and petal, plum
    amethyst, satin oxidized surface . .   **225.00**
  Sinclaire, 12", amethyst, circular feet,
    paneled blown stems twisted at the
    top, flat rimmed sockets, pr **150.00**
Iron
  6¼", spiral sits on cup on scroll feet,
    19th C **55.00**
  11", pricket on round candle cup, wire
    twisted stem, 4 delicate tooled legs,
    18th C **350.00**
  24", alter, integral bobech cast with
    cherubic faces, standard cast with
    grapevines, cherubic faces and
    names of 4 apostles cast above 4
    cherub feet, early 19th C **900.00**
Pewter, 8", gadrooned molding,
    pushups, orig felt lining on base. . . .   **185.00**
Silver Plated, 5½", cylindrical, molded
    bases, hand applied silver on copper,
    English, late 18th C, pr **150.00**
Steel, 5½", hogscraper, hanging tab pu-
    shup, brass molding around center,
    mkd on pushup thumbpiece "No Rob
    11" **375.00**
Tin
  3½", candle holder on ring handled
    cylindrical box, 5 pcs of flint and
    steel stricker **325.00**

7¾" h, 3¾" w, deep saucer base,
    large ring handle, attached snuffer   **85.00**
11¼", sconce, crimped candle cup,
    sun shaped back **275.00**

CANDY CONTAINERS

History: In 1876 Croft, Wilbur and Co. filled a small glass Liberty Bell with candy and sold it at the Centennial Exposition in Philadelphia. From that date until the 1960s glass candy containers remained popular and served to outline American and American transportation history.

Jeannette, Pennsylvania, a center for the packaging of candy in containers, was home for J. C. Crosetti, J. H. Millstein, T. H. Stough, and Victory Glass. Other Early manufacturers included: George Borgfeldt, New York, New York; Cambridge Glass, Cambridge, Ohio; Eagle Glass, Wheeling, West Virginia; L. E. Smith, Mt. Pleasant, Pennsylvania; and, West Brothers, Grapeville, Pennsylvania.

Candy containers with original paint, candy, and closures command a high premium, but be aware of reproduced parts and repainting. The closure is a critical part of each container; its loss detracts significantly from the value.

Small figural perfumes and other miniatures often are sold as candy containers.

Prices range from $10 to $1,700, the recent record price paid at auction for Soldier By The Tent.

References: Jennie Long, *An Album Of Candy Containers*, privately printed, Volume I: 1978, Volume II: 1983; Robert T. Matthews, *Antiquers Of Glass Candy Containers*, privately printed, 1970; Mary Louise Stanly, *A Century Of Glass Toys*, Forwards Color Productions, n.d.

Collectors' Club: Candy Container Collectors Of America, Box 184, Lucerne Mines, PA 15754. Dues: $10.00. *The Candy Gram* (bimonthly).

Museums: Cambridge Glass Museum, Cambridge, OH; L. E. Smith Glass, Mt. Pleasant, PA.

Additional Listings: See *Warman's Americana & Collectibles* for more examples.

Advisor: Robert Dellaposta.

Airplanes
  Patent 113053, 4⅝" l, tin wings, cork
    closure with attached propellor,
    emb Patent 113053, T. H. Stough   **45.00**
  Spirit Of St. Louis, 4½" l, glass body,
    emb W. Glass Co. Grapeville, PA,
    tin superstructure containing wings,
    carriages, and wheels, top of wings
    lithographed "Spirit of St. Louis,"
    complete. **375.00**
  U.S. P-51, 5" l, emb on wing US P-51,
    cardboard closure **30.00**
Automobiles
  Coupe, long hood, 5¼" l, 3" h, tin strip
    closure **65.00**
  Sedan, little, 3" l, cork closure, emb
    on bottom 3DR/J.S.CO **20.00**

*Sedan, streamlined, 4⅝" l, resembles 1940s sedan, cardboard closure, Victory Glass, complete **20.00**

*Station Wagon, 4⅞" l, resembles woody of late 1940s, cardboard closure, J. H. Millstein Co., complete **25.00**

Bell, Liberty, 3⅜" h, emb 1776 Centennial Exposition 1876/Proclaim Liberty Throughout The Land, pewter screw cap, Croft, Wilbur and Co., complete with orig sticker **300.00**

Bird On Mound, 2⅜" h, bird perched on glass base, tin whistle attached, tin slide on closure, complete **425.00**

Boats

*Cabin Cruiser, 4½" l, emb 4 in circle, cardboard closure, J. H. Millstein, complete **15.00**

Colorado 1914, 6⅜" l, glass body emb Colorado below nine port holes, red tin closure forms deck, 2 wooden stacks and 2 wooden masts, complete with string holding flag **250.00**

Battleship, 5½", cardboard closure, Victory Glass, complete, $25.00.

Cannon

Rapid Fire, 7¾" l, metal carriage with movable wheels, glass ammo compartment held candy balls which were shot out by turning a crank . . **325.00**

U. S. Field Defense, glass base emb with gears, black barrel is attached to base, screw cap closure printed T. H. Stough Co., Jeannette, PA . . **150.00**

Carpet Sweeper, 3 x 2¼", emb Dolly Sweeper/West Bros/Grapeville, PA/ Serial No. 2862, tin wire handle, tin wheels, tin closure, complete **350.00**

Cap, military, 3", open at top, spread eagle design on buttons, cardboard closure, Pla-Toy Co., Greensburg, PA . . **35.00**

Chick, baby, standing, 3⅜" h, painted yellow, tin closure, Victory Glass Co. **75.00**

*Chicken On Nest, 4⅝" l, emb on rim J. H. Millstein/Jeannette, PA, cardboard closure, complete **25.00**

Chicken On Round Base, oval basket 2⅛ x 2½", 2¾" h, emb on basket USA, tin screw closure **225.00**

Dogs

Kiddies Breakfast Bell, 2⅜" h, dog emb Sugar/Starch/Corn/Syrup, red screw cap, attached 2" nickel plated bell and clanger, complete with sticker **20.00**

Hound, glass hat, 3½" h, emb on base T. H. Stough/Jeannette, PA, round paper push-in closure **10.00**

Scotty, 2⅞" l, 3¼" h, cardboard closure, T. H. Stough **15.00**

Fire Engines

Fire Engine, 5" l, emb on top Fire Dept. in circle, cardboard closure, J. C. Crosetti **25.00**

Ladder Truck, 5" l, emb Jeannette, PA (backward letters)/Victory Glass Co./AVOR 1-2 OZ, driver and rear fireman painted red, tin wheels, tin snap closure, complete **125.00**

Electric Iron, 4½" l, string attached to handle with paper plug to simulate electric cord, cardboard closure, Pla-Toy, Greensburg, PA, complete **75.00**

Gas Pump, 6⅛" h, plastic, glass insert, paper sticker reads "Candy Pump/ Mfg J. H. Millstein/Jeannette, PA," gold rayon cord simulates gas hose, crank at bottom lets candy out **90.00**

Jeep, 4⅜" l, emb Willy's JEEP/J. H. Millstein/Jeannette, PA, cardboard closure **20.00**

Lamp, monkey, 2⅞", monkey emb See/ Speak/Or Hear/No Evil, attached red plastic shade, mkd Spec-Toy, complete **75.00**

Lantern, twins on anchor, metal stand shaped like golden anchor, holds two small lanterns, mkd underneath Van Styles/Specialities Corp/N.Y.C. **10.00**

Locomotives

888, double window, 4⅞", emb 888 below windows, cardboard closure, Victory Glass Co., complete **30.00**

999, man in window, 4⁷⁄₁₆", emb 999 below window, shows engineer sitting in window, screw cap closure **100.00**

1028, 5⅛" l, emb 1028 below window, cardboard closure, Victory Glass Co., complete **20.00**

Milk Bottle, emb Dolly's Milk/VG CO J'NET PA, cardboard push-in closure **35.00**

Mug, 3½" w, 2¼" h, drum shape, emb eagle on one side, painted gold

With slotted closure **200.00**

Without closure **20.00**

Nurser, 3¾" h, emb Lynne Doll Nurser/ with ingredients, etc., rubber nipple mkd HyGeiA **15.00**

Pencil, 5½" l, emb Baby Jumbo, closure
is stub of real pencil, complete with
paper sticker. **45.00**
Rabbits
In Egg, 5⅛", rabbit shown coming out
of cracked egg, rabbit painted gold,
emb VG CO/U.S.A., metal screw
cap. **65.00**
*Peter Rabbit, 6¼" h, emb on rim J.
H. Millstein/Jeannette, PA, card-
board closure, complete **25.00**
Pushing Chick in shell carriage, 4" l,
emb VG CO/JENET, PA/AVOR ¾
OZ, tin snap closure, complete . . .   **325.00**
Santa, 5⅝" h, red plastic head, white
face, emb inside Mfg J. H. Millstein/
Jeannette, PA, glass body, red suit,
black boots and belt, white fur,
complete **40.00**

CANES

History: Canes and walking sticks were an important accessory in a gentleman's wardrobe in the
18th and 19th centuries. They often served both a
decorative and utilitarian function. Collectors frequently view carved canes in wood and ivory as
folk art and pay higher prices for them. Glass canes
and walking sticks were glass makers' whimsies,
ornamental rather than practical.
Reference: Catherine Dike, *Cane Curiosa*, privately printed, 1983.

CANES

Antler horn, ell shaped handle, silver
band with London hallmarks, leather
cov bamboo shaft, lady's, 24" l **125.00**

Ivory handle, ebony, 35", $45.00.

Ebony shaft, silver handle, inscribed
"Presented to Capt. James Shearman
by the Members and Friends of the
Sabbath School as a token of Esteem,
Sidney, Jan 1st 1865", 33¾" l **800.00**
Glass
Aqua, sq twisted handle, 43" l **75.00**
Clear, blue and red swirl threading,
knob end, 32½" l. **200.00**
Inlaid mahogany on whale ivory, ell han-
dle, geometric inlays, 34½" l **600.00**
Ivory, whale, dove of peace carved han-
dle, wings outlined in incising, perched
atop knob and shaft, 40" l, c1860. . .   **4,500.00**
Maple, top screws off, contains glass
flaks, 34". **100.00**
Scrimshaw
Paneled whalebone shaft, carved
whale ivory fist, 2 baleen rings,
33" l. **375.00**
Rosewood shaft, whale ivory knob set
with 1857 dime, 29¾" l **175.00**
Sword, stag horn handle, silver finish
mountings, brass tip, 35" l **125.00**
Wooden
Carved chamelion handle, twisted de-
sign on shaft, 34" l. **70.00**
Carved dog's head, glass eyes,
32¼" l **50.00**
Carved wire haired terrier handle,
painted black. **150.00**

WALKING STICKS

Glass
Aqua, amber center, white spiral
threading, 35" l **125.00**
Cobalt blue, Nailsea type white loop-
ings, bulbous end, 48" l **275.00**
Portrait handle, whale ivory carved in likeness of James Madison, ebony
shaft, ivory tip, 35" l **400.00**
Whale Ivory, each section carved in dif-
ferent pattern, separated by spacing
rings of ebony, baleen and horn, top
of shaft with columnar carved open-
work, turned knob, 31" l. **800.00**
Wooden
Hexagonal shaft, worn black paint, 36"
l. **30.00**
Primitive carving, vine twisted shank,
figural carved handle with man's
head, painted black, 35" l. **50.00**

HANDLES

Celluloid, carved, dog's head, glass
eyes. **30.00**
Gold, 14K, monogrammed. **100.00**
Sterling Silver, walking stick, floral
design **50.00**

CANTON CHINA

History: Canton china is a type of oriental porcelain made in the Canton region of China from the early 19th century to the present and produced largely for export. Canton china is hand decorated in light to dark blue underglaze on white. Design motifs include houses, mountains, trees, boats, and a bridge. A design similar to "willow china" is the most common.

Borders on early Canton feature a rain and cloud motif (a thick band of diagonal lines with a scalloped bottom). Later pieces usually have a straight line border. The markings "Made In China" and "China" indicate wares which date after 1891.

Note: Several museum gift shops and private manufacturers are issuing reproductions of Canton china.

Cup and Saucer, coffee, loop handle, late, $60.00.

Bottle, 9″, bulbous	375.00
Bowls	
5¾″, enameled, continuous scene of scholars conversing in garden, floral borders, plain int., 18th C	665.00
8⅛″, round, shallow, 19th C	225.00
9″, scalloped rim, shallow	235.00
Butter Chip, 3³⁄₁₆″, sq, 19th C	85.00
Butter Plate, 5¾″, round	65.00
Candlestick, 7½″, cylindrical, tapered, scenic, 19th C	550.00
Charger, 13¼″, river scene with arched bridge, border of rain clouds, c1840	300.00
Condiment Jars, pr, cov, 3½″, scenic	150.00
Creamers	
3¼″	200.00
5½″, ovoid, scenic, c1845	300.00

6″, pagoda and flying crane, 19th C	250.00
Dishes	
4″ d, 1¾″ h, gray blue design, ftd, 19th C	75.00
8″, leaf shape, scenic, 19th C	200.00
14″, enameled copper, phoenix and dragon pursuing flaming pearl, multicolored, late 19th C	175.00
Egg Cup, 1⅝″, 19th C	200.00
Fruit Bowl, undertray, 8¾″ l, handles, reticulated, scenic center, 19th C	400.00
Garden Seats, pr, 18½″ h, hexagonal, multicolored, panels of figures reserved on ground of flowers, fruit and butterflies, 19th C	3,850.00
Ginger Jar, 6½″, bulbous	200.00
Gravy Tureen, underplate and cover, 4¼″ tureen, 7¾″ underplate, scenic, hog's head handles and finial, c1825	550.00
Hot Water Plates, pr, 9½″ across sq handles, octagonal, scenic centers, 19th C	450.00
Ice Cream Tray, 14″ l, rectangular, blue and white, scenic center, gold border dec, 19th C	1,200.00
Jars, pr, 12⅛″, circular, scenic, scrolled floral dec on shoulders, 19th C	2,200.00
Mugs	
2⅝″, scenic, 19th C	150.00
4″, strap handle, c1825	225.00
Pitcher, 9½″, landscape scene, blue rim, 19th C	500.00
Plates	
8½″	70.00
10″, round, 19th C	120.00
10¼″, oblong, scenic center, solid blue rim, 19th C	175.00
Platter, 13″, octagonal, deep blue and white, scenic	250.00
Punch Bowl, 15″ d, polychrome enamel, birds, flowers and court ladies	1,250.00
Rice Bowl and Saucer, handless, scenic	55.00
Sauce Boat, 7¼″, cross strap handle, 19th C	225.00
Serving Dishes	
10¼″ l, 9½″ w, flat rim on one side, scenic center, 19th C	390.00
11¾″ l, eggshell glaze	190.00
Spoon Dish, 3¾″, oval, scenic, 19th C	150.00
Sugars, cov	
4¼″, handles, continuous scene	250.00
5¾″, berry finial	300.00
Teapots, cov	
5½″, drum shape, scenic, entwined branch handle, 19th C	300.00
6″, entwined branch handle, 19th C	325.00
9⅞″, domed cov, foliate ground, figural reserves and reserves of birds, fruit and flowering branches, late 19th C	600.00
Teapot Stand, 5¾″, octagonal, scenic, 19th C	225.00

Tile, 5″, sq, scenic center, bamboo border, 19th C **175.00**
Tray, 8⅝″, oblong, scenic, 19th C **150.00**
Tureen, cov, florals, leaves, and butterflies, hog's head handles, foliate finial **650.00**
Umbrella Stands, pr, 23½″, cylindrical, flower ground, panels of figures, base with double grooved bands **2,400.00**
Vegetable Dish, 10½″ l, oval, scenic, 19th C **225.00**
Vegetable Dishes, cov, scenic
  8″, rectangular, berry finial **250.00**
  9″, oval **325.00**
  9½″ l, sq, berry finial, 19th C **425.00**
Vase, 4⅜″, pear shape body, tall neck, enameled multicolored lotus scrolls, white ground, 18th C **350.00**

CAPO-DI-MONTE

History: In 1743 King Charles of Naples established a soft paste porcelain factory near Naples which made figures and dinnerware. In 1760 many of the workmen and most of the molds were taken to Buen Retiro, near Madrid, Spain. A new factory opened in Naples in 1771 and added hard paste porcelains. In 1834 the Doccia factory in Florence purchased the molds and continued their production in Italy.

Capo-di-Monte was copied heavily by factories in Hungary, Germany, France, and Italy. Many of the pieces in today's market are of recent vintage. Do not be fooled by the crown over the "N" mark; it also was copied.

Bowl, 5″, oblong, gold ground, ext. with raised nude figures in classical landscapes, int. in burgundy with romantic landscape **145.00**
Boxes
  3″ h, 5½″ d, enameled, relief molded angels with musical instruments, florals, gilt bronze cov **140.00**
  6½″ l, raised figural dec of "Fete Champetre" **125.00**
  Patch, hunting scene **125.00**
Candleholder, 3″, raised flowers and nude figure **95.00**
Coffee Service, 3 pcs [coffee pot, cov sugar, creamer], white, gold spout, handles, and finials, raised nude figures **165.00**
Compote, 6½″ h, 13″ d, shell shape, mounted on scroll base, classical design **115.00**
Cups and Saucers
  Demitasse, ducks and herons in natural habitat, mkd crown over N . . . **65.00**

Phaeton, 1860 . . . . **75.00**
Figurines
  Carriage Group, 2 maidens riding in carriage drawn by 4 white horses with driver and footman, floral encrusted rect base, mkd pseudo crowned N, late 19th C, 35″ l **725.00**
  Gypsy holding tambourine, parrot on shoulder, 5″ **55.00**
  Man and lady, dancing, 1910, 7¼″ . . **175.00**
  Old woman, humorus, ruffled cap and cuffs, long dress, 4¼″ **85.00**

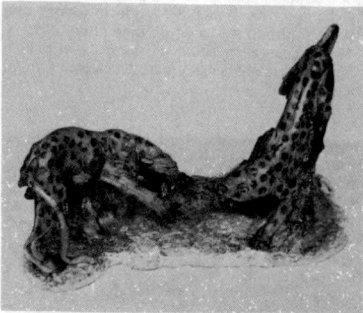

Figurine, Fighting Leopards, 17½″ l, G. Qurius, $150.00.

Perfume, 3″, cherub in garden, high relief, blue crown mark **95.00**
Pitcher, 8″, classical figures in relief, branch handle **250.00**
Plaque, 3 x 4½″, five children playing in flower garden, brass frame **175.00**
Plates
  8½″, center with 2 cherubs, border with polychromed nude figures . . . **45.00**
  Semi-nudes bathing beside brook in relief, floral festoon border **95.00**
Teapot, figure of lady with mirror, her maid in relief, serpent spout **300.00**
Tureen, cov, underplate, 15″ across handles, hp, relief molded figures, florals, and fruits, multicolored **240.00**
Vase, 10″, scalloped rim, high relief nudes and cherubs, 2 handled, ftd . . **190.00**

CARLSBAD CHINA

History: Because of changing European boundaries, German speaking Carlsbad found itself located in the last hundred years first in the Austro-

Hungarian Empire, next in Germany, and currently in Czechoslovakia. Carlsbad was one of the leading pottery manufacturing centers in Bohemia.

Wares from the numerous Carlsbad potteries are lumped together under the term "Carlsbad China." Most pieces on the market are post-1891, although several potteries date to the early 19th century.

Biscuit Jar, 5¼″, light beige, winged
   cupid scene, molded swirl, gold scalloped rim, mkd **90.00**
Bowls
   6¾″ d, 3½″ h, irid gold, pink int., 4 gold
     handles, mkd Karlsbad, Austria . . . **160.00**
   9½″, classical figures, gold trim, mkd
     Victoria Carlsbad, Austria, c1912 . . **60.00**
   16 x 9″, oval, fluted top, hp purple and
     blue flowers, gold trim **40.00**
Box, cov, diamond shape, amethyst cut
   to clear, mkd **400.00**
Butter, cov, 4½″ h, 5½″ d, sq, chamfered
   corners, white, pink, and yellow roses,
   green leaves, gold trim handles,
   c1910 . . . . **45.00**
Cake Plates
   10″, portrait of lovers, wide rim, open
     handles, maroon, chartreuse, and
     green, sgd Boucher, Carlsbad,
     Austria **65.00**
   12″, violets, pierced gold handles,
     mkd Victoria, Carlsbad, Austria . . . **35.00**
Candle Lamps, pr, intaglio florals and
   gold trim on candlesticks, shade holders and shades in silver lacework with
   green glass beaded fringe, sgd **235.00**
Chocolate Pot, 10″, white ground, multicolored daisies, gold trim, mkd **100.00**
Cups and Saucers, set of 12, figural
   scenes, sgd **150.00**
Dinner Set, 85 pcs, scalloped edges,
   white, bunches of pink roses, green
   leaves, c1903, mkd **700.00**
Dish, 7¼″, molded in shape of flower
   blossom, blue and purple irid glaze . . **85.00**
Dresser Tray, fluted rim, blue and yellow
   flowers **35.00**
Gravy Pitcher, open handled underplate,
   9¼″ l, 5⅝″ w, white ground, yellow and
   pink roses, green leaves, gold rims,
   c1908 . . . . **55.00**
Mug, 4″, decal portrait of monk with vi-
   olin, mkd Victoria, Carlsbad **65.00**
Nappy, 4¼″, white ground, shaded pink
   roses, small blue flowers, green
   leaves, gold trim, c1900 . . . . **22.00**
Pitcher, 11″, pink ground, cobalt blue
   band at top and bottom, gold trim . . . **90.00**
Plates
   7⅝″, scalloped edge, white ground,
     spray of pink and yellow roses,
     green buds and leaves, gold trim,
     c1905 . . . . **28.00**

Biscuit Jar, 6⅜″ h, 5½″ d, mkd Victoria Carlsbad, $45.00.

   8½″, off white ground, pink roses, vi-
     olets, gold trim **25.00**
Platter, 13½″, white ground, deep pink
   and yellow roses and buds, green
   leaves, gold shaped rim, imp mark . . **35.00**
Relish Dish, cream ground, multicolored
   floral dec, pink border, pierced
   handles **30.00**
Serving Bowl, underplate, bowl: 10″ d
   and 3½″ h, plate: 13″, sky blue shading to white, wide ribbing, gold flecked
   scalloped borders, L.S. & Co., Carls-
   bad, Austria **60.00**
Soup, 9½″, white with yellow and pink
   rose sprays, green leaves, shaped
   gold rim, c1900 . . . . **32.00**
Toothpick Holder, figural, monkey **42.00**
Vase, 9″, baluster shape, off white,
   shaded pink and red roses, blue violets, green leaves gold trim **65.00**
Vegetable Dish, cov, 9″, fluted, white
   ground, yellow roses, green leaves . . **60.00**

CARNIVAL GLASS

   History: Carnival glass, an American invention, is colored pressed glass with a fired on iridescent finish. It was first manufactured about 1905 and was immensely popular both in America and abroad. Over 1,000 different patterns have been identified. Production of old carnival glass patterns ended in 1930.

   Most of the popular patterns of carnival glass were produced by five companies—Dugan, Fenton, Imperial, Millersburg, and Northwood. Northwood patterns frequently are found with the "N" trademark. Dugan used a diamond trademark on several patterns.

In carnival glass color is the most important factor in pricing. The color of a piece is determined by holding the piece to the light and looking through it.

The listing below combines the variety of colors into three basic color units: marigold, dark (blue, green, or purple), and pastel (white, light blue or green, and vaseline).

References: Bill Edwards, *The Standard Encyclopedia of Carnival Glass,* Collector Books, 1982; Marion T. Hartung, *First Book of Carnival Glass* to

Tenth Book of Carnival Glass [series of 10 books], privately printed, 1968 to 1982.

Collectors' Club: American Carnival Glass Association, P. O. Box 273, Gnadenhutten, OH 44629. Dues: $5.00. *American Carnival Glass News,* quarterly; Heart of America Carnival Glass Association, 14226 E. 143 Lane, Burnsville, MN 55337. Dues: $20.00. *HOCGA,* monthly; International Carnival Glass Association, Inc., R. D. # 1, Box 14, Mentone, IN 46539. Dues: $10.00. *The Carnival Pump,* quarterly.

	Marigold	Dark	Pastel
ACANTHUS (IMPERIAL)			
Bowl, 8″–9″	45.00	48.00	70.00
Plate, 10″	110.00	—	155.00
ACORN BURRS (NORTHWOOD)			
Berry Set, master bowl, 6 sauces, 7 pcs.	275.00	360.00	900.00
Bowls			
5″	25.00	35.00	60.00
10″	80.00	125.00	300.00
Butter Dish, cov.	100.00	150.00	425.00
Creamer	75.00	100.00	200.00
Pitcher	375.00	625.00	1,000.00
Punch Bowl, base	400.00	600.00	1,800.00
Punch Cup	30.00	35.00	55.00
Spooner	70.00	95.00	200.00
Sugar, cov	80.00	125.00	240.00
Tumbler	45.00	65.00	140.00
BUTTERFLY & FERN (FENTON)			
Pitcher	320.00	445.00	—
Tumbler	35.00	50.00	—
BUZZ STAR (CAMBRIDGE)			
Cruets, orig stoppers			
4″	175.00	200.00	—
6″	185.00	210.00	—
Rose Bowl	325.00		—
COSMOS (MILLERSBURG)			
Bowl, 5″	65.00	50.00	—
Plate, 6″	70.00	75.00	—
DANDELION (NORTHWOOD)			
Mug	375.00	500.00	625.00
Pitcher, tankard	350.00	375.00	975.00
Tumbler	40.00	50.00	110.00
DRAPERY (NORTHWOOD)			
Bowl, 8″	—	—	50.00
Candy Dish, tricorn	65.00	70.00	100.00
Rose Bowl	150.00	90.00	200.00
Vase, 7½″	25.00	50.00	80.00

Dandelion, Northwood, tumbler purple, irid, $50.00.

Fisherman's Mug, Marigold, $225.00.

Flute, Marigold, vase, 6¾″, $22.50.

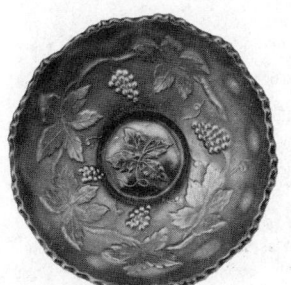

Heavy Grape, Bonbon, purple, $60.00.

Heavy Iris, tumbler, $60.00.

Louisa, Rose bowl, purple, $65.00.

EMBROIDERED MUMS (NORTHWOOD)	Marigold	Dark	Pastel
Bon Bon	—	—	100.00
Bowl, 9″	45.00	115.00	265.00
Plate, ice green	—	—	700.00

FANCIFUL (DUGAN)

	Marigold	Dark	Pastel
Bowl, 8½″	40.00	65.00	110.00
Plate, 9″	90.00	175.00	125.00

FEATHER & HEART (MILLERSBURG)

	Marigold	Dark	Pastel
Pitcher	400.00	500.00	—
Tumbler	90.00	160.00	—

FENTONIA (FENTON)

	Marigold	Dark	Pastel
Bowls			
5″, ftd, sauce	25.00	35.00	—
9½″, master berry	65.00	80.00	—
10″, fruit	60.00	70.00	—
Butter, cov	110.00	165.00	—
Creamer	60.00	80.00	—
Pitcher	300.00	425.00	—
Spooner	60.00	85.00	—
Sugar, cov	65.00	90.00	—
Tumbler	50.00	70.00	—

FISHERMAN'S (DUGAN)

	Marigold	Dark	Pastel
Mug	225.00	250.00	—

FLUTE (IMPERIAL)

	Marigold	Dark	Pastel
Bowl, 8″	20.00	80.00	—
Breakfast set, ind creamer, sugar, pr.	—	110.00	—
Goblet	15.00	—	—
Pitcher	175.00	500.00	—
Punch Bowl, base	250.00	475.00	—
Punch Cup	25.00	35.00	—
Sauce	20.00	60.00	—
Sherbet	15.00	25.00	50.00
Toothpick	60.00	75.00	125.00
Tumbler	35.00	60.00	—
Vase, 9″	40.00	60.00	—

GARDEN PATH & VARIENT (DUGAN)

	Marigold	Dark	Pastel
Bowls			
8½″	50.00	80.00	90.00
10″	75.00	100.00	150.00
Compote	185.00	300.00	500.00
Plate, 6″	245.00	500.00	300.00

GRAPE & GOTHIC ARCHES (NORTHWOOD)

	Marigold	Dark	Pastel
Bowls			
5½″	18.00	20.00	—
9½″	35.00	50.00	—
Butter, cov	95.00	125.00	—
Creamer	50.00	55.00	—
Pitcher	90.00	200.00	—

	Marigold	Dark	Pastel
Spooner	40.00	45.00	—
Sugar, cov	50.00	60.00	—
Tumbler	35.00	60.00	—

GRAPE DELIGHT (DUGAN)

	Marigold	Dark	Pastel
Nut Bowl, 6 feet	50.00	60.00	70.00
Rose Bowl, 6 feet	60.00	70.00	125.00

HEARTS & FLOWERS (NORTHWOOD)

	Marigold	Dark	Pastel
Bowl, 8½″	70.00	90.00	165.00
Compote	50.00	90.00	100.00

HEAVY IRIS (DUGAN)

	Marigold	Dark	Pastel
Compote	40.00	45.00	—
Pitcher	500.00	1,100.00	1,250.00
Tumbler	25.00	60.00	200.00

HOLLY (FENTON)

	Marigold	Dark	Pastel
Bowl, 8″	35.00	45.00	90.00
Compote	65.00	50.00	60.00
Goblet	40.00	45.00	50.00
Hat	35.00	40.00	45.00
Plate, 10″	100.00	200.00	140.00

IRIS (FENTON)

	Marigold	Dark	Pastel
Compote	50.00	80.00	275.00
Goblet, buttermilk	90.00	55.00	—

KITTENS (FENTON)

	Marigold	Dark	Pastel
Bowls			
Banana	100.00	130.00	135.00
Cereal	150.00	175.00	160.00
4 sided	70.00	—	—
6 sided	80.00	—	—
Cup & Saucer	200.00	250.00	245.00
Plate, 4¾″	115.00	150.00	145.00
Toothpick	130.00	150.00	150.00

LITTLE FISHES (FENTON)

	Marigold	Dark	Pastel
Bowls			
5½″	80.00	90.00	—
8½″	100.00	145.00	650.00
Plate, 9″, rare	—	500.00	700.00

LOUISA (FENTON)

	Marigold	Dark	Pastel
Candy Dish, ftd	55.00	65.00	—
Plate, 8″, ftd	—	120.00	—
Rose Bowl, ftd	55.00	65.00	—

MANY FRUITS (DUGAN)

	Marigold	Dark	Pastel
Punch Bowl, base	200.00	300.00	—
Punch Cups	30.00	35.00	

ORANGE TREE (FENTON)	Marigold	Dark	Pastel
Bowl, 8″	35.00	75.00	85.00
Butter, cov	135.00	150.00	400.00
Compote	30.00	50.00	70.00
Creamer	40.00	60.00	110.00
Cup	25.00	30.00	45.00
Goblet	35.00	40.00	45.00
Hatpin Holder	130.00	175.00	250.00
Loving Cup	150.00	175.00	250.00
Mug	35.00	50.00	160.00
Pitcher	130.00	200.00	400.00
Plate, 9″	50.00	100.00	130.00
Powder Jar, lid	70.00	80.00	100.00
Punch Bowl, base	200.00	265.00	350.00
Spooner	40.00	60.00	110.00
Wine	30.00	40.00	65.00

ORIENTAL POPPY (NORTHWOOD)			
Pitcher, tankard	375.00	500.00	900.00
Tumbler	50.00	50.00	90.00

PEACH (NORTHWOOD)			
Bowls			
5″	—	—	65.00
9″	—	—	220.00
Butter, cov	—	—	170.00
Creamer	—	—	85.00
Nappy	—	—	30.00
Pitcher	—	550.00	650.00
Rose Bowl	—	—	45.00
Spooner	—	—	70.00
Sugar	—	—	70.00
Tumbler	—	60.00	40.00

PEACOCK AT THE FOUNTAIN (NORTHWOOD)			
Bowls			
5″	30.00	40.00	60.00
9″	65.00	90.00	165.00
10″, fruit, ftd	210.00	275.00	1,500.00
Butter, cov	125.00	170.00	200.00
Compote	180.00	260.00	300.00
Creamer	40.00	90.00	70.00
Cup	30.00	35.00	60.00
Pitcher	135.00	350.00	400.00
Plate	125.00	275.00	180.00
Punch Bowl, base	175.00	500.00	2,500.00
Spooner	40.00	90.00	70.00
Sugar, cov	75.00	95.00	125.00
Tumbler	35.00	25.00	80.00
Water Set, electric blue	—	—	625.00

PINE CONE (FENTON)			
Bowl, 6″	40.00	60.00	—
Plate, 7″	95.00	160.00	—

QUESTION MARK (DUGAN)			
Bon Bon	35.00	40.00	60.00
Compote	40.00	45.00	70.00

Pine Cone, dish, 5½″ d, purple, irid, $38.00.

Three Fruits, Northwood, plate, 9⅛″, purple irid, $95.00.

	Marigold	Dark	Pastel
RAMBLER ROSE (DUGAN)			
Pitcher	125.00	200.00	—
Tumbler	15.00	40.00	—
RASPBERRY (NORTHWOOD)			
Bowls			
5″	30.00	50.00	—
9″	50.00	100.00	—
Compote	30.00	70.00	—
Pitchers			
Milk	125.00	150.00	—
Water	110.00	265.00	—
Tumbler	45.00	50.00	—
TEN MUMS (FENTON)			
Bowl, 8–11″	80.00	135.00	130.00
Pitcher	400.00	900.00	1,100.00
Plate, 10″	—	375.00	—
Tumbler	85.00	85.00	275.00
THREE FRUITS (NORTHWOOD)			
Bon Bon	50.00	80.00	100.00
Bowls			
8″, collar base	40.00	55.00	130.00
8″, ftd	50.00	135.00	—
Compote	35.00	90.00	260.00
Plate, 9″			
Basketweave exterior	150.00	200.00	175.00
Stippled	80.00	150.00	185.00
TREE OF LIFE (IMPERIAL)			
Berry Set, 7 pc	85.00	—	—
Perfume Bottle	45.00	—	—
Pitcher	60.00	—	—
Plate, 7½″	30.00	—	—
Tumbler	20.00	—	—
WINDFLOWER (DUGAN)			
Bowl, 8½″	60.00	85.00	90.00
Nappy, handled	40.00	65.00	70.00
Plate, 9″	50.00	170.00	

ZIGZAG (FENTON)

	Marigold	Dark	Pastel
Pitcher, tankard..................	150.00	190.00	120.00
Tumbler	40.00	60.00	75.00

MISCELLANEOUS AND SPECIAL ITEMS

Butterfly & Berry (Fenton), hatpin, marigold.....................	475.00
Butterfly & Tulip, (Dugan), bowl, sq, purple.....................	900.00
Courthouse (Millersburg), bowl, unlettered, amethyst, estate of Marion Hartung....................	1,300.00
Jeweled Heart (Dugan), water set, marigold....................	1,100.00
Marilyn (Millersburg), water set, amethyst, estate of Marion Hartung	1,200.00
Multi Fruits & Flowers (Millersburg), tulip shape punch bowl, base, cups, marigold.....................	1,400.00
Nesting Swan (Millersburg), rose bowl .	1,750.00
Persian Garden (Northwood), chop plate, purple	2,000.00

CAROUSEL FIGURES

History: By the late 17th century carousels were found in most capital cities of Europe. In 1867 Gustav Dentzel carved America's first carousel. Other leading American manufacturers include Charles I. D. Looff, Allan Herschell, Charles Parker, and William F. Mangels.

Original paint is not critical, since figures were repainted annually. Park paint indicates layers of accumulated paint; stripped means paint removed to show carving; restored involves stripping and repainting in the original colors.

In 1983 two key sales, The Edwin Ferren III collection auctioned by Guernsey and the Frederick Fried sale at Sotheby's, established record prices for many figures. A polar bear by Allan Herschell, c1918, country fair style, jeweled, and with large tassel decorations brought $28,600.00, the overall record.

Reference: Frederick Fried, *The Pictorial History Of The Carousel*, Vestal Press, 1964.

Periodical: *Carousel Art*, P.O. Box 992, Garden Grove, CA 92642.

Collectors' Clubs: The American Carousel Society, 470 South Pleasant Avenue, Ridgewood, NJ 07450; National Carousel Association, 7266 West Stanley Road, Flushing, MI 48433.

Cat, jumping, tail upright, bow at neck, wood, carved and painted, glass eyes.......................	1,750.00
Dog, 55″ l, trapping with collar, wood, carved and painted, Herschell-Spillman.....................	3,500.00
Elephant, 36″ l, 30″ h, wood, orig paint, inside row, late 1900 C	7,500.00
Giraffe, 54″ l, 67″ h, wood, carved and painted, Dentzel	14,000.00
Girl With Dog at Her Side, wood, deep carving, park paint, Herschell-Spillman Chariot.....................	2,000.00
Horses	
48″ l, 57″ h, jumper, outside row, Armitage-Herschell, c1890	2,250.00
53″ l, 51″ h, prancer, inside row, Looff, Late 19th C................	4,250.00
59″ l, 59″ h, jumper, 2nd row, park paint, Dentzel	3,500.00
64″ l, 60″ h, prancer, carved, painted, glass eyes, Dentzel	4,500.00
64″ l, 62″ h, listener, solid, carved, outside row, Dentzel.............	6,500.00
65″ l, 59″ h, prancer, middle row, Looff style mirrors, parrot saddle, peek-a-boo forlock, Looff.............	6,500.00
Lion, standing, Carmel/Borelli, Coney Island style, multi-jeweled, c1912, paint removed....................	22,000.00
Pig, leaping, wood, carved and painted, Dentzel, Philadelphia style, c1912, restored	9,350.00

Horse, $2,250.00.

Rabbit, jumping, ears upright, wood, carved and painted, glass eyes **1,750.00**
Rooster, 42″ h, strutting, wood, carved and painted, glass eyes **1,650.00**
Zebra, 50″ l, solid, painted on saddle, Herschell-Spillman............. **2,750.00**

CASTLEFORD

History: Castleford is a soft paste porcelain made in Yorkshire, England, in the 1800s for the American trade. The ware has warm, white ground, scalloped rims (resembling castle tops), and is trimmed in deep blue. Occasionally pieces are decorated further with a coat of arms, eagles, or Liberty.

Teapot, 7 x 10½″ l, salt glaze, cobalt trim, $200.00.

Bowl, 5″, white ground, blue bands, scalloped **185.00**
Creamer, 3½″, 3 brown oval medallions, one with white applied eagle and shield, second with Lady Liberty, and third with cherubs and eagle on cloud **300.00**
Sugar, cov, round, mythological scenes, vertical panels, twisted rope band near top, scalloped edge with oval medallions, blue enamel lines, dome lid, floral knob **200.00**
Teapot, cov, mythological scenes, flanked by floral panels, acanthus leaf borders top and bottom, blue enamel lines on body, lid, and handle, leaf shaped spout, florette knob **250.00**

CASTOR SETS

History: A castor set consists of a set of matched condiment bottles held within a frame or holder. The bottles are for condiments such as salt, pepper, oil, vinegar, and mustard. The most commonly found castor set consists of three to five glass bottles in a silver plated frame.

Although castor sets were known as early as the 1700s, most of the sets encountered today date from the 1870 to 1915 period when they enjoyed great popularity.

2-bottles, cut glass sq bottles, bulbous faceted stoppers, SS stand, shaped rectangular base chased with acanthus leaves, central support handle in form of ribbon tied laurel wreath, mkd K. Faberge in Cyriller, Imperial warrant, Moscow, c1910, 10⅝″ h **2,800.00**
2-bottles, Thousand Eye pattern, amber, glass stand.................. **225.00**
3-bottles, cranberry glass, cut panels, crescent moon shaped SP holder, orig salt spoon, 5½″ h, 7″ d **250.00**
3-bottles, IVT, amber, SP holder, brass ring handle **120.00**
3-bottles, opaque Mt. Washington bottles, flowers on salt and pepper, hummingbird on mustard, pastel shades, round SP hammered frame, mkd Pairpoint 724 .... **175.00**
4-bottles, cut crystal, cut and faceted stoppers, SP, sq platform, ball ftd, English, 6″ sq **135.00**
4-bottles, cut cylindrical bottles, vertical notched, flutes, pierced plated mounts, black lacquered stand, central bronzed handle, bronze mounts, English, late 19th C, 5½″ sq **825.00**
4-bottles, Daisy & Button, blue, glass holder **95.00**
4-bottles, etched bottles, triangular bail handle, SP Wilcox frame in 2 tiers .. **150.00**
4-bottles, New England Pineapple pattern bottles, glass holder **300.00**
4-bottles, opal, Stripe pattern, vaseline, glass base, ring handle **150.00**
5-bottles, Bellflower pattern, flint glass, pewter stand................... **225.00**
5-bottles, copper wheel pattern, Rogers SP stand **110.00**
5-bottles, 2 cut glass silver mounted glass bottles, 3 urn shaped castors with engraved crests, cinquefoil shaped frame, 4 leaf capped scroll and shell supports, ring handle, SS stand by Samuel Wood, London, 1743, 8½″ d **900.00**
5-bottles, cut glass, silver mounted, all over lunar and geometric cutting, SS stand, Warwick form, shell shaped ft, English, maker's mark JD, c1750, 8½″ h **550.00**
5-bottles, floral polished dot pattern, SP stand, trimmed skirt, pedestal base, loop bail..................... **145.00**
5-bottles, Heavy Paneled Finecut pattern, SP holder **75.00**

5-bottles, flint glass, Gothic Arch pattern, pewter std, c1860, Sandwich, 10½″ h, $195.00.

6-bottles, amberina, mkd Aurora, "487", metal holder, 18″ d **1,995.00**
6-bottles, cut glass, ribbed trim on pedestal base, deep skirt, bail handle holds bell and plunger, mkd Meriden B. Co., 7″ h **200.00**
6-bottles, Daisy & Button, clear, toothpick holder at top of center post, 9″ h **100.00**
6-bottles, green glass, SP stand, mkd Meridan **225.00**

CATALOGS

History: The first American mail order catalog was issued by Benjamin Franklin in 1744. This popular advertising tool helped to spread inventions, innovations, fashions, and other necessities of life to rural America. Catalogs were profusely illustrated and are studied today to date an object, identify its manufacturer, study its distribution, and determine its historical importance.

Reference: Don Fredgant, *American Trade Catalogs: Identification and Value Guide;* Lawrence Romaine, *A Guide To American Trade Catalogs 1744–1900.*

Additional Listings: See *Warman's Americana & Collectibles* for more examples.

Abercrombie & Fitch, 1930, 164 pgs . . **35.00**
Bairds Mail Order, Perth, 1939, 310 pgs **10.00**
Bannerman Sons Military Goods, 1922, 370 pgs **85.00**

L. L. Bean, Fall, 1937 . . . . **15.00**
A. C. Brown Co., Chicago, 1877, 30 pgs **35.00**
Carrom-Archaenea Co., 1912, 36 pgs, billiards. **75.00**
Cawston Ostrich Feathers **25.00**
Colt Firearms, 1930, includes orig price list **45.00**
Crescent Scoop Mfg, 1913 . . . . **10.00**
Goshen Buggy Tops, Hardware, Blacksmith Supplies, 1909, 156 pgs **18.00**
Griswold-Browning, Chicago, 1902, 20 pgs **15.00**
Louis Hanssen Hardware & Tools, Iowa, 1915, 1137 pgs, hardbound **75.00**
Heney Harness, Montreal, 232 pgs . . . **20.00**
Ives Toys, 32 pgs, 1915 . . . . **35.00**
Jacobson Architectural Ornaments, 1915, hardbound. **35.00**
Maher & Grosh Cutlery, 1894, 80 pgs . **125.00**
C. W. Marwedel Co. Tools, San Francisco, 1900, 287 pgs **40.00**
Mills Seeds, NY, 1902, 64 pgs. **6.00**
Orchard & Wilhelm Furniture, Omaha, 1928, 300 pgs, hardbound **30.00**
A. G. Parker Bisley Works, Birmingham, 1928, 170 pgs, firearms **20.00**
Quaker City Rubber Co., 1913. . . . . . . **10.00**
St. Louis Refrigerator & Wooden Gutter Co., 1894 . . . . **45.00**
A. E. Schmidt Co., 1920, 26 pgs, billiards. **10.00**

Victor Record, 1927, unnumbered, $15.00.

Schoverling, Daly, Gale Guns & Supplies, 1927, 368 pgs **20.00**
Spaulding Sports, 1922, 96 pgs. **15.00**
Springers Machinery, 1889, 80 pgs . . . **25.00**
Stanley Tools, 1929, 192 pgs **50.00**

Stark Bros. Nursery Year Book, 1911, 120 pgs	**25.00**
Sweitzer & Beer Co., 1878, 30 pgs	**40.00**
W & J Tiebout, marine hardware, 1912	**40.00**
Tiffany Co. Blue Book, 1913, 650 pgs	**35.00**
Trego Radio, 1923	**8.00**
Tufts Soda Fountain	**50.00**
Tuttle & Clark Harness Racing Equipment	**65.00**
Upson & Herrick Furniture, Rockford, IL, 1875, 8 pgs	**15.00**
A. H. Wiser, Family Cabinet Wear, 1880, 16 pgs	**35.00**
Yale & Towne, locks and hardware, 1905	**40.00**

CELADON

History: The term celadon, meaning a pale gray-ish green color, derives from a theatrical character Celadon, who wore costumes of varying shades of grayish green, in Honore d'Urfe's 17th century pastoral romance, "L'Astree." French Jesuits living in China applied it to a specific type of Chinese porcelain.

Celadon divides into two types. Northern celadon, made during the Song Dynasty up to the 1120s, has a gray to brownish body, relief decoration, and monochrome olive green glaze. Southern (Lung-ch'uan) celadon, made during the Song Dynasty and much later, is paint decorated with floral and other scenic designs and found in forms which would appeal to the European and American export market. Many of the Southern pieces date from 1825 to 1885. A blue square with Chinese or pseudo-Chinese characters appears on pieces after 1850. Later pieces also have a larger and sparser decorative patterning.

Bird Feeder, shallow, round sides, fluted rim, small loop handle, sea-green glaze, unglazed red base, Song Dynasty	**100.00**
Bowls	
5½", conical sides, ring foot, even and crackled sea-green glaze, Longquan, Song Dynasty	**1,000.00**
6", steep round sides, ring foot, lipped rim, bubble-suffused olive-green glaze, Northern, Jin Dynasty	**300.00**
Dishes	
3" h, shallow, round, imp foliate scroll center, petal molded sides, supported on column of molded squat figures, waisted plinth, olive-green glaze, Northern, Song Dynasty	**500.00**
15½", round, molded foliate spray center, radiate narrow flutes carved in well, blue-green glaze, Ming Dynasty	**675.00**
Ewer, 3⅝", ovoid, ribbed, plain shoulder, loop handle, upright spout, blue-green	

glaze, burnt orange foot rim, Southern Song Dynasty	**900.00**
Figure, Guanuin, 7¼", full robe, seated on sq pedestal base, Zhejiang, Ming Dynasty	**300.00**
Ginger Jar, globular, birds on flowering branches, leaves, teakwood base	**750.00**
Jar, 10¼" d, globular, ribbed base, red 3-clawed dragon with blue dot eyes and billowing clouds pencilled on shoulder, Kangxi	**1,800.00**
Planter, 7" l, rectangular, blue and white scrolls, scroll feet	**125.00**
Plate, 6", enameled roses, butterflies, bird and flowers, 18th C.	**150.00**

Brush Washer Bowl, 2″ h, 2¼″ d, $100.00.

Sake Pot, 5¼" h, ribbed, dome cov, green foliage, pink flowers	**75.00**
Umbrella Stand, 8½", flowering tree dec	**850.00**
Vases	
4¾", Gu shape, raised central band with incised line dec, pale green glaze, unglazed burnt red foot rim, Longquan, Ming Dynasty	**1,775.00**
5½", elongated pear shape, horizontal ribbing, 2 ring handles, crackle olive-green glaze, Southern Song Dynasty	**825.00**
7½", baluster shape, flared neck, lipped rim, flower sprigs between horizontal bands, translucent pale green glaze, Zhejiang, Ming Dynasty	**775.00**
9½", baluster shape, pale gray-green glaze, Yongzhing 6-character mark within double circle	**900.00**
18¼", trumpet neck, carved, large peony blossoms, crackled sea-green glaze, Ming Dynasty	**450.00**
Wall Pocket, 6", dark green branches, tiny white dots	**95.00**
Wine Pot, 6" d, globular, domed cov, relief modeled crisp cloud scrolls, double headed chelong forms loop handle, incised 4-character mark reading "Qi carved this in 1334"	**3,850.00**

CELLULOID ITEMS

History: In 1869 brothers J. W. Hyatt and I. S. Hyatt developed celluloid, the world's first synthetic plastic, as an ivory substitute because elephant herds were being slaughtered for their ivory tusks.

Known as "Ivorine" or "French Ivory," celluloid was made of nitrocellulose and camphor. Early pieces have a creamy color with stripes and grooves to imitate the texture of ivory or bone. The 1897 Sears catalog featured celluloid items. Celluloid was used widely until synthetics replaced it in the early 1950s. Celluloid often is used as a generic term for all early plastics.

Animals
Bear, 2½", black	25.00
Cat, 10", black and white	40.00
Elephant, 3½", gray	25.00

Bank, The Muncie Trust Company, 2",
round, blue, white and gold 30.00
Blotter, Commonwealth Casualty Co,
Philadelphia, 6 photos of young
women, c1905 . . . . 12.00
Bookmark, die cut prune, Field Prune
Syrup for constipation 25.00
Bottle Opener, figural pipe wrench, Coes
Wrench Company, c1910. . . . . 22.50
Brush, Shep Ward's Ice Cream 17.00
Button Hook, Miller's Coco, creamy ivory
handle 10.00
Comb, 7½ x 7", turquoise, blue stones 65.00
Dresser Set, 4 pcs, hair brush, clothes
brush, nail file and nail buffer with
holder, marbleized gold with amber,
letter L in black, mkd Ambassador . . 32.00
Frame, 6½ x 7", easel type, oval center,
scalloped edge, creamy ivory 20.00
Glove Box, cov, pink, cherubs and floral
dec, brass trim 27.50
Letter Opener, figural, head of rooster,
Armous's Helmet Fatted 22.00
Magnifying Glass, Buffalo Scale Com-
pany, copyright 1906 . . . . 25.00
Necktie Box, 12½ x 3½", Victorian, emb
with flowers and word Neckties 48.00
Pocket Mirror, round, King's Pure Malt 15.00
Poker Chips, marbleized, wooden box . 35.00
Powder Set, 3 pcs, box, shaker, and un-
dertray, creamy ivory, lady painted on
each 60.00
Purse, oval, ivory and pink, beaded, emb
flower dec, handle and tassel. 60.00
Rattle, 4½", cupid in wreath 14.00
Ring Box, 5" h, 3" d, cov, ftd, creamy
ivory. 13.00
Roly Poly, 3½", duck with umbrella,
c1930. . . . . 22.00
Shoe Horn, long creamy ivory handle. . 8.00
Sign, advertising, 9 x 17", Foster Hose
Supporters, lady with hose supporter
corset. 150.00
Tape Measure, figural dogs 25.00

Toy, Prince on Pig, 4½" l, 4" h, jointed legs, $25.00.

Tray, dresser, 11 x 7½", oblong, creamy
ivory. 14.00
Wall Plaque, scenic, c1930 . . . . 32.00
Whistle, Butter-Krust Bread, Sunbury,
Pa 12.00

CHALKWARE

History: William Hutchinson, an Englishman, invented chalkware in 1848. It was a substance used by sculptors to imitate marble. It also was used to harden plaster of paris, creating a confusion between the two products.

Chalkware often copied many of the popular Staffordshire items of the 1820 to 1870 period. It was cheap, gayly decorated, and sold by vendors. The Pennsylvania German "folk art" pieces are from this period.

Carnivals, circuses, fairs, and amusement parks used chalkware pieces as prizes during the late 19th and 20th century. They often were poorly made and gaudy. Don't confuse them with the earlier pieces. Prices for these chalkware items range from five to forty dollars.

Banks
Dove, 10½", perched on stump 190.00
Pomeranian dog, 11", sitting up in beg-
ging position, all white, yellow-
brown and black ears, nose, eyes,
mouth, and paws 225.00
Bust, Indian, Blackhawk 85.00
Bookends, pug dog faces 60.00
Figurines
Cat, 9", seated, brown with black, red
and yellow trim 300.00
Deer, 5⅜", olive amber with black
stripes, red and black features . . . 300.00
Doves, pr, 11", white, dec base, PA,
19th C 450.00

Ewe and lamb, 4"d, 4¼" h, 8⅝" l, reclining, black features	300.00
Frog, 3½" h, 4" w, dark green, yellow splotches	130.00
Horse, 10" standing, painted gold base, large green plant between horse's egs	150.00
Jesus, boy, sleeping, 10½" h, 9" l, 5" w	80.00
Lamb, 4¾", reclining	125.00
Man, fat, 10", standing, arms folded behind back, hole in mouth for cigar	165.00
Parrot, 9", green, yellow and red . . .	425.00
Poodle, 6½"	145.00
Rooster, 6", yellow, green and red . .	125.00
Squirrel, 6¾".	150.00
Walrus, 6½", black	125.00

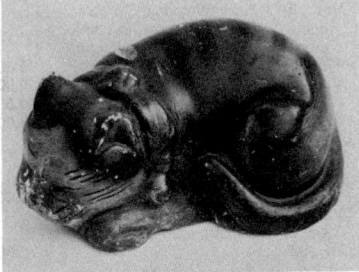

Cat, tabby, blue collar with red dots, 6", $50.00.

Garnitures	
Basket of fruit, 9", polychromed natural colors	450.00
Compote of fruit, 9" h, 8½" d, white, polychrome fruit	400.00
Statue, Geronimo, 17½", 1920s	175.00

CHARACTER AND PERSONALITY ITEMS

History: The use of the "star" product endorser began in the late 19th and early 20th centuries. By the 1930s the system was entrenched.

Two groups evolved. The first was the characters found in cartoons or portrayed on radio, in the movies, or on television by actors. Some characters, e.g., Tony The Tiger, were created by the advertising industry soley for advertising use.

The second group consists of "real" people, e.g., actors, sports, heroes, or political figures. The 1960s and 70s witnessed the pinnacle of star endorsed products.

Additional Listings: See *Warman's Americana & Collectibles* for expanded listings in Cartoon Characters, Cowboy Collectibles, Movie Personalities and Memorabilia, Shirley Temple, and Space Adventurers.

Bank, Howdy Doody, 7", $35.00.

CHARACTERS

Jack Armstrong	
Better Little Book, *Jack Armstrong And The Mystery Of The Iron Key*, Whitman, #1432, 1939	25.00
Hike-O-Meter, blue	20.00
Magic Talisman, brass, c1936	75.00
Betty Boop	
Ashtray, lusterware, c1930	100.00
Figure, 3" h, celluloid, 2 movable arms, gold trim on dress belt and garter, c1930	75.00
Buster Brown	
Bill Hook, "Buster Brown Vacation Days"	10.00
Figure, 8½", bisque, blue pants, orange shirt, green wide collar, blue hat brim, red flowers on base, c1905	200.00
Valentine, diecut heart, 8 x 8½", shows Buster and Tige, orig tassel on top, Tuck, c1905	40.00
Brownies	
Needle Case, "The World's Fair, 1492–1892 Souvenir," 3 x 4½", Brownie policeman on cover, 4 Brownies on back	50.00
Picture Frame, 5 x 6", wooden 1" sides, gray ground, red stripes, Brownies (Uncle Sam, Indian, Chinaman, Educator and Policeman), c1890	75.00

Frank Buck

Charm Bracelet, silvered brass, white metal charms of monkey, hippo, elephants, and native, plaque reads "Frank Buck–Bring 'Em Back Alive," c1930. . . . . **100.00**

Watch, "Explorer's Sun Watch," glow in dark disc with compass, sundial, reflector on reverse **50.00**

Campbell Kids

Button, 7/8", multicolored, "I Am A Campbell Kid," c1940. . . . . **25.00**

Wall Plaques, pr, painted plaster, 3 x 7", boy holds red tomato, girl holds flowers **50.00**

Dick Tracy

Badges, Secret Service Patrol

Captain. **100.00**
Lieutenant. **75.00**
Member **25.00**
Sergeant. **50.00**

Book, *Secret Detective Method and Magic Tricks*, Quaker Oats, 1939, 64 pgs, 5 x 7½". **60.00**

Toy, tin, squad car, c1949 . . . . **65.00**

Elsie The Cow

Earrings, plastic and brass, orig card "Klim Powdered Whole Milk," c1940. . . . . **20.00**

Ice Cream Dish, 4", fluted, c1940. . . **10.00**

Postcard, 3½ x 5½", unused, full color shows Elsie, Elmer, and Beuregard sitting in their living room, c1940. . **20.00**

Felix The Cat

Diecut, 2" h, celluloid, red bowtie, yellow celluloid eyes with black pupils, c1930. . . . . **50.00**

Pencil Box, 5½ x 8½", dark blue, black, Felix and 2 friends walking, copyright 1931 by Pat Sullivan . . . **35.00**

Pin, silvered brass with green nails, black enamel and silver Felix suspended in center, back inscribed "Use New Century Racing Plates," c1930. . . . . **85.00**

Postcard shows Felix walking along road next to road sign "To Wembley", caption "I Don't Know Where I'm Going, But I'm On My Way", c1924. . . . . **25.00**

Sparkler, c1930. . . . . **100.00**

Happy Holligan

Coat Hanger, wooden, 12" w, blue paint, 3 dimensional composition head, c1900 . . . . **25.00**

Nodder, 4½", papier mache. **50.00**

Hopalong Cassidy

Bank, 4", blue plastic, removable hat **25.00**

Chair, 16 x 18 x 24", wooden, folding chair with seat, back and part of arms in black fabric, bright red and white pictures, mkd "Hopalong Cassidy Official Bar 20 T V Chair" . . . **150.00**

Chow Set, 3 pc, white glass, 7" d plate, inscribed "Hopalong," 5" d bowl, and 3½" h cup, both inscribed "Hopalong Cassidy," black illustrations **75.00**

Gun, roll caps, 7" 1, black illustrations on white plastic grips, Wyandotte Toys **50.00**

Howdy Doody

Barrette, Clarabell, multicolored molded plastic, orig card. **15.00**

Bubble Bath Set, full, box pictures gang giving Flub-A-Dub a bath, MIB **30.00**

Ring, silvered plastic, raised image. . **15.00**

Jiggs, chocolate mold, tin, full figure. . . **25.00**

Little Orphan Annie

Ashtray, lusterware, c1939. . . . . **75.00**

Bandana, 16 x 18", rose, white, and dark brown, c1934. . . . . **85.00**

Manual, Secret Society, 12 pgs, full color, 1939 . . . . **65.00**

Map, 19 x 24", "Welcome To Simmons Corners," full color, Ovaltine premium, orig mailing envelope, c1936. . . . . **75.00**

Mug, Ovaltine **30.00**

Whistle, brass, figural, Sandy's head. **30.00**

Wristwatch, round, New Haven, MIB. **125.00**

Lone Ranger

Glass, 5" h, clear, white and 2 bright red bands, "Hi-Ho Silver! The Lone Ranger," 1938 copyright. **50.00**

Magnifier, silver bullet with magnifier, secret compartment and white pellet **75.00**

Pedometer, 2¾", silver, black, white and red dial, orig strap, mkd "Official Lone Ranger Pedometer". **20.00**

Mr. Peanut

Ashtray, 4" h, bisque, standing, full figure, large open peanut shell in front of feet, metal cane, c1930 . . . . . . **75.00**

Figure, 8½", wood, jointed, cane . . . **85.00**

Annie Oakley, button, 7/8", litho, black and white portrait on blue ground. . . **15.00**

Pete and Reepete, pin, multicolored molded plastic, 2 walking wolves, copyright N.Y.P.C., c1940 . . . . **40.00**

Popeye

Bank, 2½ x 2½", "Daily Dime Bank," colorful litho, bright yellow ground, red letters, copyright 1956 . . . . . . **25.00**

Coloring Book, "Popeye Coloring Book," 8½ x 11", shows Popeye punching Bluto poster just drawn by Sweet Pea, Lowe, 1958 . . . . **20.00**

Crayon Set, 8 x 10" box, Popeye in red, blue and black against bright yellow ground on cover, group of crayons in orig wrappers, unused paper strips, mkd MB (Milton Bradley), c1930 . . . . **100.00**

Pin, 1½", cello, multicolored, mkd "Made In Czechoslovakia" **20.00**

Pocket Knife, 3″ l, white handle, green
image, c1930. . . . . 75.00
Porky Pig, pencil holder, metal, tree
trunk 35.00
Red Ryder
  Game, Red Ryder's Complete 3 Game
  Set For Boys and Girls'', 1 x 6 x 11″,
  full color box, copyright 1956 Red
  Ryder Enterprises 50.00
  Gun, carbine, leather thong, name and
  trademark on stock 75.00
  Poster, 22 x 28″, ''Ride, Ryder, Ride,''
  full color, bright red ground, large
  photo of Jim Bannon, smaller photo
  of Don Reynolds, copyright 1948. . 50.00
Rin-Tin-Tin
  Cup, 3¼″ h, yellow plastic, illustration
  in blue, yellow, and black, ''Yo Ho!
  Rinty,'' copyright 1956 . . . . 45.00
  Ink Blotter, 3 x 7″, black and white,
  advertises serial ''The Lone De-
  fender,'' c1930. . . . . 25.00
  Lobby Card, serial title, c1930 . . . . . 45.00
Buck Rogers, Member's badge, brass . 70.00
Skippy, figure, 6″, bisque, movable arms,
c1930. . . . . 50.00
Straight Shooter
  Award Medal, bar covered in red and
  white checkerboard fabric, glow in
  the dark horseshoe with Tom's
  brand and checkerboard sus-
  pended below, c1945 . . . . 100.00
  Badge, silver, inset red, blue and silver
  foil checkerboard 75.00
  Belt Buckle, 1½ x 2¼″, brass, blue,
  red and silver foil insert 80.00
The Shadow, ring, glows in the dark . . 300.00
Yellow Kid
  Buttons
    #90, Kid carrying blue and white
    pennant, Columbia 65.00
    #91, Kid next to rooster, nightshirt,
    says ''Say, He Kin Lick Any Ole
    Ting'' 75.00
  Child's high chair. 650.00
  Chocolate mold, 4¾″ h, 3 dimensional
  white metal, detailed on inside and
  out, c1890. . . . . 150.00

PERSONALITIES

Gene Autry
  Button, 1¾″, black, white and red portrait of Gene and Champ, yellow
  ground 20.00
  Dixie Lid, 2¾″ d, ''Gene Autry Playing
  In 'The Strawberry Roan','' blue and
  white. 15.00
  Pennant, 10 x 26″, purple felt, bright
  yellow illustration of Gene on rearing horse, name in large letters,
  c1940 . . . . 50.00

Charlie Chaplin
  Book, Cracker Jack, flip type, 1¼ x
  1¾″, black and white 100.00
  Figure, 5½″ h, celluloid, tan outfit,
  painted features, black hat, orig pa-
  per sticker on base 65.00
  Paperweight, 4½″ h, cast iron, multi-
  colored paint 150.00
Bing Crosby
  Advertising Sign, 9 x 12″, cut out black
  and white raised picture of Bing,
  ''Mastercraft Pipes'' in raised silver
  letters, c1940 . . . . 50.00
  Lobby Card, ''Sing, Bing, Sing,'' 1933 45.00
  Ring, gold plastic, glossy black and
  white photo on top, c1940 . . . . . . 15.00
Dionne Quintuplets
  Button, 3½″, cello, ''Try Dionne Quin-
  tuplet Bread,'' blue ground, white
  and yellow letters, c1930 . . . . 25.00
  Fan, 8 x 14″, cardboard, babies play-
  ing in sand, 1936 . . . . 20.00
  Game, 3½ x 5″, ''Place The Quintu-
  plets In The Carriage,'' ball game
  under glass, c1930. . . . . 40.00
  Poster, 14½ x 32″, ''Today – The
  Dionne Quins Had Quaker Oats,''
  full color, 1935. . . . . 75.00
Judy Garland
  Mask, 7 x 9″, face, diecut paper, ''Dorothy From Wizard of OZ, 1939'' on
  back 20.00
  Souvenir Program, 9 x 12″, black and
  white photos, biography 20.00
Sonja Henie, button, 1¾″, blue drawing
  with white letters on bright green
  ground, ''Sonja Henie Ice Review,''
  c1940. . . . . 20.00
Charles Lindbergh
  Button, 1½″, black and white portrait,
  red, white, and blue rim, red, white,
  and blue ribbon, inscription ''Welcome Home Our Hero'' 45.00

**Record Duster, Bing Crosby, 3½″ d, yel-
low ground, $6.00.**

Hat, mkd "Spirit of St. Louis", c1930 — **20.00**

Jackie Robinson, doll, outfit, bat, comic, MIB, c1940 . . . . **325.00**

Roy Rogers

Button, 1¼", black and white cello, red, white and blue ribbon, gold colored white metal six gun attached below **45.00**

Tie Bar, brass, diecut metal head of Roy suspended from 2 chains, c1950 . . . . **30.00**

Babe Ruth, wristwatch **95.00**

Shirley Temple

Book, *The Poor Little Rich Girl*, authorized edition, 1936 . . . . **45.00**

Coloring Book, "The Little Princess Coloring Book," 11 x 15", Saalfield, 1939 . . . . **50.00**

Pocket Mirror, 1¾", light pink, sepia, metal rim **25.00**

Ed Wynn, mask, face, Texaco premium from Chicago World's Fair **35.00**

CHELSEA

History: Chelsea is a fine English porcelain designed to compete with Meissen. The factory began operating in the Chelsea area of London, England, in the 1740s. Chelsea products are divided into four periods: (1) Early period, 1740s, with incised triangle and raised anchor mark; (2) The 1750s, with red raised anchor mark; (3) The 1760s, the gold anchor period; and; (4) The Derby period from 1770–1783. In 1924 a large number of the molds and models of figurines were found at the Spode-Copeland Works, and many items were brought back into circulation.

Basket, 12", pierced, int. with bouquet of scattered floral sprays, ext. with applied flower heads at intersections, 2 ribbon entwined handles with flower head terminals, c1755 . . . . **550.00**

Candlesticks, pr, 5", birds in black, yellow, and red perched on tree stump; flowering bocage supporting branch for candle nozzle, c1775 . . . . **550.00**

Dishes

8½", serving, oval, raised fruit, leaves, and painted flowers, c1765 . . . . . . **500.00**

9⅝", oval leaf shape, scalloped, central floral spray and sprig, 2 molded grapevine branches and leaves in green, yellow, and puce on brown edged rim, c1755 . . . . **600.00**

Figurines

Haymakers, pr, 8½", male sharpening scythe with blue jacket and puce flowered breeches, woman holding stick with puce coat and gilt flow-

ered skirt, scroll molded bases with applied flowers, c1755 . . . . **1,200.00**

Huntsman, 2¼", stepping through raised flowers, yellow pants, black boots, rose cape, green coat, carries brown and gold gun, c1755 . . **400.00**

Shepherd musicians, seated, pr, 9¼", man, pale green jacket, flowered breeches, playing bagpipes with dog by his side, lady in blue veil, striped dress, playing mandolin with lamb by her side, scroll molded base, applied flowering bocage, c1770 . . . . **1,300.00**

Needle Case, 4⅜", figural, half figure of woman on pedestal holding a basket of flowers, c1755 . . . . **2,600.00**

Plates

8¾", central flower with scattered insects, scroll molded border, gilted and painted with flower sprays, c1758 . . . . **375.00**

Plate, 9⅞", white ground, $95.00.

9⅝", Imari Brocade, chrysanthemum spray center, panels of diaper work and flowering plants, salmon, red, yellow, turquoise, green, and gold, c1756 . . . . **500.00**

Seal, ¾", heart resting on turquoise cushion with serpent wrapped around heart, inscribed "Je La Tien En Sebre," seal missing, c1755 . . . . . . **150.00**

Scent Bottles

2¾", figural, boy seated, playing bagpipes, turquoise pants, wine jacket, black hat, flame finial **1,100.00**

3¼", painted bird on branch front and back, applied gilt floral vines on sides, floral cluster shaped stopper, gold mounted, c1760 . . . . **600.00**

Teabowl and Saucer, scalloped gilt edge, painted with foilate sprays, c1754 **1,135.00**

Toy, Dalmation, ½", seated on green base edged with gold, c1765 . . . . . . **75.00**

"CHELSEA" GRANDMOTHER'S WARE

History: "Chelsea" Grandmother's ware identifies a group of tableware with raised reliefs of either grapes, sprigs of flowers, or thistles on a white ground. Some examples are lustred.

The ware was made in the first half of the 19th century in England's Staffordshire district by a large number of manufacturers. The "Chelsea" label is a misnomer, but commonly accepted in the antiques field.

Pitcher, 6¾" h, white ground, light purple decor, $60.00.

Bowl, 10", Grape, blue grape lustre dec	45.00
Butter Pat, Thistle	15.00
Cake Set, Sprig dec, blue lustre trim on all pieces, two 9¾" sq pedestal cake plates, creamer, cov sugar, nine 7" serving plates, nine cups and saucers	500.00
Creamer, Grape	45.00
Cups and Saucers	
Grape, handleless	30.00
Sprig	25.00
Plates	
6¾", Vintage, copper lustre	18.00
7½", Grape	10.00
8", Grape, lyre with wreath mark	10.00
10", Grape, lyre with wreath mark	15.00
Sandwich Plate, handles, scalloped edge, 9½", Sprig	20.00
Sauce Dish, Sprig	5.00
Sugars, cov	
Sprig, 7½"	110.00
Thistle	75.00
Teapot, cov, Grape	100.00
Tureen, cov, Grape, applied handles	75.00
Wash Bowl and Pitcher, 6½" d, 6" h, Grape	100.00

CHILDREN'S BOOKS

History: Because there is a bit of the child in all of us, collectors always have been attracted to children's books. In the 19th century books were popular gifts for children with most of the children's classics written and published during this time. These books were treasured and often kept throughout a lifetime.

Developments in printing made it possible to include more attractive black and white illustrations and color plates. The work of these artists and illustrators has added value beyond the text itself.

References: Barbara Bader, *American Picture Books From Noah's Ark To The Beast Within*, Macmillan, 1976; Virginia Haviland, *Children's Literature, A Guide To Reference Sources*, Library Of Congress, 1966, first supplement, 1972, second supplement, 1977.

Libraries: Free Library Of Philadelphia, PA; Library Of Congress, Washington, D.C.; Pierpont Morgan Library, New York, NY; Toronto Public Library, Toronto, Ontario, Canada.

Additional Listings: See *Warman's Americana & Collectibles* for more examples.

Note: dj = dust jacket; wraps = paper covers

Advisor: Margaret L. Tyrrell.

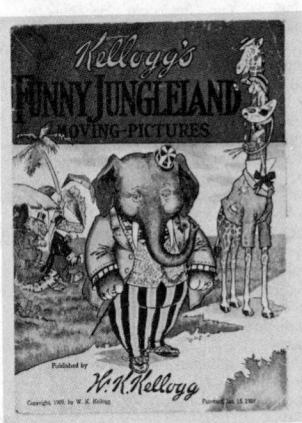

Kellogg's Funny Jungleland Moving Pictures. W. K. Kellogg, 1909, fold out, $15.00.

Adventures of Goody Two-Shoes And Her Brother Thomas. J. L. Marks, c1840, 8 pgs, hand colored, wraps	165.00
Anderson, Anne. *The Sleepy-Song-Book.* Harrap, c1910, 83 pgs	60.00
Aunt Louisa's Alphabet Book. F. Warne, c1870, unpaged	200.00

Barrie, J. M. *Peter Pan and Wendy.* Mabel Lucie Attwell, illus. Hodder & Stoughton, 1921, 186 pgs, 1st ed, dj **195.00**

Baum, L. Frank. *Ozma Of Oz.* John R. O'Neill, illus. Reilly & Britton, 1907, 270 pgs, 1st ed, 1st state **350.00**

Bemelmens, Ludwig. *The Golden Basket.* Viking, 1936, 96 pgs, 1st ed, dj . **50.00**

Bilibin, Ivan. *Vasilia Prekrasnaya (Vasilisa The Beautiful).* St. Petersburg, Russia, 1902, 12 pgs, 1st ed, wraps. **185.00**

Bradley, Will. *Peter Poodle: Toy Maker To The King.* Dodd, Mead, 1906, 166 pgs, 1st ed. **600.00**

Carroll, Lewis. *Through The Looking Glass And What Alice Found There.* Peter Newell, illus. Harper & Bros., 1902, 211 pgs, 1st ed, dj **115.00**

Cox, Palmer. *The Brownies: Their Book.* Century, 1887, 84 pgs, 1st ed, 2nd state, dj **125.00**

DeAngeli, Marguerite. *Book Of Nursery And Mother Goose Rhymes.* Doubleday, 1954, 192 pgs, 1st ed, dj, author sgd **55.00**

Disney, Walt. *A Mickey Mouse Alphabet From A To Z.* Whitman, 1936, unpaged, 1st ed.. .... **135.00**

Elkin, R. H. *The Children's Corner.* H. Willebeek LeMair, illus. Augener/McKay, 1915, unpaged, 1st ed, dj. . . **100.00**

Favorite Colored Picture Book. McLoughlin, c1870, 32 pgs. **75.00**

Field, Eugene. *Sugar Plum Tree And Other Verses.* Fern Bisel Peat, illus. Saalfield, 1930, unpaged **30.00**

Fryer, Jane Eayre. *Mary Frances Sewing Book.* Jane Allen Boyer, illus. Winston, 1913, 280 pgs, 1st ed **60.00**

Ga'g, Wanda. *The Funny Thing.* Coward-McCann, 1929, unpaged, 1st ed. . . . **65.00**

Godden, Rumer. *The Doll's House.* Tasha Tudor, illus. Viking, 1962, 136 pgs, 1st ed, dj. **35.00**

Greenaway, Kate. *Alphabet.* George Routledge, 1885, 32 pgs, 1st ed, wraps. **95.00**

Hawthorne, Nathaniel. *A Wonder Book For Boys And Girls.* Walter Crane, illus. Houghton Mifflin, 1893, 210 pgs, 1st ed. **125.00**

Heward, Constance. *Ameliaranne And The Green Umbrella.* Susan B. Pearse, illus. Jacobs, 1920, 121 pgs. **40.00**

Higgins, Violet Moore. *The Magic Circus.* Stanton, 1918, 164 pgs **50.00**

History Of The House That Jack Built, The. G. S. Peters, n.d., 18 pgs, hand colored, wraps **350.00**

Kingsley, Charles. *The Water Babies.* Ethel F. Everett, illus. John C. Winston, 1930, 228 pgs, 1st ed **50.00**

Krauss, Ruth. *A Hole Is To Dig.* Maurice Sendak, illus. Harper & Row, 1952, unpaged, 1st ed, dj **90.00**

Lamb, Charles and Mary. *Tales From Shakespeare.* Elizabeth Shippen Green, illus. McKay, 1922, 377 pgs, 1st ed **65.00**

Lang, Andrew. *Princess Nobody.* Richard Doyle, illus. Longmans, Green, c1880, 56 pgs, 1st ed **275.00**

Lowe, Constance M. *What A Surprise.* Nister, c1890, 16 pgs, movable **200.00**

MacDonald, George. *At The Back Of The North Wind.* Jessie Willcox Smith, illus. McKay, 1919, 342 pgs, 1st ed . **85.00**

MacKay, Hellen. *Stories For Pictures.* Dugald Stewart Walker, illus. Duffield, 1912, 168 pgs, 1st ed, dj.......... **65.00**

Mother Goose. *Foxy Grandpa's Mother Goose.* Bunny, illus. Frederick Stokes, 1903, 80 pgs, 1st ed **55.00**

Newell, Peter. *The Rocket Book.* Harper & Bros., 1912, unpaged, 1st ed **90.00**

Peat, Fern Bisel. *The Gingerbread Boy.* Whitman, 1941, unpaged, wraps.... **30.00**

Pogany, Willy. *Willy Pogany's Mother Goose.* Thomas Nelson, 1928, unpaged 1st ed **200.00**

Politi, Leo. *Song Of The Swallows.* Scribners, 1949, 32 pgs, 1st ed, dj, 1950 Caldecott Medal **25.00**

Potter, Beatrix. *The Tale Of Squirrel Nutkin.* Warne, 1903, unpaged, 1st ed . **200.00**

Thompson, Ruth P. *The Royal Book Of Oz.* John R. Neill, illus. Reilly & Lee, 1937, 312 pgs, 1st ed, 1st issue. . . **75.00**

Tom Thumb's Play-book. G. Angus, 1824, 48 pgs, wraps **190.00**

Tudor, Tasha. *Mother Goose.* Oxford Univ. Press, 1944, 87 pgs, dj, slipcase, limited edition of 500, sgd **400.00**

Wiggin, Kate Douglas. *Rebecca Of Sunnybrook Farm.* Houghton, Mifflin, 1903, 327 pgs, 1st ed, 1st state, sgd **135.00**

CHILDREN'S FEEDING DISHES

History: Unlike toy dishes meant for play, children's feeding dishes are the items actually used in the feeding of a child. Their colorful designs of animals, nursery rhymes, and children's activities are meant to appeal to the child and make meal times fun. Many plates have a unit to hold hot water, thus keeping the food warm.

Although glass and porcelain examples from the late 19th and early 20th century are most popular, collectors are beginning to seek some of the plastic examples from the 1920s to 40s, especially those with Disney designs on them.

Bowls

Dollie Dimples and Sammy, gold rim, mkd Buffalo Pottery, 7½″ **75.00**

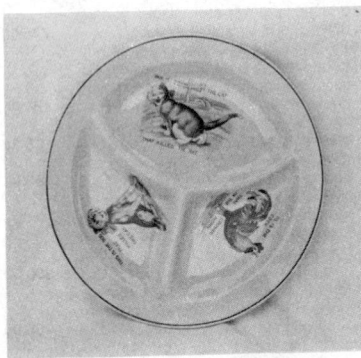

Three part dish, 7⅜″ d, decals, Roma, $50.00.

Mary Had A Little Lamb, white porcelain, scene, verse, chrome water jacket, spout and handles.	30.00
Old Mother Goose, Royal Doulton . .	15.00
Cereal Set, two children and dog sledding, Royal Bayreuth, 2 pcs	130.00
Creamer, rabbit dressed in red jacket, green band, Roseville	30.00

Feeding Dishes

Children swinging, playing with doll, horse on wheels, ABC's on side, mkd Germany	30.00
Dolly Dingle hunting with her dog, ABC border.	50.00
Little Birdies In The Nest	30.00

Mugs

China

2¼″, black transfer of "Faith" on one side, "Hope" on other, pink Lustre border	45.00
2¾″, comic, hp transfer of man falling off stool, "Devil Take The Stool," red line border.	75.00
2¾″, "Darling" in gold, children's scene, white ground, Germany. .	15.00
4¼″, 3¼″, barrel shape, blue and white pottery, "The Sisters," transfer on both sides, c1860 . .	125.00

Glass

Bryan, cov.	45.00
Little Boy Blue.	45.00
McKinley, open	35.00
Owl and Birds	30.00
Silver, "Old Mother Hubbard, Sing a Song of Sixpence," monogram MSN, mkd Gorham Sterling Silver.	225.00

Plates

6″, polychrome transfer of sleeping girls, angels, "Lay My Body Down To Sleep, Let Angels Guard . . ." .	55.00
6½″, Dr. Franklin, black line border, high relief, "It Is Hard For An Empty Bag To Stand Free," pawn shop scene	65.00
7″, "See Saw, Margery Daw," grill, green	25.00
Sets, cereal bowl, mug, and plate Bunnykins, Royal Doulton	90.00
Children Fishing, blue border, Noritake	50.00
Playful Dog, Warwick China	35.00

CHILDREN'S NURSERY ITEMS

History: The nursery is a place where children live in a miniature world. Things come in two sizes. Child scale designates items actually used for the care, housing, and feeding of the child. Toy or doll scale denotes items used by the child in play and for creating a fantasy environment which copies that of an adult or his own.

Cheap labor and building costs during the Victorian era enabled the nursery to reach a high level of popularity. Most collectors focus on items from the 1880 to 1930 period.

References: Doris Anderson Lechler, *Children's Glass Dishes, China, and Furniture,* Collector Books, 1983; Lorraine May Punchard, *Child's Play,* privately printed, 1982.

Additional Listings: Children's Books, Children's Feeding Dishes, Children's Toy Dishes, Dolls, Games, Miniatures, and Toys.

Baby Rattle, silver, whistle, dangling bells, pearl handle engraved "N.S.", 5¼″ l	100.00

Child's Captains chair, c1870, Maine, $125.00.

Beds

Doll, mahogany, well turned posts, shaped head and foot boards, old mattress, 13″ w, 23″ l. **155.00**

Youth

Rope, poplar, sq chamfered posts, scrollec head and footboards, orig rails and side guards, worn red paint, mattress size 26 x 45½″, 23½″ h **460.00**

Victorian, folding, walnut, straight slat sides, turned posts and finials. **250.00**

Blanket Chest, pine, sq posts, turned feet, lid edge moldings, old green repaint, 19½ x 12 x 12½″. **375.00**

Chairs

Ladderback armchair, worn splint seat, old red repaint, 27½″ h **325.00**

Windsor, birdcage, bamboo turnings, old dark paint finish, 12¼″ h seat, 27″ h overall **400.00**

Chest of Drawers, cherry and poplar, turned feet, paneled ends, 4 dovetailed drawers with cockbeading, orig porcelain pulls, orig finish, orig black paint on feet, 15¼ x 8¾ x 17″ **650.00**

Crib, folding, walnut, Victorian, high crested head end, rounded dowel side slats, turned finials **200.00**

Crib Quilt, Nine Patch, navy blue, white, and pink patches, line quilting, 22 x 25″, 19th C. **225.00**

Desk, walnut, top folds down to form table, pigeonholes, turned legs, 28 x 15¾ x 26″ **350.00**

Dresser, doll size, Victorian, walnut, 4 drawers and mirror in cut out frame, 10¾ x 5½ x 18¾″. **75.00**

Goat Cart, iron frame, wooden seat, wooden wheels with hard rubber treads, old worn yellow repaint, 51″ l **100.00**

High Chair, primitive, whittled legs and spindles, worn brown finish, 33½″ h. **125.00**

Hobby Horses

Bentwood frame, worn orig dapple gray, glass eyes, red dyed horsehair mane, tail, worn leather harness, worn blue velvet saddle, 36″ l. . . . **500.00**

Plush, wooden, black plush covering, glass eyes, purple plush saddle with multicolored string tassels, wooden frame painted red, yellow dec, 32″ l. **200.00**

Wooden, orig dapple gray paint, real painted harness and saddle, dark red rockers, 43″ l, 22″ h. **350.00**

Wooden, repainted white, black spots, red blanket, harness and saddle replaced, orig worn red paint and black stripes on base, 34½″ l **300.00**

Horse, wooden, riding toy, worn orig dapple gray paint on one side, green stem,

orange, yellow, and black wheels, 37″ l. **225.00**

Mule Chest, butternut and chestnut with turned feet, 2 dovetailed drawers, applied moulding, orig white porcelain pulls, 14½ x 7¼ x 11½″ **350.00**

Potty Chair, oak, pressed back, graniteware potty **85.00**

Rocker, ladderback armchair, worn red finish, worn splint seat, 20½″ h **80.00**

Sleds, wooden

Mortised and pinned construction, iron tipped runners, iron braces, old worn red paint, black and gold striping, 27″ l. **300.00**

Mortised and pinned construction, metal tipped wooden runners, worn orig floral and striping dec, 37″ l . . **200.00**

Sleigh, push, wooden, iron runners, bentwood and turned handles, folding leatherized cloth top, orig red paint, black and white striping, 56″ l **300.00**

Table, oak, 14 x 21¾ x 14″. **75.00**

Wagon, wooden, mortised construction, iron rim spoke wheels, flat bed, weathered finish, traces of red paint, 16 and 18″ d wheels, 41″ l plus tongue **85.00**

Wagon Seat, dark green paint, black and yellow striping, 10½″ w, 19½″ d **80.00**

Walker, wooden, round hoop base, round baby holder, round play tray, wooden seat fastened by springs and leather straps **150.00**

CHILDREN'S TOY DISHES

History: Dishes made for children often served a dual purpose–play things and a means of learning social graces. Dish sets came in two sizes. The first was for actual use by the child when entertaining her friends. The second, a smaller size than the first, was for use with dolls.

Children's dish sets often were made as a side line to a major manufacturing line either as a complement to the family service or as a way to use up the last of the day's batch of materials. The artwork of famous illustrators, such as Palmer Cox, Kate Greenaway, and Rose O'Neill, can be found on porcelain sets.

References: Doris Anderson Lechler, *Children's Glass Dishes, China and Furniture,* Collector Books, 1983; Lorraine May Punchard, *Child's Play,* Lorraine May Punchard, 1982; Margaret & Kenn Whitmyer, *Children's Dishes,* Collector Books, 1984.

Akro Agate

Bowl, Plain Jane, green **5.00**

Cup and Saucer, Interior Panel, opaque, pumpkin **25.00**

Plate, Oxblood & Lemonade, octagonal **15.00**

Tea Set, Trans-Optic, Interior Panel,
jade, cov teapot, creamer, cov
sugar, 4 cereal bowls, cups, sau-
cers, and plates, 21 pcs **125.00**

China

Allerton, "Punch," teapot, creamer,
sugar, 6 cups, saucers, and plates,
22 pcs **85.00**

Noritake, robin's egg blue decor, service for 4, mkd M in green wreath,
15 pcs **125.00**

Unmarked, gold band, 6" teapot,
creamer, sugar, 6 cups, saucers,
and plates, 22 pcs **65.00**

**Porcelain, Japanese Tea Set, 8 x 12", 11
pcs, $35.00.**

Depression Glass

Creamer, Cherry Blossom, pink 25.00
Cup, Doric & Pansy, teal 25.00
Pitcher, Doric & Pansy, pink 25.00

Plates

Cherry Blossom, delphite 10.00
Laurel, scotty dog decal 20.00

Sets

Little Hostess, Hazel Atlas, 14 pcs,
orig box 70.00
Little Hostess Party Set, Modern-
tone, bulbous coffee pot, sugar,
creamer, 4 cups, saucers, and
plates, orig box. 95.00

Graniteware, gray, tea set 90.00

Milk Glass

Stein, Monk's, rings on top 25.00
Table Set, Thumbelina, butter,
creamer, and sugar 40.00

Pattern Glass

Berry Set, Lacy Daisy, clear, 7 pcs . .   65.00
Butter, cov, Tulip & Honeycomb 30.00

Castor Sets

3 bottles, Drape, wire holder 75.00
4 bottles, American Shield 90.00

Creamers

Hobnail, Northwood, opal 50.00
Menagerie, owl 85.00

Mug, Wee Branches **20.00**

Pitchers

Banded Portland, yellow stain
decor **35.00**
Waffle & Button **25.00**

Punch Bowls

Inverted Strawberry **40.00**
Wheat Sheaf, Cambridge **30.00**
Whirligig **20.00**

Punch Bowl Set, Pinwheel, 6 cups . .   **70.00**

Spooners

Inverted Strawberry **40.00**
Sawtooth Mitered Corner **30.00**
Tappan **15.00**
Tulip & Honeycomb **20.00**

Sugar, cov, Alabama **80.00**

Table Sets, butter, creamer, sugar,
and spooner

Duncan & Miller #42 . . . .   **125.00**
Lion's Head **250.00**
Sweetheart **65.00**

Tray, round, Doyle's 500, vaseline . .   **30.00**
Tumbler, Pattec Cross **10.00**

Spatter, handleless cup and saucer,
blue **65.00**

Spongeware, blue on white, tea set of
teapot, sugar, creamer, and 2 cups
and saucers **350.00**

Tin, cookware, 6 pcs, early 1900 . . . . .   **20.00**

White Patterned Ironstone, tea set [cov
teapot, creamer, cov sugar, waste
bowl, 4 cups, saucers, and tea plates],
grape leaves around handles, berry
finials, 18 pcs **135.00**

CHRISTMAS ITEMS

History: The celebration of Christmas dates
back to Roman times. Several customs associated
with modern Christmas celebrations date back to
the early pagan rituals.

Father Christmas, believed to have evolved in
Europe in the 7th Century, was a combination of
the pagan god Thor, who judged both the good and
punished the bad, and St. Nicholas, the generous
Bishop of Myra. Kris Kringle originated in Germany
and was brought to America by the Germans and
Swiss who settled in Pennsylvania in the late 18th
Century.

In 1822 Clement C. Moore wrote "A Visit From
St. Nicholas" and developed the character of Santa
Claus into what we know today. Thomas Nast did
a series of drawings for Harper's Weekly from 1863
until 1886 and further solidified the character and
appearance of Santa Claus.

Reference: Maggie Rogers and Judith Hawkins,
The Glass Christmas Ornament, Old and New, Tim-
ber Press, 1979; Maggie Rogers and Peter R. Hal-
linan, *The Santa Claus Picture Book: An Appraisal
Guide*, Dutton 1984.

Additional Listings: See *Warman's Americana
& Collectibles* for more examples.

Candy Container, Santa Claus, 9½", composition body, $275.00.

Bank, 8" h, painted plaster, Santa sleeping on overstuffed chair **65.00**

Biscuit Tin, 8" d, litho, Santa with pack full of toys over shoulder, mkd Huntley & Palmer **35.00**

Candy Containers

  Father Christmas, 12" h, crepe paper and cotton costume, white ground, gold snowflakes dec, painted plaster feet and face **225.00**

  Reindeer, 8" l, painted papier mache, glass eyes, painted metal antlers .   **175.00**

  St. Nicholas, 14½" h, papier mache, stern molded face, painted facial features, fluffy white mohair wig and beard, hollow cardboard torso, orig red flannel suit and cap, gray trousers, green bough in one hand, tin pail in other, mkd Germany, c1890 . . . .   **275.00**

  St. Nicholas and Reindeer, 20" l, papier mache, painted facial features, hollow torso, orig costume, seated on rough hewn sleigh pulled by pr of plush cov papier mache reindeer, elaborate harnesses, metal antlers, reindeer heads remove to form candy containers, c1890 . . . .   **600.00**

Card, 10¼ x 13", turn wheel, open windows, close up of Santa, sgd Tony Sarg, 1941, B. F. Jay **35.00**

Creche Figures, pr, 18", wood carved and sculpted, painted facial features, hair, wire armature body, one is elderly man, long gray carved beard, other is man with short page boy hair style, middle aged features, short beard, Italian, 17th C **475.00**

Doll, Santa, 12", vinyl swivel head, molded features, 5 pc body, fur mustache, beard, red felt suit, Steiff yellow paper label on wrist **325.00**

Father Christmas, 10" h, painted papier mache, white costume, glitter trim . .   **350.00**

Game, The Christmas Tree Game, Parker Bros., litho paper on wood, 20 x 24" **200.00**

Ice Cream Mold, 11", Santa, pewter . . .   **100.00**

Kerchief, 17 x 24", litho, Santa in center, various scenes in corners **250.00**

Puzzle, cube, 10 x 12", The Night Before Christmas, Santa Claus, 5 picture sheets, McLoughlin **400.00**

Santas

  19", wooden, hand carved, jolly face, applied wooden bushy eyebrows, mustache and beard with frosted wax surface, intaglio blue eyes, tan cloth suit, white cotton and fur trim, wooden knob on back makes beard go up and down, American, 19th C.   **500.00**

  22", painted papier mache, cloth costume, working clockwork, German   **1,400.00**

  27", papier mache, standing, painted facial features, fluffy white mohair beard, orig red flannel hooded jacket, white fur trim, tin lantern hung around neck, mounted on snow cov base **1,100.00**

Santas in Sleighs

  11", wood and straw sleigh on wooden base, flocked reindeer with metal antlers, painted papier mache Santa, glitter and rabbit fur trim . . .   **500.00**

  18", Bliss litho on wood, Santa in sleigh, pr of reindeer **1,500.00**

Stocking, 27" l, litho design on both sides **300.00**

Store Window Display, 19½" h, wood and paper, clockwork, Santa face above fireplace, orig box **350.00**

Toys

  Delivery Wagon, 29" l, painted wood wagon, cloth cov horse with glass eyes on platform, sign on wagon "St. Claus - Dealer in Good Things" **750.00**

  Santa and Sleigh, 16" l, painted cast iron, red Santa, blue sleigh, white reindeer, Hubley **550.00**

Tree Lights

  Blown

    2⅞", emerald green, expanded 12 diamond with folded rim **75.00**

    3", puce, expanded diamond design, pontiled, folded rim **125.00**

    3⅜", light blue, DQ, pontiled with flared rim **75.00**

Figural
Lantern, hp, Japanese style	15.00
Santa, 4″.	40.00
Snowman	20.00

Tree Ornaments
Bird House with birds, 2⅞″, silver with polychrome dec.	25.00
Clown with banjo, 4⅛″, amber with olive green dec	25.00
Cockatoo, 6¼″, silver, red, and green, angel hair tail.	40.00
Girl in red hood, 3″, glass, glass eyes	50.00
Girl in rose, 3″, glass, pink dec.	80.00
Ice Skater, 6″, magenta costume trimmed in cotton fur and glitter . .	40.00
Man's Face, 3″, glass, triangular. . . .	110.00
Owl, 6½″, silver, gold wash with pink and blue dec, angel hair tail	30.00
Parrot, 7½″, silver with green and magenta, angel hair tail, tin clip	25.00
Santa Riding Hot Air Balloon, 5½″ h, glass, tinsel, and litho paper	80.00
Snake, 5½″, glass, twisted.	50.00
Turnip, 7″, glass, green silk top	60.00
Tree Stand, 11″ d, tin, wood, working clockwork, German	150.00
Tree Top Ornament, angel, 8¾″, printed and gilded, angel hair dec	45.00
Wall Plaque, 24″ h, Santa face, painted plaster, applied cotton beard and eyebrows	50.00

CIGAR CUTTERS

History: Counter and pocket cigar cutters were used at the end of the 19th and the beginning of the 20th century. They were a popular form of advertising. Pocket type cigar cutters often were a fine piece of jewelry that was attached to a watch chain.

Counter Type, 5 x 6½ x 3″, The Brunhoff Mfg. Co, Cincinnati, OH, $110.00.

COUNTER TOP

Advertising
Boston Trader.	185.00
Cuban Blossom, nickle font, built-in lighter	165.00
Harvester, glass, mechanical	200.00
Rogers Iron Co., Springfield, OH, cast iron halberd replica, wooden handle, 20½″ l	100.00
Spearhead Tobacco, J. P. Sorg Co., cast iron	75.00

Figural
Monkey, metal, sits on creamy onyx base, holds brass cutter over head, 5½″ h	175.00
Stag's head, brass	180.00
Wooden, cherry base, cuts 3 cigars at once	300.00

POCKET

Advertising
Bayuk Cigars, Phila, PA, c1929.	20.00
El Roi-Tan, "The JHA", SP, engraved, 1″ w, 1¾″ l	20.00
Funk, dated 1872	45.00
Morrel's Fine Hams.	20.00
Osmond Cigar Superior, 10¢—$1.00, 1913.	25.00
Pure Food Gelatin.	15.00

Knife Types
Gold filled, bell shaped portion pulls up, ribbed ring, 1″ w, 1½″ l.	25.00
Pearl handle, ring for hanging on watch chain.	35.00

Silver Plated
German castle scene, watch chain type.	20.00
Two blades, patent RR Johnstone, 2½″ l	20.00
Stag horn grip, chrome	25.00
Sterling Silver, mkd Kut Rite.	45.00

CIGAR STORE FIGURES

History: Cigar store figures were familiar sights in front of cigar stores and tobacco shops from about 1840. Figural themes included Sir Walter Raleigh, sailors, minstrels, ladies, and Indians, the most popular.

Most figures were carved in wood, although figures also were made in metal and papier mache for a short time. Most carvings were life size or slightly smaller and brightly painted. A coating of tar acted as a preservative against the weather. Of the few surviving figures, only a small number have their original bases. Most replacements are due to years of wear and usage by dogs.

Use of figures declined when local ordinances were passed requiring shop keepers to move the figures inside at night. This soon became too much trouble, and other forms of advertising developed.

Indians

Chief, full length, carved from single pine plank, wearing feathered headdress, yellow fringed green costume, holding a tobacco leaf in one hand, a pipe in other hand, shaped base, painted on both sides, 67″ h, c1860 . . . . **2,500.00**

Maiden, full length, carved in full round, wearing large feather headdress, holding a bunch of cigars, standing on sq plinth, mounted on pedestal, inscribed "CIGARS", 56¼″ h **900.00**

Princess, full length, carved in full round, wearing a feathered red and green headdress, deep yellow costume trimmed in red and gold, embellished with feathers, holding a rose in one hand, several packets of cigars in other, packet inscribed "Cigars 5¢", on plaster sq base, 61″ h, attributed to Samuel Robb, NY, c1880 . . . . **5,000.00**

Scout, full length, carved in full round, wearing feathered headdress, painted red, green and gold, lion skin mantle, fringed costume, holding bunch of cigars in one hand, other raised to shade his eyes, mounted on plaster block in trapeziodal base painted "This Is Muellers, Pipe Repairing", on wheels, 88″ h, attributed to Samuel Robb Shop, NY, c1886 . . . . **25,500.00**

Scout, single board carved in relief on both sides, tall feathered headdress, blue cloak, yellow-brown fox skin, holding a band of cigars in one hand and a calumet in other, 48¼″ h, c1850 . . . . **5,000.00**

Warrior, cast zinc, full length, wearing feathered headdress with traces of blue paint, flowing red painted cloak, green painted cloth held in place with belt, sheated dagger, silver painted arm bracelet, gold painted necklace with portrait bust of Lincoln, standing on vanquished prey, orig maker's plaque inscribed "Wm. Demuth & Co., Manufrs., 501 Broadway, New York", 68½″ h, c1870 . . . . **11,000.00**

Lincoln, full round carving, life size. . . . **8,000.00**

William Penn, papier mache, standing against tree trunk, scroll in one hand, box of Wm Penn Cigars in other, 63″ h. Theobold & Oppenheimer, c1900. **700.00**

Punch, carved in full round, brightly painted, cigars in one hand **6,000.00**

Warrior, polychrome, 108″ h, $11,000.00.

CINNABAR

History: Cinnabar is a ware made of numerous layers of a heavy mercuric sulfide and often referred to as vermilion, the red hue in which it is most commonly found. It was carved into boxes, buttons, snuff bottles, and vases. The best examples were made in China.

Bowl, cov, 7″ d, 4″ h, carved, scenic . . **400.00**

Boxes

5¾ x 4 x 2½″, deeply carved flowers, cov with Greek key border, peonies and birds, brass base, emb brass seal, mkd **125.00**

7 x 7″, hexagonal, carved, 3 Oriental figures in garden scene **135.00**

16″ d, flattened ball shape, carved, Oriental scene **700.00**

Button, ¾″ d, carved lotus flower. **35.00**

Jars, covered

6″, pr, carved, continuous landscape, Oriental figures in garden **125.00**

15¾″, stand, carved, continuous landscape, Chinese figures, flowerheads on cov and stand. **500.00**

Plate, 8″, carved, garden scene with house and bridge **225.00**

Snuff Bottle, 2¾″, carved, scenic, 2 Oriental figures, trees and florals, late 19th C **275.00**

Bracelet, 7½", plus clasp, mkd "China", $85.00.

Table, 5" h, 12½" d, sq, carved, scenic, Oriental figures and trees, Chinese . .	**800.00**
Tray, 12", oval, carved, dragons in clouds, late 19th C	**300.00**
Vases	
9", carved, scenic, Oriental figures and flowers, c1750.	**200.00**
48¾", pr, baluster shape, carved, panels of sages in forests and groves, smaller bird and flower panels, lotus scrolls, floral lappet borders, scroll feet, early 19th C . .	**15,500.00**

CLAMBROTH GLASS

History: Clambroth glass is an semi-opaque, grayish-white glass which resembles the color of the broth from clams. Pieces are found in both a smooth finish and a rough sandy finish. Sandwich Glass Co. and other manufacturers made clambroth glass.

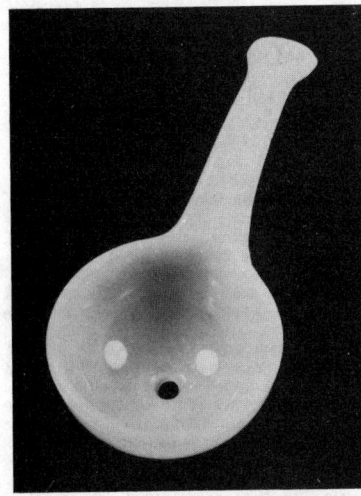

Pickle Dipper, 9½", $30.00.

Animal Dish, cov, nesting hen, 7½" l, 5½" h	**225.00**
Bowls	
Center, cranberry edge	**100.00**
Oval, Horn of Plenty pattern.	**100.00**
Candlesticks	
6⅞" h, pr, Loop and Petal, slight chips, Sandwich, c1840	**150.00**
9¼", columnar, petal top, rough sandy finish, Sandwich.	**125.00**
10", dolphin, double step base.	**200.00**
Dish, oval, Horn of Plenty pattern	**200.00**
Funnel, blown	**140.00**
Lamp, whale oil, 11" h, Star & Punty pattern, rough sandy finish, Sandwich, c1840.	**300.00**
Mug, Peacock and Stork pattern	**45.00**
Salt, Stag's Horn, lacy, Boston & Sandwich Co.	**130.00**
Spill Holder, Vine pattern, Sandwich. . .	**350.00**
Sugar, cov, Gothic Arches, Sandwich, c1830.	**350.00**

CLEWELL POTTERY

History: Charles Walter Clewell was first a metal worker and second a potter. In the early 1900s he opened a small shop in Canton, Ohio, to produce metal overlay pottery.

Metal on pottery was not a new idea, but Clewell was perhaps the first to completely mask the ceramic body with copper, brass, "silvered" and "bronzed" metals. One result was a product whose patina added to the character of the piece over time.

Most of the wares are marked with a simple incised "CLEWELL" along with a code number. Because Clewell used pottery blanks from other firms, the names "Owens" or "Weller" are sometimes found.

Because Clewell operated on a small scale with little outside assistance, a limited quantity of his art work exists. He retired at the age of 79 in 1955, choosing not to reveal his technique to anyone else.

References: Paul Evans, *Art Pottery of the United States,* Everybodys Press, Inc., 1974; Ralph and Terry Kovel, *The Kovel's Collector's Guide To American Art Pottery,* Crown Publishers, Inc., 1974.

Ashtray, 1¼ x 3¾", copper, 1922 imp mark in circle reads "Clewell, Canton, Ohio".	**150.00**
Bowl, 1½ x 4½", riveted overlay finish, sgd with circular imp "Clewell Coppers" seal.	**200.00**
Candlesticks, pr, 9½" h, 1" round standard, 4" round pedestal base, blue-green patina	**350.00**
Ewer, 5¾", paneled, bronze clad	**200.00**
Tobacco Jar, 6 x 8", cov, hammered and riveted design, dark brown patina . . .	**600.00**

Vase, 4¾", mkd 2/Owens/120, $400.00.

Vases
4", bud, green patina	**125.00**
10", jug shape, copper, butterfly design of brass inlay	**600.00**

CLIFTON

CLIFTON POTTERY

History: The Clifton Art Pottery, Newark, New Jersey, was established by William A. Long, once associated with Londhuna Pottery, and Fred Tschirner, a chemist.

Production consisted of two major lines: Crystal Patina, which resembled true porcelain with a subdued crystal like glaze, and Indian Ware or Western Influence, an adaptation of the American Indians' unglazed and decorated pottery with a high glazed black interior. Other lines included Robin's Egg Blue and Tirrube. Robin's Egg Blue is a variation of the crystal patina line but in blue-greens instead of straw colored hues and with a less prominent "crushed crystal" effect in the glaze. Tirrube is on a terra cotta ground, features brightly colored, slip decorated flowers, and is often artist signed.

Marks are incised or impressed. Early pieces may be dated and shape numbers impressed. Indian wares are identified by tribes.

Bowls
3½" d, 2½" h, red clay body, feather design, glazed black interior, Indian Ware.	**140.00**
6", Tirrube	**80.00**

Candlesticks, 9½" h, pr, Indian Ware, incised "Pueblo Viejo, Arizona," artist
sgd, c1906	**125.00**
Jar, cov, 7½", Indian Ware	**85.00**
Mug, 4", Indian Ware	**50.00**
Pitcher, Indian Ware, artist sgd	**75.00**

Teapots
5½" h, cov, finial, matte finish, yellow-green glaze, stamp mark, imp Clifton Pottery, #272-42	**145.00**
8", tan drip on green ground	**100.00**

Vases
6", bud, Crystal Patina, flambe green lip, yellow glaze inside and out, copper crystalline glaze, nearly white ground, c1906	**275.00**
9" h, 5" d, Tirrube	**145.00**

Humidor, Indian Ware, 4¼" h, 4½" d, brown, $50.00.

CLOCKS

History: The sundial was the first man-made device for measuring time. Its basic disadvantage is well expressed in the saying: "Do like the sundial, count only the sunny days."

With need for greater dependability, man developed the water clock, oil clock, and the sand clock respectively. All these clocks worked on the same principle—time was measured by the amount of material passing from one container to another.

The wheel clock was the next major step. These clocks can be traced back to the 13th century. Many improvements on the basic wheel clock were made and continue to be made. In 1934 the quartz crystal movement was introduced.

Recently an atomic clock that measures time by the frequency of radiation, that only varies one second in a thousand years, has been invented.

Identifying the proper model name for a clock is

critical in establishing price. Condition of works also is a critical factor. Examine the works to see how many original parts remain. If repairs are needed, try to include this in your estimate of purchase price. Few clocks are purchased purely for decorative value.

References: Roy Ehrhardt, *Clock Identification And Price Guide: Book I,* rev. ed., Heart of America Press, 1979; Roy Ehrhardt, *Clock Identification And Price Guide: Book II,* Heart of America Press, 1979; Roy Ehrhardt, ed., *The Official Price Guide To Antique Clocks,* House of Collectibles, second ed., 1984; Robert W. Miller, *Clock Guide: Identification With Prices,* Wallace-Homestead, 1981; Anita Schorsch, *The Warner Collector's Guide To American Clocks,* Main Street Press, 1981; Alan and Rita Shenton, *The Price Guide To Clocks, 1840-1940,* Antique Collectors' Club, 1977.

Collectors' Club: National Association of Watch and Clock Collectors, Inc., P. O. Box 33, Columbia, PA 17512. Dues: $20.00. *Bulletin* (bimonthly).

Museum: Museum of National Association of Watch and Clock Collectors, Columbia, PA.

MISCELLANEOUS

Advertising
Finzer, John & Bros, Louisville, KY, "Jolly Tar Pastime, Old Honesty, Plank Road," tobacco manuf	**1,100.00**
Schmidt, E. & Co., harness manuf, Baird Cloth Co., Seth Thomas movement, 30½"	**1,500.00**

Alarm
Ansonia, c1890, Peep-O-Day, nickel, 1 day, repeating strike, 4".......	**100.00**
Gilbert, W. L. Clock Co., c1896, basket alarm, brass, 1 day, basketwork sides, 6¼"..................	**75.00**
Ingraham, E, c1917, Premier Intermittent, solid brass, 8 day, 7½".....	**50.00**
Jennings Bros, Waterbury movement, 2" porcelain dial, plain case with semi-circular pediment, base and top have leaf band molding, 5½" .	**65.00**
Kroeber, Florence, c1888, Watermill, nickel, animated water wheel, 4" dial......................	**250.00**
Thomas, Seth, c1910, Mode, dresser type, metal case with relief floral motif, 3" dial	**45.00**
Waterbury, c1930, Trusty, 1 day, metal case, bell on top, independent second dial, 4" dial	**60.00**

Novelties, Figural
Child sleeping by basket, Ansonia, bisque, 1 day, 5½".............	**100.00**
Elephant, French, gilt dial in cylindrical case by Pignot of Paris, white porcelain elephant on shaped rococo style gilt-bronze base, surmounted by porcelain figure of Chinese man, 18"......................	**2,250.00**

Rabbit, white, from Alice in Wonderland, Terry Clock, Waterbury, CT, c1870, 30 hour brass movement, cast metal painted figure on wooden base, blinking eyes, 12 x 5½ x 3".	**750.00**
Railroad wagon, gilt-metal wagon with fixed wheels on tracks, slate base, loaded with 3 rope tied kegs forming clock, thermometer, and barometer, c1900	**700.00**

Advertising, wall, $400.00.

Violin, Seth Thomas Co., Thomaston, CT, c1890, violin shaped wooden case with applied leaf carving, glass panel with gilt dec, 29 x 13½"....	**1,200.00**
Zappler, miniature, 4 wheel movement, front mounted pendulum, chased scrollwork, engraved flowers and leaves, glass dome, fitted leather case, 1½"	**1,650.00**

SHELF AND MANTEL

Beehive
Ansonia, Tudor, 8 day, strike, veneered case, floral and Roman pillar motif, 19"	**250.00**
Brown, J. C., Bristol, CT, 8 day, rosewood, ornate molding..........	**700.00**
Jennings Bros, Brush Brass Novelty No. B5437, filigree panel beneath face, 5"....................	**80.00**
New Haven, Gothic, 1 day, strike, veneered, fruit motif, 19¼"........	**150.00**
Welch, E. N. Co., late 19th C, 30 hour time, strike and alarm, mahogany, 18¾"	**250.00**

Box or Cottage

Ansonia, c1910, Island, 8 day, strike, veneered, 9½″ **140.00**

Gilbert, Wm. L. Clock Co., Rose Cottage Time, 30 hour, gilt rose dec, 9⅞ x 7¾″ **100.00**

Jerome & Co., New Haven, CT, c1850, No. 2 Model, pine case, painted wheat dec, 30 hour brass spring movement, alarm, 11¾ x 7¾ x 3½″ **200.00**

Thomas, Seth, Concord Sessions, 8 day, mahogany, 13 x 9¾″ **150.00**

Waterbury Clock Co., Waterbury, CT, c1858, 30 hour brass spring movement, alarm, painted green wood case, 12 x 8 x 3½″ **175.00**

Bracket

Bosley, Joseph, London, c1750, George II, crown wheel escapement, musical, mahogany and gilt bronze bell topped case, pineapple finials, 21¼″ **3,850.00**

Monkhouse, John, London, mid 18th C, George II, ebony, Grande Sonnerie, arched case surmounted by ormolu cock, top and sides with pierced and engraved sound panels, floral sprays and flowerheads, 4 acorn finials, gilt metal chutes on corners cast as pendant fruited and flowered vines, scrolled feet, mounted with brass loop handles, 20½″ h **5,000.00**

Payne, London, c1810, Regency, gilt bronze mounted burr yew wood, anchor escapement, glazed on all sides, fluted border at top, ogee molded base, 4 gilt ball feet, acanthus chased bail handle, 10″ **2,000.00**

Smith, William, London, George I, red lacquer, 6⅝″ silver dial, pendulum aperature, rect case with arched top, glazed on 4 sides, molded base, low bracket feet, 19″ **3,100.00**

Calendar

Ansonia, Banker's inkstand, 1 day, bronze with nickel finish, Egyptian motif, 12″ **375.00**

Brocot, A. & Delettrez, Paris, c1900, brass, patented escapement, white enamel dial with recessed center enameled with sky scene, moon phases, day and date dials, 12¾″ **1,000.00**

Ingraham, E., Urania, 8 day, half hour strike, thermometer and barometer, oak, 25″ **250.00**

Ithaca, Octagon No. 11, 8 day strike, mahogany veneer, 21″ **800.00**

Waterbury, Office Calendar, Double Dial No. 40, time, strike, alarm, walnut, 24″ **625.00**

Carriage

Black Starr & Forest, c1900, champleve enamel, platform lever movement, porcelain dial, multicolored, 5½″ **1,200.00**

Bohler, F., Frankfurt, c1890, Grande Sonnerie, gilt metal, gilt platform lever movement, repeating, alarm, 5¼″ **1,800.00**

Le Roy et Fils, c1900, gilt metal, detached lever movement, alarm, patented bottom wind, fitted leather case, 5¼″ **1,400.00**

Limoges, 1898, Grande Sonnerie, gilt metal, platform lever movement, repeating, alarm, case with four free standing columns with corinthian capitals and acanthus chased urn

Shelf clocks (left) Gingerbread, Ingraham, Lion, 8-day, T & S, pressed oak, $300.00: (center) Massachusettes, Eli Terry & Sons, 8-day, Plymouth, CT, $450.00; (right) Ogee, Seth Thomas, 9″, $125.00.

finials, sides inset with enamel panels painted with classical women holding a jewel box, basket of flowers, gilt highlights, maroon ground, fitted leather case with key, 6¾″ **10,000.00**

Unknown, Grande Sonnerie, late 19th C, engraved oval case, detailed platform lever movement, alarm, 5½″ **2,400.00**

Voak, London, c1840, gilt metal, engraved, diamond endstone, lever movement mounted on back, 4¾″. **1,210.00**

Column, French, Charles X, mid 19th Mantel, gilt bronze, white marble set with finely chased bronze mounts in classical style, 4 pad feet, 19½″ .. **770.00**

Unknown maker, gilt bronze mounted mahogany, sq pediment applied with gilt, chased pendulum and key, 24″ h **800.00**

Crystal Regulator

Ansonia, Crystal Palace No. 2, 8 day, half hour striker, mirrors reflecting figure, 20″ **650.00**

Gilbert, W., L. Tunis, 8 day, half hour strike **675.00**

Waterbury, Bordeau, gold plated, 8 day, half hour strike **850.00**

Figural

French, late 19th C, gilt bronze mounted onyx, green, surmounted by putto, 24½″ h **1,320.00**

Louis XVI, last quarter 19th C, ormolu and marble, circular white enamel dial with black Roman and Arabic numerals, 2 train movement striking hour and half hour, drum shaped case flanked by seated female figure above bow front base flanked by laurel garlands, white marble base with ormolu flowerheads, raised on toupie feet, 13 x 11¼″.. **1,100.00**

Viennese Neoclassical, 1st quarter 19th C, ormolu, face inset with white enamel chapter ring, flanked by figures striking quarters on bells, 3 train movement within octagonal case fitted with masks, claw feet, 13 x 7½″ **1,320.00**

Figure Eight, Ingraham Co, Bristol, CT, Victorian, rosewood, 16¼″ **150.00**

Gingerbread

Ansonia, c1885, ash and black trimming, 8 day strike, 6″ dial, 22″ ... **200.00**

Gilbert, Wm. L. Clock Co.

Excelsior No. 2, c1899, oak, 8 day half hour strike, 16½″ **200.00**

Hawk, c1896, walnut, 8 day strike, 6″ dial, spider web dec on blass, 22″ h................... **185.00**

Ingraham

Cayuga, c1905, solid oak, 8 day, half hour strike, emb, 22″ **200.00**

Niagara, c1905, oak, 8 day, half hour strike, 23″............ **185.00**

New Haven Clock Co.

Councilman, c1920, oak, 8 day, half hour strike, emb glass, 22″ **225.00**

Kitchen Oak, c1882, press molded case, wood ball finials, 8 day brass spring driven movement .. **250.00**

Patrol, c1900, walnut, potted plant dec on glass, 22¾ x 14¼ **200.00**

Thomas, Seth

Golden Oak, c1904, 8 day, half hour, 25″ **210.00**

Harvard, c1910, oak, 8 day, cathedral bell, 23″ **200.00**

Waterbury, Ideal O, black walnut, 8 day, cathedral gong, wire bell **300.00**

Welch, E. N., c1880, walnut, 8 day, white dial, brass alarm bell, 23⅜ x 14½ x 15⅛″ **250.00**

Mantel

Brush Brass, B5436, Waterbury movements, 5½″ **65.00**

Thomas, Seth

Paris, dull gold plated brass, 15 day, 8½″.................. **200.00**

Tambour, c1900, pine and rosewood veneer case, brass movement, 9½ x 19½ x 5½″....... **100.00**

Brown, E. A. Co., Chelsea Clock Co., Boston, MA, c1910, fruitwood case, 8 day movement **75.00**

Tiffany & Co., c1915, gilt and enameled bronze, circular face within octagonal geometric devices, octagonal cast base with drapery swags and acanthus borders, blue enamel, face imp "Tiffany & Co./New York", base imp "Tiffany Studios/New York/1870″, 10¾″............ **1,650.00**

Waterbury Clock Co., 1930, Ship's Wheel dial, oak and brass case, 10 x 18 x 3¾″ **50.00**

Massachusetts Shelf

Balch, Daniel, Jr., Newburyport, MA, c1790, Federal, mahogany, two sets of reeded pilasters, lower door with keystone and arch, scrolled pediment, plinth with brass urn and flame finials, brass dial, 28½ x 12 x 6″....................... **12,000.00**

Reuben Tower, Hingham, MA, c1836, stenciled tablet with lyre spandrels, dished painted metal dial, 8 day weights **7,500.00**

Thomas, Seth, Plymouth, mahogany, 8 day, half hour strike, 24″ **200.00**

Willard, Aaron, Boston, MA, c1815, Federal, carved mahogany, shaped crest, hinged door below with eglomise panel, painted with lyre and foliate motifs in polychrome, circular mirror plate, convex shaped

base, gilt metal ball feet, 37 x 13 x
5½″ **11,000.00**

Metal Faced
Brass, Brush Brass, c1912, round top,
emb band, alarm, 5½″ **75.00**

Bronze
Ansonia, Composer, 8 day, half hour
strike, Japanese bronze finish,
11½″ **275.00**
Gilbert, Wm. L. Clock Co.
Mignon, c1900, marbleized base,
12 x 14¼″ **225.00**
Sportsman, c1920, marbleized
base, 13½ x 14″ **250.00**
Jennings Bros, No. 68, Art Nou-
veau, seated lady in flowing robe,
arm resting on clock, 1 day,
10½″ **200.00**
New Haven, Flute Player, gilt finish,
8 day, half hour strike, 16″ **250.00**
Thomas, Seth, Art Nouveau, woman
standing behind block, supported
on flowing leaf & stand, 1 day, 11″ **100.00**

Iron or Pot Metal
American Clock Co., New York,
NY, c1850, Victorian, Egyptian
motif, gilt metal, 30 hour move-
ment, 15½ x 10½ x 4″ **200.00**
Ansonia, c1900, gilt bust of St. Clair,
11¼ x 10½″ **225.00**
Bradley and Hubbard, John Bull,
blinking eye, 8 day, painted **750.00**
Jennings Bros, Waterbury move-
ment, 1906, gilt finish, emb cherries, leaves, 1 day, 2 inch ivory
dial, 7″ **85.00**
Kroeber, F, Gothic, MOP inlay, 8
day, 12″ **185.00**

Mirror Side
Ansonia, Windsor, silvered cupids,
bronze ornaments, 8 day, strike,
21½″ **375.00**
Gilbert, Wm. L., walnut, cherubs, 8
day **400.00**

Ogee
Ansonia, veneered case, putti with
garland in cameo reserve, weights,
1 day strike, alarm, 26″ **225.00**
Gilbert, Wm. L. Clock Co., c1870, veneered case, bird perched on
branch dec, 30 hour, weights, 15⅜
x 25⅞″ **125.00**
Ingraham, E. Co., c1894, veneered, 1
day, weight, strike, 26″ **175.00**
Jerome, Barnum, walnut, 8 day **250.00**
Johnson, Wm. S., New York, NY,
c1845, mahogany veneer, painted
flower basket on green ground, 26
x 15¾ x 4½″ **300.00**
New Haven, Weight No 2, zebra wood,
1 day, strike, 26″ **175.00**
Waterbury, O.O.G., sq containing oval
with portrait of man, 30″ **175.00**

Pillar and Scroll
Dohenes, Ephraim, Bristol, CT, c1830,
Federal, carved mahogany, shaped
crest, 3 brass urn finials above a
hinged glazed door, eglomise panel
with houses and pond, tapering columns, bracket feet, 31 x 17½″ . . . **550.00**
Leavenworth, Mark, Waterbury, CT, 3
brass finials, landscape panel,
30¾″ h **800.00**
Terry, Eli and Samuel, Plymouth, CT,
c1835, Federal, mahogany, shaped
cresting, 3 brass finials, eglomise
panel with houses in landscape,
bracket feet, 32 x 16½″ **1,350.00**
Thomas, Seth, mahogany, swan's
neck, 3 brass urn finials, painted dial
with foliate spandrels, Federal man-
sion in landscape panel, 31″ **1,650.00**

Porcelain and China
Ambrosonia, A, Paris, late 19th C, porcelain mounted, gilt bronze, surmounted by a trophy, 2 putti and
goat below, set with small plaque
painted with 18th C motifs, enamel
dial, 11″ h **935.00**
Ansonia, c1910, La Riviere, painted
with daisies, flowers, and leaves in
white, yellow, pink, and green,
12½ x 14½″ **325.00**
New Haven Clock Co., c1900, multi-
colored flowers, emb scrolls, 8 day,
strike, 9¾ x 7¾″ **175.00**
Welch, E. N., Bristol, CT, c1870, Victorian, architectural case in blue,
green, and yellow, 30 day, 19 x 16
x 8″ **225.00**

Shelf
Ansonia, Lowell, black walnut, rose-
wood trim, 8 day, strike, 23½″ . . . **200.00**
Gilbert, Wm. L., Long Branch, oak, 8
day, gong, house and tower, 28″ . . **425.00**
Ingraham, Valkyrie, oak, 8 day, half
hour strike, cathedral gong, 21¼″. **175.00**
New Haven, Oder, 8 day, strike, 24″. **200.00**
Thomas, Seth, Oxford, oak, 8 day, half
hour strike, 23″ **200.00**
Yale Clock Co., Ideal N, black walnut,
8 day, strike **300.00**

Steeple
Ansonia, Gothic, dec, 1 day, vase with
flowers, shaped molding, 20″ **200.00**
Atkins Clock Co., Bristol, CT, c1859,
Gothic, rosewood veneer case, eagle with banner and American flag
painted on blue glass, 30 hour brass
spring driven movement, 19½ x
9½ x 3¾ **450.00**
Birge & Fuller, Bristol, CT, c1844, Victorian, rosewood veneer case,
painted glass panels, 8 day, 26½″ **650.00**
Boardman, C., walnut, painted dial and
tablet, fuzee movement, 1 day . . . **475.00**

Gilbert, Wm. L., Winsted Gothic, 8 day, 17¼" **175.00**

New Haven, Gothic, rosewood, church window arch motif, 1 day, 15½" . . **150.00**

Thomas, Seth, Sharon, mahogany finish, black with oval light, 8 day, 14¼" **200.00**

Waterbury, Sharp Gothic, veneer, woman and child motif, 19½" **150.00**

TALL CASE

Bachman & Sayre, Elizabethtown, NJ, Federal, inlaid mahogany, 8 day, musical, c1805, hood with shaped cresting centering three brass steeple finials on dot inlaid plinth, glazed hinged door, white painted dial with phases of moon, minute, and date register, waisted book-end inlaid case, shaped fan inlaid door, fluted quarter columns, fan inlaid base, bracket feet, 99¾" . . **29,700.00**

Brant, Adam, New Hanover, PA, Queen Anne, carved walnut, 30 hour, c1760, hood with molded cornice, glazed hinged door, engraved brass dial, waisted case, shaped hinged door, molded base, reduced ogee bracket feet, 83", some restoration to hood . **4,950.00**

Tall Case, Frederick Dominick, Phila., PA, Chippendale, carved walnut, c1770, 95", $10,500.00.

Breneisen, Samuel, Reading, PA, Federal, inlaid walnut, 30 hour, c1798, hood with molded swan's neck cresting ending in carved rosettes, centering three turned finials, shell-carved frieze, glazed hinged door, white painted dial, date register, waisted case, shaped door inlaid with wing-spread eagle, line-inlaid chamfered corners, molded base with incised wing-spread eagle flanked by line-inlaid chamfered corners, scroll-cut bracket feet, 89" **8,500.00**

English, George IV, oak and mahogany, 14" sq brass, engraved dial, 8 day, hour strike, inlaid dec, reeded stiles, 90½" **1,500.00**

Ferguson, John, Philadelphia, PA, Chippendale, carved walnut, 8 day, c1770, hood with molded swan's neck crest ending in carved rosettes, arched glazed hinged door, engraved brass dial, waisted case, hinged door, fluted quarter columns, shaped base panel with fluted quarter columns, ogee bracket feet, 101½". **13,200.00**

French, Alph. Peyret a Eauge, pine, mid-19th C, white enamel dial, time and strike, 8 day, 78" **1,000.00**

German, mahogany, 8 day, 20th C, 2 sets of chimes, 5 tubular groups, triangular pediment, reeded columns for accents, 78½" **1,200.00**

Hill, Joakim, Flemington, NJ, Federal, inlaid mahogany, 8 day, c1815, hood with molded swan's neck pediment ending in inlaid rosettes, 3 urn form finials, vine inlaid panel, arched glazed door, white painted dial fitted with minute and date registers, phases of moon, waisted case, flanked by fluted quarter columns, bracket feet, 95" **5,000.00**

Holingshead, Joseph, Burlington, NJ, Chippendale, carved walnut, 8 day, c1785, hood with molded swan's neck cresting ending in carved rosettes, arched hinged and glazed door, white painted dial, minute register, waisted case, molded shaped door, fluted quarter columns, base with scalloped panel with fluted quarter columns, ogee bracket feet, 96". **9,500.00**

Huston, William, Philadelphia, PA, Chippendale, walnut, 8 day, c1800, hood with free standing columns, gooseneck pediment, two brass ball finials, brass face [earlier than case], brass spandrels, and engraved phoenix medallion, calendar and minute register, waisted case, cherry shaped door, ogee bracket feet, 95½", restoration to case. **4,900.00**

Hutchins, Abel, Concord, NH, Federal, inlaid mahogany, c1805, hood with pierced crest, 3 brass finials, white painted dial, rocking ship, minute and date registers, waisted case, hinged door flanked by fluted quarter columns, bracket feet, 92" 5,775.00

Meredith, William, Merthyr, Victorian, mahogany, 8 day, c1850–55, arched hood with scalloped cresting, 13" painted arch dial, date and minute register, checker & line inlaid waist and base, spiral reeded column stiles, bracket feet, 85½" 1,100.00

Rogers, John, Newton, MA, Chippendale, carved mahogany, c1770, hood with pierced crest centering three brass finials, arched glazed hinged door, engraved brass dial, waisted case, molded arched, hinged door, molded base, 95" 6,750.00

Unknown Maker, New England, Federal, inlaid mahogany, 8 day, c1805, hood with pierced and shaped cresting centering three brass finials, glazed hinged door, white painted dial, minute and date register, waisted case, hinged door, fluted quarter columns with brass capitals, inlaid base, bracket feet, 97", some restoration to feet 5,775.00

Unknown Maker, Ohio, found in Canton, Chippendale, popular, 30 hour, c1800, hood with broken-arch pediment, two urn finials, glazed hinged door flanked by free-standing columns, painted face, calendar register, waisted body, chamfered sides, molded and shaped door, 89", new platform base, glass replaced, other major restoration ... 500.00

Willard, Aaron, Boston, MA, Federal, inlaid mahogany, 8 day, 1806, hood with pierced crest centering three urn and eagle finials, white painted dial surmounted by a hunting scene with rocking skiffs, gilt spandrels, waisted case, inlaid door flanked by brass top-fluted quarter columns, inlaid and molded base, lacks feet, 96½", descended in Fenno family, Willard paper label ... 27,500.00

Williams, David, Newport, RI, Federal, inlaid mahogany, c1800, molded hood with pierced cresting centering 3 brass urn and acanthus finials, line inlaid glazed door, white painted dial, brass stop-fluted columns, waisted case with line inlay, cockbeaded door, ogee bracket feet, 94" 9,750.00

WALL

Banjo
Curtis & Dunning, Burlington, VT, c1815, mahogany, giltwood case, foliate waist, brass fillets, naval battle, 32¾" 7,000.00

Derry Manufacturing Co., Derry, NY, c1895–1900, reproduction of Willard Clock, mahogany case, eagle finial, 8 day, 35" 1,000.00

Howard, E., No. 3, mahogany case, carved scrolls, 33¼" 2,000.00

Ingraham, c1930, Nordic, eagle finial, scroll dec on tapered waist, brass fillets, sailing ship, 26" 200.00

Low, John J. & Co., Boston, MA, c1828, Empire, painted stenciled case, landscape scene, eagle on ball finial, 39½" 3,000.00

Polsey, John & Co., Boston, 32".. 1,300.00

Sessions, York, c1930, concave waist with scroll molding, eagle finial, Federal style home painted on rect... 275.00

Waltham, No. 1540, walnut case, foliate waist, brass fillets, eagle finial, rural village scene, 40½" 1,250.00

Willard, Aaron, Boston, MA, c1825, Federal, brass, mahogany case, eglomise throat, white painted dial, giltwood acorn finial, 8 day, weight driven movement, 41 x 10½" 2,750.00

Willard, Simon, Boston, MA, early 19th C, scroll painted throat glass, mahogany faced door glass, wooden finial, 32½" 1,800.00

Calendar
Ansonia, Rio, oak, 8 day, spring.... 650.00

Gilbert, Wm. L., Standard Admiral, oak, 8 day, strike, octagonal, short drop, 26½" 350.00

Calendar, Ingraham, Mosaic, 30" l, rosewood case, $850.00.

Ithaca, No. 2, Band, oak, 8 day, 61″ **2,500.00**
Jerome & Co., Register, 8 day, 33¾″ **1,250.00**
New Haven, Ionie Figure, double dial,
  8 day, 29½″ **1,200.00**
Prentise, Empire, walnut, 60 day, 2
  springs **1,875.00**
Unknown, rosewood, figure 8 style,
  27½″ **650.00**
Cuckoo
American Cook Co., Philadelphia, PA,
  c1930, Victorian, carved wood
  case, carved spread eagle at top, 8
  day brass movement, cuckoo
  painted red, blue, and black, 17 x
  14 x 7½″. **150.00**
Keebler Clock Co., Philadelphia, PA,
  1920, pressed log design, leaves,
  flowers, nest of birds, brass spring
  pendulum, 5 x 4 x 1¾″ **75.00**
Kroeber, F, c1888, walnut case, brass
  movement, 2 weights, pendulum,
  18″ **250.00**
Gallery
Ingraham, chestnut, 8 day, 12″ d . . . **250.00**
Sempire, No. 8, electric, oak, 21⅛″ . **265.00**
Thomas, Seth, Wardroom, c1905,
  5½″ d **225.00**
Girandole, Curtis, L., MA, 19th C, carved
  mahogany, eglomise and giltwood,
  glazed circular brass door, spread
  winged giltwood eagle, throat panel
  painted with American eagle, brass fillets, circular base with hinged door
  with allegorical scene in polychrome,
  acanthus carved giltwood pendant, 44
  x 12½″. **5,000.00**
Regulators
Ansonia, Office Regulator, ash, duplex
  movement, 8 day, strike **375.00**
Freres, Japy, Paris, early 20th C, gilt
  bronze, hour glass, bezel and pendulum set with pastes, colonnaded
  case, 12⅛″ **385.00**
Gilbert, Wm. L., Regulator No. 2, oc-
  tagonal top, 8 day, dead beat escapement, 33½″ **750.00**
Howard, E., #70, oak, 8 day, weight,
  time only **1,250.00**
Ingraham, Hartford, oak, octagonal, 8
  day, 32″ **350.00**
New Haven, Elfrida, 8 day, strike,
  49″ **850.00**
New Haven, Prussian Oak, 90 days,
  51½″ **600.00**
Prentiss, Standard Regulator, 8 day,
  47″ **450.00**
Thomas, Seth, Regulator No. 60, oak,
  8 day, weight, Graham escapement,
  58½″ **3,250.00**
Vienna, late 19th C, ebonized shaped
  case, 8 day, weight drive, 40½″ . . **330.00**
Waterbury, Regulator B24, 8 day,
  weight, Swiss movement, 83″ **3,750.00**

School House
Ansonia, Kobe, round top and drop, 8
  day, strike, 21½″ **300.00**
Gilbert, Wm. L., Riverside, dark finish,
  octagonal, short drop, 8 day, strike,
  23″ **350.00**
Ingraham, Lyric, oak, octagonal, short
  drop, 8 day, strike, 27″ **250.00**
New Haven, Emporer, light oak, con-
  cave faceted corners, short drop, 8
  day, 25″ **300.00**
Sempire, electric, oak, octagonal,
  short drop, 33″ **400.00**
Terry Clock Co., iron case, octagonal,
  spring, 8 day, 19″ **600.00**
Thomas, Seth, Brighton, mahogany,
  oval, short drop, 8 day, spring,
  strike, 22¼″ **275.00**
Waterbury, Digby, oak, octagonal,
  short drop, 8 day, 27½″ **275.00**
Wag on Wall
Gilbert, Wm. L., Asbury, walnut, 8 day,
  gong strike, 27″ **650.00**
New Haven, c1905, Mission, oak,
  12″ **100.00**
Terry, Eli, CT, c1790, Federal, wooden
  works, tin weight, painted dial with
  ship and flower sprigs, 16 x 11″ . . **675.00**

CLOISONNÉ

History: Cloisonné is the art of enameling on
metal. The design is drawn on the metal body;
wires, which follow the design, then are glued or
soldered on the body. The cells thus created are
packed with enamel and fired; this step is repeated
several times until the level of enamel is higher than
the wires. A buffing and polishing process brings
the level of enamels flush to the surface of the
wires.

This art form has been practiced in various countries since 1300 B.C. and in the Orient since the
early 15th century. Most cloisonné found today is
from the Victorian era, 1870–1900, and comes from
China and Japan.

Ashtray and Match Holder, 6½″ h, 5″ w,
  pedestal base, royal blue, dragon and
  flowers, turned up scalloped edge . . **165.00**
Bowls
6″, chrysanthemun design, green, yellow, red, blue, white, mkd China . . **110.00**
6″, scalloped rim, panel decor of
  birds **250.00**
12″ d, 3″ h, imperial shape, copper rim
  and collar base, deep blue, large lotus blossoms, flowers, branches,
  and leaves **195.00**
Boxes
3″ h, 4″ d, round, lift off lid, blue
  ground, red and white flowers,
  green leaves and vines **450.00**

3½" x 2½" x 12", rectangular, lift off lid, blue and rust leaves, panel of goldstone on top with colored flowers and leaves.............. **125.00**

Brush Holder, 4½" h, 3½" d, light blue ground, T-fret cloisons, multicolored peonies, green leaves, brown stems. **300.00**

Camel, 6" l, 2 removable humps, rust ground, multicolored scroll design... **450.00**

Candlestick, 8⅞" h, 3⅞" d, blue ground, rust, yellow, and white florals, green, pink, yellow buds, green leaves **110.00**

Chargers
12", turquoise ground, 3 butterflies, rust, pink, white, and lavendar flowers **440.00**
13½", dragons in pursuit of flaming pearl, Chinese, late Ch'ing **275.00**

Cup, 3¾" h, 3¾" d, white ground, wave cloisons, multicolored fish, green seaweed.................... **260.00**

Ginger Jar, 7½", pedestal base, lift off cov, multicolored flowers, green leaves and vines............... **225.00**

Horses, set of 4, 8" h, enameled in colors with floral scrolls on fish scale, wood oblong stand................. **1,100.00**

Jewel Box, 8 x 4½ x 3", rectangular, dark blue, cloud cloisons, white cherry blossoms, red, pink and yellow mums, multicolored birds, padded lid **600.00**

Planter, 8" d, 7" h, round, foo dog handles, blue ground, multicolored florals..................... **400.00**

Plates
6½", light blue ground with cloud cloisons, mums, yellow rocks, green leaves and vines **150.00**
8½", dark blue ground, 6-petal cloison pattern, multicolored flowers, green leaves and pines **500.00**

Platters
12", black ground, 3 butterflies, ginko leaves, bamboo leaves and cherries, Japanese **800.00**
12", octagon shape, stork decor.... **600.00**

Potpourri Jar, 4¼" h, 4⅛" d, cov, white panels around top, blue, green, and rust with flowers and butterflies below, black, gold, and blue with flowers, Japanese **265.00**

Salt, 3 ftd, black, colorful dragon chasing flaming pearl, lotus blossom surrounded by waves on bottom **125.00**

Teapot, 5½" h, 4" d, black, 2 yellow dragons, green, pink, red, white clouds .. **475.00**

Tray, 11" d, peacock perched on pine tree, flowering branches, Chinese, c1890.................... **400.00**

Tumbler, 5" h, 2¾" d, light blue ground, T-fret cloisons, 2 multicolored fish and marsh panels, floral bands top and bottom **350.00**

Vases
5", alternating goldstone and blue panels with flowers and butterflies, Japanese, 1890............. **195.00**
5¾", pale blue foil with large white bird on brown tree trunk, green leaves, orange and yellow daisies, 19th C **325.00**
7¼" h, 2¾" d, gray ground, gray and rose fish, green seaweed, Japanese **265.00**

Vase, Japanese, robins egg blue on body and shield, 9½" h, $700.00.

12", pale blue, red-brown neck, 4 multicolored floral shield panels, above panels multicolored dragon winding around base, Japanese, 19th C... **625.00**

18½" h, 7½" d, pink, bird in cherry tree, deep pink and white blossoms, green leaves, Japanese **2,200.00**

CLOTHING

History: While museums and a few private individuals have collected clothing for decades, it is only recently that collecting clothing has achieved a widespread popularity. Clothing reflects the social attitudes of a historical period.

Christening and wedding gowns abound and, hence are not in large demand. Among the hardest items to find are men's clothing from the 19th and early 20th centuries. The most sought after clothing is by designers, such as Fortuny, Poiret, and Vionnet.

Note: Condition, size, age, and completeness are critical factors in purchasing clothing. Collectors divide into two groups: those collecting for aesthetic and historic value and those desiring to wear the garment. Prices are higher on the west coast; major auction houses focus on designer clothes and high fashion items.

References: Maryanne Dolan, *Vintage Clothing 1880–1960*, Books Americana, 1984; Tina Irick-Nauer, *The First Price Guide To Antique And Vintage Clothes*, E. P. Dutton; Shelia Malouff, *Clothing With Prices*, Wallace Homestead, 1983.

Collectors' Club: The Costume Society of America, 330 West 42nd Street, Suite 1702, New York, NY 10036. Dues: $35.00.

Museums: Los Angeles County Museum (Costume and Textile Dept.), Los Angeles, CA; Metropolitan Museum of Art, New York, NY; Museum of Costume, Bath, England; Philadelphia Museum of Art, Philadelphia, PA; Smithsonian Institution (Inaugural Gown Collection), Washington, D.C.

Additional Listings: See *Warman's Americana & Collectibles* for more examples.

Blouses
    Dotted Swiss, shirtwaist, puffed sleeves, lace yoke **85.00**
    Embroidered Net, c1930 . . . . **75.00**
    Silk, Chinese, cream, scoop neckline, cuffs trimmed with a trio of narrow gold and silver braid, front overlaid with plaid of white silk chenille and flat white braid, "Worth" label. . . . **200.00**
Caftan, wool challis, cream, hand embroidered borders of multicolored paisley and stylized foliate motifs . . . **165.00**
Capes, Evening
    Satin and lace, cream, embroidered with black sequins, beaded floral design, ruched cream chiffon trim, black lace ruffles, c1900 . . . . **300.00**
    Wool, taupe, full length, white rabbit fur trim, cream lace collar, braid tassel closures, c1900 . . . . **125.00**
Chemises
    Cotton, white, machine sewn pleats and lace panels, 28″ l **25.00**
    Silk, deep peach, wide bands of gold lace, narrowly pleated, gold lace

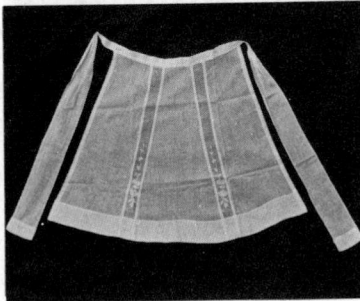

Apron, cotton, white, $45.00.

edged hem, "Callot Soeurs Paris Nouvelle Marque Déposé Made In France" label. **425.00**
Christening Dress, cotton, white, machine sewn, pleats and lace on bodice, sleeves and skirt, 40″ l **45.00**
Coats
    Brocade, gold roses and foliage woven on ivory satin ground, silk braid and ball buttons. **100.00**
    Fur, girl's, sheared beaver, lined in brown faille, "Fourrures Max Paris" label **200.00**
    Fur, lady's, sheared nutria, brown, notched collar, hood, loop wrap front closures, lined in brown and white taffeta, "Ben Thylan Furs" label **625.00**
    Lace, Battenburg, white, flowering foliate motifs, fitted sleeves, trained hem, c1900 . . . . **450.00**
    Lamé, gold, embroidered with black sequin leaf and berry motifs, batwing sleeves, hem covered in sequins, fur collar, c1920 . . . . **100.00**
    Wool, evening, cream, warp printed silk borders, collar, sleeves edged in ecru lace, pale pink chiffon ruffles, "Newfirm, Paris" label, c1890 **100.00**
    Wool, girl's, cranberry, large patch pockets, embroidered in red with interlocking rectangles of various sizes, "Jeanne Lanvin Paris Unis France" label. **350.00**
Dresses
    Daytime
        Lawn, summer, white, pintucked, embroidered, lace inserts, c1910 . . . . **185.00**
        Muslin, cream, gathered Empire bodice, lawn short puffed sleeves, skirt trimmed with embroidered ruffles at the hem, c1805 . . . . **675.00**
        Voile, summer, white, self ruffled overskirt, collar and cuffs, sash, c1915 . . . . **125.00**
    Evening
        Georgette, black, bodice embroidered with crystal beads and rhinestones, c1928 . . . . **275.00**
        Lace, cream, surplice Empire bodice, short puffed sleeves, c1805. **350.00**
        Net, black, chemise, black and blue sequins, trimmed with net at bodice and armholes, c1920 . . . . . . **300.00**
        Silk, cream, Liberty style, bodice with shaped panels, oversleeves embroidered with lilac flowers, trimmed with matching tassels, flowing mousseline undersleeves, lilac satin sash, self ruffled trained skirt, c1905 . . . . **250.00**

Silk, rose, shaped overblouse and short sleeves trimmed with terracotta and blue Venetian glass beads, inseam sgd "Fortuny De" **950.00**

Silk, silver blue, short sleeves laced with white silk cord trimmed with blue and brown striped Venetian glass beads, inseam sgd "Fortuny Dse" **600.00**

Taffeta, girl's, pale rachel-pink, sewn in triangular panels to tulle, pleated skirt sewn into waist at points, pale pink slip, "Jeanne Lanvin Paris Unis France, Model No. 40161" label **145.00**

Velvet, black, embroidered with scattered rhinestones, abstract patterns worked on waistband and skirt, "Jean Patou" label, c1925 .... **125.00**

Dressing Gown, charmeuse, peach, stitched from the center of the back with a dense sunburst, rays extending to all corners of the coat and sleeves, "Jeanne Lanvin Paris Unis France, 1929" label................. **500.00**

Jackets

Lady's, velvet brocade, Chinese, maroon, canary yellow silk lining **125.00**

Man's, wool, navy, long length **75.00**

Knickers, wool, boy's, orig label, c1910 **15.00**

Nightgown and Peignoir, machine and hand sewn, smocking, pleats, panels of intricate lace, 54" l **85.00**

Petticoats

Cotton, white, deep hem flounce worked with tuck and lace insertion **60.00**

Silk, pale green, embroidered with pink roses, foliage on lace edge ruffle.................... **65.00**

Robes, Chinese

Gauze, blue, embroidered with gilt dragons, blue and multicolored clouds, flaming pearls, breaking weave border at hem **350.00**

Silk, damask, red, white silk cuffs and borders, embroidered with multicolored birds, flowering foliage **250.00**

Romper, boy's, one piece, white, blue trim **20.00**

Slip, half, crepe de chine, black, inset at hips, hem band of Chantilly lace, narrow pleats, "Callot Soeurs Nouvelle Marque Déposé Made in France" label....................... **200.00**

Suits

Charmeuse, 3 pc, black, jacket top stitched in curved lines, curved pockets, faceted jet buttons, round collar faced in ivory, black and white chiffon chrysanthemum on one side, black skirt, ivory blouse, French cuffs, rounded neckline, row of buttons and buttonholes on one side, band of black charmeuse around hem, "Chanel Model No. 36751" on jacket label **7,250.00**

Linen, white, abstract floral embroidery **75.00**

Raw Silk, girl's, Middy blouse and pleated skirt, pocket embroidered in navy, navy blazer trimmed in white braid, "Modele Molyneux 5 rue Royale Made in France" label **500.00**

Velvet, 2 pc, black, straight skirt, smocked at waist, jacket with wide stand up collar and cuffs of brown mink, trimmed with 2 bands of brown mink around hem, black charmeuse lining, "Ventura Milano" label **2,650.00**

Wool, boy's, tweed, brown-olive, coat, knee pants, "Trump Clothes, Age 4" label.................... **40.00**

Wool, man's, gray pin stripe, high buttoned frock coat, vest with high rounded collar, c1905.......... **500.00**

Trouser's, man's, wool, black, gray stripes **80.00**

Tuxedo, black, satin lapels **175.00**

Vest, man's, velvet, gold, 5 pearl buttons.................... **100.00**

Wedding Dresses

Satin, cream, 2 pc, beaded waistband, c1900 .... **100.00**

Silk, cream, 2 pc, horizontal tucking, Battenburg lace insertions, double sleeves, train with self ruffled hem **125.00**

CLOTHING ACCESSORIES

References: Evelyn Haertig, *Antique Combs & Purses*, Gallery Graphics Press, 1983; Richard and Teresa Holiner, *Antique Purses*, Collector Books, 1982.

Additional Listings: See *Warman's Americana & Collectibles* for more examples.

Aprons

Cotton, white, embroidered flounce, long **25.00**

Homespun, hand sewn, hand made crocheted lace on hems, ends of ties, 39" l **30.00**

Belt, Russian silver, gold washed, set with small turquoise colored stones, made of 10 separate parts, each mkd "84", and maker's mark......... **400.00**

Belt Buckle and matching buttons, Art Nouveau, 3⅛" l buckle of English silver in shape of spreading butterfly wings, enameled in green and blue between chased ridges, 5 one inch d buttons of enameled green and turquoise, stamped "CYMRIC" on back, fitted case **700.00**

Bonnets, baby

Cotton, hand and machine sewn, embroidered, drawn work on ruffled edge, 9" l **35.00**

Irish Crochet **15.00**

Lace, white, embroidered **10.00**

Linen, white, white embroidery, matching shoes, 3 pcs **25.00**

Collar, lace, Battenburg **30.00**

Fur Stoles

Mink, black, black satin damask lining, "B. Weinstein" label **50.00**

Silver Fox **75.00**

Gloves

Lace, lady's, mit style **10.00**

Suede, brown, small child's, "Kayser" on snaps **25.00**

Handbags

Beaded

Black beaded design on burgundy, beaded drops, drawstring closure **35.00**

Mountain village scene, SS frame, 7" w, 12" l **250.00**

Three roses, red, orange, yellow, beaded fringe, 8" w, 14¼" l **325.00**

White, black florals, German, 8" w, 11½" l **85.00**

Evening

Brocade, dec with birds amongst flowering foliage, red satin lining, silver gilt mounted comb, lipstick, mirrored powder case, cigarette case, lighter, "Tiffany" label, 7½" l **365.00**

Satin, black, pleated and gathered, mounted on hinged gilt metal rim, clasp dec with rectangles of eggshell within panels of black enamel, "Germaine Guerin, Paris" label, c1920 . . . . **200.00**

Silk, petitpoint roses, ornate brass frame set with brilliants **150.00**

Leather

Black, basket of flowers motif, dec with rose diamonds, c1930 . . . . **350.00**

Black, frame patented July 29, 1898 . . . . **20.00**

Mesh

Brass frame, pierced scroll with florals, orig miniature purse inside, Art Nouveau **35.00**

German Silver, chain handle **20.00**

Gold, 15 round diamonds, 48 emerald cut sapphires in cathedral shape frame, mesh handle, c1920 . . . . **2,750.00**

Gold, 18K, yellow, chain handle, emb frame **1,500.00**

Sterling, scroll, floral frame, early mark, tassels **115.00**

Tapestry, courting couple and sheep, jeweled frame, 7¼" w, 8¼" l **210.00**

Hats, Ladies

Satin, white, small brim, large white feathers, jewels all over fine tan crown **30.00**

Straw

Blue, pressed, blue band and floral bouquet, "Ilten" label **40.00**

Brown, veil, 6 sets of jewels on brim, pins for fastening **25.00**

Ivory and taupe, cloche, trimmed with ribbons, "Caroline Reboux" label **100.00**

Velvet, purple, tilt style **10.00**

Hats, Men

Panama, mkd Royal Stetson, boxed. **25.00**

Top, black, beaver **50.00**

Pantaloons, silk, black, Victorian **10.00**

Shawls

Egyptian, cream net embroidered with silver tinsel, geometric, tree motifs, collar of bugle beads, sequins in floral design, silver braid tassels, c1920 . . . . **275.00**

Paisley, pierced, crimson, black, blue and white, embroidered border . . . **375.00**

Silk, cream, embroidered with deep pink peonies and purple buds, trimmed with knotted silk fringe . . . **300.00**

Shoe Buckles, pr **3.50**

Shoes, ladies, black, beaded trim, $35.00.

Shoes, ladies

Hightop, lace up, brown leather, c1900 . . . . **25.00**

Pumps, black suede, oval buckles of silver inset with onyx, cushion-cut sapphires, floral diamond clusters mkd "S. Calcagnile Roma", black ribbon tied covers for buckles **675.00**

Stockings
  Cotton, black, long, size 7, "Buster
    Brown & Tige" label. **10.00**
  Cotton, white
    Child's. **10.00**
    Ladies, seamed **10.00**
  Silk, black, orig label **12.00**
  Wedding Veil, satin, lace net, ivory,
    c1920. . . . . **45.00**

COALPORT

History: In the mid-1750s Ambrose Gallimore established a pottery at Caughley in the Severn Gorge, Shropshire, England. Several other potteries, e.g., Jackfield, developed in the area.

About 1795 John Rose and Edward Blakeway built a pottery at Coalport, a new town founded along the right-of-way of the Shropshire Canal. Other potteries located adjacent to the canal were those of Walter Bradley and Anstice, Horton, and Rose. In 1799 Rose and Blakeway bought the "Royal Salopian China Manufactory" at Caughley. In 1814 this operation was moved to Coalport.

A bankruptcy in 1803 led to refinancing and a new name, John Rose and Company. In 1814 Anstice, Horton, and Rose was acquired. The South Wales potteries at Swansea and Nantgarw were added. The expanded firm made fine quality, highly decorated ware. The plant enjoyed a renaissance in the 1888 to 1900 period.

World War I, decline in trade, and shift of the pottery industry away from the Severn Gorge brought hard times to Coalport. In 1926 the firm, now owned by Cauldon Potteries, moved from Coalport to Shelton. Later owners included Crescent Potteries, Brain & Co., Ltd., and finally in 1967 Wedgwood.

Additional Listings: Indian Tree Pattern.

Bough Pot, 11½" h, yellow, hp, scenic,
  two soldiers, one on horseback, one
  embracing girl, gilt floral border,
  pierced top, ftd, c1809. . . . . **350.00**
Compote, 12" l, banana leaf pattern,
  green, red, blue and gilt, c1815 . . . . **250.00**
Cup and Saucer, demitasse, 2⅞" cup,
  3½" saucer, pink, gold enamel dec,
  gold int., sgd, c1891 . . . . **135.00**
Figurine, Judith Anne, 7", plum dress,
  blue hat, muff, shawl, and necklace,
  1920–45 mark. **85.00**
Mustache Cup and Saucer, dark blue
  bamboo and birds, white ground, wide
  blue geometric border, 1881–91 . . . . **85.00**
Perfume Bottle, stopper, 9", pear shape,
  high relief, gilt flowering plants and foliage, flower spray finial and gilt scroll
  work, blue script Coalport mark,
  c1830. . . . . **325.00**
Plate, 10", scenic, girl holding child, wide
  green and gold border, sgd Hancock **225.00**
Potpourri Jar, cov and liner, 7½", landscape and floral reserve in gilt cartouche, heavy gilt blue ground, printed
  mark and painted signature **300.00**
Scent Bottles, pr, 3¾", globular, tur-
  quoise jeweling, heavy gilt, c1910. . . **550.00**
Tea Caddy, cov, 5½", heavy gilt pink and
  lemon ground, turquoise jeweling,
  c1910. . . . . **450.00**
Tea Set, pot, 6 cups and saucers, cobalt
  blue flowers and vignettes, orange
  and gold, 1870 mark **350.00**
Vase, 10" h, 5½" w, urn on pedestal
  base, dome cov, hp, scenic, Derwent
  River, cobalt blue ground, raised gold
  scrolls, vines, flowers, gold ram's head
  handles **215.00**

Plate, 9½", ecru with gold decor, imp 9 (1815-25 mark), $35.00.

COCA-COLA ITEMS

History: The originator of Coca-Cola was John Pemberton, a pharmacist from Atlanta, Georgia. In 1886 Dr. Pemberton introduced a patent medicine to relieve headaches, stomach disorders, and other minor maladies. Unfortunately, his failing health and meager finances forced him to sell his interest.

In 1888 Asa G. Candler became the sole owner of Coca-Cola. Candler improved the formula, increased the advertising budget, and widened the distribution. Accidentally, a "patient" was given a dose of the syrup mixed with carbonated water instead of still water. The result was a tastier, more refreshing drink.

As sales increased in the 1890s, Candler recognized that the product was more suitable for the soft drink market and began advertising it as such.

From these beginnings a myraid of advertising items have been issued to invite all to "Drink Coca-Cola."

Dates of interest: "Coke" was first used in advertising in 1941. The distinctive shaped bottle was registered as a trademark on April 12, 1960.

References: Deborah Goldstein Hill, *Wallace–Homestead Price Guide to Coca-Cola Collectibles,* Wallace Homestead, 1983; Shelly and Helen Goldstein, *Coca-Cola Collectibles* (four volumes, plus index), privately printed, 1970s; Allan Petretti and Cecil Munsey, *Official Coca-Cola Collectibles Price Guide,* Nostalgia Publishing Co., 1982.

Collectors' Club: The Cola Clan, 2084 Continental Drive N.E., Atlanta, GA 30345. Dues: $15.00.

Additional Listings: See *Warman's Americana & Collectibles* for more examples.

Advertising, 1930, magazine, 10 x 14", scene, Boy Scout camp.	10.00
Ashtray, red, silver letters, 1963.	5.00
Bank, 5½", metal, figural vending machine, red paint.	70.00
Bingo Game, 7 x 14" box, red and white, c1940.	25.00
Blotter, three pretty girls with raised glasses, 7¾ x 3½", 1944.	3.00
Brush, 8" l, celluloid, imp red slogan, c1934.	85.00
Buttons, pinback	
Member of Bottle Coca-Cola Club, hand holding bottle, c1930	25.00
World War II Air Force unit.	20.00
Calendars	
1921, 12 x 31", girl in garden.	250.00
1933, 12 x 30", "The Village Blacksmith".	175.00
Clock, round, maroon, slogan, c1950's.	45.00
Coupon, Lillian Russel, 1904	80.00
Crock, fountain, 11½" h, 29" d, unglazed int., "Drink Rum and Coca-Cola".	130.00
Cuff Links, ½" d, celluloid, white letters on red ground, c1920	50.00
Door Handle, 8" l, plastic, 3 dimensional.	28.00
Door Push, bottle shape, tin, c1942.	80.00
Fan, cardboard, bamboo handle, Japanese woman in garden, 1911.	80.00
Ice Pick, all metal.	9.00
Knife, pocket, 4" l, 3" blade, yellow celluloid handle, red inscription, c1934.	45.00
Matchbook Cover, c1940	8.00
Needle Case, folder, 1925.	35.00
Notebook, 3 ring, Sales Management Conference, 1958	15.00
Paperweight, 1916 Coca-Cola Pepsin Gum.	40.00
Pencil Box, 8½" l, 2½" w, red, gold lettering, contains 3 pencils, pen, ruler, eraser, and blotter dated 1937.	15.00
Pencil Sharpener, miniature figural bottle, iron.	22.00
Pocket Mirror, oval, Elaine, 1916.	100.00

Post Cards, set of 4, Popeye pictured, orig wrapper, 1942	22.00
Poster, 15" h, 20" l, platter of food, 2 bottles, 1956.	20.00
Ruler, 12", 1935.	6.00
Scorekeeper, baseball, c1906	30.00
Signs	
3¾ x 30", arrow shape, tin, 1927	90.00
14 x 25", cardboard, raised picture of WW II aircraft, planes on deck and taking off, "U.S. Navy Aircraft Carrier 1944".	135.00

Change Tray, "Elaine," 1917, 4⅜ x 6⅛", $55.00.

Cardboard, self frame, pretty lady wearing broad brimmed hat, frilly blouse, 1930s	125.00
Tie Clip, metal, enamel, "All Star Dealer Campaign Award," 1950s	30.00
Toy Trucks	
Buddy L., with conveyor, 1950s	175.00
Smith Miller, 13" l, metal, yellow, 5 plastic cases filled with clear bottles.	150.00
Trays	
1917, Elaine, 8½ x 19", rect.	125.00
1920, Garden Girl, 4 x 5", oval, change.	55.00
1923, Flapper, 4 x 6", oval, change.	50.00
1923, Coronation, "Cheerio," 10½ x 13".	110.00
1939, Spring Board Girl, Sunblom, artist, 14 x 10".	50.00
Wallet, leather, black, emb slogan.	45.00
Watch Fobs	
Coca-Cola, 2 bulldogs, advertisement on back, lead.	80.00
Drink Coca-Cola Sold Every Where 5¢, silvered brass	75.00

COFFEE MILLS

History: Coffee mills or grinders are utilitarian objects designed to grind fresh coffee beans. Before the advent of stay-fresh packaging, coffee mills were a necessity.

The first home size coffee grinders were introduced about 1980. The large commercial grinders designed for use in stores, restaurants, and hotels often bear an earlier patent date.

Reference: Terry Friend, *Coffee Mills*, Collector Books, 1982.

Germany, 14½″ h, $95.00.

COUNTERTOP (COMMERCIAL)

Enterprise, cast iron, 1873.	110.00
Golden Rule, cast iron	195.00
Landers, Frary, Clark, New Britain, CT, 1901, 12″ h	425.00
Swift, cast iron, 12″ wheels	190.00

FLOOR MODELS (COMMERCIAL)

John C. Dell & Sons, Pat 1884, brass hopper, sand blasted and primed cast iron, 33″ wheels, 5′6″ h	900.00
Enterprise, 6′ h.	400.00
Henry Troemner, 2 foliate cast iron wheels, ornamental base, red, gilt trim, cast inscription on each wheel "Star Mill, Philadelphia," stenciled Henry Troemner Maker Philadelphia, c1885	900.00

LAP (DOMESTIC)

Arcade, Imperial, cast iron top, oak base	70.00

Czechoslovakian, enameled wood . . . .
Kenrick, cast iron base, round white porcelain lined hopper, brass name plate, 4½″ w, 6″ h . . . .

TABLE (DOMESTIC)

Challenge Fast Grinder, wooden base, drawer, cast iron hopper, crank, and handle, wooden knob, 6½ x 6½ x 7½″	80.00
Enterprise No. 0, clamp on, cast iron, 11½″ h.	50.00

WALL (DOMESTIC)

Arcade, brass plating over iron	100.00
Grand Union Tea, red tin, advertisement, gold trim, cast iron grinder	95.00
Koffie, large red glass canister, measuring cup at base, crank handle on side, mounted on board.	75.00
Mystic, tin "V" shaped hopper, cast iron grinder	25.00
Steinfield #17, glass canister, lacy iron grinder	35.00
Telephone Mill, Arcade Mfg Co., cast iron and wood, Pat 1893, 6½″ w, 13″ h	300.00
Universal	45.00

COIN OPERATED ITEMS

History: Coin operated items include amusement games, pinball, jukeboxes, slot machines, vending machines, cash registers and other items operated by coins.

The first jukebox was developed about 1934 and played 78 RPM records. Jukeboxes were important parts of teenage life before the advent of portable radios and television.

The first pinball machine was introduced in 1931 by Gottlieb. Pinball machines continued to be popular until the advent of solid state games in 1977 and advanced electronic video games.

The first three reel slot machine, the Liberty Bell, was invented in 1905 by Charles Fey in San Francisco. In 1910, Mills Novelty Company copyrighted the classic fruit symbols. Improvements and advancements have lead to the sophisticated machines of today.

Vending machines for candy, gum, and peanuts, were popular from 1910 until 1940 and can be found in a wide range of sizes and shapes.

Because of the heavy usage these coin operated items received, many are restored and at the very least have been repainted by either the operator or manufacturer. Using reproduced mechanisms to restore pieces is acceptable in many cases, especially when the restoration will be able to perform as originally intended.

References: Jerry Ayliffe, *American Premium Guide To Coin Operated Machines*, Books Americana, 1981; Rick Botts, *1983 Jukebox Collectors Directory*, privately printed, 1983; Richard Bueschel, *An Illustrated Guide To 100 Collectible Pinballs*, Coin Slot Books, 2 volumes, 1983 and 1984; Roger Pribbenow, *Gumball Guide*, privately printed; Richard D. and Barbara Reddock, *Price Guide To Antique Slot Machines*, Wallace-Homestead, 1981.

Collectors' Club: The Society For The Preservation Of Historical Coin Operated Machines, 100 North Central Avenue, Hartsdale, NY 10630.

Periodicals: *The Coin Slot*, P. O. Box 176, Luzerne, PA 18709; *Gumball Gazette*, P. O. Box 272, Sun Prairie, WI 53590. Subscription: $21.00; *Jukebox Collector Newsletter*, 2545 SE 60th Street, Des Moines, IA 50317. Subscription: $20.00; *Pinball Collector's Quarterly*, P. O. Box 137, Lagrangeville, NY 12540. Subscription: $22.00.

Additional Listings: See *Warman's Americana & Collectibles* for separate categories for Jukeboxes, Pinball Machines, Slot Machines, and Vending Machines.

GAMES

Add-A-Ball Hurdy-Gurdy, pinball, Gottlieb	400.00
Bally Hoo, amusement, tilted wood case, glass top, plunger at front, 31" l	75.00
Kicker & Catcher, Baker Novelty Co., c1935	200.00
O. K., pinball, 5¢, mechanical, orange, yellow, green and red dec, 32½" l	85.00
Play Football, arcade, Chester Pollard Amusement Co., c1924	850.00
Rocket Ship, pinball, Gottlieb	450.00

Slot machine, 1¢, "The Little Duke," early 1930s, $2,400.00.

Select-Em, dice game, Exhibit Supply Co., Chicago	285.00
Tug-O-War, Callie	4,500.00

JUKEBOXES

Rock-Ola, Model 1426	1,100.00
Seeburg	
Symphonola, Model 146W, ash can form, wood veneered case, 20 selections, 57" h, c1946	1,200.00
Symphonola Regal, veneered wood case framed by orange plastic panels, 20 selections, 55", c1940	1,250.00
Wurlitzer	
Model 61, countertop, walnut case, red plastic panels, 12 selections, 78 RPM mechanism, 22" h, c1938, restored	1,750.00
Model 81, countertop, walnut case, yellow and red marbleized plastic panels containing 12 selections, 78 RPM mechanism, 23", c1940, restored	2,750.00

SLOT MACHINES

Callie, Duck, upright, 5¢, c1898	8,000.00
Gabel, Chicago, floor model, 5¢, c1910	13,000.00
Groetchen's, Columbia, countertop, 10¢	1,100.00
Jennings, Bronze Chief, countertop, 5¢, 1941	875.00
Mills	
Extraordinary, 5¢, three reels, double jackpot, c1933, restored	1,210.00
Operator Bell, 5¢, three reels, copper plate finish, 25", c1930	1,250.00
The Owl, 5¢, one wheel upright, oak cabinet carved with owl and foliage below color wheel, 5 way cast metal coin head, 64", c1905, restored	7,000.00
Pace, The Kitty, countertop, 25¢	3,500.00
Rock-Ola, Five Jacks, countertop, 5¢	1,400.00
Wattling, Blue Seal, 5¢, three reel, double jackpots, 24", c1932, restored	1,500.00

VENDING

Ace, 1¢, peanuts, aluminum, 8 sided base, c1930	125.00
Advance, gumball, glass globe	100.00
Ansco, Hot Nut Machine, flat glass front, c1940	65.00
Columbus 14, Profit Sharing, gum	200.00
Kitco, 1¢, sanitary towels and soap	125.00
Leebold, metal, candy, ornate, c1925	1,500.00
Lucky Strike Cigarettes, 1¢, Wilson Mfg	850.00
Nut Jewel, 5¢, 2 columns, peanuts, Lawrence Mfg Co	100.00
Select-O-Vend, penny candy bar	40.00
Silver King, gum	75.00
Stamps, mail box, red, white and blue, 18"	45.00
Yu-Chu, gum	100.00

MISCELLANEOUS

Black Jack, 5¢, trade stimulator type . . **325.00**
Cash Registers, National, brass
    Model No. 421, keys up to $9.99, re-
      ceipt machine at side, crank oper-
      ated, oak cash drawer, 23″ h **650.00**
    Model No. 542, keys up to $99.99, re-
      ceipt machine at side, running totals
      at other side, crank operated, brass
      cash drawer, 24″ h. **600.00**
Fare Box, Jonson, hand crank, patent
    1914, restored **225.00**
Fortune Cards, Lion Purtian Baby Bell . **325.00**
Knotty Peek, 1¢ **450.00**
Nickelodeon, Link, piano with violin and
    flute pipes, paper roll in oak case, art
    glass front, 68″ h, c1920 . . . . **2,000.00**

CONTINENTAL CHINA AND PORCELAIN (GENERAL)

History: By 1700 porcelain factories existed in large numbers throughout Europe. In the mid-18th century the German factories at Meissen and Nymphenburg were dominant. As the century ended, the French potteries assumed the leadership role. The "golden age" of Continental china and porcelains was from the 1740s to the 1840s.

Americans living in the last half of the 19th century eagerly sought the masterpieces of the European porcelain factories. In the early 20th century this style of china and porcelain was a "blue chip" among the antiques collectors.

Additional Listings: France—Haviland, Limoges, Old Paris, Sarregeumines, and Sevres; German—Austrian Ware, Bavarian China, Carlsbad China, Dresden/Meissen, Rosenthal, Royal Bayreuth, Royal Bonn, Royal Rudolstadt, Royal Vienna, Schlegelmilch, and Villeroy and Boch; Italy—Capodi-Monte.

FRENCH

Chantilly
    Beaker and saucer, crane and grouse,
      flowering plants, brown rims, Kak-
      iemon palette, red hunting horn
      mark, c1740 . . . . **525.00**
    Dish, 9³⁄₄″, quatrefoil shape, flower
      sprays, red hunting horn mark,
      c1745 . . . . **250.00**
    Ointment pot, 4¹⁄₄″, baluster shape,
      painted, foliage and fruit branches
      tied with red ribbon forming car-
      touche, Kakiemon palette, c1735 . **700.00**
    Potpourri, 5¹⁄₂″ h, baluster vase sur-
      rounded by molded flowers, leaves,
      branches, and seated cupid, or-
      ange, purple, green, and brown. . . **675.00**
    Vase, 8¹⁄₂″, baluster, painted, chrysan-
      themum by fence, insects, and

      flower spray, Kakiemon palette, red
      hunting horn mark, c1735 . . . . **1,450.00**
Faience
    Basket, cov, 8¹⁄₂″, oval, molded relief
      basketwork, ochre, cov with rope
      twist handle, multicolored flowers,
      Moustiers, c1740 . . . . **900.00**
    Jardinieres, pr, 7″, sq, flared, poly-
      chrome, molded with stylized
      leaves, lappets, and foliage, molded
      mask handles, c1750 . . . . **800.00**
    Jug, 9″, helmet shape, flared foot, flo-
      ral dec, bearded mask under
      molded spout, Rouen, c1760 . . . . **725.00**
    Plate, 9¹⁄₂″, polychrome, Chinoiserie
      figure, scattered flower spray rim,
      Moustiers, c1780 . . . . **200.00**
    Tureen, cov, 13³⁄₄″, blue and white,
      flower heads, foliage, scrolls, 4
      scroll feet, handled, artichoke finial,
      Strasbourg, blue mark, 1721–38 . . **1,700.00**
Mennency
    Mustard pot on fixed stand, 6″, barrel
      shape, bouquets, scattered flower
      sprays, puce rim, c1760 . . . . **150.00**
    Tureen on fixed stand, cov, 8³⁄₄″, oval,
      bouquets, scattered flower sprays,
      blue scroll and line borders, fruit
      branch finial, c1740 . . . . **350.00**
    Vase, cov, 6³⁄₄″, flower sprays, rock-
      work base, brown tree stump, ap-
      plied rose, and green florettes, mid
      18th C **700.00**
Nevers
    Jar, cov, 7¹⁄₂″, blue, flowering plants
      and birds, ochre, yellow, and white,
      scroll handles, knob finial, c1680. . **550.00**
    Vases, pr, 12″, bottle shape, blue and
      white, cupid, sportsmen, and birds,
      c1680 . . . . **2,450.00**
Niderviller
    Basket, 7¹⁄₄″ c, circular, pierced, 2 oval
      reserves, flower sprays, puce, blue,
      and green, ribbon entwined loop
      handles, int. with flower spray, blue
      interlaced, c1785 . . . . **200.00**
    Cruet stand, 10¹⁄₂″, polychrome,
      molded trailing branches, pierced
      sides with scroll and shell motifs,
      place for 2 bottles, pierced scroll
      handles, 4 scroll feet, c1760 . . . . . **700.00**
Parisian Factories
    Dessert service, 23 pcs, pink ground,
      fruit with gilt lappet border with in-
      terlaced initials, c1840 . . . . **1,400.00**
    Plates
      9¹⁄₂″, blue ground, flower spray cen-
        ter, gilt scroll border with scrolling
        flower panels, Feuillet mark, c1880 **250.00**
      9¹⁄₂″, portrait, bust of French court
        figure named on reverse, green
        borders with gilt bees and bis-
        hop's metre, mid 19th C, set of 12 **975.00**

Vases, pr, 12½" h, blue, oval panel with alpine lovers on rocky mountain ledge, gilt borders, late 19th C . . . 600.00

St. Cloud

Cups and saucers

White, blue scroll and foliage rims, ribbed below, band of diamond pattern on foot rim, c1745 . . . . . 400.00

White, plain, shaped rims, applied flowers and leaves 500.00

Mug, 2½", flowering plants, reeded borders, red and green foliage rim, loop handle with flower heads and foliage, c1730 . . . . 500.00

Potpourri, 7", 4¾" h, melon shape on molded base, all white, applied flowers, leaves, and branches, c1730 . 425.00

St. Omer, tureen, cov, and stand, 13¾", cabbage shape, molded overlapping leaves, snail finial, yellow B mark, c1755 2,100.00

Strasbourg, dish, 11½", octagonal, blue and white center, bird, flowers, and jardiniere on low table, raised flower head border, blue HK mark, 1730. . . 1,800.00

GERMAN

Faience

Enghalskrug, 11½", bulbous, powder blue, cartouche with church and buildings, flower sprays on sides, hinged pewter cov, shell thumbpiece, late 18th C 750.00

Ink stand, 10" w, white, glazed, rococo scroll molded stand, attached oval tray, c1745 . . . . 325.00

Leaf dish, 9½", green, yellow tone, brown veins, black Holic's mark, c1775 . . . . 675.00

Tankard, 8½", blue and white, flowering foliage, sponged trees, blue strap handle, hinged pewter cov, ball thumbpiece, c1740. . . . . 525.00

Tureen, cov, 11", octagonal, fluted, white, applied branch handles, flower branch terminals, branch finial, Holic's mark, c1760. . . . . . . 675.00

Frankenthal

Cup and saucer, tea, floral dec, rampant lion mark, c1755 . . . . 325.00

Dishes

9½", fruit and flowers dec, Carl Theodore mark, incised F 110, c1765 . . . . 275.00

11½", painted, birds on branches, scattered floral sprays, scroll and foliage rim, blue crowned interlaced C T mark, dated 1781 . . . 475.00

Figurine, 5", "Chinese Lady with a Bird in a Ring", modeled by Konrad G. Lueck, wears pointed hat, flowing sleeves, orange sash, rose shoes, underglaze blue Carl Theodore mark over "79", 1779 . . . . 900.00

Sauce boat, 8⅜", silver shape, birds in trees beneath meander border, gilt rim, foliate handle, crowned C T & B mark 800.00

Teapot, cov, 5¾", bouquets of flowers, strap handle, bird's head spout in puce 300.00

Hausmaler

Bowl, 6", Chinese figure in landscape, trees and building, int. with 2 figures, table, and flowers, c1740 . . . . 400.00

Knife handles, pr, stylized leaves and foliage, iron red, purple, green, yellow, and gold, c1740 . . . . 200.00

Saucer, 5⅛", allegorical scene, huntress and victim, angels above, gold border, c1750 . . . . 750.00

Nymphenburg

Coffee pot, 6½", minuet dancer in red, green foliate scroll work, imp shield mark, c1765 . . . . 575.00

Cup and saucer, coffee, painted, Bingen on the Rhine, lavender panel, heavy gold banding, gold leaf on saucer, c1770 . . . . 750.00

Perfume burner, 3¾", figural, Chinese woman seated on sq cushion, robed, hooded, molded borders, imp shield on front of base, late 18th C 500.00

Sweetmeat dishes, cov, pr, 5¼", figural, seated Moors, scantily draped, feathered headdress and skirt, beside pale yellow oval baskets with flower sprays, fruit finials, late 19th C 525.00

ITALIAN

Doccia

Beaker and saucer, flower sprays, painted and enamel 125.00

Cup, coffee, sq handle, landscape, painted, c1765. . . . . 80.00

Tea caddy, 4½", rect, arched, painted, bagpiper seated in landscape, reverse, shepherdess by river, c1775 450.00

COPELAND

COPELAND AND SPODE

History: In 1749 Josiah Spode was apprenticed to Thomas Whieldon, and in 1754 worked for William Banks in Stoke-on-Trent. In the early 1760s Spode started his own pottery, making cream colored earthenware and blue printed whiteware. In 1770 he returned to Banks' factory as master, purchasing it in 1776.

Spode pioneered the use of steam powered pottery making machinery. About 1784 he mastered the art of transfer printing from copper plates. Spode opened a London shop in 1778 and sent William Copeland there about 1784. A number of larger London locations followed. About 1800 Spode introduced bone china. In 1805 Josiah Spode II and William Copeland entered into partnership for the London business. A series of partnerships between Josiah Spode II, Josiah Spode III, and William Taylor Copeland resulted.

In 1833 Copeland acquired Spode's London operations and the Stoke plants seven years later. William Taylor Copeland managed the business until his death in 1868. The business remained in the hands of Copeland heirs. In 1923 the plant was electrified; other modernizations followed.

In 1976 Spode merged with Worcester Royal Porcelain to become Royal Worcester Spode, Ltd.

Reference: L. Whiter, *Spode: A History Of The Family, Factory, And Wares, 1733–1833,* London, 1970.

Biscuit Jar, cov, Willow, SP frame and bail, c1875	**125.00**
Bottles, pr, 4″, dark green, flowering plants in reserves, gilt rim and stopper.	**125.00**
Butter Dish, Tower, blue transfer, Spode	**60.00**
Cottage, 6½″, octagonal, elaborate flowers, moss, shrubbery, etc, Spode Felspar, c1810	**800.00**
Creamer, 4¼″ h, 5½″ d, ivory ground, blue band, gilt trim, #893, 1810. . .	**45.00**
Cups and Saucers	
Coffee, Tower, blue and white transfer, Spode.	**40.00**

Mug, 6″, "The Chase," multicolor transfer, $24.00.

Demitasse, Indian Tree	**32.00**
Dinner Sets	
Bouquet pattern, 64 pcs	**575.00**
Christine, service for 8, spode	**675.00**
Figurine, mother with baby, "Go to Sleep", Parian, Copeland, c1865, 17½″	**525.00**
Fruit Bowl, 8½″, scalloped edge, Imari type, blue, green, and orange, pedestal base, c1850	**95.00**
Pitchers	
6½″, drinking scene, dated 1897 . . .	**120.00**
6½″, Tower, blue and white transfer, Spode.	**75.00**
8″, scenic, blue and white, Chicago burning around top, 3 medallions around middle, designed by Frank E. Burley, Burley & Co, Chicago, #81, Spode	**350.00**
8¼″ h, 6½″ d, bright blue ground, raised ivory figures front and back, raised leaf trim around top, made for Columbian Expo.	**175.00**
Plates	
6″, Tobacco Leaf, c1850	**35.00**
8¾″, botanical, rose and tulip sprigs, molded grape bunches and leaves, multicolored, Spode, c1820.	**145.00**
9″, Bridal Rose	**25.00**
10″, Marathon pattern, blue floral border, gold trim.	**22.00**
Platters	
11″ l, 8½″ w, scalloped shell border, cobalt blue fuchsia blossoms, vines, gold trim, dated 1887	**135.00**
20¼″, Gothic Castle, blue and white.	**175.00**
Potpourri Bowl, 4¼″ l, oval, pierced cov, gilt scalloped edge, Bengal tiger, borders of oriental flowers, handles, iron red Spode mark, pattern #1645, c1810.	**300.00**
Salt, individual, cobalt blue with white blossoms.	**20.00**
Soup Plate, 9½″, pearlware, transfer, reserves with oriental landscapes, wide floral and diaper border, gold rim, imp Spode, 1815.	**95.00**
Tea Set, teapot, cov, 6½″ h, 9¼″ l, creamer, 3″ h, 5″ l, sugar, cov, 4¾″ h, 6½″ l, brown transfer, farm scene, imp Copeland	**100.00**
Teapot, 8½″, Jasper, blue ground, white hunting scene, mkd	**118.00**
Tiles, pr, 12 x 6″, hp, polychrome landscapes, 2 continuous scenes, sgd W. Yale, 19th C	**150.00**
Urn, cov, 6½″, white ground, Imari dec, cobalt, green, and red, gilt lion's head handles, gilt finial and trim, Copeland dated 1845.	**425.00**
Vase, 5″, Imari type, c1820	**100.00**
Vegetable Dish, cov, 10″, Tower, blue and white transfer, Spode	**85.00**

COPPER

History: Copper objects, such as kettles, tea kettles, warming pans, measures, etc., played an important part in the 19th century household. Outside, the apple butter kettle and still were the two principal copper items. Copper culinary objects were lined with a thin protective coating of tin to prevent poisoning. They were relined as needed.

Great emphasis is placed by collectors and signed pieces, especially those by American craftsmen. Since copper objects were made abroad as well, it is hard to identify unsigned examples. Many modern reproductions also exist.

Reference: Henry J. Kauffman, *American Copper And Brass.*

Additional Listings: Roycroft.

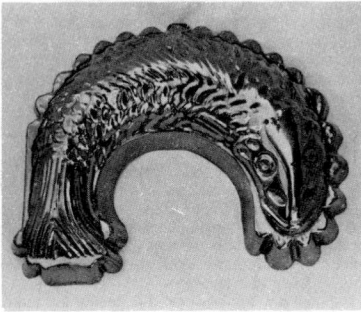

Mold, Fish, sgd Kreamer, $58.00

Apple Butter Kettle, 24″ d, 12″ h, dovetail construction, wrought iron handle, c1875.	300.00
Bedwarmer, 40″ l, circular, brass domed hinged lid with chased foliate dec, late 18th C	200.00
Boiler, 12½ x 7⅝ x 7″, flat cov, iron handles, tin lining, c1860.	110.00
Candelabras, pr, 11⅛″ w, 3 cylindrical nozzles, narrow horizontal supports on rect standard, stepped base, imp mark Dirk Van Erp.	325.00
Chestnut Pan, 13½″, pierced design cov, iron shaft, wooden handle	350.00
Chocolate Pot, 7″, steel handle, orig wooden muller, English, mid 18th C .	185.00
Clam Steamer, 18½″ h, 12″ d, screen shelves, sliding door	145.00
Coal Scuttles	
13″, hammered, swing handle	100.00
18″, cylindrical, brass bail handle, flared foot, 19th C	325.00
Coffee Pot, 7½″, cylindrical, flared, flat domed hinged lid, S-shape spout,	

turned wooden handle, English, 18th C	250.00
Coffee Urn, Queen Anne style, domed lid, late 19th C	300.00
Dipper, maple sugar	75.00
Fireplace Surround, 38″ h, hammered, repousse with conventionalized blossoming tulips, 20th C.	350.00
Funnel, 5″ h.	20.00
Lamps	
6⅝″, skater's, mkd Perkins Marine Lamp Co.	60.00
14½″ h, hammered, shallow dome shade with 4 panels, set with 4 lower mica panels, flaring cylindrical standard, flaring circular base, Roycroft imp mark, c1930	675.00
Lantern, ship's starboard, 19″	150.00
Measures	
1 gal, 10″, stamped 1 Gal Liquid	70.00
1 qt, 6⅛″, Georgian, pub style, mkd 1826/N-P on spout	225.00
Mug, 3⅞″, strap handle.	28.00
Pail, 4 gal, straight sides, pouring lip, bail handle, c1860	85.00
Powder Flask, 7½″, emb, basket weave and foliage, brass fittings	75.00
Sauce Pan, 6″ d, 7″ h, dovetail construction, copper lid, brass finial, iron handle	250.00
Scoop, 4″ l, ring handle	45.00
Soup Pot, 12″ h, cov, dovetail construction, iron handle, mkd L.F.D. & H., NY.	100.00
Smoking Set, 4 pcs, cylindrical humidor, knopped cov, rect cigarette box, hinged cov, cylindrical cigarette urn and match box with applied handle, imp Roycroft symbol, c1910.	325.00
Tea Kettles	
6⅜″, globular, dovetail construction, gooseneck spout with flap, swing handle.	155.00
10″, globular, cylindrical handle on scrolling supports, dome lid, acorn finial, S-shape spout, 18th C .	110.00
Teapot, gooseneck, wood finial and handle	85.00
Tray, 21″ d, circular, shallow bowl, hammered, heart shape motifs, 4 pierced oval handles, imp Gustav Stickley, c1910.	350.00
Washer, copper bottom tub with wringer.	110.00

CORALENE

History: Coralene is a glass or china object which has the design painted on the surface of the piece and tiny glass colorless beads applied with a fixative. The piece is placed in a muffle which fixes the enamel and sets the beads.

Several American and English companies made glass coralene in the 1880s. Seaweed or coral was the most common design. Other motifs were "Wheat Sheaf" and "Fleur-de-Lis." Most of the base glass was satin finished.

China and pottery coralene, made from the late 1890s to the post WW II era, is referred to as Japanese coralene. The beading is opaque and inserted into the soft clay. Hence, it is only half to three-quarters visible.

Reproductions are on the market, some using an old glass base. The beaded decoration on new coralene has been glued and can be scraped off.

CHINA

Bowl, 8″ d, blue matte ground, purple
plums, green leaves, c1910 . . . .   **175.00**
Box, 1½ x 2 x 3″, copper matte ground,
pink, lavender, and green thistle, mkd
Kinran Pat. 16132 Japan **110.00**
Ewer, 8″, turquoise ground, pink and
gold flowers, gold handle, Japanese   **175.00**
Plate, 8½″ d, white lilies, green leaves.   **120.00**
Vase, 8″ bulbous, scalloped and fluted
rim, shaded lavender to light blue
ground, multicolored snapdragons,
1909 . . . .   **225.00**

GLASS

Bride's Basket, 9½″ h, 10½″ d overall,
int. of pale yellow satin, Moire pattern,
MOP, ext. of white satin, coral beaded,
frosted edge, Pairpoint SP holder with
blackberries and leaves **750.00**
Lamp Base, 7¼″ h to top of font, yellow
satin raindrop ground, blue beading,
script sgd, Webb **250.00**
Mantel Lusters, pr, 14″ h, pink satin
overlay, floral dec, single row of cut
prisms **500.00**

**Vase, 8″, transparent clear orange, mkd
"Patent," $185.00.**

Pitcher, 6¼″ h, 4″ d, orange ground,
white water lilies and green leaves,
clear beading, applied amber handle,
amber rigaree around neck **200.00**
Tumbler, 3⅞″, clear, light green with
opalescent cast, applied enameled
butterfly and morning glory, cov with
coralene beading, mkd Patent **275.00**
Vases
5½″ h, 2¾″ d, shaded pink satin,
MOP, diamond pattern with cross in
center, yellow coralene snowflakes,
white lining **450.00**
7¾″, shaded green, pink coralene
beading, sgd, dated, Japanese . . .   **235.00**

CORKSCREWS

History: The corkscrew is composed of three parts: 1) handle, 2) shaft, and 3) worm or screw. The earliest known reference to "a Steel Worme used for drawing corks out of bottles" is 1681. Samuel Henshall, an Englishman, was granted the first patent in 1795.

Elaborate mechanisms were invented and patented from the early 1800s onward, especially in England. However, three basic types emerged: "T" handle (the most basic, simple form), lever, and mechanism. Variations on these three types runs into the hundreds. Miniature corkscrews, employed for drawing corks from perfume and medicinal bottles between 1750 and 1920, are among the most eagerly sought by collectors.

Nationalistic preferences are found in corkscrews. The English favored the helix worm and tended to coppertone their steel products. By the mid-18th century English and Irish silversmiths were making handles noted for their clean lines and practicality. Most English silver handles were hallmarked.

The Germans preferred the center worm and nickel plate. The Italians used chrome plate or massive solid brass. In the early 1800s the Dutch and French developed elaborately artistic silver handles.

Americans did not begin to manufacture quality corkscrews until the late 19th century. They favored the center worm and specialized in silver mounted tusks and carved staghorn for handles.

An ornate, 5¼″, silver "T" handle with floral and vine motif on the ends and silver sheetwork wrapped around an ivory base recently sold for $730.00 at the Brau Haus Auction on May 4, 1984. Items that are signed and marked are immediately more desirable to collectors.

Advisor: Charles H. Rosasco.

LEVERS

Brass, Italian, double, rack and pinion
type, steel shaft with center worm, cap
lifter in handle, c1920 . . . .   **30.00**

Chrome plated steel, Italian (Vogliotti-Torino), double, wire helix, mkd "Japan" and "Christian-Brothers - San Francisco 1908" **125.00**

Coppertone finish, "Lund's Lever," Patent No. 736 of 1855, triangular hinge, mkd "Coat of Arms & Lever," 2 fingerpull wire helix signet **110.00**

Steel, hinged, retractable, scalloped casing, nickel plated corkscrew, mkd "The Handy" and "Patented Feb. 24, 1891," round shaft with center worm   **40.00**

MECHANISM

Bone handle, polished, English rack and pinion corkscrew (King's Screw), brush and hanging ring, four plain post open barrel, narrow rack, long wire helix, side handle, sgd VERINDER, c1800. . . . .   **400.00**

Brass, solid, 4 triangular posts, open cage, uncyphered solid cutworm, probably Italian, c1890. . . . .   **220.00**

Nickel plated steel, open cage, German Pat. 1892, swivel over collar on handle to raise shaft, hanging ring, cyphered center worm **40.00**

Staghorn handle, 5" l, 3" cyphered center worm, 2 post open cage, nickel plated, ball bearing action, mkd "MONOPOL & GERMANY D.R.G.M.", c1900. . . . .   **55.00**

MINIATURES

Chromed steel, folding harp, 1½" closed, hanging loop, cyphered wire helix, c1890. . . . .   **25.00**

Ivory handle, crescent shape, 1⅜" l, chromed turned steel shaft wire helix, 2⅝" l, c1790–1820 . . . .   **70.00**

Meissen, porcelain head of Johann Von Schiller (1759–1805), poet and philosopher, uncyphered center worm, head mkd with crossed swords under glaze, c1870. . . . .   **375.00**

Nickel plated cut steel, 3" peg and worm, fluted wire helix, c1790 . . . .   **90.00**

Silver handle, 2½" l, fine ornate floral design, hallmarked "Birmingham/ 1887", 2" tapered steel shaft and wire helix. **65.00**

NOVELTY

Brass, cast, spread wing eagle, 3½" w, plain wire helix, c1930 . . . .   **15.00**

Gilted, revolver, 4" barrel is wire helix, cap lifter and can piercer on hammer, c1940. . . . .   **20.00**

Wood, horse, 5" l, tail is wire helix, c1925. . . . .   **20.00**

T-HANDLE

Staghorn handle, 5½", figural, carved horsehead with flowing mane and spirited glass eyes, tapered shaft, center worm with point, c1880 . . . .   **250.00**

Wooden
Four finger pull fitted handle, key shaped, steel center worm, c1895–1915. . . . .   **30.00**

Champagne Tap, 6" l, French Gargoyle head, c1900, $100.00.

Shaped and turned handle, "Williamson" on shaft, bell and wire cutter, cap lifter, cyphered center worm, mkd Ptd. 13 Dec. 1898. . . . .   **30.00**

Turned, 4" handle, one acorn end, other with wirebreaker/wax cutter, thick shaft tapering to wire helix, late 1800. . . . .   **60.00**

COSMOS GLASS

History: Cosmos glass is a milk glass pattern made by the Consolidated Lamp and Glass Company, c1900.

Cosmos glass is identified by its distinctive pattern. The ground is a molded cross-cut design. Relief molded flowers are painted in pink, blue, and yellow. Cosmos glass came in an extended tableware line which included several sizes and shapes of lamps.

Butter Dish, cov, pink band	**200.00**
Cologne Bottle, orig stopper	**210.00**
Condiment Set, salt, pepper, cov mustard, matching patterned stand.	**350.00**
Creamer, pink band	**140.00**
Lamps	
7½" h, minature	**250.00**
14"	**550.00**
Pitcher, milk, 9", pink band	**180.00**
Salt and Pepper Shakers, 3" h, pink band	**85.00**

Tumbler, 3¾″, pink band, $85.00.

Spooner	100.00
Sugar, cov, pink band	185.00
Sugar Shaker, orig top, bulbous	125.00
Syrup, orig top	200.00
Water Set, pitcher, 4 tumblers	500.00

COWAN POTTERY

History: R. Guy Cowan founded the Cowan Pottery in 1913 in Cleveland, Ohio. The establishment remained in almost continuous operation until 1931 when financial difficulties forced closure.

Early production was redware pottery. Later a porcelain-like finish was perfected with special emphasis placed on glazes. Lustreware is one of the most common types. Commercial type wares marked "Lakeware" were produced from 1927 to 1931.

Early marks include an incised "Cowan Pottery" on the redware (1913–17), an impressed "Cowan", and an impressed "Lakewood". The imprinted stylized semicircle with or without the initials R. G. was later.

References: Paul Evans, *Art Pottery of the United States*, Everybodys Press, Inc., 1974; Ralph and Terry Kovel, *The Kovels' Collector's Guide to American Art Pottery*, Crown Publishers, Inc., 1974.

Bookends, Rook, metallic glaze	110.00
Bowl, attached flower frog in shape of deer	250.00
Candlesticks, pr, 4″, cream white	25.00
Card Holder, 3″, cream white, imp mkd	15.00

Console Sets

3 pc, 13″ oval bowl, 2 bird heads on rim, rose int., ivory, pr of matching candelsticks	150.00
4 pc, bowl, flower frog, pr of candlesticks, blue lustre	75.00
Figurines, pr, 8″, Spanish Dancers, old ivory glaze	450.00
Flower Frogs	
6¼″, nude with drape, wave like base, white, high glaze	75.00
7½″, nude with drape, white, high glaze	140.00
Lamp, 9″, orange lustre, ink mark	120.00

Trivet, 6½″ d, Louis Mora, blue ground, rose and yellow flowers, $200.00.

Pitcher, qt, pink lustre glaze	50.00
Strawberry Jar, large, mint green glaze	75.00
Vases	
5″, bulbous, matte green to rose	50.00
5¼ x 8¼″, baluster, green tones, semi-crystalline glaze	80.00
6″, handles, yellow high glaze	45.00
11⅝″, ribbed, blue lustre	85.00

CRANBERRY GLASS

History: Cranberry glass is transparent and named for its color, achieved by adding powdered gold to a molten batch of amber glass which then is reheated at a low temperature to develop the cranberry or ruby color. The glass color first appeared in the last half of the 17th century, but was not made in American glass factories until the last half of the 19th century.

Cranberry glass was blown, mold blown, or pressed. Examples often are decorated with gold or enamel. Less expensive cranberry glass was made by substituting copper for gold and can be identified by its bluish-purple tint.

Reproductions abound. These pieces are heavier, off color, and lack the quality of older examples.

Additional Listings: See specific categories, such as Bride's Baskets, Cruets, Jack-in-the-Pulpit Vases, etc.

Banana Bowl, 12″ l, 6½″ w, oval, boat shape, 4 feet, bronze basket **575.00**

Barber Bottles
7″, SP top **90.00**
11½″, Mary Gregory type, white enamel boy in landscape **125.00**

Basket, 4½″, folded top, imp petal each side of clear handle, 3 clear petal feet **145.00**

Bells, wedding
10″ h, 6″ d, DQ, opaque cream handle. **225.00**
12″, clear applied handle **200.00**

Bowls
5½″ d, 5½″ h, crystal berries and 3 crystal fans applied around top, 3 reeded scroll feet, berry pontil. . . . **265.00**
6¼″ d, 3¼″ h, 8 crimp top, large crystal applied leaves and branches . . **245.00**
8″, hobnail, fluted opal rim **200.00**

Boxes
2½″ h, 2¾″ d, round, dome top, lift off lid, blue and white enameled flowers, yellow scrolls and leaves **85.00**
4¾″ h, 3⅜″ d, cut panels outlined in gold, crystal cut faceted knob finial **110.00**

Chalice, cov, 16″ h, enameled portrait of girl on front, gold trim **175.00**

Condiment Sets
4″ d, 7¼″ h to top of handle, pepper pot, mustard jar, open salt with spoon, Swirl, SP holder **150.00**
5½ d, 7″ h to top of handle, cut panels, mustard pot, pepper, salt with spoon, SP cresent moon shaped holder **165.00**

Creamers
3⅝″ h, 2⅝″ d, clear applied handle, 2 bands enameled white dots and white floral decor **70.00**
3¾″ h, 2⅝″ d, round mouth, clear applied handle, yellow florals and leaves, gold trim **95.00**

Cruets
7″ h, 3¼″ d, vinegar, ovoid, clear wafer foot, clear applied handle, clear cut faceted stopper, heavy gold flower and leaf decor **135.00**
8¼″ h, 4″ d, cut beveled neck, clear applied handle, matching deep cranberry bubble stopper, cut star base **200.00**

Cup and Saucer, 5½″ d, 2¾″ h, windows with gold trim, white florals, gold decor, clear applied handle covered with gold, sgd Moser **325.00**

Decanters
9¾″ h, 4¾″ d, IVT, over all lacy white enameling, clear applied handle, steeple bubble stopper. **200.00**
10¼″ h, 4½″ d, dainty white and blue enameled flowers, green leaves, gold tracery, clear bubble steeple stopper **135.00**

Vase, 4¼″ h, ormolu stand, cup neck, $55.00.

12″, enameled floral decor, clear glass stopper **225.00**

Epergne, 18″ h, 10″ d bowl, ruffled and scalloped, cone shaped center vase, engraved floral design **350.00**

Ewer, 4¾″ h, 3″ d, tiny white enameled flowers, gold trim, clear applied handle **95.00**

Fairy Lamp, 7″ d base, crackle dome, marked Clarke **165.00**

Finger Bowl and Underplate, 9⅛″ plate, scalloped, 4½″ h, 3″ d bowl, round, Webb encrusted gold vine and leaves decor, gold butterfly, pink enameled flower. **375.00**

Hat, 6″, spiral. **150.00**

Inkwells on gold washed stand, 8½ x 5 x 3″, cov box in center for stamps with red and green stones, sq, hinged brass tops, small cupid finial **225.00**

Jar, 5″ h, 4½″ d, clear and cranberry knob, enameled gray leaves and grapes, detailed in gold **145.00**

Lamp Shade, 4¾″ h, 7¾″ d, hobnail, ruffled rim. **90.00**

Lamps
5⅞″ h, 4½″ d, hand, clear applied handle, clear chimney **125.00**
20″ h, 10″ d, lace maker's, IVT shade, ruffled top, brass base, 2 small handles. **550.00**

Liqueur Set, 8″ sq, scalloped edge tray, 9¼″ h, 3″ d bottle, clear applique down sides, clear rigaree around neck, gold basket of flowers and butterfly decor, clear stopper with rigaree, 6 liqueur glasses, 2″ h, 1⅛″ d, gold decor . . . **225.00**

Perfume Bottles
4″, enameled **80.00**
5½″, cut panels, scalloped base, clear cut faceted bubble stopeer **120.00**
5¾″, cut to clear, clear stopper **110.00**

Pitchers
6″ h, 3¾″ d, bulbous, round mouth, clear reeded applied handle, dainty white enamel flowers **125.00**
6½″ h, 4″ d, mat-sur-noke flowers applique, clear thorny ball feet, crystal applied handle, clear berry prunt, engraved on base, Rd. 15353 . . . . **495.00**
7″, opal hobnails, clear applied handle. **150.00**
8½″ h, 5″ d, tankard, IVT, enameled blue florals, green leaves, applied clear braided rope handle **300.00**
10″, lemonade, molded, enameled floral decor **200.00**

Powder Jar, SP lid **85.00**
Punch Cups, 3¼″, pedestal, handled, enameled strawberry plants, set of 6 **450.00**
Ring Tree, 3″, gold and white decor. . . **58.00**

Rose Bowls
2¾″, miniature, 8 crimp top, cranberry and crystal cut. **165.00**
3½″ d, 3″ h, 8 crimp top, small blue and white enameled flowers, green leaves. **125.00**

Salts
3″, ribbed, double rows of applied vaseline rigaree, ftd holder, hallmarked **110.00**
3½″, ruffled top, 7 petal feet, white threading. **55.00**
4½″, clear rigaree trim, hallmarked holder **95.00**

Sauce Dish, 5″ d, 3″ h, sq, hobnail, 7″ h heavy SP holder **125.00**

Sugar Shaker
5″ h, 2¾″ d, cut panels, SP screw on top **70.00**
Ribbed opal lattice **80.00**

Sweetmeat Dish, 6¼″ d, 6″ h, crystal ruffle and shell trim applied around center, SP basket frame **110.00**

Tumblers
4″, baby IVT, white and blue enameled flowers **40.00**
4¼″, IVT. **35.00**

Tumble-up, (water carafe and tumbler top) IVT **100.00**

Urn, 12″ h, 4¾″ d, cov, pedestal base, gold scroll decor and flowers, thorny crystal handles and finial **275.00**

Vases
3½″ h, 1¾″ d, cylinder, IVT, applied

bunches of green grapes, gold leaves, ormolu foot **185.00**
5⅝″ h, 4¼″ d, clear applied drippy leaves top and middle, clear wishbone feet **120.00**
6½″ h, 4¼″ d, sanded gold leaves and flowers outlined in white enamel, white flowers with blue centers, pr. **175.00**
8″ h, 4¾″ d, IVT, ruffled top, clear edging. **100.00**
8½″ h, 4¼″ d, applied crystal leaves top and base **120.00**
8¾″ h, 3⅞″ d, gold leaves, white enameled flowers and outlining on leaves, small blue dots, pr **365.00**
11½″ h, 4¾″ d, swirl ftd, applied crystal ruffle around top rim, enamel floral decor, pink, blue, yellow, and green, facing pr **500.00**

Watering Can, 8½″ h, 5″ d, clear applied side and overhead handles, hollow spout, heavy gold lacy flowers, foliage, and butterflies. **600.00**

CROWN MILANO

History: Crown Milano is an American art glass produced by the Mt. Washington Glass Works, New Bedford, Massachusetts. The original patent was issued in 1886 to Frederick Shirley and Albert Steffin.

Normally it is an opaque white satin glass finished with light beige or ivory color ground embellished with fancy florals, decorations, and elaborate heavy raised gold. When marked, pieces carry an entwined CM with crown in purple enamel on the base. Sometimes paper labels were used. The silver plated mounts often have MW impressed or the Pairpoint mark as they supplied the mountings.

Advisors: Clarence and Betty Maier.

Biscuit Jar, 7″ d, melon ribbed, enamel dec of brown wild roses on a cream ground, SP lid and bail, lid sgd MW, orig paper label. **875.00**

Bowls
4″ h, 2½″ d, swirl in glass, crown-like top, enamel dec of autumn leaves on pristine white body, unsgd **385.00**
6″ h, 8½″ l, oblong shape, multicolored peonies and daisies outlined in gold over a pink floral ground, orig paper label **1,250.00**

Boxes, Dresser
4 x 6″, jeweled starfish on ground of enameled chrysanthemums over a cream base, sgd MW on SP lid . . . **500.00**
7½″, round, nine cranes in flight on top, raised gold floral dec on lower portion, unsgd **1,600.00**

Cruet, 8½″ h, raised spiral cream ground

with roses and gold floral dec, dec stopper and rope handle, extremely rare **4,250.00**

Demitasse, eggshell-thin cup and saucer dec with delicate multicolored enamel blossoms, raised gold borders, both sgd **1,250.00**

Ewers

10½", shepherd and flock by a country brook on front, medallion with country church on reverse, pale green ground dec with roses in gold tracery, rope handle, sgd **2,450.00**

10½", shepherdess reading a book beneath a tree, surrounded by sheep executed in soft lilac tones on front, roses and birds on reverse; both scenes surrounded by wreath of raised gold, similar but small wreaths in lilac as background, rope handle, sgd **3,000.00**

Muffineer, 5", melon ribbed, multicolored blossom with raised gold borders, cream ground, ornate emb SP lid, sgd **650.00**

Pickle Castor, 4 x 4½" Crown Milano bowl, enameled pansies dec, SP lid sgd MW, ornate 10" h SP holder with Pairpoint mark. **1,050.00**

Tray, 7" w, fan shaped with roll-over sides, shiny finish, enamel violets dec, brushed gold enamel on sides **350.00**

Tumbler, 3¾" h, shiny finish, raised gold blossoms and ribbons dec, sgd **700.00**

Urn, 16½", profuse gold enamel and raised gold blossoms and foliage, rare crown shaped lid, sgd **2,950.00**

Vases

8", sq with rounded corners and two

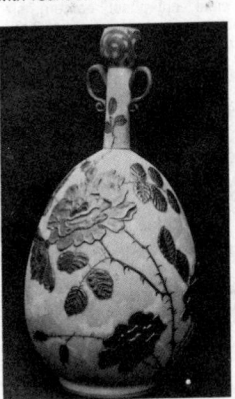

Vase, 10" h, egg body, applied gold floral deco, star mark, $825.00.

scroll handles, enamel oak leaves, gold enamel leaves and acorns, all with raised gold borders, ground of pale colored leaves and acorns, orig paper label **1,150.00**

12", tapered body, multi-floral dec., raised gold scrolls over body, sgd. **1,000.00**

13", bulbous melon ribbed base, long slender neck with tricorn fold-over top, enamel dec of gold and raised gold zinnias and spider webs **2,100.00**

15½", bulbous shape with long slender neck, enamel dec of 2 cherubs on front, one on reverse, raised gold scroll work and embellishments, shiny finish, rare steeple shaped stopper **2,500.00**

16", tapered, dancing couple in colonial garb, raised gold embellishments, thorn strap handles, shiny finish. **3,000.00**

17", slender, 4 GUBA ducks in flight over a wheat field of raised gold, shiny finish, sgd, a masterpiece. . . **3,750.00**

CRUETS

History: Cruets are small glass bottles, used to hold oil, vinegar, wine, etc., for the table. The high point of cruet use was during the Victorian era when a myriad of glass manufacturers made cruets in a wide assortment of patterns, colors, and sizes. All cruets had stoppers; and, most had handles.

Reference: Dean L. Murray, *More Cruets Only*, Killgore Graphics, Inc., 1973.

Additional Listings: Pattern Glass and specific glass categories such as Amberina, Cranberry and Satin.

Amber

8¼" h, 3¾" d, sq, dimpled bulbous shape, sapphire blue applied handle, orig sapphire blue bubble stopper **115.00**

12½" h, 3⅞" d, wine, blue applied handle, amber pedestal foot, blue applied rings, salamander applied to front, blue cut faceted stopper . . . **170.00**

Amberina, DQ, enamel decor. **350.00**

Amethyst, pedestal, blown, lily of the valley decor **165.00**

Blue, sapphire, 6¼" h, 3½" d, clear applied handle, clear cut faceted stopper, flashed green leaves and blossoms, gold trim **175.00**

Burmese, blue and white forget-me-nots, stripes on both handle and mushroom stopper. **1,475.00**

Clear

Brilliant Pattern, vaseline stain, Riverside Glass Co. **150.00**

Shaded to green, 9¼" h, 2½" d, flattened cylinder shape, lacy lavendar enamel foliage, tiny gold leaves, gold top, gold scrolls, clear applied handle, clear decorated stopper .. **145.00**

Cranberry, Polka Dot pattern, Northwood **125.00**

Milk Glass, Royal Oak pattern **150.00**

Opalescent

Daisy & Fern, clear, swirl ribbed body..................... **115.00**

Spanish Lace, blue, blue handle, clear faceted stopper **120.00**

Opalescent Herringbone, Cranberry, Hobbs, Brockunier & Co., $350.00.

Peachblow, 6½" h, amber applied handle, hand cut amber stopper, Wheeling **800.00**

Satin, 6½" h, 3½" d, yellow MOP, ribbed camphor handle, camphor stopper .. **250.00**

Spatter, white and cranberry, vaseline handle, clear faceted stopper, leaf mold **200.00**

CUP PLATES

History: Many early cups and saucers were handless, with deep saucers. The hot liquid was poured into the saucer and sipped from it. This necessitated another plate for the cup, the "cup plate."

The first cup plates made of pottery were of the Staffordshire variety. In the mid-1830s to 40s, glass cup plates were favored. Boston and Sandwich Glass Company was one of the main contributors to the lacy glass type.

It is extremely difficult to find glass cup plates in outstanding (mint) condition. Collectors expect some marks of usage, such as slight rim roughness, minor chipping [best if under rim], and in rarer patterns a portion of a scallop missing.

Reference: Ruth Webb Lee and Robert Rose, *American Glass Cup Plates*, privately printed, 1948.

Notes: The numbers used are from the Lee-Rose book in which all plates are illustrated. The book is difficult to find, even in libraries. Yet, it continues to be used extensively by dealers and collectors.

Prices are based on plates in "average" condition.

Advisors: David and Linda Arman.

GLASS

LR 1, light green, blown, plain **200.00**

LR 36, clear, eight pointed star, Sandwich or New England, slight mold underfill **50.00**

LR 51, clear, pontiled, six checkered diamonds, New England, heavy rim roughness, 2 rim chips. **150.00**

LR 61, clear, diamond motif, probably New England Glass Company, minute rim roughness.................. **60.00**

LR 67, clear, New England, one small rim chip **175.00**

LR 77, clear, triangles within six pointed star, Philadelphia area, minimal rim roughage and flaking........... **475.00**

LR 78, clear, star, circle, and other motifs, New England, one small chip under rim **30.00**

LR 81, opalescent, rope rim, New England **350.00**

LR 82, opalescent, New England, 2 rim chips, heavy roughage. **75.00**

LR 83, opaque, medium blue, swirl center, New England Glass Company .. **450.00**

LR 97, clear, octagonal, eastern, six pointed star with center rosette, 2 minor rim nicks. **45.00**

3⅝", dark blue, Battery, New York, Historical Staffordshire, $325.00.

LR 119B, blue, 10 petal floral motif, Midwestern, small rim flakes, light roughness. 250.00

LR 121, clear, lacy, eight rayed center in hexagonal border, Midwestern, chips on 2 scallops 150.00

LR 127, clear, eight pointed star, overfill roughness. 45.00

LR 130, clear, lacy, leafed diamond, Midwestern, most of one bull's-eye chipped from underside 170.00

LR 131, clear, checkered diamond, Midwestern, light rim roughness. 250.00

LR 145B, clear, checkered with center circle, Midwestern, slight roughage . . 175.00

LR 151A, clear, thistle, Midwestern, minute under rim roughness 250.00

LR 193, light green, lacy, 9 petal floral, Midwestern, one slight upper rim nick 150.00

LR 216, blue, fleur-de-lis quadrants, Fort Pitt Glass Works 575.00

LR 255, green tint, roman rosette, Sandwich, light roughage, several scallops removed by chip 45.00

LR 255A, clear, roman rosette, probably Sandwich, minimal rim roughage. . . . 15.00

LR 279, amethyst [unlisted color], 16 petal floral, New England. 200.00

LR 279, light green, lacy, 16 petal floral, New England, roughness and chips . 40.00

LR 292, opalescent [unlisted color], ten loop pattern, slight mold roughness . 190.00

LR 298, opaque, light blue [unlisted color], daisy motif 250.00

LR 323, medium amber, rayed star with miniature rayed stars in quadrants, Sandwich, mint 150.00

LR 459F, clambroth-opalescent, four loops with inverted "v" connectors, heart border, minor flaking on four scallops 40.00

LR 459M, opaque, jade, geometric and diamond center, heart border, Sandwich, 3 3/16" d, light roughage, 2 scallops partially chipped away 650.00

LR 465F, opalescent, four loops with inverted "v" connectors, heart border, rim mold roughness. 30.00

GLASS, HISTORICAL

LR 562A, Clay, clear, tiny flakes on two scallops 235.00

LR 564, Clay, clear, mold roughness . . 25.00

LR 565B, Clay, peacock blue, lacy, probably Sandwich, light rim roughage, one rim chip 150.00

LR 576, Clay, medium blue, two large scallops chipped off, flake on another. 350.00

LR 592, Log Cabin, clear, minor flaking on three serrations 210.00

LR 628, ship, Chancellor Livingston, medium blue, Sandwich, slightest rim roughness. 500.00

LR 636, clear, bridge, mold roughness 30.00

LR 660, clear, eagle, probably Sandwich, 2 small rim chips. 40.00

LR 678, clear, eagle, 2 shallow rim chips, one with possible check or bruise. . . 90.00

LR 686, clear, harp, one point and three scallops with flakes 110.00

PORCELAIN OR POTTERY

King's Rose. 115.00
Pink Lustre. 40.00
Redware, slip, crow's foot. 150.00
Staffordshire, Historical
3¾", General Jackson, The Hero Of New Orleans, carmine transfer . . . 650.00
3¾", Ship Anchored, shallow mold, partial border, dark blue, Wood . . . 325.00
4⅜", Wilkie Series, Christmas Eve, dark blue, Clews 300.00
4½", Pittsfield Elm, two medallion border, dark blue, Clews 500.00
4¾", French Views, Stone Bridge With One Arch, Wood 75.00
Staffordshire, Romantic
California, Podmore Walker & Co.. . . 75.00
Claremont, Baker & Son 40.00
Lozere, Edward Challinor 60.00
Venus, Podmore Walker & Co.. . . . . 50.00

CUSTARD GLASS

History: Custard glass was developed in England in the early 1880s. Harry Northwood made the first American custard glass at his Indiana, Pennsylvania, factory in 1898.

From 1898 until 1915, many manufacturers produced custard glass patterns, e.g., Dugan Glass, Fenton, A. H. Heisey Glass Co., Jefferson Glass, Northwood, Tarentum Glass, and U. S. Glass. Cambridge and McKee continued the production of custard glass into the Depression.

The ivory or creamy yellow custard color is achieved by adding uranium salts to the molten hot glass. The chemical content makes the glass glow when held under a black light. The higher the amount of uranium, the more luminous the color. Northwood's custard glass has the smallest amount of uranium, creating an ivory color; Heisey used more, creating a deep yellow color.

Custard glass was made in patterned tableware pieces. It also was made as souvenir items and novelty pieces. Souvenir pieces are marked with place names or hand painted decorations, e.g., flowers. Patterns of custard glass often were highlighted in gold, enamel colors, and stains.

L. G. Wright Glass Co. has reproduced pieces in the Argonaut Shell and Grape and Cable patterns. It also introduced new patterns, such as Floral and

Grape and Vintage Band. Moser reproduced toothpicks in Argonaut Shell, Chrysenthemum Sprig, and Inverted Fan & Feather.

Reference: William Heacock, *Encyclopedia Of Victorian Colored Pattern Glass, Book IV: Custard Glass From A to Z*, Peacock Publications.

Additional Listings: Pattern Glass.

Banana Boat, 11″ l, 7½″ w, ftd, Geneva, red and green dec	150.00
Berry Bowls	
Individual	
Georgia Gem	25.00
Grape, pedestal, mkd N	45.00
Master	
Chrysanthemum Sprig	175.00
Geneva, red and green dec	125.00
Georgia Gem	85.00
Jackson	120.00
Louis XV	150.00
Winged Scroll, 8½″	175.00
Berry Sets	
Geneva, oval, red and green dec, 7 pc	400.00
Winged Scroll, 5 pc	250.00
Butter Dishes, cov	
Chrysanthemum Sprig	275.00
Louis XV	150.00
Candlesticks, pr, Penumbra	45.00
Celery, Chrysanthemum Sprig	650.00
Cologne Bottles, pr, Grape & Cable, nutmeg stain, clear stoppers, mkd N	300.00
Compote, jelly, Chrysanthemum Sprig	150.00
Cookie Jar, cov, Grape & Cable, nutmeg stain	500.00
Creamers	
Chrysanthemum Sprig	95.00
Fan, mkd N	75.00
Geneva, red and green dec	65.00
Georgia Gem, souvenir LeSeur, Minnesota, Artesian Well	50.00
Maple Leaf	85.00
Tiny Thumbprint	30.00
Winged Scroll	75.00
Cruets	
Chrysanthemum Sprig, orig stopper, dec	325.00
Louis XV, clear stopper	110.00
Dishes	
Flute, ruffled edge, ftd	135.00
Waterlily & Grape, 2 handles, fluted, pink stain, 8½″ d	60.00
Dresser Tray, Grape & Cable	225.00
Fruit Dishes	
Grape & Cable, nutmeg stain, pedestal, mkd N	45.00
Winged Scroll, 8½″ d, 3½″ h	100.00
Goblets	
Beaded Swag, hp roses, mkd Heisey	70.00
Grape & Gothic Arches, nutmeg stain	55.00
Hats	
Blackeberry Spray, candy ribbon edge	35.00

Grape & Gothic Arches, nutmeg stain, mkd N	30.00
Ice Cream Bowls, Peacock & Urn, nutmeg stain, mkd N	
Individual	55.00
Large, scalloped rim, 9¾″ d	200.00
Lamps	
Crocodile Tears	60.00
Nine Panel	100.00
Mug, souvenir	55.00
Orange Bowl, Grape & Cable	275.00
Pickle Dish, Poppy, nutmeg stain	50.00
Pitchers	
Chrysanthemum Sprig	750.00
Geneva, mkd N	125.00
Louis XV	225.00
Powder Jars	
Georgia Gem	40.00
Grape & Cable	300.00
Rose Bowl, Fine Cut & Roses, mkd Northwood	65.00
Salt & Pepper Shakers, pr	
Geneva	60.00
Jackson	125.00
Louis XV	165.00
Maple Leaf, good enamel dec	425.00
Sauce Dishes	
Diamond Peg, souvenir	35.00
Louis XV	45.00
Shot Glass, Diamond Peg, enameled pink rose	40.00
Spooners	
Chrysanthemum Sprig, blue, gold dec	300.00
Fan, mkd N	75.00
Georgia Gem, souvenir	60.00
Maple Leaf	130.00
Winged Scroll	75.00
Sugars	
Covered	
Geneva, red and green dec	120.00
Georgia Gem	90.00
Grape & Gothic Arches, worn gold, mkd N	75.00
Louis XV	125.00
Maple Leaf	110.00
Open	
Grape & Cable, nutmeg stain, breakfast size	35.00
Ring Band	65.00
Syrup, Vintage, blue, orig tin cov	175.00
Table Sets, cov butter, creamer, spooner, cov sugar	
Chrysanthemum Sprig	600.00
Little Gem, enamel flowers	425.00
Maple Leaf	500.00
Tea Cup, souvenir, Harmon's Harbor, Maine	30.00
Toothpicks	
Georgia Gem	50.00
Harvard	35.00
Souvenir, McCune, Kansas	30.00
Tumbler	
Baby Thumbprint	40.00

Sugar, 6½″, Chrysanthemum Sprig, sgd, $95.00.

Chrysanthemum Sprig	75.00
Diamond Peg	40.00
Geneva	65.00
Grape & Gothic Arches	55.00
Jefferson Optic	25.00
Louis XV	35.00
Maple Leaf	90.00
Vases	
Grape Arbor, mkd Northwood	35.00
Panel Bottom	25.00
Row of Rings, calloped, scene of Underwood, ND, 6¼″ h	40.00
Water Sets, pitcher, 6 tumblers	
Grape & Gothic Arches, gold dec worn	200.00
Louis XV, excellent gold	550.00
Wines	
Beaded Swag	70.00
Diamond Peg	40.00
Honeycomb	55.00

CUT GLASS, AMERICAN

History: Glass is cut by the process of grinding decoration into the glass by means of abrasive-carrying metal wheels or stone wheels. A very ancient craft, it was revived in 1600 by Bohemians and spread through Europe, to Great Britain, and to America.

American cut glass came of age at the Centennial Exposition in 1876 and the World Columbian Exposition in 1893. The American public recognized American cut glass to be exceptional in quality and workmanship. America's most significant output of this high quality glass occurred from 1880 to 1917, a period now known as the "Brilliant Period."

About the 1890s some companies began adding an acid-etched "signature" to their glass. This signature may be the actual company name, its logo, or chosen symbol. Today, signed pieces can command a premium over an unsigned piece since the signature clearly establishes the origin.

However, caution should be exercised in regard to signature identification. Objects with forged signatures have been in existence for some time. To check for authenticity, run your finger tip or finger nail lightly over the area with the signature. As a general rule, a genuine signature cannot be felt; a forged signature exhibits a raised surface.

Many companies never used the acid-etched signature on the glass and may or may not have affixed paper labels to the items originally. Dorflinger Glass and the Meriden Glass Co. made cut glass of the highest quality, yet never acid-etched a signature on the glass. Furthermore, cut glass made before the 1890s was not signed. Many of these wood polished items, cut on blown blanks, were of excellent quality and often won awards at exhibitions.

Consequently, if collectors restrict themselves to signed pieces only, many beautiful pieces of the highest quality glass and workmanship will be missed.

References: E. S. Farrar & J. S. Spillman, *The Complete Cut & Engraved Glass Of Corning*, Crown Publishers [Corning Museum of Glass monograph], 1979; J. Michael Pearson, *Encyclopedia Of American Cut & Engraved Glass*, Volumes I to III, privately printed, 1975; Albert C. Revi, *American Cut & Engraved Glass*, Thomas Nelson, Inc., 1965.

Collectors' Club: American Cut Glass Association, P. O. Box 7095, Shreveport, LA 71107. Dues: $15.00. *Hobstar* (10 times a year).

Museums: The Corning Museum of Glass, Corning, NY; Everhart Museum Of Natural History, Science & Art, Scranton, PA; Lightner Museum, St. Augustine, FL; Toledo Museum Of Art, Toledo, OH; Margaret Woodbury Strong Museum, Rochester, NY.

Advisors: Richard and Joan Randles.

Baskets	
6″, 4″ h, hobstars, notched handles	185.00
8½″, 8½″ h, hobstars, double twist handle	395.00
Bells	
6″, "Kalana Lily," Dorflinger	85.00
Dinner Size, hobstars and cane vesicas	275.00
Bonbon	
Dish, 6″ d, triangular, handled, "Jewel," Clark	75.00
Plate, matching	75.00
Bottles	
Condiment, hobstar chain around top and bottom, engraved flowers and stars between, SS cap	60.00

Cordial, 8" h, corset shaped, "Hindoo," Hoare **185.00**

Medicine, hobstars, strawberry-diamond, notched prisms, hollow stopper **175.00**

Bowls

8", heart, hobstars. **200.00**

8", low, clusters of hobstars, sgd Clark. **200.00**

8½", bell shaped, "Marquise," Hoare **350.00**

9", "Kensington," Hawkes **325.00**

9", "Prince Of Wales," Dorflinger, blown blank, footed ambrosia, 7" h **375.00**

9", "Royal," Hunt, 4" h **395.00**

10", "Filigree," Egginton **350.00**

10", "Holland," Hawkes, salad bowl **350.00**

10", "Lansing," American **275.00**

11½ x 5½", "Bellevue," Taylor Bros. **425.00**

Boxes

Dresser, 4½ x 3 x 3", large hobstar on top with expanding rays, prisms around lid, design on lid carried to base, hinged **140.00**

Jewelry, 7 x 7", heart-shaped, Russian cut sides, diamond cut on center of top **600.00**

Miscellaneous, 6" d, daisy and intaglio with vertical prisms on edges, hinged silver rim **300.00**

Butters, cov

Harvard and floral **295.00**

Hobstars and prisms, blown blank . . **475.00**

Covered Butter, 5" d, 5" h dome, 7½" plate, hobstar & straw & fans, $395.00.

Candlesticks, pair

6" h, plain flutes, teardrop stem **295.00**

10½", butterfly, rose, leaves, teardrop tem. **275.00**

12", engraved over body, foot, and bowl, large teardrop stem, sgd Libbey. **475.00**

Canoe, 11", hobstars **235.00**

Carafes

"Albany," meriden, corset shaped . . **175.00**

Hobstars, fans, and punties, 8" h, sgd Clark. **135.00**

Russian pattern. **200.00**

Card Tray, 7 x 6", Assyrian and engraved, sgd Sinclaire **1,050.00**

Celeries

"Devonshire," Hawkes. **175.00**

"Lovebirds," Libbey, 11 x 4½ x 2" . . **1,095.00**

"Russian-Canterbury," Mount Washington **225.00**

"Wheeler," Mount Washington **150.00**

Celery Vase, 6½", hobstars and fans . . **245.00**

Cheeses, cov, large size

Blown Blank, hobstar and punty chain, hobstar on plate base **475.00**

Dome 7" d and 7" h, underplate 10" d, geometric cuttings **600.00**

Cheese & Crackers

9¼" d, 5" h, two tier, elevated center cut on sides **140.00**

9½" d, 4½" h, "Flute & Panel," Sinclaire **250.00**

Clocks

6" h, 4" w, allover "Russian," orig clock case. **195.00**

6" h, 4" w, roses, leaves, and notched prisms. **150.00**

6½" h, 4" w, "Harvard". **450.00**

Colognes

Allover hobstars and rosettes. **225.00**

"Harvard," 7½" h **115.00**

Strawberry-diamond and fans, daisies and leaves, blown blank **85.00**

Compotes

6" h, 7" d, hobstars, flared skirt **125.00**

7" h, 8" d, hobstar vase, teardrop stem, "Ribbon Star" variation **285.00**

8" h, 6½" w, twisted stem, sgd Hawkes. **250.00**

10½" h, 8" d, hobstars, scalloped hobstar base, teardrop. **350.00**

Cruets

7½" h, sgd Clark. **155.00**

"Cosmos," triple lips, double notched handle. **125.00**

Decanters

8½", ovoid whiskey, notched prisms **225.00**

11½", "Harvard & Floral," double notched handle, rayed base **195.00**

12", allover hobstars, bell shaped, goose neck **450.00**

13½", "Harvard & Floral," bowling pin shaped **435.00**

17", pedestal, hobstar foot, triple notch handle, teardrop stopper . . . **1,400.00**

Geometric cuttings, Hawkes, pr **1,870.00**

"Russian," four sided with curved corners, honeycomb neck **495.00**

Decanter Set, decanter and 12 wines, "Russian". **2,500.00**

Dishes

5½", heart shaped, hobstars	**125.00**
5½", sq, blown blank, shell and vesicas	**125.00**
8½" d, divided, four sections, SS wide border, "Brunswick," Hawkes	**235.00**
9" l, oval, "Venetian," Hawkes	**200.00**
12" d, divided, four compartments, split vesicas and hobstars, cut handle.	**235.00**
Spade shaped, floral and geometric .	**75.00**

Doorknobs, pr, 2" d, mushroom shape, int. teardrop, strawberry-diamond, star, and punties, orig mountings . . . | **45.00**

Ferners

Hobstars and fans, three ftd, 8" d, 4½" h	**115.00**
"Primrose," ftd, sgd Tuthill	**475.00**

Finger Bowl, "Gladys," Hawkes . . . . . . | **45.00**

Flower Centers

8" d, hobstars and cane, hobstar base	**225.00**
12" d, large hobstar base, "Glenwood," Bergen	**1,195.00**

Hair Receiver, SS cov in Art Nouveau stylized flowers . . . . | **115.00**

Humidors

6½" h, barrel shaped, zipper pattern, hobstar base, SS cov	**350.00**
7½", hobstar sides & base, SS cov .	**650.00**

Ice Buckets

Cross-cut diamond, hobstars, fans, and beading	**250.00**
Hobstars (large), checkered diamond, and fans, two handled	**385.00**
"Marlboro," two handled, matching underplate, Dorflinger.	**1,400.00**

Ice Cream Dishes, set of 12, 4¾" d, hobstars and vesicas . . . . | **250.00**

Ice Cream Sets

14 x 8" tray, six matching 7" plates, block cuttings of strawberry-diamond and clear hobstars and fans	**550.00**
17 x 10" tray, ten matching dishes, "Jewel," Libbey	**1,400.00**

Inkwells

2" sq, 2½" h, waffle cut base, beveled edges, SS hinged lid, repousse decor	**95.00**
2" sq, 3" h, SS repousse top	**50.00**
Small, dome shape, strawberry-diamond and fan, repousse floral SS hinged lid	**95.00**

Jars

3" h, 5½" w, underplate, panel cut, rayed base, SS cover and ladle. . .	**75.00**
4½" x 3½", cov, matching underplate, allover vertical prisms.	**135.00**
5", powder, lid.	**115.00**
6", sachet, hobstar chain, flashed fans	**125.00**

Jugs

9½" h, cross-cut diamond and fan, ornate handle, matching stopper . . . | **350.00**

10" h, 5" l, 3½" d, flat type, cross-cut diamond, pinwheel sides.	**395.00**
10" h, 5" w, flutes between cane stripes, sgd Libbey.	**525.00**
Rum, strong green color cut to clear, flutes and panels	**525.00**

Whiskey

"Japan," 8" h, 5" d, strap handle, Fry Ruby cut to clear, matching stopper	**825.00**
	485.00

Knife Rests

3½", barbell shape, stars on ends . .	**55.00**
5½", hobstars, fans, and crosshatching	**80.00**
Set of 12, orig case.	**120.00**

Ladle, 15" l, shell shaped, double pour spout, teardrop handle cut in strawberry-diamond, cross-hatch, diamond, and fan, sgd Pairpoint . . . . | **350.00**

Lamps

13" h, boudoir, mushroom shade, prisms, wheel-cut flowers and polished leaves	**375.00**
17" h, cut pansy shade and base, prisms.	**1,000.00**
17½", mushroom shade, geometric, floral roses, and leaves	**1,150.00**
24", 2 light, mushroom shade "Harvard," very fine	**5,000.00**
Hobstars and strawberry-diamond	**3,500.00**
27", sultan's hat shaped shade, "Harvard & Floral"	**3,500.00**

Loving Cups

6" h, three handled, ornate SS rim . .	**350.00**
8½" h, three handled, hobstars, fans, and strawberry-diamond, hobstar base, pedestaled, honeycomb handles	**3,250.00**

Mayonnaise, 2 pc, hobstar, nailhead diamond, and fans. . . . . | **225.00**

Miniatures

Bonbon, heart shaped, 3", sgd Hawkes.	**95.00**
Cake Stand, pedestal, 2" h, 3" w, teardrop stem, SS rim	**150.00**
Dish, triangular shaped, hobstars . . .	**55.00**
Tumbler, 1½" h, allover cut	**95.00**
Vase, 3½" h, "v" shaped, pedestal .	**145.00**

Napkin Ring, brilliant cutting . . . . | **75.00**

Nappies

Base cut in six-sided star with hobstars and cross-hatching	
Sgd Clark	**85.00**
Unsigned.	**35.00**
Hobstars and cane, one handled . . .	**60.00**
Strawberry-diamond, one handled, thumb rest, "Drape," sgd Straus . .	**125.00**

Perfumes

Flashed pinwheel, teardrop stopper, sgd Maple City. . . . . | **125.00**

Laydown Type

4" l, curved, inside stopper, ornate SS top. | **65.00**

12" l, sharp "Russian," Gorham SS
cap 275.00
Notched prism, cylindrical, 4" h, ⅝" d,
rayed base, repousse brass screw
top with long dauber 68.00

Pitchers

8", bulbous, "Colonial," Dorflinger . . 195.00
8", tankard, "New Brilliant," sgd
Libbey. 255.00
8½", bulbous, "Design #33," Elmira 325.00
9", "Brunswick," sgd Hawkes. 425.00
11", champagne, ornate SS rim and
spout 450.00
11", 3 qt, "Columbia," Blackmere. . . 475.00
12", tankard, swirled notched prism,
Tiffany SS rim 450.00
14", punties and hobstar chain, triple
notched handle, hobstar base. . . . 375.00
14½", bulbous base, notched prisms,
and hobstars, hobstar base, beaded
SS top mkd Wilcox. 650.00
Tankard, hobstar chains, vertical hobstar rosette chain vesicas. 300.00
Syrup, punties and cross-hatching,
rayed base, SP top, hinged lid, and
handle. 145.00

Plates

6", "300," Libbey 50.00
7", "Astor," Hawkes 75.00
10", "Fuchsia," sgd Sinclaire 175.00
10", "Hindoo," Hoare 195.00
12½", intaglio strawberry leaf and
vine, sgd Tuthill 350.00

Punch Cups

Hobstars and fans, strawberry-diamond, etc., handled, set of 10, each 55.00
"Prism," P.&B., set of 6, each 35.00
"Russian" bowl, hobstar foot, set of
9, each 50.00

Punch Sets, 2 pcs

Bowl, 12" d and 10½" h, geometric
cutting, 9 cups 1,650.00
Bowl, 12" d, blown blank, snowflake
& floral, 6 cups 550.00

Rose Bowls

Engraved mums, rock crystal,
Sinclaire 110.00
"Middlesex," 8" d, New England . . . 375.00

Salts

"Fern," set of 6, individual 90.00
"Parisian," master, paperweight,
Dorflinger 85.00

Salt and Pepper Sets

Cut bodies, 2¾", SS tops 35.00
Panel and notch 15.00

Spoon Holder, Brilliant period cutting,
sgd Tuthill. 235.00

Sugar and Creamers

"Colias," handled, Pairpoint 115.00
Flowers (cut), vesicas of stems and
leaves, notched handles. 125.00
Geometric (allover) and hobstars, tricorn, triple pouring spouts 385.00

Geometric and intaglio, rare flat
shape, sgd Tuthill. 425.00
Notched Prisms, emb SS rim 185.00
Pinwheel and vesicas, rayed base . . 120.00
"Rosaceae," sgd Tuthill. 425.00
Strawberries, sgd Hawkes Gravic . . . 325.00

Stemware

Cordials, set of 6
Hobstar and prism, notched stem,
rayed base. 185.00
"Princess," sgd Libbey with sword 360.00
Goblets
Single, 6" h, "Brunswick" variation 130.00
Set of 4, 7" h, "Millicent," each . . 65.00
Set of 5, 6½", brilliant cuttings, hob-
star base, notched stem 800.00
Sherbert, set of 10, underplates, swag
of flowers and foliage, swagged
lines and circles, sgd Tuthill 1,250.00
Wines
Set of 4, clarets, 4½" h, cross-
hatching, rayed foot, flared rim. . 128.00
Set of 4, hobstars, strawberry-dia-
mond, and fans, sgd Maple City 150.00
Set of 6, strawberry-diamond and
fan, all cut to clear—2 in turquoise, 2 in cranberry, 1 in amber,
and 1 in cobalt 900.00
Set of 8, green, "Flute," Dummer . 200.00

Trays

8½" l, hexagonal, "Helene," Hawkes 75.00
9" d, serving, "Russian" 275.00
12" d, "Colonna," sgd Libbey. 800.00
12½" d, 12 pt. star and geometric, sgd
Hawkes. 650.00
14 x 8", ice cream, blown blank, cut
in sculpted intaglio fruits 325.00
14½ x 7½", fold in corners, "Chrysanthemum," Hawkes 750.00
14½ x 8½","Russian," including handles 1,100.00
16 x 10½ x ½", oval, "Devonshire,"
Hawkes. 850.00
18", ice cream, Russian filled vesicas
and hobstars 1,100.00

Tumblers

Single
"Desdemona," Clark 42.00
Fans and mitres, sgd Hawkes 35.00
"Heart," P. & B. 50.00
Set of 2, cut butterflies and flowers,
each 45.00
Set of 3
Cut and engraved, Sinclaire, each 28.00
"Empress," Libbey, each 42.00
"Harvard," Libbey, each 28.00
Set of 4, sgd Clark, each 50.00
Set of 5, 5½" h, well cut, heavy blank,
sgd Hoare, each 125.00
Set of 8, hobstars, fans, and canes,
each 45.00
Set of 12, hobstars and pinwheels . . 270.00

Vases

5½", bud, corset shape, geometric

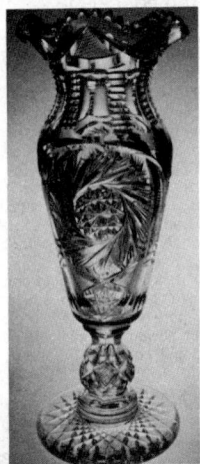

Vase, 13″ h, pattern cut teardrop knob, hobster base, sgd Bergen, $450.00.

gold tracery, green cut to clear, Honesdale.	**900.00**

Whiskey Glasses

Pair,"Daisy & Butterfly,"Pairpoint, each	**40.00**
Set of 4, geometric cutting, rayed base, each	**65.00**

CUT VELVET

History: Several glass manufacturers made cut velvet during the late Victorian era, c1870-1900. An outer layer of pastel color was applied over a white casing. The piece then was molded or cut in a ribbed or diamond shape in high relief, exposing portions of the casing. The finish had a satin velvety feel, hence the name "cut velvet."

Vase, 9½″, blue diamond quilted, $250.00.

cutting, SS banded rim sgd Gorham.	**58.00**
8″, engraved flowers and leaves, stick style, sgd Sinclaire	**160.00**
8″, wood lily (deeply carved), two pattern-cut handles, sgd Tuthill	**1,250.00**
9″, "Alhambra," SS top	**900.00**
10″, "Lace," corset shape, sgd Hunt	**265.00**
10″, "Queens," trumpet shape, hobstar base, faceted knob on stem, sgd Hawkes	**650.00**
12″, "Brunswick," trumpet shape, sgd Hawkes.	**275.00**
12″ "Chrysanthemum," trumpet shape, heavy blank, scalloped hobstar base, Hawkes	**525.00**
12″, "Harvard" and flowers	**135.00**
14″	
Cross-hatched panels frame engraved bird and flowers, pedestal, sgd Hawkes, SS top band mkd Hawkes/Sterling.	**750.00**
"Poppy," trumpet shape, sgd Tuthill	**1,100.00**
Punties, strawberry-diamond, fans, and hobstars	**325.00**
Punties & Zipper, trumpet shape, sgd Libbey	**295.00**
16″, bulbous, 28″ circumference, hobstars, notched prisms, swirled neck	**1,300.00**
16″, "Primrose," sgd Tuthill, pr	**875.00**
17½″, basketweave which crisscrosses four single stars in a sq,	

Bowl, butterscotch, applied clear feet. .	**225.00**
Creamer, 3½″, green, DQ	**325.00**
Cruet, blue, DQ	**300.00**
Ewer, pink, ruffled top.	**90.00**
Pitcher, 3¼″ h, 3″ d, rose, DQ, white cased, applied white handle	**250.00**
Rose Bowls	
3¼″, 4 crimp top, blue, DQ, white cased	**155.00**
3½″, 8 crimp top, deep rose, DQ, white cased	**195.00**
Tumble-up, 6¼″, rose, DQ, white cased.	**375.00**
Vases	
6″ h, 3¼″ d, sq top, shaded blue, DQ	**185.00**
7¼″ h, 3¾″ d, bottle shape, dusty rose, DQ.	**145.00**
8½″ h, 4⅜″ d, bottle shape, deep pink, ribbed	**150.00**
10⅜″ h, 4½″ d, ruffled top, deep rose, DQ	**275.00**

CZECHOSLOVAKIAN ITEMS

History: Objects marked "Made in Czechoslovakia" were produced after 1918 when the country claimed its independence from Austria Hungary. The people became more cosmopolitan, liberated and expanding their scope of life. Their porcelains, pottery, and glassware reflect many influences.

A specific manufacturer's mark may be identified as being much earlier than 1918; but, this only indicates the factory existed in the Bohemian or Austro-Hungarian empire period.

Reference: Ruth A. Forsythe, *Made In Czechoslovakia,* Richardson Printing Corp., 1982.

GLASS

Ashtray, 1½" sq, amber, molded floral and circle dec, jeweled over head handle	22.00
Basket, 6½", mottled green and red, crystal twisted thorn handle	190.00
Bowl, 3½", irid, pink, blue King Tut dec	225.00
Candlesticks, pr, 8½", blown, purple, sgd	65.00
Cigarette Box, cut glass, Art Deco	65.00
Lamp, 14", including 9½" shade, bell shape, irid, red, sgd	125.00
Rose Bowl, 4½", spatter, ruby	35.00
Tumble-up, blue with hp white glass over reserves of multicolored enameled blossoms, black foot and rims, sgd	75.00

Vases

7", Art Deco, cranberry, pink handles	90.00
7½", ruffled top, red, cased, applied clear rigaree	45.00
8", Art Deco, green and yellow, irid blue rim, 3 blue ball feet, sgd	100.00
8½" h, 6" d, orange, silver deposit decor of lady playing harp	75.00
Green, cased, white int, applied clear rigaree with multicolor dec	48.00

Salt and Pepper, 2¼" h, Tobys, blue coats, red britches, $20.00.

POTTERY AND PORCELAIN

Box, cov, pottery 6½" h, round, green handles, beige, multicolored molded fruit on lift off lid, pineapple knob, Erphila Art Pottery	120.00
Humidor, pottery, 8" h, 5" w, figural, man's head, brown, sgd	175.00
Pitcher, porcelain, 4½", figural duck, yellow handle	35.00
Plate, porcelain, 11½", rooster center	20.00
Salt, hanging, porcelain, floral dec, wooden hinged lid	38.00
Toby Mug, pottery 4", blue, rust, yellow, mkd	40.00
Vase, pottery, dark green and gold dec with 2 Persian figure medallions, sgd	55.00
Wall Pocket, pottery, 7¼", dark blue, peacock on flowering branch, pink, green, gold and violet	40.00

DAVENPORT

History: John Davenport opened a pottery in Longport, Staffordshire, England in 1793. His ware was of high quality, light weight and cream colored with a beautiful velvety texture.

The firm made soft-paste (Old Blue), lustre trimmed ware, and pink lustre with black transfer. There have been pieces of Gaudy Dutch and Spatterware found with the Davenport mark. Later Davenport became a leading maker of ironstone and early flow blue. His famous "Cyprus" pattern in mulberry became very popular. His heirs continued the business until the factory closed in 1886.

Biscuit Jar, 6½", Imari dec, SP cov and bail, 1870–86 mark	125.00
Bough Pots, pr, 7¼", tapering crescent shape, pearlware, scrolling foliage, iron red and olive green, no liners, imp marks, early 19th C	450.00
Bowl, 8", gold rim, floral dec, c1830	50.00
Butter Pat, flow blue	20.00
Compote, 9", hp, pink flowers, gold trim, c1830	95.00

Cup and Saucers

Blue and white, handleless	28.00
Pink lustre	45.00
Dessert Service, part, 2 sauce tureens on fixed stands, cov with lion finials, ladles, oval, pierced, handled basket with stand, 4 plates, pearlware, iron red and green, scrolling foliage in green line rims, c1815	1,450.00

Cup and Saucer, 6″ d saucer, 3¾″ cup, flowing blue, Amoy pattern, anchor mark, $65.00.

Dinner Service
Gilt molded edge, cobalt band with gilt grape leaves and tendrils, c1860, 50 pcs	**3,250.00**
White ground, green and white floral dec, two 7¼″ sauce boats with saucers, 6 shaped serving dishes, 11 dessert plates, c1825	**1,000.00**
Dish, 4″, Imari decor, orig hallmarked holder, 1870–86 mark	**135.00**
Ewer, 9″, multicolored, flower dec, c1830	**185.00**
Gravy Boat, white with blue and white flower dec	**90.00**

Pitchers
6″, tan transfer dec, serpent handle .	**175.00**
7″, scenic, blue and white	**185.00**

Plates
9¼″, scenic view, Braes Ballochmyle, gilt and pink border, printed Davenport Longford marks, mid 19th C	**45.00**
9¼″, scenic view, St. Michael's Mount, gilt and turquoise border, printed Davenport Longford marks, mid 19th C	**50.00**
10¼″, Waverly-Scotts Illustrations, dated 1852	**70.00**

Platters
9 x 12½″, Cyprus, mulberry	**95.00**
10⅜ x 13⅝″ l, chamfered corners, Amoy pattern, flow blue, incised anchor mark	**165.00**
Teapot, 6½″, Cyprus mulberry	**125.00**
Tureen, cov, underplate, 5¾″ d, Gothic, blue and whites, imp anchor mark, c1844	**125.00**
Vase, 9″, Imari dec, 1870–86 mark . . .	**135.00**
Vegetable Dish, Berry, imp anchor mark	**50.00**

DECOYS

History: Carved wooden decoys, used to lure ducks and geese to the hunter, in the past several years have become widely recognized as an indigenous American folk art form.

Many decoys are from the 1880–1930 period when commercial gunners commonly hunted over rigs of several hundred decoys. Many other fine carvers also worked through the 1930s and 1940s.

The value of a decoy is based on several factors: (1) fame of the carver, (2) quality of the carving, (3) species of wild fowl—the most desirable are herons, swans, mergansers, and shorebirds, and (4) condition of the original paint (o.p.).

The inexperienced collector should be aware of several facts. The age of a decoy, per se, is usually of no importance in determining value. Since very few decoys were ever signed, it will be quite difficult to attribute most decoys to known carvers. Anyone who has not examined a known carver's work will be hardpressed to determine if the paint on one of his decoys is indeed original.

Repainting severely decreases a decoy's value. In addition, there are many fakes and reproductions on the market and even experienced collectors are occasionally fooled.

Richard A. Bourne Co., Inc., Hyannis, Massachusetts, is one of the leading auctioneers of decoys. At the sale on July 10, 1984, a rare hollow carved Canada Goose, carved by Nathan Cobb, in a beligerent position, head gracefully extended out and canted slightly to the right, carved split tail, carved "N" on the bottom, with original paint and overall average wear, brought $19,000.00.

Decoys listed below are of average wear unless otherwise noted. O.p. indicates original paint.

Reference: Henry A. Fleckenstein, Jr., *American Factory Decoys*, Schiffer Publishing; Carl F. Luckey, *Collecting Antique Bird Decoys: An Identification & Value Guide*, Books Americana.

Periodical: *Decoy Magazine*, P.O. Box 1900, Montego Bay Station, Ocean City, MD 21842, quarterly publication.

Brant, St. Lawerence River, early 1900s, o.p., $800.00.

Artic Loon, Nova Scotia, o.p., winter plumage	**200.00**
Black Bellied Plover, P. W. Patterson, sgd on bottom, good details, o.p., minor wear to wing tips	**700.00**
Black Breasted Plover, Elisha Burr, Hingham, MA, branded "E. Burr" on bottom, o.p.	**1,750.00**

Black Duck, C. Reggie Martin, Burlington, NJ, head carved and tucked into content position with carved raised wing tip and tail feathers, o.p. **375.00**

Bluebill Drakes

Mason's Decoy Factory, Detroit, MI, standard grade, glass eyes, o.p., minor wear, neck putty damaged, 13½" l **225.00**

Stevens, H. A., Decoy Factory, humpback style, o.p. **500.00**

Bluebill Hen, hollow carved, Parkertown, NJ, old repaint worn, lightly hit by shot **75.00**

Blue Winged Drake, Mason's Decoy Factory, Detroit, MI, standard grade, glass eyes, good o.p. **475.00**

Blue Winged Teal Drake, John Baker brand on bottom, stamped on side, Bristol, PA, carved and raised wing tips and tail feathers, hollow carved, o.p. **120.00**

Brant, Reuben Corlies, NJ, branded CHM on bottom, o.p. **325.00**

Buffleheads, pr, Mason's Decoy Factory, standard grade, glass eyes, slight wear and minor age splitting to bodies **3,500.00**

Canada Goose, L. Travis Ward, c1915, hollow carved from the back, identified and sgd on bottom, traces of o.p., age splits in back and neck **1,200.00**

Canvasback Drakes

Madison Mitchell, Harve De Grace, MD, sleeping position, fine o.p., lightly hit by shot **375.00**

Mason's Decoy Factory, Detroit, MI Challenge grade, worn o.p., shot scars, age crack in bottom of back, glass eyes, 15¾" l **260.00**

Premiere grade, good o.p., worn to natural wood on sides **350.00**

Coot, Madison Mitchell, MD, o.p. **175.00**

Curlew, NJ, unknown maker, shows little wear, o.p. **300.00**

Eider Hen, carved raised wing, carved eyes, from the rig of J. C. Pike, o.p. . **700.00**

Goldeneye Drake, Mason's Decoy Factory, Detroit, MI, challenge grade, o.p., roughage to edges of bill **200.00**

Goldeneye Hen, 2 pc cork body, carved by Walter Smith, fine epaint **50.00**

Green Winged Drake, Mason's Decoy Factory, Detroit, MI, standard grade, glass eyes, o.p., lightly hit by shot .. **400.00**

Hooded Merganser Hen, Charles Clark, Chincoteaque, VA, c1900, in-use repaint **425.00**

Mallard Drake, Evans Decoy Factory, mammouth size, o.p., moderately hit by shot **200.00**

Mallard Hen, John Blair, Philadelphia, PA, and Elkton, MD, hollow carved,

orig beveled weight on bottom, well defined feathered paint all over head and body, o.p. **9,500.00**

Merganser Drake, red breasted, Capt. Henry Grant, Barnegat, NJ, 1860–1924, hollow carved, o.p. **500.00**

Mute Swan, NJ, hollow carved cedar construction, o.p. **1,050.00**

Old Squaw Duck, Hurley Conklin, branded "H. Conklin" on bottom, carved wing tips, o.p. **375.00**

Pintail Drakes

Hancock, Miles, Chinoteaque, VA, 1880–1974, balsa body, worn to natural, worn on right side and tail area **250.00**

John Blair School, hollow carved, o.p., chip at end of tail **450.00**

Redhead Drakes

Baumgartner, Frank, Houghton Lake, MI, c1930, glass eyes, old repaint, 11½" l **125.00**

Tolley, Capt. Willie, Hooperstown, MD, c1900, o.p. **175.00**

Redhead Hen, Mason's Decoy Factory, Detroit, MI, standard grade, glass eyes, o.p., minor flaking, age split in bottom **150.00**

Ruddy Duck, St. Clair Flats, unknown maker, hollow carved, o.p. **1,250.00**

Sea Gull, Robert White, Tulleytown, PA, carver's brand on bottom, hollow carved, o.p. **200.00**

Shoveler Duck, Herter's Inc., Waseca, MN, 1893–1960, o.p., minor wear ... **150.00**

Surf Scoter, carved eyes, bill and wings, from the rig of J. C. Pike, o.p. **900.00**

White Winged Scoter, Beale Island, ME, o.p. **250.00**

Widgeon Drake, Tim Eastland, Old Lyme, CT, initialed "TE" on bottom . **125.00**

Wood Duck Drake, Jay May, Langhorne, PA, finely carved feather work with raised carved wing tips **175.00**

Yellowlegs, A. E. Crowell, Cape Cod, MA, sgd rect brand, 1939, o.p. **925.00**

DEDHAM POTTERY

History: Alexander W. Robertson established the Chelsea Pottery in Chelsea, Massachusetts in 1860. In 1872 it was known as the Chelsea Keramic Art Works.

In 1895 the pottery moved to Dedham, and the name was changed to Dedham Pottery. Their principal product was gray crackleware dinnerware with a blue decoration, the rabbit pattern being the most popular. The factory closed in 1943.

The following marks help determine the approximate age of items: (1) Chelsea Keramic Art Works, "Robertson" impressed, 1876–1889; (2) C.P.U.S. impressed in a cloverleaf, 1891–1895; (3) Foreshortened rabbit, 1895–1896; (4) Conventional rabbit with "Dedham Pottery" stamped in blue, 1897; (5) Rabbit mark with "Registered", 1929–1943.

Several large sales of Dedham Pottery have occurred recently, including one held by Richard H. Bourne in Hyannis, Massachusetts in February 1984, where several pieces achieved new record prices.

Reference: Lloyd E. Hawes, *The Dedham Pottery And The Earlier Robertson's Chelsea Potteries*, Dedham Historical Society, 1968.

Ashtray, Swan, 4″	**245.00**
Bowls	
4″, Rabbit, ear handles	75.00
6″, Polar Bears	140.00
8″, Rabbit	175.00
9″, Magnolia, scalloped edge	300.00
Butter Dish, Rabbit	210.00
Butter Pats, 3⅝″ d, set of 4, star shaped, blue border stripe, crackle glaze, c1931	675.00
Candlesticks, pr, Azalea	350.00
Celery Tray, Elephant	165.00
Chocolate Pot, Grape, 9″	275.00
Coffee Pot, Rabbit	850.00
Creamers	
Magnolia, 3″	110.00
Rabbit, 4″	100.00
Cups and Saucers	
Duck	110.00
Polar Bear	120.00
Rabbit	100.00
Egg Cup, Elephant	350.00
Figurine, Rabbit	475.00
Marmalade, Rabbit	900.00
Mayonnaise, Elephant	800.00
Mugs	
Lobster	950.00
Rabbit	125.00

Bowl, 9″ d, 3½″ h, 1898, ins mkd "Dedham Pottery," $850.00.

Pitchers	
Owl	**300.00**
Rabbit, 5″	**250.00**
Plates	
6″	
Duck	65.00
Magnolia	65.00
Peacock	1,250.00
Polar Bear	200.00
6½″	
Lobster, 2 marks	185.00
Rabbit	70.00
Tulip, 2 marks	120.00
7½″	
Elephant	125.00
Turkey	145.00
8″, Owl	900.00
8½″	
Azalea	100.00
Dolphin & Mask	1,500.00
Duck, sgd Maude O., Davenport	275.00
Rabbit, stamped and impressed mark	100.00
Snowtree	150.00
Tapestry Lion	950.00
10″, Golden Gate, San Francisco, blue floral border, landscape with rising sun	3,500.00
10½″, Grape	125.00
Salts, figural	
Rabbit	125.00
Walnut shape on leaf, pr	1,650.00
Sugar, cov, Rabbit	200.00
Tiles	
Magnolia	120.00
Rabbit	125.00
Swan	150.00
Vases	
3″, volcanic glaze	200.00
7½″, green flambe, ivory, brown highlights, mkd Dedham/HCR	320.00
Vegetable Dish, cov, Rabbit	500.00

DELFTWARE

History: Delftware is pottery of a soft red clay body with tin enamel glaze. The white, dense, opaque color came from adding tin ash to lead glaze. The first examples had blue designs on a white ground. Polychrome examples followed.

The name originally applied to pottery made in the region around Delft, Holland, beginning in the 16th century and ending in the late 18th century. Tin came from the Cornish mines in England. By the 17th and 18th century English potters in London, Bristol, and Liverpool were copying the glaze and designs. Some designs unique to English potters also developed.

In Germany and France the ware is known as Faience and in Italy as Maiolica.

Note: Much souvenir type Delft material has been produced in the late 19th and 20th centuries to appeal to the foreign traveler. Don't confuse these modern pieces with the older examples.

Basin, 9″, blue and white, center flower and stylized rock work, geometric brick pattern rim, Bristol, c1760 .... **350.00**

Basket, 8¾″, round, pierced interlaced circle border, int., vase, flowers, table of shrubs, ext., trailing flowering branches, Liverpool, c1760 .... **1,325.00**

Bottle, 10″, blue and white, pagoda, trees, fenced garden, trellis pattern and flowers on shoulder, scrolls and geometric foliage on flared neck, Liverpool, c1760 .... **365.00**

Bowls
10¾″, manganese, int., flower spray within diaper border, ochre line rim, Lambeth, c1780............. **425.00**
12½ x 8″, scallop lattice handles, blue and white, harbor with ships, windmills, people in boats, sgd Crown RC Lion D'or Germany......... **125.00**

Butter Tub, 4½″, polychrome, harbor scenes on cov and sides, gold final and handles, mkd VA, Dutch, c1740–1760 .... **350.00**

Charger, 24″, tavern scene center, floral border, sgd................... **750.00**

Dish, 12¼″, octagonal, blue and white, cupid among shrubs within hatched pattern well, trellis and flowerhead border, Bristol, c1750 .... **225.00**

Miniature Lamp, 6⅛″ h, $200.00.

Figures
Lady, 6½″, polychrome, yellow and green bodice, brown apron, flowered skirt, sq grass mound base, Dutch, blue JE mark, 19th C..... **200.00**
St. Francis, 5¼″, manganese and orange, Dutch, late 18th C........ **200.00**

Jar, 16″, octagonal, polychrome, blue, iron-red, and green, putti holding baskets of fruit above hounds, alternate panels with peacocks on rockwork, Dutch, c1760 .... **950.00**

Pastille Burner, 5¼″, cottage with sign "Inde Rokende Moor"........... **325.00**

Pilgrims Bottle, 9″, blue and white, Victorian man walking, sgd, Dutch..... **450.00**

Plaque, 16″, blue and white, central flower basket, scroll design, border, Victorian red velvet frame, Dutch, 18th C..................... **750.00**

Plates
9″, blue and white, chrysanthemum issuing from pierced rock work, date and initials A. V/1753 in center, Bristol, 1753 .... **575.00**
12″, powder blue ground, cartouche with Oriental seated beneath flowering tree, border with 4 leaf shaped panels of trailing branches, brown line rim, Bristol, c1750 .... **350.00**
12″, scalloped rim, Bianco-Sopra-Bianco decor on border, center pagoda with Chinese figure in doorway, manganese, blue and yellow, Bristol, c1760 .... **400.00**

Platter, 15¼″, octagonal, blue and white, shrubs and bamboo in fenced garden, pagoda on rocky, shrubby island, trellis and flowerhead border, ochre line rim, Dublin, blue F mark, c1765 .... **775.00**

Salt, 3½″, rococo scroll molded, blue and white, painted flower sprays and foliage, flared base with blue molded scrolls, Dutch, c1750........... **200.00**

Spittoon, 5″ w, octagonal, flower sprays, everted rim with band of scrolling flowering foliage, Dutch, c1740........ **715.00**

Tiles, 4 mounted in wood frame, octagonal cartouches with blue baskets of flowers, manganese ground, carnations in corners, Bristol, c1740 ..... **190.00**

Tobacco Jar, 11¾″, oviform, blue and white, SPANJOLA within cartouche of rococo scroll, foliage and flowering plants, Dutch, blue P mark, c1720 .. **2,640.00**

Vase, 11¼″, baluster, blue and white, Oriental figures in landscape, terraces, stage and hunter, bands of scroll, stiff leaves top and bottom, Dutch, c1700 .... **525.00**

Wall Pocket, 7¾″, V shape, blue and white, molded, masks, scrolls, foliage, Liverpool, c1770 .... **350.00**

DEPRESSION GLASS

History: Depression glass is a glassware made during the period of 1920–40. It was an inexpensive machine made glass, produced by several companies in various patterns and colors. The number of pieces within a pattern also varied.

Depression glass was sold through variety stores, given as premiums, or packaged with certain products. Movie houses gave it away from 1935 until well into the 1940s.

Like pattern glass knowing the proper name of a pattern is the key to collecting. Collectors should be prepared to do research.

References: Gene Florence, *The Collector's Encyclopedia of Depression Glass,* Collector Books, 1984, 6th ed.; Ralph and Terry Kovel, *The Kovels' Illustrated Price Guide to Depression Glass And American Dinnerware,* Crown, 1983, 2nd ed.; Carl F. Luckey and Mary Burris, *An Identification & Value Guide to Depression Era Glassware,* Books Americana; Sandra McPhee Stout, *Depression Glass,* Book One (1970), Book Two (1971), Book III (1980), Wallace Homestead, updated pricing guides issued in 1980; Hazel Marie Weatherman, *1984 Supplement & Price Trends for Colored Glassware Of The Depression Era, Book 1,* privately printed, 1984.

Periodical: Depression Glass Daze, Box 57, Ottisville, MI 48463. Subscription: $14.50.

Collectors' Club: National Depression Glass Association, Inc., 8337 Santa Fe Lane, Shawnee Mission, KS 66212. Dues: $8.00.

Additional Listings: See *Warman's Americana & Collectibles* for more examples.

ADAM, Jeannette Glass Co., 1932–34. Made in green and pink; limited production in crystal and yellow.

	Green	Pink		Green	Pink
Ashtray.	15.50	20.00	Pitcher, 8″, 32 oz.	28.00	25.00
Bowls			Plates		
4¾″, berry	9.00	10.00	6″, sherbet.	3.50	4.00
5¾″, cereal	16.00	26.00	7″, salad, sq	7.00	6.75
7½″, fruit.	13.00	14.00	8″, luncheon	7.50	10.00
9″, salad	12.00	16.00	9″, dinner, sq.	12.00	16.50
9″, veg, cov.	38.00	40.00	9″, dinner, grill	12.00	12.50
10½″, oval.	12.00	20.00	Platter	14.00	14.00
Butter, cov	250.00	85.00	Relish, 2 part	15.00	12.00
Cake Plate, ftd	17.00	14.00	Salt and Pepper Shakers, pr	70.00	55.00
Candlesticks, pr.	70.00	55.00	Saucer, 6″, sq.	3.00	3.00
Candy Dish, cov	48.00	60.00	Tumblers		
Casserole, cov, 9″.	38.00	40.00	7 oz	15.00	18.00
Coaster	11.00	14.00	9 oz	34.00	36.00
Creamer	10.00	16.00	Vase	35.00	70.00
Cup	15.00	17.00			

AMERICAN PIONEER, Liberty Works, 1931–34. Made in crystal, green, and pink; limited production in amber.

	Crystal	Green	Pink
Bowls			
5½″, handled.	7.50	8.00	7.75
8¾″, cov	55.00	68.00	60.00
9″, handled	10.00	15.00	12.00
9¼″, cov	65.00	77.00	63.00
10¾″, console	35.00	45.00	35.00
Candlesticks, 6½″, pr.	45.00	55.00	45.00
Candy Dish, cov, 1 lb.	42.50	52.00	42.50
Cheese & Comport	15.00	18.00	15.00
Coaster, 3½″	13.00	15.00	12.50
Creamer, 3½″	6.00	8.00	6.50
Cup & Saucer	4.75	8.50	5.00
Goblets			
4″, 3 oz, wine	13.00	15.00	12.50
6″, ftd, 8 oz, water	14.00	16.00	14.00
Ice Bucket, 6″.	18.00	30.00	30.00
Lamp, 8½″ h.	55.00	70.00	65.00

	Crystal	Green	Pink
Pitchers			
5″, cov, urn	80.00	160.00	85.00
7″, cov	100.00	140.00	95.00
Plates			
8″, luncheon	9.00	4.00	6.00
11″, handled	9.00	10.00	8.00
Rose Bowl, ftd, flared	—	60.00	—
Saucer	3.00	3.00	2.50
Sherbets			
3½″	6.00	9.00	6.00
4¾″	10.00	13.00	10.00
Sugar, 3½″	5.00	8.00	6.00
Tumblers			
5 oz, juice	11.25	14.00	11.75
8 oz, 4″	13.00	18.00	12.50
12 oz, 5″	15.75	28.00	15.50
Vase, 7″	50.00	55.00	53.00

BOWKNOT, manufacturer unknown, late 1920s. Made only in green.

	Green		Green
Bowls		Sherbet, ftd	8.00
4½″, berry	8.00	Tumblers	
5¼″, cereal	10.50	5″, 10 oz	10.00
Cup	4.50	5″, 10 oz, ftd	10.00
Plate, 7″ salad	6.50		

COLONIAL FLUTED (Rope), Federal Glass Co., 1928–33. Made in crystal and green. Crystal made only in bridge sets consisting of plates, cups and saucers with a decal dec.

	Green		Green
Bowls		Plates	
4″, berry	4.00	6″, sherbet	2.00
6″, cereal	5.00	8″, luncheon	3.75
6½″, salad	10.00	Saucer	1.50
7½″, master berry	12.00	Sherbet	4.00
Creamer	12.00	Sugar, cov	12.00
Cup	4.50		

DIAMOND QUILTED, Imperial Glass, late 1920s, early 1930s. Made in black, blue, green, and pink; limited production in amber and crystal.

	Black	Blue	Green	Pink
Bowls				
4¾″, cream soup	13.75	13.00	10.00	6.50
5″, cereal	8.00	7.50	4.50	4.75
5½″, nappy, one handle	9.00	8.50	5.50	5.50
7″, crimped edge	18.00	17.00	5.50	5.75
Candlesticks, pr	30.00	26.00	14.00	13.00
Candy Dish, cov	28.00	26.00	18.00	16.50
Compote, cov, 11½″	—	—	40.00	40.00
Creamer	10.00	9.50	6.00	8.00
Cup	6.00	7.50	4.00	5.00
Goblets				
1 oz, cordial	—	—	6.00	6.00
2 oz, wine	—	—	6.00	6.00

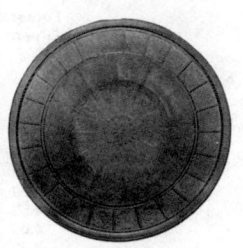

(Left) Adam, candlesticks, 3¾" h, pinks, $55.00: (center) Dorie & Pansey, plate 6", $10.00; (right) Iris, wine, 4½", $11.00.

	Black	Blue	Green	Pink
3 oz, wine	—	—	7.50	7.50
9 oz, 6", champagne	—	—	8.00	8.25
Ice Bucket	75.00	75.00	40.00	42.00
Mayonnaise, 3 pc	—	—	20.00	18.00
Pitchers, 64 oz	—	—	32.00	30.00
Plates				
6", sherbet.	4.00	4.50	3.00	3.50
7", salad	7.00	6.50	4.00	4.25
8", luncheon	12.00	10.00	5.00	6.50
14", sandwich	—	—	8.50	9.00
Sandwich Server, center				
handle.	25.00	25.00	15.00	18.00
Saucer	4.00	4.00	2.50	2.00
Sherbet	10.00	12.00	8.00	8.50
Sugar.	10.00	12.00	8.00	8.00
Tumblers				
6 oz	—	—	6.00	6.00
9 oz, water	—	—	10.00	10.00
12 oz, iced tea.	—	—	12.75	12.75

DORIC & PANSY, Jeannette Glass Co., 1937–38. Made in crystal, pink, ultramarine.

	Crystal	Pink	Ultramarine
Bowls			
4½", berry.	6.00	8.00	12.00
8", berry, master	20.00	20.00	60.00
9", handled	10.00	12.50	25.00
Children's Dishes			
Cup.	—	—	18.00
Saucer	—	—	25.00
Creamer.	65.00	65.00	175.00
Cup & Saucer	14.00	15.00	17.50
Plates			
6", sherbet.	6.00	8.00	10.00
7", salad	—	—	30.00
9", dinner	5.00	5.00	20.00
Sugar, open	65.00	65.00	165.00
Tray, 10", handled1	—	—	20.00
Tumbler, 4½", 9 oz	—	—	35.00

FOREST GREEN, Anchor Hocking Glass Co., 1950–57. Made only in forest green.

	Forest Green		Forest Green
Ashtrays		10″, sq, dinner	12.00
3½″	2.50	Platter, 8 x 11″	10.00
6½″, maple leaf shape	3.00	Punch Bowl, base, cups	40.00
Bowls		Salt and Pepper Shakers, pr.	8.50
4¾″, dessert	3.00	Tumblers	
6″, cream soup	6.50	4″, hourglass shape	2.50
7″, salad	9.00	5¾″, hourglass shape	2.50
Mixing, small	4.50	6½″, straight sides	4.50
Creamer	4.00	Vases	
Cup	2.00	3″, ruffled top	1.00
Pitcher, 22 oz, juice	15.00	6⅜″	
Plates		Coolidge	2.50
6½″, salad	2.00	Harding	2.50
8½″, luncheon	4.00		

IRIS (Iris and Herringbone), Jeannette Blass Co., 1928–32, 1950s, 1970s. Made in crystal and iridescent; recently in bicolor combinations.

	Crystal	Irid
Bowls		
4½″, beaded berry	35.00	8.00
5½″, fruit	5.50	5.00
8″, beaded, master berry	70.00	10.00
9½″, ruffled	7.50	7.00
11″, ruffled	8.00	6.00
Butter Dish, cov.	28.00	32.50
Candlesticks, pr.	17.25	25.00
Coaster	35.00	—
Creamer	7.00	6.00
Cup and Saucer	14.00	11.50
Demitasse Cup	21.50	50.00
Goblets		
5¾″, cocktail	12.50	22.50
8″, 9 oz, water	13.00	24.00
Lamp Shade	21.00	—
Pitcher	20.00	26.50
Plates		
6″, bread and butter	10.00	4.75
8″, luncheon	6.50	—
9″, dinner	27.50	20.00
11¾″, sandwich	15.00	12.00
Saucer	4.50	4.00
Sherbet	15.00	7.25
Sugar	12.00	10.00
Tumblers		
6″, ftd	9.75	11.00
6¾″, ftd	12.50	11.50
Vase, 9″	13.25	12.75
Wine, 4″	12.50	19.75

MADRID, Federal Glass Co., 1932, 1939. Made in amber, blue, crystal, green and pink. This pattern was reissued by Federal in 1976 and by Indiana Glass in the 1980s as "Recollection." The reissue was made using some of the original molds and with some variations to the original styles, colors and marks.

	Amber	Blue	Crystal	Green	Pink
Ashtray, 6″ sq	125.00	—	125.00	80.00	—
Bowls					
4¾″, cream soup	12.00	—	12.00	—	—

	Amber	Blue	Crystal	Green	Pink
5″, sauce	4.50	7.50	5.00	5.00	4.50
7″, soup	9.00	12.50	9.00	10.00	—
8″, salad, sq	12.00	60.00	12.00	15.00	—
9⅜″, master berry	20.00	—	20.00	—	—
9½″, salad	22.00	—	20.00	—	—
10″, veg, oval	13.00	19.00	13.00	14.50	14.00
11″, console	13.00	—	13.00	—	8.00
Butter Dish, cov	65.00	—	65.00	70.00	—
Cake Plate, 11½″	14.75	—	150.00	20.00	10.00
Candlesticks, 2¼″, pr	18.00	—	15.00	—	14.00
Coaster	30.00	—	25.00	—	—
Cookie Jar	30.00	—	32.50	—	29.00
Creamer	5.00	12.00	5.00	8.50	—
Cup	3.50	10.00	3.50	6.50	5.50
Jello Mold, 2⅛″, h	7.50	—	8.00	—	—
Marmalade Dish, 7″	10.00	25.00	10.00	14.00	—
Pitchers					
5½″, 36 oz, juice	27.00	—	27.00	—	—
8″, 60 oz, sq	40.00	145.00	40.00	115.00	32.50
8½″, 80 oz	47.50	—	50.00	175.00	—
8½″, 80 oz, ice lip	45.00	—	45.00	175.00	—
Plates					
6″, sherbet	2.50	7.00	2.50	3.25	3.00
7½″, salad	8.00	12.50	7.50	7.50	8.00
8⅞″, luncheon	4.25	17.00	4.25	8.00	8.00
10½″, dinner	24.00	40.00	24.00	26.00	—
10½″, grill	9.00	—	—	14.00	—
Platter, 11½″, oval	12.00	20.00	10.00	15.00	10.00
Salt and Pepper Shakers, 3½″					
Flat	32.50	—	32.50	25.00	—
Footed	60.00	110.00	60.00	80.00	—
Saucer	2.50	5.00	2.50	3.00	2.50
Sherbet	4.75	10.00	4.75	7.50	—
Sugar	25.00	80.00	25.00	28.00	—
Tumblers					
3⅞″, 5 oz	10.00	20.00	10.00	20.00	—
4″, 5 oz, ftd	18.00	—	18.00	35.00	—
4¼″, 9 oz	11.00	20.00	12.00	18.00	12.50
5½″, 10 oz, ftd	17.50	—	17.50	30.00	—
5½″, 12 oz	23.00	25.00	24.00	30.00	—

MT. PLEASANT (Double Shield), L. B. Smith Co., 1920s-1934. Made in amethyst, black, cobalt blue, green and pink.

	Black/ Amethyst	Cobalt Blue	Green	Pink
Bon Bon, 8¾″, center handle	20.00	—	8.50	8.25
Bowls				
5″, ftd, rolled edge	15.00	14.00	12.00	10.00
8″, sq, 2 handles	24.00	24.00	12.00	13.00
9″, ftd, fruit	35.00			
Cake Plate, 10½″, sq, open handles	27.00	18.00	14.00	13.50
Candlesticks, pr, double stem	36.00	34.00	15.00	15.00
Creamer	10.00	6.50	5.00	5.00
Cup	7.00	6.00	5.00	5.00
Plates				
8″, luncheon	12.00	8.00	7.00	6.50
9″, grill	9.00			
Saucer	3.00	3.00	2.50	2.75
Server, center handle	40.00			

	Black/Amethyst	Cobalt Blue	Green	Pink
Sherbet	13.00	13.00	6.00	6.75
Stirrers, set of 6	15.00	—	—	—
Sugar	12.00	15.00	8.00	7.75
Tumbler, ftd, water	—	14.00	—	—
Vase, 7", ribbed optic	40.00	12.00	—	—

OVIDE, Hazel Atlas Glass Co., 1930–35. Made in black, green, platonite with fired on colors and white.

	Black	Green Platonite White		Black	Green Platonite White
Bowls			8", luncheon	5.00	1.75
4¾", berry	6.50	—	9", dinner	7.50	—
5½", cereal	7.00	—	Platter, 11"	10.00	—
8", master berry	14.00	—	Salt and Pepper Shakers, pr	20.00	8.00
Candy Dish, cov	25.00	15.00	Saucer	3.00	1.00
Creamer and Sugar	16.00	5.00	Sherbet	6.50	1.50
Cup	6.00	2.00			
Plates					
6", sherbet	2.50	1.00			

PATRICIAN (Spoke), Federal Glass Co., 1933–37. Made in amber, crystal, green, and pink.

	Amber	Crystal	Green	Pink
Bowls				
4¾", cream soup	10.00	9.00	8.00	8.75
5", berry	9.50	6.00	6.50	10.00
6", cereal	15.00	6.50	12.00	12.50
8½", master berry	25.00	16.00	19.00	18.50
10", vegetable, oval	22.50	16.50	16.50	16.50
Butter Dish, cov	65.00	68.00	90.00	200.00
Cookie Jar	65.00	50.00	85.00	—
Creamer, ftd	9.50	9.50	6.50	7.00
Creamer and sugar, pr	12.00	12.00	13.50	14.50
Cup	7.00	6.00	8.00	9.00
Marmalade	25.00	25.00	25.00	20.00
Pitchers				
8", 75 oz	62.50	48.00	100.00	80.00
8¼", 75 oz	65.00	75.00	90.00	85.00
Plates				
6", sherbet	7.50	6.50	5.00	4.00
7½", salad	9.50	5.00	9.00	14.00
9", luncheon	7.00	5.75	6.50	6.50
10½", dinner	6.00	5.00	18.00	15.00
10½", grill	7.50	7.50	12.00	12.50
Platter, 11½"	25.00	12.00	18.00	12.00
Salt and Pepper Shakers, pr	47.50	45.00	50.00	75.00
Saucer	4.25	4.25	4.00	4.00
Sherbet	8.50	6.50	9.50	12.00
Sugar				
Cover only	30.00	25.00	40.00	45.00
Open	8.50	7.00	7.50	8.00
Tumblers				
4", 5 oz	22.00	22.00	22.00	22.00
4½", 9 oz	19.00	18.00	19.00	14.50
5½", 8 oz, ftd	30.00	—	35.00	—
5½", 14 oz	30.00	25.00	32.00	28.00

(Left) Madrid, pitcher, 5¾″, gold, $35.00, (center) Patrician, sherbet, 3″ h, 3½″ d, $8.50; (right) Windsor, bowl, 12″, $20.00.

ROUND ROBIN, manufacturer unknown, early 1930s. Made in green and iridescent.

	Green	Irid		Green	Irid
Bowl, 4″, berry	3.50	4.00	8″, luncheon	3.00	3.50
Creamer, ftd	5.00	6.00	12″, sandwich	4.50	5.00
Cup, ftd	3.50	4.50	Saucer	1.50	1.50
Domino Tray	20.00	—	Sherbet	3.50	4.00
Plates			Sugar	4.50	5.00
6″, sherbet	1.50	1.50			

TEAROOM, Indiana Glass Co., 1926–31. Made in pink and green; limited production in amber and crystal.

	Crystal	Green	Pink
Banana Split, 7½″	—	35.00	36.00
Bowls			
8¾″, master berry	—	45.00	40.00
Vegetable, oval	—	47.50	45.00
Candlesticks, pr.	—	27.50	45.00
Ceiling Fixture	100.00	—	—
Celery, 8½″	14.00	16.50	17.00
Center Handle Plate	—	55.00	70.00
Creamers			
3½″	—	15.00	15.00
5½″, ftd	12.00	10.00	10.00
Cup	—	27.00	23.50
Finger Bowl	—	—	25.00
Glacé, 7 oz	29.00	49.00	45.00
Goblet	—	49.00	45.00
Ice Bucket	—	70.00	60.00
Lamp	165.00	45.00	40.00
Marmalade, cov.	—	125.00	—
Mustard	37.50	48.00	48.00
Pitcher	—	95.00	95.00
Plates			
6½″, sherbet	—	22.50	17.00
8½″, luncheon	—	32.50	29.00
10½″, 2 handles	—	42.50	35.00
Relish, 2 parts	15.00	13.50	15.00
Salt and Pepper Shakers, pr.	50.00	35.00	40.00
Saucer	—	15.00	16.00
Sherbets			
Low	18.00	20.00	17.50

	Crystal	Green	Pink
Tall	—	30.00	—
Sugar			
3½"	—	15.00	14.00
4½"	12.00	8.00	10.00
Sundae	—	23.00	20.00
Tray for 3½" creamer and sugar	—	35.00	30.00
Tumblers			
6 oz, ftd	—	16.50	18.00
9 oz	—	18.00	20.00
12 oz, ftd	—	12.50	30.00
Vases			
6", ruffled	13.00	47.50	35.00
9", ruffled	—	42.50	40.00
11", ruffled	45.00	40.00	52.50

WINDSOR (Windsor Diamond), Jeannette Glass Co., 1936–46. Made in crystal, green and pink; limited production in amberina and delphite.

	Crystal	Green	Pink
Ashtray, 5¾"	15.00	35.00	35.00
Bowls			
4¾", berry	2.00	8.50	4.00
5", cream soup	6.00	15.00	12.00
5½", cereal	8.00	12.00	12.50
7⅛", console, 3 legs	6.00	—	17.50
8", two handles	6.00	14.00	18.00
8½", master berry	6.00	12.00	15.00
9½", vegetable, oval	8.00	12.00	12.00
12½", fruit, console	12.00	—	60.00
Butter Dish, cov	22.50	40.00	38.00
Cake Plates			
10¾", ftd	8.00	12.00	15.00
13½", thick	8.00	12.00	13.00
Candlesticks, 3", pr	12.50	—	30.00
Candy Jar, cov	8.00	—	20.00
Coaster, 3¼"	5.00	10.00	8.00
Compote	5.00	12.00	10.00
Creamer	3.00	10.00	7.00
Cup	2.50	7.25	6.00
Pitchers			
4½", 16 oz	20.00	—	80.00
5", 20 oz	6.00	—	—
6¾", 52 oz	15.00	55.00	22.50
Plates			
6", sherbet	1.50	4.00	2.25
7", salad	4.00	8.50	14.00
9", dinner	3.50	9.50	12.50
10¼", sandwich, handled	4.00	8.00	12.00
13⅝", chop	9.00	15.00	22.50
15½", serving	10.00	—	—
Platter, 11½", oval	8.00	10.00	15.00
Relish, 11½", divided	3.00	9.00	60.00
Salt and Pepper Shakers, pr	15.00	30.00	30.00
Saucer	3.00	4.00	3.50
Sherbet	3.00	12.50	6.75
Sugar, cov	5.00	25.00	22.00
Trays			
4", sq	10.00	25.00	30.00
4⅛ x 9"	12.00	24.00	20.00

	Crystal	Green	Pink
8½″ x 9¾″, handles	14.00	32.00	30.00
Tumblers			
3¼″, 5 oz	6.00	20.00	9.00
4″, 9 oz.	7.00	17.50	10.00
4″, ftd	4.00	—	—
5″, 12 oz	7.50	16.25	16.00
7¼″, ftd.	8.00	—	—

DISNEYANA

History: Walt Disney and the creations of the famous Disney Studios hold a place of fondness and enchantment in the hearts of people throughout the world. The release of "Steamboat Willie" featuring Mickey Mouse in 1928 harolded an entertainment empire.

Walt and his brother, Roy, showed shrewd business acumen. From the beginning they licensed the reproduction of Disney characters in products ranging from wrist watches to clothing. In 1984 Donald Duck celebrated his 50th birthday, and collectors took a renewed interest in material related to him.

The market in Disneyana has been established by a few determined dealers and auction houses. Hake's Americana and Collectibles has listed and sold Disney material for over a decade. In October, 1981, Phillips in New York held a sale devoted exclusively to Disneyana. Sothebys collector carousel auctions and Lloyd Ralston Toys auctions have continued the trend.

References: Marcia Blitz, *Donald Duck*, Harmony Books, 1979; Robert Heide & John Gilman, *Cartoon Collectibles*, 1984 (only covers Disney material); Cecil Munsey, *Disneyana*, Hawthorne Books, 1974; Richard Schickel, *The Disney Version: The Life, Times, Art and Commerce of Walt Disney*, Avon Books, 1968; Carl Terison, Jr., and Mel Morrison, *Price Guide To: Walt Disney Collectibles 1928–1939*, privately printed, nd.

Archives: Walt Disney Archives, 500 South Buena Vista Street, Burbank, CA 91521

Collectors' Club: Mouse Club, 13826 Ventura Blvd, Sherman Oaks, CA 91423

Additional Listings: See *Warman's Americana & Collectibles* for more examples.

Alice in Wonderland, fan card, full color, caption "Walt Disney's All Cartoon Feature—Alice in Wonderland," 8 x 10″ 65.00

Bambi
Book, "Walt Disney's Cut Out Book," 4 still cardboard sheets, 9½ x 4½″, Australiian ed., unused 60.00
Picture, framed, "Bambi and Mother," c1940, Courvoisier Galleries sticker, c1940 . . . . 250.00

Donald Duck
Celluloid, Donald Duck as musketeer on the defense, 9¼ x 6¼″ 100.00
Comic Book Art, orig 8 panel strip, pen and ink by Al Taliaferro, Walt Disney Comics #55, page 29, 19 x 13″ . . 600.00
Egg Cup, glazed china, Donald with wheelbarrow, 2 x 4 x 3″ 30.00
Poster, Donald fading from fatique while Horace Horsecollar whistles as he works, "You Can't Breakfast Like A Bird And Work Like A Horse," 1943 copyright, "Designed by Walt Disney For The California Food & Nutrition Committee," orig mailing envelope with 1947 postmark 65.00
Toy, long billed Donald carrying briefcase, 4 yellow wheels, colorful paper labels, 2 x 3 x 4″ 90.00

Dumbo
Figure, wearing clown hat, mkd Vernon Kilns #40, 3 x 5 x 4″ 250.00
Sketchpad, 24 ink drawings in sequence, stamped Disney Studios, c1940, 13 x 17″ 300.00

Fantasia
Celluloid, satyrs and unicorns dancing in pasture, applied to airbrushed ground, Courvoisier Galleries label, sgd "Walt Disney" in pencil on mat, 1940, 11½ x 8″ 1,250.00
Toy, carousel, unicorns, 25″, 1940 . . 225.00

Goofy
Celluloid, surprised Goofy about to be hit on nose with a mousetrap, applied to watercolor ground, sgd Walt Disney, c1940, 12 x 9″, ... 1,210.00
Figure, bisque, 2″, c1930 . . . . 25.00
Plate, china, Goofy seated on a crate, brick wall and flowers in back, cameos of Bambi, Thumper, Flower, 2 butterflies, and bluebird around edge, mkd Beswick, England, 7″ . . 45.00

Mickey Mouse
Bank, treasure chest, red leatherette, brass trim, emb Mickey and Minnie on top, mkd Zell Products. 175.00
Coloring Book, "A Mickey Mouse

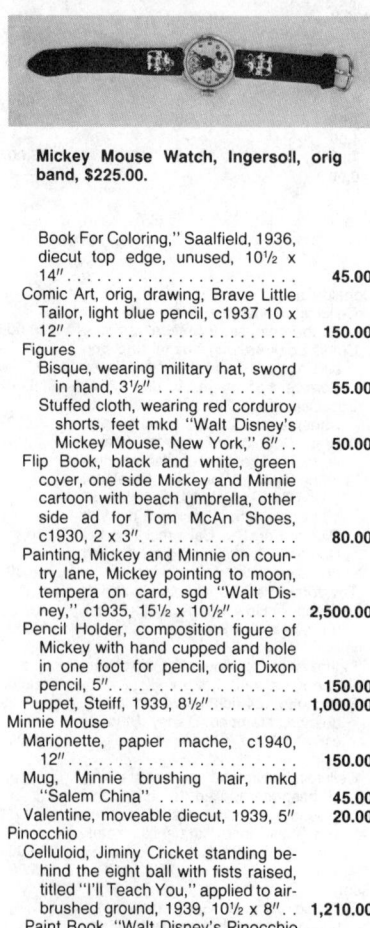

Mickey Mouse Watch, Ingersoll, orig band, $225.00.

Book For Coloring," Saalfield, 1936, diecut top edge, unused, 10½ x 14" **45.00**
Comic Art, orig, drawing, Brave Little Tailor, light blue pencil, c1937 10 x 12" **150.00**
Figures
Bisque, wearing military hat, sword in hand, 3½" **55.00**
Stuffed cloth, wearing red corduroy shorts, feet mkd "Walt Disney's Mickey Mouse, New York," 6".. **50.00**
Flip Book, black and white, green cover, one side Mickey and Minnie cartoon with beach umbrella, other side ad for Tom McAn Shoes, c1930, 2 x 3".................. **80.00**
Painting, Mickey and Minnie on country lane, Mickey pointing to moon, tempera on card, sgd "Walt Disney," c1935, 15½ x 10½"........ **2,500.00**
Pencil Holder, composition figure of Mickey with hand cupped and hole in one foot for pencil, orig Dixon pencil, 5"................... **150.00**
Puppet, Steiff, 1939, 8½"......... **1,000.00**
Minnie Mouse
Marionette, papier mache, c1940, 12" **150.00**
Mug, Minnie brushing hair, mkd "Salem China" **45.00**
Valentine, moveable diecut, 1939, 5" **20.00**
Pinocchio
Celluloid, Jiminy Cricket standing behind the eight ball with fists raised, titled "I'll Teach You," applied to airbrushed ground, 1939, 10½ x 8".. **1,210.00**
Paint Book, "Walt Disney's Pinocchio Paint Book," Whitman, 1939, 48 pgs, unused, 11 x 15" **35.00**
Pluto
Bank, china, black, white, and tan, Pluto with head turned toward slot on back, Disney copyright on base edge, mkd "Leeds China Co. 1949".................... **50.00**
Celluloid, Sheep Dog, Pluto walking across desert with bone in mouth, 1949, 9 x 27" **100.00**
Figure, bisque, labeled "Pluto The Pup" on base, 2½" **75.00**

Toys
Friction, bright yellow plastic, Marx, 3 x 6 x 4" **30.00**
Wood, 4 red wood wheels, orig paper labels, c1935, 2 x 5 x 2"... **80.00**
Snow White
Banner, premier, silk screen, 3 x 4½" **525.00**
Celluloid, Snow White kissing Grumpy on forehead, applied to watercolor ground, Walt Disney Enterprises label, 1937, 9½ x 7½" **950.00**
Doll, Doc, velvet, Knickerbocker Toy Co., 1938 .... **145.00**
Pie Bird, Dopey, ceramic, rosy cheeks, purple hat, yellow tinting, c1939, 2" d, 4½" h **50.00**
Pin, molded celluloid, multicolored, Snow White surrounded by dwarfs with musical instruments, orig 3½ x 4" white, blue, and yellow card, pin 1¾ x 2" **35.00**
Three Little Pigs
Bisque Set, litho box, 2 x 3½ x 5", top shows wolf puffing at brick house, 3½" figures, c1930........... **125.00**
Comic Art, orig, 10 panels, Sunday strip in pen and ink sgd Al Taliaferro, copyright Walt Disney Enterprises, July 24, 1938, 17 x 27" **1,800.00**
Salt & Pepper Shakers, black jackets with sailor collars, orig corks, mkd Japan, 3¼" h................ **20.00**
Uncle Remus, book, "Walt Disney's Uncle Remus," Simon and Schuster Little Golden Book, 1947....... **15.00**
Zorro, book, "Walt Disney's Zorro," Golden Press, 1958............. **10.00**
1001 Dalmations, celluloid, two puppies walking, 6¼ x 9¼" **150.00**

DOLL HOUSES

History: Doll houses date from the 18th Century to modern times. Early doll houses often were handmade, sometimes with only one room. The most common type was made for a young girl to fill with replicas of furniture scaled especially to fit into a doll house. Special sized dolls also were made for doll houses. All types of accessories and styles allowed a doll house to portray any historical period.

References: Flora Bill Jacobs, *Dolls' Houses in America: Historic Preservation in Miniature*, Charles Schribner's Sons, 1974; Donald and Helene Mitchell, *Dollhouses, Past and Present*, Collector Books, 1980.

Museums: Margaret Woodbury Strong Museum, Rochester, NY; Washington Dolls' House and Toy Museum, Washington, D.C.

Additional Listings: See *Warman's Americana & Collectibles* for more examples.

Litho on cardboard, folding, 2 rooms, 2 stories, Victorian, McLoughlin Brothers, NY, 15 x 16″ 650.00
Litho on wood
American, Bliss, Pawtucket, RI
  1 room, stable, rectangular, steepled roof with overlapping half moon shingles, attached chimney, steepled gable with pulley for hay bails, shaped architectural columns, simulated bricks and other features, 2 papier mache horses, c1875 . . . . 300.00
  2 rooms, 2 stories, steeple roof, gable windows, first story porch with metal grill work front, cut out and dec windows, hinged front facade, wallpapered interior, mkd "R. Bliss" on doorway, c1900 . . 575.00
  4 rooms, 2½ stories, steepled roof, steepled dormer, flat roof for 2nd floor porch, good architectural details including stained glass windows, curtains, 20″ h 600.00
English, 4 rooms, opens from middle, 4 columns with 2 balconies on front facade, restored, 27″ h. 150.00
German, Christian Hacker, Nürnberg, painted, stucco on front facade, 5 rooms, 2½ stories, steepled roof, 2 chimneys, papered inside, bay window, FAO Schwarz label, 34″ . . . 450.00
Wooden
  1 room, butcher shop, papered interior of shop displaying painted composition cuts of meat and carving instruments, bisque butcher doll at counter, 13½ x 15 x 5″ 600.00
  1 room, general store, painted balsa, handmade, primitive windowed front door and facade, interior fitted with counters, sectioned wall shelves displaying various goods, bisque storekeeper, helper and customer dolls, 14 x 24 x 15″ 300.00
  2 rooms, 2 stories, pitched roof, cov side porch, painted gray with green trim, hinged side, c1900, 31 x 19 x 11″. 350.00
  2 rooms, 2 stories, wood and pressed board, red shingled roof, green shuttered windows, Schoenhut decal on base, 16 x 15 x 11. . . . . . . 265.00
  4 rooms, 2 stories, 2 halls, stairs, roof opens to top rooms, plank floors, yellow and white hinged facade, colonial style, 42″ h. 1,650.00
  4 rooms, 2 stories, hinged, balconied facade, cream and red highlights, plank floors, Victorian styling, 42″ h 600.00

DOLLS

History: Dolls have been children's play toys for centuries. Dolls also have served other functions. During the 14th through 18th century doll making was centered in Europe, mainly in Germany and France. The French dolls produced in this era represented adults and were dressed in the latest couturier designs. They were not children's toys.

During the mid 19th century, child and baby dolls, made in wax, cloth, bisque, and porcelain, were introduced. Facial features were hand painted; wigs were made of mohair and human hair. They were dressed in baby or children's fashions.

Marks from the various manufacturers are found on the back of the head, neck, or back area. These marks are very important in identifying the doll and date of manufacture.

Doll making in the United States began to flourish in the 1900s with names like Effanbee, Madame Alexander, Ideal, and others.

References: Jean Bach, *Collecting German Dolls*, Main Street Press, 1983; Jan Foulke, *5th Blue Book Dolls and Values*, Hobby House Press Inc. 1982; R. Lane Herron, *Herron's Price Guide To Dolls and Paper Dolls*, Wallace-Homestead, 1982; Wendy Lavitt, *American Folk Dolls*, Alfred Knopf, Inc., 1982; Wendy Lavitt, *Dolls*, Alfred A. Knopf, 1983.

Periodicals: *Collectors Unlimited*, P. O. Box 1160, Chatsworth, GA 30705; *Doll Times*, 1675 Orchid, Aurora, Il 60506; *Doll Reader*, Hobby House Press, Inc., 900 Frederick Street, Cumberland, MD 21502; *Doll Values Quarterly*, Hobby House Press, Inc., 900 Frederick Street, Cumberland, MD 21502; *Dolls The Collector's Magazine*, Acquire Publishing Co., 170 Fifth Avenue, NY, NY 10010; *The Dollmasters*, Theriaults, P. O. Box 151, Annapolis, MD 21404.

Collector's Clubs: Madame Alexander Fan Club, P. O. Box 146, New Lenox, IL 60451; United Federation of Doll Clubs, 2814 Herron Lane, Glenshaw, PA 15116.

Museums: Margaret Woodbury Strong Museum, Rochester, NY; Yesteryears Museum, Sandwich, MA.

Additional Listings: See *Warman's Americana & Collectibles* for more examples.

Alt, Beck & Gottschalck, 28″, child, bisque socket head, composition and wooden ball jointed body, brunette human hair wig, gray glass sleep eyes, real lashes, painted facial features, open mouth, 4 teeth, antique blue cotton sateen pleated dress, c1915, marks: ABG/1362/Made in Germany/4½ 400.00

(Right) Emile Jumeau, mkd Jumeau 5″, $5,700.00. (Left) Emile Jumeau, mkd "Depose E57," $4,800.00.

Amberg, Louis & Co., 10″, character, solid dome bisque head, flanged neck, orig muslin body, composition arms, painted tinted brown hair, blue glass sleep eyes, open mouth, 2 upper teeth, c1925, marks: LA & S/371.2/ DRGM **250.00**

A. W., Special, 24″, child, bisque socket ad, fully jointed composition body, blue set eyes, painted facial features, open mouth, short brown hair, pink dotted swiss dress with tucked bodice and skirt, straw hat with flower trim, marks: 29/A-W, Special,/Germany. **375.00**

Bahr & Proschild, 12″, character baby, bisque socket head, 5 pc composition baby body, blonde human hair, blue sleep eyes, open mouth, 2 teeth, brown and white cotton romper, chip on left thumb, marks: BP with swords/0 585 2/Germany **225.00**

Belton, French, 17″, child, solid dome bisque socket head, jointed composition French body, long auburn human hair wig, blue paperweight eyes, closed mouth, dimpled chin, pierced ears, white taffeta dress, blue ribbon and lace trim, matching poke bonnet, mark: L. & C. **2,000.00**

Bergmann, C. M., 30″, child, bisque socket head, fully jointed composition body, deep blue sleep eyes, molded and painted facial features, open mouth, light blonde mohair wig, white dress with tucked yoke, deep flounce of anglaise embroidery, white cotton chemise and bloomers, pale blue wool and china silk coat, wide brimmed hat of ruffled pale blue silk and satin, marks: C. M. Bergmann/Simon & Halbig/13½ **975.00**

Bergner, Carl, 12″, character, bisque head with 3 faces (smiling, sleeping, crying) 2 with blue eyes, composition body, operative voice box, white cotton and lace dress, marks: C. B. . . **900.00**

Biedermeir, 19″, child, china shoulderplate, cloth body, china lower arms and legs, orig blonde mohair wig, painted blue eyes, closed mouth, molded black heeled boots, pink cotton print dress **375.00**

Bru, Casimir, 36″, child, bisque swivel head on kid lined bisque shoulderplate, kid torso, kid over wooden upper arms and legs, carved wooden forearms and lower legs, auburn mohair wig over cork pate, almond shaped blue glass paperweight inset eyes with spiral threading and dark blue outer rims, rose blushed eyelids, delicately painted facial features, closed mouth, dimpled blushed chin, pierced ears, aqua silk dress trimmed with multirows of tucking, lace, gold braid and embroidered with wild flowers, matching straw bonnet, c1875, marks: Bru Jne 15 (head)/Bru Jne (left shoulderplate)/N. 15 (right shoulderplate) . . . **11,000.00**

Century Doll Co., 15″, baby, solid dome bisque socket head on cloth body, composition hands, molded and shaded brown hair, pale blue sleep eyes, 2 glazed pearly upper teeth, long white cotton infant gown with ruffled hem, hooded white wool cape, marks: Germany/K inside diamond/ Century Doll Co. **450.00**

Chase, Martha, 25″, character, stockinette, cotton sateen cov over body, oil painted lower arms and legs, pressed and painted facial features and short blonde inpasto style hair, brown painted eyes, painted facial features, rosy complexion, antique costume with embroidered capelet, silk ribbons, ruffled bonnet, c1900 . . . . . **450.00**

Cloverleaf, 23″, child, bisque socket head on jointed composition French body, jointed wrists, long brown human hair wig, brown paperweight eyes, open mouth, 5 porcelain teeth, dimpled chin, pierced ears, pink bloused dress with flounced hem, marks: incised Cloverleaf/13 . . . . . **500.00**

C.O.D., 22″, child, bisque socket head, kid body, bisque lower arms, pin jointed hips and knees, blue sleep eyes, open mouth, orig dark blonde human hair wig, green polka dot dress with lace bodice and sleeves, marks: COD/93-4/DEP **250.00**

Denamar, E., 11″, child, bisque socket head, French composition and wooden jointed body, blonde human hair over cork pate, blue glass paperweight inset eyes, painted facial features, closed mouth, antique embroidered white dress, crocheted stockings, c1885, marks E 4 D **1,000.00**

Doleac, 17″, fashion, bisque swivel head, gusseted kid body, lower bisque arms, cork pate, blue-gray glass eyes, delicately painted facial features, well costumed, marks: L & Cie/L. Depose/4 D **1,350.00**

Dressel, 8″, Admiral Dewey, bisque socket head, 5 pc composition body, gray glass inset eyes, painted facial features, molded and painted hair, closed mouth, handlebar moustache, painted on boots, orig uniform, belt, sword, c1898, marks: 17D **275.00**

Eden Bebe, 27″, child, bisque socket head on fully jointed composition French body, jointed wrists, orig cork pate, dark brown human hair wig, deep blue paperweight eyes, open mouth, upper teeth, pierced ears with blue French glass earrings, 2 pc French coat dress of blue grosgrain and pink crepe, white braid and lace trim, matching bonnet, brown leather French shoes, marks: Eden Bebe/ Paris **1,500.00**

Effanbee, 14″, character, Skippy, composition socket head on wooden dowel neck, fabric torso, composition legs to above knees, composition arms, painted brown hair with long forecurl, blue side glancing eyes, rosebud mouth, painted tall brown boots, orig army uniform, matching cap with gold emblem, c1935 marks: Effanbee/Skippy/P.L. Crosby Copr **425.00**

Ellis, Joel, 15″, jointed wood, molded black hair, antique costume **375.00**

Fulper, 25″, character, bisque socket head, composition and wooden ball jointed toddler body, blonde human hair, bright blue glass inset eyes, open mouth, 2 upper teeth, white cotton dress with lace trim, matching bonnet, marks: CMU in triangle/Fulper in vertical scroll **450.00**

Gaultier, Ferdinand, 15″, adult lady, bisque swivel head on kid lined bisque shoulderplate, kid fashion body, gusset jointing, shapely waist, brunette mohair wig over cork pate, almond shaped blue glass paperweight inset eyes, painted facial features, 2 pc walking suit, turquoise with gilt beads, dangle earrings, c1875, marks: 1 on back of head/FG on shoulderplate/

red stamp on shoulderplate reads "France" **1,600.00**

Georgene Novelty, 13½″, character, Nancy and Sluggo, pr, cloth, pink muslin body and head, applied pink cotton satin mask face, painted facial features black "O" eyes, pug nose, watermelon smile, stiched on fabric shoes and socks, mitten hands, orig costumes of orange skirt, black vest, blue trousers, black patched jacket, orange trimmed cap, c1935; marks: A Georgene Doll/Georgene Novelty Inc./New York/Sluggo/ Nancy, orig paper label on wrists . . . **650.00**

Girard, Paul, 11½″, character, bisque, jointed composition body, blue stationery eyes, open mouth, pink dress, ribbon trim, small cameo, matching bonnet, marks: A/P7G. **250.00**

Handwerck, Heinrich, 28″, child, bisque socket head, composition and wooden ball jointed body, long blonde human hair wig, blue glass spiral threaded sleep eyes, painted facial features, open mouth, 4 teeth, pierced ears, antique white school dress, c1890, marks: 15/79/DEP **650.00**

Handwerck, Max, 27″, child, bisque socket head, composition and wooden ball jointed body, blonde human hair, brown glass sleep eyes, painted facial features, open mouth, 4 teeth, soft rose wool dress trimmed with silk bodice, tiny gold buttons and black velvet ribbon, c1900, marks: 50 H **525.00**

Ideal, 13″, personality, Shirley Temple, composition socket head, 5 pc composition body, curly blonde mohair wig, green sleep eyes, painted facial features, open mouth, orig tagged red percale dress with pleated front, white ruffled collar, matching hair ribbon, c1938, marks: 13 Shirley Temple Copyright Op. Ideal N. & T./Shirley Temple. **425.00**

Jumeau, Emile
  19″, child, bisque socket head with soft rose complexion, French composition and wooden ball jointed body, auburn mohair wig over cork pate, blue glass paperweight inset eyes, delicately painted facial features, closed mouth, antique pink satin dress with lace trim, antique white fur coat, matching cap, c1880, marks: Depose Tete Jumeau Bte SGDG 8/Jumeau Medaille d'Or Paris **2,500.00**
  28″, child, bisque socket head, French composition and wooden jointed body, brunette human hair, large

dark blue glass paperweight inset eyes, delicately painted facial features, closed mouth, well costumed, c1880, marks: Depose Tete Jumeau Bte/SGDG 13 Bebe Jumeau Diplome d'Honneur **2,900.00**

Kammer & Reinhardt

12½", Carl, bisque socket head, fully jointed composition body, painted facial features, painted blue eyes, closed pouty mouth, short ash blonde mohair wig, brown velvet Fauntleroy suit, white shirt, lace trimmed collar, matching cap, orig brown leather boots, marks: K * R/107/30 . . . . **4,400.00**

18", character, bisque socket head, composition and wooden ball jointed body, brunette mohair wig with side coiled braids, painted facial features, intaglio gray eyes, closed mouth with pouty lips, antique gold velvet dress, lace collar, orig body finish scuffed, c1912, marks: K * R/224/46 . . . . **3,500.00**

19", character, bisque socket head, composition and wooden ball jointed body, boyish blonde human hair wig, painted facial features, intaglio smoke gray eyes, closed mouth, antique gold velvet Buster Brown type suit with lace collar, orig matte body finish, c1912, marks: K & R 114/46. . . . . **4,250.00**

Kestner

12", character, bisque socket head, composition and wooden ball jointed body, brunette curly fleeced hair, brown painted eyes, closed mouth, molded teeth, impressed dimples, orig oily patina body finish, antique white dress, lace trim, c1900, marks: 185 . . . . **1,300.00**

19", character, bisque socket head, composition and wooden ball jointed body, blonde mohair wig over plaster pate, brown glass sleep eyes, painted facial features, open mouth, 2 upper teeth, white wool costume, orig pull string mama crier, marks: H/ Made in Germany/ 12 143 (head); Germany/ 2 (red stamp on body) **600.00**

Kley & Hahn, 23", child, bisque socket head, fully jointed composition body, painted facial features, brown sleep eyes, open mouth, upper teeth, short blonde mohair wig, orig pink crepe dress, underclothes, redressed due to frail orig garments, marks: 9/ Walkure /Germany **450.00**

Konig & Weinicke, 22½", character, boy, bisque head, jointed body, brown wig,

J.D. Kestner, Hilda, $3,000.00.

brown sleep eyes, smiling mouth, black velvet suit, marks: K & W 170 . . . . **625.00**

Koppelsdorf, Heubach

9", character, solid dome composition head, rich dark brown 5 pc composition bent limb baby body, painted black baby hair and mohair topknot, brown glass sleep eyes, pierced nostril with gold nose ring, open mouth, wide smile, row of painted teeth, pierced ears with gold bangle earrings, matching gold necklace, c1925, marks: Heubach Koppelsdorf/463 15/0 Germany . . **400.00**

9", child, bisque socket head, composition 5 pc body, long slender limbs, brunette bobbed wig, gray glass sleep eyes, painted facial features, open mouth, 4 teeth, painted white socks, brown sandals, c1925, marks: Heubach Koppelsdorf/ 409-5/0/Germany **325.00**

A. Lanternier & Cie, 28", child, bisque head, composition and ball jointed body, blue paperweight eyes, pierced ears, open mouth with row of teeth, marks: Depose/ Fabrication/ Francaise/ Favorite/ No. 14/Ed Tasson/ SC/AL & Cie/Limoges. **800.00**

Lenci, 25", character, felt swivel head, muslin adult torso with felt arms and legs, pressed mask, painted facial features, intaglio blue side glancing eyes, closed mouth, blonde mohair wig in elegant coiffure, orig white puffed sleeve dress, long black satin skirt, lace trim, velvet ribbons, flowered hat, elaborate undergarments, rose felt garter, c1930, marks: orig label . . . **400.00**

Limoges, 21″, walker, bisque socket head, composition French body, brown human hair wig, blue paperweight eyes, 5 upper teeth, dimpled chin, pierced ears with orig earrings, yellow satin dress with lace trim, hands repainted, marks: Limoges/ France 9 . . . . **325.00**

Madame Alexander

11″, character, Scarlett O'Hara, composition socket head, 5 pc composition body, black curly human hair, green sleep eyes, real lashes, closed mouth, orig red and white striped dress, elegant red velvet bonnet, red plume, c1939, marks: Scarlett O'Hara/Madame Alexander/ New York/USA. **450.00**

11″, personality, Annette of Dionne Quintuplets, composition socket head, 5 pc toddler body, brunette human wig, brown sleep eyes, real lashes, pug nose, closed rosebud mouth, c1935, marks: Dionne/ Mme. Alexander. **475.00**

Marseille, Armand, 14″, character, solid domed bisque socket head, composition bent limb baby body, brown molded hair in upraised topknot, molded forelock curls, intaglio blue side glancing googly eyes, painted facial features, pug nose, closed mouth in watermelon smile, c1915, produced for George Boegfeldt, marks: GB 252/Germany/A. O. M./DRGM **1,200.00**

Morimura Brothers, 15″, character baby, bisque socket head, composition bent limb baby body, blonde human hair, bright blue glass sleep eyes, painted facial features, open mouth, 2 upper teeth, embroidered antique baby gown, c1917, marks: MB in circle/ Japan 5 . . . . **225.00**

Montanan, English Artist, 20″, baby, poured wax shoulderhead, orig muslin body, poured wax lower arms, hands, lower legs and feet, blonde human hair inserted into scalp in small tendrils, half moon shaped blue glass inset eyes, heavily modeled upper lids, real lashes, closed mouth, painted facial features, soft blush on cheeks and ears, orig frail pink silk gown, matching cape, ruffled bonnet, c1840, unsigned. **1,900.00**

Nippon, 21″, baby, solid dome bisque socket head, 5 pc composition baby body, brush stroked light brown hair, blue sleep eyes, open mouth, 2 upper teeth, double chin, red velvet 2 pc suit,

white collar, white crochet bonnet, c1920, marks: F Y/Nippon/106 . . . **175.00**

Putnam, Grace S., 11″, Bye-lo, baby, solid domed bisque head with flanged neck, muslin body, celluloid hands, brown painted baby hair and lashes, brown glass sleep eyes, painted facial features, c1923, marks: Copyright by Grace S. Putnam/Made in Germany **300.00**

Queen Louise, 25″, child, bisque socket head, fully jointed composition body, painted facial features, light brown hair, open mouth, upper teeth, 3 pc walking suit, maroon and navy striped satin skirt, front dickey trimmed with lace, maroon velvet jacket with back bustle, matching velvet bonnet trimmed with feathers and lace, marks: 29/Queen Louise/100/ Germany **225.00**

Que San Baby, 4½″, baby, all bisque, jointed at shoulders, Oriental painted facial features, painted black hair, green ribbons, lavendar slippers, orig red paper label on tummy, marks: red label "Que San Baby" 1918 on back **50.00**

Rabery & Delphieu, 17″, child, bisque socket head, French composition and wooden jointed body, straight wrists, blonde fleece wig over cork pate, large brown glass paperweight inset eyes, corners of closed mouth turned up, antique clothes, pin striped dress, lace trim, brown leather slippers, carries own trunk of vintage clothing, c1875, marks: R.O.D. **3,000.00**

Sannier & Caut. 32″, bisque socket head, composition and wooden ball jointed body, blonde mohair wig, blue glass sleep eyes, painted facial features, open mouth, 4 teeth, pierced ears, modeled double chin with dimple, orig body finish, antique red wool dress, trimmed with black velvet, matching bonnet, carries wooden handled black carved parasol, c1900, marks: S & C/Germany/15 . . . . **1,100.00**

Schmidt, Bruno, 19″, bisque socket head, composition and wooden ball jointed toddler body with side hip jointing, brunette braided hair, brown glass inset eyes, open mouth, 2 teeth, antique blue calico dress, embroidered trim, antique shoes, c1920, marks: Made In Germany/BSW in heart/ 2097 . . . . **550.00**

Schmitt et Fils, 24″, child, bisque socket head, French composition and wooden jointed body, straight wrists, almond shaped dark blue glass paperweight eyes, painted facial features, brunette human hair over cork pate,

Simon and Halbig, orig gown, turquoise beads and gold trim, sapphire and gold topped walking stick, $5,000.00.

royal purple velvet costume, c1875, marks: SCH in a shield/45 on head ... **8,000.00**

Schoenhut, 15″, baby, bent limb wooden body, painted blue eyes, blonde mohair wig, white cotton night dress ... **250.00**

Simonne, 17″, French Fashion, bisque shoulderplate, kid lined swivel neck, bisque lower arms, kid over wood torso, upper legs and arms, delicate painted features, pierced ears, blue paperweight eyes, closed mouth, blonde mohair wig on orig cork pate, 2 pc long blue brocade walking dress, satin underskirt, panieried jacket trimmed with black pleats, minor damage to hands, marks: oval blue stamp "Simonne, Paris". ... **2,000.00**

Societe Francasie de Bebes et Jouets, 21½″, child, bisque socket head, French composition and wooden jointed body with straight walker legs, blonde wig, almond shaped light blue glass sleep eyes with spiral threading, painted facial features, open mouth, 4 upper teeth, walker legs, embroidered lace dress, matching bonnet, ribbon trim, c1915, marks: 21 D S.F.B.J. 60 Paris 5 on head/Fabrication Francaise S.F.B.J. Paris label on torso ... **900.00**

S.P.S., 17″, toddler, bisque socket head, 5 pc composition body, purple cardboard pate, orig gold mohair wig, blue set eyes, 2 upper teeth, antique white baby dress, made in Saare, France, marks: 1920/SPS in shield/12 ... **350.00**

Steiner, Bourgoin, 8¼″, baby, bisque socket head, fully jointed French composition body, straight wrists, upper leg and arm parts of turned wood, pale blue inset eyes, painted facial features, closed mouth, ash blonde mohair wig, minor paint chips, marks: handwritten in red script letters "Steiner Bte, Bourgoin"/incised Ste. C/4/0 ... **1,300.00**

Steiner, Edmund, 14″, child, bisque, socket head, composition and wooden ball jointed body, brunette human hair wig, brown glass inset eyes, painted facial features, open mouth, 4 teeth, red gingham school dress, c1910, marks: Majestic/3 reg'd ... **475.00**

Steiner, Jules Nicholas, 27″, child, bisque socket head, plump baby limbs, French composition and wooden jointed body, early straight wrists, brunette mohair wig over cork pate, almond shaped dark blue glass paperweight inset eyes, painted facial features, closed mouth, pierced ears, frail ivory lace and satin dress with matching bonnet, ribbon trim, c1875, marks: J. Steiner Bte S.G.D.G./Paris Fl Re A 15 plus elaborate antique pencil script on back torso ... **5,700.00**

Strobel & Wilkins, 17″, character, bisque socket head, composition bent limb baby body, blonde human hair wig, moon shaped brown glass inset eyes which glance to the right, long painted curly sunburst type lashes, closed mouth in molded watermelon smile, white baby dress, matching bonnet, c1915, marks: 165/9/Jubilee trademark ... **2,300.00**

Unknown Maker, 22″, lady, bisque swivel head on kid lined bisque shoulderplate, kid gusseted jointed adult body, brunette human hair wig over cork pate, pale blue glass inset eyes, delicate painted facial features, closed mouth, French, c1875, marks: 5 on head and shoulderplate ... **1,200.00**

Wellings, Norah, 34″, character, Little Bo Peep, felt mask, pressed face, painted facial features, blue side glancing eyes, closed mouth, brunette mohair wig, muslin torso, felt legs, stitched fingers, long pink satin dress, 7 rows of ruffles, laced vest, black lace gloves, pink bonnet, fabric flowers, c1935, marks: cloth label on wrist "Made Expressly by Norah Wellings" ... **525.00**

DOOR KNOCKERS

History: Before the advent of the mechanical bell or electrical buzzer and chime, a door knocker was considered an essential door ornament to announce the arrival of visitors. Metal was used to cast or forge the various forms; many cast iron examples were painted. Collectors like to find knockers with English registry marks.

BRASS

Anchor	55.00
Bear standing by barren tree, 3½"	35.00
Boar's Head	32.00
Butterfly, oval back plate	30.00
Eagle, 8½"	60.00
Elephant's Head	55.00
Indian's Head, 7½"	125.00
Woodpecker, 4"	75.00

BRONZE

Cat, 3½" h, arched back, English, c1900	25.00
Lion's Head, 4 x 6" backplate	25.00

CAST IRON

Basket of Flowers, 4", painted	25.00
Cat's Head, 4"	35.00
Horseshoe	40.00
Lady's Head, c1870	75.00
Owl on Branch, oval back plate, brown, yellow eyes, green ribbon	75.00
Parrot on Branch, 4½", pink and rose body, oval back plate	35.00

Parrot, green, yellow paint, $55.00.

DOORSTOPS

History: Doorstops became popular in the late 19th century. They can be found flat or three dimensional and were made in cast iron, bronze, wood, and other material. Hubley, a leading toy manufacturer, made many examples.

Note: Pieces described below contain at least 80% or more of the original paint and are in very good condition. Repainting drastically reduces price and desirability. Poor original paint is preferred over repaint.

B + H = Bradley and Hubbard.

Reference: Marilyn Hamburger and Beverly Lloyd, *Collecting Figural Doorstops*, A.S. Barnes and Company, 1978.

Advisor: Craig Dinner.

Boston Bulls	
9" h, full figure, facing left, black with white markings	70.00
9½" h, full figure, facing right, brown with tan markings	55.00
Boxer, 8¾", dog, full figure, facing forward, brown with lighter markings . . .	110.00
Cat, 8", flatback, on pillow, black with red bow and ribbon around neck	65.00
Cat, Persian, 9½" h, 7" w, full figure, sitting, gray with lighter markings, sgd Hubley	80.00
Clipper Ship, 5¼", flatback, full sails, waves at base, small American flag on top mast, two rubber stoppers on back for door, sgd CJO	45.00
Cottages	
5¾" h, 8⅝" w, flatback, blue roof, flowers in fenced garden, path, cape type, sgd Eastern Speciality Mfg. Co. –14	75.00
6" h, 8" w, flatback, flowers, Dutch dormer, chimney, path to arched door, sgd Hubley 211	55.00
Dog, Art Deco, 6⅜", white with black markings, prong for door, sgd Spencer, Guilford, CT	55.00
Drum Major, 12⅝", full figure on sq base, ivory pants, red hat with feather, yellow baton in right hand, left hand on waist	210.00
Dwarf, 9⅞", full figure, red cap, blue apron, yellow shirt, keys in left hand, lantern in right hand, red shoes, beard	165.00
Fox Terrier, Wire Haired, 8" h, 9" l, full figure, facing sideways, tail straight in air	75.00
Frog, 3⅝" h, 4" l, full figure, solid casting, sitting, yellow chest, green body with yellow rimmed black eyes	45.00
*Fruit Bowl, 7" h, 7" w, flatback, variety of fruits, natural colors, green-blue bowl, natural colors on fruit, sgd Hub-	

Elephant, 10⅜″, flatback, gray with white tasks, sgd B & H 7999, $145.00.

ley 456 (Note: example with brown
bowl is reproduction) **75.00**

Girls

French, 9″, flatback, with hat, holding
skirt out at sides, sgd Hubley 23 . . **95.00**

Spanish, 9″, flatback, black dress with
colored flowers, fan in right hand,
left hand on hip, unsgd but Hubley
193 . . . . **85.00**

Horse, 10¾″, full figure, brown with white
markings, unsgd but Hubley 345 . . . . **115.00**

London Mail Coach, 7¼″ h, 12″ l, two
sided, horses, driver, bugler on back
of coach, passengers, orange, green,
and red, prongs on both sides of rear
wheels **45.00**

Mammy, 8½″, full figure, blue dress,
white apron, red kerchief with white
spots on head, sgd Hubley 327 on
inside **125.00**

Pan, 7″ h, flatback, with flute, sitting on
mushroom, green outfit, red hat and
sleeves, green grass at base **95.00**

Penguin, 10″ h, full figure, facing side-
ways, top hat, bow tie, white chest,
black wings and back, yellow feet and
beak, unsgd Hubley **165.00**

Polly, 8″ h, flatback, bird with crest, on
perch, blue bird, tan face, yellow back,
orange chest, dark tan perch, sgd
Hubley 180 . . . . **65.00**

Poppies and Cornflowers, 7¼″ h, 6½″
w, striped pot, sgd Hubley 265 . . . . . **55.00**

Poppies and Snapdragons, 7½″ h,
7¼″ w, flatback, handle on basket,
multicolored, triangular base, sgd
Hubley 484 . . . . **60.00**

Rabbit, 15¼″, flatback, tan natural color
for rabbit, sitting on hind paws, front

paws at chest level, green grass, detailed casting, sgd B+H 7800 . . . . . **235.00**

Rose Basket, 11″ h, ivory colored wicker
basket with bow on handle, natural
colored flowers, sgd Hubley 121 . . . . **65.00**

Windmill, 6¾″ h, 6⅞″ w, ivory colored
mill, red roof, small house at side,
green base **65.00**

Zinnias

7¼″ h, 7″ w, flatback, multicolored
flowers in fancy bowl, sgd Hubley
267 . . . . **65.00**

11⅝″ h, blue-black vase, multicolored
flowers, detailed casting, 2 rubber
stoppers for door, sgd B+H **115.00**

DRESDEN/MEISSEN

History: Augustus II, Elector or Saxony and King
of Poland, founded the Royal Saxon Porcelain Manufacture in the Albrechtsburg, Meissen, in 1710.
Johann Frederick Boettger, an alchemist, and
Tschirnhaus, a nobleman, experimented with kaolin
clay from the Dresden area to produce porcelain.
By 1720 the factory produced a whiter hard paste
porcelain than that from the Far East. The factory
experienced its golden age in the 1730–50s period
under the leadership of Samuel Stolzel, kiln master,
and Johann Gregor Herold, enameller.

Many marks were used by the Meissen factory.
The first was a pseudo-oriental mark in a square.
The famous crossed swords mark was adopted in
1724. A small dot between the hilts was used from
1763–74 and a star between the hilts from 1774 to
1814. Two modern marks are swords with a ham-
mar and sickle and swords with a crown.

The Meissen factory was destroyed and looted
by forces of Frederick the Great during the Seven
Years War. It was reopened, but never achieved
its former greatness. In the 19th century, the factory
reissued some of its earlier forms. These later
wares are called "Dresden" to differentiate them
from the earlier examples. Further, there were several other porcelain factories in the Dresden region;
and, their products also are grouped under the
"Dresden" designation by collectors.

DRESDEN

Cache Pot, 5¼″ d, 5″ h, hp, pink roses,
florals, gilt border, 2 handles, crown
mark/Dresden, c1870 . . . . **145.00**

Chocolate Pot, 8″, chinoiserie scenes in
ovals with gilding and florals, gilt and
floral cov, c1750 . . . . **800.00**

Clock, 17½″, cherub with doves on top,
French movement, porcelain dial . . . **525.00**

Cups and Saucers
 Demitasse, 2⅛" cup, six feet, 4" saucer, white, applied clusters of multicolored flowers, painted flowers and leaves, sgd C. S. Dresden . . . **125.00**
 Tea, cream ground, inside cup hp children playing, gold trim, large gold monogram on saucer is covered by cup, A. Lamm **165.00**
 Tea, Oriental flowering branches and birds, gilt highlighting **125.00**
Figure, colonial couple, 8¼", oval base with gold scrolls in relief, ormolu brass base, Dresden **160.00**
Lamp, miniature, 8¼", scattered polychrome floral decor, P & A burner, Pairpoint, sgd Dresden. **435.00**
Loving Cup, 3 handles, 3 panels of garden scenes, gold decor, sgd Dresden **230.00**
Plates
 8⅞", reticulated border, center decor of Dutch 18th C port scene, sgd Dresden **75.00**
 10", cabinet, wavy edge with panels of pierced trellis alternating with pierced reserves of bouquets, center with molded basket of spring flowers, set of 15. . . . . **725.00**
Tea Caddy, 5¼" h, 3½" d, sq, floral lift off lid, 2 sides with lacy gold and flowers, other sides courting scenes, sgd Dresden **125.00**
Trays, pr, 15½", shell corners, 2 handles, Dresden style flowers **350.00**
Vase, cov, 10", blue, gold biblical figures near sea, mkd Dresden Germany "Lohengrin's Storkunfit". **150.00**

Figurine, three putti around campfire, 5⅞" h, mkd, $750.00.

MEISSEN

Beaker and Saucer, Flying Dragon pat, kakiemon decor, red and gold, 2 handles, molded saucer with brown border, c1730 . . . . **650.00**
Bowl, serving, 14" d, 10¾" h, cobalt center, white and gold oak leaves **275.00**
Box, 3½" sq, white, small blue and pink flowers, gold edging **250.00**
Cake Plate, 11½", shape of grape leaves and grapes, pink, gold and white, 19th C **150.00**
Candlesticks, pr, 8½", Greek columns with painted scenes, 4 lady's face masks with white drapery over hair, separated by large scrolls on top of each column, sq bases with molded wreaths wound with pink ribbons, . . . **850.00**
Charger, 15⅛", scalloped rim, 2 central wheat sheaves with scattered kakiemon flowers, brown rim with geometric raised border design, c1730. . . . . . . **400.00**
Chocolate Pot, cov, 6⅞", cylindrical, blue and white, reeded, branch shaped spout, right angle handle, underglaze blue 36, c1760. . . . . **225.00**
Coffee Pot, 6½", pear shape, 4 panels with chinoiserie decor of 3 or more Oriental figures, landscapes, birds, foliate, and scrolling gilt border, gilt 19, c1730. . . . . **325.00**
Compote, 10¾" d, 6¾" h, ftd, white with emb gold trim and multicolored emb fruit and alternating "Deutsche Blumen," c1860. . . . . **375.00**
Condiment Dish, cov, 2⅞", alternating panels of sea battles and gilt ground reserved with single flower, spade shaped handles, stalk finial, leaves and applied flowers on cov, c1740 . . **225.00**
Creamer, 4⅝", yellow, 2 large cartouches with purple sailing vessels, elaborate rococo handle, beak spout, c1740. . . . . **300.00**
Cups and Saucers
 Coffee, harbor scenes in gilt framed cartouches, kakiemon flowers, gold borders, gilt L, c1740 . . . . **350.00**
 Tea, white with pastoral scenes in colors, flowers, and birds between scenes, rococo style molding, brown edges, c1750. . . . . **375.00**
Figures
 Children, one with bird coming out of open birdcage, the other with huge mask and dog jumping through its open mouth, H88. . . . . **875.00**
 Chinese couple seated in arbor with roses, woman holding book on lap, 8", imp mold # 2653. . . . . **1,050.00**

Hound dog lying with legs askew, resting on front paw, white decor, 5" l, 1¼" h **165.00**
Vendor, blue striped shirt, dark green britches, holding cloth cov basket, grassy rock base with flowers, c1745 .... **450.00**
Jar, cov, 4¼", globular, 3 paw feet, scrolling J handle, quatrefoil panels with kakiemon flowers, c1725 ...... **300.00**
Knives and Forks, silver gilt 3-pronged forks and blades, birds on branches-and flower sprays within molded scroll borders, gilding, c1750, set of 24 .... **1,650.00**
Plates
  9¼", courting couple in garden, band of blue and red ribbon broken by floral bouquets, reticulated wavy edge, gilt decor, star mk **125.00**
  9¾", central butterfly on flowering stalk, brown bordered rim with scattered kakiemon flowers, c1730 ... **225.00**
Salts, 6", open, figural, man and woman representing winter and summer, each sitting on side of basket, late 18th C, pr **2,200.00**
Sauce Boat, 9¾", Sulkousky pattern raised border, flowers, molded Indian head spouts, 4 gold scroll feet, 2 handles, c1745 .... **500.00**
Scent Bottle, 3", monk carrying girl hidden in sheaf of wheat and holding basket of eggs and fowl, round base, c1750 .... **1,000.00**
Soup Plate, 9", children in landscape, shaped dentil rim, green mosaic border with gilt scrolls and flower sprays, c1765 .... **400.00**
Soup Tureen, cov, 9¾", underglaze dark blue lappets, gold, brown, or red, cov with scalloped rim and acorn finial, c1725 .... **2,200.00**
Tea Bowl and Saucer, chinoiserie scenes in colors and gold, floral interior, landscape in saucer, floral sprays outside, c1750 .... **550.00**
Tea Caddy, 5⅛", rectangular, underglaze blue and purple flowers, gold highlights **400.00**
Teapot, 4", rose scale ground, exotic birds and flowers, flower finial, gold # 62, c1750 .... **900.00**
Vase, 13½", flared, powder blue, small round gold foot rim, 2 large gilt framed cartouches with kakiemon flowers and leaves sprouting from rock work, bottom band of horizontal kakiemon flowers, FA mk, c1733 .... **5,750.00**
Waste Bowl, 6½", purple, hunter shooting fowl, deer on reverse, mosaic border outlined in gilt rococo scrolls, c1765 .... **350.00**

DUNCAN AND MILLER

History: George Duncan, Harry B. and James B., his sons, and Augustus Heisey, his son-in-law, formed George Duncan & Sons in Pittsburgh, Pennsylvania, in 1865. The factory was located just two blocks from the Monongahela River, providing easy and cheap access by barge for materials needed to produce glass. The men from Pittsburgh's southside were descendents of generations of skilled glass makers.

The plant burned to the ground in 1892. James E. Duncan, Sr., selected a site for a new factory in Washington, Pennsylvania, where operations began on February 9, 1893. The plant prospered, producing fine glassware and table services for many years.

John E. Miller, one of the stockholders, was responsible for designing many fine patterns, the most famous being "Three Face." The firm incorporated, using the name The Duncan and Miller Glass Company until its plant closed in 1955. The company's slogan was "The Loveliest Glassware in America." The U. S. Glass Co. purchased the molds, equipment, and machinery in 1956.

References: Gail Krause, *The Encyclopedia Of Duncan Glass,* privately printed, 1984, 3rd printing; Gail Krause, *A Pictorial History Of Duncan & Miller Glass,* privately printed, 1976; Gail Krause, *The Years Of Duncan,* privately printed, 1980.

Collectors' Club: National Duncan Glass Society, P. O. Box 965, Washington, PA 15301. Dues: $10.00. *National Duncan Glass Journal* (quarterly).

Additional Listings: Pattern Glass.

Advisor: Gail Krause.

Ashtrays, Adoration, etched
  4½" **17.50**
  5½" **19.50**
Baskets
  Canterberry, # 115, 12", oval **75.00**
  Etched, # 80, 5" **45.00**

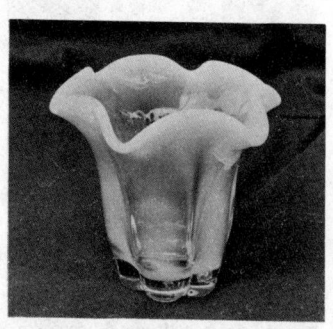

Vase, 4¼" h, blue, opal rim, $16.00.

Milk Glass, 5″ 55.00
Tavern, 3″ 30.00
Bitter Bottles, Pall Mall, #30
  Engraved 40.00
  Plain 25.00
Bowl, Canterberry, #115, 12″, oval . . . 35.00
Butter Dishes, cov
  Maltese Cross, #1003, 8″ 85.00
  Polka Dot, #47, 6″ 125.00
  Sandwich, #41, oblong, quarter
    pound 37.50
  Teardrop, #301, glass lid 27.50
Candlesticks, pairs
  Candlelight garden set, #153, 2″ . . . 45.00
  Festive, 5½″, crystal 24.00
  First Love, 5″, two light 75.00
  Sculptured Glass, #128, crystal. . . . 35.00
Candy Boxes, 8″, three compartments,
  cov
  Canterberry, #115 . . . . 37.50
  Language Of Flowers 65.00
Celeries
  Diamond, #75, 11″, handled, com-
    partment 23.50
  Madri Gras, #42, 7½″, oblong 25.00
  Ripple, #100, 11″, oblong 12.00
  Sanibel Opalescent, #130, 9″ 45.00
  Terrace, #111, 8″, handled 35.00
Compotes
  Festive, #155, 7½″. 27.50
  Hobnail, #118, 6″, crimped, ftd,
    crystal. 17.00
  Sandwich, #41, 5″ h, green, amber,
    or pink 32.50
Creamers
  Bag Ware [Same as Heavy Paneled
    Finecut, #800, without panels.
    Name listed in 1884 catalog of
    George Duncan & Son], George Duncan &
    Son 55.00
  Colonial, #54
    3 oz, individual, crystal 8.00
    8 oz, berry, crystal 9.00
    10 oz, hotel. 9.00
  Laguna, #154, 7 oz, crystal. 12.50
  Radiance, #113, 6 oz, crystal 12.50
  Ripple, #101, 6 oz, crystal 9.00
  Tavern, #83, 10 oz. 8.50
  Starlight, #152, 7 oz. 22.50
  Wild Rose, 7 oz, cut 23.00
  [Note: colored ware in mint condition
    commands approximately 30%
    more]
Decanters
  Gordon, #55, amber, cobalt, or ruby
    stopper
    16 oz 55.00
    32 oz 75.00
  Laguna, #154, 32 oz 25.00
  Flip Pitcher, Plaza, #21, 32 oz 35.00
Grapefruits
  Colonial, #54, 5 oz, crystal 11.50
  Georgian, #103, 5 oz, crystal 8.50

Sandwich, #41, 6″, color. 17.50
Hats
  Hobnail, #118, 10″, white milk glass 275.00
  Lacey Dewdrop [George Duncan
    made this in the early 1870s in crys-
    tal only]. 55.00
Herons
  Clear 135.00
  Frosted 185.00
Horseradish Bottle, Block, #331 . . . . . 55.00
Ice Cream, Heavy Paneled Finecut,
  #800. . . . . 95.00
Ice Tub, Block, #331 . . . . 65.00
Juice Glasses
  Chanticlear, 5 oz, clear [Amber, co-
    balt, green, opalescent, or ruby
    commands 50% more] 15.00
  Starlight, 5 oz 20.00
  Sundown, 5 oz 10.00
Ladle, Venetian, #126, clear or colored
  handle 35.00
Lamp Shades, gas
  Amberette, 9″ 55.00
  Diamond Ridge, #48, small. 30.00
Lamps [If decorated, add 30% more]
  Barred Oval 95.00
  Duncan Bar 85.00
  Heavy Paneled Finecut, #800 . . . . . 150.00
  Three Faces, #500. . . . . 225.00
  Zipper Block, #90 . . . . 85.00
Molassas Can, Block, #308, plated
  top. 55.00
Muddlers
  Clear 18.00
  Cobalt, green, or ruby 25.00
Nappies, colored [Amber, apple green,
  blue, and vaseline priced higher than
  crystal]
  Amberette, #48, 4½″ 32.00
  Ellrose, 4″ 28.00
Oil Bottles, cut or pressed, stopper
  Beaded Swirl, #335 . . . . 65.00
  Craquelled 65.00
Orange Bowl, Ellrose, 8″ [Patent date in
  March 6, 1886, by George Blair; but,
  illustrated in 1884 catalog. Color
  baked on to achieve amber panels]
  With stand 75.00
  Without stand 55.00
Pidgeon (dove), separate crystal base . 325.00
Pitcher, All Over Diamond 95.00
Plates, Harp and Thistle, 9½″
  Clear 35.00
  Amber, green, or pink 55.00
Powder Box, Astaire, #22, crystal, co-
  balt stopper 75.00
Puff Box, Astaire, #22, crystal, cobalt
  stopper [Pattern also produced at Tif-
  fin, OH, but called Hilton for blue and
  Kimberly for ruby. Duncan Miller made
  set along with perfume bottles and co-
  balt tray in 1930.] 65.00
Quart, hotel jug, #83 . . . . 22.50

Syrup, Block Band, #27, crystal **65.00**
Swans
  Swan Vase, #3, 9″
    Clear. **175.00**
    Amber, cobalt, green, or ruby **250.00**
  Sylvan, #122, 12″, pink opalescent . **350.00**
Tumblers
  Bar, #30 . . . . **15.00**
  Barney Toy. **14.00**
  Zippered Block, #90. . . . . **27.50**
Tumblers, ftd
  Fish, 3 oz, cut. **15.00**
  Fish, 12 oz, cut, colored bottoms . . . **25.00**
  Owl, 14 oz, cut, crystal **18.00**
  Rooster, 7 oz, cut, crystal **11.50**
  Sea Horse, 4 oz, cut, colored bottom **16.50**
  Waikiki, 8 oz, cut, colored bottom. . . **25.00**
Umbrella, Daisy and Button, ftd, 6¼″
  [Made also without base. Crystal plus
  amber, blue, and vaseline. Pat'd by
  Augustus Heisey on Dec. 14, 1886;
  but listed in 1884 catalog.]. **135.00**
Viking Boat, crystal [Not a standard fac-
  tory item; made for another company.
  Limited quantities in pink and blue
  opalescent]. **250.00**
Wine Set, Heavy Paneled Finecut,
  #800, eight pcs [Decanter with cut or
  pressed stopper, 6 wine goblets, and
  round tray] **275.00**

DURAND

History: Victor Durand (1870–1931), born in Baccarat, France, apprenticed at the Baccarat glassworks where several generations of his family
worked. In 1884 Victor came to America to join his
father at the Whitall-Tatum & Co. in New Jersey.
In 1897 father and son leased the Vineland Glass
Manufacturing Company in Vineland. Products included cheap bottles, jars, and glass for scientific
and medical purposes. By 1920 four separate companies existed.

When Quezal Art Glass and Decorating Company failed, Victor Durand recruited Martin Bach,
Jr., Emil J. Larsen, William Wiedebine, and other
Quezal men and opened an art glass shop at Vineland in December 1924. Quezal style iridescent
pieces were made. New innovations included
cameo and intaglio designs, geometric Art Deco
shapes, Venetian Lace, and oriental style pieces.
In 1928 crackled glass, called Moorish Crackle and
Egyptian Crackle, was made.

Much of Durand glass is not marked. Some bears
a sticker lableled "Durand Art Glass"; some has
the name "Durand" scratched on the pontil or "Dur-
and" inside a large "V". Etched numbers may be
part of the marking.

Durand died in a car crash in 1931. The Vineland
Flint Glass Works was merged with Kimble Glass
Company a year later, and the art glass line dis-
continued.

**Vase, 7½″ h, orange ground, blue
leaves, $750.00.**

Bowl, 10″, flat, yellow with pulled decor
  similar to King Tut pattern **300.00**
Candle Lamps, 18″ black and gold
  metal, 7″ gold irid shades with pulled
  feathers and random threading, elec-
  tric, pr **850.00**
Compote, 6″, blue over gold, King Tut
  decor, sgd **750.00**
Goblet, 6″, gold ruby, clear pedestal
  foot **100.00**
Jar, cov, 11½″, gold, threaded. **600.00**
Lamp, 30″, irid blue, threaded, opaque
  white heart shape leaves, wrought iron
  mounting with leaves and flowers . . . **350.00**
Parfait glasses, cobalt blue, opal pulled
  feather, pale yellow foot, pr **425.00**
Plates
  6¾″, cobalt blue, paneled, applied
    rim **90.00**
  7½″, cobalt blue, opal pulled feather,
    crosshatch pontil **225.00**
  8¼″, green, opal pulled feather, cross-
    hatch pontil **200.00**
Rose Bowl, 2¾″, miniature, Moorish
  crackle, cranberry and white. **175.00**
Sherberts
  Footed, green and yellow, opaque
    pulled feather **150.00**
  Tall, ruby and gold amber, opal pulled
    feather **275.00**

Vases

4⅛″, cobalt blue, cut to clear	**400.00**
6⅛″ h, 5¼″ d, blue irid, random threading, No 1710-6, sgd Durand	**750.00**
7″, bulbous, irid blue, circular paneled foot, No 182, sgd Victor Durand	**425.00**
7¾″, art glass, irid blue, white leaves and veining, No 1900-8, sgd Victor Durand	**800.00**
8″, irid gold and orange, No 1722-8, sgd Victor Durand	**400.00**
8¾″, cylinder, green to rust, King Tut decor, 3 layer cased, unsigned, c1915	**425.00**
9″, art glass, green, opaque white leaves and veining, gold interior, unsigned	**500.00**
10¼″, apple green, King Tut decor, platinum, gold inside, sgd	**750.00**
13¾″, amethyst, paneled, No 012017, sgd	**275.00**

ENGLISH CHINA AND PORCELAIN (GENERAL)

History: The manufacture of china and porcelain was scattered throughout England, with the majority of the factories located in the Staffordshire district. The number of potteries was over one thousand.

By the 19th century English china and porcelain had achieved a world wide reputation for excellence. American stores imported large amounts for their customers. The special production English pieces of the 18th and early 19th centuries held a position of great importance among early American antiques collectors.

References: Peter Bradshaw, *18th Century English Porcelain Figures, 1745–1795*, Antiques Collectors' Club; Geoffrey A. Godden, *Godden's Guide To Mason's China And The Ironstone Wares*, Antique Collectors' Club, Geoffrey A. Godden, *Lowestoft Porcelain*, Antique Collectors' Club; R. K. Henrywood, *Relief Molded Jugs, 1820–1900*, Antique Collectors' Club.

Additional Listings: Castleford, Chelsea, Coalport, Copeland and Spode, Liverpool, Royal Crown Derby, Royal Doulton, Royal Worcester, Historical Staffordshire, Romantic Staffordshire, Wedgwood, and Whieldon.

BOW

Candlesticks, pr, 10″, figural, Liberty and Matrimony, Liberty with turquoise and yellow flowered skirt, holding bird cage, Martrimony with pink coat, flowered breeches, holding bird cage, flowering borcage candle supports, c1760	**1,200.00**

Pickle Dish, 3½″, leaf shape, blue and white molded veins, painted flowers, foliage and grapes, c1760	**150.00**
Sauce Boat, 3¾″, blue and white, leaf molded, grapes and foliage, int. with painted grapes	**225.00**
Tea Bowl and Saucer, chrysanthemum and trailing prunus blossoms, c1755	**3,350.00**
Vase, 4¾″, flared foot, floral sprays in scroll molded cartouches, applied flower head at neck, c1735	**150.00**

COALBROOKDALE

Colonges, pr, 7½″ h, heavily encrusted with raised flowers, c1820	**750.00**
Cottage, 7″, large white mansion, sq base, 2 chimneys, windows and doors outlined in gold, encrusted floral and oak leaf roof, flowers and moss on ground, c1820	**2,000.00**
Vases, cov, pr, 15″ h, pear shaped bottle vases, applied flowers in high relief, gilt rims and cov, flower spray finials, c1840	**750.00**

DERBY

Basket, 11¼″ w, oval, pierced, cherries, butterflies, and insects, 2 entwined loop handles, c1780	**475.00**
Candlesticks, pr, 10″, figural, Mars and Venus, Mars in plumed helmet, breastplate, and striped shirt, Venus in flowered skirt with cupid beside her, repaired, c1758	**700.00**
Dish, 20″, oval, King's pattern, red, blue and gilt, iron red crowned crossed batons, D mark, 1820	**800.00**
Figurine, squirrel, 4″, wearing turquoise collar, gnawing nut, grass base, c1770	**675.00**
Scent Bottle, 3½″, 2 doves on tree stump holding ribbon in their beaks, inscribed "Nous L'Amitie Unit" in puce, flower spray stopper, c1780	**250.00**
Tureen, cov, oval, King's pattern, red, blue, and gilt, handled, lion's mask and paw feet, gilt, iron red crowned crossed batons, D mark, c1820	**1,000.00**

JACKFIELD

Cheese Dish, cov, 12½″ d, 11½″ h, black glaze, enameled ferns and butterflies	**275.00**
Coffee Pot, cov, 9¾″ h, black glaze, relief molded vine dec, double scroll handle, narrow feet, gilding	**250.00**
Figurines, Spaniel Dogs, pr, sitting, black glaze, red glass eyes, 10¼″ h	**225.00**
Jug, 7½″, oak leaf dec, brown and black, S handle, c1920	**225.00**

Pitcher, 6″, black glaze, white enamel
floral dec **100.00**
Syrup Jug, 7½″ h, black glaze, pewter
top **80.00**
Teapot, 6¼″, black glaze, green leaves,
gilt **150.00**

LONGTON HALL

Dishes
5¼″, leaf shape, painted flower
sprays, green rope twist handle,
c1755 . . . . **450.00**
8″, peony relief molded, pierced, puce,
green, and yellow, c1755 . . . . **625.00**
Figurine, parrot, white, glazed, 2⅜″,
c1750. . . . . **900.00**
Vases, pr, 6¾″, scroll shape, rococo,
painted floral dec **425.00**

LOWESTOFT

Bowl, 10½″, pedestal base, sce-
nic,Chinese family in outdoor setting. **400.00**
Box, cov, cricket dec **200.00**
Coffee Pot, cov, 9″, underglaze dark
blue, river scene, Chinese man fishing,
trellis diaper border, c1770–75 . . . . . **880.00**
Cup and Saucer, demitasse, underglaze
blue **100.00**
Feeding Cup, 7″ d, blue, flower sprays
and butterflies, c1765 . . . . **250.00**
Gravy Boat, 4¼″, underglaze blue, floral
spray dec, c1775. . . . . **285.00**

MASON'S

Dish, dessert, Oriental floral dec,
c1830. . . . . **45.00**
Dinner Service, 20 pcs, Chinese scene,
2 figures, trees, river, and house,

flower head and scroll borders, imp
mark, c1820 . . . . **450.00**
Platter, 10¾″, bird on fruiting and flow-
ering branch, black banner mark,
c1810. . . . . **150.00**
Soup Plate, 9½″, underglaze blue, flam-
boyant dragon. **150.00**
Tureen, cov, underplate, 7½″, Oriental
dec, underglaze blue, iron red and
gilding, imp mark, c1825 . . . . **180.00**

NEW HALL

Creamer, painted Chinese figure on ter-
race, c1790 . . . . **150.00**
Cups and Saucers
Blue ground, transfer printed and
painted figures in roundels, c1825. **130.00**
Floral dec, green, red, and yellow. . . **65.00**
Dish, underglaze deep blue, large
leaves, small flowers with orange cen-
ters, gilt, 1825. . . . . **100.00**
Sugar Bowl, pink lustre dec. **125.00**
Tea Service, 43 pcs, pale blue ground,
gilt sprig borders, pattern #1092 . . . **2,300.00**
Teapot, cov, quatrefoil shape, painted
Chinoiserie figures on terrace, c1790 **250.00**

WOOD AND BROWNFIELD

Dinner Service, blue transfer, bird feeding young, flowers, foliage, and fruit,
12″ tureen, cov with seated lion finial,
7″ sauce tureen, cov and stand, 6
soup plates, 13 dinner plates, 15 side
plates, 12 breakfast plates, imp B &
W mark, c1840 . . . . **2,300.00**

ENGLISH SOFTPASTE

History: Between 1820 and 1860 a large number
of potteries in England's Staffordshire district produced decorative wares with a soft earthenware
(creamware) base and a plain white or yellow
glazed ground.

Design or "stick" spatterware was created by a
cut-sponge (stamp), hand painting, and transfer.
Blue is the dominant color. The earliest patterns
were carefully arranged geometrics and generally
covered the entire piece. Later pieces have a decorative border with a center motif, usually a tulip.
In the 1850s Elsmore and Foster developed the
Holly Leaf pattern.

King's Rose features a large, cabbage type rose
in red, pale red, or pink. The pink rose often is called
"Queen's Rose." Secondary colors are pastels of
yellow, pink, and occasionally green. The borders

**Lowestoft, saucer, 4¾″ d, Chinese
style, blue dec, $75.00.**

vary: a solid band, vined, lined, or sectional. The King's Rose exists in an oyster motif.

Strawberry China ware comes in three types: strawberries and strawberry leaves (often called strawberry lustre), green feather-like leaves with pink flowers (often called cut-strawberry, primrose, or old strawberry), and a third type with the decoration in relief. The first two types are characterized by rust red moldings. Most pieces have a creamware ground. Davenport was one of the many potteries who made this ware.

Yellow-glazed earthenware (canary lustre) has a canary yellow ground, transfer design which is usually in black, and occasional lustre decoration. The earliest pieces date from the 1780s and have a fine creamware base. A few hand painted pieces are known. Not every piece has lustre decoration.

Marked pieces are uncommon. Because the ground is softpaste, the ware is subject to cracking and chipping. Enamel colors and other types of decoration do not hold well. It is not unusual to see a piece with the decoration rubbed off.

Additional Listings: Adams Rose, Gaudy Dutch, Salopian Ware, Staffordshire Items.

DESIGN SPATTERWARE

Bowls

6¾" d, 3½" h, blue stick spatter, gaudy floral band, mkd Baker & Co, Ltd. England	125.00
9½", serrated rim, blue, white, and black trim	285.00

Cups and Saucers

Florals, blue, green, ochre, and red	125.00
Peony, red and green	175.00
Cuspidor, 7¼" d, 5" h, blue and white dec	75.00

Jugs

4", geometric design, red, green, and brown	85.00
7", barrel shape, Rosettes, fern prongs, blue	150.00
Holly Leaf, purple and green dec	100.00

Mugs

4¼", brown and blue stick spatter design	85.00
6", Holly Leaf, red and green dec	110.00
6", Rosettes, blue, green bands	85.00

Plates

8⅜", green stick spatter, gaudy 4 color floral center, red rim stripes	120.00
8½", black stick spatter border, center flower, red and blue, green leaves	175.00
8¾", stick spatter, red concentric circles in center, narrow red line border with stars circled in blue	85.00
9", stars in center, pin wheels around narrow red line border	90.00
9¼", green flowers, red center, stick spatter	100.00

Platters

12" red and green	180.00
16", purple and green	225.00
Sugar, cov, 5" h, white, blue and red flowers, green leaves, closed ring and shell handles	85.00
Teapot, cov, Rosettes, blue	215.00

KING'S ROSE

Coffee Pot, 11½", dome lid, vine border	750.00
Creamer, helmut shape, brick red rose	225.00

Cups and Saucers, handleless

Line border, plain ext., int. with pink rose	110.00
Oyster pattern, pink border	125.00
Scalloped rim	140.00

Plates

4½", pink rose, 4 spray border	60.00
6½", brick red rose, c1820	75.00
7", brick red rose, pink lustre stripe border	110.00
7¾", brick red rose, pink lustre stripe border	150.00
9⅞", pink border design	85.00
Platter, 13", brick red rose	280.00
Sauce Boat, 6", brick red rose	145.00
Soup Plate, 10", brick red rose, broken border	160.00
Tea Set, brick red rose, teapot, cov, 4 cups, handleless, 4 saucers, imp Wood	550.00

STRAWBERRY CHINA

Bowl, 6¼", pink lustre, red and green enamel, wide strawberry border, c1820	175.00
Coffee Pot, cov, 11¼", Strawberry Lustre, dome cov, strawberry finial	450.00
Creamer, 4½", Cut Strawberry	175.00
Mug, handled, 2½"	80.00

Plates

6½", strawberries and morning glories, pink lustre border	185.00
7½", Cut Strawberry	150.00
10", Strawberry Lustre	180.00
Platter, 10½" l, Cut Strawberry	180.00
Sugar, cov, sq, Strawberry Lustre	200.00
Teapot, 9½", Strawberry Lustre	325.00
Vegetable Dish, cov, oval	375.00

YELLOW-GLAZED EARTHENWARE

Bowl, 5¼" d, 4¼" h, red flowers, green buds and leaves, rust line on scalloped rim	500.00

Cups and Saucers, handleless

Brown transfer, man and lady at tea, 3" d cup, 4¾" d saucer	300.00
Red-brown transfer, couple in garden, mkd Newell	275.00
Jug, 5½", black transfer, silver lustre roundel with young men threshing	

Yellow glazed earthenware, mug, silver lustre, 2″ h, 1⅞″ d, $250.00.

wheat, silver lustre neck band, c1810–20	375.00
Mugs, Children's	
2″, brown transfer, boys flying kite, "For A Favorite," silver lustre rim	225.00
2⅝″, black transfer, rabbit in garden, "A Rabbit For William," c1820	425.00
Pitcher, 3¾″, red and orange flowers, wine dec on neck	625.00
Plates	
6¼″, "Thomas" in center, bright green band, sponged border, c1820	410.00
7⅜″, bright red and green floral dec, emb floral rim	300.00
8½″, red transfer center scene, molded acanthus border, imp Wood	275.00
Waste Bowl, 5⅜″ d, 2⅞″ h, red and green floral dec, emb floral rim.	240.00

FAIRINGS, MATCH-STRIKERS, AND TRINKET BOXES

History: Fairings are small, charming china objects which were purchased or given away as prizes at English fairs in the 19th century. Although fairings are generally identified with England, they actually were manufactured in Germany by Conte and Boehme of Possneck.

Fairings depicted an amusing scene either of courtship and marriage, politics, war, and children or animals behaving as children. Over four hundred varieties have been identified. Most fairings bore a caption. Early examples, 1860–70, were of better quality than later ones. After 1890 the colors became more garish, and gilting was introduced.

The manufacturers of fairings also made match-strikers and trinket boxes. Some were captioned. The figures on the lids were identical to those of the fairings. The market for the match-strikers and trinket boxes was identical to that for the fairings.

Advisor: Barbara and Melvin Alpren.

FAIRINGS

After The Ball, mother and father pig in bed	225.00
After The Race, two pussy cats in a basket	175.00
An Awkward Interruption, cat disturbing couple going to bed.	175.00
Baby's First Step, three small children, dressed-up	200.00
Children's Meeting, three small Victorian girls	200.00
Coming Home From The Seaside, family of three, dressed as pigs	325.00
Don't Awake The Baby, two small girls rocking a baby in a cradle	275.00
Gentlemen Of The Jury, three rakish pug dogs	225.00
Go Away Mamma I Am Busy, mother and child at table.	250.00
Her First Ball, young girl primping at mirror, mother and sister look on	200.00
Little Bo Peep, three sheep.	200.00

MATCH-STRIKERS

Boot, woman's	175.00
Boy, young, with pig and basket	200.00
Elephant and rider, howdah is striker	225.00
Girl, paddling colorful canoe	175.00

TRINKET BOXES

Boy, young, and dog on dresser	175.00
Boy, young, in bed, putting on pajamas	225.00
Child's Prayer, young girl in bed.	200.00
Girl, young, reading.	200.00
Girl, young, sitting on dresser	175.00
Punch, seated on chair	200.00

Fairing, Three O'Clock In The Morning, 3⅝ x 2 x 3″, $245.00.

FAIRY LAMPS

History: Fairy lamps, originating in England in the 1840s, are candle burning night lamps. They were used in nurseries, hallways, and dim corners of the home.

Two leading candle manufacturers, the Price Candle Company and the Samuel Clarke Company, promoted fairy lamps as a means to sell candles. Both contracted with other manufacturers of glass, porcelain, and metal to produce the needed shades and cups. For example, Clarke used Worcester Royal Porcelain Company, Stuart & Sons, and Red House Glass Works in England, plus firms in France and Germany. Clarke's trademark was a small fairy with a wand surrounded by the words "Clarke Fairy Pyramid, Trade Mark."

Fittings were produced in a wide variety of styles. Shades ranged from pressed to cut glass, from Burmese to Nailsea. Cups are found in glass, porcelain, brass, nickel, and silver plate.

American firms selling fairy lamps included Diamond Candle Company of Brooklyn, Blue Cross Safety Candle Co., and Hobbs-Brockunier of Wheeling, West Virginia.

Fairy lamps are found in two pieces (cup and shade) and three pieces (cup with matching shade and saucer). Married pieces are common. Reproductions abound.

Cobalt blue, 2 pc, sgd "Geo. Davidson/ Est 1867/England," $85.00.

Baccarat, 4½" h, 5¼" d, rose teinte, pinwheel pattern, matching base, mkd Baccarat.	245.00
Brass	
3¾" h, 4½" d, multicolor glass jewels set in openwork brass, Mooris Moorish.	165.00
Brass holder attached to mirror base, Burmese scalloped cup, Burmese dome shade, acid finish, sgd Thomas Webb.	700.00
Burmese	
4¾" h, 3⅞" d, salmon pink shading to yellow, acid finish, Webb, clear Clarke base.	195.00
6½" h, 4¼" d, fluted bowl, 3 yellow feet, acid finish, pressed Burmese insert mkd Clarke, clear candle cup, large Burmese dome.	820.00
6½" h, 4⅞" d, acid finish, red flowers, green leaves on dome, light gray, gold decor base, Tunnecliffe, S. Clarke's Patent Trademark Fairy.	750.00
Cranberry	
3½" h, 2⅞" d, DQ, clear Clarke base.	95.00
4" h, 3" d, all over emb hob design, clear Clarke base.	100.00
Frosted, 4½" h, 2⅞" d, orange, emb diamond design, clear base, unmarked.	120.00
Lace de Bohme, 6" h, 7" d, rose, white flowers, cream ceramic base, white flowers, sgd S. Clarke's Patent Trademark Fairy	285.00
Opalescent, 4½" h, 3" d, crown shape, clear, overshot, clear pressed base, mkd Clarke.	195.00
Opaque, 3½" h, 2⅞" d, yellow, overshot emb swirl, clear Clarke base	125.00
Overlay, 4⅜" h, 3⅞" d, dark green, white lining, clear Clarke base.	110.00
Overshot, 3¾" h, 2⅞" d, cranberry, emb ribs, clear Clarke base.	100.00
Owl Shape, 4½" h, frosted, painted eyes, Clarke base	225.00
Peachblow, 6¼" h, 7⅞" d, fluted, cream, floral decor dome, tapestry flower bowl base, acid finish, cream lining, Webb, mkd Tunnecliffe	700.00
Satin Glass	
3¾" h, 4" d, green, emb swirl, Clarke base.	180.00
4¾" h, 3⅞" d, blue, DQ, MOP, white lining, clear Clarke base.	175.00
5¼" h, 6" d, pyramid size, pink, emb swirl, tapestry base, gray-green, pink band, white flowers, gold branches.	345.00
Spatter Glass	
3½" h, 2⅞" d, blue, white spatter, clear Clarke base.	125.00
4⅝" h, 3⅞" d, emb swirl, pink, yellow and white, white lining, clear Clarke base.	135.00
Stevens and Williams	
5¼" h, 4" d, striped, white and green, satin finish, clear Clarke base.	175.00
Verre Moire (Nailsea)	
4" h, rose, white loopings, clear	

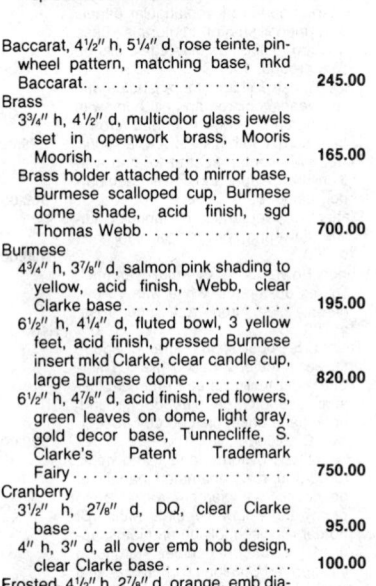

pressed base, mkd S. Clark's Patent
Trademark Fairy. **215.00**
5¼" h, blue, frosted, opaque white
loopings, matching ruffled base,
clear Clarke insert **435.00**
6" h, 7½" d, green, white loopings,
matching ruffled base, clear Clarke
insert **450.00**
6½" h, 7¾" d, yellow-chartreuse,
white loopings, matching ruffled
base, clear Clarke insert. **550.00**

FAMILLE ROSE

History: Famille Rose is Chinese export enameled procelain in which the pink color predomi-
nates. It was made primarily in the 18th and 19th
century. Other porcelains in the same group are
Famille Jaune (yellow), Famille Noire (black), and
Famille Verte (green).

Decorations include courtyard and home scenes,
birds, and insects. Secondary colors are yellow,
green, blue, aubergine, and black.

Mid to late 19th century Chinese export wares
similar to Famille Rose are identified as Rose Canton, Rose Mandarin, and Rose Medallion.

Basin, 15½", turquoise ground, central
panel of nobles in pavilion, floral vignettes, 19th C. **900.00**
Bowl, tasting, 5¾", int. with 2 windblown
orchids, ext. with spray of yellow and
red chrysanthemums, red, white, and
lilac poppies, 18th C **880.00**
Box, cov, 12½" d, celadon ground, im-
mortals dec **250.00**
Brush Box, 7½ x 3¾ x 2½", multicolored
florl dec **550.00**
Candlesticks, pr, 8¾", figural elephants,
white glazed body, saddlecloth with lotus flower, *gu* shape holder with raised
central band with lotus meander. . . . **1,200.00**

Plate, 8¼", $225.00.

Charger, 14" d, peonies, magnolia, and
birds, c1760 . . . . **400.00**
Cup and Saucer, reticulated, openwork
honeycomb pattern set with 3 flowerheads, enameled bands of peony,
18th C **275.00**
Dish, 7¾", center, lady seated beside
table holding fly wisk, 3 boys, rabbits,
2 large jars, cell pattern band with 3
peony cartouches, Yongzheng **350.00**
Figurines
Boys astride toy leopards, pink, turquoise and lime-green robes scat-
tered with flowers, c1900, 6". **775.00**
Phoenix bird, enameled, multicolored
with gilt dec, standing on rock work
base, 19th C, 14½" **975.00**
Garden Seats, pr, 18⅛", pavilion with
warriors at combat, false gadroons,
ruyi-head borders, sides pierced with
double cash medallions, top Eight
Daoist emblems and cash **1,400.00**
Jar, baluster shape, cov, 18", 2 panels
with basket of flowers flanked by 2
other panels on pink-rose ground,
petal borders, floral color, chrysanthe-
mum knop **700.00**
Lantern, 13½", hexagonal barrel shape,
pierced, interlocking cash and U-
shaped openwork rectangular panels
with medallions of immortals, base
and top molded as blue sq scrolls on
pink ground, 18th C. **2,200.00**
Mug, 6", barrel shape, loop handles with
ruxi heads, colored and gilt body with
monograms below ribboned crown,
blue border with gilt stars, Qianlong . **275.00**
Plate, 8¼", center, seated woman with
3 children, diaper and flower head bor-
der, early 18th C **300.00**
Platter, 10", serpentine rectangular out-
line, flowering springs, gilt highlights,
c1760. . . . . **400.00**
Punch Bowl, 15½", overglaze enamel,
figures on terrace, white with yellow,
green, blue, iron red, and rose,
c1780. . . . . **1,400.00**
Teapot, 5", pear shape, straight spout,
sq ear handle, 2 raised pierced florettes and trailing green enamel blossoming cherry on pink dot ground,
petal band base, pierced cov. rose fi-
nial, Qianlong **520.00**
Vase, 29½", oviform, long flared neck,
ruby ground, 2 enameled panels of
peacocks on pierced rocks, rose
peony and yellow lovebirds within gilt
borders, incised foliage and lotus, applied gilt dragon handles, turquoise
int., iron red Qianlong 6 character seal
mark **15,500.00**
Wine Ewer, 7" w, peach shape, high re-
lief openwork leafy tendrils top, curv-

ing spout, loop handle, green foliage and black seed ground, lotus and butterflies, iron red tooth pattern on foot, early 19th C **775.00**

FENTON GLASS

History: The Fenton Art Glass Company began as a cutting shop in Martins Ferry, Ohio, in 1905. In 1906 Frank L. Fenton started to build a plant in Williamstown, West Virginia, and produced the first piece of glass in 1907. Early production included carnival, chocolate, custard, and pressed and mold blown opalescent glass. In the 1920s stretch glass, Fenton dolphins, jade green, ruby, and art glass were added to their line.

In the 1930s boudoir lamps, "Dancing Ladies," and various slags were produced. The 1940s saw crests of different colors being added to each piece by hand. Hobnail, opalescent, and two-color overlay pieces were popular items. Handles were added to different shapes, making the baskets they created as popular today as then.

Through the years Fenton has added beauty to their glass by decorating it with hand painting, acid etching, color staining, and copper wheel cutting. Several different paper labels have been used. In 1970 an oval raised trademark also was adopted.

References: Shirley Griffith, *A Pictorial Review Of Fenton White Hobnail Milk Glass,* privately printed, 1984; William Heacock, *Fenton Glass: The First Twenty-Five Years,* O-Val Advertising Corp, 1978; William Heacock, *Fenton Glass: The Second Twenty-Five Years,* O-Val Advertising Corp, 1980.

Collectors' Club: Fenton Art Glass Collectors Of America, P. O. Box 2441, Appleton, WI 54913. Dues: $10.00. *Butterfly Net* (bimonthly).

Additional Listings: Carnival Glass.

Advisor: Ferill J. Rice

Baskets

Aventurine green and blue, 9" h, c1964 .... **75.00**
Burmese, small, maple leaf decal ... **50.00**
Hobnail, colonial green **15.00**
Opalescents
  Blue, miniature, hobnail **28.00**
  Cranberry, 4½" **55.00**
Satin Glass, rose, swirled, 11" h, c1974 .... **90.00**
Spangled Glass (Vasa Murrhina), Autumn Orange, small, c1965 ...... **65.00**
Bowls
Finger, underplate, Lincoln Inn, jade green **30.00**
Hamilton Beach Mixing Bowl, Chinese yellow, large size **10.00**
Petal, 2 candlesticks, Chinese yellow, c1933 .... **105.00**

Epergne, 12″ d, 9½″ h, white opal, green rims, $150.00.

Rosalene Leaf & Orange Tree **42.50**
Waterlily and Cattail, 8″, c1910. .... **25.00**
#203, Emerald Crest **40.00**
#847
  Lilac, crimped, 10″ **90.00**
  Mandarin Red, cupped, c1933. ... **30.00**
Candlesticks
Dolphin, ruby, poinsettia under base, pr **55.00**
Petal, moonstone, pr **20.00**
Candy Dishes
San Toy, etched, satin crystal, flower knob.................... **45.00**
Valencia, cov, ftd, any color **20.00**
Compotes
Colonial Blue, Ftd. Thumbprint **25.00**
Green Opalescent, hobnail, 6″ **32.50**
Ruby, dolphin handles, c1926. ..... **60.00**
Creamers and Sugars
Aqua Crest, #680
  Dark, c1949. .... **50.00**
  Light, c1948 .... **80.00**
Orchid, Lincoln Inn **60.00**
Cruets
Cranberry, Coin Dot. **60.00**
Dusk, black stopper, c1953 .... **130.00**
Decanters
French Opalescent, #1934, six shot glasses and stopper........... **200.00**
Ruby Georgian, six short glasses and stopper **150.00**
Egg, ebony, white daisies, pedestal ... **30.00**
Epergnes
Ivory Crest, one lily, base, frog..... **150.00**
Peach Crest, one lily **60.00**
Hats, hobnail, hurricane, 2 pcs
Milk Glass **25.00**
Peach Crest **75.00**
Rose Pastel **50.00**
Macroon Jar, Big Cookies, Chinese yellow, wicker handle............ **150.00**

Nappies and Bon-bons
Aquamarine, dolphin handles, small,
cut 20.00
Blue Opalescent, 4″ sq, handles. . . . 18.00
Green, 7″, dolphin handles. 35.00
Perfume Bottles, 9″
Mulberry. 50.00
Pink Overlay 30.00
Pitchers and Jugs
Pitcher Set, milk glass, hobnail, 6
tumblers 75.00
Plate, Crystel Crest, 10″, dinner 20.00
Rose Bowls
Cranberry Opalescent, hobnail, 5½″. 65.00
Peach Crest 50.00
Slipper, blue marble cat 10.00
Syrup, Topaz Opalescent, 5½″ 40.00
Vases
Burmese, maple leaf decal 35.00
Dancing Ladies, 6½″, flared 225.00
Ivory Crest, cornucopia, pr. 54.00
Jaqueline, blue, 7½″ 30.00
Mandarin Red, 6″, flared 60.00
Peacock, 7¾″, Periwinkle blue 160.00
Rose overlay, 7½″ 25.00
Silver Jamestown, c1958 . . . . 35.00
Wild Rose, triangle crimped Bubble
Optic. 55.00
#192, mulberry, sq 60.00
#621, Pekin blue, flared, 6″. 30.00
#847, fan, Mongolian green, c1934. 46.00

FIESTA

History: The Homer Laughlin China Company
introduced Fiesta dinnerware in January 1936 at
the Pottery and Glass Show in Pittsburgh, Pennsylvania. Fredrick Rhead designed the pattern; Arthur Kraft and Bill Bensford molded it. Dr. A. V.
Bleininger and H. W. Thiemecke developed the
glazes.

The original five colors were red, dark blue, light
green (with a trace of blue), brilliant yellow, and
ivory. A vigorous marketing campaign took place
between 1939 and 1943. In 1938 turquoise was
added; red was removed in 1943 because of the
war effort and did not reappear until 1959. In 1951
light green, dark blue, and ivory were retired and,
forest green, rose, chartreuse, and gray added to
the line. Other color changes took place in the late
1950s, including the addition of a medium green.
Production ceased in 1972.

References: Linda D. Farmer, *The Farmer's
Wife Fiesta Inventory And Price Guide,* privately
printed, 1984; Sharon and Bob Huxford, *The Collectors Encyclopedia Of Fiesta,* Collector Books,
1984, fifth edition.

Additional Listings: See *Warman's Americana
& Collectibles* for more examples.

Ashtray, gray 30.00
Bowls
4¾″, fruit, rose 13.50
6″, dessert, cobalt. 13.00
6″, soup, cream, medium green 25.00
8½″, fruit, dark green. 25.00
Set of 5, nested, mixing, green. 135.00
Soup, onion, cov, yellow 130.00
Candlesticks, pr, bulbous, red 45.00
Carafe, turquoise 55.00
Casseroles, cov
French, yellow. 120.00
Regular, red 85.00
Coffee Pots
After Dinner, yellow. 85.00
Regular, red 95.00
Compote, 12″, ivory 36.00
Creamer, reg, ring handle, chartreuse. . 12.00
Creamer and sugar set, individual size,
red. 125.00
Cups
Green. 30.00
Ivory. 16.00
Demitasse Cup and Saucer, ivory 20.00
Egg Cups
Chartreuse 40.00
Cobalt 25.00
Gravy Boats
Dark Green. 25.00
Yellow 20.00
Jug, 2 pt, yellow 20.00
Marmalade, cov, cobalt. 80.00
Mugs
Light Green 25.00
Red 50.00
Nappy, 5½″, rose 10.00
Pitcher, 2 qt, ice lip, cobalt 30.00
Plates
6″, dessert, chartreuse. 6.50
7″, bread and butter, medium green 9.50
10″, dinner, red. 16.00

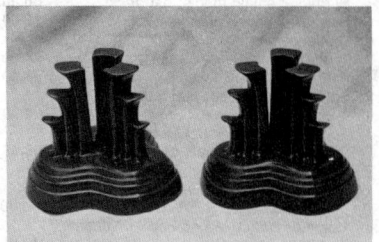

Candleholders, pr. cobalt blue, $95.00.

15", chop, yellow.	18.00
Platter, 12", oval, dark green.	20.00
Salt and Pepper Shakers, pr, ivory. . . .	8.00
Sugar, cov, reg, gray.	15.00
Teapot, 6 cup, turquoise	45.00
Tumblers	
5 oz, juice, turquoise	12.00
8 oz, cobalt	15.00
10 oz, red.	27.00
Vase, 10", red	130.00

FIGURAL BOTTLES

History: Figural bottles, made of porcelain either in glaze or bisque form, achieved popularity in the late 1800s and remained popular to the 1930s. The majority of figural bottles were made in Germany, with Austria and Japan accounting for the balance. They average in size from three to eight inches.

The figural bottles were shipped to the United States empty and filled upon arrival. They were then given away to customers by brothels, dance halls, hotels, liquor stores, and taverns. Some were lettered with the names and addresses of the establishment; others had paper labels. Many were used for holidays, e.g., Christmas and New Year.

Figural bottles also were made in glass and other materials. The glass bottles held perfumes, foods, or beverages.

References: Al Cembura and Constance Avery, *A Guide to Miniature Bottles,* privately printed, 1972; Hugh Cleveland, *Bottle Pricing Guide,* Collector Books, 1980; Ralph & Terry Kovel, *The Kovels' Bottle Price List,* Crown Publishers, 1982, 6th ed., Carlo & Dot Sellari, *The Illustrated Price Guide To Antique Bottles,* Country Beautiful Corp, 1975.

Periodicals: Antique Bottle World, 5003 West Berwyn, Chicago, IL 60630; Old Bottle Magazine, P.O. Box 243, Bend, OR 97701. Subscription: $10.00.

Additional Listings: See *Warman's Americana & Collectibles* for more examples.

BISQUE

Boy holding up night shirt, exposing himself, German, 3½".	100.00
Children emb on front with doctor's case giving whiskey to another child, "Nature's Way to Perfect Health," brown ground, 4¼" h, 3¾" w.	60.00
Elk, emb antlers, bark back.	45.00
Fireman with pink pig, 5".	125.00
Goat, naughtily dressed, German, 7½"	50.00
Jolly Man, toasting "Your Health," flask style, tree bark back, 4½" h.	75.00
Monk, round, long brown habit, white apron front, carrying 4 bottles of liquor, orig stopper in form of hat, German .	85.00
Rabbit, coming out of egg.	75.00
Sailor, cartoon type, high gloss front,	

His Master's Breath, glass, white, green, tree bark edge and back, 3¾" h, 3½" w, $35.00.

white pants, blue blouse, hat, mkd "Made In Germany," 6½"	100.00

GLASS

Acrobat, lady standing on ball, frosted, pontil	100.00
Baby in cabbage leaf, clear.	40.00
Charlie Chaplin, clear, 12¾"	100.00
Cherub holding a medallion, clear, 14"	45.00
Chestnut, handle, amber	30.00
Cigar, amber, 5".	40.00
Claws holding egg, clear, 14"	10.00
Czarina, white milk glass.	250.00
Elephant, seated, raised trunk, clear, 8½".	30.00
Hessian soldier, clear	65.00
Oyster, orig cap, painted.	35.00
Pear, clear.	15.00
Pipe, orig stopper mouthpiece, amber .	110.00
Potato, clear	20.00
Santa Claus, hand painted, red suit, pack on back	75.00

FINDLAY ONYX GLASS

History: Findlay onyx glass, produced by Dalzell, Gilmore & Leighton Company, Findlay, Ohio, was patented in 1889 for the firm by George W. Leighton. Due to high production costs resulting from a complex manufacturing process, the glass was made only for a short time.

Layers of glass were plated to a bulb of opal glass through repeated dippings into a glass pot. Each layer was cooled and reheated to develop opalescent qualities. A pattern mold then was used to produce raised decorations of flowers and leaves. A second mold gave the glass bulb its full shape and form.

A platinum lustre paint, producing pieces identified as silver or platinum onyx, was applied to the raised decorations. The color was fixed in a muffle kiln. Other colors such as cinnamon, cranberry, cream, raspberry, and rose were achieved by using an outer glass plating which reacted strongly to reheating. For example, a purple or orchid color came from the addition of manganese and cobalt to the glass mixture.

Sugar Shaker, 5¼″ h, white ground, platinum dec, $375.00.

Bowl, 8″, cinnamon.	750.00
Celery Vases	
Onyx	350.00
Rose ground, white decor	950.00
Mustard, cov, onyx	410.00
Pitcher, rose ground, white decor, handle has small chip	200.00
Spooner, rose ground, white decor	400.00
Sugar, cov, onyx.	375.00
Sugar Shaker, raspberry, orig top	1,800.00
Toothpicks	
Onyx	425.00
Rose ground, white decor, small flake chip at top.	500.00
Tumbler, cranberry	350.00
Vase, 6½″, butterscotch, white lining, long neck, bulbous	1,600.00

FIREARM ACCESSORIES

History: Early rifles and pistols were hand loaded with shot and powder, often carried in separate containers. Horn was the favored medium for early containers. Many were hand decorated with figures, maps, names, and geometric designs.

In the mid-19th century, containers of brass, tin, white metal, and other substances entered the mar-

ket. Brass was the most common. These flasks were embossed with relief designs, often of a hunting motif.

Flasks are divided into two groups—pistol (4 to 5″) and rifle (6¾ to 10″). Pistol flasks usually command higher prices. Completeness of parts also effects price.

Note: The amount of reproduction and fake powder horns is large. Be very cautious!

Flasks, Powder

Brass	
4½″, pear shape, emb on both sides with spread-winged American eagle clutching small flask and revolver	60.00
4¾″, leaf and scroll pattern, brass bottom with two sliding doors	120.00
7″, stag standing next to tree	65.00
8½″, pear shape, emb on both sides with a hunter standing next to his horse in field, scrolled cartouche border	75.00
8¾″, hunter and dog next to tree	70.00
Copper, 9″, emb rococo designs, brass fittings	60.00
Horn, Caucasian, 5¾″, tin flattened horn, large nielloed silver mounts and dispensing lever, circular designs	650.00
White Metal, 4½″, pear shape, emb on both sides with shell pattern and fitted with brass top	50.00
Flasks, Shot, Leather	
7¼″, initials "HM/1860"	45.00
8½″, pear shape, emb on both sides with dead hanging game scene, brass adjustable top for 1¼ and 1½ ounce charges	50.00

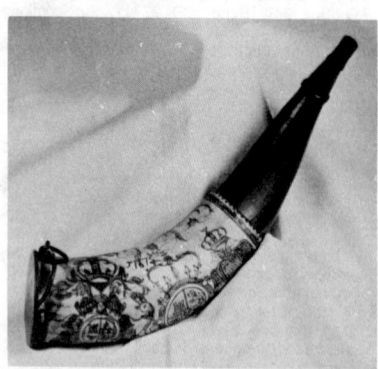

Powder horn, engraved, German, 18th C, 13″ l, $775.00.

Horns

10″, Joel Munger, Lake George, engraved "Joel Munger His Horn Made At Lake George July ye 29 1758," also engraved sailing vessel, fish, birds in trees, pinwheels, engrailed edge, raised ring faceted spout and wood base.......... **500.00**

10½″, Henry Muller, engraved "Henry Muller/His Horn/12th Penna Regt. Dauphin County/Jan Ye 19, 1781," engraved with townscape of Frederickstown, sides with large tulips, bird, wood base, metal ring, turned throat, wood plug............ **400.00**

11″, Orrangh Stoder, Lake George, engraved "Orrangh Stoder, His Horn Made at Lake GEORGE 1758, Briant Stoder His Horn," large flowering trees, birds, inscribed "A Royal Oak," fish, fox, engrailed edge, smooth spout, wood base.. **800.00**

11″, professionally engraved, base with spread-winged American eagle, crescent moon, PA state house, other PA locations, brass base and throat, 19th C **500.00**

12½″, Samuel Gridley, Lake George, engraved "Samuel Gridley, at Lake George, Novr. 9, 1756," plans of forts, pinwheels, faceted spout, raised ring................. **725.00**

13½″, unknown engraver, engraved with many individual paneled scenes of ships with American flags, Indian with box, Masonic emblems, eagle, initials "GE" or "GF," hearts, etc, later brass butt cap, copper spout............... **800.00**

13¾″, unknown engraver, engraved map, early Boston, buildings, wharf, vining tulips, zig-zags, chip carving on spout, small engraved silver plate on end **825.00**

15½″, Capt. John Wentworth, engraved "Cap. John Wentworth/his horn made at—NNOX, Oct. 18th 1760," engraved deer, Indian, serpents, lion with crown, initials "GR," trees, fish, carved ring at spout... **4,250.00**

16½″, scrimshaw, engraved lighthouse, crossed American flags, house with weeping willow, star, and weathervane, early to mid 19th C . **350.00**

FIREARMS

History: The 15th century arquebus was the forerunner of the modern firearm. The Germans refined the wheelock firing mechanism during the 16th and 17th centuries. English settlers arrived in America with the smoothbore musket; German settlers had rifled arms. Both used the new flintlock firing mechanism.

A major advance was achieved when Whitney introduced interchangeable parts into the manufacturing of rifles. The warfare of the 19th century brought continued refinements in firearms. The percussion ignition system was developed by the 1840s. Minie, a French military officer, produced a viable projectile. By the end of the 19th century cartridge weapons dominated the field.

Two factors control pricing of firearms—condition and rarity. The value of any particular antique firearm covers a very wide range. For instance, a Colt 1849 pocket model revolver with a 5″ barrel can be priced from $100.00 to $700.00 depending on whether or not all the component parts are original, whether some are missing, how much of the original finish (bluing) remains on the barrel and frame, how much silver plating remains on the brass trigger guard and back strap, and the condition and finish of the walnut grips. Be careful to note any weapons negative qualities. A Colt Paterson belt revolver in fair condition will command a much higher price than the Colt pocket model in very fine condition. Know the production run of a firearm before buying it.

References: Norman Flayderman, *Flayderman's Guide To Antique American Firearms. . . And Their Values,* DBI Books, 1983, 3rd ed.; Joseph Kindig, Jr., *Thoughts On The Kentucky Rifle In Its Golden Age,* 1960, available in reprint; H. Michael Madaus, *American Longarms,* Main Street Press, 1981.

Percussion Pistol, English, silver trim, c1820, $250.00.

FLINTLOCK PISTOLS—SINGLE SHOT

British, Queen Anne, center hammer, 12¼″, 7″ round brass barrel with Birmingham proofs, cannon turned muzzle, brass box lock with floral engraving, walnut grip with floral embossed hallmarked silver butt cap, inlaid silver dec **1,150.00**

French, military, 16″, 9″ round iron barrel, flat beveled lockplate with faceted pan fitted with flat beveled reinforced hammer, brass furniture, unmarked.. **500.00**

Kentucky, Bird & Brothers, 10.1" round smoothbore barrel, mkd "JD" (Jos. Dale), "P" and "US," stamped ed "BIRD / BROTHERS / PHILADEL-PHIA" in three lines on lockplate, .56 cal., walnut stock **1,500.00**

Kentucky, T. P. Cherington, 12.2" octagonal smoothbore barrel, stamped "T. P. CHERINGTON" on barrel and lockplate, .45 cal., brightly polished iron parts, walnut stock **2,250.00**

Kentucky, Hodgson & Thompson, 9" pin fastened octagonal, smoothbore, brass barrel, engraved "Baltimore" in script, Tower proof marks, .55 cal., American eagle with an escutcheon in its breast surmounted by thirteen tars engraved on trigger guard, lockplate engraved "Hodgson & Thompson" in script, light dec engraving on locks, tangs, and barrel breeches, pr **2,750.00**

U. S. Model 1807, J. Henry, 10" pin fastened round steel barrel stamped "J. HENRY. PHILa.," stamped "C. GIERSH" inside lockplate, stamped "J. HENRY. PHIL" behind hammer, stamped "U.S." in lockplate between hammer and frizzen, .55 cal., walnut stock **6,750.00**

U. S. Model 1808, North, Navy Contract, 10.2" round, smoothbore, unmarked barrel, stamped with an eagle and "U. STATES" on lockplate, stamped "S. NORTH/BERLIN/CON." behind hammer, .64 cal., walnut stock, reconverted to flint **2,500.00**

U. S. Model 1819, North, 10" round, smoothbore barrel, stamped "JDJ/P/ US," stamped "S. NORTH" in a curve over an eagle with a shield between letters "U S" over "MIDLTN CONN" in a curve on lockplate between cock and battery, stamped "1821" on lockplate behind cock and under sliding safety bolt, stamped "LS" in cartouche on left side of stock, .54 cal., walnut stock, reconverted to flint . . . **750.00**

PERCUSSION PISTOLS—SINGLE SHOT

Note: Conversion of flintlock pistols to percussion was common practice. Most British and U. S. military flintlock pistols listed above can be found in percussion. Values for these persussion converted pistols may be from 40 to 60% of the flintlockvalues given.

Dueling, pair, cased, J. E. Evans, 10.1" octagonal, smoothbore barrel, patent breeches stamped "J. E. EVANS/PHI-LADA," scroll and border engraved patent breeches, trigger guards, and

Percussion Pistol, single shot, French Naval, smooth base, barrel 6", 11¾" l, lock mkd "Mre Ble de Chatellerault," metal ramrod on pivot, belt hook, $200.00.

trigger plates, set triggers, .50 cal., French style brass bound mahogany casing lined in purple velvet containing a powder flask, a can of Eley percussion caps, a screw driver, a nipple wrench with a screw top containing a nipple-prick, cleaning rod, rammer, mallet head and handle, quantity of bullets, brass plaque on lid inscribed "Mr. Charles Cambos Jr. Philadelphia, Pa" **5,500.00**

Confederate, J. and F. Garret & Company, 8.5" round, browned barrel stamped "US/NWP/P," the breechplug stamped "I" and "C," the frame, fore-end, and grip straps of one-piece brass casting, the barrel held in place by a bolt and a hook on the breech plug engaged in a slot of the false breechplug, brass sideplate, .54 cal., varnished walnut grips **1,650.00**

Elgin Cutlass Pistol, Morrill, Mosman & Blair, 4" round barrel rifled with six grooves, a bowie blade 10" long and 1½" wide fastened to the barrel and etched with a vase containing fruit surmounted by "Elgin's Patent" in script in a rectangle and an eagle holding a pennant in his beak (right), vase containing fruit surmounted by "Morill Mosman/& Blair/Amherst Mass" and eagle holding pennant in beak (left), .34 cal., leather scabbard. **3,850.00**

Marston, W. W., Breech-Loading, 5.6" half octagonal and half round barrel, stamped three times "WW MARSTON/NEW YORK/PATENTED 1850," .36 cal., side-hammer, iron frame with scroll border engraving . . **825.00**

U. S. Model, 1842, 8½" round, smoothbore barrel, marked "US/H. ASTON" and "MIDDᵀᴺ/CONN," .54 cal., walnut half stock, swivel ramrod attached to barrel, brass butt and trigger guard. . **750.00**

PERCUSSION PISTOLS—MULTI SHOT (REVOLVERS)

Colt

Dragoon, Second Model, 7½" part round, part octagonal barrel stamped "ADDRESS SAM⸤ COLT NEW-YORK. COLT'S/PATENT" with "U.S." centered beneath, .44 cal., 6 shot, one piece walnut grip, squareback trigger guard and rectangular cylinder stop slots, Texas Ranger and Indian fight scene roll engraved on cylinders **4,250.00**

Navy, Model 1861, 7½" round barrel, creeping style loading lever, barrel stamped "ADDRESS COL. SAM⸤ COLT NEW-YORK U.S. AMERICA—.36 CAL," 6 shot, cylinder roll scene depicts battle between Texas Navy and that of Mexico, one-piece walnut grip **850.00**

Paterson Belt Model, No. 2, 5½" octagonal barrel, stamped "Patent Arms M'g Co Paterson N:J. Colt's Pt.," .31 cal., 5 shot, engraved cylinder, disappearing trigger, no trigger guard, flared walnut grips **4,000.00**

Pocket, Model 1849, barrel lengths of 3", 4", 5", and 6", octagonal with attached loading lever, stamped "ADDRESS COL. SAM⸤ COLT NEW-YORK U. S. AMERICA," .31 cal., 5 or 6 shot, cylinder engraved with stage-coach holdup scene, round trigger guard, walnut grips .. **450.00**

Police, Model 1862, 5½" barrel, stamped "ADDRESS COL. SAM⸤ COLT NEW-YORK U.S. AMERICA," .36 cal., 5 shot, half fluted cylinder, walnut grips **625.00**

Remington

Belt, New Model, 6½" octagonal barrel, stamped "PATENTED SEPT. 14, 1858/E. REMINGTON & SONS, ILION, NEW YORK U.S.A./NEW MODEL," .36 cal., 6 shot, round cylinder, threads visible at breech end, safety notches on cylinder shoulders between nipples **525.00**

Navy, 1861, 7⅜" octagonal barrel, stamped "PATENTED DEC. 17, 1861/MANUFACTURED BY REMINGTON'S ILION, N.Y.," .36 cal., 6 shot, round cylinder, walnut grips **650.00**

Remington-Beals 3rd Model Pocket Revolver, cased, 4" octagonal barrel stamped "BEALS' PATENT 1856 & 57 & 58/MANUFACTURED BY REMINGTONS' ILION, N.Y.," .31 cal., 5 shot, orig cardboard box with brass bullet mold, quanity of bullets, eagle and shield flask, mushroom shaped cleaning rod with screw-in type extension, extra pawl spring, can of Eley percussion caps **2,150.00**

Other

Allen & Wheelock, Army Percussion, 7½" round and partly octagonal barrel, mkd "ALLEN & WHEELOCK. WORCESTER. MASS. US ALLEN'S PAT'S. JAN. 13. DEC. 15. 1857. SEPT. 7," .44 cal., walnut grips ... **1,650.00**

Butterfield, Army Percussion, 7½" octagonal barrel stamped with serial no. (91) as are various other parts, stamped "BUTTERFIELD'S/PATENT DEc 11 1855/PHILADa" on top of silver plated frame, .40 cal. walnut grips **5,500.00**

Joslyn, Army Model, 8.2" octagonal barrel, stamped "B.F. JOSLYN. PATd MAY 4th 1858," stamped serial no. (123) on frame and other parts, .44 cal., checkered walnut grips **800.00**

Manhatten, Series I, 4" octagonal barrel, "MANHATTEN FIRE ARMS/MANUF'G. CO. NEW-YORK," .31 cal., 5 shot, cylinder engraved with stagecoach holdup scene, scroll and border engraved frame and back-strap.................. **825.00**

Nichols and Childs, 6.2" part octagonal and part round barrel, stamped "2," eight groove rifling, engraved "S.M.V." in script on small silver escutcheon on left side of wood stock, stamped "NICHOLS & CHILDS/PATENT/CONWAY/MASS." on left frame side plate, .34 cal., 6 shot, cherry grip................. **4,500.00**

North & Savage Figure-8, First Model, 7" octagonal barrel, stamped "E. SAVAGE. MIDDLETOWN. CONN./H. S. NORTH. PATENTED JUNE 17 1856" and "CAST STEEL," .36 cal., 6 shot, round brass frame and sharp spur on grip frame, stamped "76" on several parts, walnut grips **2,750.00**

Starr, Double Action, Navy, Model 1858, 6" round barrel, stamped "STARR ARMS Co. NEW YORK" (right) and "STARR'S PATENT JAN. 15, 1856" (left), .36 cal., 6 shot, walnut grips, casehardened hammer, trigger, and lever **1,250.00**

Walch, John, Pocket Model, 3.2 octagonal barrel, stamped "WALCH FIRE-ARMS Co. NEW-YORK/PAT'D FEB. 8, 1850," .31 cal., 10 shot, brass frame engraved on left with deer motif and on right with hunting dog motif, ivory grips **675.00**

REVOLVERS, CARTRIDGE

Allen & Wheelock and Ethan Allen & Co.,
32 Sidehammer Rimfire, 5″ octagonal
barrel, stamped "ALLEN & WHEE-
LOCK WORCESTER, MASS. U.S./
ALLEN'S PATENTS SEPT. 7, NOV. 9,
1858," iron frame, .32 cal., walnut
grip **200.00**
Colt Bisley Model Single Action Army
Revolver, 7½″ barrel, stamped
"COLT'S PT.F.A.MFG.C°. HART-
FORD, CT.U.S.A.," .45 cal., check-
ered hard rubber grips **625.00**
Moore, Front Loading Teat-Fire Re-
volver, 3¼″ round barrel, stamped
"MOORE PAT. FIRE ARMS Co.
BROOKLYN N.Y.," .31 teat-fire cal., 6
shot, frame, scroll, and border en-
graved, silver plated barrel, gold
washed cylinder with floral patterns,
two piece pearl grip **575.00**
Smith & Wesson, Model No. 1, First Is-
sue, 3³⁄₁₆″ octagonal barrel, stamped
"SMITH & WESSON. SPRINGFIELD,
MASS." (barrel) and "PATENTED
APRIL 3. 1855 & JUNE 15. 1858" (cylinder), .23 rimfire, 7 shot, silver plated
frame, rosewood grip **935.00**

FLINTLOCK LONG ARMS

French Model, 1763 Musket, 44½″
round barrel, .75 cal., lockplate
marked "St. Etienne, "full length walnut stock with three iron barrel bands,
iron trigger guard and butt plate, the
major weapon of French infantry
troops during the Revolutionary War   **925.00**
Kentucky, H. Deringer, Philadelphia,
59⅜″ total length, 43⅜″ octagonal
barrel, .60 cal., brass furniture, patchbox with scalloped edges and stylized
eagle head finial, tiger stripped stock   **2,000.00**
U.S. Model 1803 Musket, 36″ half oc-
tagonal, half round barrel, .54 cal.,
lockplate marked "U.S." and "Harper's Ferry" with eagle, dated 1816,
walnut half stock with brass patch box
on right side **2,750.00**
Whitney, 1798, U. S. Contract, .69 cal.,
43¾″ round barrel, iron mountings,
steel ramrod, black walnut stock with
comb, Style III, evenly rounded rear of
lock **1,750.00**

PERCUSSION LONG ARMS

Note: Conversion of flintlock long arms to percussion was common practice. Most British,
French, and U.S. military flintlock model longarms
listed in the previous section can be found in percussion. Values for these percussion converted pistols may be from 40 to 60% of the flintlock values
noted previously.

Kentucky, P. H. Laufman, Pittsburgh,
58½″ total length, 42″ full octagonal
deeply rifled barrel, .36 cal., brass furniture, tiger stripped stock **600.00**
Remington, Model 1863, Zouave Rifle,
.58 cal., 33″ round barrel, brass furniture, steel ramrod, brass patchbox,
walnut stock **975.00**
U.S. Model 1841 Rifle (Mississippi Rifle),
c1850, 33″ round barrel, .54 cal., lockplate marked "HARPERS/FERRY/
1850," full walnut stock with two barrel
bands, large brass patchbox on right
side of butt, brass trigger guard, and
butt plate **1,000.00**
U.S. Model 1861, 40″ round barrel, .58
cal., full walnut stock with three iron
barrel bands, lock marked "U.S./
SPRINGFIELD/(date)," American ea-
gle stamp **675.00**

FIREHOUSE COLLECTIBLES

History: The volunteer fire company has played
a vital role in the protection and social growth of
many towns and rural areas. Paid professional firemen usually are found only in large metropolitan
areas. Each fire company prided itself on equipment and uniforms. Conventions and parades gave
the fire companies a chance to show off their equipment. These events produced a wealth of firehouse
related memorabilia.

Reference: Mary Jane and James Piatti, *Firehouse Collectibles*, The Engine House, 1979.

Museums: Insurance Company of North America
(INA) Museum, Philadelphia, PA; Oklahoma State
Fireman's Association Museum, Oklahoma City,
OK; San Francisco Fire Dept. Memorial Museum,
San Francisco, CA.

Additional Listings: See *Warman's Americana
& Collectibles* for more examples.

Alarms
   Gamewell **55.00**
   Hartley Fire Awakener, nickel over
     copper, spring works, boxed **20.00**
   Unmarked, cast iron, huge bronze bell,
     dated 1872 . . . .   **275.00**
   Victorian, cast iron case and door,
     cast iron pole with fluted column . .   **165.00**
Axe Head, cast iron, cast intwined letters
   "C.I.P.", wood handle **150.00**
Belts, red, white and black leather
   Pumgustu **80.00**
   Suction Hose **85.00**
Belt Buckle, orig paint, red, white
   and black, mkd "Staff, Boston
   Volunteers" **100.00**

Speaking trumpet, presentation, brass, engraved, $600.00.

Billy Club, 17″ l, turned wood, painted brown graining, dec with yellow hearts and "G * O"................. 55.00

Blotter, Westchester Fire Ins. Co. of New York, unused, 1911............. 15.00

Buckets, leather
 11″ h, old black paint, white letters "B. O. Vis. No. 5"................ 95.00
 12″ h, old black paint, insignia of crossed arrows, imp signature Tilley, worn.................. 200.00
 13″ h, painted green, red trim, gold letters, dec "L. Baker No. 1, M.F.S.", Marblehead (MA) Fire Society.................. 750.00

Daguerrotype Cases, gutta-percha, 3¼″ w, 3¾″ h
 Black, fireman on cover rescuing child................... 55.00
 Brown, fireman on cover, tintype of 2 girls.................. 95.00

Extinguisher, Phoenix, Norwich, CT, patent April 25, 1899............. 35.00

Hook, 4 prong, cast iron, 9½″ h...... 30.00

Marks, cast iron
 Fire Insurance of Phila, shows hydrant and hose.................. 200.00
 Germantown, National, 1843...... 150.00

Helmets
 Brass, American, eagle finial...... 225.00
 Leather
  Chief, AFD, white paint......... 150.00

Clifton, NJ, 6″ shield.......... 125.00
Fireman's Active, Phila, red paint . 400.00
Pioneer Fire Co., No. 1, shield ... 75.00

Tin, eagle crest................ 50.00

Lamp, pole, pr, "Torrent 18" emb on round glass panels............ 3,200.00

Lantern, presentation, nickel, 1865 .. 300.00

Nozzle, 12″ l, brass............. 15.00

Paperweight, 5″ h, cast iron, fire hydrant on base, mkd Insurance Ed. Datty.................. 135.00

Parade Hat, "Western Hose Co., 1836," red, black trim, gold letters and dec, Phila.. 3,300.00

Parade Plaque, brass, mkd "Jon Waser, Maisbil-Ballm No. 4"..... 50.00

Parade Torch Helmet, serpent holder, brass front piece, mkd "Cataract 4 Steamer 1836," oil torch on top .. 1,450.00

Siren, hand pumped, brass, 24″ h, mkd Tyfon, made in Sweden..... 65.00

Steam Gauge, Ahrens Fox Fire Engine Co...................... 300.00

Trumpets
 Brass, 18″ h, presentation, inscribed "Presented to 1st Assist. Engineer E. K. Shaw by Ringgold Hose Co., No. 1, May 19th, 1875", orig red tassel........ 500.00
 Nickel, 15½″ h, inscribed "Washington Hook & Ladder Co., No. 1", orig blue tassel.......... 350.00
 Nickel Plated, engraved "W.V.F.A." 400.00
 Silver, 21¼″ h, 9½″ fluted bell, inscribed "Presented to Chief Peter L. T. Van Tienen by Victory Engine Co. No. 4, Aug 5, 1932", orig tassel.................. 900.00

FIREPLACE EQUIPMENT

History: The fireplace was a gathering point in the colonial home for heat, meals, and social interaction. It maintained its dominate position until the introduction of central heating in the mid-19th century.

Because of the continued popularity of the fireplace, accessories still are manufactured, usually in an early American motif. Modern blacksmiths also are reproducing the old iron implements.

Additional Listings: Brass and Iron.

Andirons
 Brass
  Empire, turned acorn finial over a faceted baluster turned standard on spurred arched legs, melon reeded and ring turned feet, stamped "E. Smylie Patent", NY, c1825, 19¾″ h............. 800.00

Screen, rosewood, floral panel, $500.00.

Federal, turned oval finial, hexagonal upper section and plinth, brass gallery, ball turned log stop, spurred arched legs with shod slipper feet, Boston, c1800, 18½″ h **450.00**

Federal, urn shaped finial over tapering columnar standard, sq plinth, spurred arched legs, claw and ball feet, urn shaped log stops, c1810, 28¼″ h **2,000.00**

Steeple top, lemon font, claw and ball feet, 29½″ h **400.00**

Cast Iron, full figural Indian, 19¼″ h.   **550.00**

Wrought Iron

  Heart finial, crock necks, tapered, chamfered and tooled posts, widely spaced penny feet, Berks County, PA **500.00**

  Round faceted finial above rect standard on arched legs, 19th C, 19″ h **275.00**

Ash Scraper, brass, oval turned finial above flat iron arm inlaid with brass and copper panels, engraving, "1644" above iron rake, scrolled ornament, 20″ h **1,200.00**

Bellows, turtle back, orig yellow ochre paint, free hand and stenciled dec in red, black, green, brass nozzle, leather worn, 17¼″ l **100.00**

Coal Box, brass, hinged, slanted lid . . .   **100.00**

Coal Scuttle, copper, cylindrical, one open side, brass bail handle and grip, flaring cylindrical foot, 19th C, 18″ h.   **325.00**

Crane, hearth, wrought iron, 18th C, 31″ l **125.00**

Fan, brass, dec, 27½″ h **300.00**

Fenders

  Brass

    D Shape, 3 brass baluster shaped finials, brass rail above woven iron wire screen, brass base, 19th C, 47″ w, 15¼″ h **450.00**

    Serpentine, pierced gallery above beaded molding over vertically pierced sides, engraved foliate dec, molded base, George III style, late 18th C, 31¼″ w **1,000.00**

    Serpentine, pierced, greyhounds flanking urn in center, English, 18th C, 48″ w **400.00**

  Wrought Iron, alternating twisted and wavy spindles, cast ball finials, scrolled feet, 41″ w, 12″ d, 11″ h.   **225.00**

Firebacks, cast iron

  Arched crest, tulips, dated 1794, 22½″ h **500.00**

  Rectangular, arched top, shell in center flanked by 2 dolphins, Ceres, scrolling acanthus border, English, 17th C, 23½″ w, 26″ h **1,000.00**

Fireplace, Victorian, Franklin-style, iron, brass molding, tile facing, orig brass finials, pair of brass ball top andirons, American, late 19th C, 35″ h, 26½″ d, 32″ l **800.00**

Fire Screens

  Brass, 4 brass framed arched panels, each 13″ w, 33½″ h **175.00**

  Wooden

    Folk Art, central panel with scalloped top, 2 hinged sides, painted landscape, 25″ w, 32½″ h **75.00**

    Mahogany, baluster turned pedestal, tripod cabriole legs, shod slipper feet, rect screen, canvaswork panel in polychrome crewel landscape with sheep, deer, rabbit, fox, and butterfly, Queen Anne, Newport, RI, c1760, 16¾″ w, 14¼″ h panel, 45¼″ h overall . .   **2,000.00**

    Mahogany, columnar standard with urn shaped finial on baluster turned pedestal, tripod cabriole legs, slipper feet, needlework screen, Federal, NY, c1800, 55″ h **1,000.00**

Grill, wrought iron, circular, 4 sections of scrolled foliate openwork, revolving on tripod base, strap handle, 22⅜″ h **300.00**

Hod, copper, iron feet, handle, bail . . .   **125.00**

Kettle Holder, wrought iron, dec scrollwork, 21″ w, 15″ h **100.00**

Peal, wrought iron, simple well shaped
   handle, 37¾" l **100.00**
Roasting Oven, tin, spit, 25" l, 22" h . . **200.00**
Skimmer, brass and wrought iron,
   18¾" l **125.00**
Tongs, wrought iron
   Primitive, 26¾" l **100.00**
   Shaped tips, bevelled arms, elaborate
     cut and chamfered hinge, cylindrical
     handles with turned elements, 18th
     C, 11⅞" l **350.00**
Tool Sets, brass
   3 pc, obelisk shaped handles, match-
     ing molded base with gallery trim. **200.00**
   3 pc, round finial handles, round dish
     base **100.00**
Trammels, wrought iron
   Chain, 50" l **75.00**
   Sawtooth, adjusts from 40½" **125.00**
   Scrolled terminals, notched sliding
     hook, Chester County, PA, 41" l . . **500.00**
Trivets
   Brass, D shaped surface pierced with
     circular design, engraved with fol-
     iate ornament, turned wooden han-
     dle, cabriole legs joined by
     stretcher, English, c1775, 15¼" d,
     12" h **700.00**
   Steel, rect, slats on top, baluster and
     ring turned legs, English, 19th C,
     30" l, 9" h **200.00**
Utensil Rack, wrought iron, 5 hooks, styl-
   ized floral detail, old blue and green
   paint, 16¼" l **450.00**

FISCHER J. BUDAPEST.

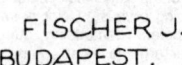

FISCHER CHINA

History: In 1893 Moritz Fischer founded his factory in Herend, Hungary, a center of porcelain production from the 1790s.

Confusion exists about Fischer china because of
its resemblance to the wares of Meissen, Sevres,
and Oriental export. It often was bought and sold
as the product of these firms. Forged marks of other
potteries are found on Herend pieces. The mark
"MF," often joined, is the mark of Moritz Fischer's
pottery.

Fischer's Herend is hard paste ware with lumi-
nosity and exquisite decoration. Pieces are designated by pattern names, the best known being
Chantilly Fruit, Rothschild Bird, Chinese Bouquet,
Victoria Butterfly, and Parsley.

Fischer also made figural birds and animal
groups, Magyar figures (individually and in groups),
and Herend eagles poised for flight.

This past year the nation's leading collector of
Fischer china died. His absence from the market
is expected to cause prices to drop.

**Vase, 13¾", cornucopia body, pierced
rim, painted floral motif, four feet with
fish scales, stamped and imp mark,
1913, orig paper label, $275.00.**

Bowl, 6¾", reticulated edge, birds, butterflies, and flowers, multicolored,
   late **50.00**
Charger, 13", floral dec, multicolored,
   gold trim. **345.00**
Dish, 4½", triangular, Victoria Butterfly,
   gold trim **150.00**
Ewer, 16", reticulated, multicolored,
   handle **325.00**
Jar, cov, 9½", floral dec, multicolored,
   gold trim. **250.00**
Pitcher, 12", reticulated, floral dec, multicolored, gold tracing **400.00**
Plates
   7½", luncheon, Chantilly Fruit. **90.00**
   10½", dinner, Parsley **110.00**
Sauce Boat, underplate and ladle, Vic-
   toria Butterfly **250.00**
Tureen, cov, 8½", Chantilly Fruit, natural
   fruit molded finial, 2 handles **300.00**
Urn, 12", reticulated, blue floral dec,
   shield mark. **350.00**
Vases
   8", reticulated, blue flowers, green
     leaves, gold handles, shield mark . **250.00**
   8½", barrel shape in holder, reticu-
     lated, much gold **350.00**
   12", reticulated, emb floral dec, ornate
     handles. **325.00**
   13" h, 8" d, reticulated, blue, pink, and
     gold bands and accents, 2 winged
     serpent handles, stamped, Fischer
     J. Budapest. **400.00**
   15", reticulated top and bottom, red
     and blue, gold trim **385.00**
Vegetable Dish, open, 9½", Victoria But-
   terfly, gold trim **190.00**

FITZHUGH

History: Fitzhugh, one of the most recognized Chinese Export porcelain patterns, was named for the Fitzhugh family for whom the first dinner service was made. The peak period of production was 1780 to 1850.

Fitzhugh features an oval center medallion or monogram surrounded by four groups of flowers or emblems. The border is similar to that on Nanking china. Occasional border variations are found. Butterfly and honeycomb are among the rarest.

Blue is the common color. Color is a key factor in pricing with rarity in ascending order of orange, green, sepia, mulberry, yellow, black, and gold. Combinations of colors are scarce.

Spode Porcelain Company, England, currently is producing a copy of the Fitzhugh pattern in several colors. Oriental copies also are available.

Plate, 9⅝″ d, orange, $300.00.

Basket, underplate, 9⅛″ basket, 9½″ underplate, oval, reticulated, blue, pine cone and beast medallion, basket with 2 upright, fluted scroll handles, 1790–1810 .... **2,000.00**
Basin, 11⅝″, blue, pine cone and dragon medallion, 1790–1820 .... **450.00**
Bottle, 9¾″, blue, pine cone and beast medallions, 19th C **675.00**
Bouillon Bowl, 4¾″ d, blue, c1820 .... **85.00**
Center Dish, 12⅜″ l, lozenge shape, blue, c1820. .... **600.00**
Cup and Saucer, tea, 2½″ cup, 6¼″ saucer, blue, beast and leaf medallion, 19th C **125.00**
Hot Water Dish, 10⅞″ d, circular, orange, pine cone and dragon medallion, c1820. .... **425.00**

Plates
  6¼″, blue, c1820. .... **135.00**
  8¾″, green, late 19th C **185.00**
  9½″, green, ... **225.00**
Platters
  12⅞″, oval, green, c1860. .... **225.00**
  20¼″, oval, blue, c1820. .... **935.00**
Potes de Creme, cov, set of 8, 3¼″ h, blue, entwined strap handles, pod knops, c1820 .... **1,000.00**
Saucer, 5⅜″, green, flower and beast medallion, c1850. .... **95.00**
Serving Dish, 10¾″, oval, orange, flower and beast medallion, c1820 .... **375.00**
Soup Tureen, cov, and underplate, 13⅝″ l soup, 13⅛″ underplate, blue, basket of flowers knob, c1810 ..... **1,100.00**
Vegetable, cov, and underplate, 11½″ l, blue **1,150.00**

FLASKS

History: A flask is a container for liquids, usually having a narrow neck. Early American glass companies frequently formed them in molds which left a relief design on the front and/or back. Historical flasks with a portrait, building, scene, or name are the most desired.

A chestnut is hand blown, small, and has a flattened bulbous body. The pitkin has a blown globular body with vertical ribs with a spiral rib overlay. Teardrop flasks are generally fiddle shaped and have a scroll or geometric design.

Dimensions can differ for the same flask because of variations in the molding process. Color is important, with scarcer colors demanding more money. Aqua and amber are the most common colors. Bottles with "sickness," an opalescent scaling which eliminates clarity, are worth much less.

Reference: George L. and Helen McKearin, *American Glass,* Crown Publishers, 1941 and 1948.

Chestnuts
  5⅛″, greenish-aqua, ½ pint, blown, 16 ribs, broken swirl [swirled ribs are bold, vertical ribs faint], Mantua, minor sickness in base, ex-collection Wettlaufer and Jim and Eileen Courtney **215.00**
  5⅜″, brilliant yellow amber, 10 diamond, Zanesville, minor wear, illus. in *Antiques* (June 1967, pg 745), ex-collection Jim and Eileen Courtney **1,800.00**
  5½″, golden amber, 24 vertical ribs, Zanesville, minor wear and pinpoint rim flakes, ex-collection of Jim and Eileen Courtney **300.00**
  6½″, aqua, pint, blown, 24 swirled ribs, Zanesville, ex-collection Jim and Eileen Courtney **150.00**
  6⅝″, golden olive-amber, pint, blown, 20 swirled ribs, Kent, small flake on

lip, some external scratches, ex-collection Jim and Eileen Courtney . . **450.00**

8⅝", amber, "popcorn" flask, 24 ribs, broken swirl, Zanesville, minor int. scratches, illus. *Antiques* (June 1967, pg 746), ex-collection Jim and Eileen Courtney **2,700.00**

Gemel

8⅛", clear, white looping, fancy applied rigaree, sheared mouth, minor wear on sides **75.00**

11⅛", clear, pink and white loopings, sheared mouth, applied white collar, polished pontil **100.00**

Flasks, Historical

Anchor/Log Cabin, aquamarine, pint, Spring Garden Glass Works, McKearin G-XIII-58 . . . . **50.00**

Army Dragoon/Dog, citrine, qt, McKearin G-XIII-6. . . . . **150.00**

Eagle/Masonic, olive-amber, pint, sheared mouth, pontil mark, Keene Marlboro Street Glassworks, Keene, NH, McKearin G-IV-21. . . . **110.00**

Eagle/Masonic, olive-green, half pint, sheared flared mouth, pontil mark, Keene Marlboro Street Glassworks, Keene, NH, McKearin G-IV-24. . . . **170.00**

Eagle/Willington, amber, pint, double collared mouth, smooth base, Willington Glass Works, Willington, CT, McKearin G-II-64 . . . . **75.00**

Lafayette, Coventry, C-T/Liberty Cap on pole with "S & S," 7⅜" h, aqua, pint, pontiled, McKearin G-I-85, some wear and int. broken blister in

neck, ex-collection Jim and Eileen Courtney **4,150.00**

Masonic/Eagle, clear, brilliant green, pint, tooled mouth, Keene Marlboro Street Glassworks, Keene, NH, McKearin G-IV-1 . . . . **235.00**

Masonic/Eagle, pale yellow-green, pint, sheared mouth, pontil base, Kensington Glass Works, Phila., PA, McKearin G-IV-37 . . . . **70.00**

Pine Tree, clear, yellow-green, pint, McKearin G-X-15 . . . . **100.00**

Sunburst, 6¼", olive green, pontiled, McKearin G-VIII-18, ex-collection Jim and Eileen Courtney. **325.00**

Traveler's Companion/Ravenna Glass Co., 6⅝", deep grass green, pint, iron pontil, ex-collection George McKearin and Jim and Eileen Courtney **1,100.00**

Washington/Taylor, portrait, clear green, qt, sheared mouth, smooth base, Dyottville Glass Works, Phila., PA, McKearin G-I-37 . . . . **130.00**

Pitkins

4½", olive-green, 36 vertical ribs, spiral ribs over, New England, early 19th C **275.00**

6⅝", yellow with slight olive tone, pint, ribbed and swirled to right, sheared mouth, pontil base, New England . **260.00**

6¾", deep olive yellow, blown, half post neck, 30 ribs, broken swirl, ex-collection Jim and Eileen Courtney **400.00**

Olive-green, pint, 32 vertical ribs, 32 swirled ribs, New Jersey or New England **200.00**

Teardrops

7⅜", opaque white, red and blue looping, tooled "three-ring" sheared mouth, polished pontil **170.00**

9", rounded, clear, white loopings, double ringed tooled collar, tubular pontil **80.00**

FLOW BLUE

History: Flow blue or flowing blue is the name applied to china of cobalt and white whose color, when fired in a kiln, produced a flowing or smudged effect. The blue varies in color from dark cobalt to a grayish or steel blue. The flow varies from very slight to a heavy blur where the pattern can not be easily recognized. The blue color does not permeate through the china.

Flow blue was first produced around 1835 in the Staffordshire district of England by a large number of potters including Alcock, Davenport, J. Wedgwood, Grindley, New Wharf, Johnson Brothers, and many others. The early flow blue, 1830s to 1870s, was usually of the ironstone variety. The late patterns, 1880s to 1910s, and modern patterns, after

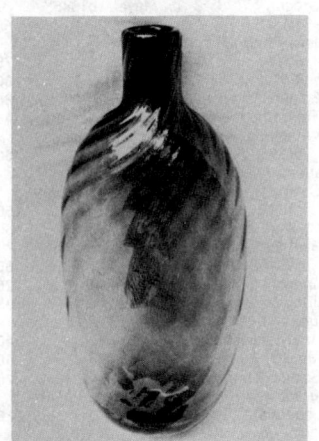

Pitkin, medium green, 14 right hand swirls, pontil, $325.00.

1910, usually were made of the more delicate semi-porcelain variety. Aproximately 95% of the flow blue was made in England, with the remaining 5% made in Germany, Holland, France, and Belgium. A few patterns also were made in the United States by Mercer, Warwick, and Wheeling Pottery companies.

References: Mary F. Gaston, *The Collector's Encyclopedia Of Flow Blue China*, Collector Books, 1983; Veneita Mason, *Popular Patterns of Flow Blue*, Wallace Homestead, 1983; Petra Williams, *Flow Blue China—An Aid To Identification*, Fountain House East, 1981, revised edition; Petra Williams, *Flow Blue China II*, Fountain House East, 1981, revised edition; Petra Williams, *Flow Blue China and Mulberry Ware—Similarity and Value Guide*, Fountain House East, 1981, revised edition.

EARLY PATTERNS: c1825–1850

Bowls
Birmah, Wood & Brownfield, mkd "C", c1845	90.00
Chapoo, Wedgwood, c1850, oval, 6"	175.00
Manilla, Podmore Walker, c1845, 8"	100.00

Butters, cov
Chusan, J. Clementson, c1840	120.00
Oregon, T. J. & J. Mayer, c1845	180.00
Pelew, E. Challinor, c1840	200.00

Creamers
Corean, Podmore Walter, c1850	100.00
Formosa, W. Ridgway, c1834	90.00
Hong Kong, Charles Meigh	85.00
Leipsic, Clementson, c1850, octagonal	165.00
Penang, Ridgway, c1840	90.00

Cups
Arabesque, T. J. & J. Mayer, c1845	40.00
Manilla, Podmore Walker, c1845	45.00

Cups and Saucers
Indian Jar, T. Furnival, c1843	80.00
Kyber, J. Meir & Son, handleless	80.00
Pelew, E. Challinor, c1840, handleless	100.00
Tulip & Sprig, Thomas Walker, 1845	65.00
Whampoa, Mellor & Venables, c1835	75.00

Gravy Boats
Arabesque, T. J. & J. Mayer, c1845	115.00
Cashmere, Francis Morley, c1850	225.00
Gothic, T. E. Mayer, mkd imp Davenport anchor, c1844, underplate	165.00
Melbourne, W. H. Grindley, c1842, underplate	95.00
Tonquin, J. Heath, c1850	225.00
Jam Dish, Cashmere, Ridgway & Morley, c1842, 3½" h, 7" d underplate, lion head handles	200.00

Pitchers
Chen-Si, John Meir, c1835, 2 qt	225.00
Chinese, Thomas Dimmock, c1840, 9" h	275.00

Early Pattern, Cashmere, creamer, 5⅜" h, 5½" w, $175.00.

Plates
Arabesque, T. J. & J. Mayer, c1845, 9½"	65.00
Bamboo, Alcock, c1845, 10½"	65.00
Beauties of China, Mellor, Venables & Co., c1845, 9½"	70.00
Canton, Maddock, c1850, 7¾"	35.00
Chapoo, Wedgwood, c1850, 9¼"	80.00
Chen-Si, John Meir, c1835, 10½"	85.00
Indian Jar, T. Furnival, c1843, 9", glaze worn	45.00
Kyber, W. Adams & Co., 10"	58.00
Oregon, Longport, c1845, 7½"	65.00
Oregon, T. J. & J. Mayer, c1845, 6½"	50.00
Pelew, Challinor, c1840	
8½"	75.00
9½"	85.00
Scinde, Thomas Walker, c1847, 9"	60.00
Troy, Charles Meigh, c1840, 7¾"	45.00
Whampoa, Mellor & Venables, c1835, 7⅝"	50.00

Platters
California, Podmore Walker & Co., c1849	150.00
Chusan, J. Clementson, c1840	165.00
Feather Edge, Clementson & Young, c1845, 12½" l, 8 sided	85.00
Oregon, T. J. & J. Mayer, c1845	225.00
Relish, Chusan, Morley, c1850	95.00

Sauces
Amoy, Davenport, c1844	40.00
Manilla, Podmore Walker c1845	40.00
Scinde, Thomas Walker, c1847	25.00
Sauce Tureen, Tivoli, T. Furnival, c1845, underplate	275.00

Sugars, cov
Amoy, Davenport, c1844	150.00
Oregon, T. J. & J. Mayer, c1845	275.00
Teapot, Scinde, J. & G. Alcock, 1840	400.00

Toothbrush Holder, cov, Botanical, C.
M., c1845. . . . . **200.00**
Vegetable Dishes
Chen-Si, John Meir, c1835, 9", open **125.00**
Chusan, Morley, c1850, 10", open . . **135.00**
Tulip & Sprig, Thomas Walker, c1845,
cov **325.00**

MIDDLE PATTERNS: c1850–1870

Bone Dish, Chinese, Josiah Wedgwood,
c1870, 6½" l, 4" w **100.00**
Bowl, Honc, Regout, c1858, 6" d,
3¼" h **125.00**
Butter, cov, Kirkee, John Meir & Son,
c1861. . . . . **185.00**
Creamer, Rhoda Gardens, Hackwood,
c1850, paneled. **125.00**
Cups and Saucers
Kinshan, E. C. & Co., c1855. . . . . . **80.00**
Strawberry, T. Walker, c1856, handle-
less **100.00**
Plates
Indian Stone, Edward Walley, c1850,
7". **55.00**
Kinshan, E. C. & Co., c1855. . . . . . **60.00**
Rock, Challinor, c1850, 9½". **60.00**
Shangae, T. Furnival, c1860, 10" . . . **75.00**
Shell, E. Challinor, c1860, 9¾". **65.00**
Platter, Formosa, T. J. & J. Mayer,
c1851, 15¾" l, 12" w. **275.00**

LATE PATTERNS: c1880–1900s

Bowls
Ashburton, W. H. Grindley, c1891, 8"
Dainty, John Maddock & Son, c1896,   **45.00**
6". **25.00**
Iowa, Wilkinson, c1907 . . . . **20.00**
Lugano, Ridgway, c1910, serving,
oblong, small **35.00**
Persian, Johnson Bros., c1902, 9½"
l, applied handles. **95.00**
Spinach, Libertas, c1900, 10". **45.00**
Butter Pat, Non Pareil, Burgess &
Leigh, c1891. . . . . **20.00**
Cake Plate, Dainty, John Maddock &
Son, c1896, 10", shaped handles. . . **85.00**
Coffee Server, LaBelle, Wheeling,
c1900, hinged SP lid **250.00**
Cup and Saucer, Italia, W. & E. Corn,
c1891. . . . . **60.00**
Gravy Boats
Andorra, Johnson Bros, c1901 . . . . . **75.00**
Ashburton, W. H. Grindley, c1891. . . **70.00**
Madras, Doulton & Co., c1900 . . . . . **100.00**
Poppy, Wedgwood & Co., c1908 . . . **225.00**
Hatpin Holder, Watteau, New Wharf
Pottery, c1891. . . . . **80.00**
Lamp, Watteau, Doulton–Burslem,
c1900, Bradley & Hubbard fittings,
ftd base, urn shape with handles,
21" h to top of harp **400.00**

Pitchers
Chrysanthemum, Myott, Son & Co.,
c1907, 7" h **135.00**
Touraine, Henry Alcock, c1898, milk **325.00**
Plates
Ashburton, W. H. Grindley, c1891,
9¾" **65.00**
Brunswick, Wood & Son, c1891, 9" . **45.00**
Clover, W. H. Grindley, c1910,
dinner **50.00**
Dainty, John Maddock & Son,
c1896, 6" **30.00**
Harwood, New Wharf Pottery, c1891,
8⅞" **30.00**
Knox, New Wharf Pottery, c1891,
dinner **20.00**
Kyber, Adams, c1891, 10" **65.00**
Mikado, W. & E. Corn, c1900, 8" . . . **40.00**
Non Pareil, Burgess & Leigh, c1891,
9¾" **50.00**
St. Louis, Johnson Bros, c1900, 8⅞" **30.00**
Superior, Petrus Regout, c1891, 9". . **35.00**
Togo, F. Winkle, c1900, 10". **45.00**
Touraine, Henry Alcock, c1898, 10",
dinner **75.00**
Verona, Wood, c1891, 8". **65.00**
Waldorf, New Wharf Pottery, c1892,
8⅞" **45.00**
Platters
Argyle, W. H. Grindley, c1896, 13" l . **95.00**
Ashburton, W. H. Grindley, c1891,
15". **80.00**
Beatrice, Maddock, c1896, 16". **90.00**
Clover, W. H. Grindley, c1910, 16". . **100.00**
Dainty, John Maddock & Son,
c1896, 10½" **55.00**
LaDas, Ridgway, c1905 . . . . **25.00**
LePavot, W. H. Grindley, c1896,
12½" oval **75.00**
Melbourne, W. H. Grindley, c1900 . . **50.00**
Richmond, Alfred Meakin, c1891,
16" l **125.00**
Togo, F. Winkle, c1900, 16". **95.00**
Warwick, c1900, 10½". **65.00**
Sauce, Osborne, W. H. Grindley,
c1900. . . . . **15.00**
Saucer, Temple, British Anchor Pottery
Co., Ltd, c1910 . . . . **35.00**
Soup Bowls
Dainty, John Maddock & Son,
c1896, 8", no flange. **40.00**
Duchess, W. H. Grindley, c1891, 9",
flange **45.00**
Waldorf, New Wharf Pottery, c1892,
9", flange **45.00**
Teapot, cov, Touraine, Henry Alcock,
c1898. . . . . **325.00**
Tureens, cov
Ashburton, W. H. Grindley, c1891,
round 12½" d, 12" ladle **200.00**
Marguerite, W. H. Grindley, c1891 . . **300.00**
Princess, Booths Ltd, c1900, 12" . . . **60.00**
Sugar, cov, LaBelle, Wheeling, c1900 . **125.00**

Late Pattern, Lancaster, New Wharf Pottery, vegetable dish, cov, raised emb dec, 12½", $120.00.

Vegetable Dishes, cov
Beatrice, Maddock, c1896	**85.00**
Hofberg, W. H. Grindley, c1891	**80.00**
Kelvin, Meakin, c1891	**165.00**
LaBelle, Wheeling, c1900.	**40.00**
Touraine, Henry Alcock, c1898, 9⅝"	**250.00**
Waldorf, New Wharf Pottery, c1892 .	**335.00**

Wash Bowl and Pitcher, Roma, Wedgwood & Co. Ltd, c1905 . . . .   **250.00**

Waste Bowls
Spinach, Libertas, c1900	**35.00**
Waldorf, New Wharf Pottery, c1892 .	**40.00**

FOOD BOTTLES

History: Food bottles were made in many sizes, shapes, and colors. Manufacturers tried to make an attractive bottle that would ship well and allow the purchaser to see the product, thus assuring him that the product was as good and as well made as home preserves.

References: Hugh Cleveland, *Bottle Pricing Guide,* Collector Books, 1980; Ralph & Terry Kovel, *The Kovels' Bottle Price List,* Crown Publishers, Inc, 1982, 6th ed.; Carlo & Dot Sellari, *The Illustrated Price Guide to Antique Bottles,* Country Beautiful Corp, 1975.

Periodicals: *Antique Bottle World,* 5003 West Berwyn, Chicago, IL 60630; *Old Bottle Magazine,* P. O. Box 243, Bend, OR 97701. Subscription: $10.00.

Additional Listings: See *Warman's Americana & Collectibles* for more milk bottle listings.

Catsup, Heinz, H. J. Co., Patent June 17, 1890, 8 sided, sample, clear	**8.00**

Cider
Findlater Brand, oval, dark olive green, 11" h, 4¼" w.	**25.00**
Green & Clark Missouri Cider, Aug. 27, 1878, amber	**25.00**
Condensed Milk, Aroostock Condensed Milk Co., Maine, emb baby on lid . . .	**15.00**

Cream Pot, sepia transfer of milk maid, Wigtownshire Creamery Stranraer, 4½"	**15.00**

Horseradish
Becker's Pure Horse-Radish, Buffalo, aqua, 4¼".	**10.00**
Heinz, emb "Heinz Noble & Co", 2 anchors and words "Horseradish," solid glass horsehead on lid, clear, 5", 1873	**275.00**

Horseradish, 8 panels, dark green, $8.00.

Lemonade, Eiffel Tower, reverse with G. Foster Clark & Co., Manuf, clear, 2¾"	**5.00**
Maple Syrup, Champion Vermont, amethyst, 8½".	**8.00**

Milk
Abbotts Dairy, Conway, NH, round, emb, quart.	**10.00**
Elm Farm Dairy, Yarmouth, ME, scene, blue	**12.00**
Oakhurst Dairy, Portland Restaurant Service, round, emb, ⅝ pint	**15.00**
Pine Tree Dairy, Butte, MT, squat. . .	**20.00**
Rainiers Cream Top Dairy, Bridgeton, NJ, round, emb, quart.	**10.00**
Mustard, G. C. Giessen Mustard, NY, open pontil	**35.00**
Olive Oil, Wood Cooper Pure Olive Oil, Santa Barbara, CA, crude blob seal on shoulder, band collar, round, aqua, 11"	**10.00**
Peanut Butter, Jumbo, clear, 5".	**10.00**

Pepper Sauce
Diamond Packing Co., Bridgeton, NJ, aqua.	**10.00**
Durkee's beehive shape, blue-green	**45.00**

Lewis, W. K., 8 sided, open pontil, aqua **50.00**

Pickles
Atmore, R. F., cathedral, aqua, 11″ h, 4″ w **155.00**
Davis, Wm, Boston, Gherkins, 6 sided, metal label **325.00**
Skilton, Foote & Co., Bunker Hill Pickles, emb trees, tower and railroad track, round, clear **10.00**
Whitney Glass Works, 6 sided, cathedral, aqua, 12″ **45.00**

Vinegar, Old Duffy's 1842 5 Year Old Apple Juice Vinegar, name emb on top shoulder, "Duffy's" emb in diamond shape, 8 panels, amber, 6³⁄₄″ **20.00**

FOOD MOLDS

History: Food molds were used both commercially and in the home. For the most part, pewter ice cream molds and candy molds were used on a commercial basis; pottery and copper molds were used in homes. Today both types are collected largely for decorative purposes.

Pewter ice cream molds were made primarily by two American companies: Eppelsheimer & Co. [molds marked E & Co., N.Y.] and Schall & Co. [molds marked S & Co.]. Both companies used a numbering system for their molds. The Krauss Co. bought out Schall & Co., removed the S & Co. from some, but not all the molds, and added more designs [marked K or Krauss]. The majority of pewter ice cream molds are individual serving molds. When used, one quart of ice cream would make eight to ten pieces. Scarcer, but still available, are banquet molds which used two to four pints of ice cream per example. European pewter molds [CC is a French mold mark] are available.

Chocolate mold makers are more difficult to determine. Unlike the pewter ice cream molds, maker's marks were not always on the mold or were covered by frames. Eppelsheimer & Co. of New York marked many of their molds, either with their name or a design resembling a child's toy shop with "Trade Mark" and "NY". Many chocolate molds are imported from Germany and Holland and are marked with the country of origin and, in some cases, the mold maker's name.

Reference: Eleanore Bunn, *Metal Molds,* Collectors Books, 1981, out-of-print.

Additional Listings: Butter Prints.

Advisor: Lorry and Bruce Hanes.

CHOCOLATE MOLDS

Clamp Type, no hinge, two piece
Cat, mkd E & Co./toy top **55.00**
Hen On Basket, mkd E & Co./toy top **38.00**
Rabbit **34.00**
Stork, mkd E & Co./toy top **45.00**

Frame or Book type [Measurements based on single cavity size]
Donkey Pulling Car, 7½ x 3″, one cavity **64.00**
Easter Bunny, 4 x 2½″, four cavities **25.00**
Easter Egg, scene, 3½ x 2″, three cavities **40.00**
Hearts, decorated, 6½ x 6″, two cavities **48.00**
Owl, 5 x 2½″, three cavities **50.00**
Rabbits, one cavity
13½ x 6½″ **50.00**
21 x 9½″ **200.00**
Rooster, 8 x 5½″, one cavity **54.00**
Santa Claus, 4½ x 2″, six cavities. . **70.00**
Teddy Bear, 10½ x 5½″, one cavity . **135.00**
Turkey, 4½ x 3½, two cavities **45.00**
Witch, 4½ x 2″, four cavities **55.00**
Tray type [Measurement is overall tray size]
Circus Peanuts, 28 x 13″, one hundred and five cavities **48.00**
Rabbit Playing Saxophone, 14 x 10″, six cavities **40.00**
Santa Claus, 14 x 10″, four cavities . **45.00**
Turkey, 14 x 10″, eight cavities. **45.00**

ICE CREAM MOLDS

Banquet Size
Owl, mkd S & Co./7, four pints **550.00**
Oyster Plate, mkd E & Co. 116, one pint **350.00**
Puss in Boots, mkd S & Co./2, four pints **575.00**
Steamship, mkd E & Co./44, four pints **625.00**
Individual Size
Acorn, mkd S & Co./135 . . . . **35.00**
Apple, mkd S & Co./149 . . . . **22.00**
Basket, mkd E & Co./305 . . . . **38.00**
Basketball, mkd E & Co./1150 . . . . . **45.00**
Chick, mkd 603 . . . . **40.00**
Child of Spring, mkd E & Co./682 . . **48.00**
Christmas Tree, mkd E & Co./1154 . **60.00**
Cucumber, mkd E & Co./226 . . . . . . **28.00**
Dahlia, mkd 313 . . . . **35.00**
Diploma, mkd K/633 . . . . **38.00**
Drum, three part, mkd S & Co./511 . **44.00**
Dove Of Peace, mkd E & Co./677 . . **45.00**
Flag, American, mkd K/282 . . . . **50.00**
Four Leaf Clover Medallion, mkd 505 . . . . **38.00**
Grape Leaf, mkd E & Co./256 . . . . . **38.00**
Indian, mkd S & Co./458 . . . . **58.00**
Morning Glory, mkd 239. . . . . **40.00**
Old Mother Hubbard, mkd E & Co./ 981 . . . . **65.00**
Pineapple, mkd E & Co./253 . . . . . . **38.00**
Pipe, mkd S & Co./374 . . . . **32.00**
Poinsettia, mkd E & Co./1144 . . . . . **58.00**
Pumpkin, mkd 617. . . . . **24.00**
Puss in Boots, mkd E & Co./657 . . . **46.00**

Roast Turkey, mkd S & Co./364. . . .	28.00
Santa Maria, ship, mkd E & Co./ 1018.	42.00
Shamrock, mkd E & Co./1030	38.00
Tiger, three part, mkd 462	52.00
Tomato, mkd E & Co./208.	26.00
Turkey, mkd E & Co./650	38.00
Twenty Dollar Gold Piece, mkd 469 .	65.00
Uncle Sam, mkd S & Co./407	65.00
Valentine Letter, mkd S & Co./506. .	42.00
Violin, mkd E & Co./985	40.00
Washington, George, mkd S & Co./ 460.	65.00
Washington, Martha, mkd S & Co./ 461.	65.00
Zeppelin, mkd E & Co./1140	56.00

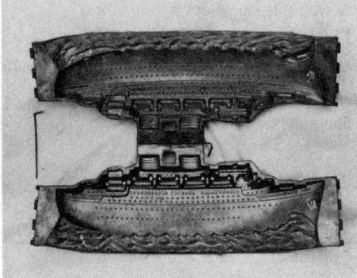

Ice Cream, ocean liner, pewter, 16¾ x 4¼ x 6″, mkd E & Co., 44, $625.00.

MISCELLANEOUS

Biscuit, melon ribbed, tin, 9″ long.	22.00
Cake, rabbit, 6½ x 7″	30.00
Cookie, pewter, six designs, 6 x 3″ . . .	55.00
Fish, tin, curved, 9″.	55.00
Lamb, cast iron, two piece, 8 x 12″ . . .	65.00
Maple Sugar, wood, hand carved, three designs, 14 x 14″	110.00

POTTERY [Center design indicated]

Ear of Corn, 8″.	60.00
Grape Cluster, 7″.	48.00
Lion, 7″	70.00
Sheaf of Wheat, 4″.	38.00
Strawberries, 4″	54.00

FOSTORIA GLASS   FOSTORIA

History: Fostoria Glass Co. began operations at Fostoria, Ohio, in 1887, and moved, in 1891, to Moundsville, West Virginia, its present location. By 1925 Fostoria had five furnances and a variety of special shops. In 1924 a line of colored tableware was introduced. Fostoria was purchased by Lancaster Colony in 1983, and continues to operate under the Fostoria name.

Reference: Hazel M. Weatherman, *Fostoria, Its First Fifty Years*, privately printed, c1972.

Collectors' Club: Fostoria Glass Society of America, P.O. Box 826, Moundsville, WV 26041. Dues: $10.00.

Museum: Huntington Galleries, Huntington, WV.

Ashtray, American, 2½″ sq, #2056 . . .	25.00
Bookends, pr, crystal	
Colt, standing, 5¼″ h.	21.00
Owl, 7½″ h.	25.00
Bowls	
Baroque, crystal, 9½″, oval vegetable	18.00
Versailles, topaz, 12″.	25.00
Butter, cov, American, round	120.00
Cake Stand, American, sq, pedestal. . .	75.00
Candlesticks	
Lyre, pr	100.00
Navarre, pr	32.00
Celery Tray, Versailles, green, 12″, oval	35.00

Goblet, Colonial Mirror, 9″, c1930, $15.00.

Champagnes	
Fascination, burgandy	12.00
Fostoria Rose.	15.00
Victoria.	15.00
Clarets	
Dolly Madison.	18.00
Fostoria Rose.	20.00
Cocktails, Chintz.	18.00

Compotes

June, yellow, small	20.00
Vintage, blown, cov, 8½″ h, 6¼″d, #204, c1904	40.00

Creamers

Fairfax, amber	7.00
Romance	10.00
Cup and Saucer, Fairfax, amber	6.00
Decanter, stopper, American, #2506	65.00

Goblets

Distinction, blue	10.00
Dolly Madison	20.00
Fascination, burgandy	15.00
Fostoria Rose	22.00
June, yellow, 8″	28.00
Moonstone, blue	7.00
Regis	20.00
Renaissance	25.00
Victoria	15.00
Ice Bucket, Baroque, yellow	60.00

Iced Tea Glasses

Fascination, burgandy	15.00
Moonstone, blue	7.00
Pavilion, gray	17.00
Regis	20.00
Victoria	15.00
Jug, American, 3 pint, #2056	25.00
Mustard, cov, spoon, American	30.00

Pitchers

Heritage, yellow	40.00
June, ftd, blue	425.00

Plates

Fairfax, amber, 11⅜″	5.00
Navarre, crystal, 9½″, dinner	40.00
Romance, 14″, torte	60.00
Platter, Vesper, green, 14″, oval	35.00
Punch Bowl, Regal, 2 pcs, 10½″ d, 11¾″ h	45.00
Relish, Coronet, 3 part divided	12.00
Salt and Pepper Shakers, Navarre, crystal	75.00

Sugars, cov

Fairfax, pink	8.00
Romance	20.00

Tumblers

June, topaz, ftd, 5 oz	20.00
Versailles, blue, ftd, 9 oz	25.00
Whiskey, American	10.00

Wines

Distinction, blue	10.00
Gazebo, rust base	12.00
Victoria	15.00

FRAKTUR

History: Fraktur, the calligraphy associated with the Pennsylvania Germans, is named for the elaborate first letter found in many of the handdrawn examples. Throughout its history printed, partially printed-handdrawn, and fully handdrawn works existed side by side. Fraktur often were made by the school teachers or ministers living in rural areas of Pennsylvania, Maryland, and Virginia. Many artists are unknown.

Fraktur exists in several forms—geburts and taufschein (birth and baptismal certificates), vorschrift (writing example, often with alphabet), haus sagen (house blessing), bookplates and marks, rewards of merit, illuminated religious text, valentines, and drawings. Although collected for decoration, the key element in Fraktur is the text.

Fraktur prices rise and fall along with the American folk art market. The key market place is Pennsylvania and the Middle Atlantic states.

References: Donald A. Shelley, *The Fraktur-Writings Or Illuminated Manuscripts Of The Pennsylvania Germans,* Pennsylvania German Society, 1961; Frederick S. Weiser and Howell J. Heaney (compilers), *The Pennsylvania German Fraktur Of The Free Library Of Philadelphia,* Pennsylvania German Society, 1976, two volumes.

Museum: The Free Library of Philadelphia, Philadelphia, PA.

Printed, Copy Book Cover, $300.00.

HANDDRAWN

Brechall, Martin, birth, baptism, and marriage record, Berks Co., PA, 1756–1778, 13 x 8½″, calligraphy text, four facing hearts each inscribed with pious verse, brightly colored flowers in corners, center	800.00
Cross Legged Angel artist, birth and baptismal, S.E. PA, 12½ x 15″, 1813	1,200.00
Farber, Wilhelm Antonius, birth and baptismal, Bucks County, PA, 1794, cut work border, 14½ x 12″	1,500.00
Flying Angel Artist, birth and baptismal, Northampton Co., PA, 1796, 15½ x 13″	1,000.00
Krebs, Frederick, birth, baptismal, and marriage, 1804, 12½ x 15½″	1,350.00
Seibecker, Ludwig, vorschrift, European, March 1816, 12¾ x 15¼″, calligraphy text, diamonds of blue, yellow, red, and orange, inscribed with pious verses, upper border of crested bird, double headed eagle, lower border with paired swans and angel's head.	500.00

Taufzegen Artist, birth and baptismal, Northampton Co., PA, 1803, 13 x 15½″ text enclosed within sawtooth border, corners with large birds, birth of Johannes Stortts. 750.00

Unknown artist, baptismal, Dauphin County, PA, 1788, 16¼ x 12¼″, calligraphy text inscribed within an arched frame work entwined with brightly colored blossoms, central chandelier with lighted tapers, two grape vines, for Christian Johannes Schenct 900.00

Unknown artist, birth and baptismal, York Co., PA, March 18, 1845, 15¼ x 12″, English script, text flanked by two angels carrying a wreath and bird, lower portion with birds and leafage, upper corners with hearts, based on printed forms which were in great currency during the latter half of the 19th C, for Levi Craly. 500.00

Unknown artist, drawing of town scene, PA, 19th C, 13 x 13″, orange, blue, green, red, and pink watercolor on paper, several brightly colored houses, pots of flowers, birds and trees 725.00

Unknown artist, haus segan, S.E. PA, early 19th C, 10¾ x 14″, German calligraphy, text within heart shaped reserve, corners with red, yellow, and green flowers and tulips, borders with meandering tulip vines and birds . . . 650.00

Young, Henry, birth and baptismal, Lycoming Co., PA, 10½ x 7¾″, single woman. 2,500.00

HANDDRAWN-PRINTED

Berchall, Martin, birth and baptismal, printed form by Hutter, Easton, PA, 1821, 13 x 16″, central heart, borders hand painted with filigrees and flowers in red, yellow, blue, and green, for Lea Schull. 775.00

Dulheuer, Henrich, birth and baptismal, 13¼ x 17″ 825.00

Otto, Henrich, birth and baptismal, 13 x 15¾″ 1,250.00

Unknown artist, birth, Northampton Co., PA, 1821, 7¾ x 12″, German calligraphy, inscription within a keystone device, handpainted paired birds and large flowering tulip plants, birth of Maria Margaretha Scherner 650.00

Unknown artist, broadside, Lancaster Co., PA, 1786, 15 x 19″, text with scripture and hymn texts, drawings illustrate the stories. 2,450.00

PRINTED

Adam and Eve
Baumann, Ephrata. 300.00

Sage, H., Reading. 175.00
Birth and Baptismal
Baumann, J., Ephrata 500.00
Baumann, S., Ephrata 325.00
Blumer & Bush, Allentown 65.00
Currier and Ives, New York 15.00
Dreisbach, Bath 100.00
Eagle Bookstore, Reading 35.00
Ebner, Allentown. 90.00
Hantsch, Reading 110.00
Lutz & Scheffer, Harrisburg 20.00
Peter, Harrisburg 60.00
Ritter, Johann, Reading, late form . . 40.00
Schnee, Joseph, Lebanon 300.00
Note: If signed by Scrivener, increase value by 50%
Haus Sagen
Blumer & Bush, Allentown 125.00
Ritter, Reading 85.00

FRANKART

History: Arthur Von Frankenberg, artist and sculptor, founded Frankart, Inc., in New York City in the mid-1920s. Frankart, Inc., mass produced practical "art objects" in the Art Deco style into the 1930s. Pieces include aquariums, ashtrays, bookends, flower vases, lamps, etc. Although Von Frankenberg used live female models as his subjects, his figures are characterized by their form and style rather than specific features. Nudes are the most collectible; caricatured animals and other human figures were produced, no doubt, to increase sales.

With few exceptions, pieces were marked Frankart, Inc., with a patent number or "pat. appl. for."

Pieces were cast in a white metal composition in the following finishes: cream - a pale iridescent white; bronzoid - oxidized copper, silver, or gold; french - a medium brown with green in the crevices; fun metal - art iridescent gray; jap - a very dark brown, almost black, with green in the crevices; pearl green - pale iridescent green; and, verde - a dull light green. Cream and bronzoid were used primarily in the 1930s.

Note: All pieces listed are in very good condition unless otherwise indicated.

Advisor: Walter Glenn.

Ashtrays
Coyote, seated, caricature, gazes into 3½″ pottery insert, insert missing, orig finish, 7″ h, good cond. 45.00

Monkey, whimsical, spans removable 6″ yellow pottery insert, curled tail acts as handle, insert cracked and repaired, orig finish, 8¾″ h 75.00

Nude, arms outstretched at sides, stands on stacked geometric base which holds 3″ opaque green glass ashball, all orig, 10″ h 310.00

Nude, dancing, round scalloped base, one knee raised, arms stretched for-

Figurine, elk, bronze patina, 6¼″ l, $125.00.

ward, holds removable 3½″ green pottery bowl	
Near Mint, 10″ h, all orig	285.00
Repainted, bowl missing, replaced with non-orig glass	125.00
Nude, kneeling on cushion, arms stretched forward, holds 3″ removable oxidized copper bowl, 6″	
All parts orig	180.00
Bowl missing, orig finish	60.00
Nude, standing, octagonal base, holds overhead 6″ removable pottery insert (missing, and replaced with non-orig glass), orig finish 13″ h . .	145.00
Bookend, Leaping Deer, sq base, orig finish, 4½″ h.	35.00
Bookends, prs	
Nude, knees drawn up and arms outstretched at sides, sits atop metal book, all orig, 10″ h	210.00
Nude, standing, head turned to right, arms straight down at sides, hands back to support books, all orig, 9¼″, near mint cond	195.00
Candlestick, nude on tiptoes stands on sq base, supports candle holder on left shoulder, all orig, 9″ h, near mint cond	70.00
Candlesticks, nude, seated, gazes skyward, knees drawn to chest, arms encircling candle, all orig, 4½″ h, pr . .	225.00
Clock, rectangular stepped base, two nudes stand on either side of rectangular clock dial of carved frosted glass which screens a light behind it, all orig, 10½″ h	845.00
Lamps	
Horse, prancing, caricature, stands on a flat round base, silk shade replaced, orig finish, 14″ h. . . . . ⌐	125.00
Nude, sitting atop a ribbed column, octagonal base, holds in her lap a 3″	

green crackled glass globe, all orig, 9″ h	370.00
Nude, standing, holds fan, both entirely of clear and frosted rose colored glass, rests on stepped metal base which contains light bulbs, all orig, 11½″ h, near mint cond	710.00
Nude, standing, octagonal base, holds overhead a 6″ round amber colored crackled glass glove, all orig, 18″h	390.00
Nudes, two, standing, face each other and embrace a glass bar cylinder made of amber colored glass rods which diffuse light inside, rectangular base, all orig, 12″ h, near mint	675.00
Silhouettes	
Nude, standing, multi-stepped base, holding overhead a bar with two rings which suspends a frosted glass panel, light behind it, all orig, 15″ h, good.	435.00
Nude, standing on tiptoes, arms outstretched at sides, multistepped base in front of a rectangular frosted glass panel with cut corners which diffuses the light behind it, 10½″	
All orig, near mint	365.00
Repainted	180.00

FRANKOMA POTTERY

History: John N. Frank founded a ceramic art department at Oklahoma University in Norman and taught there for several years. In 1933 he established his own business and began making Oklahoma's first commercial pottery. Frankoma moved from Norman to Sapulpa, Oklahoma, in 1938.

A fire completely destroyed the new plant later the same year, but rebuilding began almost immediately. The company remained in Sapulpa and continued to grow. Frankoma is the only American pottery to be permanently exhibited at the International Ceramic Museum of Italy.

In 1983 Frankoma celebrated its fiftieth anniversary. In September 1983 a disastrous fire struck once again, destroying 97% of Frankoma's facilities. The rebuilt Frankoma Pottery reopened on July 2, 1984. Production has been limited to 1983 production molds only. All other molds were lost in the fire.

Prior to 1954 all Frankoma pottery was made with a honey-tan colored clay from Ada, Oklahoma. Since 1954 Frankoma has used a brick red clay from Sapulpa. During the early 1970s the clay became lighter and is now pink in color.

There were a number of early marks. One most eagerly sought is the leopard pacing on the FRANKOMA name. Since the 1938 fire, all pieces have carried only the name FRANKOMA.

References: Phyllis and Tom Bass, *Frankoma Treasures,* privately printed, 1983; Susan N. Cox, *Collectors Guide To Frankoma Pottery,* Book I, privately printed, 1979, and Book II, privately printed, 1982.

Additional Listings: See *Warman's Americana & Collectibles* for more examples.

Advisor: Phyllis Bess.

Ashtray, Texas	8.00
Banks	
Advertising	25.00
Dog, 7½" h.	20.00
Bookends, Boot & Horseshoe, pr.	25.00
Bowls	
Knobby Cactus, #203	20.00
Oriental, #217, oval, 17"	30.00
Rectangular, #207, flat, 9"	15.00
Candelabrum, five holes	
FRANKOMA logo	60.00
Pacing Leopard logo	85.00
Chop Plate, 15"	15.00
Christmas Cards	
1955 Frankoma	70.00
1960 Frankoma	50.00
1972 Frankoma	20.00
Christmas Plates	
1966, Joy To The World	75.00
1970, King Of Kings	25.00
1975, Peace On Earth	20.00
Flower Girl, 5½"	60.00
Gardeners	
Boy, 7"	95.00
Girl, 5¾"	70.00
Jewelry	
Bolo	25.00
Ear Clip, pr	15.00
Lamp Base, Dreamer Girl, 5⅝"	55.00
Lazy Susan, wagon wheel, seven section, 15"	50.00
Pitcher, Eagle, #555	8.00
Planters	
Cactus, 10½"	
Ada clay	25.00
Sapulpa clay	6.00
Log, 11"	10.00
Rose Jar, cov.	95.00
Sculptures	
Cocker Spaniel, sleeping	45.00
Colt, prancing, 8"	185.00
Cowboy, 7¾"	85.00
Coyote, 12½", Willard Stone	8.00
Fan Dancer, 8½" h	
Ada clay	195.00
Sapulpa clay	140.00
Greyhound, 14", Flame	30.00
Madonna, praying, 9½", Gracetone.	65.00
Puma, reclining	
Ada clay	70.00
Supulpa clay	10.00
Puma, seated	
Ada clay	70.00
Sapulpa clay	10.00

Squirrel, 6", Willard Stone	5.00
Swan, miniature, 3"	25.00
Trojan Horse, miniature, 2½"	30.00
Salt and Pepper Shakers	
First National Bank	15.00
Puma	40.00
Teepee	12.00
Sign, curved, display	15.00
Spoonrest, advertising	20.00
Trivets	
Cattlebrand, #94TRC	12.00
Horseshoes, #94TRH	3.00

Vase, 5½", bulbous, green mottled glaze, cloud like design along incised line, imp mark "Frankoma," $25.00.

Vases	
Crocus, #43, 8"	12.00
Leaf Handled, #71	
Ada clay	30.00
Sapulpa clay	15.00
Modelled, #74	35.00
Scalloped top, 7½"	40.00
V-2, limited edition	50.00
V-5, limited edition	65.00

FRATERNAL ORGANIZATIONS

History: Benevolent and secret societies played an important part in American society from the late 18th to the mid-20th centuries. Initially the societies were organized to aid members or their families in times of distress or death.

They evolved from this purpose into important social clubs by the late 19th century. In the 1950s, with the arrival of civil rights, an attack occurred on the secretiveness and often discriminatory practices of these societies. The fraternal movement, with the exception of the Masonic organizations, suffered serious membership loss. Many local chapters closed and sold their lodge halls. This resulted in many items arriving in the antiques market.

Additional Listings: See *Warman's Americana & Collectibles* for more examples.

MASONIC

Knights Templar
Mug, 3", red transfer with polychrome
enamel, motto **135.00**
Watch Fob, 14K gold. **300.00**
Masons
Apron, 18 x 14", white silk, painted,
Masonic devices, trumpeting angels, two men wearing green waist-
coats and Masonic medals, framed,
c1815 . . . . **1,800.00**
Butter Dish, cov, ruby flashed, thumb-
print, souvenir of Masonic Temple,
Chicago. **85.00**
Gravy Tureen, cov, undertray and la-
dle, black transfer, symbols on side,
7 lines of verse surrounded by symbols on reverse, flower dec, Sun-
derland lustre **450.00**
Jugs
8", 3 Masonic panels, fluted base
band, threaded band on neck,
Leeds **400.00**
8", transfers, symbols, and verse on
one side, 11 lines of verse on reverse, Sunderland lustre **180.00**
Lantern, Paul Revere type, 15" plus
ring handle, punched tin, shields,
hearts, and stars, hasp is missing. **475.00**
Mug, 5½", symbols, creamware,
Leeds, c1800. . . . . **275.00**
Punch Bowl, 12" d, symbols in panels
on opposite sides, Chinese export. **275.00**
Rug, scatter, hooked, lavender
ground, ivory Masonic squares and
compasses, 50 x 29½". **125.00**
Wine Glass, 5", gold and ruby, 2 gold
sabers, St. Paul, Minn, 1908 . . . . . **70.00**
Order of Eastern Star; medal, "Watch-
man of Shepherds," 14K gold **165.00**
Shrine
Chalice, clear glass, Pittsburgh, 1900 **75.00**

Vase, 7¼" h, 3 handles, blue, gold rim, mkd in wreath "50th Anniversary, celebrated Jan. 28th 1915," Thomas Maddock & Son's Co, Trenton, NJ, $85.00.

Cup, fish handle, 1904. . . . . **45.00**
Humidor, camels, pyramids, dessert,
Shriner emblem on finial, Royal
Bayruth **215.00**

OTHERS

Ancient Order of Foresters, A.O.F.,
sword, ivory handle, etched blade, SP
sheath, Fraternal by Paquale & Sons,
San Francisco. **150.00**
Benevolent & Protective Order of the
Elks, B.P.O.E.
Mirror, oval, brass frame, BPOE Elks
emblem at top **155.00**
Pen Knife **85.00**
Stained Glass Windows, set of 7, 4' x
8½', from an Elks Club, 1915 . . . . **17,000.00**
Stein, purple, gold encrusted elk and
clock, artist Covfal of Pickard **225.00**
Grand Army of the Republic, G.A.R.,
matchsafe, brass, emblem on one
side, troops and cannon on reverse . **125.00**
Knights of Pythias
Ashtray. **50.00**
Document Box, walnut. **65.00**
Mug, 11-55 . . . . **125.00**
Sword, etched blade, Pettibone Bros,
Mfg, Cinn, Ohio **90.00**
Independent Order of Odd Fellows,
I.O.O.F.
Graveside Flag Holder, 28½", CI,
heart in hand, Odd Fellow insignia,
Pat'd Sept. 17, 1901, G.H. Dawson,
Rockford, IL, worn white metal
plating. **115.00**
Lapel Badge, large, 30 year **125.00**
Pocket Watch, 17 jewel, Illinois Watch
Co. **125.00**
Knights of Columbus
Shaving Mug. **95.00**
Watch Fob, large, gold **80.00**

FRUIT JARS

History: Fruit jars are canning jars used to preserve food. Thomas W. Dyott, one of Philadelphia's
earliest and most innovative glass makers, was pro-
moting his glass canning jars in 1829. John Landis
Mason patented his screw-type canning jar on November 30, 1858. This date refers to the patent
date, not the age of the jar. There are thousands
of types of jars in many colors, types of closures,
sizes, and embossings.

References: Alice M. Creswick, *The Red Book
of Fruit Jars No. 3*, Collector Books, 1978; Bill
Schroeder, *1000 Fruit Jars, Revised 4th Edition*,
Collector Books, 1976.

Agnew, aqua, qt, handmade, wax seal,
bottom reads "John Agnew & Son" . **50.00**

Amazon Swift Seal, clear, qt, glass lid, wire bail **5.00**

Atherholt Fisher & Co., clear, qt, hand-made, ground glass stopper **175.00**

Atlas Mason's Patent Nov. 30th, 1858, aqua, pt, zinc lid **6.00**

J. C. Baker's, aqua, qt, handmade, glass lid, iron yoke, patent Aug 14, 1860 . . **145.00**

Ball, clear, qt, glass lid, mkd "Ideal Pat'd July 14, 1908" **5.00**

BBGM Co., green, qt, glass lid, wire bail, Patent Nov. 30, 1858. . . . . **35.00**

Bosco Double Seal, clear, qt, glass lid **7.00**

Bulach, green, qt, glass lid, wire clip . . **3.00**

Carrolls True Seal, Star, clear, pint, glass lid **9.00**

Clark's Peerless, aqua, qt, glass lid . . . **10.00**

Clyde Improved Mason, green, qt, glass lid, metal band **12.00**

Crown Cordial & Extract Co. New York, clear, ½ pt **10.00**

Curtis & Moore Trade Mark, Boston, MA, clear, qt, handmade. **25.00**

Dexter, aqua, qt, glass lid, screw band **30.00**

Doolittle, aqua, qt, metal hook **40.00**

Eagle, green, qt, handmade, wax seal . **75.00**

Electric Fruit Jar, aqua, qt, glass lid, spherical grid shape on front **65.00**

F & S, aqua, qt, glass lid, wire bail, ma-chine made. **10.00**

Fahnstock Fortune & Co., green, qt, handmade, name printed on bottom **45.00**

Four Seasons Mason, clear, pt, zinc lid, mkd "4 Seasons Mason". **5.00**

Gem 1908, clear, ½ gal, glass lid, screw band **8.00**

Glenshaw, clear, qt, zinc lid, mkd "Glen-saw in rectangle,/G in sq,/Mason". . **5.00**

Green Mountain Ga. Co., green, pt, glass lid, wire bail **15.00**

Hamilton Glass Works, aqua, qt, metal yoke. **180.00**

Hazel Atlas E-Z Seal, clear, qt, glass lid **8.00**

Hom-Pak Mason, clear, pt, zinc lid **4.00**

Hormel Good Food, clear, pt, metal lid **3.00**

Ivanhoe, clear, qt, metal lid, name on bottom **4.00**

Johnson & Johnson, cobalt blue, qt, glass lid, emb "Johnson & Johnson/ New Brunswick, NJ/USA" **40.00**

Kivlan & Onthank, light amber, qt, glass lid, bottom emb with name and "Patd June 28, 21, Boston" **25.00**

Lamb Mason, aqua, ½ gal, zinc lid. . . . **5.00**

Lamont Glass Co., aqua, pt, glass lid . . **35.00**

Lustre, aqua, qt, name in script in keystone. **15.00**

Mason's Improved, green, qt, handmade **3.00**

Mason's Patent Nov. 30th 1858, aqua, qt, intertwined letters C and I **12.00**

Metro Easy-Pak, clear, pt **2.00**

Ball Special, quart clear, $45.00.

Mothers Jar, aqua, qt, emb "Mothers Jar/Trade Mark/R. E. Tongue & Bros. Inc/Phila. Pa." **35.00**

My Choice, aqua, ½ gal, glass lid, clamp, lid and bottom read "Pat Jan 3rd 1888". **185.00**

PCG Co., aqua, qt, handmade, emb let-ters on bottom **18.00**

Pearl, aqua, qt, handmade, emb "The Pearl" **25.00**

Pint Standard, aqua, pt, wax seal. **50.00**

Potter & Bodine, Philadelphia, aqua, qt, name emb in script **90.00**

Protector, aqua, qt, 6 sided, name emb vertically **40.00**

Quick Seal, clear, pt, name in script in oval, "Pat'd July 14 1908" emb below name **3.00**

Royal, aqua, qt, glass lid, emb "Royal of 1876". **80.00**

Samco Super Mason, clear, pt. **2.00**

Schram Automatic Sealer, aqua, qt, name emb in script **10.00**

Sierra Mason Jar, clear, qt, name emb above "Made In California" **12.00**

Star Glass Co., aqua, qt, wax seal, emb "The Star Glass Co., Albany, Ind" . . **30.00**

Stone, pottery, gray, qt, zinc lid, label reads "Stone/Mason Fruit Jar/Union Stoneware/Redwing Minn" **20.00**

Telephone Jar, aqua, qt, oval emb "The/ Wide Mouth / Telephone / Jar / Trade Mark / Reg. **7.00**

Victory, clear, pt, glass lid, top emb "Vic-tory Reg'd 1925" **5.00**

Wan-Eta Cocoa, Boston, amber, pt, zinc lid **6.00**

B. B. Wilcox, aqua, qt, emb "Patd March 26, 1867/B.B. Wilcox/8 . . . . **50.00**

FRY GLASS

History: The H. C. Fry Glass Co. of Rochester, Pennsylvania, began operating in 1901 and continued until 1933. Their first products were brilliant period cut glass. They later produced depression tablewares. In 1922 they patented heat resisting ovenware in an opalescent color. This "Pearl Oven Glass" was produced in a variety of oven and table pieces including casseroles, meat trays, pie, and cake pans, etc. Most of these pieces are marked "Fry" with model numbers and sizes.

Fry's beautiful art line, Foval, was produced only in 1926–27. It is pearly opalescent, with jade green or delft blue trim. It is rarely signed, except for occasionaly silver overlay pieces marked "Rockwell." Foval is always evenly opalescent, never striped like Fenton's opalescent line.

In the 1970s, reproductions of Foval were made in abundance in Murano, Italy. These pieces, including candlesticks, toothpicks, etc., have teal blue transparent trim.

Collectors' Club: H. C. Fry Glass Society, P. O. Box 41, Beaver, PA 15009.

Baking Pan, ovenware, 9 x 12″	**18.00**
Candlesticks, pr, Foval, fiery opal, blue wafers, Delft blue spiral stems, 10½″	**250.00**
Casserole, cov, round, ovenware	**25.00**

Creamer & Sugar, Foval, Delft blue handles	**175.00**
Cup & Saucer, Delft blue handle	**70.00**
Goblet, Foval, pink loopings over fiery opal	**80.00**
Hot Plate, ftd, ovenware, sgd, dated	**25.00**
Lemonade Glass, jade	**55.00**
Nappy, opaline, ring handle	**45.00**
Pie Plate, 9″, ovenware	**18.00**
Pitcher, 9¾″ h, 6¼″ d, Diamond Optic, ground pontil, rich chrome green	**65.00**
Plates	
8½″, Foval, light green border	**40.00**
10½″, Ovenware, grill, mkd "Pearl Oven Ware"	**30.00**
Punch Cup, clear deep blue handle, crackle finish	**25.00**
Reamer, pearl glass	**40.00**
Teapot, Foval, jade green handle and spout	**125.00**
Toothpick, Foval, Delft blue handles	**65.00**
Vases	
5¼″, silver overlay, green base, sgd Rockwell	**400.00**
9¾″, pr, Foval, opal, opal green feet and stems, applied rims	**250.00**
12″, opal, pink loopings	**200.00**
Water Set, tankard pitcher, 6 glasses, Delft blue base and handles	**250.00**

Tumbler, Icicle, green handle, 5¼″ h, $60.00.

Centerpiece Bowl, Foval, opal, opal green ft, flaring rim, 5⅝″ h, 14″ d	**100.00**
Compotes, Foval, opal	
6¾″ h, 6″ d, green stem	**100.00**
6¾″ h, 8¾″ d, blue foot, pale blue loopings	**165.00**
7″ h, 6″ d, blue stem	**125.00**

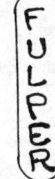

FULPER POTTERY

History: The American Pottery Company of Flemington, New Jersey, made pottery jugs and housewares from the early 1800s. They made Fulper Art Pottery from approximately 1910 to 1930.

Their first line of art pottery was called Vasekraft. The shapes were primarily either rigid and controlled, being influenced by the arts and crafts movement, or of Chinese influence. Equal concern was given to the glazes which showed an incredible diversity.

Pieces made between 1910 and 1920 were of the best quality, because less emphasis was put on production output. Almost all pieces are molded.

Reference: Robert Blassberg, *Fulper Art Pottery: An Aesthetic Appreciation,* Art Lithographers, 1979.

Advisor Robert Berman.

Bottle, round, 8″, thin neck and handle, green on green glaze, music box inside	**135.00**

Mug, light green ground, mottled oil glaze, stamped mark, 4¾" d, 3¾" h, $60.00.

Bowls
 3½" d, square handles, green crystalline glaze, vertical ink stamp . . . **45.00**
 7¾", effigy supports, blue high glaze over gray-blue glaze. **300.00**
 7 x 6", "Normandy" style, three applied shields on sides, blue, brown, and green glaze. **225.00**
 8" d, mottled green and brown glaze **60.00**
 10 x 4", "x" shaped base, blue to gray glaze. **160.00**
 10½ x 3", ribbed band around top, mustard drip glaze **90.00**
Box, 6 x 4", Art Deco lady, 4 to 5 colors. **135.00**
Lamp, bisque, parrot, 9½". **375.00**
Perfume Lamp, bisque, ballerina **145.00**
Pitcher, 5¼", coiled, green and gray glaze **60.00**
Vases
 6 x 6", two thin handles, brown to beige flambe glaze. **65.00**
 6½ x 10", squat, bulbous vase, 2 large angular handles, Chinese blue flambe glaze **300.00**
 6¾", slight flares at top and lip, entirely copperdust with good consistency to glaze. **225.00**
 7½", bulbous, shoulder handles, green flambe glaze with crystals . . **85.00**
 8¼", four sided, impressed molds at top, arts and crafts form, wisteria . **160.00**
 8½", simple Chinese form, pink famille rose **70.00**
 10", cylindrical form, mushrooms around base, butterscotch glaze . . **350.00**
 10", seven sided teardrop shape, chunky mirror black glaze **270.00**
Wall Pocket, pipes of pan, gray matte glaze **135.00**

FURNITURE

History: Two major currents dominate the American furniture marketplace–furniture made in Great Britain and furniture made in the United States. American buyers continue to show a strong prejudice for objects manufactured in the United States. They will pay a premium for such pieces and accept them above technically superior and more aesthetic English examples.

Until the last half of the 19th century formal American styles were dictated by English examples and design books. Regional furniture, such as the Hudson River Valley [Dutch] and the Pennsylvania German styles, did develop. A less formal furniture, often designated as the "country" or vernacular style, developed throughout the 19th and early 20th centuries. These country pieces deviated from the accepted formal styles and have a genre charm that many collectors find irresistible.

America did contribute a number of unique decorative elements to English styles. The American Federal period is a reaction to the English Hepplewhite period. American designers created furniture which influenced, rather than reacted, to world taste in the Gothic Revival style, Arts and Craft Furniture, Art Deco, and Modern International movement.

FURNITURE STYLES [APPROX. DATES]

William and Mary.	**1690–1730**
Queen Anne.	**1720–1760**
Chippendale	**1755–1790**
Federal [Hepplewhite]	**1790–1815**
Sheraton	**1790–1810**
Empire [Classical]	**1805–1830**
Victorian	
French Restauration.	**1830–1850**
Gothic Revival	**1840–1860**
Rococo Revival	**1845–1870**
Elizabethan	**1850–1915**
Louis XIV	**1850–1914**
Naturalistic	**1850–1914**
Renaissance Revival	**1850–1880**
Neo-Greek	**1855–1885**
Eastlake	**1870–1890**
Art Furniture	**1880–1914**
Arts and Crafts	**1895–1915**
Art Nouveau	**1896–1914**
Art Deco.	**1920–1945**
International Movement	**1940–Present**

1983 and 1984 proved record price setting years for American formal furniture. Four pieces sold at auction for over $300,000.00. Among these were a Chippendale, New York, carved mahogany, marble top pier table for $302,500.00 and a Chippendale, block-and-shell carved mahogany kneehole dressing table from the Goddard-Townsend school, Newport, Rhode Island, for $385,000.00. The best examples of early American furniture clearly have recaptured their position as one of the leading "blue chip" investments in the American antiques market.

Country pieces, with the exception of Windsor chairs, seem to have stabilized and even dropped off slightly in value. The country-designer-look no longer enjoys the popularity it did during the American Bicentennial period.

Furniture is one of the few antiques fields where regional preferences are a factor in pricing. Victorian furniture is popular in New Orleans, and unpopular in New England. Oak is in demand in the Northwest, not so much in the Middle Atlantic states.

Prices vary considerably on furniture. Shop around. Furniture is plentiful unless you are after a truly rare example. Examine all pieces thoroughly. Too many furniture pieces are bought on impulse. Turn furniture upside down; take it apart. The amount of repairs and restoration to a piece has a strong influence on price. Make certain you know about all repairs and changes before buying.

Beware of the large number of reproductions. During the American centennial of 1876 there was a great revival in copying furniture styles and manufacturing techniques of earlier eras. These centennial pieces now are over one hundred years old. They confuse many dealers and collectors.

The prices listed below are "average" prices. They are only a guide. High and low prices are given to show market range.

References: Helen Comstock, *American Furniture: Seventeenth, Eighteenth, and Nineteenth Century Styles,* Viking Press, 1962; Joseph Downs, *American Furniture: Queen Anne and Chippendale Periods In The Henry Francis du Pont Winterthur Museum,* Macmillan Co., 1952; William C. Ketchum, Jr., *Furniture, Volume 2: Chests, Cupboards, Desks, & Other Pieces,* Alfred A. Knopf [Knopf Collectors' Guides To American Antiques], 1982; Charles F. Montgomery, *American Furniture: The Federal Period In The Henry Francis du Pont Winterthur Museum,* Viking Press, 1966; Milo M. Naeve, *Identifying American Furniture: A Pictorial Guide To Styles and Terms, Colonial to Contemporary,* American Association for State and Local History, 1981; Wallace Nutting, *Furniture Treasury,* Macmillan, 3 vols [1928 and 1933], available in reprint; Don & Carol Raycraft, *Collector's Guide To Country Furniture,* Collector Books, 1984; Marvin D. Schwartz, *Furniture: Volume 1: Chairs, Tables, Sofas & Beds,* Alfred A. Knopf [Knopf Collector's Guides To American Antiques], 1982; Dina von Zweck, *The Woman's Day Dictionary Of Furniture,* Citadel Press, 1983.

There are hundreds of specialized books on individual furniture forms and styles. Two examples of note are: Monroe H. Fabian, *The Pennsylvania-German Decorated Chest,* Universe Books, 1978, and Charles Santore, *The Windsor Style In America, 1730–1830,* Running Press, 1981.

Additional Listings: Arts and Craft Movement, Art Deco, Art Nouveau, Children's Nursery Items, Orientalia, Shaker Items, and Stickley.

BEDS

Carolean, inlaid and carved oak, back paneled in geometric panels flanked by stylized foliate pilasters, paneled top with overstepped hanging cornice, baluster shaped fluted upright posts on sq pedestal bases, some restoration, 80 x 60 x 82″ **9,500.00**

Chippendale

English, c1770, carved mahogany, four poster, tester, fluted and ring turned footposts, tapered headposts, shaped headboard, frontal shell carved claw and ball feet, 85 x 64 x 96″................. **3,300.00**

Newport, RI, c1775, carved mahogany, four poster, tapered and ring turned headposts and footposts, shaped headboard, sq legs, Marlborough feet, 78½ x 52½ x 89½″ **6,000.00**

Classical, Charles Honore Lannuier, NY, c1812, mahogany, giltwood and gesso, S-scroll head and foot boards, gilt eagle finials on headboard, brass inlaid support mounted with repousse pressed brass portrait bust, gilt acanthus carved animal paw feet, mkd and orig paper labels, 95 x 57¼ x 42½″ . **36,500.00**

Empire

American, c1820, high post, mahogany, sq tapering posts and gadrooned terminals, paneled headboard and footboards, sq tapered legs, 85 x 63 x 85″ **1,000.00**

American, c1820–30, low post, maple, heavy carved posts, pineapple carved stems, shaped headboard, 50″..................... **1,300.00**

American, c1830–1850, low post, maple, turned columnar posts, urn shaped finials, shaped headboard and footboards with cylindrical crest with vase shaped finials, 3 panels with circular carving, 55 x 49½″ .. **800.00**

Massachusetts, c1820, carved mahogany, ring turned posts with ball finials, carved foliage shaped headboard and footboard with cylindrical scrolled crest with ball finials, 53½ x 42½″ **1,000.00**

Federal

Duncan Phyfe School, NY, c1820, four poster with tester, inlaid and carved mahogany and giltwood, headposts and footposts with acanthus and spiral carving, paneled standards, shaped mahogany headboard, gilt animal paw feet, 80 x 66 x 106″ .. **28,600.00**

Massachusetts, 1790–1820, four poster, mahogany and birch, footposts reeded and carved with reeded urns, columnar headposts with vase turnings, baluster and ring turned feet, 89″ **2,000.00**

Massachusetts, 1800–1815, high post, mahogany, tapering ring turned and reeded posts on block and tapering reeded legs, arched and shaped headboard, 71 x 50¾ x 99½″ **4,400.00**

New England, c1815, 4 poster, curly maple, turned and carved, sq tapering headposts, shaped headboard, reeded footposts, 55½ x 80 x 64″ **2,875.00**

New England, 1830–1850, four poster, birch, ball finials over block, ring and baluster turned posts, shaped headboard, baluster turned legs, 75 x 40⅛ x 48½″ **1,750.00**

Salem, MA, c1805, four poster, tester, inlaid mahogany, reeded and ring turned footposts, ring turned headposts, shaped headboard, line inlaid legs, cross banded cuffs, 78 x 59 x 62½″ **6,875.00**

Mission, Limbert, c1910, oak, sloping sides form backrest, headboard pierced with heart form handles, branded label, 74½ x 23″ **750.00**

Shaker, mid 19th C, maple, shaped headboard, sq tapered legs, wooden wheel casters, green, 35½ x 74″ . . . **1,250.00**

Sheraton

American, c1800, four poster, orig curved high tester, maple, finely turned and fluted posts, pine headboard, refinished, 62½″ h posts . . **3,500.00**

American, c1800–20, four poster, tester, rope and acanthus carved, maple with mahogany finish, 71″. . **1,800.00**

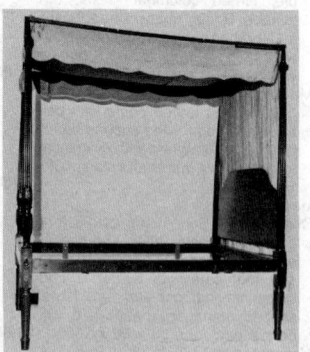

Sheraton, mahogany, tester, turned and fluted posts, $5,000.00.

American, c1800–24, four poster, plain turned maple headposts, footposts of mahogany finished maple, acanthus and pineapple carving, refinished, 82″ **1,500.00**

Late, four poster, flat tester, rope and acanthus leaf carving of all posts, paneled mahogany headboard, 91″ **1,200.00**

Victorian, carved mahogany, high rounded arched headboard, eschutcheon cresting, paneled side rails, double, 60″ **450.00**

BENCHES

Cabinetmaker's, pine and maple, mortised construction, 2 wood screw vices, 2 steel bench stops, early 20th C, 59 x 25″. **450.00**

Cobbler, poplar, tool and nail holders, 45 x 22½ x 44¼″. **250.00**

Deacon's, PA, mid 18th C, carved pine, rect back, 4 inset panels, shaped arms, bootjack feet, 79½″ l **2,000.00**

Kneeling

Pine, cut out feet, mortised, 51″ l . . . **100.00**

Shaker, pine, green paint, Canterbury, NH, 84′ x 25¾ x 7½″. **150.00**

Mammy, arrowback, turned legs, plank seat, scrolled arms, old weathered repaint, rockers, 55″ l **425.00**

Plank Seats

Arrow back, turned legs, turned front stretchers with flat segments, smoked red paint, yellow striping and stenciled. Floral and Foliage dec on front stretchers, spindles, and crest, 75″ l **5,500.00**

Rocking, turned posts, plank seat, half arrow back spindles, scrolled arms with turned posts, dark olive green paint, yellow and black striping, foliage designs in crest, 57½″ l **700.00**

Stencil decor, PA, c1830, 85½ x 21¼″ d seat **900.00**

Shaker, carved, cherry rectangular top, bootjack feet, c1850, 8′ l x 10″ w . . . **2,000.00**

Sheraton, country, maple, curl, bird's eye, 8 turned legs, turned stretchers, corner legs curve outward, orig rush seat, 17 x 72 x 18″ **1,700.00**

Walnut, cut out feet, mortised through top, 78 x 10 x 19″. **200.00**

Water

Ash, poplar backboards, scalloped top, sides, old worn blue-gray paint, Indiana, 49 x 12 x 34¾″. **450.00**

Pine, attributed to NE, c1820, refinished in natural pine curved sloped side, shelf, recess, platform shelf, round arches in base of side, 27 x 17¼ x 35″. **750.00**

Windsor

Bamboo turned legs, spindles, plank seat, splayed legs, turned stretchers, finish stripped to green stain, 75½" l 3,500.00

Bamboo turned legs, shaped back continuing to scrolled knuckle handholds, 39 tapered spindles, plank seat, 84" 6,750.00

Bamboo, 2 chair bases as supports, orig, gray-tan, green and red paneled striping, early 19th C, 96" l 2,500.00

Work, heavy maple top, 2 all wooden clamps, end clamp with dovetail frame, well for tools, holes for bench stops, 25 x 80 x 32" h 375.00

Saddle Stitcher's, chestnut, 25" l, 41" h, $150.00.

BENTWOOD

In 1856, Michael Thonet of Vienna perfected the process of bending wood using steam. Shortly after, Bentwood furniture became popular. Other manufacturers of Bentwood furniture were Jacob and Joseph Kohn, Philip Strobel and Son, Sheboygan Chair Co. and Tidoute Chair Co. Bentwood furniture is still being produced today by the Thonet firm and others.

Chairs

Arm, child's, worn red paint 150.00
Rocker, child's 250.00
Side, three horizontal turned wood slat back, carved cornice, 5 turned wood vertical rods, solid seat, stencil de-

cor on 4 straight legs, paper label, Joseph Hoffman, 36" h 200.00

Side, attr. Samuel Gragg, Boston, c1815, shaped crest above shaped uprights, slat seat on shaped legs ending in hoof feet, turned stretchers 1,750.00

Cradles

22" high 300.00
50" high, on stand with bonnet top, swing-type, all original 1,500.00

Easel, Artist's................... 75.00
Hall tree, 19th C................. 425.00

Screen, 3 fold, Thonet, c1904, inset with green glass above laminated panels cut with geometric devices, "Spanish Wand" model 3,000.00

Settee, flanking swirl center, side loop decor, cane inset seat, 4 cabriole legs, paper label Model #2001, Thonet 38" h 900.00

Shaving Stand and Mirror, designed by J. Hoffman, Thonet, c1906, 54" h... 2,250.00

Sleep Sofa, adjustable backrest raised on scrolling legs, Model #9752, Thonet, 5'10" l 950.00

BLANKET CHESTS

Oak, English, gothic, hinged rectangular top, elaborately carved front, bracket feet, 44" l, 21½" h 1,250.00

Oak and pine, Pilgrim Century, E. Massachusetts, c1760–90, rectangular hinged lid, facade of 3 molded diamond panels centering black painted split balusters, 4 short molded drawers, stiles form feet, minor restoration, 35½" h x 4'4" l x 21" d 2,000.00

Pine, Pennsylvania, c1785, Chippendale, rectangular molded top, molded base, straight bracket feet, orig blue paint, sliding till with secret compartment, iron strap hinges, 49¾ x 20¼ x 23⅝" 900.00

Pine, orig brown vinegar painting on yellow ground, scalloped base, stiles inset with herringbone reeding in contrasting reddish sponging, 2 dovetailed drawers in base, interior till, 4 pigeonholes beneath, 44 x 19 x 42" 8,000.00

Pine, six board construction, nailed drawer, red flame graining 39 x 14¼ x 32" plus crest. 500.00

Poplar, dovetailed, till, yellow paint with diagonal green stripes, old brown varnish, ogee feet, 49½ x 21 x 28".... 475.00

Poplar, Ohio, raised panels on front and ends, grain dec, shades of olive brown to olive and rust, panels with fans and finger painted polka dot, till, turned black painted feet, 45¾ x 20 x 24¾ 3,250.00

Walnut, Chippendale, Pennsylvania, c1760, rectangular molded top, dovetailed case, 2 thumb molded drawers, molded skirt, shaped bracket feet, 48½ x 22 x 30″. **2,650.00**

BOOKCASES

Biedermeier, c1830, pr, Palissander wood, dentiled triangular pediment, turned disengaged column stiles, glazed doors, base with drawer, sq block feet, 40 x 17 x 65″. **1,650.00**

Classical, attributed to Emmons & Archibald, Boston, MA, c1825, carved mahogany, molded removable cornice, 2 hinged glazed doors, brass stop, lower section with white marble top, 1 fitted long drawer, 2 acanthus carved cupboard doors, molded and acanthus carved scrolled pilasters, shaped base, 49 x 23 x 95½″ **7,150.00**

Federal, c1805, carved mahogany, removable molded cornice over 6 bookcase sections, each with glazed hinged door, sides fitted with brass carrying handles, base of 2 long drawers on sq tapered legs, 67 x 15 x 101″ **13,750.00**

George II, mahogany, upper section with molded cornice, 2 glazed doors, lower section with 2 cupboard doors, bracket feet, 44 x 14½ x 81″ **450.00**

George III, early 19th C, mahogany, molded cornice, 2 glazed doors, freestanding reeded columns, 4 long drawers, plinth base, 60 x 23 x 92½″ **1,100.00**

Regency, ebonized and parcel gilt, breakfront, dwarf, ¾ galleried back over open shelves, center grill door, 6 turned feet, 40¼ x 13 x 35″. **350.00**

Victorian, late, c1880, black walnut and ebonized breakfront, architectural form, setback upper part with arched glazed doors, fluted engaged columns, foliate capitals, door, 4 mahogany front drawers over pr of arched panel doors, carved foliate and shell ornaments, plinth base, 52 x 19½ x 99½″ **1,250.00**

William IV, c1830, pr, carved mahogany, molded cornice, 3 glazed doors, Gothic astragals, pilasters, lower case outset with 3 paneled doors, pilasters, raised on plinth, each with paper transport label "Lady Larraway, Rockshire, Waterford, Ireland," 86 x 19 x 120″. **22,000.00**

BOXES

Ballot

8½ x 11 x 16″, walnut, wide dovetailing, brass hardware **150.00**

9½ x 6 x 4½″, walnut, scrimshaw, balls, black cubes, whale ivory and wood handle **375.00**

Band

Oval, bentwood, dark green paint, red striping, gold stenciling, 9½ x 12¼ x 17¾″ **375.00**

Oval, red, blue, yellow & white stylized flowers, laced seems, 9 x 5½″ . . . **475.00**

Pennsylvania, white floral pattern on rainbow ground, black beaver hat by C. Nickerson, 8″ h **110.00**

Bible

7 x 15¼ x 21¾″ w, walnut, dovetailed, diamond inlays, initials MG Chester County, PA, 18th C **500.00**

9½ x 14½ x 25½″ w, walnut, dovetailed, turned feet, base and lid edge molding, wrought iron strap hinges with rosehead fastening nails **450.00**

Bride's

17 x 10¼ x 7″, pine, oval, floral dec of tulips and stylized flowers **325.00**

17¼ x 10½ x 6¼″, pine, bentwood, oval, orig green paint, polychrome floral dec, lid with couple standing arm in arm, German border inscription. **675.00**

19¼ x 11¾″, detailed colorful bride and groom surrounded by tulips, flowers, calligraphy on bottom, Scandinavian, late 18th C **1,150.00**

Candle

4¼ x 14 x 7″, pine, sliding cov, orig blue paint **175.00**

5 x 7½ x 15¼″, hanging, dovetailed, orig blue paint **265.00**

6 x 9 x 13″ l, carved, sliding lid **225.00**

15 x 11½ x 7″, hanging, carved, love-

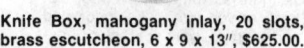

Knife Box, mahogany inlay, 20 slots, brass escutcheon, 6 x 9 x 13″, $625.00.

birds, step carved molding at sides, front panel, orig red paint, late 18th C **400.00**

Cigar, 5″ l, brass, top and bottom covered with letters and numbers, sgd, dated 1787, Dutch. **125.00**

Document
Pine, hinged cov, tapered legs, brown finish, brass lock and hasp, 16 x 9¾ x 19″. **225.00**
Tole, dome top, orig black paint, yellow striping, 8¼″ l **115.00**

Handkerchief, brass, inlaid, 2⅝″ w x 7″ d x 6″ l **100.00**

Hat
9 x 20, triangular pine, applied diamond shape decor. **150.00**
9¾″ h x 14½ x 16½″, oval, wood, wallpaper covering, white ground, brown, blue decor **125.00**

Knife
Empire, leaf carved, veneer paneled square top, rectangular case, carved front, 18¼″ h x 14½″ w, Phila, c1820, pr **2,000.00**
George III, English, c1880, inlaid mahogany, hinged sloping bow-front, fitted int., 15½″, pr. **1,250.00**
Regency, late, satinwood, incurved square hooded lifting top, finial, fitted interior, gilt metal paw feet, 29½″, pr **1,000.00**

Letter, walnut, divider, scalloped detail, chamfered sides, old dark finish, wire nail construction, 5½ x 7½″ **75.00**

Liquor Box, Continental, walnut, relief carving of interlocking flowers, elaborate finial, 4 decanters, 11 glasses **450.00**

Pantry, cov, round, single lap construction, pegged and nailed, imp "B Murdock, Jr./Boston," 9¾″ d. **85.00**

Puzzle Box, Am, 14″ l, sturdy base with trick top, 2 int. compartments, stenciled name "C.B. Jauss" **125.00**

Salt, hanging, pine, slant top, lift lid, curved crest, 11½ x 7 x 16¼″ **110.00**

Seed, wooden, orig paper labels, J. M. Philips Sons, Mercerburg, Pa, interior with unused paper seed packs, 12 x 25½″ **205.00**

Sewing, American, c1860, walnut, velvet lined int., lift out tray, mirror on lid, multiple wood inlay of diamonds and triangles, 15½ x 9 x 8″. **200.00**

Shoe shine, pine, primitive, high cut out legs, drawer, lift lid, compart mentalized int. with foot rest, old blue paint, 16½ x 14½ x 17½″. **175.00**

Spice
Curly Maple, Country Hepplewhite, 8 drawers, French feet, 20½ x 8¾ x 18½″ **800.00**

Pine, c1800, 8 drawer, 15¾ x 7¼ x 14⅞″ **450.00**

Poplar, hanging, 2 drawers, dovetailed carved crest, slant top lid, scroddleware knob, 12¼ x 9½ x 13″ **175.00**

Snuff, 4½″ d, turned, portraits of Washington & Lafayette, label A. Goodyear & Sons, Manufacturers, Waterbury, Conn. **250.00**

Stationery, Victorian, leather covered, 9″ **65.00**

Strong Box, dovetailed, decor wrought iron hardware with strap hinges, handle, lock with large face plate and stylized applied leaves, 7 x 7¼ x 12½″ **200.00**

Tool, pine, dovetailed, wrought iron bound corners, decor lock hasp, worn dark green paint **175.00**

Trinket, Turnbridge, hinged, floral decor, 3½″ **70.00**

Utility, hanging, old red paint, 16¾ x 5 x 19″ **750.00**

Writing
Cherry, table top, walnut, orig dark brown paint, yellow striping, stenciled birds, eagle on lid, front panel, interior fitted with pigeon holes, dovetailed drawer, 24½ x 21 x 16¾″ h **400.00**
Mahogany, military, brass banding, 20″, c1810 . . . . **200.00**

CABINETS

China
Chippendale, Centennial, elaborate fretwork. **1,500.00**
French Provincial, oak, 2 pairs of doors over 2 pairs of cupboard doors, arched glass panels in doors, central shell cartouche at top, recessed and carved cupboard doors, fluted quarter columns on side, 74½ x 14 x 91″ **1,600.00**
Mahogany, satinwood banding, 2 doors, shaped apron, carved cabriole legs, paw feet, 3½ x 10″ w, mid 18th C **1,500.00**
Oak, c1875, arched door, surmounted by carved mask, separated from bowed sides by flat reeded and ring turned pilasters, carved paw feet, 53″ w **800.00**
Victorian, c1900, Golden Oak, two columns with leaf carving, rounded, glass, paw feet **900.00**
Dye, Putnam, slant front, metal and wood, litho of General Putnam **300.00**
Hardware, bolts, octagonal, revolving base, oak, 4 drawers. **400.00**
Jewelry, Victorian, mahogany, inlaid, boxwood, string borders, 9¾″ w **275.00**

Spool or yarn cabinet, oak, 18¾ x 17⅛ x 16″, $560.00

Kitchen, oak with glass inserts in door, porcelain work surface with blue agate edges, flour bin, spice racks, etc., brass McDougall plates, orig factory tags **400.00**

Liquor, George IV, mahogany, inlaid, brass banded corners, 18″ w, c1830 **400.00**

Mahogany, oak drawer fronts, inlays of holly, walnut, teak, whalebone inlay sides in hexagonal design, beveled mirrors on 2 front doors, 3 shelves interior, secret compartment, brass knobs, escutcheons, Nantucket, John Baker, c1860, 20¼ x 6¼ x 32″ **3,650.00**

Music
 Art Nouveau, walnut **350.00**
 Edwardian, mahogany, 6 drawer, squat cabriole legs, 21″ **185.00**
 Renaissance Revival, rosewood, Gustave Herter, NY, c1865, 35 x 21⅛ x 47½″ **2,000.00**

Parlor, Renaissance Revival, inlaid, ebonized, gilt decor, 51 x 21 x 87¾″ **4,000.00**

Side
 Louis XV, kingwood, gilt bronze mounted, tulipwood parquetry, marble top, 44″ h x 60″w, late 19th C **5,225.00**
 Louis XVI, ebonized, gilt bronze mounted, central door mounted with bronze plaque, 27″ w, 36″ h, late 19th C, pr **18,800.00**

Smoking, oak, Gustav Stickley, one drawer above cabinet door, compartment interior, copper hardware, c1912, 20 x 15 x 29″ **1,430.00**

Spool, Merrick's, six cord, cherry, 2 large drawers over 2 small drawers, refinished **375.00**

Vitrines
 Art Nouveau, French, c1925, wrought iron, door with foliate surround, shelved int., mirrored back, 30½″ w, 66″ h **2,550.00**
 Louis XV, kingwood, gilt bronze mounted, marble top, 45″ h x 4′ 8″ w, c1900. . . . . **6,000.00**
 Louis XVI, kingwood, gilt bronze mounted, 6 legs, 51″ w, 52″ h c1900 **3,575.00**

CANDLE SHIELDS

47″, Regency, finely carved base, brass mounts, c1820 . . . . **1,200.00**

56½″, Chippendale, RI, mahogany, sliding oval screen on pole, column and vase turned support, 3 arched legs, cat's paw feet. **900.00**

64½″ Centennial, late 19th C, mahogany, oval frame, needle point panel of flowers, tripod base, cabriole legs, bulbous turned base for pole, urn finial **150.00**

CANDLESTANDS

Chippendale, mahogany, tilt top, circular dish top, bird cage support, tapering columnar and turned ball pedestal, tripod cabriole legs, pad feet, 19 x 27¼″ **300.00**

Federal
 Massachusetts, 1790–1820, inlaid cherry, oval tilt top, 2 bands of stringing, column and urn turned pedestal, 3 arched sq tapering legs, spade feet, 20 x 13⅝ x 27½″ **1,210.00**

Mahogany, 18″ d top, 27½″ h, American, serpent feet, $750.00.

Massachusetts, 1790–1810, mahogany, elongated octagonal tilt top, banded edge, flared column and urn turned baluster, 3 arched sq tapering legs, 25¼ x 16⅝ x 30½″. **825.00**

New England, c 1815, carved mahogany, tilt top, oblong shaped top, ring turned and petal standard on reeded scrolled legs, 27¼ x 19½ x 29¼″ **1,550.00**

New Hampshire, c1805, inlaid birchwood, octagonal top, birds eye maple diamond inlay, reeded and ring turned urn form standard, light and dark bellflower inlay, 13½ x 21 x 28½" **3,500.00**

Philadelphia, 1785, inlaid mahogany, tilt top, oval, line inlaid edge, birdcage support, urn form standard, cabriole legs, snake feet, 22 x 16 x 27½" **4,125.00**

Hepplewhite, American, late 18th C, cherry with mahogany band around top, spider base with spade feet. . . . **775.00**

Queen Anne

American, c1750, mahogany, 2 small drawers, vasiform stem, snake feet, 20 x 13½ x 26½". **2,500.00**

Pennsylvania, c1770, carved mahogany, tilt top, circular dished top, ring and vase turned standard, cabriole legs ending in snake feet, 17 x 29". **1,775.00**

Pennsylvania, c1780, carved walnut, tilt top, circular molded and dished top, bird cage support, ring turned urn form standard, cabriole legs, snake feet, 21½ x 28½". **8,250.00**

Victorian, English, c1870, black lacquered and gilt, circular tilt top, painted floral arrangement on keystone, turned shaft, tripod legs, 16 x 29". . . **750.00**

William & Mary, walnut, molded octagonal top, turned baluster shaped pedestal, tapered scrolled legs, 9½ x 34" **550.00**

CHAIRS

Arrowbacks

Full, plank seat **250.00**

Half, plank seat, orig stenciling. **200.00**

Art Deco

Arm, c1940, pr, lucite mounted, pale pink silken fabric **450.00**

Arm, designed by Gilbert Rohde for Troy Sunshade Co, c1935, pr, tubular metal, upholstered in tan vinyl **800.00**

Slipper, pr, matching footstool, lucite mounted, upholstered in pale pink and blue print fabric **500.00**

Balloon back, side, yellow striping, stenciled foliage, black ground, eagle on rest. **200.00**

Banister back, arm, sausage turnings, front posts terminating in mushroom tops, old worn black paint over red, NE, early 18th C **3,250.00**

Belter, side, rosewood, pierced, carved grapes and roses, upholstered needlepoint set and back . . **3,500.00**

Children's

Arm, ladderback, 3 splat back, sausage turnings, mushroom posts, wicker like seat, orig black paint . . **1,500.00**

High chair, NE, 1720–60, turned maple, back with 3 slats, bulbous finials, sausage turned arms, ring turned legs **950.00**

High Chair, Queen Anne, NE, fruitwood, rush seat, bulb and wheel frontal stretcher, splayed legs, molded vertical slats, 18th C. **1,600.00**

Potty, pine, painted and stenciled . . . **250.00**

Windsor, yoke back, flat outscrolled arms, serpentine braces, curly maple seat, legs, oak arms and back **2,500.00**

Chippendale

Arm, PA, 1765–1785, walnut, shaped crest rail, rounded ears, pierced Gothic splat, serpentine arms, slip seat, molded seat frame on Marlborough legs, 28 x 22 x 37" **1,225.00**

Arm, wing, PA, 1775, carved mahogany, upholstered serpentine crest above upholstered back, ogival wings, scrolled arms, sq molded legs **7,500.00**

Chinese, mahogany square molded legs, H stretcher, fretwork, high back, needlepoint upholstery. **1,500.00**

Corner, Newport, RI, c1770, carved mahogany, U shaped backrail, shaped hand holds, 2 pierced splats, slip seat, sq legs **2,750.00**

Dining, Phila, walnut, claw and ball feet, gothic form, pierced back splat, set of 5 . . . . **12,500.00**

Side, Eastern MA, c1770, shaped fan-carved crest, pierced volute-carved splat, slip seat, angular cabriole legs, pad feet, turned bulbous and block stretchers **3,000.00**

Side, Newport, RI, 1760–1790, pr, mahogany, serpentine crest rail, molded ears, cross hatched fan, pierced strapwork splat with punched dec, sq slip seat, Marlborough legs, 37½" h **8,250.00**

Wing, Phila, mahogany, shaped crest, wings continuing to scrolled arms, squared leg, joined by stretchers. . **4,500.00**

Eastlake, Victorian

Arm, walnut, upholstered back and seat **300.00**

Side, walnut, small arms, cane seat . **200.00**

Empire

Arm, Baltimore, 1828–1835, pr, white paint and gilt, straight crest flanked by scrolling stiles, carved arms, lotus terminals, padded arms, palmette grips, sq slip seat, scrolled front legs, flaring rear legs, 24 x 20½ x 39". **3,750.00**

Side, mahogany, veneer, fiddleback, serpentine seat, saber leg **185.00**

Federal

Arm, NE, c1810, bamboo turned crest, spindles, arms, splayed legs, cane seats, painted ochre, green, red florals, 34″ h, pr **1,650.00**

Lolling, MA, 1790–1810, Mahogany, rect padded back with arched crest, serpentine arms with molded sloping arm supports, over upholstered seat, molded sq tapered legs, 26¾″ w 43¾″ h **6,250.00**

George II

Side, Baltimore, 1790–1810, mahogany, molded oval back, 3 vertical banisters molded and pierced, over upholstered bowed seat, molded sq legs, 20¼″ w, 38¾″ h **450.00**

Armchair, corner, c1750, mahogany, carved, scrolled top rail, double interlaced balustered backrest, drop-in seat, acanthus-carved cabriole leg, ball and claw foot **2,750.00**

Dining chairs, set of 6, c1740, scrolled top rail, pierced baluster splat, shell carved cabriole legs, turned H-stretcher, restorations. **16,000.00**

George III

Armchair, c1800 tub, revolving, mahogany, leather upholstered, circular seat, sq tapered legs, block toes **5,500.00**

Side chairs, c1765, mahogany, carved, scrolling leaf-carved shaped top rail, pierced interlaced baluster splat, stop fluted free-

Shaker, ladderback, hardwood, splint seat, sgd Sick, 1840, $1,100.00.

standing stiles, upholstered seat, sq molded chamfered legs, H-stretcher, pr. **4,250.00**

Gothic style, arm, walnut, upholstered seat, c1845. . . . . **880.00**

Hepplewhite

Arm, Newburyport, MA, mahogany, square legs, spade feet, line inlay, curved arm supports, oval back, gold damask upholstery **3,800.00**

Side, mahogany, shield backs of 5 splats, molded tapered legs, H stretcher, reupholstered seats, set of 6 . . . . **7,800.00**

Side, NY, mahogany, tapered molded legs, H stretcher, well detailed shield backs, carved classical detail, seats reupholstered, old finish, pr **6,000.00**

Hitchcock, plank seat, orig paint and stenciling, c1840 . . . . **625.00**

Ladderback

Arm, Shaker, Lebanon, NY, mid 19th C, acorn finials, turned stiles, 4 shaped splats, shaped arms, mushroom finials, strap seat, turned legs and stretchers, 24 x 18½ x 41¼″ **700.00**

Side, Delaware Valley, c1740–70, 6 arched graduated slats, rush seat, turned legs, frontal ring and baluster stretcher, black **2,200.00**

Mission

Arm, Gustav Stickley, c1910, oak, V back, branded mark **500.00**

Arm, L. & J. G. Stickley, c1910, wing, oak, clamp decal mark . . . . **900.00.**

Side, Gustav Stickley, oak, three slat, back jointed to square padded seat on 4 straight legs, 39″ h **200.00**

Morris

Oak, Limbert, c1910, pierced wide stretchers, paper label **525.00**

Oak and leather, L. & J. G. Stickley, c1912, flat open arms, orig decal . **1,320.00.**

Office, desk, arm, oak, flat spindles, revolving seat, tilt back, c1910 . . . . . . **250.00**

Potty, wing back, pine, lifting lid, sliding back door, light brown graining, 19½″ w x 17¼″ d x 40¾″ h **305.00**

Queen Anne

Arm, MA, c1755, mahogany, shaped crest, ogival wings, outward scrolling arms, loose cushion, cabriole legs ending in pad feet, turned stretchers **10,500.00**

Corner, American, c1760, walnut, balloon, slip seat, cabriole legs **1,500.00**

Corner, NE, c1750, maple, dark finish, orig rush seat, flame stitch slipcover **2,000.00**

Side, CT, 1730–1760, maple, yoke crest rail, vase shaped splat, rush seat, block and vase turned legs, 20 x 14 x 40½″ **1,000.00**

Side, Hudson Valley, 18th C, fruit-wood, yoke crest, solid splat, turned styles, trumpet turned front legs, pad feet, replaced rush seat, natural wood finish **500.00**

Side, NE, 1730–1760, maple, yoke crest rail, solid spoon back, vase shaped splat, flat stiles, trapezoid rush seat, block and baluster turned legs, turned feet, 19″ w, 40¼″ h . . **1,850.00**

Wing, mahogany, banty feet with high pads, chamfered back legs, turned H stretcher, old finish, reuphol-stered **9,500.00**

Sheraton
Country, side, curly maple, Hitchcock type, turned legs, cane seat, plain splat, crest **900.00**

Side, mahogany, tapered carved legs with spade feet, carved back, clas-sical urn design, drapery swags, fluted fans, old dark finish, ivory da-mask upholstered seats, pr **2,100.00**

Victorian Style
Arm, NY, c1870, walnut incised crest rail, skirt, upholstered, pr **7,700.00**

Side, walnut, balloon back, uphol-stered seat **200.00**

Wallace Nutting, early 20th C, pilgrim century style, turned oak, arm, spindle back, rush seats, sgd, pr . . . . **700.00.**

William and Mary, Connecticut River Val-ley, 1730–1750, side maple, bannister back, shaped tablet crest rail, 5 turned half-balusters, block and baluster turned stiles, rush seat, block and turned legs, 18¼ x 12½ x 45½″ **800.00**

Windsor
Arm, continuous, NE, late 18th C, pr, 8 turned spindles continuing to shaped armrests above 2 spindles, shaped saddle seat, turned legs, 17 x 17¼ x 35″ **4,000.00**

Arm, Phila, c1785, lowback, walnut, broad saddle seat, molded out scrolled arms. **3,000.00**

Side, NE, 18th C, bow back, 9 spindle, chalked D under seat **700.00**

Side, MA, late 18th C, set of 4, comb-back, serpentine crestrail, 9 turned spindles, shaped seat on turned legs, 21¼ x 16¾ x 35″. **3,500.00**

Side, I. Clark, Hartford CT, 18th C, fan back, deeply shaped pine seat, deep turnings. **1,500.00**

Side, Samuel Vinson, RI, 18th C, fan back, carved ears, sunburst de-sign **1,250.00**

Side, hoop back, 10 spindles, bamboo turnings, deep saddle seat **750.00**

Writing armchair, NE, possibly VT,

c1790–1810, sack back, bowed crestrail above seven tapering spin-dles, shaped leather-upholstered writing surface fitted with short drawer, shaped seat fitted with drawer, turned legs and stretchers, painted cream with green high-lights. **6,750.00**

Windsor, bow back, arm, comb, NE, c1800 hardwoods, pine seat, $1,350.00.

CHESTS OF DRAWERS

Chippendale
NE, Cherry, late 18th C, oxbow front, ogee bracket base, fluted quarter columns, maker's brand LF in square with sawtooth edge on sec-ond and fourth drawers, 37⅞″ w . . **18,000.00**

PA, 1760–1790, cherry, rect top, ap-plied molding, 4 graduated thumb molded drawers, fluted quarter col-umns, molded base, ogee bracket feet, 39½ x 21¾ x 34″ **3,500.00**

PA, 1765–1790, maple rect top, molded edge, 4 graduated thumb molded drawers, molded base, bracket feet, 38½ x 18 18½ x 34″ **2,450.00**

Country, NE, 18th C, curly birch, orig hardware, 37½″ w. **8,250.00**

Eastlake, walnut, 3 long graduated draw-ers, white marble top, mirror flanked by candle stands, 32″ w **550.00**

Empire, country, curly, maple facade, top and sides are cherry and walnut, 7 dovetailed drawers, turned feet and pi-lasters, 43 x 19⅝ x 47½″ **700.00**

Federal

MA, North Shore, 1810–25, carved mahogany, bowed rect top, reeded edge and out set rounded corners, 4 drawers, reeded ¾ columns with carved capitals, spiral molded skirt, ring and baluster turned legs, turned feet, 44¾ x 23¼ x 41″ **2,650.00**

PA, 1790–1810, inlaid mahogany, bowed top, 4 graduated beaded drawers inlaid with stringing, deeply valanced skirt, French feet, 38½ x 21 x 36″ **2,000.00**

George III, English, c1770, mahogany, molded rectangular top, two short and three graduated drawers, bracket feet, 32 x 19½ x 30″ **2,350.00**

Hepplewhite

American, late 18th C, mahogany, swell front, French splay bracket base, fine inlaid bands top, bottom, 4 graduated drawers, 41¾″ l. **1,300.00**

New England, c1800, cherry, country, four graduated drawers, bracket feet with scrolls, orig hardware, old finish, 34 x 18½ x 42½″ **1,750.00**

Hepplewhite, American, 18th C, inlaid maple and curly maple, swell front, 47″ h, 40″ l, $1,750.00.

Southern, c1780–1800, 4 graduated drawers, checkered band around top, diamond inlaid band above shaped skirt, fan inlay in center of skirt, French feet, replaced hardware, 39¾″ w **3,250.00**

Mission, Gustav Stickley, c1910, oak, 2 small drawers, 3 long graduated drawers, partial paper label, 43″ h **3,250.00**

Queen Anne, country, cherry, high cut out bracket feet, dovetailed case, 2 small drawers, 4 long graduated drawers, wide molded cornice, new brasses, 35¼ x 15¾ x 48¾″ **3,250.00**

Sheraton, country, tiger maple, 4 graduated drawers, simple turned legs, paneled ends, front facings of curly maple and bird's eye maple veneer, c1800, 40½ x 20 x 40″ **900.00**

Victorian, veneer, 3 long graduated drawers, top drawers extend out from body, scored and molded side posts, red Italian marble top, 42⅛ x 17⅞ x 33″ **675.00**

William and Mary, CT, pine, 2 small drawers, 3 long graduated drawers, ball foot, painted, 37½ x 21 x 39″ **6,750.00**

CHESTS, OTHER
[See also Blanket Chests and Chests of Drawers]

Chest-on-Chest

Chippendale, MA, c1775, carved maple, bonnet-top, molded swan's neck crest, 3 spiral finials, 3 short and 4 long molded graduated drawers, center drawer fan carved, lower case with 4 molded graduated long drawers, bracket feet, orig brasses, 38½ x 18½ x 84″ **15,000.00**

George I, inlaid walnut, molded rectangular cornice above 2 short over 3 long crossbanded drawers, lower section with writing slide over 3 graduated drawers, lower drawer with central concave cavity inlaid with a half star, bracket feet, 45½″ w x 74½″ h **4,400.00**

Commode

Biedermeier, walnut, 2 fitted drawers, gray marble slab, tapered legs, 33″ h x 34″ w **1,000.00**

Regency, Provincial, oak, molded rectangular top, 3 drawers, 30¾″ h x 36½″ w **2,400.00**

Highboy

Chippendale, Delaware Valley, c1750, high grained walnut, fluted chamfered corners, upper case with three full-length graduated drawers with five drawers above, lower case with one shallow full-length drawer and three drawers below, cabriole legs, shell carved knees, stocking feet, shaped skirt, illus. *Antiques* (June 1969, pg 837), known as John Gill Highboy. **31,000.00**

Queen Anne, Phila., attributed to Joseph Armitt, c1755, carved walnut, 2 parts, top with molded swan's neck crest, 3 urn and flame-carved finials, five short and three long molded graduated drawers, center drawer shell and volute-carved, stop-fluted pilasters, lower with 1 long and 3 short drawers, shaped skirt centering volute-carved shell reserve, stop-fluted pilasters, shell carved cabriole legs, paneled pad feet, 42 x 22½ x 86″ **55,000.00**

William and Mary, inlaid, upper case and molded cornice, 2 small drawers, 3 long graduated drawers, lower case with 3 small drawers, deeply valanced skirt, vase and trumpet turned legs, 39½ x 21¼ x 63″ **22,000.00**

Linen Press, Chippendale, Phila., 1760–1780, walnut, two parts, upper part with scrolled and molded pediment, plinth and finial in scalloped opening, two scalloped arched cupboard doors, 4 sliding shelves, lower part with two rect paneled cupboard doors, molded base, ogee bracket feet, 44 x 23 x 87″ **22,000.00**

Mule, pine, 6 board, scalloped base, 2 overlapping dovetailed drawers, orig staple hinges, 38″ w x 18″ d x 38¾″ h. **750.00**

Spice Chest, Queen Anne, PA, 1760, carved walnut, two parts, upper part with molded cornice, 9 short and 1 long molded, graduated drawers, lower part with one molded long drawer, cabriole legs, slipper feet, 26½ x 15 x 4 ″ **12,000.00**

CRADLES

Cherry, Pennsylvania, early 18th C, heart cutouts in head and foot boards, scrolled sides, rockers, 42½″ **550.00**

English, provincial, pine, flat canopy, sloping sides, 38½ x 16½ x 24¼″ . . **500.00**

Federal, swing, mahogany, cylindrical, 2 supports, baluster shaped posts, trestle base, saber legs, 39¼ x 40″ **900.00**

Maple, open hand holds, trestle rockers, refinished, 38″. **275.00**

Pine

Hooded, rosewood finish, gold stenciled designs of swans, assorted fruit, and striping, orig blue painted int., 38″. **350.00**

Open, primitive, mortised and pinned construction, sq maple corner posts with well turned finials, old dark finish, 35½ x 28¾″ h **225.00**

Walnut, shaped sides, heart shaped hand holds, heart design in circular top of end boards, rockers with cut out ends, 41½″. **400.00**

Bonnet top, spindled, 27¼ x 38″ l, modern, $350.00.

Windsor, country, c1800, arched hood and foot board, shaped rockers, 38″ **1,250.00**

CUPBOARDS

Apothecary, 9 drawers, primitive, 21 x 11½ x 6¼″ **175.00**

Corner

Butternut, poplar, open, 1 pc, primitive fluting on sides, 2 batten doors, 2 full shelves, 2 set-back shelves on top, arched top, square cut relief carving, 44″ w x 80″ h **1,150.00**

Cherry, PA, early 19th C, green painted interior, 2 panel doors on base section, 1 shelf, upper door of 9 panes, 2 shelves, arched panes at top, dentil border, 46½ x 23 x 74½″ **1,700.00**

Mahogany, Empire, New York, upper case of 2 glazed doors, half columns, base of 2 closed doors carved paw feet. **850.00**

Maple, country, Am., c1800–20, upper section with glazed door with 9 lights, 2 int. shelves with spoon cuts, base with 2 paneled doors, single shelf, chamfered sides throughout, ribbed molded band across top, refinished, traces of early green paint, 41 x 23 x 77″ **3,250.00**

Pine, American, lower panel door, upper door with 12 lights of glass, butterfly hinges, 6 shells inside, poplar backing, 44 x 19 x 37″ **2,000.00**

Pine, Chippendale, ogee cornice over 2 cupboard doors, 3 fielded panels, 3 shelves, over 1 cupboard door, straight bracket feet, 78½″ h **2,850.00**

Pine, Federal, Southern, 1790–1820, molded and reeded bowed cornice, 2 cupboard doors, reeded muntins in geometric pattern, 2 bowed shelves, fluted pilasters, lower section with 2 paneled cupboard doors, applied moldings, reeded pilasters, shaped skirt, block feet,, 44½ x 27½ x 77¼" **5,000.00**

Pine, paneled sides, doors, applied moldings, glazed top doors, brass thumb latches, porcelain knobs, 52½" w x 87" h, refinished **2,250.00**

Poplar, Federal, PA, 1770–1800, painted, molded and reeded cornice over diagonally and horizontally reeded frieze and vertical panels, 2 paneled doors, molded mid band above 2 drawers, 2 paneled doors, molded base, scalloped skirt on bracket feet, 54¾ x 30¼ x 87½".. **6,500.00**

Walnut and poplar, Chippendale, American, 1760–1790, molded cornice, glazed rect 12 pane door, 3 scalloped shelves, applied mid-molding over double paneled cupboard door, base molded w straight bracket feet, 44 x 26 x 83½" **3,000.00**

Country Store, 10 drawers, pull out bin on side with 5 drawer fronts, scalloped base, chamfered corners, applied molding, 51 x 22¼ x 37" ... **625.00**

Flat: Wall or Side

Butternut, cut out feet, paneled door, CI thumb latch with porcelain knob, gallery top, 27 x 13½ x 3½" **525.00**

Cherrywood, PA, c1800, 2 parts, glazed doors, drawers, 84 x 50¾ x 18¾" **4,250.00**

Pine, 1 pc, raised panel doors base, open top, 3 shelves, molded cornice, 53 x 18½ x 86" **1,150.00**

Pine, 2 board and batten doors, interior shelves, old red paint, 49¾ x 13¼ x 69" h **325.00**

Poplar with curly maple drawer fronts, cutout feet, scalloped apron, scalloped trim at pie shelf, single board doors in base, double door above, 2 panes of glass each, 46 x 22¼ x 77½" **700.00**

Victorian, English, c1860, incised and ebonized rosewood marquetry, gilt bronze mounts, column front, concave sides, 59" w x 41" h....... **2,250.00**

Walnut, Eastlake, single panel glazed doors, 2 drawers over 2 blind doors, machine carvings............ **700.00**

Hanging

Chippendale, PA, 1760–1790, painted pine, molded cornice, rect glazed door, molded muntins, 9 glass panels, 2 iron rattail hinges, 2

Corner, Chippendale, PA, pine, $3,500.00.

molded shelves, notches for spoons, molded base, 34⅝" w, 41¼" h.................. **1,100.00**

Country, CT, c1800, pine with cherry finish, 2 int. shelves, glazed door with 4 panes, 2 small drawers at bottom, nicely molded, 24 x 9 x 32½" **2,000.00**

Country, NE, early 19th C, pine, 2 panel doors, 3 int. shelves, flat dovetail construction, orig green paint, 39 x 9 x 48".......... **750.00**

George III, English, c1770, mahogany, dentil molded broken triangular pediment centering later finial, blind fret carved frieze, paneled door enclosing shelves, flanked by fluted canted corners, 35" w, 48½" h... **1,250.00**

Poplar, painted graining, one shelf, blind door, 20 x 29" h **485.00**

Jelly

Pine, turned feet, paneled doors and ends, 3 dovetailed drawers, old red paint, 49¾ x 20 x 55¾".... **500.00**

Poplar, paneled doors, 2 overhanging drawers, shaped skirt, red and black graining, orig hardware, 41¼ x 21½ x 46".................. **600.00**

Pie Safes

Pine, pierced tin panels, red painted interior, old natural finish, early 19th C, 42½ x 18 x 62"............ **900.00**

Pine and walnut, c1830, bottom drawer, 46 x 25 x 66¼" **600.00**

Walnut, square corner posts, paneled sides, single door, 3 punched tin panels with stars, circles, old green paint, replaced feet, 30½ x 21 x 60" **225.00**

Schranks

Walnut, corner, 1 pc, bracket feet, 1 dovetailed drawer, single raised panel door, rattail hinges, cover molded cornice, 1 shelf, 7 hooks, 43½ x 48½ x 77" **5,750.00**

Walnut, carved, PA, c1770, Chippendale, molded cornice, pr of paneled cupboard door, red painted shelved int., 3 short molded drawers, replaced bracket feet, 81½ x 20 x 89½" **6,750.00**

Walnut, inlaid, Southeastern PA, 1765, molded projecting cornice above frieze, inlaid inscription GEO. R. 1765, pr of paneled hinged doors, center inlaid stellate devices, molded base with 2 drawers, flattened ball feet, 71 x 23 x 79½" . . . **12,000.00**

DRY SINKS

Butternut, 20 x 35 x 42", 2 doors, one shelf inside, original stippling and finish **425.00**

Maple, 60½ x 30½", rectangular top, single drawer, 2 doors painted, Pa. German **750.00**

Oak, 19 x 34 x 44", zinc lined, 2 doors **500.00**

Pine

32½ x 17¼ x 34", primitive, c1840, door, interior shelves, bootjack feet. **400.00**

44¾ x 42 x 21", grained to resemble oak, 3 drawer top, 2 doors, American, c1850 . . . . **550.00**

51 x 23½", pencil post legs, shaped apron, zinc liner, original blue paint **375.00**

72 x 21½ x 27" sq nail construction, center pull out bin, doors, narrow shelf **500.00**

Pine and poplar, paneled doors, shallow well dovetailed gallery, CI thumb latches with porcelain knobs, 72 x 19½ x 31" **600.00**

Poplar, Amish (Holmes Co., OH), 49 x 20¼", paneled doors, shaped skirt, 2 drawers, yellow paint with black graining over original blue paint **1,900.00**

Poplar, 2 paneled doors, 2 dovetailed drawers, galvanized sheet metal liner, top shelf, 41 x 17 x 44½" **550.00**

DESKS

Art Deco, Wolfgang Hoffman, c1935, painted wood and enameled metal, 2 drawers, chrome pulls, orig decal: Howell/St. Charles, Ill./Exclusive Design, 42" l, 30" h. **450.00**

Art Nouveau, Austrian, gilt metal, repousse panels of country scenes, glass top, brocade lining, matching arm chair **1,150.00**

Chippendale

Slant front, MA, 1760–1790, mahogany, thumb molded slant lid, fitted interior, 3 fan carved drawers, valanced pigeonholes, document drawers, 2 friezes of short drawers, 4 graduated long drawers with beaded dividers, ogee bracket feet, 40¼ x 23⅜ x 43¾" **7,750.00**

Chippendale, American, late 18th C, cherry, slant front, 39½" w, 45½" h, $5,000.00.

Slant front, North Shore, MA, 1760–1790, mahogany, thumb molded slant front, fitted interior of prospect door opening to blocked fan carved small drawers with applied columns, valenced pigeonholes, 2 tiers of blocked fan carved small drawers, frieze of small drawers, case of 4 graduated blocked drawers, molded base, carved pendant fan, 4 claw and ball feet, 40¾ x 23 x 44" **30,000.00**

Slant front, PA, 1785–1800, walnut, thumb molded slant lid, compartmented interior of 4 short drawers, 6 valanced pigeonholes, center prospect door flanked by 2 document drawers, over 4 graduated thumb molded drawers, ogee bracket feet, 40 x 21⅝ x 43½" . . . **2,425.00**

Davenport, walnut and burl walnut, c1845, carved "S" supports, 21" w x 36³/₄" h. **1,350.00**

Eastlake, Victorian, c1890, walnut, drop front, machine carvings, gallery top, fitted interior 35 x 62" **650.00**

Federal

Butler's, inlaid mahogany, hinged writing surface, 7 small drawers, pigeonholes, 3 graduated drawers, French feet, 48" w **2,500.00**

New York, c1805, mahogany, writing, top with shaped gallery, hinged leather insert lid opening to well fitted with sliding writing surface, 1 small divided drawer, frieze faced to simulate 1 long drawer, circular reeded tapering legs, 32¹/₂" h x 27" w x 23¹/₄" d **1,500.00**

Hepplewhite, slant front, cherry, French feet, scalloped apron, inlay of banded diamonds, inlaid compass star on lid, figured mahogany veneer interior, 9 dovetailed drawers, 42³/₄" w x 21" d x 45³/₄" h. **1,150.00**

Lap Desk, Victorian, brass fitted, rosewood **175.00**

Mahogany, Peruvian, folding, c1835 light, dark mahogany inlay, MOP escutcheon, initials EBS, ivory cross hatch corners on bottom, interior compartments, 18¹/₄" w x 7" h x 9¹/₄" d. . **1,045.00**

Partner's Writing Table

George III, English, c1780, mahogany, molded rectangular top, green leather insert, each side with three frieze drawers, above three drawers, in each pedestal, ogee bracket feet, 57 x 39¹/₂ x 32", restorations **5,000.00**

Mission, L. & J. G. Stickley, oak, rectangular top over 2 short drawers, 4 straight legs, stretchers, paper label, 29" h x 40" l **350.00**

Queen Anne, slant front, Mass., 18th C, cherry, turned feet, slightly stepped interior, 16 drawers, 6 pigeonholes, 39³/₄" w **2,000.00**

Roll Tops

Oak, S shaped roll top, 3 drawers one each side, plain interior. **1,000.00**

Oak, S shaped roll top, Victorian, wooten type doors on sides, elaborate carving, fancy interior **2,750.00**

Schoolmaster's, walnut, one piece, turned legs, 1 dovetailed drawer, dovetailed top, lift lid, 10 pigeonholed, refinished, 34 x 22¹/₄ x 37³/₄". **325.00**

Sheraton, Am, c1800–10, cherry and bird's-eye maple, slant top, int with two rows of drawers above open sections, 3 graduated drawers, reeded and ring turned side columns, bulbous reeded feet, replaced hardware, 39³/₄" **1,250.00**

Traveling

Ivory inlays, engraved garlands, reticulated ivory carving, 12¹/₄" l. **475.00**

Painted, earthworm like graining, 22" **550.00**

Victorian, burr walnut, pedestal, rectangular top, molded edge, 3 small drawers, kneehole opening flanked by 6 drawers, molded plinth base, 51" w . **500.00**

Wooton, c1875, walnut and burl walnut, standard grade, pierced and carved ³/₄ gallery over a double panel lifting frieze, maple veneer fitted interior, trestle feet, 41" closed, 69¹/₂" h **5,500.00**

DOUGH TROUGHS

Cherry, dovetailed corners, turned feet, white porcelain knobs, name "Hardin" scratched on base. **250.00**

Chestnut, 18 x 28 x 28", pine legs. . . . **400.00**

Pine

28¹/₂ x 48 x 29¹/₄", chip carved detail, 2 board top, hardwood base, turned splayed legs, H stretcher **235.00**

29¹/₂ x 41³/₄", rectangular top, exposed dovetails, over skirt, turned cylindrical legs **150.00**

Oak, French Provincial, 2 parts, base with scalloped apron on sq cabriole supports, 57¹/₂ x 26¹/₂ x 29¹/₄" **700.00**

Poplar, turned splayed legs, dark brown finish, 16¹/₂ x 34³/₄ x 31¹/₂ . . **150.00**

Primitive, hollowed out from 1 log, pencil post legs, drain hole with wooden plug, old red finish, 18¹/₄ x 45¹/₂ x 26¹/₂" **275.00**

Primitive, cov, sawbuck type base, traces of red and white paint, 30¹/₄ x 12¹/₄ x 25" **175.00**

FRAMES

Brass

6¹/₂ x 4¹/₂", floral scroll decor **85.00**

8 x 14", Florentine styling, easel back. **65.00**

Curly maple, cherry, butternut, 19¹/₂ x 15¹/₂ x 3" w, pr **250.00**

Empire, mahogany veneer, wide molding, 20 x 26". **50.00**

Folk Art, pine, one piece, carved, sunburst crest, American, 10¹/₂ x 17¹/₂". . **125.00**

Ivory, carved, 3³/₁₆ x 2⁹/₁₆" **50.00**

Mahogany, gold liner, 9 x 16" opening **85.00**

Maple, birds-eye veneer, gilded liner, 1⁷/₈ x 13³/₄ x 16¹/₂" **90.00**

Pine, 15 x 18", flat, block, corners with metal stars **60.00**

Poplar, beveled, orig red flame graining, 14¹/₂ x 16¹/₂" **135.00**

Shadow Box, Victorian

Circular, 21¹/₂", deep **90.00**

Oval, 19³/₄ x 22³/₄", deep **90.00**

Rectangular, 28 x 32″, walnut, double
liner 115.00
Tramp Art, 47 x 40″, deeply layered and
chip carved geometrics, top panel with
heart in center, American, c1930, pr 500.00

HAT RACKS AND HALL TREES

Art Deco, c1935, rectangular, chromed
metal, shelf above 6 knobs for hanging, mirrored back, umbrella holder,
31½″ w, 74½″ h 600.00
Bamboo, old dark finish, mirror, 2
shelves. 500.00

**Iron holder with 8 prongs, lamp, 16¾″
h, dated 1869, 150.00.**

Brass, 3 butterfly type hooks, porcelain
knobs. 135.00
Cast iron, 10″ beveled mirror, 12 hooks,
umbrella holder, 4 arched legs,
c1880. . . . . 250.00
Victorian, solid brass, large beveled
plate glass mirror supported by side
posts with hooks, base of mirror supported by rectangular shelf with round
legs joined at base by identical shelf,
cast paw feet, brass scrolls, sunflower
rosettes at mirror corners, foliate crest
with cartouche, 38 x 12 x 81″. 1,800.00
Walnut, Reform style, rectangular mirror,
5 brass hooks, 2 short drawers, Herter
Bros., c1875, 43½ x 18 x 74″. 1,500.00

ICE CREAM PARLOR FURNITURE

Chairs
   Heart back, refinished 70.00
   Spectacle, refinished 80.00
   Arm, wood seat. 125.00
Stools
   26½″ high, refinished. 50.00
   30″ h, 12″ d, seat, refinished 60.00
Tables
   27″ square, oak top. 200.00
   30″ d, oak top. 250.00

Table and 2 chairs, child's, table 18″ d;
chairs, 9½″ d seat, set 200.00
Table and 4 chairs, table, 30″ d, wood
top; Chairs, 14″ d replaced seats, refinished, set 550.00

LOVE SEATS

Empire, French, mahogany and parcel
gilt, upholstered, carved sphinx heads,
tapering supports, claw feet, c1810 . 800.00
Federal, NE, inlaid mahogany, removable rect crest, upholstered back, line
inlaid curving arms, upholstered seat,
reeded legs, 51″ l 750.00
George III, mahogany, adjustable armrests, square chamfered legs, upholstered, c1779, 4'9½″ l 3,300.00
Renaissance, gilt bronze mounted rosewood, American, c1865 . . . . 990.00
Rococo, laminated rosewood, bird carving, attributed to Alexander Roux,
American, c1855. . . . . 15,000.00
Venetian, rococo, gilt carved wood, floral
brocade upholstered cushion, carved
frieze, cabriole leg, 19th C, 15″ h x
24½″ w x 21½″ d 700.00

MAGAZINE RACKS

Canterbury
   George III, mahogany, 3 bays, short
   turned feet, casters, 23 x 17 x 20″ . 450.00
   George III, late, mahogany, fieze
   drawer, 2 bays, short turned legs,
   casters 18 x 12½ x 20″ 400.00
   New York, c.1810, 4 x-form uprights,
   single drawer case, turned legs
   mounted on casters, 19½″ l,
   20½″ h 3,750.00
Gallé, Emile, inlaid mahogany, floral
frieze on drawer, 4 open compartments, carved apron, saber legs,
side inlays of floral, butterfly,
45¾″ h x 24″ w x 12¾″ d 1,880.00
Mission
   Roycroft, oak, c1910, carved emblem,
   37″ h 450.00
   Stickley, L. & J. G., oak, c1910, rectangular decal mark, 45″ h 475.00
Victorian, Eastlake, walnut, 13½ x 26″,
pierced sides, turned posts, machine
carved 125.00

MIRRORS

Adam style, veneer frame, ebonized
molding, gilt crest in form of urn of
flowers, 48″ l 250.00
Chevals
   67″ h, mahogany oval frame, 4 paw
   feet. 500.00

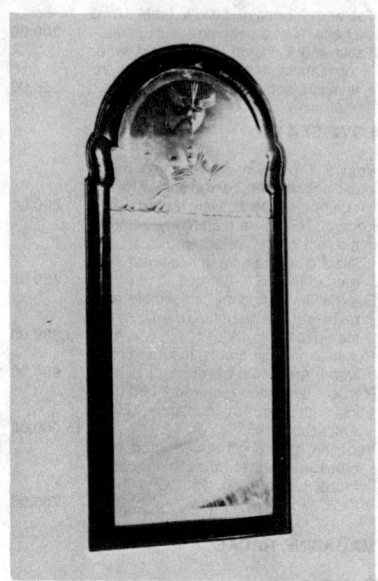

Queen Anne, walnut, piercing heart and crown, beveled 2 pc mirror, $5,600.00.

75" h, Empire, arch shape mirror frame supported by 2 columns, urn turned finials, double brass candle arms, arched bracket feet 1,000.00

Chippendale

Country primitive, early 19th C, old label on back, 13¾ x 22½ 300.00

Mahogany veneer on pine, gilded carved and geossoed trim, broken arch pediment with carved foliage rosettes, removable carved phoenix, orig mirror, 28¾ x 57" 17,000.00

Mahogany veneer, Am, c1750, high crest, fretwork sides, triangular lob cut in top, molded sides around orig beveled glass, 32½" 800.00

Dresser

Brass, oval, cupid and floral decor, 15 x 16" 175.00

Centennial, inlaid mahogany, 5 drawers, large oval mirror, 26¼ x 11 x 26" 135.00

Cherry, oval mirror on set drawer, lift top lid, 13½ x 33 x 34½" 300.00

Federal, shaving, bow front, mahogany on pine, 3 dovetail drawers, line inlay, cherry turned mirror posts, 19¾" w x 71½" d x 20½" h 240.00

Hepplewhite, mahogany, inlaid stripes, 2 drawers, glass knobs . . . 650.00

Empire

Cherry, split turnings with corner blocks, black paint and gilding, reverse painting, youth and maiden on country road, 15½ x 34" 400.00

Shaving, mahogany, carved acanthus posts 2 curved front dovetailed drawers, turned mirror supports, 22 x 9¼ x 27½" 225.00

Federal

Architectural, gilt molded cornice hung with gilt spherels, leaf molding, white painted and gilt panel, reeded pilaster, 48¾" h x 25½" w 715.00

Convex, carved spread eagle finial, gilt egg and dart molding and acanthus leaf molding, ebonized reeded molding, acanthus carved pendant, 52" h x 31" d 1,750.00

Rectangular, Am, crest molding with ball drops, reverse painting of ship, reeded and twist columns, leaf vertical dividers, 20½" h 600.00

Rectangular, Portland, ME, label of James Todd, battle between Am. and British warship on reverse painting on top, top molding with ball drops, ring and bulbous turned side columns, 28" 950.00

George II, English, c1740, parcel-gilt walnut, shaped rectangular plate, C-scroll, flowering swag hung sides, swan's neck crest centering a cartouche, shaped apron, 24 x 48½", some restoration 4,250.00

Hepplewhite, mahogany, scrolled base, ears inlaid, gilded frame, scrolled gilded pediment with inlaid shell, urn finial with flowers, grain, side garlands with bellflower detail, old mirror, reverse painted panel in white, silver with black, gold scene of cabin, 25¼ x 65" 1,300.00

Overmantel, Empire, carved and gilt, broken cornice, acorn shaped spheres over stylized egg and dart molding, applied frieze of classical figures, 3 panels of glass divided by colonettes, fluted pilasters, acanthus carved molding with applied garlands, 77½ x 31" 1,350.00

Pier, 42 x 8½" h, gilted, ornate shell type crest, fluted columns, marble shelf . . 1,000.00

Plateau, 14", silverplate, ornate base, beveled mirror 95.00

Queen Anne

Bronze painted finish, Cape Cod style, late 18th C, 20½" h x 12" w 225.00

Country, shaped, molded crest centering eglomise polychrome floral panel, floral border, 17" h x 12" w 550.00

Walnut and gilt, 1740–60 pierced and scroll crest centering pierced & carved gilt floral cartouche, beveled glass, 19½ x 50½". **2,650.00**

Rococo, gilt, shaped vertical plate, pierced frame, scrolling acanthus, 50½ x 34" **500.00**

Sheraton
Architectural, reverse painting of municipal building flying American flag, c1800, 21⅜" h. **400.00**
Shaving, mahogany, serpentine, small cut out ogee feet, 3 conforming drawers, dovetailed, line inlay, mirror frame of cross banded inlay, cut out crest, 18¼" w x 8" d x 24½" h **550.00**

ROCKERS

Arrowback, bamboo turnings, scrolled arms, 3 slat back, red and black graining, stenciled floral designs on slats **325.00**

North Carolina, rocker, hand pegged, late 18th C, $500.00.

Bannister back, NE, 18th C, fruitwood, ash, maple, rush seat **400.00**
Boston, sgd Hitchcock, orig paint and decor **400.00**

Country, American, c1830, carved and painted, shaped comb above rectangular back rails, curved seat, turned legs joined by stretchers, trestle rockers, painted with eagles, pears, floral motif, rosewood ground, yellow, black striping **3,850.00**

Eastlake, late 19th C, mahogany platform, incised and pierced cresting over square panel back, center, pad arms, seat upholstered in pink velvet, reeded arms, supports. **275.00**

Ladderbacks
Arm, Shaker #7, Mt. Lebanon label, turned arm supports, turned finials, replaced woven splint seat **625.00**
Arm, turned posts and arms, 4 slats, turned finials, woven splint eat . . . **200.00**
Child's, arm, 3 slats, spindle arms, spindle stretchers, dark finish, homemade fabric seat, 23½" h. . . . **125.00**

Mission
Gustav Stickley, c1907, mahogany, 9 spindle back, rush seat, 1" red decal **715.00**
Roycroft, c1915, oak, rectangular back, sides with vertical slats **625.00**

Oak
Child's, dog head and gallery, turned spindles, cane seat, 30" h **250.00**
Pressed back, 7 spindle back, 4 arm support spindles. **200.00**

Windsor
Bamboo turnings, old pale yellow paint, floral decor on crest **550.00**
Comb back, 7 spindle back, orig black paint, American, 19th C **1,250.00**

SECRETARIES

Chippendale, CT, cherry, top with flaring cornice over pair of paneled cupboard doors, fitted interior, bottom with slant top, fitted interior, 4 graduated drawers, ogee bracket feet, 38 x 19½ x 84" **8,250.00**

Country, cherry, 2 pc, square turned legs, 1 dovetailed drawer, slant top lift lid base, bookcase top with 2 drawers, simple cornice, one pane of glass in door, mullions removed, 27" w x 21½" d x 70¾" h **745.00**

Federal, CT, 1790–1820, inlaid cherry, molded cornice above frieze with vine and berry inlay, 2 cupboard doors with line inlay, inlaid corner fans with urns and stylized flowers, slant lid inlaid with stringing fans, vines, and pendant husks, fitted interior, inlaid prospect door, small drawers above valanced pigeonholes, 4 graduated line inlaid drawers, shaped skirt, 40 x 19¾ x 84½" **9,500.00**

Hepplewhite, mahogany, bracket feet, 3 dovetailed drawers, line inlay rectangles with invected corners, 4th drawer with inlaid ovals, pull out desk fitted with 7 dovetailed drawers, 10 pigeonholes, top 2 doors, line inlay, frieze, removable cornice with scrolled pediment, carved rosette, inlaid almond sunburst, dentil molding, gilt eagle finial, geometric arrangement of glass panes in doors, attributed to Wm Appleton, Salem, MA, 43″ w x 23½″ d x 101½″ h. **12,000.00**

Country Victorian, c1860, pine, brass hardware, 24¼ x 45¼ x 87″, $1,750.00.

Sheraton, mahogany, string and band inlays on drawers and 2 cupboard doors, oval inlay on prospect door, turned feet, 38½″ w, 49¾″ h **3,500.00**
Victorian, Renaissance, walnut, arched pediment, 2 glazed doors, fitted interior, bureau style base. **1,750.00**
William and Mary, English, c1690, inlaid burr walnut, molded cornice above pair of glazed doors, shelves, pair of candleslides, hinged sloping front, fitted step int., two loper drawers, two short drawers, two long drawers, bun feet, 39 x 24 x 78″, restorations **11,750.00**

SETTEES

Classical, maple, shaped crest, pierced splats, ring turned legs, brass castors, painted in chinoiserie in yellow and gold on black ground, 76″ l **1,430.00**
English, country, pine, high back, yew wood seat, curved paneled back, refinished, 81″ **375.00**

Queen Anne, English, 18th C, carved walnut, chairback, 80″ l, $1,000.00.

Federal, late, NE, 1810–1830, bird's-eye maple, tablet crest rail, 3 raking stiles connected by horizontal rail, scrolling arms, turned arm supports, rush seat, turned legs, 60″ w, 33¼″ h **6,100.00**
George III, English, c1770, mahogany, arch backrest and scrolled armrests, needlepoint upholstered, loose cushioned seat, square molded chamfered legs joined by stretchers, 84″ l **8,250.00**
Rococo, pickled rosewood, John Henry Belter, NY, triple arched back carved with floral bouquets, scallop shells, upholstered in lavender damask, 84″ l . **4,500.00**

SIDEBOARDS

Art Nouveau, French, c1900, oak, overhanging top above panel sides and 2 drawers with bronze drop handles, lily pad backplates, 2 panel doors carved in relief with lily pads, bracket feet, 51½ x 20½ x 39″ **950.00**
Classical, attributed to Joseph Barry, Philadelphia, PA, 1815–20, carved mahogany, oblong top, shaped splashboard, 5 short drawers and pr of paneled cupboard doors, center of 2 convex cupboard doors, reeded, acanthus and hairy paw foot carved colonnette ring turned tapering legs ending in brass animal paw feet, 82 x 25 x 49″. **3,500.00**
Federal
Baltimore, c1790, inlaid mahogany, oblong top, serpentine front,

shaped frieze, 1 long drawer, 2 cupboard drawers, sq tapered line and bell flower inlaid legs, cross banded cuffs, 72 x 26 x 40″ **9,625.00**

New York, c1820, cross banded mahogany, oblong top, shaped splashboard, 2 short drawers, candleslides, 2 cupboard doors, center bowed section with 5 short drawers above 2 cupboard doors, reeded, circular legs, brass caps, 80 x 28 x 51″ **2,750.00**

George III, c1870, inlaid mahogany, bowed center section with 3 frieze drawers flanked by 2 pedestals with single drawer and one cupboard door, sq legs, block toes, 96 x 44″ **4,400.00**

Georgian, English, late 18th C, inlaid mahogany, 2 cupboard doors, central drawer, 6 sq tapered legs, 63½ x 26 x 38½″. **1,500.00**

Louis XV, oak and fruitwood, panel sides, 2 drawers over shaped panel doors, short sq cabriole front supports, 50 x 22½ x 42″ **1,225.00**

Louis XVI, walnut, rect top, panel sides, 2 shaped fielded doors, carved scalloped apron, 52 x 25 x 48″ **900.00**

Neoclassical, inlaid and painted mahogany pedestal, brass rail gallery, in-

verted breakfront, 3 medallions, husk and swag inlaid frieze drawers, end cupboards with arched doors painted with classically draped maidens, 81¼ x 26½ x 43″ **850.00**

SOFAS

Chippendale, NY, c1770, mahogany, camel back, shaped crest, outward scrolling arm supports and seat, square molded legs, flat stretchers, 80″ **10,000.00**

Classical, NY, 1825, carved mahogany and bird's eye maple, columnar crest, acanthus and flowerhead carved terminals, upholstered back and armsupports, 73″ l **3,125.00**

Empire, Boston, 1825–35, mahogany, tablet crest rail, raised veneered panel flanked by carved palmettes, scrolled and padded back, 5 scrolled molded arms, straight skirt, carved paw feet, scrolled and leaf carved knees, 80 x 23½ x 37½″ **1,900.00**

Federal, Phila., rectangular and slightly stepped crest, downward sloping arms, reeded vase form supports, bowed seat, square tapered legs, 75½″ **4,500.00**

Federal, NY, attr. Duncan Phyfe, rectangular crest, swag carving, reeding in arms, seat rail, and tapered legs, 81¼″ **6,500.00**

George III, c1800, mahogany, upholstered, sq tapered legs, castor ends, stretchers, 50″ l **2,900.00**

Hepplewhite, mahogany, square moulded legs, spade feet, cabriole back, rosette carved arms, upholstered in gold raw silk damask, NY, 81″ w. **9,000.00**

Mission, oak, Gustav Stickley, c1905, red decal mark, 72″. **1,850.00**

Rococo, laminated rosewood, John Henry Belter, NY, c1855, applied floral cresting, 74″ **2,000.00**

Victorian, early, mahogany, shaped back, center medallion with carved leaf motif, bowed side arms with flat shaped front board, scroll, leaf, and sunburst relief carving on front apron, incised winged style feet, 85″. **750.00**

SPINNING WHEELS

Flax Wheels (Saxony), Mixed woods, PA, c1840, turned **300.00**

Wool Wheels (Walking)
Oak, 44½″ d wheel, turned legs, posts, spindles, bobbin reel missing **225.00**

Victorian, walnut, marble top, carved with game birds and fish, $850.00.

Oak, 45″ d wheel, 60″ h 285.00
Walnut, PA, mid 19th C 450.00

STANDS

Cottage, rustic, natural bark base, worn
gold, brown painted top, 13½ x 14½
x 27″ 75.00
Country
Cherry, turned legs, 1 dovetailed
drawer, 2 board top, red finish,
20¾ x 22 x 29″ 225.00
Walnut, Hepplewhite sq. tapered legs,
banded inlay around base of apron,
herringbone inlay on posts, 1
drawer, 19 x 22¾ x 29″ 300.00

**Pine, cherry stain, turned spindle towel
holders, 13¾ x 22½ x 32″, $200.00.**

Empire, mahogany, 2 drawer, square
top, tapered feet, 28½ x 34½ x 17″ . 275.00
Federal, 19th C, cherry, rect. top, 1
drawer, baluster turned tapering legs,
18″ x 18¾ x 29″ 300.00
George II, English, c1750, reading, mahogany, hinged ratcheted adjustable
rectangular top, baluster stem, tripod
cabriole legs ending in pad feet, 19½
x 15½ x 28½″, restorations 800.00
Cherry, square one board top, dovetailed drawer, 20 x 28″ h 400.00
Mahogany, corner washstand, 3 draw-
ers, slightly splayed legs 550.00
Walnut, country, square turned legs,
one dovetailed drawer, 20½ x 24 x
28¾″ h 235.00

Sheraton
Cherry, poplar, turned, reeded legs, 2
dovetailed drawers with cockbeading, one board top, 20¼ x 16¾ x
28¼ h 375.00
Cherry and tiger maple, 2 drawers,
beaded, mushroom pulls, 20 x
28¾″ 350.00
Mahogany, turned legs, posts, one
dovetailed drawer, top cut out for
bowl, gallery, some veneer damage,
20″ w x 16″ d x 30½″ h 250.00
Umbrella, cast iron, ring grip, pierced
scalloped disk, baluster support,
pierced circular umbrella holder, scalloped drip pan, 3 scroll feet, 40″ . . . 275.00
Victorian, brass, 33″ h, marble inserts . 300.00
Wash, pine, turned legs and posts,
dovetailed drawer, dovetailed scalloped gallery, dark red and black
graining, yellow striping, fruit stenciled
crest, 17 x 14 x 29½″ h plus crest . . 275.00

STEPS

Bed
Federal, NY, 1800–20, mahogany,
serpentined open sides, 3 leather
cov steps, ring and baluster turned
supports, ring turned tapered legs,
ball feet, 17 x 24½ x 22¾″ 1,250.00
Regency, hinged rectangular inset
leather top above two steps, circular
ring turned legs, 16½″ w 1,210.00
Library
Georgian, mahogany, embossed
green leather insets, top step
hinged, compartment beneath second step contains holder for chamber pot, 17⅜ x 25 x 25⅝″ 425.00
Regency, English, early 19th C,
quarter spiral, 45½″ 850.00
Victorian, oak, 4 steps, arm rail support,
76″ h 450.00

STOOLS

Foot
Country, NE, rectangular, chamfered
sides, peg legs, top painted and
grained in shades of red and black,
yellow line decor, 7″ h x 12″ l 400.00
Country, pine, board, dark red paint,
7¾ x 16 x 6¾″ 40.00
Empire, carved mahogany, rectangu-
lar half upholstered seat above
scrolling side rails, scrolling curule
legs, carved lotus petals, turned
stretcher, 15½″ h 800.00
Flemish, baroque, walnut, upholstered
needlepoint rect. seat 675.00
Inlaid fruitwood, Conn, c1780, rectan-

gular, ebony, ironwood, scalloped
skirt, 11″ l **1,760.00**
Georgian, English, late 18th C, ma-
hogany, sq tapered legs, molded
corners, upholstered seat, 19½ x
13¾ x 18½″ **200.00**
Louis XV, circular seat, painted, upholstered, floral sprig carved ca-
briole legs **200.00**
Queen Anne
Mahogany, cabriole legs with cyma
scrolls, slipper feet, upholstered
in contemporary crewel, 13½ x
16″ **300.00**
Walnut, NE, c1740, stretcher base,
19″ l x 15¾″ h **2,250.00**
Sheraton, English, mahogany, adjust-
able top leather and cloth cover, 14
x 18″ **175.00**
Victorian, 19th C, mahogany, carved
rectangular seat, upholstered in flo-
ral needlepoint, cabriole legs **385.00**
William and Mary, c1700, upholstered
circular seat, trumpat turned legs,
shaped cross stretchers with turned
pediment, painted black, 17″. **3,250.00**
Milking
Country, primitive, 3 legs, heart cut out
handle, relief carving of cow, old
dark finish, 7¼ x 18″ **275.00**
Country, primitive, 3 legs, burl top, old
red paint, 8½ x 10″ **130.00**
Monk's, Gustav Stickley, c1909, oak
leather, square oak splayed feet, pa-
per label, 1½″ red decal **500.00**
Organ, Victorian, circular, 3 fancy metal
legs, ebonized stem, needlepoint top **125.00**
Piano, Victorian, mid-19th C, circular, upholstered, rosewood frame, adjusta-
ble, shaped base, scroll feet, 21″ h . **125.00**

TABLES

Card
Chippendale, c1780, cherrywood, rectangular, single drawer, 29¾ x
35¼ x 16⅜″ **3,500.00**
Empire, attributed to Issac Vose, Bos-
ton, 1825–1835, mahogany, folded
rect top, rounded corners, carved
scrolls and lotus blossoms, sq pedestal, shaped base, scrolled feet,
34⅝ x 17½ x 30⅝″ **400.00**
Federal, MA, 1790–1815, mahogany,
D shaped top, outset rounded corners, conforming skirt, figured veneer flanked by ring turned stiles,
reeded tapering cylindrical legs, 36
x 17¾ x 30″ **1,125.00**
Federal, Salem, MA, c1798, carved
and inlaid mahogany, carving attributed to Samuel McIntire, semi-circular top, hinged leaf, flowerhead

**Card, Sheraton, Philadelphia, c1810,
mahogany, 29 x 36 x 35″, $2,750.00.**

and glyph carved edge, top inlaid
with fan centering conch shell, felt-
lined playing surface, frieze with
beaded edge centering basket of
flowers and fruit, carved paterae
dies flanking on acanthus carved
circular reeded tapered legs, acanthus carved feet, 48¾ x 24¼ x
30″ **308,000.00**
George III, mahogany, D shape hinged
top, frieze inlay, square tapering
legs, 36″ w **500.00**
Hepplewhite, maple, country, sq ta-
pered legs bowed apron and conforming top, refinished 17 x 35¼ x
27¼″ **750.00**
Queen Anne, PA, 1770, carved wal-
nut, rect top, hinged leaf, 1 cock
beaded drawer, cabriole legs,
paneled trifid feet, 34 x 18½ x 27″ **4,775.00**
Regency, c1815, satinwood and rose-
wood, inlaid, 29 x 36″. **1,600.00**
Corner, Queen Anne, Southern, 1750–
70, carved walnut, triangular top,
hinged D shaped leaf, shaped skirt,
circular tapering legs, pad feet, 43 x
39 x 29″. **7,500.00**
Dining
Art Deco, Donald Desky style, c1935,
burl walnut, lyre base, 52 x 26″. . . **1,550.00**
Chippendale, Phila, mahogany, drop
leaf, claw and ball feet, 28 x 48 x
54″. **5,000.00**
Duncan Phyfe, mahogany, D shaped
ends, 3 pedestals with reeded te-
trapods, brass paw castors, ... **4,250.00**

Empire, mahogany, drop leaf, 1 drawer, paw feet, 28 x 51″ 600.00

Federal, NE, c1800, drop leaf, walnut, 30 x 61″ 700.00

George I, walnut, gateleg, rounded rectangular twin flap top, circular tapering legs, pad feet, 64″ w 1,600.00

Hepplewhite, 2 part, inlay mahogany, D shape top, rectangular drop leaves, 42 x 81½ x 30″ 1,800.00

Mission, Limbert, c1910, oak, oval top, branded mark, 44¾″ 775.00

Regency, mahogany, oval, single board top, baluster pedestal on 3 molded sabre legs, castors, 27¼ x 21½ x 20″ 6,500.00

Sheraton, mahogany, 2 parts, 5 fluted legs on each section, 45¼″ x 22½″ 1,250.00

Dressing, Continental, mahogany with pine, painted dark blue, salmon drawer front and end panels, molded edge trimmed in yellow, 43 x 26¾ x 35″ 1,200.00

Drop Leaf

Empire, mahogany, rectangular top over ogee frieze, square baluster pedestal, concave cut platform base, 57½ x 39½″ 275.00

Federal, MA, 1800–1820, mahogany, rect top, 2 drop leaves with rounded corners, straight skirt, cock beaded drawer, reeded and turned tapering legs, tapering cylindrical feet, 36⅞ x 39¾ x 29″ 1,000.00

Queen Anne, cherry, square legs with turning below apron, duck feet, 1 board top, 41⅞ x 13⅜ x 27″ 1,250.00

Queen Anne, PA, 1740–1760, walnut, rect top, 2 leaves, shaped skirt, cabriole legs, stocking carved trifid feet, 47 x 41½ x 28¼″ 2,275.00

Sheraton, country, NY or PA, cherry, leaves scalloped near corners, turned spindle legs, 42 x 22¾″ x 29″ 225.00

Stuart, 17th C, oak, gateleg, oval twin flap top, spool turned legs, 45″ w . 1,320.00

Game, George III, c1770, mahogany, serpentine front, bead and reel carved, hinged rectangular top, outset corners, shaped apron with leaf-carved brackets, bead and reel-carved molded sq chamfered legs, 35½ x 16½ x 28½″, restoration. .. 3,650.00

Harvest

Pine, NE, mid 19th C, oblong, X form legs, 28½ x 156″ 2,250.00

Sheraton, pine, turned legs, 22 x 72 x 29″ h, 9½″ leaves 600.00

Hutch, Am, c1740–60, pine, traces of old red paint, scrubbed top, shoe foot, one of pr, 35 x 45½ x 27¾″ 2,000.00

Library

Federal, Am, c1820, carved mahogany, rect top, 2 shaped drop leaves, concave frieze, urn form standard, brass animal paw feet, 41½ x 59 x 29½″ 2,125.00

Victorian, c1840, mahogany, 2 drawers in frieze, 2′5″ x 4′4″ w 1,000.00

William IV, c1835, rosewood, top of leaf carved molded edges, frieze of 2 bead molded drawers, 2′4½″ h by 4′4″ w 11,000.00

Marble Top

Giltwood, cabriole legs, 3′9″ w 1,145.00

Regency, c1720, console, carved giltwood, mottled top, 3′4″ w.....11,350.00

Renaissance Revival, American, c1865, library, walnut, burl veneer, banded top, 5″................ 450.00

Mission, Stickley, c1900, oak, rect top, small shaped splash rail, decal, 40″ w, 38″ h 650.00

Papier Mache, Victorian, game, chess board top, shaped apron, inlaid MOP, gilt floral pearl motifs, lyre shaped end supports, scrolled central stretcher, 28″ h x 24″ w x 20½″ d......... 500.00

Pembroke

Chippendale, PA, c1750–75, drop leaf, mahogany top, walnut base, straight legs chamfered on inner corners, flat reticulated x-stretcher, 34⅜ x 28 (open) x 28¼″ 3,200.00

Federal, NY, 1790–1810, maple, oval top with 2 drop leaves, 1 drawer, 4 chamfered legs, 39 x 32¼ x 27¾″ 3,375.00

George III, English, c1790, inlaid satin wood, serpentine shaped, hinged cross-banded top, frieze drawer, square tapered legs ending in brass casters, 29 x 20½ x 28″ 5,000.00

Mahogany, Chinese Chippendale, square legs, pierced cross stretcher, fretwork brackets, dovetailed drawer, sgd Ingles, NY, orig finish, 9″ leaves, 19¼ x 28½ x 27¾″ 3,250.00

Tavern, NE, spade foot, 27¼ x 44 x 28½″, $1,000.00.

Poker, oak, swivel iron pedestal base, 36″ d **650.00**

Tavern

Queen Anne, NE, 1730–1750, maple, oval top, shaped skirt, splayed and turned legs, pad feet, 35 x 24¾ x 25½″ **4,000.00**

Maple, Buxton, Maine, c1800, stretcher base, orig dark red paint, 33″ l x26½″ w x 26¼″ h. **7,500.00**

Pine and Maple, Am, 18th C, single pine board with breadboard ends, one drawer, turned maple base, legs joined by stretchers, refinished, 26 x 24½ x 35½″. **2,250.00**

Tea

Chippendale, NE, 1770–1790, cherry, tilt top, sq top, baluster turned pedestal, tripod cabriole legs, elongated ball and claw feet, 33 x 33 x 27″. . **7,250.00**

George II, English, c1750, mahogany, tilt-top, shaped molded top, bird cage support, spirally turned columnar stem, acanthus carved tripod cabriole legs, call and ball foot, 27½″ d, 27″ h, restorations. **2,650.00**

Queen Anne, bird's eye maple, snake feet, molded toes, tilt top, 27½″ top x 27½″ h. **1,600.00**

Queen Anne, Maple, tray top, rectangular, 29 x 20¼ x 25½″ h. **7,000.00**

Regency, rosewood, circular, tilt top, octagonal swelling pedestal, triangular base, embonized paws, 49½″ d **5,000.00**

Work

Biedermeier, 19th C, mahogany, 3 drawers. **250.00**

Federal, late, MA, 1815–25, mahogany and maple veneer, rect top, 2 drawers, spool ¾ columns, lyre base, 4 sabre legs, brass paw feet, 17¾ x 16 x 29½″. **1,100.00**

Hepplewhite, country, c1800, maple or birch, reversed serpentine top with incut corners, single drawer, square tapered legs, old dark finish **450.00**

George III, English, c1810, penwork and polychrome decorated parquetry inlaid rosewood, canted rectangular frame, hinged lid with classical reserve, fitted int. above basket, sq splayed legs, concave sided stretchers, 20½ x 15½ x 28½″ . . . **4,500.00**

Queen Anne, country, bread board ends, single drawer, turned legs, pad feet, 29 x 45″ **1,750.00**

Sheraton

Cherry, maple and bird's eye maple, serpentine chased top, rope and pineapple carved legs, lacy glass draw pull **650.00**

Mahogany and rosewood, Boston

or Salem, c1800, two drawers, finest quality banding and select grain facings, delicately turned and reeded legs, mid-shelf with scalloped gallery, orig lion head brasses **7,000.00**

Tiger maple, Vermont, c1800, fine reeded legs, split drawer construction. **1,700.00**

Victorian, check inlaid octagonal rising top over fitted interior, turned and lobed circular base, 3 scroll feet, 19¾″ **250.00**

TEA WAGONS

Black lacquer finish, raised Chinese figures in landscape, D drop leaves, turned legs, support, 2 wheels **300.00**

Victorian, brass, glass **700.00**

Wicker, wrapped reed and rattan, close weave, removable glass/top, c1880 **450.00**

YARN WINDERS

Floor Type, Primitive oak, mortised frame, two reels, one stationary, one adjustable, 51″ h. **75.00**

Niddy Noddy, Maple, mortised, 17¼″ l **75.00**

Spoke Type

4 spoke table model, chip carved base, turned standard, geared counter, one spoke folds back, old red paint, reel 24″ **65.00**

4 spoke, primitive, reel in frame, shoe feet, worn black paint, 28″ h. **75.00**

4 spoke, Shaker, Sabbathday Lake, combination of hard and soft woods, square nail construction, geared side counter needle, reel 26″ , 32″ h **375.00**

6 spoke, old red paint, semicircular base, 3 splayed legs, counter wheel, turned hub with radiating spokes, 24 x 47″ **125.00**

6 spokes, walnut, turned legs, reel spindles, chip carved details, geared counter, old worn finish, worn paper counter dial with name, 1845, 28½″ d x 41¾″ h **175.00**

WAGON SEATS

Wagon seats cannot be classified with seats from a wagon. Early wagon seats were usually constructed with a double frame and a basketry-type seat. They served a dual purpose: in the house and in the family wagon for additional seating.

Country, board along back and sides above seats, trestle feet, board across front below seat, orig black, red, and gold paint, 34½″ l, 14″ h **525.00**

Ladderback

Two slat back, turned stiles, splint
seat, red paint, 35″ 550.00

Three slat back, turned stiles, worn
orig red paint with yellow striping,
polychrome floral decor, painted
scenes in ovals on top slats, replaced paper rush seat, 34¾″ l . . . 355.00

Pine, 3 boards mortised together,
rounded top on side boards, painted
black with green and gold striping,
32¾″ w, 13½″ h 175.00

WICKER

Bird Cage, painted metal cage, circular
open woven reed wicker base 200.00

Carriage, baby, rattan, woven design on
body, movable hood, wooden handle 250.00

Chairs

Arm, close weave, rattan wrapped,
geometric diamond shaped panel
on back, upholstered seat. 350.00

Arm, child's, scroll work, continuous
crestrail braiding, rattan wrapped
legs 200.00

Corner, solid wood and cane seat,
wrapped arms and legs 135.00

Rocker, upholstered back and seat,
curved arms 175.00

**Stool, foot, painted white, 13½ x
16½″ x 12″, $150.00.**

Chest, 32 x 27 x 18″ d, 3 drawer, rattan
wrapped, close weave, c1900 . . . . . 310.00

Desk, kneehole, 34 h x 35 w x 24″ d, 1
drawer. 2 ornate compartments on
solid wood rectangular top, wrapped
legs, c1900. . . . . 390.00

Etragere, 69″, 6 tier, arch crest insert
with oval mirror, X stretchers, cabriole
legs, rattan wrapped, fancy scroll . . . 1,000.00

Ferner, 31″, cane and wicker, wrapped
legs 210.00

Footstool, rect, reed scroll work, chintz
cov cushion 50.00

Lamp, table, rattan, domical shade,
fringe beading. 100.00

Plant stand, victorian, circular top above
openwork frieze, 4 cabriole legs,
16½″ w, 27½″ h 185.00

Settee, 40½ h x 46 w x 15½″ d, scrolled
and pierced back in variety of weaves,
curved arms, scalloped skirt, 6 legs . 390.00

Sofa, closely woven rattan, caned inset
diamond panel on back, braided trim
from arms continuing on back, shaped
skirt with braid trim, 6 slightly flaring
legs, 3 upholstered cushions 425.00

Swing, porch, hanging, rattan, loosely
woven center back panel, tightly
woven border on back, arms and seat,
mounted on 2 wooden slats with orig
chains 275.00

Table, 30 x 30 x 20″ d, rectangular, solid
wood molded top, scrolled legs 400.00

GAME PLATES

History: Game plates, popular between 1870
and 1915, are specially decorated plates used to
serve fish and game. Sets originally included a platter, serving plates and a sauce or gravy boat. Many
sets have been divided. Today individual plates are
used for wall hangings.

BIRDS

Plates

9″

Duck, shades of brown and yellows,
artist A. Porter 100.00

Game bird, blue and gold border,
artist sgd, Limoges, pr. 340.00

Game bird over marsh grasses, artist Braun, Limoges 50.00

Quail, artist sgd, Limoges 200.00

10″, long beaked flying bird, colorful
sky, sgd R. K. Beck 65.00

10¼″, Pheasant and quail, dull gold
scalloped border, sgd MAX, Lim-
oges, pr 250.00

12″

Pheasant, artist sgd 85.00

Quail, artist sgd, Limoges 250.00

12⅞″, two colorful birds, florals,
scene, hp, rococo gold scallop emb
border, sgd DuBois 225.00

15″, three hanging birds, gold scalloped border, sgd Duvall, Limoges 375.00

Platter, 18½″ l, partridge, dark green border, gold trim, mkd Theodore Havi-
land, Limoges, artist sgd 275.00

Ducks, burgundy with gold border, Limoges, French, sgd Vitet, $145.00.

Sets
7 pcs, platter, 6 plates, Limoges, artist sgd	**700.00**
13 pcs, platter, 12 plates, gold leaf dec, French	**900.00**

DEER

Plates
13", 2 deer, scenic, blues and green	**300.00**
13½", sgd R. K. Beck	**100.00**
13¾", hp, stag in woods, raised enameling	**200.00**

ELK

Plate, 9", scalloped edge	**35.00**

FISH

Plates, 9"
Bass, sgd Morley, Lenox	**60.00**
Trout, cobalt border, sgd M. Z. Austria	**50.00**

Platters
14", bass on lure, sgd R. K. Beck. . .	**100.00**
16½", bass, waterlilies, emb, sgd MAX, Limoges	**150.00**

Sets
7 pcs, platter, 6 plates, R. K. Beck, Buffalo Pottery	**250.00**
7 pcs, 20" platter, six 8" plates, gravy boat, painted fish, water, mkd Victoria, Austria	**250.00**
11 pcs, platter, 10 plates, sgd Muville, Limoges	**550.00**

FOX

Plate, 13", fox stalking quail, gold scalloped border, artist sgd, Limoges . . .	**350.00**

GAMES

History: Mass production of board games did not take place until after the Civil War. Firms like McLoughlin Brothers, Milton Bradley, and Selchow and Righter were active in the 1860s, following by Parker Brothers, who began in 1883. Parker Brothers bought the rights to the W. & S. B. Ives Co., who had published some very early games in the 1840s, including the "first" American produced board game, The Mansion of Happiness. All except McLoughlin Brothers are giants in the game industry today.

McLoughlin Brothers's games are a challenge to find. Not only does the company no longer exist [Milton Bradley bought them out in 1920], but the lithography on their games was the best of its era. Most board games are collected because of the bright, colorful lithography on their box covers. In addition to spectacular covers, the large McLoughlin games often had lead playing pieces and fancy block spinners, thus making them even more desirable.

Common games like Anagrams, Authors, Jackstraws, Lotto, Tiddledy Winks, and Peter Coddles do not command high prices, nor do the games of Flinch, Pit, and Rook, which still are being published.

Condition is everything when buying. Do not buy games that have been taped or that have price tags stickered on the face of their covers. Also, beware of buying games at outdoor flea markets where weather elements can cause fading and warping.

References: R. C. Bell, *The Board Game Book*, The Knapp Press, 1979; Brian Love, *Great Board Games, 1895–1935*, Macmillan Publishing Co., 1979; Brian Love, *Play The Game: Over 40 Games From The Golden Age Of Board Games*, Reed Books, 1978.

Museums: The Game Preserve, Peterborough, NH; Washington Dolls' House and Toy Museum, Washington, D.C.

Additional Listings: See *Warman's Americana & Collectibles* for more examples.

Advisor: Lee and Rally Dennis.

Air Mail, 1920s bi-plane on cover, Milton Bradley.	**35.00**
All Around The World, Mother Goose on cover, McLoughlin Bros., 1908	**175.00**
American Boy, Boy Scout game, Milton Bradley, 1930s	**60.00**
Base Ball, players in old time uniforms on cover, lead playing figures, McLoughlin Bros., 1886	**325.00**
Bear Hunt, wood game board folds in half, graphics of bears, McLoughlin Bros., 1870.	**125.00**

Boy Scouts Progress Game, board pictures all Boy Scout badges, Parker Brothers, 1926 . . . . **85.00**
Captain Kidd And His Treasure, pirate on cover, 20 x 15″, Parker Brothers, 1896 . . . . **65.00**
Check and Double Check, small size, Milton Bradley, 1920s **10.00**
Columbus, small wood game, issued for 400th Anniversary, Milton Bradley, 1892 . . . . **35.00**
Corn and Beans, E. G. Selchow, 1875 [before merger with Righter] **28.00**
Country Store, colorful cover, 12 x 8″, J. H. Singer, pre-1900 . . . . **40.00**
Errand Boy, boy delivering parcels on cover, 14 x 14″, McLoughlin Bros., 1891 . . . . **95.00**
Excursion To Coney Island, early, small size, Milton Bradley **25.00**

Race For The Cup, Parker Brothers, 1896, $30.00.

Flivver Game, board, box of playing pieces, Milton Bradley, 1922 . . . . . . **65.00**
Fun At The Zoo, animals on cover, large size, Parker Brothers, 1902 . . . . **50.00**
Good Old Aunt, old woman on cover, McLoughlin Bros., 1892 . . . . **60.00**
International Yacht Race, McLoughlin Bros., 1903 . . . . **30.00**
Jack and Jill, good graphics, medium size, Milton Bradley **20.00**
Jr. Auto Race, All-Fair [Alderman Fairchild], Milton Bradley **18.00**
Kings and Queens, royal court on cover, large size, McLoughlin Bros., 1892 . . **40.00**
Knockout Andy, skittles-type game, spring top, Parker Brothers, 1926 . . . **22.00**
Letter Carrier, mailman on Victorian style cover, McLoughlin Bros. **35.00**
Lindy, card game, yellow box, Parker Brothers, 1927 . . . . **18.00**
Major League Baseball, wood hinged box, played with metal spinner, large size, 1912 . . . . **125.00**

Mrs. Casey Wants To Know, card game, small size, Parker Brothers **12.00**
Mystic Wanderer, Ouija-type game, colorful, J. H. Singer, 1895 . . . . **35.00**
Nations, flags of world, small size, Milton Bradley **15.00**
Ouija Board with planchette, all wood, Fuld Bros., issued 1890 . . . . **45.00**
Over The Fence, Milton Bradley, 1920s **18.00**
Polly Put The Kettle On, wooden parts, Milton Bradley, 1920s **15.00**
Puss In Boots, cat on cover, large size, McLoughlin Bros., 1888 . . . . **165.00**
Quiz Of The Wiz, caricature of Thomas Edison on cover, small size, H. J. Phillips Co., 1921 . . . . **15.00**
Rough Riders, Teddy Roosevelt era, large size, Clark and Sowdon **55.00**
Round The World Fliers Game, metal board and planes, Wolverine, 1927. . **45.00**
Round The World With Nellie Bly, first woman reporter to circle the globe, McLoughlin Bros., 1890 . . . . **85.00**
Spoof, small size, Milton Bradley, 1920s **12.00**
Sports, implements of most sports on cover, 15 x 9″, Milton Bradley, early 1900s **40.00**
Stars And Stripes, lead soldier figures carrying American flag, large size, McLoughlin Bros., 900 . . . . **200.00**
Street Car, trolley with animals on cover, 14 x 9″, Parker Brothers, c1900 . . . . **45.00**
Ticker, stock market game on cloth, Glow Products, 1929 . . . . **40.00**
Toll Gate, colorful graphics, 15 x 13″, McLoughlin Bros., 1890s **75.00**
Witticisms, small size, Selchow and Righter, 1878 . . . . **22.00**
World To World Airship Race, metal planes, large size, Chicago Game Co., 1913 . . . . **85.00**
Yankee Pedlar, early, small size, McLoughlin Bros. **30.00**

GAUDY DUTCH

History: Gaudy Dutch is an opaque, soft-paste ware made between 1790 and 1825 in England's Staffordshire district. Many pieces are unmarked; various potters marks, including the impressed marks of Riley and Wood, have been found on some pieces.

The pieces were first hand decorated in an under glaze blue, fired, and then received additional decoration over the glaze. Many pieces today have the over glaze decoration extensively worn. Gaudy Dutch found a ready market with the Pennsylvania Dutch because it was inexpensive and intense with color. It had little appeal in England.

Cup plates, bearing the impressed mark "CY-BRIS," have been reproduced and are collectible in their own right. The Henry Ford Museum has issued pieces in the single rose pattern, although they are of porcelain and not soft-paste.

References: Eleanor and Edward Fox, *Gaudy Dutch*, privately printed, 1970, out-of-print; Sam Laidacker, *Anglo-American China Part I*, Keystone Specialties, 1954, out-of-print; Earl F. Robacker, *Pennsylvania Dutch Stuff*, University of Pennsylvania Press, 1944, out-of-print.

Advisor: John D. Querry.

Butterfly
Coffee Pot, 11″	3,750.00
Creamer	850.00
Cup Plate	750.00
Plates	
6³⁄₈″	550.00
9³⁄₄″	1,500.00
Sugar Bowl	1,500.00
Tea Bowl and Saucer	775.00
Teapot	2,100.00
Waste Bowl	1,275.00

Carnation
Plate 8″	575.00
Tea Bowl and Saucer	550.00
Teapot	1,275.00

Dahlia
Sugar	850.00
Tea Bowl and Saucer	700.00

Double Rose
Plate, 8³⁄₄″	600.00
Sugar	775.00
Tea Bowl and Saucer	425.00
Teapot	675.00

Dove
Plates, 9³⁄₄″	775.00
Tea Bowl and Saucer	575.00
Waste Bowl	650.00

Grape
Plate, 8″	375.00
Tea Bowl and Saucer	325.00
Teapot	675.00

Leaf, Tea Bowl and Saucer 750.00

Oyster
Plate, 8³⁄₄″	425.00
Tea Bowl and Saucer	350.00
Toddy Plate	325.00

Primrose, plate, 8³⁄₄″, impressed Riley . 450.00

Single Rose
Coffee Pot	675.00
Plate, 8³⁄₄″	325.00
Tea Bowl and Saucer	275.00

Strawflower, plate, 8¼″ 575.00

Sunflower
Creamer	400.00
Plate, 8¼″	575.00
Tea Bowl and Saucer	750.00

Urn
Plates, 8¼″	375.00
Tea Bowl and Saucer	375.00

Plate, oyster, 8″, $350.00.

War Bonnet
Creamer	500.00
Plate, 7½″	575.00
Tea Bowl and Saucer	575.00
Teapot	975.00
Toddy Plate	525.00

Zinnia, plate, 9″ 575.00

GAUDY IRONSTONE

History: Gaudy Ironstone was made in England c1850. Most pieces are impressed "Ironstone" and bear a registry mark. Ironstone is an opaque, heavy body earthenware which contains large proportions of flint and slag. Gaudy ironstone is decorated in patterns and colors similar to Gaudy Welsh.

Biscuit Jar, Imari type dec, SP lid, bail .	150.00
Bowl, 9½″, handles, orange and yellow dec, Carlton	75.00
Coffee Pot, 10″ h, Strawberry	500.00
Cups and Saucers	
Imari type dec.	70.00
Strawberry, handleless.	125.00
Dish, 9¼″ d, 10¼″ l, leaf shape, Imari type dec, mkd Ironstone China Patent	45.00
Handkerchief Box, hp, mkd SMF	40.00
Pitcher, 5⅞″ h, blue, polychrome flowers, birds, trees, English registry mark	100.00
Plates	
7″, Sunflower	60.00
9″, polychrome floral dec, gilt, mkd Davenport Stone China, James Radley, Adelphi Hotel.	30.00
9¼″, polychrome Oriental dec, Lion and Unicorn mark	50.00
9½″, Grape.	60.00

Soup Plate, 7⅝" d, unmarked, $40.00.

10½", Amherst Japan, blue and orange dec.	50.00
10¾", Imari type dec, gilt, imp Spode's New Stone, rim flakes	20.00
Platter, 11 x 7¼", Imari type dec, leaf shape	80.00
Sugar, cov, 8½" h, Strawberry	400.00
Vegetable, 12", Indiana, blue, red rim	60.00

GAUDY WELSH

History: Gaudy Welsh is a translucent porcelain that was originally made in the Swansea area of England from 1830 to 1845. Although the designs resemble Gaudy Dutch, the body texture and weight differ. One of the characteristics is the gold lustre on top of the glaze.

In 1890, Allerton made a similar ware. These wares are heavier opaque porcelain and usually bear the export mark.

Reference: Howard Y. Williams, *Gaudy Welsh China,* Wallace Homestead.

Columbine	
Cup and Saucer	60.00
Plate, 5½"	40.00
Daisy and Chain	
Creamer	75.00
Sugar, cov	125.00
Teapot, cov	165.00
Feather	
Cup and Saucer	40.00
Plate, 8"	40.00
Flower Basket (also known as Urn or Vase)	
Bowl, 10½"	175.00
Creamer	85.00
Cup and Saucer, handleless	85.00
Mug, 4"	65.00
Plate, 8½"	45.00

Sugar, cov	95.00
Grape	
Creamer	50.00
Cup and Saucer, handleless	85.00
Morning Glory	
Compote, 10¼" d, 5¾" h	225.00
Cup and Saucer	65.00
Pitcher, 6½", Allerton, c1890	75.00
Plate, 9"	75.00
Teapot, cov, 5½"	150.00
Oyster	
Bowl, 6¼"	60.00
Creamer	85.00
Cup and Saucer	75.00
Jug, 5¾" h, c1820	200.00
Plate, 8½"	80.00
Shanghai	
Creamer	100.00
Plate, 5½"	75.00

Cup and Saucer, Flower Basket, cup 4", saucer 5¼", $600.00.

Strawberry	
Creamer	95.00
Mug, 4⅛" h	125.00
Plate, 8¼"	85.00
Spill Holders, 4⅜" h, pr	200.00
Teapot, cov	175.00
Tulip	
Creamer, 5¼" h	75.00
Cup and Saucer	60.00
Pitcher, Milk	150.00
Plate, 9"	45.00
Sugar, cov, 6¾" h	100.00
Teapot, 7¼", ornate cov	135.00
Waste Bowl, 6⅜" d	75.00
Wagon Wheel	
Cup and Saucer	65.00
Mug, 2¾"	60.00
Pitcher, 8"	135.00
Plate, 8¼"	65.00

GEISHA GIRL PORCELAIN

History: Geisha Girl porcelain is a Japanese export ware whose production commenced during the last quarter of the 19th century and continued heavily until WWII. The ware features kimono-clad Japanese ladies and children amidst Japanese gardens and temples. There are over 125 brightly colored scenes depicting the pre-modern Japanese lifestyle. Over 100 different marks have been identified on pieces.

Geisha Girl ware may be totally hand painted, hand painted over a stenciled design, or occasionally decaled. The stenciled underlying design is usually red-orange, but also is found in brown, black, and green (rare).

All Geisha Girl items are bordered by one or a combination of blues, reds, greens, rhubarb, yellow, black, browns, or gold. The most common is red-orange. Borders may be wavy, scalloped, or banded and range from 1/16" to 1/4". The borders themselves often are further decorated with gold, white or yellow lacings, flowers, dots, or stripes. Some examples even display interior frames of butterflies or flowers.

Geisha Girl is found in many forms including tea, cocoa, lunch, and children's sets, dresser items, vases, serving dishes, etc. Large plate or platters, candlesticks, miniatures, and mugs are hardest to locate. Geisha Girl advertising items add to a collection.

Geisha Girl porcelain's popularity continued after WWII; it is being reproduced today. Chief reproduction characteristics are a red-orange border, very white and smooth porcelain, and sparse coloring and detail. Reproduced items include dresser, tea, and sake sets, toothpick holders, small vases, table plates, and salt and pepper shakers.

Periodical: The Geisha Girl Porcelain Newsletter, P.O. Box 394, Morris Plains, NJ 07950. Subscription: $12.00.

Additional Listings: See *Warman's Americana & Collectibles* for more examples.

Advisor: Elyce D. Litts

Bowl, soup, Geisha in Sampan, brown with gold, mkd Blue Maple Leaf, Nippon. **25.00**

Bouillon Set, cup, cover, and dripplate, mint, aquamarine, and pine greens, red and gold, Garden Bench, mkd "TN" in wreath and "Japan," $40.00.

Cake Platter, Boat Festival, delft blue with gold interior frame, mkd Cherry Blossom. **25.00**
Cake Set, platter plus 6 individual plates, River's Edge, mint green and red with gold, mkd C. O. N. Nippon. **75.00**
Celery Set, rectangular master with 4 salts, Porch, red, mkd Torii Nippon. . **35.00**
Cocoa Pots
  Meeting, 9", blue with gold, roses as backdrop, fluted body. **80.00**
  To The Teahouse, 9", yellow, mkd Torii Nippon. **65.00**
Cup and Saucer, tea, Servant with Sack, red-orange, pattern on ext., int. of cup with floral sprays. **8.00**
Egg Cup, single, Cherry Blossom Ikebana, red-orange. **7.00**
Hair Receiver, Garden Bench, red-orange **20.00**
Hatpin Holder, Parasol, multicolor with gold, mkd Japan **35.00**
Lunch Set, cup, saucer, and 7" plate, Parasol and Lesson, blue with gold, mkd Japan **25.00**
Marmalade Jar, large, Cloud, red-orange with yellow, ribbed body, mkd Dai Nihon Tashiro zo **28.00**
Mustard Pot, Lady in Kago, blue with gold **25.00**
Pitchers
  Doll size, 3", Parasol, red, mkd Made in Japan **7.00**
  Lemonade, 9", Fishing, red-orange with yellow **75.00**
Plates
  6¼", Circle Dance, red-orange with yellow, swirl fluted scalloped edge. **12.00**
  7", Garden Bench, green grass with gold, plain round **20.00**
Salt and Pepper Shakers, 3¼", Parasol, red-orange with gold, mkd Nippon . . **15.00**
Teapot, Waterboy, blue with gold, mkd Torii Nippon **30.00**
Vase, 3⅜", Geisha on Parade, blue-green. **32.00**

GIRANDOLES AND MANTEL LUSTRES

History: A girandole is a highly elaborate branched candleholder, often featuring cut glass prisms surrounding the mountings. A mantel lustre is a glass vase with attached cut glass prisms.

Girandoles and mantel lustres usually are found in pairs. It is not uncommon for girandoles to be part of a larger garniture set. Girandoles and mantel lustres achieved their greatest popularity in the last half of the 19th century both in the United States and Europe.

GIRANDOLES, prs

13³/₄″, crystal and gilt bronze, cut with
bands of diamonds above matching
drip pans, scrolling scale arms, central
acorn finial, barrel knopped standards,
rectangular stepped bases **575.00**
15″, Victorian, pink, enameled and colored wild flowers, notched prisms . . . **275.00**
17″, brass, 8 lustres around each candle
section, 10 lustres across back **350.00**
18″, oval base, ormolu mounted, gilt
brass foliage, porcelain flowers, maroon parrots, oriental birds as giran-
doles, electrified **350.00**
21″, crystal, cut, star cut drip pans, scroll
arms, cental knopped standard with
gilt bronze finials, George III, early
19th C **2,100.00**

**Mantel Lustres, ruby glass, 14″, enamel
floral dec, $425.00.**

MANTEL LUSTRES, prs

10¹/₂″, cranberry, gold dec, hp portrait of
woman, cut glass prisms **700.00**
11¹/₄″, ruby flash, small white floral dec,
crystal prisms, cornucopia shape . . . **350.00**
12″, opalene, green fold over top, white
satin glass bodies, gold trim **225.00**
14″, Bristol glass, custard color ground,
hp portrait of young girl, enamel
shasta daisies, gold leaves, cut
prisms **875.00**
14¹/₄″, Bristol glass, pink, hp flowers, cut
glass prisms, cut ball bases **595.00**
14¹/₄″, pink cased, scalloped bulbous
bowl, swags of enamel painted flowers with gilt scrolls, 2 rows of clear
faceted glass prisms **275.00**
18³/₄″, white cased, gilted lustres, flaring
scalloped rims with line borders,
painted figural scenes, overall gilted
scrollwork, circular bases **310.00**

GLASS, EARLY AMERICAN

History: Early American glass covers glass
made in America from the colonial period through
the mid-19th century. As such it includes the early
pressed glass and lacy glass made between 1827
and 1840.

Major glass producing centers prior to 1850 were
Massachusetts with the New England Glass Com-
pany and the Boston and Sandwich Glass Com-
pany, South Jersey, Pennsylvania with Stiegel's
Manheim factory and Pittsburgh, and Ohio with
Kent, Mantua, and Zanesville.

Early American glass was collected heavily during the 1920 to 1950 period. It now is regaining
some of its earlier popularity. In April 1984 Garth's
sold the Jim and Eileen Courtney Early American
Glass Collection, a major landmark sale. Other
leading sources are the mail auctions of David and
Linda Arman and the sales of Richard A. Bourne
and Early Auction Company.

References: William E. Covill, *Ink Bottles and
Inkwells*, 1971; Lowell Inness, *Pittsburgh Glass:
1797–1891*, Houghlin, Mifflin and Company, 1976;
George and Helen McKearin, *American Glass*,
Crown, 1975; George and Helen McKearin, *Two
Hundred Years of American Blown Glass*, Double-
day and Company, 1950; Helen McKearin and Ken-
neth Wilson, *American Bottles And Flasks*, Crown,
1978; Adeline Pepper, *Glass Gaffers Of New Jer-
sey*, Scribners, 1971; Jane S. Spillman, *American
And European Pressed Glass*, Corning Museum of
Glass, 1981; Kenneth Wilson, *New England Glass
And Glassmaking*, Crowell, 1972.

Additional Listings: Blown Three Mold, Cup
Plates, Flasks, Sandwich Glass, and Stiegel Type
Glass.

Amelung, wine, 6³/₈″, clear, blown, applied dome foot with folded rim, hollow
stem, small bubbles in thick solid base
of bowl, attributed to Amelung, ex-
Courtney **250.00**
Ellenville, New York
Creamer, 3³/₄″, brilliant yellow-amber,
blown, Jacob Relyea, Ellenville,
NY **500.00**
Pitcher, 5³/₄″, deep amber, blown, lily
pad, applied foot and handle, long
cylindrical neck with flaring rim, tubular pontil, illus. *Antiques* (June
1967, pg 745), ex-McKearin who
made Ellenville attribution, ex-
Courtney **2,850.00**
Vases, pr, 7³/₄″, amber, applied foot,
globular body, long cylindrical neck,
illus. *Antiques* (June 1967, pg 745),
minor scratches and flakes at pontil,
ex-McKearin who made Ellenville
attribution, ex-Courtney **700.00**
Engraved, 800–1835
Cider Mug, 5¹/₈″ h, 3³/₄″ d, clear, ribbed

base, heavy₄ applied handle, band of leaves and berries dec, attributed to Baltimore-Philadelphia area **145.00**

Decanter, pint, three applied rings, ribbed base, mushroom stopper, swirling leaf dec **85.00**

Tumbler, 3⅜" h, 2⅞" d, clear, non-lead glass, band of ribbing formed by shallow mold dip, swirling leaf dec **40.00**

Kent

Bottle, half post, 4¾", light yellow-green, twenty ribs, broken swirl, minor sickness and flake at pontil, ex-Courtney **600.00**

Pan, 5⅜" d, 2¼" h, golden-amber, twenty ribs, broken swirl, folded in rim, very shallow flake at pontil, ex-Wettlaufer, ex-Courtney **2,450.00**

Pan, 7¾" d, 2⅛" h, yellow-amber, blown, folded out rim, ex-Courtney **500.00**

Tumbler, 4⅝", brilliant yellow-amber, twenty ribs, broken swirl, pinpoint rim flakes, ex-Wettlauber, ex-Courtney **2,000.00**

Lockport, NY, salt, 3½", bluish-aqua brown, applied foot, knop stem, ex-Courtney **300.00**

Mantua

Bottle, 5¾", amethyst, blown, sixteen vertical ribs, faint terminal ring, in-the-making heat check at pontil, ex-Courtney **750.00**

Condiment or Perfume bottle, 5¾", amethyst, blown, sixteen swirled ribs, terminal ring, flared lip, attributed to Mantua, ex-Courtney **500.00**

Pan, 5" d, 1⅜" h, aqua, blown, sixteen ribs, broken swirl, folded in rim, very minor flakes at pontil and one pinpoint on inner edge of folded rim, illus. *Antiques* (Feb. 1935, pg 66, fig 10A), ex-Courtney **650.00**

Pan, 5¼" d, 1¾" h, light green, blown, fifteen diamond, folded in rim, attributed to Mantua, illus. *Antiques* (Feb. 1935, pg 67; June 1967, pg 746), ex-Courtney **1,950.00**

Midwestern, pitcher, 7½", clear with greenish tint, pattern molded, 20 ribs, swirled right, folded rim, applied hollow handle **475.00**

New Geneva, PA, wine, 5⅛", light green, blown, applied foot, some wear and scratches, ex-Courtney **250.00**

New Jersey

Bottle, 6½", pale aqua, globular, short cylindrical neck, collared mouth, applied disc foot, 32 rib mold, large pontil mark on base **475.00**

Creamer, 3¾", cobalt blue, free blown, applied foot and handle, nice curl

on handle tip, attributed to New Jersey **325.00**

Creamer, 6¼", deep aqua, type I lily pad dec, elongated shape, tooled and pincered mouth, applied ear handle, circular foot with scarred base, piece of slag in center of pouring lip **5,250.00**

Jug, 7⅛", aqua, blown, applied crimped foot, applied handle and lip collar, attributed to New Jersey, roughness at base of handle where excess glass napped off, illus. *Antiques* (June 1967, pg 745), ex-Courtney **850.00**

Pitcher, 6⅝", deep sapphire blue, blown, applied crimped foot, applied double rib handle, long neck with flared rim and pinched spout, tubular pontil, some int. sickness, ex-Courtney **650.00**

Pitcher, 7½", pale green, lily pad dec, crimped foot, 2 ribbed handle, ex-Wettlaufer **2,250.00**

Pitcher, 9¼", deep cobalt blue, free blown, ringed foot, drawn out from body, heavy applied handle, polished pontil, attributed to Ruhlander, c1870–1900 . . . . **200.00**

Salt, 2⅞" d, 2⅛" h, sapphire blue, blown, wide applied foot, bowl with flaring rim, attributed to New Jersey, ex-Courtney **425.00**

Sugar Bowl, 7¼", deep aqua, type I lily pad dec, applied foot, scarred base, matching lid with folded out rim, solid button finial with pontil mark **5,500.00**

New York, pitcher, 5⅞", aqua, blown, sturdy strap handle, threaded neck and shoulder, attributed to Saratoga, minor wear and pinpoint chips on threading, ex-Courtney **525.00**

Pittsburgh

Bowl, 7⅛" d, 2⅞" h, cobalt blue, blown, folded rim, pinpoint rim flake, ex-Courtney **450.00**

Celery Vase, 9¼", clear, pillar molded, 8 pillars, slight chemical deposit . . **125.00**

Compote, 11" d, 7" h, deep amethyst, blown, pillar molded, wide applied foot, flaring bowl, ex-Courtney **16,100.00**

Cordial, 3⅜", canary, blown, applied foot, wafer stem, flared bowl with six cut panels, ex-Courtney **250.00**

Creamer, 5", clear, blown, applied foot, ribbed handle, bowl has copper wheel engraved floral dec, neck has tooled threading, heat check and chips at base of handle, ex-Courtney **1,450.00**

Cruet, 7¼" h plus stopper, deep amethyst, blown, sixteen vertical ribs, applied hollow handle, orig stopper, ex-Courtney................. **1,700.00**

Cruet, 7⅞" h plus stopper, sapphire blue, blown, fifteen vertical ribs, applied hollow handle, orig stopper, ex-Courtney................. **1,200.00**

Decanter, 9¾", amethyst, pillar molded, 8 pillars, bar lip........ **1,500.00**

Decanter, 10¾" plus top, canary, pillar molded, eight ribs with collar, pewter jigger top, ex-Courtney....... **600.00**

Flask, chestnut, 4⅛", sapphire blue, blown, nineteen ribs, broken swirl, ex-Courtney................. **625.00**

Goblet, 5¼", clear, blown, wide applied foot, flaring stem and bowl, engraved coat of arms with eagle, laurel, and banner reading "E Pluribus Unum," illus. *Antiques* (June 1967, pg 747), ex-Courtney.......... **900.00**

Jigger, 2¼", sapphire blue, fifteen arched ribs, ex-Courtney........ **55.00**

Pitcher, 5¼", deep amethyst, twenty-four vertical ribs, spiraled tooling at neck, applied handle, minor traces of sickness, ex-Courtney........ **2,100.00**

Pitcher, 5¼", puce, blown, eight ribs, tooled lip, applied ribbed handle, shallow flakes at pontil, ex-Courtney.......................... **2,050.00**

Pitcher, 8½", violet, blown, pillar molded, eight swirled ribs, applied hollow handles, ex-Courtney....... **7,200.00**

Sweatmeat, cov, 14¾", clear, free blown, heavy applied pedestal foot, cov with ball finial drawn from cov, attributed to Pittsburgh......... **160.00**

Sugar Bowl, 7¾", emerald green with white looping, blown, flaring foot, galleried rim, dome asymetrical lid with applied finial, small rim flake on under edge of lid, illus. Innes (plate 46), ex-Wettlaufer, ex-Courtney................. **2,600.00**

Sugar Bowl, 8", clear, blown, applied foot, flattened knop stem, bowl and lid have copper wheel engraved foliage dec, lid with applied wafer finial, illus. *Antiques* (June 1967, pg 747), ex-Courtney............. **1,000.00**

Syrup, 11" h, clear, pillar molded, applied foot, eight ribs, applied hollow handle, wire collar at neck, pewter top, hinged lid and bird finial, ex-Courtney................. **450.00**

Vase, 8⅜", clear, blown, applied foot, wafer stem, base of bowl with impressed diamond diapering, copper wheel engraved floral swags with bows, illus. *Antiques* (June 1967, pg 747), ex-Courtney............ **735.00**

Whiskey, 2", clear, blown, applied blue rim, ex-Courtney............. **65.00**

Saratoga, NY

Compote, 4⅛" d, 3¾" h, amber, blown, one pc, hollow bulbous base and stem, flared bowl with folded in rim, very minor sickness and some residue in hollow foot, ex-Courtney.................. **150.00**

Hat, whimsey, 2" h, 3⅞" w, olive-green, blown, ex-Courtney...... **65.00**

Mug, 5", dark olive-amber, blown, applied handle, illus. *Antiques* (June 1967, pg 745), ex-Courtney...... **375.00**

Vase, 6½", amber, blown, one pc, hollow flared base, knop-like stem, bell shaped bowl with folded over rim, some sickness and residue in hollow foot, ex-Courtney.......... **200.00**

Saratoga (Congressville), NY

Bowl, 7¼" d, 4⅞" h, emerald green, blown, folded rim, ex-Courtney... **600.00**

Pitcher, 6⅜" plus cover, grayish-emerald green, blown, pinched spout, applied handle, hollow blown egg-shaped witch ball cov, ex-McKearin, ex-Courtney................. **500.00**

South Bend Glass Works (Thomas Cains), bowl, shallow, 6⅝" d, 1½" h, clear, free blown, applied eleven link chain dec, folded rim, attributed to South Boston Glass Works, minor wear on base of bowl........... **1,200.00**

Unknown Makers

Free Blown

Baptismal bowl, 4⅛" d, 3¾" h, purple-blue violet, folded rim, applied blown foot................. **180.00**

Bottle, ½ pint, clear, fine, light glass, circular body, extended cylindrical neck, rolled mouth......... **35.00**

Compote, 4⅝" d, 3⅜" h, amber, twenty-four swirled ribs in bowl and stem, applied foot and knop stem, ex-Gest, ex-Courtney.... **2,500.00**

Hat, 7½" d, 3¼" h, golden amber, applied threading around brim, folded rim, made from quart bottle.................. **180.00**

Pitcher, clear, double tooled rim, heavy applied handle, probably blown from qt decanter....... **95.00**

Plate, 7¾", green, folded rim, probably made from pint bottle..... **120.00**

Sugar Bowl, 4¾" d, 5⅞" h, clear, applied foot, galleries rim, domed cov, folded rim, flat button finial part of cov [not applied]...... **450.00**

Wine Rinser, 4¾" d, 4⅛" h, pale citron, polished pontil........ **50.00**

Pattern Molded

Bowl, 4" d, 3¼" h, deep purple-blue, sixteen rib, ribs swirl to left, plain applied foot with folded rim, ex-Gest.................... **275.00**

Christmas Lights

Amber, sixteen diamonds, rolled rim, 3⅛″ h, 3″ d **45.00**

Amethyst, fifteen expanded diamonds, rolled rim, 3⅜″ h, 2½″ d **45.00**

Clear, thirteen expanded diamonds, rolled rim, 3¼″ h, 3⅛″ d **25.00**

Emerald green, rolled rim, 3½″ h, 2½″ d **40.00**

Creamer, 3⅛″ h, opaque white, twelve rib, applied handle and foot, molded collar ring between spout and ribbing, pontil base, nice curl on tip of handle. **245.00**

Creamer, 3¼″, cobalt blue, twenty expanded diamond, applied foot and handles **300.00**

Pitcher, 9¼″, clear, three rows of cleats around body, row of cleats at base, applied handle, roughness to one cleat **135.00**

Salt, 2¼″ d, 3⅛″ h, clear, twenty-four ribs, slight swirl to right, applied foot **50.00**

Salt, 3⅛″ d, 1¾″, opaque powder blue, fiery opalescent, thirty-one ribs, pontil base **160.00**

Zanesville

Beaker, 2¾″, amber, blown, ex-Courtney **150.00**

Bottle, 4⅞″, aqua, blown, club shape, twenty-four swirled ribs, applied lip, illus. *Antiques* (June 1967, pg 746), ex-Courtney **1,005.00**

Zanesville, flask, brilliant amber, expanded vertical ribbing, 24 rib-mold, 8¼″ h, 6⅞″ w, $1,200.00.

Bottle, 5″, golden amber, blown, globular "popcorn," twenty-four ribs, broken swirl, some int. sickness, illus.*Antiques* (June 1967, pg 746), ex-McKearin, ex-Courtney **2,700.00**

Bottle, 8½″, grass green, blown, globular, twenty-four swirled ribs, ex-Courtney **1,100.00**

Compote, 5⅜″ d, 3½″ h, amber, blown, applied foot, knop stem, ex-Courtney **2,000.00**

Creamer, 4″, brilliant light green, blown, ten diamonds, applied handle with heat checks in body at base and top of handle, ex-Hicken, ex-Courtney **1,750.00**

Flip, 5¾″, pale green, blown, twenty-four swirled ribs, flake on rim, illus. *Antiques* (June 1967, pg 746), ex-Courtney **375.00**

Inkwell, 1⅞″ h, golden amber, blown, twenty-four vertical ribs, illus. Covill (pg 317, fig 1335), ex-Courtney . . . **800.00**

Inkwell, 2¼″ h, brilliant light green, blown, ten diamonds, ex-Wettlaufer, ex-Courtney **5,750.00**

Pan, 5½″ d, 1⅜″ h, brilliant light green, blown, ten diamonds, folded in rim, illus. *Antiques* (June 1967, pg 745) and *Journal of Glass Studies* (Vol. II, pg 123), ex-Courtney **2,000.00**

Salt, master, 3¾″, amber, blown, twenty-four vertical ribs, applied foot, well shaped bowl, flaring rim, ex-Courtney **3,900.00**

Sugar Bowl, 5¼″, brilliant light green, blown, ten diamonds, small flakes at pontil on finial, ex-Gast, ex-Wettlaufer, ex-Courtney **11,250.00**

Sugar Bowl, 6¾″ h, bluish-aqua, blown, sharply rounded shoulders and wide galleries rim, double domed cov has folded rim and ball finial, small flake at finial, ex-Courtney **2,600.00**

Sugar Bowl, 7″ h, 5½″ d, golden amber, twenty-four vertical ribs, double domed lid with folded rim, pinpoint rim flakes and small broken blister in bottom of int., illus. *Antiques* (June 1967, pg 746), ex-Best, ex-Courtney **8,100.00**

GONDER POTTERY

History: Lawton Gonder established Gonder Ceramic Arts, Inc., at Zanesville, Ohio, in 1941. He gained experience while working for other factories in the area. Gonder experimented with glazes, including Chinese crackle, gold crackle, and flambe.

Lamp bases were manufactured under the name Eglee at a second plant location.

Gonder pieces are clearly marked. The company ceased operation in 1957.

Candlesticks, 4³/₄", turquoise outside, pink coral interior, mkd "E-14 Gonder," $15.00.

Bowl, 12" d, shallow, pink glaze 15.00
Cornucopia, 8¹/₂" h, upright, blue, pink
    int. 8.50
Creamer and Sugar, cov, brown and
    cream spatter glaze. 15.00
Figurines
    Cat, 12¹/₄", lime green 45.00
    Oriental man, 8", pink and green mot-
       tled glaze 20.00
Pitcher, 7", blue, white, high pointed
    handle 25.00
Planter, swan, 9" l, pink-gray glaze . . . 12.00
Vases
    8", flower shape, pink-brown glaze . . 10.00
    9", sea horse, irid glaze. 15.00
    21", Chinese crackle, blue 100.00

GOOFUS GLASS

History: Goofus glass, also known as Mexican Ware, Hooligan glass, and Pickle glass, is a pressed glass with relief designs. The back or front was painted. The designs are usually in red and green with a metallic gold ground. It was popular from 1890 to 1920 and was used as a premium at carnivals.

It was produced by several companies: Cresent Glass Company, Wellsburg, West Virginia; Imperial Glass Corporation, Bellaire, Ohio; LaBelle Glass Works, Bridgeport, Ohio; and Northwood Glass Co., Indiana, Pennsylvania, Wheeling, West Virginia, and Bridgeport, Ohio. Northwood marks include "N," "N" in one circle, "N" in two circles, and one or two circles without the "N."

Goofus glass lost its popularity when people found the paint tarnished or scaled off after repeated washings and wear. No record of its manufacture has been found after 1920.

Reference: Carolyn McKinley, *Goofus Glass,* Collector Books, 1984.

Additional Listings: See *Warman's Americana & Collectibles* for more examples.

Berry Set, master and 3 bowls, apples
    and pears, red, gold leaves 70.00
Bowls
    Blossom and Palm, 9", white opal, red
       and gold 35.00
    Jolly Bear 80.00
    Thistles, 7" 25.00
    Wild Rose, 9" 28.00
Bread Tray, The Last Supper, gold, red
    grape border. 60.00
Cake Plate, Morning Glory, 12" 27.50
Dish, Cherries, 4¹/₂" 15.00
Lamp, Cabbage Rose, 7¹/₂", miniature,
    paneled bulbous chimney. 15.00
Mug, Cabbage Rose, large 30.00
Plates
    Apples, 7¹/₂" 18.00
    Rose and Lattice, 6" 20.00
Powder Box, Puffy Rose, 4" d, 3" h, gold,
    red roses 40.00
Salt and Pepper, Cabbage Rose, milk
    glass, painted gold, 3¹/₂" 38.00
Sugar Shaker, Grapes, milk glass, 4¹/₂". 30.00

Vase, 5³/₄", bulbous, gold, green leaves, red flowers, $30.00.

Syrup, Cabbage Rose, 5¹/₂", paint worn   28.00
Vases
    Cabbage Rose, 7", gold paint, red
       rose 35.00
    Grapes, 10", 3 bunches of grapes with
       lattice design in between 20.00
    Poppies, 8¹/₂", bulbous. 32.00
Water Bottle, basketweave, white paint
    ground, red rose, gold vine and
    leaves 42.00

MARK

W H GOSS

GOSS CHINA AND CRESTED WARE

History: In 1858 William H. Goss opened his Hanley factory and produced terra cotta wares. A year later he moved to Stoke-on-Trent and added Parian wares to his line. In 1883 Adolphus, William's son, expanded on his father's idea of decorating small ivory pots and vases, with the coat of arms of schools, hospitals, colleges [especially Oxford and Cambridge], and other motifs to appeal to the souvenir seeking English "day-tripper." The forms used were copied from ancient artifacts in museums.

William died in 1906, his son in 1913. Following business setbacks, the firm was sold in 1929 to Geo. Jones & Sons Ltd., who had previously acquired Arcadian, Swan, and other firms that made crested wares. As late as 1931 the Goss name was still being used. In 1936–37 Cauldon Potteries purchased the Goss assets. Production ceased in 1940. In 1954 Ridgeway and Adderley acquired all Goss assets [molds, patterns, designs, and right to use the Goss name and trademark].

From 1883 to 1931 pieces carry the mark of GOSHAWK, with W. H. Goss beneath, and "England" on later pieces. Many early examples carry an impressed "W. H. Goss," either with or without the printed mark.

Other manufacturers of crested ware in England were: Arcadian, Carlton China, Grafton China, Savoy China, Shelley, and Willow Art. Gemma in Germany also made crested wares.

Crests are of little value unless they match, e.g., Shakespeare's jug with Shakespeare's crest. Collectors tend to collect one form (vase, ewer, jug, etc.), one particular crest, or one type of object (boat, cat, dog, etc.). Price is determined not by crest, but size, condition, and bottom mark.

References: Sandy Andrews, *Crested China: The History of Heraldic Souvenir Ware*, Milestone Publications [England]; John Galpin, *A Handbook Of Goss China*, Milestone Publications; Nicholas Pine, *The 1984 Price Guide To Goss China*, Milestone Publications, 1984; Nicholas Pine and Sandy Andrews, *The 1984 Price Guide To Crested China* (including revisions to *Crested China*), Milestone Publications; Roland Ward, *The Price Guide To The Models Of W. H. Goss*, Antiques Collectors' Club.

Collectors' Clubs: The Goss Collectors Club, 3 Carr Hill Gardens, Barrowford, Nelson, Lancashire BB9 6PU; The Crested Circle, 26 Urswick Road, Dagenhem, Essex RM9 6EA.

Advisor: Mildred Fishman.

Vase, 2⅝", model of Roman vase found at Walmar Lodge, mkd No. 382437, $30.00.

GOSS

Ewers

Chichester, Roman	19.00
Ilkley, Roman	19.00
Oxford, matching crest, impressed mark only	58.00
Shrewbury, matching crest, Romano Salopian	30.00
York, Roman	19.00

Jugs

Kendal	19.00
Litchfield	25.00
Reading	18.00
Roman Bath, large	50.00
Shakespeare's Jug, matching crest, impressed mark	40.00

Worchester

Large	25.00
Small	19.00

Miscellaneous

Bristol Puzzle Cider Cup, four crests	80.00
Channel Island Fish Basket, Jersey	35.00
Milk Can, lid, Jersey	40.00
Norwegian Horse Beer Bowl	40.00
Parian Ware, Shakespeare's bust, 4¼" h	75.00

Urns

Leek, British	20.00
Lewkesbury	20.00
Penmaenmawr	25.00
Reading, Roman	15.00
Seaford	
Impressed Mark	30.00
Roman	20.00

Vases

Glastonbury	20.00
Pineapple, impressed mark	30.00
Reading	14.00
Swindon	15.00

OTHER CRESTED WARE MANUFACTURERS

Arcadian
Bathing Wagon	30.00
Castle, chess piece	24.00
Statue, small, model of Cenotaph . . .	25.00
Urn, two handles, "Double-Double-Toil & Trouble"	25.00

Clifton
Bulldog.	15.00
Elephant.	20.00

Coronet Ware
Pitcher, spout	11.00
Pot, three ftd, 2 handles	12.00

Gemma
Cheese Dish, cov	20.00
Coal Pail.	15.00
Teapot, lid	30.00

Savoy
Boat, small	30.00
Rabbit	20.00

Shelley
Cockermouth Cycle Oil Head Lamp, matching crest	45.00
Olive Jar, eastern, #208	24.00
Rose Bowl, silver, #147	35.00
Sea Shell, #166	30.00
Tea Caddy, model Lang Hi, #144 . .	24.00
Urn, Penmaenmawr, #108	20.00

Victoria
Cheshire Cat, matching crest	24.00
Watering Can	25.00

Willow Art
Shakespeare's cottage, medium size	100.00
Tewkesbury urn.	15.00

MADE IN

Zuid Holland

GOUDA POTTERY

History: Gouda and the surrounding areas of Holland have been one of the Dutch pottery industry centers for centuries. Originally the potteries produced a simple utilitarian Delft type earthenware with a tin glaze and the famous clay smokers' pipes.

When the pipe making portion declined in the early 1900s, the Gouda potteries turned to art pottery. Influenced by the Art Nouveau and Art Deco movements, artists expressed themselves with free form and stylized designs in bold colors.

Note: With the Art Nouveau and Art Deco revival of recent years, modern reproductions of Gouda pottery currently are on the market. They are difficult to distinguish from the originals.

Tobacco Humidor, cov, Verona pattern, 5″ h, $75.00.

Ashtrays
3½″, schoolhouse mark	35.00
4⅛″ d, 1¼″ h, green, cobalt, multicolor int., house mark "Anne Royal" . . .	40.00

Basket, 7¾″ h, 6″ d, high matte glaze, floral dec	150.00
Biscuit Jar, 8″.	125.00
Bowl, 5½″ d, 3½″ h, Damascus mark. .	50.00
Box, cov, round, floral dec.	85.00

Candlesticks
13″ h, 7½″ d base, vine, flower, and dot design, house mark, pr	410.00
19″, crimped drip pan, lobed flaring base, polychrome glaze with stylized foliage, printed mark	125.00

Carafe, 11″, cov, sunflower dec	110.00

Chambersticks
6½″, saucer base, handle	60.00
14½″, handled, schoolhouse mark . .	145.00

Charger, 12″, multicolored flowers, rope border and black rim	150.00
Cigarette Box	45.00
Compote, 7⅝″, black ground, geometric design, multicolored scroll int.	165.00
Dish, 8½″ l, 8″ w, leaf shape, house mark	35.00

Ewers
4¾″, stylized flowers	55.00
9½″, matte finish, Anjer house mark.	125.00

Humidors
6″ h, white high glaze, floral dec, Jilliana Gouda house mark.	250.00
7¾″ h, matte finish, black base, orange, blue and green, Ali Gouda Holland House mark.	175.00

Inkwell with attached pen tray, 8″ w, matte finish, blue, Purdah Gouda, orange and black house mark	190.00
Jug with stopper, 10″, black matte ground, multicolored design	175.00

Pitchers
2½″ h, miniature, black matte, gold

trim with blue matte, red dots, turquoise and high glaze dec, house mark, "Z Waro" 25.00

5½", schoolhouse mark 65.00

Planter, 12" l, 7" w, 4" h, oblong, Yssel pattern 150.00

Plate, 10½", matte finish, multicolored design 100.00

Potpourri Jar, 4" high glaze, multicolored, black bottom 85.00

Stein, raised figure of cavalier playing instrument, floral pattern, shaded brown, pewter cov and thumb rest, marked 75.00

Sweetmeat Dish, 6", cov, Art Deco, marked 125.00

Tray, 10½", leaf dec, autumn colors. . . 150.00

Vases

5¼" h, 6" across handles, black matte finish, wide cobalt and multicolored band, house mark, "Blareth" 50.00

10¾" h, 9" d, gourd shape, 2 handled, high glaze, blue tulip on green and multicolored Art Nouveau ground, house mark, 19th C 450.00

11½", pitcher shape, extended bark neck, twig handle, scenic, windmill on obverse, lake on reverse, Springer & Co./Elfagen, Germany, c1890 .... 145.00

Sunflower dec, rust, blue, and yellow, sgd 85.00

Wine Barrel on wooden stand, 11½" h, matte finish, black ground, yellow, orange, blue, and white design, C. M. Bergen, Gouda 125.00

GRANITEWARE

History: Graniteware is the name commonly given to iron or steel kitchenware covered with enamel coating.

The first graniteware was made in Germany in the 1830s. Graniteware was not produced in the United States until the 1860s. At the start of World War I, when European manufacturers turned to the making of war weapons, American producers took over the market.

Colors commonly marketed were white and gray. Each company made their own special color, including shades of blue, green, brown, violet, cream, and red. Graniteware still is manufactured with the earliest pieces in greatest demand among collectors.

Older graniteware is heavier than new graniteware. Pieces with cast iron handles date from 1870 to 1890; wood handles date from 1900 to 1910. Other dating clues are seams, wood knobs, and tin lids.

Reference: Vernagene Vogelzang and Evelyn Welch, *Graniteware, Collectors' Guide With Prices,* Wallace Homestead, 1981.

Collectors' Club: American Graniteware Association, Box 605, Downers Grove, IL 60515. Dues: $12.00. *The Granitegram* (quarterly).

Additional Listings: See *Warman's Americana & Collectibles* for more examples.

Advisors: Linda Buehrer and Diane Erpenbach

Bread Boxes

Rectangular, 15 x 12", "Bread" written in black letters, white with cobalt blue trim 85.00

Round, 11" d, 11" h, "Bread" in black letters, side handles and matching lid, gray mottled 37.00

Bucket, 2½ gal capacity, wire bail, dark green with white marbling 75.00

Butter Pail, 10" d, oval shape, matching dome lid, wood knob, wide tin movable handle, gray mottled 62.00

Cake Pan, 13" l, oblong shape, white inside, hole to hang, dark green with white marbeling 68.00

Canister Set, 5 pcs each with granite cover, nested, smallest 3" d and 5¾" h, largest 4½" d and 8½" h, snow on the mountain color, white ground with fine lines of blue running through it like veins 225.00

Chamber Pot, 7½" d, side handle, blue with white marbling 42.00

Chamberstick, leaf shaped, green 48.00

Coffee Pot, 4 cup capacity, small, tin hinged lid, gray mottled 38.00

Colander, cobalt blue with white marbling 65.00

Cook Set, child's, 4 pcs, coffee pot, frypan, steamer, and stockpot, baby blue with white speckles 105.00

Dishpans

16" d, 5½" h, two handled, blue with white mottling 56.00

Teapot, gray, $85.00.

19" d, two handles, dark green with white marbling 60.00
Fish Boiler, 20 x 9", twisted cast iron handles on side, gray mottled, "Granite Steelware" label in enamel on bottom 78.00
Flask, coffee, screw top, metal lid, gray 95.00
Frypan, 9" d in pan, black handle, white int., enameled on cast iron, dark green with white marbling 95.00
Funnel, child's size, 2½" h, blue side handle, white funnel with sky blue trim 30.00
Kettle, large, heavy in weight, wire bail handle, dark chocolate color with white marbling, metal plate mkd "Majestic" 90.00
Kettle and Lid, bail handle, riveted side handle near top for tipping, pouring spout on opposite side, blue with large white mottling, pouring spout and cover have some gray in white part of mottling 36.00
Measurer, 6½" h, 4 cup capacity, powder blue with white mottling, mkd "Elite" on bottom. 62.00
Milk Kettle, 12" h, tin lid, gray 34.00
Mold, cake, fluted, 4 cup, gray. 38.00
Salt Box, wall hanging type, hinged wooden lid, "Salt" written in cobalt blue, white 48.00
Saucepan, 11 x 4", flat bottom, heavy in weight, white int., 9" l handle, cobalt blue with white marbling. 68.00
Scale, hanging, round flat granite tray suspended by cast iron handle, hung from round hanging scale, pan 12" d, azure blue 85.00
Scoop, thumb handle, robin egg blue with fine white mottling 75.00
Skimmer, long handled, gray 32.00
Sugar Bowl, bulbous, two side handles, no cover, cobalt blue with white swirls 90.00
Syrup, 5½" h, cover has thumb lift and also covers spout, gray with dark tiger mottling 92.00
Tea Strainer, hand held with wire mesh bottom, gray 30.00
Tea Kettle, enameled over cast iron, cobalt blue with white marbling 150.00
Teapot, Sugar, and Creamer, cov sugar, hinged cov creamer, gray with pewter trim 495.00
Teapots
  4 cup capacity, cobalt with white marbling, black handle, hinged lid, gooseneck spout 85.00
  4 cup capacity, shaded blue (royal blue shading to pale blue and back to royal), matching hinged lid and gooseneck spout 30.00

8 cup capacity, dark brown with white speckles (called onyx ware), tin cover, gooseneck spout 70.00
Tray, 10 x 8¼ x 1¼", oval shell shaped tray, solid cobalt color 45.00
Tumbler, child's size, 2½" h, heavy in weight, blue int., sky blue with small veinings of white throughout. 30.00
Water Pitcher, 12" h, white ground with blue fine vein-like swirls (snow on mountain) 50.00

GREENAWAY, KATE K.G.

History: Kate Greenaway, or "K.G." as she initiated her famous drawings, was born in 1846 in London. Her father was a prominent wood engraver. Kate's natural talent for drawing soon was evident, and she began art classes at the age of 12. In 1868 she had her first public exhibition.

Her talents were used primarily in the world of illustration. She did cards for Marcus Ward, which are largely unsigned. China and pottery companies soon had her drawings of children appearing on many of their wares. By the 1880s she was one of the foremost children's book illustrators in England.

Some Greenaway buttons have been reproduced in Europe and sold in the United States.

Basket, porcelain, boy and girl on each side 65.00
Books
  Birthday Book For Children 100.00
  Marigold Gardens, F. Warner & Co., 1880 . . . . 85.00
Boxes
  5", sq, child laying on bear skin rug . 250.00
  6", round, cov, 3 children having a tea party on lid, base with florals and white beading on blue ground with gold dappled brushmark finish, sgd Nakara 700.00
Button, 1¾", metal, children on fence under umbrella 15.00
Cards, set of orig 4 seasons, litho, framed, c1882. . . . . 115.00
Child's Foot Bath, 15 x 10¾", oval, division in center with open handle grip, children in interior, bottom and exterior, mkd "Germany" with Sarreguemines shield mark 225.00
Compote, porcelain, oval, child leaning against tree, mkd Royal Worcester, 1885 . . . . 275.00
Cup and Saucer, children and dog. . . . 35.00
Dish, 8¼", children in 7 scenes around edge 75.00
Fan, 10½", children playing ring-around-a-rosie 40.00

English softpaste, brown hat, gray dress, yellow-green floral vase, imp #10257, 5½" h, 4⅜" w, $80.00.

Figurines

5¼", bisque, pr, boy and girl in blue and pink Victorian clothes.	150.00
6¾ x 2¾ x 3½", girl with basket, off white, gold trim, flesh tones, mkd Royal Worcester, 1882	475.00
Hair Receiver, 5" d, apricot ground, 3 children playing, mkd Nakara	250.00
Inkwell, metal, 3", boy seated behind nest with eggs, hinged.	65.00
Jewelry Box, 5 x 4½ x 3½", SP, figural, 2 girls on top with outstretched arms, 4 pillar posts form corner and footing, swing out drawers in half circle, blue satin lining, James W. Tufts	225.00
Match Holders, bisque	
Boy holding rabbit, striker on base . .	75.00
Girl holding tea cup	65.00
Mug, boy and girl playing	25.00
Napkin Ring, SP, girl feeding yearling. .	100.00
Nodders, pr, 5", boy with book, girl knitting, seated on pale blue chairs, white and gold clothing.	175.00
Piano Baby, 7", bisque	100.00
Pin Tray, children playing on see-saw. .	65.00
Plates	
7½", girl with umbrella	35.00
8½", girls blowing bubbles	50.00
12", children having tea party.	65.00
Powder Jar, cov, child with dog	175.00
Salt and Pepper Shakers, pr, boy and girl peeping out of barrels	50.00
Spoon, SS, figural girl handle, entire Lucy Locket poem engraved on bowl	50.00
Toothpick Holder, boy standing behind basket	50.00
Tumbler, 3½" h, porcelain, children playing, enamel highlights	25.00
Watch Holder, SP, girl standing, fancy dress, holds watch holder in front, ornate base, mkd James Tufts	155.00

GREENTOWN GLASS

History: The Indiana Tumbler and Goblet Co., Greentown, Indiana, produced its first clear, pressed glass table and bar wares in late 1894. Initial success led to a doubling of plant size in 1895 and other subsequent expansions, one in 1897 to allow for the manufacture of colored glass. In 1899 the firm joined the combine known as the National Glass Company.

In 1900, just before arriving in Greentown, Jacob Rosenthal developed an opaque brown glass, called "chocolate" which ranged in color from a dark, rich chocolate to a lighter "cream" coffee hue. Production of chocolate glass saved the financially pressed Indiana Tumbler and Goblet Works. The Cactus and Leaf Bracket patterns were made almost exclusively in chocolate glass. Other popular chocolate patterns are Austrian, Dewey, Shuttle, and Teardrop and Tassel. In 1902 National Glass Company bought Rosenthal's chocolate glass formula so other plants in the combine could use the color.

In 1902 Rosenthal developed the Golden Agate and Rose Agate colors. All work ceased on June 13, 1903, when a fire of suspicious origin destroyed the Indiana Tumbler and Goblet Company Works.

After the fire, other companies, e.g., McKee and Brothers, produced chocolate glass in the same pattern designs used in Greentown. Later reproductions also have taken place, with Cactus among the most heavily copied pattern.

References: Brenda Measell and James Measell, *A Guide To Reproductions of Greentown Glass,* The Printing Press, 1974, 2nd ed.; James Measell, *Greentown Glass, The Indiana Tumbler & Goblet Co.,* Grand Rapids Public Museum, 1979.

Collectors' Club: National Greentown Glass Association, 1807 West Madison, Kokomo, IN 56901. Dues: $4.00. *N.G.G.A. Newsletter,* quarterly.

Museums: Greentown Glass Museum, Greentown, IN; Grand Rapids Public Museum [Ruth Herrick Greentown Glass Collection], MI.

Additional Listings: Holly Amber and Pattern Glass.

Animal Dishes, cov	
Chicken, choc	350.00
Dolphin, choc	225.00
Dolphin, golden agate	450.00
Rabbit, amber	150.00
Biscuit Jars, cov	
Cactus, choc.	225.00
Herringbone Buttress, emerald green	300.00
Bowls	
Dewey, green opaque, cov.	150.00
Geneva, choc, large berry	250.00
Phenix, Cactus, choc.	900.00
Box, cov, 3¼" h, "Collars," choc.	365.00
Butters, cov	
Geneva, choc	350.00
Leaf Bracket, choc	150.00
Cake Stand, Cactus, choc.	1,400.00

Syrup, Geneva pattern, chocolate glass, orig tin top, $600.00

Child's Set, Wild Rose & Bowknot, butter
  dish, creamer, spooner, cov sugar
  bowl, choc, 4 pcs **1,300.00**
Compotes, Cactus, choc
  5½" **85.00**
  10", open, high standard **175.00**
Creamer, Shuttle, choc **90.00**
Cruets, orig stoppers
  Cactus, choc. **125.00**
  Leaf Bracket, choc **95.00**
Dustpan, canary, 3¾" w **125.00**
Lamp, Wild Rose, choc font, 8" **600.00**
Mugs
  Cactus, choc. **65.00**
  Shuttle, Nile gren, 5" **50.00**
Mustard Pot, Greentown Daisy, frosted **65.00**
Nappies
  Cactus, green **90.00**
  Shuttle, choc **135.00**
Parfait, Strigil, choc. **60.00**
Pitchers, water
  Leaf Bracket, choc **250.00**
  Panel, choc **400.00**
  Running Deer, choc. **325.00**
  Serenade, choc. **175.00**
  Squirrel, choc **400.00**
  Wild Rose, green satin. **190.00**
Plates, Serenade
  6¼", choc **175.00**
  6¼", green **35.00**
  8¼", choc **150.00**
Punch Cup, Herringbone Buttress, em-
  erald green **120.00**
Relish, Strigil, choc. **35.00**
Sauces
  Cactus, green **40.00**
  Leaf Bracket, choc **35.00**

Steins
  Dog & Child, clear, 5" **90.00**
  Indoor Drinking Scene, choc, 8" **200.00**
Spooner, Overall Lattice, clear. **35.00**
Sugar, cov, Wild Rose & Bowknot,
  choc **215.00**
Syrups, choc
  Cactus **85.00**
  Star & Shuttle **60.00**
Sweetmeat, cov, Cactus, choc. **450.00**
Toothpicks
  Dog Head, frosted blue **300.00**
  Indian Head, amber. **300.00**
  Sheaf of Wheat, Nile green **325.00**
  Witch Head, Nile green **200.00**
Tumblers
  Cactus, choc. **85.00**
  Shuttle, choc **60.00**
  U Needa Biscuit, cov. **150.00**
Vase, corn shape, amber, 4⅝" h **165.00**
Wheelbarrow, blue **70.00**

GRUEBY POTTERY

History: William Grueby was active in the ceramic industry for several years before he developed his own method of producing matte glazed pottery and founded the Grueby Faience Company in Boston, Massachusetts, in 1897.

The art pottery was hand thrown in natural shapes, hand molded, and hand tooled. A variety of colored glazes, singly or in combinations, were produced with green being the most prominent. In 1908 the firm was divided into the Grueby Pottery Company and the Grueby Faience and Tile Co., the latter making art pottery until bankruptcy forced closure shortly after 1908.

References: Paul Evans, *Art Pottery of the United States,* Everybodys Press, Inc., 1974; Ralph and Terry Kovel, *The Kovels' Collector's Guide to American Art Pottery,* Crown Publishers, Inc., 1974.

Bowl, 3", turned in rim, green **115.00**
Candlestick, 5½", blue **250.00**
Tiles, 6" sq
  Set of 3 forming a scene of green and
    brown lily pads and cream water lil-
    ies on a dark green ground, each
    imp "Grueby Boston" **425.00**
  Turtle, painted brown, coffee, and pale
    yellow, green leaves, mustard
    ground **250.00**

Vase, 7½", bulbous bottom, outward tapering extended neck, inelsed stamp mark, green, $400.00.

Vases

3¼ x 5¼", squat bulbous shape, incised dec, very thick green matte glaze. **150.00**

7½", cylinder, straight sides, thick lavender glaze. **165.00**

7½", cylindrical with a trefoil rim, molded with broad leaves and narrow flower buds on a cucumber green ground, imp "Grueby Faience Co. Boston U.S.A." **375.00**

13", bulbous base, overlapping leaves dec, green, silver overtones, sgd "Ruth Erickson". **800.00**

13 x 6½", green, yellow trefoils encircling rim, several glaze misses (in firing) **3,100.00**

22½", ovoid, molded with lappets, typical green glaze, imp factory mark, c1900 . . . . **1,500.00**

HAIR ORNAMENTS

History: Hair ornaments, one of the first accessories developed by primitive man, were used to remove tangles and keep hair out of one's face. Remnants of early combs have been found in many archeological excavations.

As fashion styles changed through the centuries, hair ornaments kept pace through design and use changes. Hair combs and other hair ornaments are found in a wide variety of materials, e.g., precious metals, ivory, tortoise shell, plastics, and wood.

Combs were first made in America during the Revolution when imports from England were restricted. Early American combs were made of horn and treasured as valued toiletry articles.

Reference: Evelyn Haertig, *Antique Combs and Purses*, Gallery Graphics Press, 1983.

Barettes
Enameled flowers, pink, yellow and green, hallmarked silver, 2" l. **85.00**
Gold setting, open leaf shape, seed pearl border, c1920 . . . . **250.00**
Bodkins (Hair Pins)
Brass, ornate flower on top, 5½" l . . **15.00**
Gold Plated **10.00**
Chigon Comb, crescent shape, rhine stones, steel comb **80.00**
Combs
Jade, mouse and flower design, king fisher feathers, Oriental, c1840 . . . **250.00**
Sterling Silver
Filigree flower, 5 petals, 5 seed pearl stamens, tortoise shell hair comb, c1895 . . . . **145.00**
Filigree wreath, tortoise shell hair comb, c1895 . . . . **150.00**
Tortoise Shell
Open scroll work, 2 prongs. **75.00**
Spanish style, black, rose, leaves, scrollwork. **65.00**

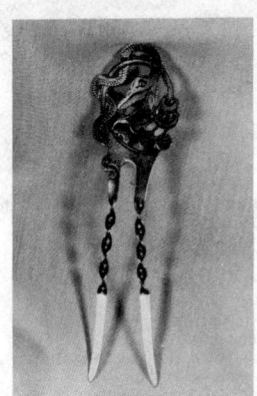

Comb, SS, Serpent top, 4" l, $50.00.

HALL CHINA COMPANY

History: Robert Hall founded the Hall China Company in 1903 in East Liverpool, Ohio. He died in 1904 and was succeeded by his son, Robert Taggart Hall. After years of experimentation, Robert T. Hall developed a leadless glaze in 1911, opening the way for production of glazed household products.

The Hall China Company made many types of kitchenware, refrigerator sets, and dinnerware in a wide variety of patterns. Some patterns were exclusive, such as Cameo Rose for Sears.

One of the most popular patterns was Autumn Leaf, an exclusive premium designed in 1933 for the Jewel Tea Company by Arden Richards. Still a Jewel Tea property, Autumn Leaf has not been listed in catalogs since 1978 but, is produced on a replacement basis with the date stamped on the back.

References: Jo Cunningham, *The Autumn Leaf Story,* Haf-A-Productions, 1976; Jo Cunningham, *The Collectors Encyclopedia of American Dinnerware,* Collector Books, 1982; Jo Cunningham, *Hall China Price Update,* Haf-A-Productions, 1982.

Collector's Club: National Autumn Leaf Collectors Club, 6505 W. Cameron, Tulsa, OK 74127. Dues: $15.00.

Additional Listings: See *Warman's Americana & Collectibles* for more examples plus a separate section on Autumn Leaf.

Teapot, maroon, gold trim, mkd "0116-6 cup", 6¼" h, 10½" w, $20.00.

Bakers
Autumn Leaf, 10½", oval	20.00
Seashell, pink, #228	10.00
Basket, handle, No. #44, squirrels, white and rose	40.00
Bean Pot, tab handles, Rose Parade	50.00

Bowls, mixing, nested sets
Autumn Leaf, 3 pcs	35.00
Red Poppy, 3 pcs, #3, #4, #5	35.00
Breakfast set, 5½" cereal bowl, 3¼" d, 5½" h pitcher, 4" mug, PA Dutch design	20.00
Cake Plate, ftd, Red Poppy	12.00
Canister, flour, Chinese Red, sunshine mark	75.00

Casseroles, cov
Chinese Red, individual, saf handle	30.00
Rose Parade	25.00
Clock, wall, electric, Autumn Leaf	450.00
Coaster Set, 8 coasters, hot pad, orig box, Autumn Leaf	45.00

Coffee Pots
Bell, flamingo decal, mkd Dripolator	40.00

Crest, aluminum inserts, daffodil dec	25.00

Cookie Jars
Flare Ware, white and gold	30.00
Tritone, Zeisel	40.00
Creamer and Sugar, Blue Bouquet	15.00

Cups and Saucers
Crocus, sprig decal, D shape, platinum dec	10.00
Mt. Vernon	8.00

Custard Dishes
Autumn Leaf	6.50
Blue Bouquet	5.00
Jug, Red Poppy, Sunshine, #5	10.00
Marmalade, underplate, Autumn Leaf	55.00
Pie Plate, Heather Rose, 9½"	15.00
Pitcher, Orange Poppy, 6¼"	20.00

Plates
Autumn Leaf, 10½"	10.00
Cameo Rose, 10"	8.00
Crocus, 8", sprig decal, platinum dec	5.00
Monticello, 10"	5.00
Silhouette, 9"	10.00

Platters
Autumn Leaf, 13½"	40.00
Orange Poppy, 11¼"	10.00
Red Poppy, 13", oval	15.00
Punch Set, pedestal bowl, 6 cups, "May You Always Have an Eagle (picture of gold coin) in Your Pocket, a Turkey (picture) on Your Table and Old Crow (picture) in Your Glass", 13" d, 8" h.	225.00
Reamer, lettuce, rare	250.00

Salt and Pepper Shakers, pr
Blue Garden	35.00
Crocus, handled, border decal	15.00
Souffle Dish, Autumn Leaf, 4½", individual	5.00
Stein, beer, 12 oz, lettuce green ground, hp tavern scene	35.00
Sugar, cov, Red Poppy	10.00
Table Cloth, cotton, 54" w, 64" l	100.00

Teapots
Autumn Leaf, Aladdin, infuser	35.00
Birdcage, yellow	135.00
Cleveland, cobalt	50.00
Los Angeles, cobalt and gold	28.00
New York, Red Poppy decal	45.00
Twinspout, Tea Master, yellow	35.00

Trays, Autumn Leaf
Glass, wooden handles	70.00
Metal, oval	50.00
Vase, bud, Autumn Leaf	155.00
Water Server, Aristocrat, cobalt	40.00

HAMPSHIRE POTTERY

History: In 1871 James S. Taft founded the Hampshire Pottery Company in Keene, New Hampshire. Production began with redwares and stonewares, followed by majolica decorated wares in 1879. A semi-porcelain, with the recognizable matte glazes plus the Royal Worcester glaze, was introduced in 1883.

Until World War I the factory made an extensive line of utilitarian and art wares including souvenir items. After the war the firm resumed operations, but only made hotel dinnerware and tiles. The company dissolved in 1923.

Vase, 5⅞", green over white ground, dandelion type leaf dec, imp. mark, $185.00.

Bowls
5" d, 4" h, green, scroll work in relief	80.00
6" d, 2½" h, dark blue, florals in relief	90.00
Creamer, 4", applied handle, multicolored handle, flowers dec, imp mark.	85.00
Inkwell, cov, 4".	85.00
Jug Vase, squat spout, basket handle, matte green	50.00

Lamps, oil
6½", matte green	65.00
15", dark green, Tulip & Leaf design, monument base.	400.00
Mug, snakeskin	70.00

Pitchers
5½", snakeskin	90.00
7½", souvenir, Volunteer Soldier Statue, Newburyport, MA	85.00
Plate, 7", scenic, Ft. Ticonderoga	55.00
Relish, 9", scenic, Huntsville, AL, spring.	60.00
Toothbrush holder, Aster.	70.00

Vases
6" h, 5½" d, matte green, dandelions in relief	95.00
9½", dark blue, irises in relief.	100.00

HAND PAINTED CHINA

History: Hand painting on china began in the Victorian era and remained popular through the 1920s. It was considered an accomplished art form for women in the upper and upper middle class households. It developed first in England, but spread rapidly to the Continent and America.

China factories in Europe, America, and the Orient made the blanks. Bellek, Haviland, Limoges, and Rosenthal are among the European firms. American firms include A. H. Hews Co., Cambridge, Massachusetts; Willetts Mfgs. Co., Trenton, New Jersey; and Knowles, Taylor and Knowles, East Liverpool, Ohio. Nippon blanks from Japan were used heavily during the 20th century.

The quality and design of the blank is a key factor in pricing. Some blanks were very elaborate. Many pieces are signed and dated by the artist. Aesthetics is critical. Value is added to a piece when a decorator goes beyond the standard forms and creates a unique and pleasing design.

Bowl, 9", sq, flowers, pink and blue	35.00
Box, cov, 6" d, orange poppies	80.00
Candlestick, 5¾", shaded yellow and blue, pink roses, gold trim	25.00
Cheese Dish, cov, 9" h, 6¼" d, pale blue top to white bottom, pink floral sprays, green leaves, gold trim, applied handles	95.00
Charger, 13", peaches, green leaves, Limoges, artist sgd	60.00
Cruet, blue and white flowers	50.00
Dresser Tray, 16" l, 11" d, white, pink border, center spray of flowers, gold wreath of flowers and multicolored flowers, sgd	75.00

Tobacco Jar, multicolored Indian, gold trim and finial, initials on finial artist Florence Weaver, mkd "Favorite/Bavaria," 7" h, $200.00.

Dish, 6″, small pink roses, gold trim,
Lenox, sgd **35.00**
Pitcher, 6″, berries, leaves, gold handle
and trim, Limoges **90.00**
Planters, pr, 10¾″ h, 6″ d, light blue
ground, floral dec, multicolored. **115.00**
Plates
9½″, red rose border, Limoges, sgd .   **25.00**
10″, fish swimming, sgd **40.00**
Tankard, 12¼″, dark green band top and
bottom, dark green handle, 2¼″ green
and gold center band, large pink and
burgundy flowers. **90.00**
Tray, 10¾″, white, yellow border, raised
gold tracery, gold handles, T&V
France, sgd **35.00**
Vase, 4¾″, floral and gold dec, Bavarian,
sgd **15.00**

HATPINS AND HATPIN HOLDERS

History: When the vogue for oversized hats developed around 1850, hatpins became popular. Designers used a variety of materials to decorate the
pin ends, including china, crystal, enamel, gem
stones, precious metals, and shells. Decorative
subjects ranged from commemorative designs to
insects.

Hatpin holders are porcelain containers which set
on a dresser to hold these pins. These holders were
produced by major manufacturers, among which
were Meissen, Nippon, R. S. Germany, R. S. Prussia, and Wedgwood.

Reference: Lillian Baker, *Handbook for Hatpins
& Hatpin Holders,* Collector Books, 1983.

Collector's Club: International Club for Collectors of Hatpins and Hatpin Holders, 15237 Chanera
Avenue, Gardena, CA, 90249. Dues: $15.00.

Museum: Los Angeles Art Museum, Costume
Dept., Los Angeles, CA

HATPINS

Amber set with marcasites **20.00**
Art Nouveau
Black faceted glass on wire frame, ab-
stract fleur-de-lis **200.00**
Sterling, peacock blue enamel petals,
hallmarked, 1909 . . . .   **95.00**
Blue stone, 2″ head, center stone, 2
rings of rhinestone brilliants, 11″
shaft **35.00**
Brass
Bird, turquoise stone **35.00**
Flower **25.00**
Bulldog, carved amethyst, bull's eye
glass eyes **265.00**
Carnival, green-blue, peacock design . .   **35.00**
Egyptian motif, brass, celluloid. **125.00**

Enamel shield, multicolored, people,
pine tree, deer, "Dirigo," "Maine,"
8″ l. **20.00**
Flower, gold filled, large rhinestone cen-
ter, 8 small rhinestones on stamens,
9⅛″ l **15.00**
Grasshopper, 14K gold, figural. **150.00**
Pearls, 5 seed pearls mounted on 14K
gold setting. **135.00**
Repousse, SS, purple stone, 6¾″ l . . .   **40.00**
Satsuma, 7¼″ **50.00**
Silver ball, 11″ **30.00**
Teardrops
Gold filled lacy wire applied over large
jade type stone, 8¾″ l **25.00**
10K gold, 6¼″ l. **15.00**
Wooden ball, 1½″, black 7½″ l. **10.00**

**Nippon, green mark, green leaves, pink
roses, purple daisies, 4½″ h, $40.00.**

HATPIN HOLDERS

Bavarian
4½″, hp pastel flowers. **50.00**
5″, violets, gold trim, white ground,
mkd "Favorite Bavaria" **35.00**
Celluloid, pearlized, 4 blue jewels, 1 red
jewel **15.00**
Geisha Girl, red trim, 3 legs. **45.00**
Hand Painted, 6″, black ground, roses,
gold trim. **45.00**
Nippon, cornucopia shape, wall hanging,
pink roses, gold, mkd **140.00**
R. S. Germany, 6 sided, yellow ground,
white roses. **45.00**
R. S. Prussia evergreens decor 4½″,
Mold 728, swans. **225.00**
5″, Mold 726, 3 ftd, yellow roses . . .   **165.00**

6", attached tray, large pink and white roses **175.00**

Torquay, motto ware, blue and green decor **35.00**

Unmarked, slender tapered body molded in swirls, vertical vines, dainty pink roses **75.00**

H & C°
L
FRANCE

HAVILAND CHINA

History: In 1842 David Haviland, an American, went to Limoges, France. There he commissioned porcelain companies to make products according to his designs. Eventually he set up his own decorating studio. The porcelain was exported to the United States via New York, where David and Daniel, his brother, had an importing firm.

In 1865 David began making his own porcelain in Limoges. Havilands married into the French porcelain manufacturing families; the Alluard works were obtained through marriage. A multiplicity of firms using the Haviland name organized, reorganized, and dissolved during the 1863 to 1941 period.

The peak period of production during which the dainty all-over flowered patterns typical of Haviland china were made covers only a short period, roughly 1890 to 1910. Earlier larger flowers, many in darker colors, were produced. Later the conventional border patterns became more prevalent.

Theodore Haviland contracted with the Shenango pottery to make Haviland wares in the United States beginning in 1936. The wares produced by Shenango for Haviland gained great popularity as a choice of brides for their wedding china. As a result, many of these patterns are being sought as replacements or for extensions of sets already in existence.

In 1941 W. David Haviland, representing the Theodore Haviland Co., bought the assets of Haviland and Co. from the French heirs of Charles Edward Miller Haviland. In 1946 the Limoges plant was furnished with electrically controlled kilns. A gift line was introduced in America in 1963; and, the first Christmas plate was issued in 1970.

References: Mary Frank Gaston, *Haviland Collectibles & Art Objects*, Collector Books, 1984; Gertrude T. Jacobson, *Haviland China*, 2 volumes, Wallace Homestead, 1979; Arlene Schleiger, *Two Hundred Patterns of Haviland China*, Books 1 through V, privately printed, 1950–1977. Book II contains a history of the company by Theodore Haviland, 2nd.

Additional Listings: See *Warman's Americana & Collectibles* for more examples.

Dessert Plate, 7¼" sq, varied fruits, mkd Limoges, $25.00.

Bone Dish, floral dec, brown and yellow, fluted rim **9.00**

Bread Plate, 9½", Moss Rose, molded rope edge **32.00**

Butter Pat, Chrysanthemum **10.00**

Chocolate Pot, cov, Taranto **125.00**

Chop Plate, 12⅞", Ranson blank, hp, pastel ground, purple and green grapes, green foliage, gold trim, artist sgd, Haviland & Company **95.00**

Cream and Sugar, Ranson, gold trim .. **85.00**

Cups and Saucers

Delaware, demitasse, Theodore Haviland, New York **15.00**

Holly pattern, demitasse, red berries, green leaves, gold scalloped border, Theodore Haviland **40.00**

Montebello, tea **30.00**

Silver Anniversary, coffee **30.00**

Cuspidor, pink, white, and gold **140.00**

Dessert Service for 8, including coffee pot, sugar and creamer, Moss Ross. **650.00**

Dinner Set for 12, Garden Flower, 91 pcs, American **850.00**

Gravy Boat, Autumn Leaf **40.00**

Mustard Jar, cov, attached underplate, Chrysanthemum **75.00**

Oyster Plates

8⅝", hold 5 oysters, salmon pink, dark green and brown trim, gold, Haviland Limoges **55.00**

8¾", holds 6 oysters, lemon yellow, brown and gold trim, Haviland Limoges **48.00**

Plates

9½", Clover Leaf, green leaves, red

blossoms, gold trim, Haviland & Co 30.00
9¾", dinner, Autumn Leaf 22.00
Platters
12¾", Silver Anniversary 45.00
16½", Princess, Haviland & Co. 65.00
Ramkins and Saucers, set of 8, pale blue flowers, pink roses, green leaves, brown lines 200.00
Sauce Dish, 5", Apple Blossom 9.00
Soup Plate, flange rim, pale blue and gray flowers, brown and gray dec . . . 10.00
Syrup, 6", cream, grapes and green leaves 50.00
Tea Set, 3 pcs, Moss Rose, molded rope edge 165.00
Teapot, 8", blue flowers, gold trim 75.00
Vase, 5¼" h, 3¾" d, ladies with large hats in beige panels, alternating floral panels, C. Field Haviland/Limoges . . 335.00
Vegetable Dishes
9¼" l, 7¼" w, oval, open, Clover Leaf 55.00
Princess, oval, cov 48.00

HEISEY GLASS ⬦Ⓗ

History: The A. H. Heisey Glass Co. began producing glasswares in April, 1896, in Newark, Ohio. Heisey was not a newcomer to the field, having been associated with the craft since his youth. Many blown and molded patterns were produced in crystal, colored, milk (opalescent), and Ivorina Verde (custard) glass. Decorative techniques of cutting, etching, and silver deposit were employed. Glass figurines were introduced in 1933 and continued until 1957 when the factory ceased production. All Heisey glass is notable for its clarity.

Some Heisey molds were sold to Imperial Glass of Bellaire, Ohio, and certain items were reissued. These pieces may be mistaken for the original Heisey. Some of the reproductions were produced in colors which were never made by Heisey and have become collectible in their own right. Not all Heisey glassware is marked with the familiar "H" within a diamond.

References: Mary Louise Burns, *Heisey's Glassware of Distinction,* 2nd edition, privately printed; Virginia and Loren Yeakley, *Heisey Glass In Color: Book II,* privately printed, 1978.

Collectors' Club: Heisey Collectors of America, P. O. Box 27, Newark, OH, 43055. Dues: $15.00. *Heisey News* monthly.

Museum: National Heisey Glass Museum, Newark, OH.

Advisor: Joyce Clement.

Ale Glass, 8", Priscilla, crystal, sgd . . . 45.00
Animals
Angelfish 95.00

Donkey. 275.00
Elephant, large 350.00
Pheasant 200.00
Plug Horse 85.00
Scottie 90.00
Ashtrays
Bow Tie, moongleam. 50.00
Horsehead 50.00
Twist, turned up, 2 handled, flamingo 20.00
Yeoman, flamingo, set of 4 with holder 80.00
Bonbons
Kalonyal, sgd 35.00
Ridgeleigh, 2 handled 18.00
Bowls
8", Criss Cross, sgd. 75.00
8½", Cross Lined Flute, sgd. 40.00
9", Ridgeleigh, sgd 26.00
9", Star and Zipper, emerald 175.00
11", Orchid, 3 seahorse, ftd 85.00
12", gardenia, Crystolite. 28.00
Floral, Coleport 35.00
Salad dressing, Lariat, divided, crystal. 38.00
Whipped cream, Saturn, zircon. 50.00
Butter Dish, covered
Rose etched. 175.00
Waverly, horse finial, crystal. 65.00
Candlesticks
6¾", silver deposit, crystal, sgd 65.00
2 light, Trident, Tea Rose etched, pr 50.00
Candy Jar, 5½", Provincial, cov, ftd, sgd 285.00
Celery
9", Coarse Rib, flamingo 26.00
9", Priscilla, sgd 16.00
10", Twist, flamingo, sgd 20.00
Champagnes
Carcassone 45.00
Danish Princess 18.00
Rose etched. 30.00
Wabash, Pied Piper etched, saucer. . 14.00
Coasters
Plantation, crystal 20.00
Twist, flamingo 7.00
Cocktail Glasses
Creole, Alexandrite, crystal stem and foot. 100.00
Minuet, crystal. 40.00
Rooster 47.00
Cocktail Shaker, Fisherman etched . . 125.00
Cologne, Punty and Diamond Point, silver top 40.00
Compotes
7", Albermarle, Old Colony etched, diamond optic, Sahara, ftd, sgd. . . 85.00
8", Rib and Panel, cov, silver overlay, flamingo 125.00
Creamers
Empress, Lafayette etched, sgd 26.00
Swingtime. 17.00
Creamers and Sugars
Cabachon, sgd 40.00

Half Circle, moongleam, sgd.	85.00
Wide Flat Panel, flamingo, sgd	60.00

Cruets
Greek Key	60.00
Rib and Panel.	32.00

Cups and Saucers
Empress, Sahara, sgd	35.00
Orchid	45.00
Yeoman, flamingo, sgd	22.50

Goblets
Carcassone, Sahara, short stem. . . .	15.00
Ipswich, crystal	12.00
King Arthur, crystal bowl, moongleam stem and base, sgd	35.00
Old Dominion, Sahara	20.00
Oxford, sgd.	12.00
Tyrolean, Orchid etched.	39.00
Yeoman	27.00
Ice Bucket, Queen Anne, silver overlay	70.00
Iced Tea Glass, Old Williamsburg	20.00

Jelly Dishes
5″, Hawthorne, handled, sgd	38.00
5″, Revere, handled, sgd	19.50
6″, Queen Anne, handled, ftd.	27.50
Peerless.	37.00
Prince of Wales Plumes, ftd, sgd . . .	45.00

Jugs
3 pt, Pleat and Panel, flamingo, sgd.	65.00
½ gal, Narrow Flute, sgd	60.00
½ gal, Winged Scroll, emerald, sgd. .	245.00
54 oz, Fairacre, diamond optic, moongleam base and handle, sgd.	155.00

Mayonnaise
Octagon, cut.	25.00
Twist, crystal, sgd	24.00
Mug, 12 oz, Old Sandwich, Sahara, handled, sgd	145.00
Mustard, Narrow Flute, cov, sgd	27.50
Nappy, 5″, Rib and Panel	12.50
Nut Dish, swan.	12.00
Pitcher, Fancy Loop, ½ gal, squat . . .	95.00

Plates
4½″, Narrow Flute, crystal, sgd	7.00
7½″, Revere, cut.	9.50
8″, Empress, tangerine	135.00
8″, Rose etched	27.50
8″, Toujours, Minuet etched	7.50
8¼″, Minuet, crystal.	12.50
8½″, Orchid etched.	16.00
Punch Bowl, Lariat, 15 piece	160.00

Punch Cups
Banded Flute, sgd.	6.00
Pinwheel and Fan, moongleam.	25.00
Whirlpool	8.00

Relish Dishes
3 part, Plantation.	35.00
4 part, Lariat.	42.00
4 part, Zodiac, crystal	30.00

Salt and Pepper Shakers
Empress, Sahara.	95.00
Orchid etched.	75.00
Ridgeleigh	90.00
Yeoman, flamingo	45.00

Sherbet, Victorian, crystal, footed, sgd, $15.00.

Sherbets
Carcassone, low	12.00
Crystolite	16.00
Minuet, crystal.	18.00
Orchid etched, low	27.50
Plantation, Ivy etched	18.00
Ridgeleigh	18.00
Whirlpool	12.00
Yeoman, low.	10.00
Soap Dish, Medium Flat Panel, cov . . .	32.00

Soda Glasses
5 oz, Ipswich	10.00
12 oz, New Era, ftd, sgd	10.00
13 oz, Victorian, crystal	18.00
18 oz, Impromptu	22.50
Stein, Hunt Scene etched	140.00

Sugars
Empress, Sahara, individual, sgd . . .	20.00
Queen Ann, sgd	15.00
Waverly, Orchid etched, sgd.	22.00

Toothpicks
Beaded Swag, ruby	36.00
Winged Scroll, custard.	95.00
Tray, 15″, Fern, Belvedere etched, handled	45.00

Tumblers
Provincial, ftd	11.50
Twist, marigold	30.00
Winged Scroll, custard, sgd	85.00

Vases
2½″, Warwick, sgd	18.00
8″, Thumbprint and Panel, sgd	50.00
Lariat, fan, cut.	85.00
Saturn, violet, zircon, sgd.	110.00
Warwick, cornucopia	38.00

Wines
Beaded Swag, ruby souvenir	36.00

Park Lane.	**22.50**
Victorian, cry.	**18.00**
Yeoman, Sahara	**25.00**

Salt and Pepper, pr	**450.00**
Spooner.	**460.00**
Sugar, cov, 4½″ d	**650.00**
Syrup, metal lid	**600.00**
Toothpick, ftd.	**1,700.00**
Tray, water, round, 9¼″ d	**800.00**

HOLLY AMBER

History: Holly Amber, originally called Golden Agate, was produced by the Indiana Tumbler and Goblet Works of the National Glass Co., Greentown, Indiana. Jacob Rosenthal created the color in 1902. Holly Amber is a gold colored glass with a marbleized onyx color on raised parts.

A new pattern, Holly [No. 450], was designed by Frank Jackson for Golden Agate. Between January 1903 and June 1903, when the factory was destroyed by fire, more than 35 items were made in this pattern.

References: Brenda Measell and James Measell, *A Guide To Reproductions of Greentown Glass,* The Printing Press, 1974, 2nd ed.; James Measell, *Greentown Glass, The Indiana Tumbler & Goblet Co.,* Grand Rapids Public Museum, 1979.

Collectors' Club: National Greentown Glass Association, 1807 West Madison, Kokomo, IN 56901. Dues: $4.00. *N.G.G.A. Newsletter,* quarterly.

Museums: Greentown Glass Museum, Greentown, IN; Grand Rapids Public Museum [Ruth Herrick Greentown Glass Collection], MI.

Additional Listing: Greentown Glass.

Bowl, 8½″, berry	**325.00**
Cake Stand, 9″.	**1,900.00**
Compote, cov, 4½″, jelly.	**650.00**
Creamer	**625.00**
Mug, handled, 4½″.	**375.00**
Nappy.	**350.00**
Pitcher, water.	**1,700.00**
Plate, 7½″, sq	**450.00**
Relish, 7¼″ l, oblong	**250.00**

Compote, open, 6¾″ h, 7⅜″ d, $850.00.

HORN

History: For centuries horns from animals have been used for various items, e.g., drinking cups, spoons, powder horns, and small dishes. Some pieces of horn have designs scratched in them. Around 1880 furniture made from the horns of Texas longhorn steers was popular in Texas and the southwestern United States.

Additional Listings: Firearm Accessories.

Tumbler, 2½″ h, $20.00.

Beakers	
3¼″ h, name incised at lip by pattern of dots	**35.00**
6½″, scratch carved compass star	**50.00**
Box, cov, 2¾″ h, brass hinges.	**25.00**
Cup, 3″ d, 5″ h, scratch carved hunting scenes, applied handle	**75.00**
Furniture, made from Texas longhorn steers	
Chair, arms, back and legs of horn, leather seat cushion.	**300.00**

Foot Stool, velvet upholstered seat,
horn legs **150.00**
Rocker, wooden rockers, horn back
and arm rests, upholstered seat . . **450.00**
Ladle, scratch carved reindeer in bowl. **95.00**
Offering Box, 7¼ x 3½ x 2″, hanging
type, slant top, arched back **35.00**
Scoop, 12″ l **25.00**
Snuff Box, 1¾″ h, wooden plug at top,
ring handle **40.00**
Wall Hanging, 72″ l, Texas longhorn
steer, mounted in bound leather and
set on wood base **125.00**

HULL POTTERY

History: In 1905 Addis E. Hull purchased the Acme Pottery Company, Crooksville, Ohio. In 1917 the A. E. Hull Pottery Company began making a line of art pottery, novelties, stoneware, and kitchenware, later including the famous Little Red Riding Hood line. Most items had a matte finish with shades of pink and blue or brown predominating.

After a disasterous flood and fire in 1950, J. Brandon Hull reopened the factory in 1952 as the Hull Pottery Company. New, more modern style molds, mostly with glossy finish, were produced. The company currently produces pieces, e.g. the Regal and Floraline lines, for sale to florists.

Hull pottery molds and patterns are easily identified. Pre-1950 vases are marked "Hull USA" or "Hull Art USA" on the bottom. Many also retain their paper labels. Post-1950 pieces are marked "Hull" in large script or "HULL" in block letters.

Each pattern has a distinctive number, e.g., Wildflower with a "W" and number, Waterlily with an "L" and number, Poppy with 600 numbers, Orchid with 300 numbers, etc. Early stone pieces have an H.

References: Brenda Roberts, *The Collectors Encyclopedia Of Hull Pottery*, Collector Books, 1980.

Additional Listings: See *Warman's Americana & Collectibles* for more examples.

Advisor: Joan Hull

PRE-1950 (MATTE)

Bowknot
B-9-8½″, vase **45.00**
B-16-13½″, console bowl and
candleholders **115.00**
B-28-10″, plate **200.00**
Wallpockets [cup and saucer, iron,
pitcher, whiskbroom, etc.] **40.00**
Camellia (Open Rose)
106-13¼″ **175.00**
118-6¼″, swan vase **30.00**
126-8½″, hand vase **50.00**
Dogwood (Wild Rose)
502-6½″, vase, suspended **35.00**

Cornucopia, green tones, pink int. high glaze, $18.00.

511-11½″, cornucopia, large **65.00**
521-7″, planter **35.00**
Iris (Narcissus)
402-7″, vase **35.00**
402-8½″, vase **45.00**
412-7″, basket, hanging **50.00**
Jack-in-the-Pulpit (Calla Lily)
556-33-10″, vase **55.00**
530-33-9 x 9″, vase, large **85.00**
Little Red Riding Hood
Cookie Jar **75.00**
Tea Set, creamer, and sugar **150.00**
Magnolia
3-8½″, vase **40.00**
20-15″, vase, large **150.00**
26-12½″, console bowl **60.00**
Orchid
301-8″, vase **40.00**
301-10″, vase **65.00**
302-6″, vase **30.00**
Pinecone, # 55-6½″, vase **35.00**
Pink Magnolia [glossy]
H-13-10½″, vase **50.00**
H-15-12″, double cornucopia **60.00**
H-20-6½″, tea set, two lids **125.00**
Poppy
601-12″, basket **175.00**
604-8″, cornucopia, boat shaped . . . **50.00**
605-8½″, base **40.00**
Rosella
R-5-6¼″, vase **30.00**
R-9-6½″, pitcher **30.00**
R-10-6¼″, heart wallpockets **35.00**
Stoneware, marked with H
Beer Pitcher **100.00**
Beer stein **25.00**
Thistle, # 51-54, 6½″, vases **35.00**
Tulip
103-33-6″, vase, suspended **45.00**
109-33-8″, pitcher **40.00**
110-33-6″, vase **30.00**
Waterlily
L-12-10½″, vase **50.00**
L-18-6″, tea set with two lids **125.00**
L-25-5½″, planter with saucer **50.00**

Wildflower
W-2-5½", pitcher	25.00
W-13-9½", vase	45.00
W-16-10½", basket	125.00

Woodland [matte]
W-3-5½", pitcher	25.00
W-9-8½", basket	45.00
W-29, console bowl, boat shaped	60.00

POST 1950 (GLOSSY)

Blossomflite
T-8, ruffled oval basket	35.00
T-13, pitcher	75.00

Butterfly
B-2 and B-22, large round three footed console bowl and candleholders	75.00
B-12, cornucopia, tall	30.00
Ebbtide, 11", double fish vase	30.00
Parchment & Pine, scroll planter	40.00

Serenade
S-4, vase, hat shaped	25.00
S-14, basket, large	65.00

Tokay
Basket, moon shaped, large	50.00
Candy Dish, stemmed	25.00

HUMMEL ITEMS

History: Hummel items are the original creations of Berta Hummel, born in 1909 in Massing, Bavaria, Germany. At age 18, she was enrolled in the Academy of Fine Arts in Munich to further her mastery of drawing and the palette. Berta entered the Convent of Siessen and became Sister Maria Inconnentia in 1934. In this Franciscan cloister, she continued drawing and painting images of her childhood friends.

In 1935 W. Goebel Co. in Rodental, Germany, began reproducing Sister Berta's sketches into 3 dimensional bisque figurines. The Schmid Brothers of Randolph, Massachusetts, introduced the figurines to America and became Goebel's U.S. distributor.

In 1967 Goebel began distributing Hummel items in the U.S.; and, a controversy developed between the two companies involving the Hummel family and the convent. Law suits and countersuits ensued. The German courts finally effected a compromise. The convent held legal rights to all works produced by Sister Berta from 1934 until her death in 1946 and licensed Goebel to reproduce these works. Schmid was to deal directly with the Hummel family for permission to reproduce any pre-convent art.

All authentic Hummels bear both the signature, M.I. Hummel, and a Goebel trademark. Various trademarks were used to identify the year of production. The Crown Mark (CM) was used in 1935, Full Bee (FB) 1940–1959; Small Stylized Bee (SSB) 1960–1972; Large Stylized Bee (LSB) 1960–1963; Three Line Mark (3L) 1964–1972; Last Bee Mark (LB) 1972–1980, Missing Bee Mark (MB) 1979–Present.

References: John F. Hotchkiss, *Hummel Art II,* Wallace Homestead, 1981; Carl F. Luckey, *Hummel Figurines and Plates, 5th Edition,* Books Americana, 1984.

Collectors' Clubs: Goebel Collectors' Club, 105 White Plains Road, Tarrytown, NY 10591. Insight quarterly newsletter. Dues: $17.50.

Additional Listings: See *Warman's Americana & Collectibles* for more examples.

Ashtrays
Let's Sing, #114, LSB	75.00
Singing Lesson, #34, LB	40.00

Bookends

Figurine, Chick Girl, stylized bee, $95.00.

Angelic Song, #14A, SSB, single. . .	75.00
Apple Tree Boy & Girl, #252A, 252B, LSB	140.00
Candy Box, Joyful, III/53, CM, 6¼″ h. .	350.00
Dealer Sign, Merry Wanderer, LSB. . . .	55.00

Figurines

Accordian Boy, #185, SSB	75.00
Angelic Son, #144, LB	40.00
Auf Wiedersehen, #153/0, SSB, 5½″ h	85.00
Barnyard Hero, #195/I, 3L	100.00
Begging His Share, #9, FB	300.00
Blessed Event, #333, LB, 5½″ h . . .	135.00
Book Worm, #3/II	
4½″ h, SSB.	300.00
8″ h, FB	630.00
Boots, #143/I, MB.	55.00
Busy Student, #367, LB	75.00
Cinderella, #337, LB.	465.00
Confidentially, #314, LB	325.00
Duet, #130, LSB	125.00
Eventide, #99, SSB	125.00
Farewell, #65, FB	300.00
Festival Harmony, flute, #173/II, MB, 10¼″	225.00
For Father, #87, LSB	90.00
Happy Days, #150/I, LSB, 6¼″. . . .	250.00
Hello, #124/0, FB, green pants. . . .	250.00
Homeward Bound, #334, LB, 5¼″. .	165.00
Latest News, #184, LB.	95.00
Little Band, #392, 3L, on base	135.00
Little Fiddler, #2/1, CM, 11″	1,000.00
Little Guardian, #145, FB	110.00
Little Helper, #73, SSB.	70.00
Little Sweeper, #171, FB	165.00
Little Tailor, #308, LB.	50.00
Mail Coach, #226, LSB.	280.00
Mother's Helper, #133, SSB	100.00
Mountainner, #315, 3L	100.00
Not For You, #317, SSB, 6″	100.00
Out of Danger, #56/B, SSB	110.00
Puppy Love, #1, FB	220.00
Retreat to Safety, #201/1, 3L.	125.00
St. George, #55, LB, 6¾″ h	145.00
Surprise, #94/1, SSB.	85.00
To Market, #49/0, LSB	115.00
Watchful Angel, #194, FB.	225.00

Fonts

Angel Cloud, #206, 3L	25.00
Angels at Prayer, #91B, SSB	75.00
Madonna & Child, #243, MB.	25.00

Lamps

Good Friends	175.00
Out of Danger, 3L	225.00
She Loves Me, She Loves Me Not. .	175.00
Wayside Harmony	190.00
Nativity Set, #260/A/S, 17 pc, large, stable.	2,500.00

Plaques

Madonna, #48/0, SSB	55.00
Vacation Time, #195, FB, oversize .	200.00
Wall Vase, pr, boy and girl, #360/A, 6¼″ h	75.00

IMARI

History: Imari derives its name from a Japanese port city. Although Imari ware was manufactured in the 17th century, the wares most commonly encountered are those made between 1770 and 1900.

Early Imari was decorated simply, quite unlike the later heavily decorated brocade pattern commonly associated with Imari. Most of the decorative patterns are an underglaze blue and overglaze "seal wax" red supported by turquoise and yellow.

The Chinese copied Imari ware. Important differences of the Japanese type include grayer clay, thicker glaze, runny and darker blue, and deep red opaque hues.

The pattern and colors of Imari inspired many English and European potteries, such as Derby, Meissen, and others, to adopt a similar style of decoration for their wares.

Many reproductions of Imari have been made.

Vase, 9½″ h, blue birds on white ground flying over blue water, blue dec on top of planter, $140.00.

Bowls

7¼″, blue and white, ship dec, Japanese, 19th C	175.00
7⅝″ w, 9⅝″ l, oval, underglaze blue with orange painted floral dec	145.00
8¼″, blue and white, mums and cranes, c1860	90.00
10″, barber, deep, wide everted rim,crescent indentation, Japaneselady peering from behind screenoverlooking garden, underglaze blue and multicolored enamel, 18th C	750.00
Cache Pot, 9½″, sq, chamfered corners, blue and white, birds flying over water, scroll and floral border, ftd . . .	175.00

Chargers

    12″, central basket of flowers, cobalt, green, red and yellow **185.00**

    17¼″, dark blue and white, central Hoo bird and flaming pearl, outer rim, 3 medallions of blossoms, 3 shields of diapering with scattered mum blossoms in between, c1860 .... **550.00**

    18½″, petal rim, dark blue, central shore scene, floral medallions, geometric diapering on wall, c1860 .... **300.00**

Cup, 2¾″ h, 3½″ d, sq panels of red and green plums, pine and bamboo, corners with red folding fan panels, c1830 .... **55.00**

Dishes

    6⅛″, underglaze blue, iron red and gilt, Chinese, 1710 .... **350.00**

    7″, shell shape, florals and temples, c19th C **225.00**

    8½″, shaped rim, bamboo forest scene, 19th C **90.00**

Fish Bowl, 10″ h, 13½″ d, globular, inturned rim, painted, multicolored immortal and dragon scenes, mid 19thC **900.00**

Hibachi, 12″ h, 18″ d, blue and white, plum tree, reserved white petals, brown berries and leaves, c1880 ... **650.00**

Jar, cov, 24¾″, baluster shape, phoenix birds in flight and blossoming peony branches rising from open fence, lappet borders foot and shoulder, blue bud knop, Chinese, Kangxi Period .. **3,750.00**

Mug, bell shape, continuous river scene, underglaze blue, iron red, green and gilt, Chinese, c1735. .... **190.00**

Plates

    7¼″, petal rim, multicolored, 3 garden scene panels, 3 medallions, c1860 **75.00**

    8½″, seto plate, red and blue with green and gold trim, 4 round bird medallions, 4 lotus panels, c1900 . **70.00**

Platter, 12⅜″, center, leaves, feathers, and berries, iron red and cobalt border with leaves, vines and fruit, c1875 .. **120.00**

Sake Bottles, pr, 10⅜″, sq, Japanese lady, florals, vines, in sq wooden bases, late 19th C **350.00**

Saucer, 6¼″, iron red, translucent green and gilt, Chinese, c1710 .... **90.00**

Teapot, 5⅝″, beehive shape, castellated borders, painted gibbons in peach trees, Chinese, Kangxi Period...... **1,100.00**

Urn, blue and undgerglaze red, designs of winged dragon and fantasy animals. **375.00**

Vases, 18½″, pr, dome cov, octagonal baluster shape, cartouches of flowers and butterflies, matching cov and knobs, 19th C. **2,100.00**

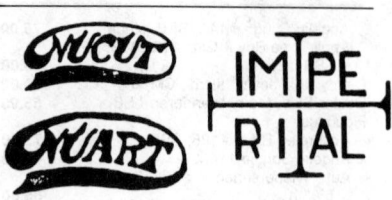

IMPERIAL GLASS

History: Imperial Glass Co., Bellaire, Ohio, was organized in 1901. Its primary product was the manufacture of pattern (pressed) glass. Soon other lines were added including carnival glass, NUART, NUCUT, and NEAR CUT. In 1916 the company introduced "Free-Hand," a lustred art glass line, and "Imperial Jewels," an iridescent stretch glass that carried the Imperial cross trademark. In the 1930s the company was reorganized in to the Imperial Glass Corporation and continues to produce a great variety of wares.

Imperial recently has acquired the molds and equipment of several other glass companies—Central, Cambridge and Heisey. Many of the "retired" molds of these companies are once again in use. The resulting reissues are marked to distinguish them from the originals.

Reference: Margaret and Douglas Archer, *Imperial Glass,* Collector Books, 1978.

Collectors' Club: Imperial Glass Collectors Society, P. O. Box 4012, Silver Spring, MD 20904. Imperial Collectors Glasszette, quarterly.

Additional Listings: See Carnival Glass, Pattern Glass, and *Warman's Americana & Collectibles* for more examples of Candlewick.

ENGRAVED OR HAND CUT

Bowls

    5½″, nut, 3 hand cut floral sprays, 3 butterflies **12.00**

    9½″, salad, 3 hand cut floral sprays, molded star in cut base **18.00**

Console Set, stretch glass, blue irid, 10¼″ d bowl, 3¼″ h candlesticks, $80.00.

Pitcher, 3 qt, tankard shape, hand engraved cherries and foliage **45.00**
Plate, 5½", 5 hand cut daisy sprays. . . **10.00**
Sundae, ftd, hand engraved stars **7.00**
Syrup, SP top, Etched Design No. 102, 7½" oz. **18.00**
Tumbler, 3 hand cut side stars, molded star in cut base. **8.00**

JEWELS

Bowls
  7", blue irid, ftd, sgd **65.00**
  8½", amethyst, sgd. **75.00**
Compote, 6½", white irid. **50.00**
Rose Bowl, amethyst, pearl green lustre **75.00**
Spitton, gold, small **70.00**
Vase, flared, silver lustre on amethyst, sgd **85.00**

LUSTRED (FREE HAND)

Candlesticks
  10¾"
    Drag Loop, opaque white, green drag loop dec, applied green socket and base. **110.00**
    Leaf and Vine, opaque white with dec on clear glass body, applied cobalt blue socket, base **95.00**
  11", irid dark blue, white loops **150.00**
Lamp Shade, 5", opal leaves edged in green on gold base, threaded, 2¼" fitted collar, sgd. **245.00**
Rose Bowl, 5½", cobalt, spun **125.00**
Vases
  5½" h, 6" d, vines and leaves embedded on cobalt ground. **175.00**
  7", gold swags on calcite ground . . . **225.00**
  8", orange lustre **100.00**
  10½", irid blue loopings on ivory, deep blue foot **120.00**

NEAR CUT

Bowl, berry, 7", crimped edge **16.00**
Butter, cov, Pattern 292 . . . . **35.00**
Cucumber Dish, shell shape **15.00**

NUCUT

Bowls
  7", berry, sq **15.00**
  9", salad. **14.00**
Compote, 4½", ftd, c1940. . . . . **25.00**
Creamer **10.00**
Nappy, 6", heart shape. **15.00**
Olive, 5", round, handle **10.00**
Spoon Tray, 7½", oval **15.00**
Sugar **10.00**
Tumbler, flared top, molded star, polished base **5.00**
Vase, 6" **18.00**

PRESSED

Almond Set, 5 pc, Cape Cod. **50.00**
Basket, 5", Sugar Cane, blue opal **15.00**
Bowl, 6½", crystal, brocade etched with orchids, MOP wash **35.00**
Candlesticks, pr, 8½", Cathay, servants figural. **300.00**
Candy Jar, cov, handled, Cape Cod. . . **60.00**
Champagne, Cape Cod, ball stem, 5". . **7.00**
Cigar Jar, cov, Candlewick, #400-44 . . **20.00**
Cigarette Box, cov, Candlewick, #400-134 . . . . **30.00**
Cologne Bottle, orig stopper, Cape Cod **35.00**
Console Bowl, Cathay, Chen, dragons . **285.00**
Cruet, Cape Cod **24.00**
Cup and Saucer, coffee, Cape Cod . . . **8.50**
Ice Tub, 6½" w, 4½" h, handled, light aqua blue **20.00**
Lemon Tray, Candlewick, #400-221 . . **30.00**
Mayonnaise Set, 3 pc, milk glass, Holly Band, Delft blue stain trim **55.00**
Mint Tray, closed handles, light green, etched roses, gilded **12.00**
Mirror, dresser, Candlewick **65.00**
Pagoda, Cathay, 3 pcs **285.00**
Pitcher, 60 oz, ice lip, Cape Cod **65.00**
Plates, Cape Cod
  7" **6.00**
  8" **6.50**
Relish, 10½", 3 part, ruby **45.00**
Sherbet, wafer ft, Cape Cod **8.00**
Tumblers, Cape Cod
  Juice, flat **3.00**
  Water, 12 oz. **5.00**
Vase, 8", Royal Blue opal hobnail **75.00**
Whiskey Tumbler, 2½ oz, Cape Cod . . **20.00**
Wine, Cape Cod, 5 ball stem. **4.00**

MISCELLANEOUS

Animals, Heisey mold, caramel slag
  Dog **30.00**
  Elephant. **35.00**
  Horse. **20.00**
Candlestick, clear, dolphin. **20.00**

INDIAN ARTIFACTS, AMERICAN

History: During the historic period there were approximately 350 tribes of Indians, grouped into the following regions: Eskimo, Northeast and Woodland, Northwest Coast, Plains, and West and Southwest.

American Indian artifacts are quite popular. Material from the Eskimo and Northwest Coast is down slightly from the high prices it enjoyed a few years ago.

Note: American Indian artifacts listed below are

objects made on the North American continent during the pre-historic and historic periods.

Advisor: Fred Boschan.

Acoma Pottery Jar, dark brown on white slip, 9¼", $275.00.

ESKIMO

Bow Drill, ivory, 2¼" mouthpiece,
  Thule **715.00**
Dolls, ivory, Okwik
  2⅜" h **1,800.00**
  3" h **1,400.00**
Needlecase, ivory, 4", 19th C **1,100.00**
Pipe, ivory, carved, 9" l, 19th C **800.00**

NORTHEAST & WOODLANDS

Cigar Case, birch bark, 5½" l, quilled,
  Huron. **300.00**
Container, birch bark, lid, 7 x 9", incised,
  Chippewa **300.00**
Knife sheath and knife, sheath quilled,
  antler handle knive, 14" l, Iroquois . . **6,000.00**
Mask, wood, 11" h, Iroquois **950.00**
Moccasins, child's, quilled on hide, Eastern Woodlands **385.00**

NORTHWEST COAST

Blanket, 68" l, wool, fringed, Tlingit/
  Chilkat **4,200.00**
Bowl, Seal, wood, carved, 12½" l,
  Tlingit. **1,200.00**
Chest, wood, 17" l, carved and painted,
  Bella Bella **13,750.00**
Frontlet, wood, carved, painted, shell inserts, Kwakiutl. **4,400.00**
Rattle, wood, carved, 12½" l, painted,
  Haida. **22,000.00**

PLAINS

Boots, woman's, 21" h, hide, beaded,
  Cheyenne. **190.00**
Cradle Board, model, 30" l, hide, beaded, Sioux **800.00**
Holster, 10½" l, hide, beaded, Cheyenne **500.00**
Pipe Bag, 36" l, hide, beaded and
  fringed, Sioux **550.00**
"Possible Bag," 19" l, hide, quilled,
  Sioux **900.00**
Shirt, 45" l, hide, beaded and fringed,
  North Plains **275.00**
Vest, man's, 20" l, hide, beaded, Sioux **660.00**

WEST AND SOUTHWEST

Baskets
  Apache, coiled tray, 18" d **460.00**
  Apache, tray, 7" d **350.00**
  Pima, tray, 12" d **700.00**
  Pomo, gift, multicolored bird feathers
    and shells, 6" d **950.00**
  Yokuts, polychrome, 9" d **660.00**
Doll, Hopi Kachina, 13" h **880.00**
Pottery, Prehistoric
  Casas Grandes, polychrome jar,
    10"d **570.00**
  Four Mile, polychrome bowl, 11½" d **950.00**
  Mimbres, bowl, geometric, 13" d. . . . **750.00**
  Tonto, polychrome Ola, 14" d **700.00**
  Tularosa, black on white Ola,
    14½"d. **900.00**
Pottery, Historic
  Acoma, polychrome jar, 12" d **880.00**
  Hopi, polychrome jar, Nampeyo,
    12"d **16,500.00**
  San Ildefonso, blackware
    Jar, "Marie & Julian" **600.00**

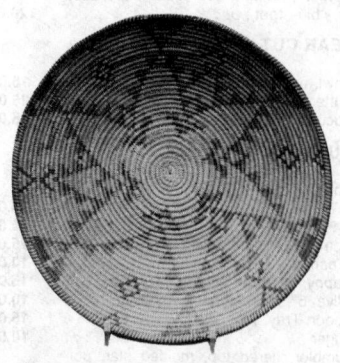

Basket Tray, coiled, Apache, red and black designs, 13½" d, $200.00.

Plate, "Marie & Julian"	**880.00**
Tesuque, polychrome jar, 9½" d	**1,100.00**
Zia, polychrome jar, 11" d	**825.00**
Zuni, polychrome	
Effigy Vessel, 10" h	**2,100.00**
Jar, 11½"	**1,000.00**
Textiles, Navajo	
Blankets	
Chiefs, 3rd phase, 73 x 56"	**3,600.00**
Chief's 3rd phase, woman's	**7,700.00**
Child's, 47 x 24"	**2,200.00**
"Germantown," 51 x 34"	**700.00**
Saddle, "Germantown", 33 x 22"	**400.00**
Rugs	
Transitional, 73 x 50"	**400.00**
"Two Gray Hill," 96 x 51"	**900.00**
Yei, 81 x 63"	**750.00**
Textile, Saltillo Serape, 90 x 46"	**1,800.00**

INDIAN TREE PATTERN

History: The Indian Tree pattern is a popular pattern of porcelain made from the last half of the 19th century until the present. The pattern consisting of an Oriental crooked tree branch, landscape, exotic flowers, and foliage is found in predominately greens, pinks, blues, and oranges on a white ground. Several English potteries, including Burgess and Leigh, Coalport, and Maddock, made wares with the Indian Tree pattern.

Bouillon Cup, underplate, Coalport	**30.00**
Bowl, 7", Coalport	**40.00**
Butter Dish, cov	**45.00**
Cake Stand	**25.00**
Creamer, 3", Maddock	**20.00**
Cups and Saucers	
Coalport	**15.00**
Minton	**25.00**
Demitasse Cup and Saucer, mkd John	
Maddock Sons, Ltd	**25.00**
Egg Cup, 4" h, Maddock	**20.00**
Gravy Boat, cov, mkd Brownfield & Son,	
c1856	**30.00**
Pitcher, 8¼", gold trim	**25.00**
Plates	
6", Maddock	**2.50**
7", Maddock	**4.00**
9"	
Burgess, Leigh	**15.00**
Maddock	**10.00**
9½", Maddock & Sons	**20.00**
10", Johnson Bros	**25.00**
Platters	
11", Maddock	**10.00**
11½", Hancock	**30.00**
12½", Maddock	**15.00**
16½", Maddock	**25.00**
Soap Dish, 3pc	**35.00**
Soup Plates	
Coalport, 7½"	**15.00**

Bowl, 7¼", handled, mkd "Johnson Bros," $15.00.

Myott	**30.00**
Teapot, cov, Maddox	**85.00**
Tureen, cov, ladle, 10", Maddox &	
Sons	**125.00**
Vegetable Dish, cov, Coalport, 11½"	**25.00**

INK BOTTLES

History: Ink was sold in glass or pottery bottles in the early 1700s in England. Retailers mixed their own formula and bottled it. The commercial production of ink did not begin in England until the late 18th century and in America until the early 19th century.

Initially, ink was supplied in pint or quart bottles, often of poor manufacture, from which smaller bottles could be filled. By the mid-19th century when writing implements were improved, emphasis was placed on making an "untippable" bottle. Shapes ranging from umbrella style to turtles were tried. Since ink bottles were displayed, shaped or molded bottles became popular.

The advent of the fountain pen relegated the ink bottle to the back drawer. Bottles lost their decorative design and became merely functionable items.

References: Hugh Cleveland, *Bottle Pricing Guide,* Collector Books, 1980; Ralph & Terry Kovel, *The Kovels' Bottle Price List,* Crown Publishers, 1982, 6th ed.; Carlo & Dot Sellari, *The Illustrated Price Guide To Antique Bottles,* Country Beautiful Corp., 1975.

Periodicals: *Antique Bottle World,* 5003 West Berwyn, Chicago, IL 60630; *Old Bottle Magazine,* P. O. Box 243, Bend, OR 97701. Subscription: $10.00.

Additional Listings: See *Warman's Americana & Collectibles* for more examples.

Staffords Ink green, 3″ h, 2¼″ d, $20.00.

Angus & Co., cone, aqua, 3½″	**10.00**
Brickett, J. Taylor, cylindrical, flared lip, 4½″	**125.00**
Cardinal Bird Ink, turtle shape, aqua. . .	**75.00**
Carter's emb on shoulder, 3 part mold, ring collar, pouring lip, light green, pink	**20.00**
Caswell Hazard & Co., Chemist, NY, cobalt.	**30.00**
Central Dome Ink, 8 sided, open pontil, rolled lip, light olive green	**50.00**
Clam shape, cobalt.	**125.00**
Club Ink, Carter ink label, hexagon, 4 leaf clover emb, cobalt, 4 oz	**25.00**
David's Thaddeus, & Co., cream crock, label reads "Thaddeus David's & Co. Writing Fluid, NY", 5¾″	**45.00**
Igloo Ink, dome shape, neck on side, cobalt.	**150.00**
Nicholas & Hall, house type, clear, 2⅞″	**10.00**
Stafford Ink. lime green.	**25.00**
Thomas Master Ink, aqua	**15.00**
Umbrella type, 8 sided, rolled lip, aqua.	**25.00**
Waterman's Ink, orig paper labels, contents, emb wood stopper, "8 oz" emb on shoulder, orig box, c1920	**15.00**

INKWELLS

History: The majority of the commonly found inkwells were produced in the United States and Europe from the early 1800s to the 1930s. The most popular materials were glass and pottery because these substances resisted the corrosive effects of ink.

Inkwells were a sign of the office or a wealthy individual. The common man tended to dip his ink directly from the bottle. The period from 1870 to 1920 represented a "golden age," when inkwells in elaborate designs were produced.

References: William E. Covill, Jr., *Inkbottles and Inkwells,* William S. Sullwold Publishing, 1971, 1st edition; Betty and Ted Rivera, *Inkstands and Inkwells: A Collector's Guide,* Crown Publishers, Inc., 1973, 2nd edition.

Collectors' Club: The Society of Inkwell Collectors, 5136 Thomas Avenue, Minneapolis, MN 55410. Dues: $24.50.

Additional Listings: See *Warman's Americana & Collectibles* for more examples.

Advisor: Karen Bauman.

CERAMIC

Delft, 7½″, blue and white, two cherubs, windmill dec, two removable wells with loose lids	**380.00**
French porcelain, pump type, 4¼″ h, floral dec, three quill holes, brass regulating knob	**300.00**
Meissen, 4½″ l, white with hp purple and green flowers, two hinged lidded wells in tray.	**220.00**
Sarreguemines, French, 6″ l, double sofa, loose cushions cover wells	**190.00**
Staffordshire, 3″ h, fat gentleman in suit with spotted vest, holds sack with quill hole	**140.00**

GLASS

Amethyst, barrel shape, 2¼″ h, fountain well, teakettle type	**300.00**
Apricot cut, 2¼″ h, double, matching separate glass lids, penledge across front.	**240.00**
Blue cut, cube, 3″ h, cut penledge on shoulders, matching hinged lid, four feet	**210.00**
Clear	
Cut, oval shape, 2⅝″ h, sunray cut on bottom, SS hinged lid, penledges on shoulders	**125.00**
Pressed, Columbian Exposition building, 3⅝″ h, dome lifts off	**200.00**
Sphere, 3″ h, controlled bubbles, ground and polished base, hinged SS lid	**175.00**
Spherical, paperweight type, 4½″ h, millefiori base, matching millefiori in stopper	**170.00**
Cobalt cut, cube, 1¾″ h, matching hinged lid	**290.00**
Green cut, cubes, 3″ h, matching hinged lids, green cut sponge cup, all on mahogany stand	**400.00**
Loetz type, irid amber web pattern, 3″ sq, hinged brass lid	**230.00**

Vaseline cut, hexagon with tapering
sides, 3″ h, matching hinged lid 310.00

METAL

Brass, French, 6″ h, bear in clothing sitting next to table with book, oval brass
base, bear has ruby eyes and MOP
buttons. 550.00
Bronze, 7½″ l, dog in center holding um-
brella, hatbox and boots on one side,
bag on other side, all bronze base . .   250.00
Bronze, writing case, oriental, 7½″ l,
brush and ink holder 260.00
Iron, skull from insurance company resting on iron crossed bones, 2″ h, top
half of skull opens to reveal glass
insert 95.00
Silver
Casket style, 4¾″ l, two wells inside,
English 120.00
Dog in center, oval shape, 9¾″, two
crystal and silver wells, geometric
design on wells and stand, two han-
dles, four ball feet 300.00
Man standing in center holding tray
with lid, pedestaled sander and
inkwell with four quill holes, ornate
base. 625.00

**CI, hinged lid, pressed glass insert,
c1900, $80.00.**

IRONS

History: Ironing devices have been used for
many centuries, with the earliest references dating
from 1100. Irons from the Medieval, Renaissance,
and early industrial era can be found in Europe, but
are rare. Fine brass engraved irons and hand
wrought irons dominated the period prior to 1850.
After 1850 irons began a series of rapid evolution-
ary changes.

Between 1850 and 1910 irons were heated in
four ways: 1) a hot metal slug was inserted into the
body, 2) a burning solid, e.g., coal or charcoal, was
placed in the body, 3) a liquid or gas, e.g., alcohol,
gasoline, or natural gas, was fed from an external
tank and burned in the body, and 4) conduction
heating, usually drawing heat from a stove top.

Electric irons have not yet found favor among
iron collectors.

References: Esther S. Berney, *A Collectors
Guide To Pressing Irons And Trivets,* Crown Pub-
lishers, Inc., 1977; A. H. Glissman, *The Evolution
Of The Sad Iron,* privately printed, 1970.

Museums: Henry Ford Museum, Dearborn, MI;
Shelburne Museum, Shelburne, VT; Sturbridge Village, Sturbridge, MA.

Additional Listings: See *Warman's Americana
& Collectibles* for more examples.

Advisors: David and Sue Irons.

ACCESSORIES

Laundry Stove, Keeley Stove Co., Columbia, PA, conical body, heats 10 flat
irons, c1900 . . . .   250.00

IRONS

Alcohol, revolving multipurpose [fluting,
round, and flat], self heating with alcohol tank and wick, USA, c1880. . .   75.00
Charcoal, combination [flat; fluter when
turned on side], detachable fluter in
handle, USA, c1900. . . . .   60.00

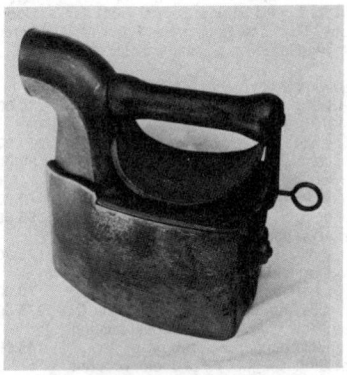

**Charcoal, wood handle, mkd #3,
$45.00.**

Fluter, machine, table clamp on base, orig black paint with striping, Crown, Philadelphia, PA, c1880 . . . .   **100.00**

Gasoline, Coleman, self heating, operated like typical camping stove, c1925. . . . .   **35.00**

Goffering, hand wrought, single barrel, spiral decoration on tripod base, inset iron, European, c1800 . . . .   **300.00**

Hat, curved shape with ridge for brim, wood handle, iron rod posts, USA . .   **35.00**

Slugs
  American, Mrs. Streeters Gem Polisher, detachable, top opens for slug, round back, tapered straight cut front, USA, 1900 . . . .   **60.00**
  Russian, brass and iron, top lifts off for slug, tear drop shape, elaborate handle and posts, c1750 . . . .   **250.00**

Dough Scraper, triangular, 4¾″ w base, 4½″ l handle, $25.00.

MINIATURES

Flat, 2″, trivet **35.00**

Goffering, for ribbons, 2½″ barrel, insert, "S" shaped stand with round base, English, sgd Kenrick, c1900 . . . .   **90.00**

Sleeve, 1⅞″, cast iron, USA, c1880s . .   **45.00**

IRONWARE

History: Iron, a metallic element that occurs abundantly in combined forms, has been known for centuries. Items made from iron range from the utilitarian to the decorative. Early hand-forged ironwares are of considerable interest to Americana collectors.

Reference: Kathryn McNerney, *Antique Iron*, Collector Books, 1984.

Additional Listings: Banks, Boot Jacks, Doorstops, Fireplace Equipment, Food Molds, Irons, Kitchen Collectibles, Lamps, Tools, and Trivets.

Andirons, pairs
  15½″ h, cast and wrought, polished .   **130.00**
  19½″, gooseneck, arched feet, ball finial **250.00**

Bookends, pr, deer, 8¼″ h, black paint.   **30.00**

Broiler, 10″ w, 18″ l to end of handle with ring for hanging **70.00**

Bundt Pan **55.00**

Calipers, double, 17″ l, twisted wrought handle **75.00**

Candle Holder, 6¾″ l, sticking tommy, socket has interior threads **70.00**

Candlestand, 29″ h, tripod feet, 18th C   **375.00**

Candlestick, 7″, primitive, sprial pushup and lip hanger, wooden base **145.00**

Cauldron, 6½″ h, 6½″ d, 3 feet, wrought bail handle **45.00**

Charcoal Iron, 7½″, cast, wooden handle, satyr head latch **40.00**

Cobbler's shoe last, man's, c1870 . . . .   **20.00**

Coffee Grinders
  5½″, brass hopper, emb brass medallion with lion and unicorn, old brass paint **65.00**
  25½″ h, 13″ sq base, 19½″ d each wheel, one with handle, sliding riveted lid, wooden drive, emb Enterprise Manufacturing Co., Philadelphia, PA, U.S.A., Pat'd May 12, '98 . . . .   **425.00**

Curry Comb, 5″ w, 7½″ l to end of wooden handle, figural horse, wooden handle **75.00**

Dipper, 16″ l, brass bowl, handle mkd F.B.S. Canton, O, Pat Jan 26, '86. . .   **125.00**

Door Knocker, 9½″ l, bat finial. **30.00**

Doorstop, Airdale, 8½″, gold paint, rhinestone eyes, leather collar. **50.00**

Figurines
  Cardinal on stump, 5½″ h, old red paint, yellow beak, green base . . .   **75.00**
  Horse, 5¼″, realistic paint, worn. . . .   **60.00**

Fork, 18″ l, 2 tine, hand-wrought, straight handle with ring for hanging, c1850 .   **65.00**

Garden Ornament, rabbit, 11½″, old white paint **125.00**

Garden Seat, 75″ l, wooden slat seat, scroll and floral back and sides, saw feet, mid 19th C **450.00**

Garden Urn, 20″, fluted sides and stem, sq base, mid 19th C **185.00**

Gate and Posts, 43″ w, 53″ h, tree trunk posts, branch and foliage deco gate, old white paint **975.00**

Grate, fireplace, 18 x 12″ **20.00**

Grease Lamp, hanging, 4″ h, spout and hanger **40.00**

Hinges, pr, 13″ l, wrought iron **65.00**

Hitching Post Finial, 13¾″, figural circus horse's head. **345.00**

Ladle, for pouring lead, 2 lips, 11″ l . . .   **25.00**

Match Holder, hanging, 8⅝″ black, gold design	35.00
Meat Press, 10″ , serrated, 2 tenderizers	15.00
Mortar and Pestle, 4″, urn shape, 1890	75.00
Muffin Pan, 8 flat sections, imprinted, Griswold MFG. Co. Erie, PA, U.S.A., c1870.	45.00
Plant Stands, pr, 33½″ h, wrought iron bowl on tripod scroll feet	350.00
Potholder, fireplace, swivel, hand-forged	15.00
Sadiron, tailor's, twisted and forged on handle, c1850	25.00
Sausage Grinder, 11″ l, hand crank, patented Aug 2, 1859, Ext, Aug 2 1873.	24.00
Scales, 11½″ l, brass crescent shaped gauge, mkd Germany	35.00
Shelf Brackets, 8 x 9¾″, scroll and tulip detail	40.00
Shoe Shine Foot Rest, 6¾″ figural horse base, gold paint	35.00
Shovel, ashes, 35½″ l, ring handle. . . .	10.00
Skimmer, 16″, wrought iron, brass bowl	50.00
Spatula, 9¼″, hand-wrought, twisted handle, ring for hanging	25.00
Stove Foot, 8½″, grotesque face with wing mask	25.00
Stringholder, beehive shape, fluted edge, bolts to counter top	25.00
Trammel, sawtooth, 49″ l, adjustable . .	70.00
Utensil Rack, 17″ l, 5 hooks, simple scroll design	185.00
Waffle Iron, hearts and star design, 418, Griswold	75.00
Wheel Measure, 12″ l, mkd Wiley & Russell Mfg. Co., Greenfield, Mass.	40.00
Wick Trimmer, scissors, 7″ l	30.00

IVORY

History: Ivory, a yellowish-white organic material, comes from the teeth or tusks of animals and lends itself well to carving. It has been used for centuries by many cultures for artistic and utilitarian items.

Ivory from elephants shows a reticulated crisscross pattern in a cross section. Hippopotamus teeth, walrus tusks, whale teeth, narwhal tusks, and boar's tusks also are ivory sources. Vegetable ivory, bone, stag horn, and plastic are ivory substitutes which often confuse collectors.

Note: Dealers and collectors should be familiar with The Endangered Species Act of 1973, amended in 1978, which limits the importation and sale of antique ivory and tortoise shell items.

Box, 4½″ h, rect, sliding cov, carved, high relief intricate village setting, bottom with low relief figures in garden, int. has vertical panel pierced with horizontal bar, early 19th C. . . .	1,210.00
Brush Pot, 5⅝″, circular, plain with in set ivory base, 17th C	600.00
Bust, Buddha, small figure sitting on crown, teakwood base, 14″	500.00
Candle holder, 5″, carved, 11-layer mystery ball with Greek key base, high relief flowers around neck.	200.00
Card Case, 4¼″, carved, high relief both sides, scholars in setting of pavilions and willow trees, 19th C	350.00
Cribbage Board, pegs store inside, 6 x 11″, painted and etched, Alaskan. . .	75.00
Doctor's Lady, 4″, fully carved figure of lying woman, wearing movable bracelet	75.00
Figurines, Animals	
Elephant and calf, 3″ h, 4″ w	200.00
Phoenix birds, pr, 10″, perched on tall flowering stump, sq, pierced wood base	500.00
Polar bears, pr, carved, Alaskan. . . .	350.00

Figurine, Elephant, 1¾″ h, $35.00.

Figurines, People	
Billiken, 4″ h, 2″ w, Alaskan	65.00
Cavalier, 7¼″, plumed hat, loose trousers, playing trumpet, ivory socle.	550.00
Man and woman, fishing, pr, 6″, holding rods with fish hanging on lines	300.00
Mother and child, 20″, mother in revealing classical robe embracing infant, wood socle, Continental, late 19th C	2,200.00
Warrior, female, 16½″, full armor, quiver of arrows on her back, holding lance and sword, honey tone with black detailing, 19th C . .	1,210.00
Wise man, 9½″, long beard, hat, staff and fan, boy at his feet holding	

shrine and apple in his hand, artist sgd, 19th C **685.00**

Frame, 3″ h, 3½″ w, easel type, carved, reticulated dragons, sgd **125.00**

Glove Stretcher, 9½″ **50.00**

Incense Burner, 10″, carved, dragon medallions body and cov, foo dog finial, loose rings, handles, intricate cut wood base **550.00**

Jewel Casket, 8¼″ l, rect, cut corners, 8 panels on sides with allegorical subjects, corners and hinged cov set with gilt bronze cast with foliage, 4 toupie feet, Continental, mid 19th C . **2,640.00**

Letter Opener, 5″ l, complete filigree work **50.00**

Magnifying Glass, 4″, carved, whale ivory handle in form of walrus **175.00**

Match Box, 1⅝″, book shape **65.00**

Mystery Ball, 7½″ h, 2½″ w, 12-layer, carved, intricate base **275.00**

Napkin Ring, carved dragon, black eyes **50.00**

Needle Case, 4″ l, carved, flower, dragon **175.00**

Pagoda, 23″, seven tier, hexagonal, hung with bells, 19th C **825.00**

Pen Holder, 4″, cylindrical, carved, 3 monkeys, tree, ftd wooden base **125.00**

Plaque, 4⅝″ h, 7⅜″ w, rect, central cartouche with 2 immortals astride lions, house, pagoda, and floral sprigs, fitted frame, 19th C **550.00**

Plate, 3″, carved flowers with stand . . . **120.00**

Ruler, 6″, folding center, brass fittings . **35.00**

Sceptre, 19¾″, carved, eight immortals on clouds, ruyi border, reverse side plain, Ming date **600.00**

Tankard, 13″, carved, battling Romans and Saracens, foliage handle, helmeted warrior thumb rest, gilt metal foot and hinged cov, strap work, knight on horseback finial, late 19th C **4,400.00**

Teapot, 5½″, scenic panels, immortals in garden, Greek key fret cov with flower finial, footed wooden base . . . **225.00**

Thermometer, 21¼″, tusk set with thermometer above carved leafage, set with polychromed bronze sparrows on ivy vines, sq ivory base, c1900 . . . . **1,000.00**

Thimble, scrimshawed, needles, spool, scissors and buttons **20.00**

Tray, 5¼″ l, rect, carved on one end with female nude and ball, late 19th C **200.00**

Wrist Rest, 11⅜″, carved, high relief, immortal and attendants, pavilion setting with tall peaks and clouds, reverse with low relief, female immortal, deer on cloud, landscape, 19th C **775.00**

JACK-IN-THE-PULPIT VASES

History: Jack-in-the-Pulpit glass vases, made in the trumpet form, were in vogue during the late 19th and early 20th centuries. The vases were made in a wide variety of patterns, colors, and sizes.

Additional Listings: See specific glass categories.

Amberina Swirl, 11½″ h, 6″ d, fluted top, amber edging **185.00**

Amethyst shaded to vaseline, ribbed, 6″ **65.00**

Art Glass, 6¼″, bulbous bottom, ruffled top, ribbed inside, purple shading to pale green **75.00**

Burmese, 12″, ruffled top, satin finish . . **425.00**

Cased
5½″ h, 5⅜″ d, blue, ruffled top with crystal edge, white lining **100.00**
6″, bud, white to clear, paper weight bottom **55.00**

Cranberry, 10¾″ h, 6″ d, ruffled edge, clear pedestal base **100.00**

Opalescent
4¾″ h, 2¼″ d, ruffled top, shell feet, vaseline, applied rigaree around center **60.00**
6¼″ h, 5″ d, green, ribbed, crystal applied flower and leaf, ruffled **100.00**

Rubena Verde, 8¼″ h, 4″ d, opal, vaseline veining applique, applied feet . . . **100.00**

Spangled
6¾″ h, 4½″ d, multicolors, silver mica flakes **75.00**
7¾″ h, 4⅝″ d, green ground, brown

8½″ h, crystal to cranberry opal, four modeled pedal feet, $150.00.

and white spatter, silver mica flakes **100.00**

Spatter, 7″, yellow ground, white, orange, blue and green stripes **50.00**

Transparent, 10½″, clear, gilt dusted pink ruffle **45.00**

Vaseline, 7½″ h, 3¾″ d, ruffled top, opal swirl, applied pink ruffle around body. **90.00**

JADE

Floral centerpiece, 21½″ w, 12½″ h, $325.00.

History: Jade is the generic name for two distinct minerals, nephrite and jadite. Nephrite, an amphibole mineral from Central Asia and used in pre-18th century pieces, has a waxy surface and ranges in hues from white to almost a black-green. Jadite, a pyroxene mineral found in Burma and used from 1700 to the present, has a glassy appearance and comes in various shades of white, green, yellow-brown, and violet.

Jade cannot be carved because of its hardness. Shapes are achieved through sawing and grinding with wet abrasives, such as quartz, crushed garnets, and carborundum.

Prior to 1800 few pieces are signed or dated. Stylistic considerations are used for dating. The Ch'ien Lung period (1936-95) is considered the "golden age" of Jade.

Museum: Avery Brundage Collection, de Young Museum, San Francisco.

Bangle, pale lavender shaded to pale green **170.00**

Belt Hook, 4⅜″, pale green-white, carved, taotie mask and archaistic designs, dragon head hook **150.00**

Bird Pole Finial, 3¾″, bird, crouched, outstretched tail and head, incised wings and tail, mottled yellow-green and russet, pierced on 2 sides for attachment **225.00**

Bowl, 4½″, mottled pale green jadite, thinly carved, flared sides, ring foot. . **1,475.00**

Box, 6″ d, round, dark green, carved, top with 2 dragons encircling shou medallions, sides with Buddhist emblems and clouds, Qianlong seal mark on base **1,430.00**

Brush Washer, 2¾″, double gourd, flecked white, hollowed out fruit carved and pierced in relief with branches and geese **550.00**

Censer, 6″ l over handles, globular, gray-green, 3 stubby mask feet, horned animal head handles with loose rings, domed cov, pierced knop with coiled dragon **775.00**

Cups

2⅛″, sq, flared sides, mottled pale brown, incised key fret border. . . . **375.00**

4¾″ long over handle, conical sides, mottled gray-green with russet, loop handle, small ring foot, Ming Dynasty. **715.00**

Dish, 5⅜″, leaf shape, pale gray-white, coiled stem handle, veins in low relief, Moghul style, 19th C **660.00**

Figurines

Fish, 1½″ h, 3½″ l, fan-tail goldfish, pop eyes, carved, mottled green . . **125.00**

Immortal, female, standing, 5¾″, yellow-white with dark brown mottling, long robes, billowing scarf, holding peach, phoenix standing behind her, 17th C **1,760.00**

Tiger, 1⅝″, block form, sitting, ribbed tail running up back, gray-white with brown markings **665.00**

Pendants

Grape cluster, 2″, pale celadon **175.00**

Magnolia bud opening, 2½″, white with russet, carved, stem forms loop **150.00**

Perfume Holder, 10½″, slender cylinder, dark green, pierced and carved, high relief, sage, attendants, trees, pale green cov and base, carved wood stand, late 18th C **4,400.00**

Planter, 5⅛″ h, 7¼″ l, rect, dark green, wooden base, Chinese, late 18th C . **450.00**

Plaque, 7¾″, circular, green-white, carved, obverse with scholar and attendant, carrying flower bough, on mountain footbridge, reverse with deer and crane beside pine tree, wood stand **660.00**

Sash Buckle, carp and horned dragon biting each other's tail, 4¾″ w, mottled celadon **185.00**

Sceptre, 14½″ l, flat, mottled white, plain shaft, gilt bronze mount and hinged enamel pendant in form of ruyi-shaped pouch, bat and dragon dec, 19th C **935.00**

Snuff Bottle, 3″, mottled brown, incised design, animal with body raised vertically, hand carved, green jade stopper. **385.00**

Spoon, 4″ l, white, flute handle, bowl carved with archaistic cicada **350.00**

Table Screen, 8″ h, 5¾″ w, rectangular, spinach green with black flecks, carved on both sides, pair of birds on flowering plum branch, bamboo reeds, wood stand. **990.00**

Thumb Ring, white, carved, dragon in relief **100.00**

Vases

3³/₁₆″, tree trunk shape, mottled white and brown, carved, blossoming prunus branches, late 17th C. **1,650.00**

4⅜″, baluster, white, carved, high relief, dragon wrapped around sides, bird shaped handles at neck, base of cresting waves, flaming pearl finial **625.00**

Waterpot, 6″ l, lotus flower shape, green-white, scalloped rim, incised veining, stems and blossoms form handle, wood stand, 19th C. **1,760.00**

Wine Ewer, cov, 6½″, pale green jadite, curved spout, loop handle **455.00**

Vase, Sumida Guwa, two monkeys, dragon costume, red ground, crackle glazed top, 7″ h, sgd Cartouche, $350.00.

JAPANESE CERAMICS

History: Like the Chinese, the Japanese spent centuries developing their ceramic arts. Each region established its own forms, designs, and glazes. Individual artists added to the uniqueness.

Japanese ceramics began to be exported to the west in the mid-19th century. Their beauty quickly made them a favorite of the patrician class.

The ceramic tradition continues into the 20th century. Modern artists enjoy equal fame with older counterparts.

Reference: Sandra Andacht, Nancy Garthe, and Robert Mascarelli, *Wallace-Homestead Price Guide To Oriental Antiques*, Wallace-Homestead, 1984, 2nd ed.

Periodical: *The Orientalia Journal*, P. O. Box 94P, Little Neck, NY 11363. Subscription: $12.00.

Additional Listings: Imari, Kutani, and Satsuma.

Airta

Barber's bowl, 9⅞″, wide everted fan shape rim, cresant indentation, white ground, underglaze blue, int. with kirn below lotus head band, ext. with figures in landscape below trellis band, 19th C **200.00**

Vase, 16¾″, bottle shape, blue and white, scrollwork pattern, raised foot with alternating X and O symbols, late 18th C **900.00**

Banko, teapot, cov, 6″ h, 7½″ w, figural, man holding fish, fish's mouth forms spout, hat is cov, bow finial, polycolor, glazed and unglazed **350.00**

Bernard Leach, vase, rect section, ovoid foot, round mouth, lozenges of blue and gray emblazed with red characters, front and back, imp mark BL, 20th C **1,500.00**

Hirado, cov dishes, pr, 5″, abalone shape, realistically molded, brown slip and underglaze blue, encrusted with shells and other crustaceans, stippled cov, shell finial with moveable tongue, late 19th C **700.00**

Kakiemon, dish, 5½″ d, blue, green, and red enamels with alternating discs of objects and stylized flowers surrounding pannel of birds and flowers, late 17th C **300.00**

Kawai Kanjiro, vase, 9½″, bottle shape, rect foot, round neck, molded whirling plum blossom design, glazed, purple and gray-blue, sgd wooden box, 20th C **1,900.00**

Kensan, box, cov, 7½″ h, underglaze blue, landscape with scholar's pavilion, poetic inscription at back, rock shape knop, sgd on lid and base, early 19th C **400.00**

Kinkozan, vase, 15½", ovoid, cream crackle glaze ground, light green molded grasses, gray rabbits, imp mark **1,400.00**

Kiokuzan Kaga, bowl, 11½" d, red with gilt highlights, int. with continuous landscape with clouds around rim, ext. with 3 iron red panels of figures, green enameled ground and peony heads, restored, mid 19th C **400.00**

Seto

Chatsubo, 5½" h, cylindrical with sloping shoulder, wide mouth, irid brown glaze pooling to long brown drips, wooden base, early 19th C **475.00**

Plate, 11¼", sq, blue and white, transfer scene, rocks and flowering trees, floral border, mid 19th C **175.00**

Teapot, cov, 4½" h, squat, round, gray ground, blossoming tree, pine, yellow, green, and gold, c1900 . . . . . **300.00**

Shoju Hamada, tea bowl, 2½" h, tapering conical shape, high foot, dark green glossy glaze on rim, rough pale green bowl, brown foot, sgd wooden box, 20th C **1,800.00**

Sumida, jar, cov, 8", round, unglazed lower section with 2 molded figures, marblized flowing green, sitting figure finial, sgd Inoue Ryosai **350.00**

Toyozo Arakawa, sake cup, 1½", thick walled, irregular straight sides, underglaze red patterns and unglazed red patches, sgd wooden box, 20th C. . . **1,400.00**

Yuko, chaire, 3½", cylindrical, irregularly potted walls, sloping shoulder, green crackle glaze, knife cut foot, imp mark, wooden box, 19th C **450.00**

JASPERWARE

History: Jasperware is a hard, unglazed porcelain with a colored ground, varying from the most common blues and greens to lavender, yellow, red, or black. The white designs are applied in relief and often reflect a classical motif. Jasperware was first produced at Wedgwood's Etruria Works in 1775. Josiah Wedgwood described it as "a fine Terra Cotta of great beauty and delicacy proper for cameos."

Many other English potters, in addition to Wedgwood, produced jasperware. Two of the leaders were Adams and Copeland and Spode. Several continental potters, e.g., Heubach, also produced the ware.

Jasperware still is made today, especially by Wedgwood.

Note: This category includes all pieces of jasperware which were made by companies other than Wedgwood. Wedgwood jasperware is found in the Wedgwood listing.

Additional Listings: Copeland and Spode and Wedgwood.

Biscuit Jar, 6" h, 5½" d, blue, white hunting scene, SP cov. rim and bail handle, imp Adams, England **175.00**

Bowl, 7", dark blue, white classical figures, unmarked, c1875 . . . . **225.00**

Box, cov, 6" l, 4½" h, gray-green, white cherub, birds, and clouds. **125.00**

Cheese Dish, 11", dark blue, white angels, grapevine border, Staffordshire, c1890. . . . . **175.00**

Coffee Pot, 10", green, white classical figures, unmarked **185.00**

Cream and Sugar, dark blue, white classical figures, Adams **150.00**

Hair Brush, ladies, lavender, white lady with cupid, brass rim and handle . . . **95.00**

Hatpin Holder, 4¼", deep blue, white classical figures, band of flowers at top, imp Adams. **50.00**

Jam Jar, SP cov, 4" h, 4" d, dark blue, white classical figures, imp Adams . . **75.00**

Jardinere, 7½", light blue, white Columbus landing, Copeland **175.00**

Jugs

8" green, white fox hunting scene, unmarked, c1820. . . . . **170.00**

12", hinged cov. green, white grape and leaf dec, branch handle, Adams **375.00**

Planter, coblat blue, white hunting scene, imp Adams. **190.00**

Salt Shaker, dark blue, white classical figures, unmarked **60.00**

Pitcher, 5⅜", brown ground, Copeland, Football/JMSD&S/1895, Reg. 180288, $250.00.

Scent Bottle, 2½", flattened oval, blue, 2 white classical figures on both sides within stiff leaf border, SP cov and stopper, unmarked **200.00**

Sugar Shaker, 6" dark blue, white classical figures, unmarked **175.00**

Syrup, SP hinged cov, 5½", medium blue, white grape and leaf dec, unmarked. **165.00**

Tankard, 8", dark blue, white classical figures, unmarked **200.00**

Tumbler, 4¼", dark blue, white classical figures, unmarked **55.00**

Vase, 7", dark blue, white classical figures, imp Adams. **140.00**

JEWEL BOXES

History: The evolution of jewelry was paralleled by the development of boxes in which to store it. Jewel box design followed the fashion trends dictated by furniture style. Many jewel boxes are lined.

Gilt metal, 7" l, rect, 4 ball feet, each side chased and repousse with panels of noble people within rural scenes, bevelled cov chased with band of ribbon, bunch of wheat and poppies, and reclining cupid holding foliate cartouche **325.00**

Silver plated, ftd, floral trellis like bail, bird finial, made by Mermod Jaccard & Co./St. Louis, c1870, resilvered, $275.00.

Glass
4½ x 2½ x 4¾", clear glass, ftd, hinged, cov with gold, heavy enamel flowers in white, pink and blue **250.00**

7 x 5 x 3", sand painting under glass lid, creamy velvet lining, c1830 . . . **225.00**

Pewter, 5½" w, 9½" d, engraved brass, frame-like ornament on top enclosing oval mosaic work, purple velvet lining, mkd "Marshall & Sons, Edinburgh, Scotland". **250.00**

Silver Plated
4½" d, 8" h, cylindrical, 3 swing out drawers, knob handles, ornate base and foot, full figure Art Nouveau nude lady holding scarf as finial **200.00**

9" h, musical, jeweled crown shape, chased scrollwork, colored glass jewels on outside, velvet int. **200.00**

Sterling Silver
Dutch, 4½ x 3¼ x 4¾", emb scenes of dancing people, children, men in rowboat, lighthouse, ftd, hinged, import mark of Chester, England, 1728. . . . . **750.00**

English, 6¾" l, rect, hinged lid, emb and chased with foliate scrolls and cupid kissing a maiden on a bed of clouds, applied rim of foliate scrolls and rosettes, base with simulated drawer, hinged wreath forms handle, lined with blue velvet, mkd "J & S, Birmingham, England, 1903" **400.00**

Wood
3¾" d, 2½" h, round, hinged, red stain, heavy enamel flowers in pastel colors, gold ground **115.00**

6 x 7 x 2½", inlaid patridgewood, octagonal, hinged cov, divided int., late George III, c1800. . . . . **225.00**

JEWELRY, ANTIQUE

History: Jewelry has been a part of every culture. It was a way of displaying wealth, power, or love of beauty. The metals, stones, and gems used in jewelry have proven endurable over time.

Jewelry items were treasured and handed down as heirlooms from generation to generation. This practice continues. Style and fashion may change, but jewelry craftsmen have a knack of redesigning their product to fit any fashion trend.

The jewelry found in this listing tends to be handmade, often by special order, and of high quality for its time period. Mass produced quality jewelry and inexpensive costume jewelry is covered in *Warman's Americana & Collectibles.*

In examining antique jewelry take into account the current value of gold and silver. Also identify the cut of stones, since some cuts are no longer fashionable. Finally, if possible, have all stones graded.

Several major auctions houses, especially Christie's, Doyle's, and Sotheby's in New York City, hold specialized antique jewelry auctions several times each year.

References: Lillian Baker, *Art Nouveau And Art Deco Jewelry,* Collector Books, 1981; Jeanne Bell, *Answers To Questions About Old Jewelry, 1840 to 1950,* Books Americana, 1982.

Pin, Lalique, jet center, marquisete stones, SS mounting, $325.00.

Bar Pin, platinum setting, 9 marquise diamonds, 2 trapezoid diamonds, 10 baguette diamonds, 8 sq diamonds, assorted round diamonds, approx weight 7.50 carats **4,250.00**

Beads
  Amethysts, 22", tapered from 5.5 to 9.5 mm, 14K yg bead spacers . . . **225.00**
  Coral, red, 89 graduated beads, 6.9 to 19.0 mm, gold oval clasp with oval cabochon, deep blue and green enamel dec. **1,450.00**
  Lapis Lazuli, 32", 8 mm, individually knotted, 14K yg clasp. **115.00**
  Pearls, single strand
    Cultured, 46 pearls 8.9 to 9.33 mm, ball clasp of 60 round diamonds, approx 2.40 carats **3,850.00**
    Natural, 92 pearls 3.8 to 8.5 mm, yellow metal clasp **1,450.00**

Bracelets
  Bangle
    Art Nouveau, enamel band and pearl rings over silver bangle. . . . **975.00**
    Half hoop design, silver and gold hinged bangle claw set with 9 circular cut diamonds alternating with 7 pearls, c1880 . . . . **1,200.00**

Knife wire, yg, center of openwork scalloped panel of white gold, 65 round diamonds, border of 60 smaller round diamonds, approx 3.25 carats, c1920 . . . . **2,750.00**

Cable, 18 yg links
  Lapis-lazulis in 4 rect cuts, hallmarked and maker's mark "E". . **525.00**
  Triple form, 35 small brilliant full cut diamonds. **1,850.00**

Identification, gentleman's 14K yg, 1⅞ x ⁷/₁₆" curved center panel with 16 pane cut brilliant white diamonds, ¼" rope sides, safety clasp. **1,300.00**

Pearls, cultured, triple strand, pearl and diamond slide center, 24 tiny rose cut diamonds set in yellow and white gold **325.00**

Victorian
  Braided hair, encased in glass, inscribed "Opehelia", orig bos . . . **60.00**
  Gilt, large faceted and engraved links, large heart pendant engraved with floral motifs and set with garnet. **225.00**
  15 K yg, 2 old mine cut diamonds and one natural pearl **650.00**

Brooches
  Art Nouveau, gold scroll mount set with seed pearls, octagonal cut peridot center, pear shaped amethyst and 3 pearl collets suspended from center **300.00**
  Cameo, oval shaped gray and white agate of woman with upswept hair, headdress of ivy leaves, gold frame of modified fret design with 8 pearls, c1785 . . . . **1,350.00**
  Crescents
    Diamonds, approx .75 carats. **525.00**
    Gold mount, turquoise and seed pearls **75.00**
  Hand painted porcelain, boy in green hat and cape, brown jacket, holds tamborine, claw frame, 1¾" h, 1"w. **85.00**
  Georg Jensen, round, raised raven and berries **135.00**
  Lalique, central female figure in long windswept skirt, 2 extended wings in pale blue plique-a-jour enamel against deep blue translucent ground, set with old mine and rose cut diamonds, stamped "Lalique" twice, 2⅛" l, c1900 . . . . **6,200.00**
  Platinum round mount set with graduated circular cut diamonds, rows of calibre cut sapphires, diamond set bow, total diamond weight approx 3.00 carats, Edwardian **1,600.00**

Chains
  Collet set with 33 rounded diamonds,

approx 2.35 carats, joined by small circular links, rod shaped links, and 4 seed pearls, 20″ l **1,325.00**

Double circular links, 14K yg, slide of hardstone cameo quartered by 4 seed pearls, scrollwork, black tracery enamel borders, 58″ l, late 19th C **1,000.00**

Chateline, Canmetille style, fancy shaped openwork set with 6 round and oval cut pink topaz suspending a lozenge shaped openwork pendant set with 5 cushion cut pink topaz and seed pearls, 19th C **425.00**

Clip, Art Deco, yg, rect amethyst, small diamonds and synethic rubies **800.00**

Crosses

Platinum setting with 4 sq diamonds, eight round diamonds, approx 1.5 carats. sgd "Cartier," white gold chain **1,300.00**

Yellow gold, red and white enamel . . **225.00**

Cufflink and Tie-Tac Set, single mount, set with rect white jadeite enhanced by openwork gold dragon, matching tie tac **150.00**

Cufflinks, double mount

Engraved nautilus shell, conch shell, 18K yg, "Schlumberger, Tiffany & Co.", orig box **550.00**

Sapphires, sq cut, platinum mounts. . **250.00**

Earrings

Bow knots, platinum, 37 small diamonds, center diamond approx $3/16$ carat, clip backs. **1,800.00**

Pendants, flexible platinum setting, elongated, 174 old European cut and single cut diamonds, approx 4.00 carats, fitted box stamped "Ramond C Yard Inc.", c1915 . . . . . . **3,575.00**

Star shape, blue enamel, 7 large mine cut brilliant white diamonds, center stone 3 carats, gold mounted lapis teardrop with 9 tiny rose cut diamonds near top of drop, yg mounts, clip backs **800.00**

Jabots

Arrow shape, platinum and gold, 24 gold European cut diamonds, French cut black onyx, mkd "Black Starr & Forest", c1915 . . . . **850.00**

Platinum setting with 1 triangular cut diamond, approx .40 carat, 1 approx .30 carat marquise diamond, 3 French cut diamonds approx .44 carats, 49 round diamonds approx total 2.45 carats. **3,000.00**

Lavaliere, lozenge shaped white gold pendant set with 16 circular cut diamonds, bezel set diamond approx 1.0 carat center, fine link chain **1,300.00**

Lockets, 18K yg. oval

Crystal intaglio of lily of the valley spray, tinted, reverse with glazed locket compartment, c1880. . . . . . **775.00**

Pink coral, white enamel and 4 sq emeralds in center **950.00**

Necklaces

Art Deco, topaz colored kite shaped stone, brass chain enameled in orange, green, and blue **135.00**

Coral, 6 inlays, 2 white jade and gilt metal fu lion masks, 2 gilt metal and kingfisher feather dragon heads with pearls, all within finely worked gilt metal hinged frame, 7½″ d, Chinese, 19th C. **1,760.00**

Tourmaline, pink and green, 14K white gold chain, ovals, rect, round cuts, pearls **425.00**

Victorian, braided hair with compass, orig box, label "So Turns My Heart To Thee" **100.00**

Pendants

Bow shaped

Aquamarine, approx 35 carat, surmounted by diamonds. **2,850.00**

44 sq cut rubies, 65 rose cut diamonds mounted in bow flowing over ruby set bar, foliate motif under bar, French yg, hallmarks "MD" and eagle's head, platinum chain **1,150.00**

Heart shape, 17 pearls, 17 round diamonds in center, 17 pear shaped diamonds on outer border, pin clasp, 14K white gold **525.00**

Owl shape, outstretched wings, emerald eyes, diamond chip in claws, 16″ woven chain **150.00**

Rings

Art Deco, 14K yg, 4.00 carat blue

Ring, cameo, "Atlas," mkd Wedgwood, SS mounting, $225.00.

aquamarine center, raised platinum
leaf side trim, 2 diamonds. **275.00**
Cameo
  Carved pink ¾″ oval cameo, 14K yg
    setting **100.00**
  Jasper agate cameo, yg setting. . . **300.00**
Cluster mount, 18K gold and silver,
  center of cushion cut sapphire surrounded by rose cut diamonds
  within a border of larger round sap-
  phires, late 19th C **1,100.00**
Diamonds
  5 round diamonds, total .50 carat,
    14K white gold **225.00**
  Solitaire, one brilliant cut diamond
    of approx 5 carats with yellow tint,
    2 tapered baguette diamonds of
    approx .30 carat each, platinum
    setting **14,500.00**
Gentleman's, star sapphire, approx
  15.00 carats, silver setting **800.00**
Wedding Set, platinum mount with cir-
  cular cut 3.75 carat diamond center
  flanked on each side by tapered dia-
  mond baguette, white gold wedding
  band set with 3 tapered diamond
  baguettes **4,750.00**
Shirt Studs, pr, sapphires **100.00**
Stick Pins
  Blackamoore face, enameled, hoop
    earrings, set with cabochon coral
    and a round garnet in spotted black
    and white enameled turban, gold
    mount, continental hallmark, Aus-
    trian, late 19th C **225.00**
  Game Bird, gold and silver set with
    rose cut diamonds and old Euro-
    pean cut diamonds, reddish enamel
    on head and feet, late 19th **385.00**
  Shell, stylized, 1 round .40 carat dia-
    mond surrounded by calibre cut sim-
    ulated emeralds in navette shape,
    10 round diamonds, purple velvet
    box, c1920 . . . . **330.00**
Tiara, old mine and rose diamonds, im-
  itation multicolored French pearls . . . **3,500.00**

JUDAICA

History: As members of the Jewish faith spread
throughout the world, artifacts used in their syn-
agogues and religious celebrations in the home assumed the artistic attributes of each individual region. Thus each basic form, whether Hanukah lamp
or Torah breast plate, may come in a wide variety
of styles.

Silver is a favored medium for many objects.
Hence, objects have value both by weight as well
as artistic content. Signed items are the most desired. Sotheby's and Christie's both hold at least
one special auction of Judaica each year.

Beaker and Tray, SS, repousse work
  of grapes hanging from vine on
  3″ beaker, 6¼″ tray with Star of
  David, grapes on vine, Hebrew inscrip-
  tion **335.00**
Belt Buckle, Yom Kippur, SS, oval, emb
  with lions of Judah flanking wreath
  framed with Hebrew inscription, Austrian hallmarks, 1 oz, 10 dwt, 5″ l . . . **275.00**
Bread Tray, SS, rippled border, Hebrew
  inscription around border, center of
  tray emb with 2 loaves of bread
  flanked by Star of David with shafts of
  wheat going into side of tray, emb in
  gold, 15½ x 11″ **1,175.00**
Circumcision Knife Set, steel blade,
  ebonized wood handle, SS mounts,
  matching SS shield, c1800. . . . . **825.00**
Esther Scrolls
  Italian Illuminated, scroll finely written
    on parchment, dec along borders
    with polychrome and gilt flowers,
    front panel with elaborate fruit, floral
    and scrolling foliate illumination in
    polychrome and gilt surrounding
    cartouche painted with a pomegran-
    ate, illumination terminating approx
    two-thirds from beginning with crest
    of a pelican, on wood roller, scroll
    7″ w, 18th C **3,850.00**
  Mediterranean, silver filigree case with
    applied floral motifs, 3 tiered finial,
    light brown parchment scroll with
    finely written hamelech text, case
    16″ h, scroll 5″ w, 19th C **1,350.00**
Etrog Containers
  Continental, silver, fluted oval, detach-
    able lid and body emb and chased
    with floral swags and scrollwork,
    floriform knop on lid, int. gilt lined,
    5″, c1900 . . . . **600.00**
  Syrian, inlaid silver and copper, rect,
    cut corners, depicting Moses,
    Aaron, and stylized foliage lid with
    vignette in Hebrew, entitled the Ex-
    odus from Egypt, lock and key,
    wood lined, 5¾″, early 20th C. . . . **1,550.00**
Kiddush Cup
  German, silver, hexagonal bowl en-
    graved with Hebrew inscription at
    the rim, cast with flowers and
    scrolls, set on knopped stem,
    domed circular foot, 5¾″ h, c1920 **300.00**
  Persian, silver and niello, dec of gra-
    pevine design enclosing 2 car-
    touches, one with crowned Star of
    David flanked by lions, other with
    bird and Hebrew inscription, "To
    Honor the Sabbath," 3¼″, early
    20th C **1,100.00**
Matzo Cover, 20″ sq, linen, "Matzo" in
  Hebrew embroidered in white within a
  wreath above Hebrew inscription for

the family of Menachem Nurzi, dated
1802, lace border **450.00**
Menorah, SS
    Branches with acanthus leaves, bul-
    bous repousse base with heavy flo-
    ral work, Star of David in center of
    branches, 7½ x 6½" **450.00**
    Scenes of the Ten Commandments
    Tablets, Judaic lions, Pillars of the
    Temple with everburning flame and
    drapery, repousse, oil burning, 10 x
    8½" **675.00**
Purim Noisemaker, grogger form, ap-
    plied with cast SS figure of a man lead-
    ing another on horseback, 4¾" **225.00**
Passover Seder Towels, pr, undyed
    linen, lower section embellished with
    flowering tree above floral border,
    fringed, 92 x 21", 19th C **600.00**
Rose Water Sprinkler, Balkan, silver gilt,
    flattened fig form, pierced and applied
    with flowers and foliage, stamens with
    touches of red enamel, oval base, up-
    per section terminating in a floral bou-
    quet, 12¾" h, second half of 19th C   **700.00**
Sabbath Candelabra, pr, Polish, 5 light,
    brass, baluster stem over domed cir-
    cular base, upper section pierced and
    chased with lions amidst foliage, mid
    19th C **1,870.00**
Spice Boxes, SS
    Pyramid shape, claw feet, tower turret
    with flag, repousse foliage work,
    7" **215.00**
    Turret shape, 4 smaller towers
    mounted on pedestal ending in
    round foot, dec swags and floral
    work, 8" **385.00**
Spice container, German, porcelain, fish
    form, gilt details and polychrome foli-
    age, head with hinged metal fitting re-
    vealing hollow int., underglaze blue
    mark of crowned caduceus, 5¼" . . .   **550.00**
Torah Crown, SS, multitiered openwork,
    bird finial, set with rows of flower
    heads and pendant bells, Hebrew in-
    scription, dated 1930, 17½" h, 85 oz,
    10 dwt **900.00**
Torah Mantle, German stumpwork,
    worked in silver metallic thread on
    ecru ground, upper section with He-
    brew inscription in oval reserve em-
    bellished with foliage, lower section
    worked with large flower filled urn,
    crowned Solominic columns, fringed,
    34" l, early 18th C. **3,550.00**
Wall Plaque, silvered brass, relief with a
    scene of Jews praying in synagogue,
    inscripted in Hebrew, Bezalel, Jeru-
    salem, 5½ x 17", c1920. . . . .   **725.00**
Yad, Middle East, SS, applied wirework
    dec, presentation inscription, chain at-
    tachment, 11¾", 3 oz **200.00**

JUGTOWN POTTERY

History: In 1920 Jacques and Julianna Busbee
left their cosmopolitan environs and returned to
North Carolina to revive the state's dying craft of
pottery making. Jugtown Pottery, a colorful and
somewhat off-beat operation, was located in Moore
County, miles away from any large city and acces-
sible only "if mud permits."

Ben Owens, a talented young potter, turned the
wares. Jacques Busbee did most of the designing
and glazing. Julianna handled promotion.

Utilitarian and decorative items were produced.
Although many colorful glazes were used, orange
predominated. A Chinese blue glaze that ranged
from light blue to deep turquoise was a prized glaze
reserved for the very finest pieces.

Jacques Busbee died in 1947. Julianna, with the
help of Owens, ran the pottery until 1958 when it
was closed. After long legal battles, the pottery was
reopened in 1960. It now is owned by Country
Roads, Inc., a non-profit organization. The pottery
still is operating and using the old mark.

Advisor: Robert Berman.

Bowls
  2 x 6", crimped, Chinese blue and red
    glaze. **75.00**
  3 x 5½", green frogskin glaze **35.00**
Cup and Saucer, cobalt blue **40.00**
Candlesticks, pr, 11", orange. **90.00**
Jar, 6", salt glaze, pebbles in glaze . . .   **75.00**

**Sugar bowl, tobacco spit glaze, imp
stamp mark, $25.00.**

Jar, cov, 4″, frogskin glaze **40.00**
Pitchers
  6″, Chinese white, exposed clay bottom of body **90.00**
  8″, salt glaze **70.00**
Vases
  5″, squat bottom, Chinese white **65.00**
  9″ h, 10″ w, stovepipe neck, two handles, Chinese blue and red glaze .   **200.00**
  10″ h, 5″ w, four small handles at neck, salt glaze **135.00**
  13″ h, 10″ w, stovepipe neck, Chinese blue **250.00**

KPM   *K.P.M*

History: The mark, KPM, has been used separately and in conjunction with other symbols by many German porcelain manufacturers, among whom are the Königliche Porzellan Manufactur in Meissen, 1720s; Königliche Porzellan Manufactur in Berlin, 1832-1847; and Krister Porzellan Manufactur in Waldenburg, mid-19th century.

Collectors now use the term "KPM" to refer to the high quality porcelain produced in the Berlin area in the 18th and 19th centuries.

Basket, 16¼″ d, oval, 2 sq handles, pierced border, pale green ground, flowers and butterflies, blue scepter, iron red KPM, c1840 . . . .   **325.00**
Bowl, 13¼ x 11¼″, oval, applied floral dec, c1880 . . . .   **375.00**
Compote, 7½″ h, pedestal base, pierced border with gilt drapery, green ground, floral dec, mkd, c1860 . . . .   **275.00**
Creamer and Sugar, pink roses, gold handles **125.00**
Cup and Saucer, emb floral and gold dec   **42.50**
Dinner Service, Armorial, 24 pcs, blue and gilt rims with Hohenzollern Wappen and initials, center with crown suspending an order, gilt borders, blue scepter, iron red KPM, date 1903-1913 . . . .   **2,350.00**
Figurine, classical youth in 18th C costume, bright colors, c1830 . . . .   **650.00**
Inkwell and Pounce Pot on 7″ l dish base, apple green, painted Watteauesque, gilted **200.00**
Plaques
  Dice players, group of Neopolitan urchin boys playing dice, painted after Murillo, sgd, imp KPM, scepter, late 19th C, 10⅜ x 7⅝″ **2,250.00**
  Queen Louise of Prussia decending palace steps, raised gold dec on dress and jewelry, gilt frame, artist sgd Wagner, 19th C, 9¼ x 6¼″ . . .   **2,800.00**
  Ruth holding a sheaf of wheat, imp KPM, scepter, c1900, 16 x 10¼″ . .   **1,400.00**

Statue, 24″ h, male and female on pedestal, $3,600.00.

Ships at sea, 2 clipper ships tossing on stormy sea, imp KPM, scepter, paper label, late 19th C, 13⅜ x 11¼″ **900.00**
The Three Fates, spinning the thread of life, measuring and cutting off the allotted length, imp KPM, scepter, letter H, 9¼ x 6¼″ **2,000.00**
Plate, 7″, hp yellow daisies **80.00**
Tea Set, 4 pcs, teapot, cov sugar, cov pitcher and 16¼″ tray, floral and bird dec, late 19th C **700.00**
Vases, pr, 17″, cov, reserves of lovers under tree, cobalt blue ground, white borders, gilt, late 19th C **1,550.00**
Wall Pocket, 15″, ornate floral dec. . . .   **275.00**

KAUFFMANN, ANGELICA

History: Marie Angelique Catherine Kauffmann was a Swiss artist who lived from 1741 until 1807. Her paintings were copied by many artists who hand decorated porcelain during the 19th century. The majority of the paintings are neo-classical in style.

Bowl, 9½″ d, sleeping warrior and maiden, cobalt border, gilt dec, gold rim, mkd Victoria, Austria **55.00**
Box, cov, round, woman and cherub on top of cov, red, green, and gold design, mkd Royal Vienna **125.00**
Chocolate Pot, cov, 9½″ h, reserve panel scene of classical maidens, mkd Victoria, Austria **80.00**

Cup and Saucer, ftd, gold handles, portrait dec, beehive mark 60.00
Planter, bulb, 6¼" d, 2½" h, brown shading to white, gold florals, seated maiden with cupid at her side, two attending maidens behind her, mkd Victoria, Austria 125.00
Plaque, 12", four classical ladies, red border, gold highlights, pierced for hanging 125.00

Tobacco Jar, 7½" h, portrait front, dark green muted with hints of orange and yellow, sp rim and lid, pipe finial, $300.00.

Plates
  8½"
    Cherub and maiden, green and gold border, hp, mkd Crown China, Austria. 85.00
    Cherub and three classical women, blue and gold border, sgd Kauffmann, Victoria, Austria 85.00
    9", 1½" openwork border, dark green ground, seated sleeping warrior, woman holding garland of flowers, sgd Kauffmann 90.00
    9¾", Shepherd and three draped maidens, ¼" blue border 100.00
Tea Set, teapot, cov, creamer, cov sugar, two cups and saucers, green ground, cherubs and maiden, sgd. . . 250.00
Toothpick, garden scene, three maidens picking grapes for cupid. 110.00
Tray, 16½" d, reserve portrait scene, burgandy, gold beads 175.00
Vases
  9¼", 2 ornate handles, classical scene, pearlized ground, lacy, gold dec. 100.00
  16", handled, portrait, cobalt ground, sgd. 150.00

KEW BLAS

History: Amory and Francis Houghton established the Union Glass Company, Somerville, Massachusetts, in 1851. The company went bankrupt in 1860, but was reorganized. Between 1870 and 1885 the Union Glass Company made pressed glass and blanks for cut glass.

Art glass production began in 1893 under the direction of William S. Blake and Julian de Cordova. Two styles were introduced. A Venetian style consisted of graceful shapes in colored glass, often flecked with gold. An iridescent glass, labeled Kew Blas, was made in plain and decorated forms. The pieces are close in design and form to Quezel products, but lack the subtlety of Tiffany items.

The company ceased production in 1924.

Bowl, 14" d, 5" h, pulled feather, red ground, sgd 1,200.00
Compote, 4½" h, irid gold, fluted top . . 525.00
Creamer, 2¼", bulbous, fishnet pattern. 400.00
Finger Bowl, 6" underplate, ribbed, scalloped border, metallic gold lustre, platinum highlights 475.00
Pitcher, 4⅛" h, irid gold and green feather dec on irid white ground 750.00
Rose Bowl, 4½" d, shaped base, green, gold zipper dec on tan ground 600.00
Salt, open, irid gold. 200.00
Sherbet, 5" h, irid gold, sgd. 200.00
Tumbler, 3½" h, tapered, rounded foot, ribbed interior, irid gold, sgd. 150.00
Vases
  4¼" h, green and gold irid pulled threading on opal ground 800.00

Vase, 7" h, pulled feather, sgd, $1,225.00.

5″, gold, petal top 625.00
7½″, rich blue irid 900.00
8″, inverted funnel body, bulbous
   shoulder, dec, sgd 1,200.00
8¾″, jack-in-the-pulpit, gold, pulled
   lines, stretch marks in flowers 800.00
10″, King Tut, green and irid gold . . . 1,000.00
Wine Glass, 4¾″, curving stem, irid
   gold 150.00

KITCHEN COLLECTIBLES

History: The kitchen was a central focal point in a family's environment until the 1960s. Many early kitchen utensils were handmade and prized by their owners. Next came a period of utilitarian products of tin and other metals. However, the housewife did not wish to work in a sterile environment, so color was added through enamel and plastic while design began to serve both an aesthetic and functional purpose.

The advent of home electricity changed the type and style of kitchen products. Many items went through fads. The high technology field already has made inroads into the kitchen, and another revolution seems at hand.

References: Jane H. Celehar, *Kitchens and Gadgets*, 1920 to 1950, Wallace Homestead, 1982; Linda Campbell Franklin, *300 Hundred Years of Kitchen Collectibles*, Books Americana, 1982, second edition; Glydon Shirley, *The Miracle In Grandmother's Kitchen*, privately printed, 1983.

Periodical: Kitchen Collectibles News, Box 383, Murray Hill Station, New York, NY 10016.

Additional Listings: Baskets, Brass, Butter Prints, Copper, Fruit Jars, Food Molds, Graniteware, Ironware, Tinware, and Woodenware. See *Warman's Americana & Collectibles* for more examples.

Apple Butter Scoop, 12″ l, pine, open
   "D" handle 150.00
Apple Peeler, Shaker type, wood,
   clamps to table top 125.00
Baker's Rack, 6½″ h, 5″ d, wrought iron,
   5 shelves, grapevine pattern sides,
   c1910. . . . . 450.00
Batter Bowl, small, orig bail handle . . . 250.00
Bread Board, round, maple, carved
   motto along edge 35.00
Butter Churns
  16″ h, ovoid, Ohio stoneware, applied
    handles, splashes of blue, imp "3" 100.00
  23″, wood, green paint, stave con-
    struction, metal bands, turned top,
    dasher 355.00
Butter Crock, cov, daisy pattern, blue
   and white 75.00
Cabbage Cutting Board, 34½″ l, 12¼″
   w, wood 15.00
Canister Set, 12 pcs, 6 large, 6 small,

cov, sq, windmills, blue and white, mkd
   Germany 150.00
Cheese Strainer, 21″ l, woven, splint . . 145.00
Cherry Pitter, CI, 3 legs, 1863 . . . . 50.00
Coffee Pot, cov, 10″, drip, 2 sections,
   graniteware, cream, green trim 18.00
Colander, 13″ d, copper, hand-wrought
   brass loop handle 75.00
Cookie Board, 14¾ x 18¾″, oval, poplar,
   fish tail crest 80.00
Corn Bread Pan, 13″ l, 6″ w, CI, wire
   handles, "Wagner Ware", 1880 . . . . 18.00
Custard Cup, crockery, fishscale pattern,
   blue and white 45.00
Dutch Oven, 24″ w, 22½″, h, tin, hearth-
   side with wrought iron spit, black
   paint 130.00
Flour Scoop, tin, dated 1869 . . . . 25.00
Flour Sifter, 5 cup size, tin, double lids,
   yellow wood handle 30.00
Fork, 17″ l, wrought iron, detailed
   handle 175.00

Cutting Board, wood, round top, shaped base, metal blade, 6⅛″ w, 18″ h, $85.00

Funnel with filter, 7″ h, 4″ w, copper,
   brass thumbrest 25.00
Hot Plate, 6¾″, tin, punched compass
   star design, wooden base, brass stud
   trim 170.00
Kettle, 14″ d, CI, ftd, bail handle, swivel
   hook for fireplace 42.00
Ladle, 11½″ l, pierced design on bowl 115.00
Lemon Squeezer, CI, hinged, Universal 14.00
Mayonnaise Maker, 9½″, glass jar base,
   directions emb on side, iron crank top,
   Universal 24.00
Mixing Bowls
  7″, blue enameled tin 12.00

10″, crockery, cottage scene	22.00
Pastry Cutter, 4⅜″, brass	12.00
Pitcher, water, 9″, tin, wide spout	65.00
Potato Masher, 9½″, l, twisted wire, turned wooden handle	15.00
Roaster, 10″ h, 10″ w, 8″ d, tin, dome top	125.00

Rolling Pins

Tin, wooden handles	40.00
Yellow ware, 15½″ l, wooden handles	110.00
Skewer Holder, 11¾″ l, tin plated, 9 skewers	55.00
Skillet, forged iron, long handle, 3 peg legs	45.00
Skimmer, 18½″ brass and wrought iron	90.00
Toaster, stove top, one piece, wire	12.00
Tongs, ice, 14″, iron, Butler Ice Co.	12.00
Washboard, 24½″ h, 12″ w, wood frame, brass corrugated scrubbing surface	14.00
Washtub, 11½″ d, 5″ h, wood, 12 staves	45.00

KUTANI

History: In the mid 1600s Kutani originated in the Kaga province of Japan. Kutani comes in a variety of color patterns, one of the most popular being Ao Kutani, a green glaze with colors such as green, yellow, and purple enclosed in a black outline. Wares made since the 1870s for export are enameled in a wide variety of colors and styles.

Berry Set, 7 pcs, large bowl, 6 small bowls, enamel floral dec, red border.	150.00

Bowls

7″, center, fish leaping, floral diaper border, green glaze, Ao Kutani	300.00
9″, One Thousand Butterflies, black and gold border	175.00
Coffee Pot, cov, scenic, mythological figures	200.00

Dishes

7½″, octagonal, rimmed, 5 children playing in garden	190.00

10″, band of birds and floral roundels, Ao Kutani	250.00
10½″, rimmed, magpies in bamboo forest	260.00
Ginger Jar fitted as table lamp, 19″, scenic	150.00
Hair Receiver, heart shape, One Thousand Faces, green glaze, Ao Kutani.	85.00
Jar, cov, 14¾″, birds and grasshoppers in foliage, gold bands, bud finial, sgd, 19th C	250.00
Pitcher, 6″, birds and flowers, c1840	150.00
Tea Set, 3 pcs, teapot, creamer, sugar, cov, turquoise, dragons and clouds, lotus leaf finials	250.00
Teapot, cov, white, red birds and clouds	95.00
Tobacco Jar, cov, 6″, mask handles	200.00
Tray, red ground, river scene, boatmen, gold	150.00
Umbrella Stand, 28″, butterflies, flowers, foliage, and medallions	500.00

Vases

9¾″, bulbous, stick, flowers and birds	200.00
15″ h, 7¾″ d, obverse, war lords, reverse, grouse, flying bird, and enameled mums, gold trim, geometric diapered border, Ao Kutani	375.00
16″, ovoid, waterfall, mountains, and lakes, multicolored pastel shades	475.00
18″, octagonal, white ground, red panels with medallions of beautiful women	500.00

LALIQUE

LALIQUE **A.LALIQUE**

History: Rene Lalique (1860–1945) first gained prominence as a jewelry designer. Around 1900 he began experimenting with molded glass brooches and pendants, often embellishing them with semiprecious stones. By 1905 he was devoting himself exclusively to the manufacture of glass articles.

In 1908 Lalique began designing packaging for the French cosmetic houses. He also produced many objects, especially vases, bowls, and figurines, in the Art Noveau style in the 1910s. The full scope of Lalique's genius was seen at the 1925 Paris International Exhibition of Decorative Arts. He later moved to the Art Deco form.

The mark "R. LALIQUE FRANCE" in block letters is found on pressed articles, tableware, vases, paperweights, and mascots. The script signature, with or without "France", is found on hand blown objects. Occasionally a design number is included. The word "France" in any form indicates a piece made after 1926.

Miniatures, left, red, 3½″, $75.00, right, red, 3¾″, $75.00.

The post-1945 mark is "Lalique France" without the "R"; but, there are exceptions to this rule. Much faking of the Lalique signature occurs, the most common being the addition of an "R" to the post-1945 mark.

References: Katherine Morrison McClinton, *Introduction to Lalique Glass*, Wallace Homestead, 1978.

Additional Listing: Lamps and Lighting.

Ashtray, 6¾" d, Fauvette, clear and frosted, rim form of triangular projections each containing birds and branches, molded R. Lalique, c1922 ..... **275.00**

Bookends, Hirondelle, birds, frosted, Lalique, pr **375.00**

Bottles
  Atomizer, 6", green, dancing nudes around base, sgd **350.00**
  Perfume, 4¼", heart shape, Coeur Joie **235.00**
  Perfume, frosted stoppers with figures of court lady and gentleman, block letters Lalique, pr **300.00**
  Perfume, Thorn pattern, mauve stain on clear glass, sgd raised block letters **450.00**
  Scent, 2⅓", molded emerald green, swirl design, R. Lalique, c1930 ... **750.00**

Bowls
  5¼", fruit, honey, stylized wheat, acid etched, R. Lalique, c1930 .... **320.00**
  8", Vernon pattern, opal sunflowers . **325.00**
  8½", round, Gui, No 1, clear, molded mistletoe on ext with frosted intaglio leaves and branches, opal berries in relief, block letters R. Lalique **400.00**
  11¼", round, flared rim, frosted, leaping gazelles and leafy branches molded in relief, block letters R. Lalique **350.00**
  14¼", opal, 8 pr kneeling angels with vases of flowers, sgd R. Lalique, c1930.................... **2,275.00**
  14¼", round, ribbed, flared collared rim molded with frosted marguerites, script Lalique, France **225.00**

Boxes
  2½" h, 3½" d, round, carved, deep emb floral top, frosted sgd R. Lalique **275.00**
  3¾", round, rose tint ground, 3 dancing nudes holding hands, sgd **185.00**
  3¾", 3 dancing nudes on lid, design around sides, frosted, block letters R. Lalique **215.00**
  Nude horseback riders........... **300.00**

Car Mascots
  3½" l, molded boar, topaz, Sanglier, sgd R. Lalique, c1929.......... **1,700.00**
  4¾", sparrow, Timide, frosted and clear with head pecking, tail down,

script R. Lalique, France, # 115, molded R. Lalique, c1927....... **220.00**

Ceiling Globe, 12" d, Grand Cyprins, R. Lalique..................... **750.00**

Figure, nude, 2⅝" h, 1⅜" d, frosted opal, standing, flowing drapery, block letters R. Lalique, wax seal **285.00**

Fingerbowl, underplate, 4⅜" bowl, 7½" plate, double row of fish, blue trim, R. Lalique..................... **225.00**

Fish, 4" h, 6½" l, frosted, orig paper label, sgd Lalique, France......... **265.00**

Inkwell, cov, 2" h, Papillons, molded butterfly wings, frosted, c1932 .... **550.00**

Jardiniere, 19¼", Saint-Hubert, frosted and clear with handles of bounding gazelles amidst foilage, wheel cut R. Lalique, France, c1926 .... **1,200.00**

Liqueur Glass
  1 oz, 2 panels, cherubs **35.00**
  2", Coquelicot pattern, overlapping poppy petals with black enamel stamen, R. Lalique **50.00**

Mirror Frame, 4¼", sq, frosted with 6 mermaids around opening, script R. Lalique, France, c1930 .... **150.00**

Pendant, lilies, orange-red, weeping lilies highlighted with dark enameling, unsigned.................... **375.00**

Plate, 10½", black, tree molded in relief **125.00**

Ring Tree, 5" h, 3¾" d, figural center, frosted madonna, R. Lalique, France "288".................... **195.00**

Scent Burner, 3½", artichoke shape, butterscotch, oil lid and wick holder, R. Lalique, c1930 .... **295.00**

Tumbler, 4", Hesperides, clear with frosted swirling leaves **95.00**

Vases
  4¾", Rampillon, yellow, molded with diamond cut projections on floral ground, wheel cut R. Lalique, c1922.................... **1,300.00**
  5½", Amiens, sq, molded, topaz brown, 2 handles with 4 small curled fern fronds, R. Lalique **920.00**
  6¼", trumpet shape, African violet leaf design and frosting int, corn flower blue enamel ext, R. Lalique, France, c1929.................... **725.00**
  6⅓", opal, molded eucalyptus leaves with birds at base, R. Lalique, c1920.................... **600.00**
  7¾", molded, clear, 6 panels of veiled figures, script R. Lalique, c1930.................... **800.00**
  9⅓", cylindrical, Epicea, clear, evergreen motif in relif, R. Lalique, c1930.................... **550.00**
  11", frosted, 4 vertical bands of scrambling lizards in relief, script R. Lalique, # 898, c1925 .... **1,095.00**

Vase, 3½″ h, lion face, script sgd, $45.00.

Wine Glasses
3½″, underside of pedestal ft cov with graduating raised dots, R. Lalique, set of 8 . . . .   250.00
Etched "S" design, cut stem, R. Lalique 45.00

LAMP SHADES

History: Lamp shades were made to diffuse the harsh light produced by early gas lighting fixtures. These early shades were made by popular Art Nouveau manufacturers including Durand, Quezal, Steuben, Tiffany, and others. Many shades are not marked.

Reference: Jo Ann Thomas, *Early Twentieth Century Lighting Fixtures*, Collector Books, 1980.

American Makers, unmarked
5¼″ h, opal, bell shaped, green feathering, edged in green 75.00
13″ h, pr, stained glass globes, radiating panels of green glass tiles, medial band of blue, white, and red butterflies 1,650.00
22″, d, conical, leaded glass, ochre and pale green radiating panels above border of ochre, blue, and green 1,870.00
Carnival, 5¼″ h, 5″ d at base, marigold, bell shaped, floral, stylized flowers and leaves 25.00
Cased Glass, 7″ h, hall, gold ruby outer casing with blue vines and paper-weight inset flowers in pink, white, and yellow, green leaves 200.00
Fostoria
King Tut dec, gold interior, dark green shade with platinum dec. 375.00
Wave pattern, dark brown with gold zipper dec, brilliant gold int. 450.00
Galle, 10¼″ d, cameo, ivory glass overlaid in amber and brown and cut with a leafage and petals to resemble a blossom, firepolished, inscribed in elaborate cameo "Galle", c1900 . . .   2,325.00
Handel
10″ d, dome, blue, green dec, fits floor lamp 275.00
16″, chipped ice, reverse painted fish, lily pads, water. 1,400.00
16″ d, dome radiating panels of green glass tiles against lower border of pink and cherry blossoms, green leaves, white and green ground. . .   1,320.00
Lundberg, 7″ h, dome, blue and green dec   200.00
Lustre Art
5¼″ h, pr, green border with brown and white pulled feathers on irid gold ground, sgd 265.00
8″, lily shape, gold irid, sgd 250.00
Muller-Fres, 6″ h, opaque off-white with hues of mottled purple, green, and orange, sgd 75.00
New England, 4½″ h, 6½″ d, 2¼″ fitter, peachblow, shiny finish 385.00
Opalescent, hanging hall fixture, cranberry with white stripes 75.00
Quezal
5¼″ h
Calcite, gold, pulled blue feather pattern on ivory 275.00
Opal, ribbed bell form, amber irid striated feathers, sgd 100.00
Opal, snakeskin on gold, green border 125.00
9¼″
Amber, irid, sgd 150.00
Lily, gold, blue, and purple 250.00
Opal, green feathers, sgd 175.00
Pendant, compressed teardrop form, opal dec with pulled lattice devices, inscribed, sgd 200.00
19″, dome, amber irid sides dec with striated feathers in amber and wintergreen irid. 1,760.00
Steuben
4″, h, Aurene, creamy chocolate, applied border, mkd #206 . . . .   350.00
4½″ h, Ivrene acid cutback, irid, electric 85.00
5¼″, h
Amber irid
Bulbous shape, sgd 110.00
Flaring base, sgd 115.00
Aurene, tan, gold leaf and vine, sgd, R. #191 . . . .   185.00

Calcite, ribbed, gold and white . . .   **100.00**
Diamond Quilted, short green
feather. **150.00**
9½" h
Amber irid, sgd **100.00**
Opal, trumpet form, amber irid
feathering, sgd **125.00**
Tiffany
5" h, King Tut, green dec on opal,
sgd. **575.00**
16" d, dome, radiating panel of mot-
tled, green glass tiles, medial band
of mottled ochre and green scrolling
acorns, imp Tiffany Studios, NY . .   **2,000.00**
/enini Glass
10½" d, sconce shape, pyriform, milky
glass striped in pale blue, frosted
int., paper label Venini/Murano/
Venezia. **75.00**
12" d, dome, milky glass striped with
pink, paper label Venini/Murano/
Venezia. **85.00**

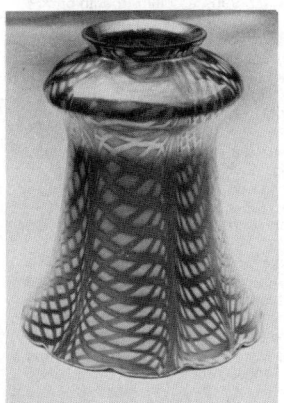

**Steuben, 5½" h, 2½", collar; green, pur-
ple, and gold irid, opal ground, fish net
pattern, gold irid, int, $175.00.**

LAMPS AND LIGHTING

History: Lighting devices have evolved from simple stone age oil lamps to the popular electrified
models of today. Aimé Argand patented the first oil
lamp in 1784. Around 1850 kerosene became a
popular lamp burning fluid, replacing whale oil and
other fluids. In 1879 Thomas A. Edison invented
the electric light bulb, causing fluid lamps to lose
favor and creating a new field for lamp manufacturers to develop. Companies like Tiffany and Han-

del developed skills in the manufacture of electric
lamps, having their decorators produce beautiful
aesthetic bases and shades.

References: J. W. Courter, *Aladdin, The Magic
Name in Lamps*, Wallace Homestead, 6th Printing,
1980, J. W. Courter, *Collectors Manual & Price
Guide Nine, 1983*, privately printed, 1982, Jo Ann
Thomas, *Early Twentieth Century Lighting Fixtures*,
Collector Books, 1980, Catherine M. V. Thuro, *Oil
Lamps*, Wallace Homestead, 1976, Catherine M. V.
Thuro, *Oil Lamps II*, Thorncliffe House, Inc., 1983.

Collectors' Club: Mystic Light of the Aladdin
Knights, J. W. Courter, Simpson, IL 62985, *The
Mystic Light of the Aladdin Knights*, (bi-monthly).

Museum: Winchester Center Kerosene Kerosene Lamp
Museum, Winchester Center, CT

Additional Listings: See specific makers and
Pattern Glass.

**Tavern, fat lamp, tin with brass caps,
5" l, 1¾" h, $115.00**

AMERICAN, EARLY

Betty Lamps
4", wrought iron, wire wick pick, small
bird silhouette on front lid **300.00**
5"
Double, wrought and cast iron. . . .   **125.00**
Single, wrought iron, twisted han-
ger, wire-link wick pick, old black
paint **110.00**
Canting, 7", tin, flat lard type wick,
varnished **375.00**
Chandelier, tin, 4 gooseneck style can-
dle arms, 24" h. **800.00**
Cruise, 6", double, wrought iron, twisted
hanger, worn tin plating **85.00**
Lacemaker's Lamp, 18" h, 10" d, satin
glass, shaded rose with emb leaves,
scrolls and overlapping petals design,
white lining, brass handled base,
chimney, orig kerosene burner **550.00**
Lard Lamps
7¼" h, tin, emb label on side of font
"D. Kinnear's Patent Feb. 4, 1851",
traces of old black paint. **515.00**
11½" h, tin
Brown paint, copper tube, tin hood,
mkd "Swopes Patent". **350.00**

Saucer base, ring handle, orig tin reflector, shade mkd "Ufford/Kinnear Patent" **500.00**

Loom, 18" l, wrought iron, rush holder, candle socket counterweight **215.00**

Peg Lamps

19½" h, 3½" d, satin glass, pink swirl MOP, ruffled top, clear chimney, classical lady candlestick brass base **600.00**

19¾" h, lime green font, alternating frosted and glossy stripes, enameled white daisies, lime green to clear tulip form shade, orig burner, brass beehive candlestick with pushup **300.00**

Petticoat Lamps

5½" h, clear, well shaped applied handle, floral cut dec, brass collar and fluid burner, snuffer caps **75.00**

6" h, pewter, orig camphene burner, attributed to J. B. Woodbury, RI, c1820 . . . . **250.00**

Rushlight, 14" h, wrought iron, twisted detail, coiled base, candle socket counterweight **135.00**

Sparking Lamp, 4½" h, pewter, single whale oil burner, turned pedestal, disc base **225.00**

Whale Oil, 5" h, pewter, acorn font, brass burner, mkd "E. Capen" **400.00**

CHANDELIERS

6 Lights

16½" h, 19" d, scrolling gilt bronze candle arms, joined by winged masks to waisted standard, cast with classical motifs, Louis XVI style, French, late 19th C **1,100.00**

40" h, gilt metal circular dished candle holders, drip pans on arms, circular corona over concaved hexagonal tier, cut glass pendants, chains, Regency, c1910 . . . . **6,100.00**

8 Lights

35" h, 33½" d, scrolling gilt bronze candle arms, baluster standard, alternating female heads and pineapple terminals, pineapple finial, Louis LXI style, French, late 19th C **3,000.00**

40" h, 4 wrought iron arms supporting 2 lights each, center spherical terminal, pendant from ceiling cap and chain, mkd "Edgar Brandt", French, c1925 . . . . **1,350.00**

12 lights, 36" h, gilt bronze scrolling arms, faceted glass standard, upper tier hung with prisms, ropes of beads and drops, chain links between tiers, French **2,750.00**

18 lights, 38" h, 34" d, Serves, gilt bronze mounts, vase form standard printed

and painted with panels of rustic lovers and sprays of flowers, blue ground **3,850.00**

DESK LAMPS

Handel, 14¼" h, oblong white milk glass shade, painted green scroll work band, patinated metal C-scroll support and adjusting curving standard **625.00**

Pairpoint, 14¼", SP base, bell shaped frosted shade dec with landscape, sgd **250.00**

Quezal, solid brass, goose neck, ball feet, cast leaf base, gold shade with blue and irid highlights, sgd **365.00**

FLOOR

Aladdin, #1254, 60" h, 18" d shade, No. 470 Whip-O-Lite shade, openwork fluted base, fluted riser **200.00**

Tiffany Studios, 86", figural palm tree, crystal drops as palm fronds, bronze parrot perched halfway, glass feathers in blue, green, and red, clear comb, bird mkd "Tiffany Studios, NY," base mkd "France" **2,000.00**

FLUID

8¼" h, clear, lacy base, free blown font, orig double drop whale oil burner, Sandwich **225.00**

9¼", Waffle, clear, removable reservoir, Sandwich **300.00**

10¼"

Clear font in Bullseye and Fleur-de-lis pattern, fluted brass stem, stepped marble base **135.00**

Double cut overlay pear shaped font, white cut to cranberry with fiery opal base, attributed to Boston and Sandwich Glass Co **350.00**

11½"

Heavy stepped serpentine pressed base, wide knop stem, engraved free blown teardrop font **275.00**

Squat thumbprint cut crystal font, mounted on double cut overlay base, white cut to clear with aventurine, circular emb brass font **300.00**

12½"

Large clear molded glass ball font molded with stars and circles, supported on a short brass band above a triple dolphin white opal glass base, Sandwich **425.00**

Large squat pear shaped triple cut overlay font, pink to white to clear, brass tapered, fluted stem, double stepped bronze ornamental base, Sandwich **1,400.00**

13″, pr, powder blue pyriform font in Punty & Loop pattern, pewter fittings mounted on tapering brass columnar standards, white marble bases, Sandwich **500.00**

14″, frosted pyriform font cut with stars and circles supported on a celery green triple dolphin base, Sandwich. **2,750.00**

22″, dark red and tan floral dec, fancy brass foot. **265.00**

HANGING

Albert Cheuret, 26″ l, ovoid alabaster shade, figural gilt bronze owl mounts, pendant from chains, ceiling cap cast and finely chased with pine motifs, mkd, c1930. . . . . **8,000.00**

Handel, 12″ d, Birds of Paradise, red, blue, orange, yellow, and green, sgd. **1,200.00**

Lalique
12″ d, molded yellow glass, all over blossom design, silken corn, silken ceiling cap, molded "R. Lalique", c1925 . . . . **1,550.00**

20″ d, molded glass, domical shade set with 6 coiling blossoms, hung from twisted silken cords, c1925 . . **2,500.00**

NIGHT LIGHTS

7½″ h, figural, obverse and reverse painted parrots and flowers on crackle glass shade, gilt metal and teakwood style base, sgd Handel, c1920 . . . . . **800.00**

20½″, figural, owl, white, glass eyes, pink ruffled satin shade. **575.00**

STUDENT

19¾″ h, single, orig green overlay glass ribbed shade, brass reservoir and lamp adjustable on rod standard, mkd "Miller's Ideal No. 2 Burner, Made In U.S.A.". **325.00**

20½″
Orig green and white cased shade, brass, electrified. **425.00**

Orig white cased shade, brass, old soldered repair, polished and electrified **300.00**

22½″, green shade cased in white, brass, chimney bracket mkd "Pat'd May 23, '76/Manhattan Brass Co., NY," electrified **300.00**

29″, double, orig green and white overlay shades, brass reservoir and lamps adjustable on rod standard, mkd "Manhattan Brass Co." **700.00**

TABLE

Aladdin Mfg Co., 23″ h, leaded glass shade, red flowers, irregular edge,

hangs in umbrella fashion, green mottled vase standard, sgd "Aladdin Mfg Co., Muncie Indiana No. 500" **1,750.00**

Art Deco, 13″ h, shade, 10½″ d, gold frosted dome shade, Art Deco figure in center, gold finished metal lamp . . **170.00**

Banquet style, 35″, cameo, cut green to frosted white globular shade, white metal base with onyx stem, brass reservoir, electrified **325.00**

Bradley and Hubbard, 15″ d shade, leaded glass, red and green panels, 6 sided base **325.00**

Classique, 23″ h, 18″ d, domed chipped ice shade, reverse painted in pastels with sailboat, lakes and woods, bronzed base, sgd. **1,650.00**

Cut Glass, brilliant, American, 17½″ h, etched rose pattern, mushroom shade, crystals **1,150.00**

Daum Nancy
14″ h, 5″ d, conical shade, trumpet base of translucent white mottled glass with blue, green-brown overlay, 10 opal wheel carved flower heads, lighted base and shade, wrought iron shade supports, sgd . **3,650.00**

15″ h, 6″ d, landscape cameo, mottled yellow and orange glass overlaid in claret, bellform shade cut with bay scene, sailing junket, baluster standard cut with pendant pine leaves and branches, shade sgd in cameo Daum/Nancy with croix de Lorraine, c1900 . . . . **2,750.00**

33½″ h, 15½″ d, cameo, shallow dome shade, baluster standard, domed circular foot in pale gray glass mottled with pale dusty rose, overlaid in dusty rose and shaded lime and forest green, wheel carved apple blossoms, leaves, martele ground, 3 arm wrought iron shade support, sgd in intaglio Daum/Nancy with croix de Lorraine, c1900 . . . . **27,500.00**

Fostoria
15¼″ h, 6⅝″ d, cased dome shade, baluster base, opal glass dec with striated green feathers, edges in amber irid, c1912. . . . . **900.00**

15½″ h, 6½″ d, cased cone shade, baluster standard in opal glass, amber and green irid leaves and trailing vines, amber irid applied stringing on shade and base, c1912 . . . . . . **1,900.00**

Genet & Michon, 10½″ d, spherical frosted white glass globe molded in low relief with world map, wrought iron circular support, circular domed base raised on beaded foot, molded "Genet/&/Michon/Made In/France/", c1930. . . . . **1,325.00**

Handel
19″ d
　Leaded, caramel, amber, and green
　　panels, pointed tab border, metal
　　base, sgd. **700.00**
　Leaded, scale-like design, smoky
　　opal on top, ruby scroll and drape
　　against green and smoky opal
　　ground, bronze handled base. . . **400.00**
24″ h, 18″ d, dome chipped ice shade,
　clear stippled enamel on ext., re-
　verse painted with yellow ground,
　black border, red roses, white dog-
　wood, small blue flowers, ftd,
　bronzed Oriental style base with 3
　applied handles, sgd **2,300.00**
Imperial, 21″, leaded shade of mottled
　green, browns, and white on top, al-
　ternating pink and blue flowers,
　painted metal base **325.00**
Lalique, 19″ h, molded glass base of thin
　rect form etched with central upright
　scrollwork, chrome mounts, sloping
　rect base, finial, isinglass shade, in-
　scribed "R. Lalique, France", c1932. **2,900.00**
Miller, 12″ d, reverse painted floral
　shade, light blue ground, red flowers,
　metal base **325.00**
Muller Freres, 26″ h, 18¾″ d, dome
　shade in mottled yellow and gray
　glass, overlaid in sea blue, cut with
　pendant wisteria blossoms and
　leaves, raised on 3 foliate arms, swell-
　ing wrought iron standard pierced with
　wisteria vines, circular pierced foot,
　shade sgd in cameo "Muller/Freres/
　Luneville", base inscribed "Virtz/
　Luneville", c1925 . . . . **4,500.00**
Pairpoint
　21″ h, 13″ d, dome shade, molded and
　　painted with red Oriental poppies,
　　green leaves, ftd, SP, engraved
　　base, brass font and trim **1,750.00**
　23″ h, 16″ d, scalloped border, acid
　　texture white glass, reverse painted
　　with silhouetted white flowers and
　　roses, band of multicolored flowers
　　bordered by obverse gilt scrolls,
　　brass base engraved with band of
　　scroll work, sgd **1,300.00**
Pittsburgh Lamp, Brass & Glass Co.
　16″ d, reverse painted shade with
　　swans and pond scene, brass
　　base. **850.00**
　20″ h, 14″ d, reverse and obverse
　　painted dome shade, tropical jungle
　　scenes, antiqued silvered base . . . **800.00**
Rayo, 17¾″ h, 12″ d shade, orig green
　cased shade, brass, electrified **110.00**
Stevens & Williams, 15″, oil, cameo
　glass, slightly flaring shade, ruffled rim,
　bulbous base raised on 3 branch form
　feet, turquoise glass overlaid in white

and cut with blossoming branches,
　acid stamped factory mark. **2,200.00**
Tiffany
　13¼″ h, spiral base, opaque and
　　green feathers, insert reservoir, oil
　　burner, irid gold Favrille paneled
　　chimney, mkd "The Twilight," sgd
　　"Tiffany Favrille" **2,100.00**
　14½″, Arabian, deep blue lustered
　　glass, 3 prunts at top, 3 prunts on
　　stem, shade mkd "L.C.T. Favrile",
　　base mkd "L. C. Tiffany" **3,400.00**
　18½″ h, 5½″ d, candle, ruffled and
　　stretched shade of heavy red and
　　blue irid, bronze base in wave pat-
　　tern, sgd "Tiffany Studios" **1,100.00**
　23″, base gold finished bronze with
　　enamel-like inlay in an Indian design
　　on the upper part of foot in green,
　　orange, blue, and black supporting
　　vasiform irid DQ green stem, orig
　　conical shade set with red, green,
　　and black enamel on bronze frame,
　　base mkd "Louis C. Tiffany Fur-
　　nances Inc. Favrille 88", "LCT"
　　monogram above, shade mkd
　　"Louis C.Tiffany Furnances,Inc.906" **2,250.00**

LANTERNS

History: A lantern is an enclosed, portable light
source, hand carried or attached to a bracket or
pole to illuminate an area. Many lanterns can be
used both indoors and outdoors and have a pro-
tected flame. Fuels used in lanterns include can-
dles, kerosene, whale oil, coal oil, and later gasoline, natural gas, and batteries.

**Photographic, 9¼″h, tin, kerosene
"Simplex" burner, green, gold lettering,
"Common Sense Lantern," 2 colored
plates, burner mkd E. Miller & Co, Meriden, CT, c1880, $150.00**

Barn, 22" h, tin, kerosene burner, dark
green paint 150.00
Bicycle, brass, carbide type, "Duplex" by
Miller, Daniels & Walsh, c1899 . . . . . 85.00
Campaign Torch, 60" h, tin keg shaped
font with 3 tubular burners and central
air tube, worn green, yellow, and red
paint, wooden handle 100.00
Candle, multipurpose
Tin
8" h, folding, mica glazing, brass
fittings 55.00
12", hexagonal, deep cup with can-
dle socket removable from bottom, pierced pyramidal top, ring
handle, brown japanning, old
glass 135.00
12½", punched detail of circles, half
circles, quarter circles, ring
handle 150.00
15½", hexagonal, fixed candle-
holder, additional candle socket
on top of handle, early 19th C,
electrified 200.00
16", semicircular, punched conical
top with ring handle, carrying handle on back, old black paint 145.00
Whalebone, 8¼", brass hinges, ring
handle, mic 19th C 2,700.00
Wooden
11", fixed tin candleholder, sliding
tin back, glass replaced, age
crack on base 100.00
11¾", mortised wooden frame,
hinged door, tin heat deflector
and socket, small dowel like feet,
old glass 225.00
12", fixed candleholder, 2 orig glass
panes, hinged top 175.00
Coach, 11¾", tin, brass trim, beveled
glass, emb name plate reads "Weite
Manf'g Co. Bridgeport, Conn. Pat.
1874," removable brass font with orig
kerosene burner 60.00
Hall, pr, 14½" h, elongated urn shaped
blown amethyst shade fitted with
brass pendant and suspended from a
domed font 3,000.00
Kerosene Burners
9", tin, truncated hinged top 85.00
11", brass, kerosene, orig globe, bottom mkd "Pat 1874, 1880" 65.00
Miner's, mkd "Patterson Lames, Ltd.,
Gateshead on Tyne" 50.00
Ship's, 21" h, brass, carved clear lens
and red curved insert, brass trim, emb
label "Bakboord," kerosene burner,
polished 50.00
Whale Oil Burners
8", tin, pierced pyramidal top, orig font,
indistinct patent mark, orig brown japanning, ring handle 185.00
11", tin, clear blown globe, removable

base, mkd "Patent Applied For N.E.
Glass Co.", orig glass font, pewter
collar and orig burner, traces of old
japanning 200.00

LEEDS CHINA

History: The Leeds Pottery in Yorkshire, England, began production about 1758. Among its
products was creamware that was competitive with
that of Wedgwood. The initial factory closed in
1820, but various subsequent owners continued until 1880. They made exceptional cream colored
ware, either plain, salt-glazed, or painted with colored enamels, and glazed and unglazed redware.

Early wares are unmarked. Later pieces bear
marks of "Leeds Pottery," sometimes followed by
"Hartley-Green and Co." or the letters "LP". Reproductions also have these marks.

**Nut dish, 4¾" d, white ground, blue ori-
ental dec, $140.00.**

Bowl, 3¾", creamware, Dutch dec,
Prince of Orange and wife flanked by
orange tree and initials PVOR, int. inscribed in iron red, c1770 . . . . 225.00
Charger, 12¼", blue feather edge, peafowl in tree, 5 colors, rim wear 785.00
Chestnut Bowl, cov, 7¼", creamware,
reticulated, flaring foot, domed reticulated cov, floral knop, entwined strap
handles, imp mark, c1775–1880 . . . . 725.00
Coffee Pot, cov, pear shape, creamware,
leaf molded and curved spout, entwined rope handle ending in floral
clusters, dome cov, flower head finial,
c1785 . . . . 450.00

Cream Pot, cov, 6¼", soft paste, cream
with brown sponge dec, green border,
button finial. **225.00**
Creamer and Sugar, cov, miniature,
pearlware, blue, yellow, and ochre, flo-
ral band **285.00**
Creamers
 4⅝", floral and leaf dec, blue, gold,
 and dark brown **150.00**
 Large bud against a sunburst, 5
 colors **275.00**
Cup, handless, gaudy dec, 5 colors . . **95.00**
Egg Cup, 2¾", creamware, pierced rim,
 c1790. . . . . **135.00**
Loving Cup, 5½", soft paste, 2 handles
 with leaf terminals, floral dec, 3 colors,
 inscribed Robert Hill 1791 . . . . **400.00**
Mug, 3⅝", band of pale blue and cream
 panels centered between narrow blue
 and white checker bands, blue band
 top and bottom, c1790 . . . . **200.00**
Pitchers
 9", gaudy floral dec, 3 colors **185.00**
 Miniature, blue, white classical figures,
 white twisted handle. **120.00**
Plates
 5¾", leaf shape, soft paste, blue
 feather edge **110.00**
 6¾", floral dec, 5 colors **125.00**
 7¼", emb swag border, center floral
 dec, 5 colors **145.00**
 14", white, blue transfer, Great Wall of
 China, imp mark, c1800–10. . . . . . **425.00**
Platters
 4¾", miniature, floral dec, 3 colors . . **275.00**
 16½", creamware, blue feather edge. **190.00**
Sauce Boat, 8" l, figural duck, creamware, tail forms pouring lip, some
 wear, c1770 . . . . **625.00**
Snuffbox, cov, 2¾", creamware, floral
 spray dec, When This You See Re-
 member Me, 1779. . . . . **550.00**
Soup Bowl, 8¼", gaudy blue and white
 floral dec **90.00**
Sugar Bowl, cov, gaudy, 5 colors, button
 finial, shell shape handles **250.00**
Sugar Shaker, 4", green dec **125.00**
Tea Caddy, 5¾", rect, arched, cream-
 ware, molded portraits of George III,
 c1765. . . . . **575.00**
Tea Service, miniature, creamware, flo-
 ral and sprig dec, teapot, milk jug, tea
 caddy, 5 tea bowls and saucers, 1775 **450.00**
Teapots, covered
 6", soft paste, Dahlia dec, 5 colors,
 acorn finial **575.00**
 7", enameled, scenic, chinoiserie fig-
 ures in shaped panels, foliage
 molded spout, c1775 . . . . **625.00**
Teapot Stand, 6⅞", oval, creamware,
 pierced rim, c1790. . . . . **95.00**
Vegetable Dish, cov, 10¼" d, 8" h,
 creamware, guady blue floral dec . . . **500.00**

LENOX CHINA

History: In 1889 Jonathan Cox and Walter Scott
Lenox established The Ceramic Art Co. at Trenton,
New Jersey. By 1906 Lenox formed his own com-
pany, Lenox Inc. Using potters lured from Belleek,
Lenox began making an American version of this
famous ware.

Older Lenox china has two marks: a green wreath
and a pallette. The pallette mark appears on blanks
supplied to amateurs who hand painted china as a
hobby. The Lenox Company still exists and currently uses a gold stamped mark.

Reference: Mary Frank Gaston, *American Belleek,* Collector Books, 1984.

Additional Listings: Belleek.

Candlestick, 8", mkd "930/E41," $80.00

Box, 4 x 5", hp, pink floral dec **45.00**
Cake Set, 7 pcs, 10½" low pedestal
 plate, six 7½" plates, Mimosa pattern,
 green wreath mark **170.00**
Candy Dish, cov, round, coral, white bird
 finial. **115.00**
Coaster, 3" d, cobalt blue, SS overlay,
 gold washed **75.00**
Compote, 7" d, 5" h, fluted edge, light
 blue stem, white top, green wreath
 mark **50.00**
Creamer and Sugar, 2¾" creamer, 4"
 cov sugar, brown ground, SS lily of the
 valley dec, monogram **95.00**
Cup and Saucer, demitasse, hp, bird on
 branch, sgd Nosek **55.00**
Figurines
 Bird, 6½", white **75.00**
 Swan, 5", pink, green wreath mark . . **30.00**

Honey Pot, beehive shape, ivory, gold bee finial, green wreath mark **52.00**

Mug, 7¼", Art Nouveau, hp, black and red band, gold leaves and trim, sgd, pallette mark. **85.00**

Pitcher, William Penn, pink, white handle, green wreath mark **160.00**

Plate, 10½", The Pointer (dog), Richard E. Bishop, black wreath mark. **75.00**

Relish Jar, 4½", cov, ivory and gold, Wallace SS holder **95.00**

Tea Strainer, holder, floral and gold dec, lavender wreath mark **200.00**

Toby Jug, 7", William Penn, white, Indian handle, green wreath mark. **150.00**

Torchiere Lamp, 11", pedestal base, ivory, raised classic columns and trees, mkd **275.00**

Vases
  5", urn shape, ribbed bulbous base, 4 claw feet, green wreath mark **45.00**
  8¼", coral cornucopia, gold dec, pedestal base, green wreath mark, pr. **225.00**

LIBBEY GLASS

History: In 1888 Edward Libbey established the Libbey Glass Company in Toledo, Ohio, after the closing of the New England Glass Works of W. L. Libbey and Son in East Cambridge, Massachusetts. The new Libbey company produced quality cut glass for the "Brilliant Period." In 1930 Libbey's interest in art glass production was renewed. A. Douglas Nash was employed as a designer. The factory continues production today as Libbey Glass Co.

Additional Listings: Amberina Glass and Cut Glass.

Candlestick, 6", made by Nash, acid mkd, $375.00.

Bowl, 4" d, amberina, sgd **80.00**

Compote, 7" d, 4" h, cut and etched floral design, bulbous, swirled stem, 8 sided rimmed base, sgd. **125.00**

Finger Bowl, underplate, engraved. . . . **50.00**

Glass, ftd, 3" h, crystal with dark green applied units, sgd **110.00**

Pitcher, 9", water, heavy cut crystal, sgd on thumb piece of handle **200.00**

Tumbler, maize, green and brown leaves, pearlized kernels **120.00**

Vases
  10", "Moderne," #1023 inscribed in base. **160.00**
  10¼", 3¾" d, internal wavy green lines, vertical molded braids, oval polished pontil **225.00**
  14", cylindrical, blue ripple decor, thumbprint design running horizontally **100.00**

Wine, 5¾" h, black kangaroo stem, sgd **150.00**

LIMITED EDITION COLLECTOR PLATES

History: Bing and Grondahl made the first collector plate in 1895. Royal Copenhagen issued their first Christmas plate in 1908.

In the late 1960s and early 1970s, several potteries, glass factories, mints, and artists began issuing plates commemorating people, animals, events, etc. Christmas plates were supplemented by Mother's Day plates, Easter plates, etc. A sense of speculation swept the field, fostered in part by flamboyant ads in newspapers and flashy direct mail promotions.

Collectors often favor the first plate issued in a series above all others. Condition is a prime factor. Having the original box also increases price.

Limited edition collector plates, more than any other object in this guide, should be collected for design and pleasure and only secondarily for rise in value.

References: Bradford Exchange, Ltd., *The Bradford Book of Collector's Plates*, Charles Winthrope & Sons, 1983; Susan K. Jones, ed., *Collectibles Market Index Guide: To Plates, Figurines, Bells, Graphics, Steins, and Dolls, 1984*, Schiffer Publishing.

Periodical: *The Plate Collector*, Collector's Media, P. O. Box 1729, San Marcos, TX 78667. Subscription: $24.95.

Collectors' Club: International Plate Collectors Guild, P. O. Box 487, Artesia, CA 90701. Dues: $8.50.

Museum: Bradford Museum, Miles, IL.

Additional Listings: See *Warman's Americana & Collectibles* for more examples of collector plates plus many other limited edition collectibles.

Bing and Grondahl, 1908, St. Petri Church of Copenhagen, $85.00.

BING AND GRONDAHL

Christmas Plates

1895 Behind The Frozen Window...	4,000.00
1896 New Moon Over Snow-covered Trees	2,000.00
1897 Christmas Meal Of The Sparrows	1,000.00
1898 Christmas Roses And Christmas Star	700.00
1899 The Crows Enjoying Christmas	1,250.00
1900 Church Bells Chiming In Christmas	700.00
1901 The Three Wise Men From The East	400.00
1902 Interior Of A Gothic Church . . .	275.00
1903 Happy Expectation of Children	175.00
1904 View of Copenhagen From Frederiksberg Hill	125.00
1905 Anxiety Of The Coming Christmas Night	130.00
1906 Sleighing To Church On Christmas Eve	100.00
1907 The Little Match Girl	125.00
1908 St. Petri Church of Copenhagen....................	85.00
1909 Happiness Over The Yule Tree	100.00
1910 The Old Organist	90.00
1911 First It Was Sung By Angels To Shepherds In The Fields........	80.00
1912 Going To Church On Christmas Eve....................	80.00
1913 Bringing Home The Yule Tree .	85.00
1914 Royal Castle of Amalienborg, Copenhagen	75.00
1915 Chained Dog Getting Double Meal On Christmas Eve	125.00
1916 Christmas Prayer Of The Sparrows....................	100.00
1917 Arrival Of The Christmas Boat	75.00

1918 Fishing Boat Returning Home For Christmas	85.00
1919 Outside The Lighted Window..	80.00
1920 Hare In The Snow..........	65.00
1921 Pigeons In The Castle Court ..	45.00
1922 Star Of Bethlehem	60.00
1923 Royal Hunting Castle, The Hermitage	50.00
1924 Lighthouse In Danish Waters..	65.00
1925 The Child's Christmas	60.00
1926 Churchgoers On Christmas Day....................	60.00
1927 Skating Couple	115.00
1928 Eskimo Looking At Village Church In Greenland	50.00
1929 Fox Outside Farm On Christmas Eve....................	75.00
1930 Yule Tree In Town Hall Square Of Copenhagen	85.00
1932 Lifeboat At Work..........	90.00
1934 Church Bell In Tower........	75.00
1936 Royal Guard Outside Amalienborg Castle In Copenhagen	80.00
1938 Lighting The Candles	100.00
1940 Delivering Christmas Letters ..	175.00
1942 Danish Farm On Christmas Night....................	150.00
1944 Sorgenfri Castle	100.00
1946 Commemoration Cross In Honor Of Danish Sailors Who Lost Their Lives In World War II	80.00
1948 Watchman, Sculpture Of Town Hall, Copenhagen	80.00
1950 Kronborg Castle At Elsinore...	140.00
1952 Old Copenhagen Canals At Wintertime With Thorvaldsen Museum In Background...............	85.00
1954 Birthplace Of Hans Christian Andersen, With Snowman........	110.00
1956 Christmas In Copenhagen	145.00
1958 Santa Claus	100.00
1960 Danish Village Church.......	180.00
1962 Winter Night.............	80.00
1964 The Fir Tree And Hare	45.00
1966 Home For Christmas........	50.00
1968 Christmas In Church	40.00
1970 Pheasants In The Snow At Christmas	20.00
1972 Christmas In Greenland......	20.00
1974 Christmas In The Village	20.00
1976 Christmas Welcome	25.00
1978 A Christmas Tale	30.00
1980 Christmas In The Woods.....	40.00
1982 The Christmas Tree	55.00

Mother's Day Plates, Henry Thelander artist, 6″ d

1969 Dog And Puppies, FE	450.00
1970 Bird And Chicks	40.00
1972 Mare And Foul	20.00
1974 Bear And Cubs...........	20.00
1976 Swan Family.............	22.00
1978 Heron	22.00

1980 Woodpecker And Young	35.00
1982 Lioness And Cubs.	45.00
1984 Stork And Her Nestlings	40.00

HAVILAND & PARLON (France)

Christmas Series, various artists, 10″

1972 Madonna And Child, Raphael, FE	100.00
1973 Madonnina, Feruzzi.	90.00
1975 Madonna And Child, Murillo . . .	45.00
1977 Madonna And Child, Bellini . . .	40.00
1979 Madonna Of The Eucharist, Botticelli	150.00

Lady And The Unicorn Series, artist unknown, 10″

1977 To My Only Desire, FE	55.00
1979 Sound	40.00
1981 Scent.	65.00

Haviland, Parlon, 1975, Unicorn Surrounded, $75.00.

Tapestry Series, artist unknown, 10″

1971 The Unicorn In Captivity	140.00
1973 Chase Of The Unicorn.	120.00
1975 The Unicorn Surrounded	75.00

LALIQUE (France)

Annual Series, lead crystal, Marie Claude Lalique artist, 8½″ d

1965 Deux Oiseaux (Two Birds), FE	1,500.00
1967 Ballet de Poisson	200.00
1969 Papillon (Butterfly).	90.00
1971 Hibou (Owl)	80.00
1973 Petit Geai (Jayling)	60.00
1975 Due de Poisson (Fish Duet) . . .	80.00

LENOX (United States)

Boehm Bird Series, Edward Marshall Boehm artist, 10½″ d

1970 Wood Thrush, FE	225.00
1971 Goldfinch	65.00
1973 Meadowlark	50.00
1975 American Redstart	50.00
1977 Robins.	45.00
1979 Golden-Crowned Kinglets	50.00
1981 Eastern Phoebes	100.00

Boehm Woodland Wildlife Series, Edward Marshall Boehm artist, 10½″ d

1973 Raccoons, FE.	60.00
1975 Cottontail Rabbits	70.00
1977 Beaver.	60.00
1979 Squirrels.	75.00
1981 Martens	100.00

ORREFORS (Sweden)

Christmas

1970 Notre Dame Cathedral.	40.00
1971 Westminster Abbey	45.00
1972 Bascilica di San Marco	60.00
1973 Cologne Cathedral	70.00
1974 Rue de la Victorie	75.00
1975 Bascilica di San Pietro.	90.00
1976 Christ Church	75.00
1977 Masjid-E-Shah	120.00
1978 Santiago de Compestela	100.00

REED & BARTON (United States)

Christmas Series, Damascene silver, 11″ d through 1978, 8″ d 1979 to present

1970 A Partridge In A Pear Tree, FE	200.00
1972 Hark! The Herald Angels Sing .	60.00
1974 The Adoration Of The Magi . . .	60.00
1976 Morning Train.	60.00
1978 The General Store At Christmas Time.	70.00
1980 Gathering Christmas Greens . .	75.00

ROSENTHAL (Germany)

Christmas Plates, various artists, 8½″ d

1910 Winter Peace	575.00
1912 Shooting Stars	255.00
1914 Christmas Song	350.00
1916 Christmas During War	235.00
1918 Peace On Earth	200.00
1920 The Manger In Bethlehem	325.00
1922 Advent Branch	200.00
1924 Deer In The Woods.	200.00
1926 Christmas In The Mountains . .	175.00
1928 Chalet Christmas	175.00
1930 Group Of Deer Under The Pines	225.00

1932 Christ Child.	195.00
1934 Christmas Peace.	200.00
1936 Nurnberg Angel	185.00
1938 Christmas In The Alps.	190.00
1940 Marien Church In Danzig	250.00
1942 Marianburg Castle.	300.00
1944 Wood Scape	275.00
1946 Christmas In An Alpine Valley .	250.00
1948 Message To The Shepherds . .	875.00
1950 Christmas In The Forest	175.00
1952 Christmas In The Alps.	200.00
1954 Christmas Eve	185.00
1956 Christmas In The Alps.	190.00
1958 Christmas Eve	195.00
1960 Christmas In Small Village	190.00
1962 Christmas Eve	185.00
1964 Christmas Market In Nurnberg	225.00
1966 Christmas In Ulm	250.00
1968 Christmas in Bremen.	195.00
1970 Christmas In Cologne	165.00
1972 Christmas Celebration In Franconia	100.00
1974 Christmas In Wurzburg	100.00

ROYAL COPENHAGEN

Christmas Plates, various artists, 6″ d 1908–10, 7″ d 1911 to present

1908 Madonna And Child.	1,700.00
1909 Danish Landscape	150.00
1910 The Magi	130.00
1911 Danish Landscape	115.00

Royal Copenhagen, 1920, Mary with the Child Jesus, $75.00.

1912 Elderly Couple By Christmas Tree	130.00
1913 Spire Of Frederik's Church, Copenhagen	135.00
1914 Sparrows In Tree At Church Of The Holy Spirit, Copenhagen	100.00
1915 Danish Landscape	175.00
1916 Shepherd In The Field On Christmas Night	100.00
1917 Tower Of Our Savior's Church, Copenhagen	70.00

1918 Sheep and Shepherds.	80.00
1919 In The Park	80.00
1920 Mary With The Child Jesus . . .	75.00
1921 Aabenraa Marketplace.	75.00
1922 Three Singing Angels	70.00
1923 Danish Landscape	70.00
1924 Christmas Star Over The Sea And Sailing Ship	100.00
1925 Street Scene From Christianshavn, Copenhagen	85.00
1926 View of Christmas Canal, Copenhagen	75.00
1927 Ship's Boy At The Tiller On Christmas Night.	140.00
1928 Vicar's Family On Way To Church	75.00
1929 Grundtvig Church, Copenhagen	100.00
1930 Fishing Boats On The Way To The Harbor	80.00
1931 Mother And Child	90.00
1932 Frederiksberg Gardens With Statue Of Frederik VI	80.00
1933 The Great Belt Ferry	110.00
1934 The Hermitage Castle	115.00
1935 Fishing Boat Off Kronborg Castle	145.00
1936 Roskilde Cathedral	130.00
1937 Christmas Scene In Main Street, Copenhagen	135.00
1938 Round Church In Osterlars On Bornholm	200.00
1939 Expeditionary Ship In Pack-Ice Of Greenland.	200.00
1942 Bell Tower of Old Church In Jutland	300.00
1944 Typical Danish Winter Scene . .	160.00
1946 Zealand Village Church	150.00
1948 Nodebo Church At Christmastime	150.00
1950 Boeslunde Church, Zealand . . .	175.00
1952 Christmas In The Forest	120.00
1954 Amalienborg Palace, Copenhagen	150.00
1956 Rosenborg Castle, Copenhagen.	160.00
1958 Sunshine Over Greenland	140.00
1960 The Stag	140.00
1962 The Little Mermaid At Wintertime	200.00
1964 Fetching The Christmas Tree . .	75.00
1966 Blackbird At Christmastime . . .	55.00
1968 The Last Umiak	40.00
1970 Christmas Rose And Cat	45.00
1972 In The Desert.	25.00
1974 Winter Twilight	25.00
1976 Danish Watermill.	35.00
1978 Greenland Scenery	40.00
1980 Bringing Home The Christmas Tree	50.00
1982 Waiting For Christmas	65.00

Mother's Day Plates, various artists, 6½″ d

1971 American Mother	15.00

1972 Oriental Mother.	**10.00**
1974 Greenland Mother.	**12.00**
1976 Mermaids.	**20.00**
1978 Mother and Child	**25.00**
1980 An Outing With Mother	**35.00**
1982 The Children's Hour	**45.00**

SCHMID (Japan)

Disney Christmas Series, undisclosed artists, 7½″ d

1973 Sleigh Ride, FE.	**300.00**
1974 Decorating The Tree.	**80.00**
1976 Building A Snowman.	**15.00**
1978 Night Before Christmas	**15.00**
1980 Sleigh Ride.	**30.00**
1982 Winter Games	**20.00**

Disney Mother's Day Series

1974 Flowers For Mother, FE.	**50.00**
1975 Snow White And The Seven Dwarfs	**25.00**
1977 Pluto's Pals	**15.00**
1979 Happy Feet	**18.00**
1981 Playmates	**25.00**

Peanuts Christmas Series, Charles Schulz artist, 7½″ d

1972 Snoopy Guides The Sleigh, FE	**70.00**
1973 Christmas Eve At The Doghouse.	**115.00**
1975 Woodstock, Santa Claus	**15.00**
1977 Deck The Doghouse	**15.00**
1979 Christmas At Hand	**20.00**
1981 A Christmas Wish.	**20.00**

Peanuts Mother's Day Series, Charles Schulz artist, 7½″ d

1972 Linus, FE.	**10.00**
1973 Mom?	**20.00**
1975 A Kiss For Lucy	**18.00**
1977 Dear Mom	**15.00**
1979 A Special Letter	**12.00**
1981 Mission For Mom	**15.00**

Peanuts Valentine's Day Series, Charles Schulz artist, 7½″ d

1977 Home Is Where The Heart Is, FE	**15.00**
1979 Love Match	**18.00**
1981 Hearts-A-Flutter	**45.00**

Raggedy Ann Annual Series, undisclosed artist, 7½″ d

1980 The Sunshine Wagon, FE	**60.00**
1981 The Raggedy Shuffle.	**20.00**
1983 Winning Streak.	**40.00**

WEDGWOOD (GREAT BRITAIN)

Christmas Series, jasper stoneware, 8″ d

1969 Windsor Castle, FE.	**250.00**

1971 Piccadilly Circus, London.	**40.00**
1973 The Tower Of London.	**45.00**
1975 Tower Bridge	**40.00**
1977 Westminster Abbey.	**35.00**
1979 Buckingham Palace.	**55.00**
1981 Marble Arch	**75.00**
1983 All Souls, Langham Palace	**80.00**

Mothers Series, jasper stoneware, 6½″ d

1971 Sportive Love, FE.	**25.00**
1973 The Baptism of Achilles.	**15.00**
1975 Mother and Child	**35.00**
1977 Leisure Time	**30.00**
1979 Deer and Fawn.	**35.00**
1981 Mare And Foul	**50.00**
1983 Cupid and Butterfly	**55.00**

LIMOGES

History: Limoges porcelain has been produced in Limoges, France, for over a century by numerous factories other than the famed Haviland. One of the most frequently encountered marks is "T. & V. Limoges" which is the ware made by Tressman and Vought. Other identifiable Limoges marks are A. L. (A. Lanternier), J. P. L (J. Pouyat, Limoges), M. R. (M. Reddon), Elite and Coronet.

References: Mary Frank Gaston, *The Collector's Encyclopedia Of Limoges Porcelain*, Collector Books, 1980.

Additional Listings: Haviland China.

Asparagus Set, 10 pcs, platter with insert, gravy with underplate, six 7″ plates, hp asparagus, mauve tones, artist sgd, LD & C mark	**450.00**
Basket, candy, 8″ l, yellow, crows and cherries, sgd G Remy	**75.00**
Biscuit Jar, underplate, 8″ jar, 7½″ underplate, hp, pink and white florals, porcelain raised scrolls, gold figural scroll knob, CFH/GDM, dated 1894 .	**200.00**
Bone Dish, 6¼″ l, 4″ w, scalloped border, scattered brown and yellow floral design, GDM	**25.00**
Bowl, 8¼″ d, 2″ h, sq. scalloped, salmon pink ground, rust, pink and gold flowers, leaves, gold trim	**75.00**
Box, 5″ d, 3″ h, blue, hp, cupid leaning on branch of blue flowers, green leaves, gold trim	**90.00**
Butter Pat, 3″ d, violets with gold, L. Strauss mark	**10.00**
Cache Pot, 9 x 5 x 12¾″, oval, hp, scenic, fox hunting rabbit in forest, gold bun feet, gold handles, artist sgd, Heidrick, W. C. & Co mark	**850.00**
Celery Dish, 13½″ l, 6½″ w, gold scalloped border, green and gray floral border, pink floral center, green GDA/France.	**35.00**

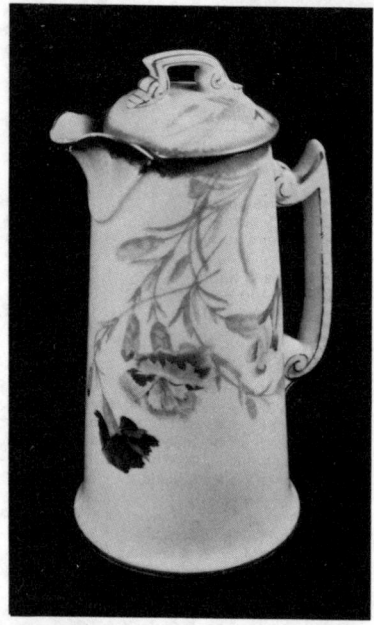

Chocolate Pot, 9¼″ h, carnation dec on white ground, gold trim, $175.00.

Chamberstick, 4″ h, 7″ d, applied handle, hp roses, gold trim edge, T&V **68.00**

Cheese and Cracker Dish, 2 tiers, hp roses **75.00**

Chocolate Set, pot, 5 cups and saucers, delicate gold and green on white, T&V/France **350.00**

Chop Plates
  12¼″, scalloped 8 sided edge, hp purple and green grapes, green and brown leaves and shadow foliage, mkd **100.00**
  13¼″, hp flowers, green leaves, scalloped edge, gold trim, mkd H & Co Limoges **95.00**

Cookie Jar, 7½″, curving, slightly molded lines, cream to pale brown, gold dec, 3 blue and gilt flower sprays **85.00**

Creamer and Sugar, 4″ creamer, basket shape sugar, 5″ to top of handle scalloped, raised scrolls, hp purple flowers, sgd, T&V **125.00**

Cup and Saucer, tea, gold rim and handle, scattered pink and green floral design, green GDM/CFH. **20.00**

Dish, 11⅞″, leaf shape, light blue flowers, gold dec, green D & C/France. . **45.00**

Fruit Bowl, 8¾″ d, 4½″ h, cream ground, large pink, purple and yellow astors, shaded foliage, gold rim, 3 gold feet, artist sgd, Guerin mark **70.00**

Game Plate, 9½″, pheasant center, heavy gold rim, artist sgd, "Coronet" mark **50.00**

Game Platter, 12½″, flying game birds, hp, heavy gold scalloped edge, emb rocco, artist sgd Rogin. **255.00**

Game Set, 16″ platter, seven 8½″ plates, birds in flight **300.00**

Hair Receiver, hp bluebirds, gold trim, 3 feet **95.00**

Mug, 5″, hp cherries, artist sgd Markwith, green T&V **75.00**

Mush Set, milk pitcher, bowl and underplate, white ground, purple wildflower bouquets, gold rims, gold twig handle on pitcher. **60.00**

Pitcher, cider, 6″ h, 8″ d, hp blackberries, artist sgd, green B & Co/France **85.00**

Plaque, 9¼″ h, fencer in elaborate costume, standing on grassy knoll, deep blue ground, framed, sgd P. Bonnaud/Limoges, late 19th C **385.00**

Plates
  8½″, blue, cupids, scroll and shell rim, Lanternier double mark. **45.00**
  10¼″, set of 12, ivory rim with enameled floral medallions joined by gilt scrollwork, emb gilt and blue enamel borders, Ahrenfelt, for Stern Brothers, NY, C1910 . . . . **450.00**
  11⅛″, pr, hanging, winter scene, woman with basket walking across snow landscape with windmill, scalloped gold edges. **250.00**
  12⅛″, hanging, hp peaches, grapes and strawberries, beaded scalloped gold border, artist sgd C. Fernand, Limoges/France **175.00**

Powder Box, 3″ h, 6″ d, round, pastel green, pink flowers, artist sgd, T&V/Limoges France **175.00**

Punch Bowl, 13″ d, 5½″ h, wisteria, gold trim, T&V mark, dated 1895 . . . . . . **195.00**

Tankard, 15″ floral dec, artist sgd, J.P./L. France **215.00**

Tray, 13″ l, 9″ w, scalloped border, hp roses inner border, green J.L./L. France. **72.00**

Vases
  6½″, bulbous, large pink, yellow and purple mums, 1½″ wide reticulated gold collar, sgd J.P./L. France . . . **145.00**
  12″, 18″ d, 4″ base tapers to 3″ scalloped top, dark green pond lilies at base, trees at top **145.00**
  14″, portrait, European courtier, gold

handles and around panel, mkd
Limoges, AK France. **275.00**
19¾" pr, baluster shape, painted
sprays of roses between black
sponged borders, gilt necks, shoulders and bases, green printed Lim-
oges/France, c1900. . . . . **1,200.00**
24", silver ground, enameled raspber-
ries and leaves, magenta to rose
and green, sgd Sarlandie/Limoges,
c1900 . . . . **725.00**
Vegetable Dish, cov, 9" l, 7" w, 3" h, oval,
tiny pink flowers, Elite **60.00**

LITHOPHANES

History: Lithophanes are highly translucent porcelain panels with impressed designs. The design
is formed by the difference in thickness of the
plaque. Thin parts transmit an abundance of light
while thicker parts represent shadows.

Lithophanes were first made by the Royal Berlin
Porcelain Works in 1828. Other factories in Germany, France, and England later produced them.
The majority of lithophanes on the market today
were made between 1850 and 1900.

Collectors' Club: Lithophane Collectors Club,
Blair Museum of Lithophanes and Carved Waxes,
2032 Robinwood Avenue, Toledo, OH 43620. *Lithophane Collectors Club Bulletin* (bimonthly).

Museum: Blair Museum of Lithophanes and
Carved Waxes, Toledo, OH.

Candle Shield, 9" h, panel with scene of
2 country boys playing with goat, cas-
tle in background **250.00**
Cups and Saucers
Coffee, 3 oval panels of classical
maidens, gilded int., saucer painted
in black, calendar of Sundays for
1837, gilt ground border with
molded shells and scrolls, puce
highlights, mkd "Berlin, K P M". . . **600.00**
Tea, blue Oriental dragon with nude
lady **135.00**
Fairy Lamp, 9", lady leaning out of tower
window, 3 panels, rural romantic
scenes **1,200.00**
Lamps
Night, pr, 5 panels, scenes of children,
galleries on upper and lower edges
of shade, nickel-plated brass base,
mkd "PPM". **1,900.00**
Table
5 panel shade, children playing,
mkd "KPM" **650.00**
5 panel shade, each 4½ x 6¼",
scenes of children, lovers, emb
floral brass framing, each panel
sgd "PPM", overall 8⅛" h, 8" d **400.00**
6 panel shade, 22" h, portraits of
young ladies, bronze base. **450.00**

Mug, monk. **100.00**
Panels
KPM
4½" x 6", woman carrying nude
child on back, leading leashed
sheep, scenic background, gilded
wooden frame **175.00**
4¾ x 6½", man kneeling, mosque
type building, mkd. **225.00**
PPM
3¼ x 5¼", castle scene **125.00**
4½ x 5¼", woman holding muscial
instrument, seated on rock **150.00**
P.R. Sickle
4 x 4⅝", Suitor, dwarf-like man presenting flower to lady, mkd
#1393. . . . . **110.00**
4¼ x 5¼", nudes in garden **110.00**

**Plaque, windmill and ship, 5⅜" h, 3⅞"
w, imp "KPM/365," c 1860, $145.00**

Unmarked
4½ x 5⅜", man and woman with
whippet overlooking water
scene **100.00**
4½ x 5⅜", young man playing flute
in garden, woman seated, holding
music. **100.00**
7¼ x 9", girl playing with cat. **130.00**
Stein, souvenir, embracing couple on
bottom, French Lick Springs Hotel,
French Lick, IN **140.00**
Tea Warmer, 6 x 6", 4 panels, romantic
scenes, Sheffield silver frame, orig
burner **275.00**

LIVERPOOL CHINA

History: Liverpool is the name given to products made at several potteries in Liverpool, England, between 1750 and 1840. Among the early potters were Seth and James Pennington and Richard Chaffers who made tin enameled earthenwares.

By the 1780s tin glazed earthenware gave way to cream colored wares decorated with cobalt, enamel colors, and blue or black transfers.

The Liverpool glaze is characterized by bubbles and most often there is clouding under the foot rims. By 1800 about 80 potteries were working in the town producing not only creamware, but soft paste, soapstone and bone porcelain.

Jug, 7³/₄″ h, The Farmers Arms, The Grave Robbers, multicolored, c1810, $800.00.

Bowls
  8¼″ d, scene of houses on wooded river islands, underglaze blue, overglaze dec of iron red, green, gilding, sgd Phillip Christian, c1770 ..... **800.00**
  10¼″ d, blue and white dec, Oriental seated and holding a parasol, rocky landscape, slight rim chips, c1760 ..... **625.00**
Dish, 13½″, blue and white dec, two fighting cocks beneath a flowering tree in fenced garden, border of scrolling flowering branches, c1760 ..... **600.00**

Jugs
  8⅝″ h, three black transfers relating to Masonry, traces of orig gold dec **300.00**
  8¾″ h, short spout, strap handle, transfer print in black on one side with Masonic devices, reverse with sailing ship flying American flag, green, yellow, red and blue paint, inscribed "James McDonald" enclosed by a wreath beneath the spout **800.00**
Plate, painted blue underglaze, white ground, shrubs and bamboo among rocks **175.00**
Saucer, painted blue underglaze, scene of houses on river island beneath flowering branch, c1760 ..... **150.00**
Soup Plate, 10″, black transfer of British ship firing a cannon **100.00**
Tea Caddy, creamware, rect, painted with chinoiserie in inky blue, 3¾″ h. . **200.00**
Tiles, set of 11, manganese, 6 painted with vases of flowers, corners with stylized flower heads, 5 with vases of flowers and birds within octagonal cartouches, corners with carnations and powdered manganese ground, 1 repaired, 6 with minor chips, 5 x 5″ ... **300.00**

LOETZ

History: Loetz is a type of iridescent art glass made in Austria by J. Loetz Witwe in the late 1890s. Loetz was a contemporary of L. C. Tiffany and worked in the Tiffany factory before establishing his own operation; therefore, much of the wares are similar in appearance to Tiffany. Some pieces are signed "Loetz," "Loetz, Austria," or "Austria." The Loetz factory also produced ware with fine cameos on cased glass.

Bowls
  3½″, wide mouth, lemon yellow ruffled lip, lower section navy blue with deep green scrolling, pink-amber irid oil spots, inscribed Loetz/Austria, c1900 ..... **1,400.00**
  5″ h, 9″ d, pinched, rainbow coloring, Damasene pattern of swirls, oil spots **450.00**
  6½″, ruffled, irid purple, raindrop pattern, sgd **200.00**
Bride's Basket, large, amber, silver-blue irid oil spots, metal holder **350.00**
Cane, 54″ l, striped **150.00**
Cuspidor, 4½″ h, 5″ d, melon ribbed, dimples, irid green, polished pontil, unsigned **125.00**
Inkwell, 3½″, sq, irid green, brass lid with copper flowers **300.00**

Vase, 4″, orange glass with silver irid waves highlighted by gold threading; silver overlay, floral pattern, unsigned, $275.00.

LOTUS WARE CHINA

History: Knowles, Taylor and Knowles Co., East Liverpool, Ohio, made a translucent, thinly potted china between 1891 and 1898. It compared favorably to Belleek. It first was marked "KTK." After being exhibited at the 1893 Columbian Exposition in Chicago, Col. John T. Taylor, company president, changed the marking to Lotus Ware, because the body resembled the petals of the lotus blossom.

Blanks also were sold to amateurs who hand painted them. Most artist signed pieces fit this category.

Bowl, 4″ d, raised floral dec, filigree handles	**200.00**
Creamers	
Fish net dec in gold, white ground . .	**320.00**
Rose dec, hp	**360.00**
Cup and Saucer, mkd KTK	**120.00**
Dish, shell shaped, shell pink and pale green, small green floral, gilt coral feet, mkd KTK	**400.00**
Ewer, 7½″ h, bulbous, narrow neck, gilt highlights on spout, pastel daisies and buttercups, twig handle, sgd.......	**600.00**
Pitchers	
Fish net dec in gold, hp, sgd "Dillingham, 1898"..............	**500.00**
Plain white, mkd KTK	**235.00**
Wild rose dec, gold trim, hp	**400.00**
Rose Bowl, 5″ d, 4½″ h, white, gold flowers and branches, mkd KTK.......	**400.00**
Syrup, SP dispenser top, mkd KTK ...	**300.00**
Teapot, cov, fish net dec, bamboo handle	**375.00**
Vases	
4¾″, cylindrical, 3 ball feet, fish net dec, lavendar raised floral dec ...	**375.00**
6″, raised floral dec, dated August 1896, mkd KTK..............	**450.00**
6½″, hp, rose dec, gold filigree rim, gold border	**525.00**
8″, hp, wisteria, gold handles, mkd . .	**600.00**
10″, gold fish net, 4 hp figures in panels, mkd...............	**650.00**
11″, gold floral panels, white fish net over entire body, ftd, mkd.......	**750.00**

Rose Bowl, 4″, irid gold, rose to lavender, pink oil spots, silver overlay....	**475.00**
Sweetmeat Jar, cov, wavy textured amber, irid pink and green, brass bail, pewter raspberry finial...........	**265.00**
Syrup, 6½″, tall and slender, irid blue, SS handle and hinged cov, sgd	**400.00**
Vases	
4½″, dimple sided, irid gold, blue and gold lava dec................	**475.00**
4½″, tapered, translucent pink with silver-blue swags conforming to shape, sgd Loetz-Austria	**525.00**
6½″, Art Nouveau shape, irid turquoise-green feathered, sgd Loetz, Austria	**850.00**
7½″, amphora shape, red int., silver-blue irid concentric waves, sgd Loetz/Austria, c1900	**1,000.00**
9½″, flower form, irid dark blue, random crisscross threading, unsigned....................	**425.00**
9⅞″, baluster form with spreading foot, pale green, irid gold-green, silver-blue undulating waves, sgd Loetz/Austria, c1900	**660.00**
10″, irid green to silver, SS Berry & Leaf dec, sgd L..............	**325.00**
10¼″, irid red and blue, serpent encircling vase	**450.00**
13″, twisted baluster with undulating lip, irid blue, red, purple, c1900 ...	**400.00**
14″ h, 7″ w, flower form opening, irid green with gold dust, 3 dimples. . .	**350.00**

LUSTRE WARE

History: Lustering on a piece of pottery creates a metallic, sometimes iridescent, appearance. Josiah Wedgwood experimented with the technique in the 1790s. Between 1805 and 1840 a wealth of lustered earthenware pieces was created in England by makers such as Adams, Bailey and Batkin, Copeland and Garrett, Wedgwood, and Enoch Wood.

Lustre decorations often were used in conjunction with enamels and transfers. Transfers used for lustre decoration covered a wide range of public and domestic subjects. They frequently were accompanied by pious or sentimental doggerel as well as the humors of everyday life.

Copper lustre was created by the addition of a copper compound in the glaze. It was very popular in America during the 19th century and experienced a collecting vogue from the 1920s to the 1950s. Today it has a limited market. The market stagnation can partially be attributed to the large number of reproductions, especially creamers and the "polka" jug, which fool many new buyers. Reproductions are heavier in appearance and weight than the earlier pieces.

Pink lustre was made by using a gold mixture. Silver lustre was first covered completely with a thin coating of a "steel lustre" mixture, containing a small quantity of platinum oxide. An additional coating of platinum, worked in water, was applied before firing.

Sunderland is a coarse type of cream colored eathenware with a marbled or spotted pink lustre decoration which shades from pink to purple. A solution of gold compound applied to the white body developed the many shades of pink.

The development of electroplating in 1840 created a sharp decline in the demands for metal-surfaced earthenware.

Additional Listings: English Softpaste.

COPPER

Beaker, 3¼", blue band with applied floral band, polychrome enameling. . . .	**60.00**
Chalice, 4", relief design, colored enamel.	**55.00**

Copper, creamer, 4", blue dec, $65.00.

Compote, 8" d, 4¾" h, scalloped edge, floral dec	**60.00**
Creamers	
3⅛", white reserves with purple transfer scenes, polychrome enamel "Hope," purple lustre trim.	**90.00**
4⅝", white band with blue stripes and emb copper foliage	**65.00**
5⅜", raised basket of polychromed flowers, pink lustre sunburst in white band around center	**65.00**
Cup, 3", handleless, blue and copper leaf dec, pink inner rim	**45.00**
Cup and Saucer, scalloped rim, floral dec	**65.00**
Goblets	
4¾", black transfer scene, oriental landscape with figures	**100.00**
5", canary band, reserves of mother and child, c1825	**135.00**
Jugs	
6⅜", commemorative, black transfer, General Jackson, wide blue band, c1828	**450.00**
12¼", cov, painted in colors and pink lustre, scrolling flowering foliage, rose sprays at neck, Staffordshire, dated 1821	**300.00**
Mugs	
2½", sanded band.	**35.00**
2¾", Sunderland lustre band	**60.00**
2¾", yellow band, teal stripe, purple lustre int. rim	**30.00**
3", blue band, floral dec.	**35.00**
Pitchers	
2½", blue band, yellow flowers.	**35.00**
3¾", polychrome floral band	**50.00**
4", white band with relief design. . . .	**45.00**
4½", blue band with ram and hound	**60.00**
5½", blue band with emb hunting scene	**135.00**
5½", sanded band.	**85.00**
6¾", bittersweet band with emb polychromed cherubs and ram . . .	**85.00**
8", emb, children at play	**125.00**
Salts, pr, 2", pedestal bases, white band with pink and purple lustre house dec	**95.00**
Shakers	
3½", pedestal base, white band with green and orange floral enameling	**35.00**
4½", blue band.	**30.00**
Shaving Mug, 4", blue with copper diagonal stripes, pink inner rim	**55.00**
Spill Vase, 3½", pedestal base, applied polychrome floral dec	**45.00**
Teapots	
6", emb ribs, polychrome enameled floral dec.	**120.00**
6½", blue band, figural bud handle . .	**95.00**
Toby Jug, 4½", man seated holding pipe and mug, cobalt blue coat	**125.00**
Tumbler, 2⅝", blue floral band	**35.00**

Waste Bowls

5½", ribbed.	**35.00**
Ftd, blue band, figures in relief	**40.00**

PINK

Bowl, 6½", House	**90.00**
Creamer, 4½", House.	**75.00**
Cup, handleless and deep saucer, Butterfly.	**65.00**

Dishes

7½", freehand, large bird in tree, multicolored enamel and lustre.	**85.00**
7½", House	**75.00**
Flower Pot and Stand, 4½", wide floral borders, satyr's mask and ring handles, c1820.	**250.00**

Jugs

4½", cottage scene, Greek key border, c1820.	**95.00**
5¾", buff ground, bird perched on small tree in landscape, band borders, c1815.	**225.00**
Mug, 4", black transfer, ruin in wooded landscape, Greek key border	**85.00**
Pitcher, 7", ftd, House.	**150.00**

Plates

8½", black transfer, maiden and dog on garden path	**55.00**
8⅝", black transfer, turbanned couple, exotic landscape, green enamel foliate border, imp Staffordshire, c1810	**60.00**
Sugar Bowl, ribbed, floral dec	**85.00**
Tea Set, 28 pcs, House, cov teapot, sugar bowl, creamer, waste bowl, 12 cups and saucers, c1820.	**275.00**
Teapot, ribbed base and lid.	**185.00**
Vases, pr, 4¼", butterfly in oval panel, floral sprays, wigglework borders, Leeds, 1810	**250.00**

SILVER

Bowl, 5⅛" d, 3" h, ftd, ribbed, beaded rim, copper lustre int.	**80.00**
Chamberstick, 4" h, 6" saucer, emb scroll dec	**75.00**
Coffee Pot, cov, 11", urn shape, ribbed, bead dec, high dome cov, button finial, pedestal base	**250.00**
Creamer, 3⅛", emb	**35.00**
Jug, 5½", floral and leaf pattern, broad band around center.	**100.00**
Salt Shaker, 4", bulbous, pedestal foot, beaded dec	**80.00**
Teapot, cov, 6", ftd, ribbed design	**120.00**

SUNDERLAND

Bowls

6½", black transfer, Queen Victoria	**150.00**

8", House.	**125.00**
Box, cov, 4" w, 6" l, 2½" h, black transfer, English landscape	**125.00**
Cake Plate, 10", pink, mottled	**145.00**

Cups and Saucers

Babes in Woods	**85.00**
Pink, mottled, black transfer, country scene	**50.00**
Goblet, 5½" h, pink, mottled	**150.00**
Jug, 9½", black transfer, Sailor's Farewell, rhyme "The Sailor's Tale," wavy iron red enamel and pink lustre bands, c1825.	**550.00**

Mugs

4", pink, mottled, black transfer, English country scene	**160.00**
4⅞", pink lustre, Sailor's Farewell on one side, poem "The Sailor's Tear" on other, int. with floral clusters and applied frog, c1825	**175.00**
Mustache Cup, black transfer, ship and verse	**110.00**

Pitchers

6", mottled	**180.00**
8⅝", black transfer, ship and verse on side, poem "The Sailor's Tear" on the other side, mariner's compass under spout.	**325.00**

Plates

7", pink, floral dec.	**75.00**
9", pink, black transfer, Sailor's Farewell	**150.00**

Salts

Cloud motif, pink lustre trim	**35.00**
Ftd pedestal base, pink splash.	**30.00**
Sugar Bowl, cov, 8" h, octagonal, pink, mottled, handled, pear finial	**60.00**
Sugar Shaker, 5½", Cloud.	**75.00**
Teapot, 6½", pink, mottled, black transfer, Sailor's Farewell	**230.00**
Toothpick Holder, pink, mottled, enameled white daises, canary lustre leaves and base band	**65.00**

Wall Plaques

9¼" h, 7¾" d, mask, woman's face, framed	**250.00**
9¼" l, rect, landscape, black transfer, foliate molded self frame in pink lustre, c1820	**160.00**
Waste Bowl, pink splash.	**55.00**

LUTZ TYPE GLASS

History: Lutz type glass is an art glass attributed to Nicholas Lutz. He made this type of glass while at the Boston and Sandwich Glass Co. from 1869 until 1888. Since Lutz type glass was popular, copied by many capable glass makers, and unsigned, it is nearly impossible to distinguish genuine Lutz products.

Lutz is believed to have made two distinct types of glass, striped and threaded glass. This style often is confused with a similar style Venetian glass. The striped glass was made by using threaded glass rods in the Venetian manner. Threaded glass was blown and decorated by winding threads of glass around the piece.

Tumbler, 3½", white, green, and orange, $150.00.

Cake Stand, clear and white threads . .	**100.00**
Compote, underplate, aquamarine twisted threads	**170.00**
Epergne, 3 parts, pink threads.	**250.00**
Lamp, 6 blue and white stripes, swirled to the left, brass collar, brass stem, sq marble base, 8¼" h	**650.00**
Tumbler, ftd, 3" h, gold and white latticino, 6 applied strawberries, threading	**100.00**
Whimsy, 6⅜" h, tiny "Frozen Charlotte" doll in clear glass tube, bulbous finial, knob stem and clear foot dec with latticino rings	**300.00**

MAASTRICHT WARE

History: Maastricht, Holland, is where Petrus Regout founded the De Sphinx pottery, in 1836. The firm specialized in transfer printed earthenwares. Other factories also were established in the area, many employing English workmen and their techniques. Maastricht china was exported to the United States in competition with English products.

Bowl, 6⅛" d, 3⅛" h, Hone pattern, mkd "Maastricht Petrus Regoulec Co, Made in Holland," $75.00.

Bowls	
6", Pompeia pattern.	**45.00**
7½", Pajong pattern	**55.00**
7⅝", Timor pattern	**30.00**
Coffee Pot, cov, blue and white flowing dec	**75.00**
Cups and Saucers	
Roman Key pattern, flow blue, mkd "Societe Ceramique, Maastricht". .	**20.00**
Stick spatter dec.	**25.00**
Plaque, 10", FDR portrait, green wreath	**30.00**
Plates	
7⅛" d, gaudy stick dec, pr	**45.00**
8¼", transfer, native on horseback selling fruit, blue ground	**40.00**
8½", gaudy stick spatter, floral design in red, blue, green, ochre, and lavendar, mkd "Maestricht".	**20.00**
9", gaudy stick spatter, floral design in blue, green, and ochre, mkd "Maestricht, Made in Holland"	**40.00**
Soup Plate, 8⅝" d, rooster and foliage in red, green, ochre, and black, mkd "Maastricht".	**40.00**
Tumbler, 3⅛" h, mkd "Maastricht". . . .	**20.00**

MAJOLICA

History: Majolica, an opaque, tin glazed pottery, has been produced by many countries for centuries. It originally took its name from the Spanish Island of Majorca, where figuline (a potter's clay) is found. Today majolica denotes a type of pottery which was made during the last half of the 19th century in Europe and America.

Majolica frequently depicted elements in nature: leaves, flowers, birds, and fish. Human figures were rare. Designs were painted on the soft clay body using vitreous colors and fired under a clear lead glaze to impart the rich color and brilliance characteristic of majolica.

Among English majolica manufacturers who marked their works were: Wedgwood, George Jones, Holdcraft, and Minton. Most of their pieces can be identified through the English Registry mark and/or the potter-designer's mark. Sarreguemines in France and Villeroy and Boch in Baden, Germany, produced majolica that compared favorably with the finer English majolica. Most continental pieces had an incised number on the base.

Although 600 plus American potteries produced majolica between 1850 and 1900, only a handful chose to identify their wares. Among these manufacturers were George Morely, Edwin Bennett, the Chesapeake Pottery Company, the New Milford-Wannoppee Pottery Company, and the firm of Griffen, Smith, and Hill. The other hoped their unmarked pieces would be taken for English examples.

References: Mariann K. Marks, *Majolica Pottery: An Identification And Value Guide*, Collector Books, 1983; M. Charles Rebert, *American Majolica 1850–1900*, Wallace-Homestead, 1981.

Advisors: Herb and Joyce Krueger.

Baskets
  8″ l, 5½″ h, handled, yellow DQ ground, pink feet and cherub faces at base of handles, pink int. 185.00
  8″ l, 5½″ h, twig handle, yellow basketweave ground, pink flowers and turquoise int. 200.00
Bread Trays
  13″ l, 10″ w, oval, green ground, yellow wheat heads, brown mottled center, brown border inscribed "Eat Thy Bread with Thankfulness". 175.00
  13″ l, 10″ w, oval, yellow pineapple textured with brown mottled center 150.00
Compotes
  9″, top of pink and green maple leaves, twigs on white ground, supported on 5″ bark textured base, mkd GSH on underside 115.00
  9½″, green pond lily and floral center, 3 storks forming 5″ pedestal base. 275.00
Creamer, 3″, pewter top, textured brown bark ground with oak leaves and acorns, turquoise int. 85.00
Cups and Saucers
  3¼″ cup, 6″ saucer, bamboo design in yellow and brown, pink int., mkd GSH Etruscan Majolica. 85.00
  3¼″ cup, 6″ saucer, shell and seaweed pattern in green, pink, and brown, green mottled underside, mkd GSH Etruscan Majolica 125.00
Cuspidor, 7½″ d, 2½″ h, cobalt shell center surrounded by white shells, brown basketweave ground 140.00
Egg Caddy, 5½″ sq, 4 eggs, brown bas-

ketweave body, yellow rope trim, brown rope handle 115.00
Mugs
  3¾″, blackberries, leaves and blossoms on cream ground, brown handle, rim and bottom, pink int. 65.00
  5″, corn textured, green leaves at base, green cornstalk handle 55.00
Pickle Dish, 7″, textured begonia leaf, mkd GSH 35.00
Pitchers
  Butterfly spout, yellow ground, brown basketweave bottom and blue ribbed top band, mkd GSH Etruscan Majolica
    4½″ 45.00
    6″ 85.00
    8″ 125.00
  Corn textured, colored, green leaves curling up from base and forming handle
    4″ 75.00
    6″ 95.00
    8″ 135.00
    10″ 175.00
  Face, figural, 5½″, man with beard and mustache, lavender hat and striped band, turquoise int., mkd Sarreguemines 95.00
  Fish, figural, 8″, tail forms handle, pours through mouth 95.00
  Goat, figural, 8″, sitting on haunches; glaze shading from green to cream to brown 235.00
  Grazing deer in field, 6¾″, yellow ground, brown handle. 125.00
  Hawthorne flower, raised pink flower on green, pink and brown mottling, mkd GSH Etruscan Majolica
    4½″ 55.00

Teapot, 6″ h, 10″ d, pink, blue, white, tan, green seaweed, seashell finial, pink interior, mkd "Etrascan, Majolica," $240.00

6½"	**95.00**
8"	**185.00**

Pond Lily, 7", green, base with pink ribbed top, brown bud on handle. . **85.00**

Pug Dog, figural, 8½", brown textured body, red collar and tag **200.00**

Tree Bark, 8", brown, textured with pink flowers and green leaves. . . . **85.00**

Plates

7"

Basketweave ground in brown or blue, yellow textured center with blackberry flowers and leaves, brown mottled underside **35.00**

Realistic lettuce leaf, mkd with a "W" inside a sunburst. **110.00**

8"

Textured green leaves edged in pink with cauliflower center, mkd GSH on mottled green underside **85.00**

White ground, textured design of 3 birds on branches and fans joined at center, mkd Wedgwood with English registry mark. **175.00**

9"

Basketweave ground in brown or blue, yellow textured center with blackberry flowers and leaves, brown mottled underside **95.00**

Pineapple textured, green leaves and brown mottled center, edged in brown rope design **85.00**

Pond lily leaf, green with white flower at center, green underside **45.00**

10½"

Scalloped border in brown and green florals, center showing shaggy dog in front of dog house **85.00**

Scalloped border in brown or yellow, center showing man on stool with mug in his hand **65.00**

Sardine Boxes

7" l, 7½" w, cobalt with pond lilies and white flowers, brown border, lavender int. and green bottom, 2 crossed sardines forming handle on cover **275.00**

8" l, 7" w, yellow pineapple textured with green leaves, 3 crossed sardines on cover form handle, attached underplate **225.00**

Syrups

7½", alternating pink and blue vertical panels edged with yellow caning and brown handle, mkd GSH Etruscan Majolica, pewter top. **175.00**

8", sunflower on pink or blue pebbled ground, brown bark handle, mkd GSH Etruscan Majolica, pewter top **195.00**

Tea Sets, cov teapot, creamer, cov sugar

Bird on a branch, cobalt, drum shaped body, cream ground, brown branch handles and covers **300.00**

Cauliflower, textured green leaves edged in pink with cauliflower in center, lined in either pink or green, mkd GSH Etruscan Majolica **325.00**

Floral, cream basketweave ground edged in light blue, brown handles and lids. **250.00**

Toothpick, 1½", blue textured ground with 3-dimensional moths, one with wings opened, one with wings closed **125.00**

MAPS

History: Maps provide one of the best ways to study the growth of a country or region. From the 16th to the early 20th century, maps were both informative and decorative. Engravers provided ornamental detailing which often took the form of bird's eye views, city maps and ornate calligraphy and scrolling. Many maps were hand colored to enhance their beauty.

Maps generally were published in plate books. Many of the maps available today result from these books being cut apart and sheets sold separately.

In the last quarter of the 19th century, representatives from firms in Philadelphia, Chicago, and elsewhere traveled the United States preparing county atlases, often with a sheet for each township and a sheet for each major city or town. Although mass produced, they are eagerly sought by collectors. Individual sheets sell for $25 to $75. The atlases themselves can usually be purchased in the $200 to $400 range. Individual sheets should be viewed solely as decorative and not as investment material.

Principatus Walliae Pars Borealis Vulgo, 1667 chart of North Wales, hand colored, German text on verso, sgd by Joannes Janssonius, 16 x 22¾", $375.00.

Canada, "The British Possessions in North America From the latest Authorities," engraved by W. Robinson, Philadelphia, M. Carey, c1814, engraving with outline color, 15⅝ x 18¼" **175.00**

Mexico

"Mexico," Philadelphia, A. Finley, 1825, hand colored engraving, 9⅝ x 12⅛" **75.00**

"Plan of the Port of Veracruz," published in Humboldt, *Political Essay on the Kingdom of New Spain,* London, Longman & Co., 1811, uncolored, 8 x 10" **150.00**

North America

"A Map of North America With the European Settlements and whatever else is remarkable in ye West Indies, from the latest and best Observations," drawn and engraved by R. W. Seale, published in Rapin de Thoyras, *The History of England,* London, 1744, uncolored engraving, 14¾ x 18⅜" **700.00**

"A New and accurate Map of North America, Laid down according to the latest, and most approved Observations, and Discoveries," inset of Hudson's Bay, published in *The Universal Magazine,* London, J. Hinton, c1763, hand colored engraving, 10⅜ x 13¾" **150.00**

United States

"Map of the American Coast, from Lynhaven Bay to Narraganset Bay, by John Melish," engraved by H. S. Tanner, Philadelphia, 1813, hand colored engraving, 16⅛ x 18¼" .. **825.00**

"A Map of the British Empire in North America, by Samuel Dunn, Mathematician," London, Robert Sayer, 1774, hand colored engraving, 19⅜ x 12¼" **400.00**

Kentucky, "Kentucky," Philadelphia, A. Finley, 1825, hand colored engraving, 9⅝ x 12" **90.00**

Maryland and Delaware, "Map of the States of Maryland and Delaware," engraved by Amos Doolittle after J. Denison, Boston, 1796, uncolored engraving, 7⅜ x 9½" **175.00**

New Hampshire, "The State of New Hampshire. Compiled chiefly from Actual Surveys by Samuel Lewis, 1813," Philadelphia, M. Carey, hand colored outlined engraving, 19⅛ x 12" **350.00**

New York, "The State of New York, Compiled from the most Authentic Information," New York, J. Reid, 1796, uncolored engraving, 15⅜ x 18¼" **450.00**

Ohio and Indiana, "Ohio and Indiana," published in *American Atlas,* Philadelphia, H. S. Tanner, 1819, hand colored engraving 23⅝ x 28" **650.00**

South Carolina, "South Carolina," Philadelphia, A. Finley, 1825, hand colored engraving, 9¾ x 12¼" ... **100.00**

Southern New Jersey to Georgia, "Carte Reduite des Cotes Orientales de l'Amerique Septentrionale Contenant Partie de Nouveau Jersey, la Pennsylvanie, le Mary-land, la Virginie, la Caroline Serptentrionale, la Caroline Meriodionale et la Georgie....Par Ordre de M. De Sartine," engraved by Petit, Paris, 1778, uncolored engraving, 23 x 34¼" **1,000.00**

"Territories of the United States," published in *Morse's General Atlas of the World,* New York, D. Appleton and Company, 1856, colored wax engraving, 14½ x 12" **150.00**

"United States, Exhibiting the Railroads and Canals," New York, Bradford, 1835, hand colored engraving, 8⅜ x 10¾" **60.00**

Vermont, "Vermont from actual Survey/Delineated & Engraved by Amos Doolittle, N.H.," Philadelphia, M. Carey, c1790, hand applied color outline, 15¼ x 12¼" **300.00**

Washington, D.C., "Map of the City of Washington Established as the Permanent Seat of the Government of the United States of America," D. McClelland, 1846, uncolored engraving, 13 x 17", orig boards **350.00**

MARBLEHEAD POTTERY

History: This hand thrown pottery had its beginning in 1905 as a therapeutic program introduced by Dr. J. Hall for the patients confined to a sanitorium located in Marblehead, Massachusetts. In 1916 production was removed from the hospital to another site. The factory continued under the directorship of Arthur E. Baggs until it closed in 1936. Most pieces found today are glazed with a smooth, porous, even finish in a single color. The most desirable pieces are decorated with conventionalized design in one or more subordinate colors.

Bowls

3" h, 6" d, dark blue **70.00**

3" h, 8" d, plum, semi-matte finish .. **80.00**

Vase, 5½″ h, 6″ d, blue, imp mark, $165.00.

Candlesticks

2⅞″ h, 3¾″ w at base, light green, concave standard, scroll "S" handles	35.00
4″ h, chamber style, rose matte glaze	45.00
Creamer, 3″ h, bulbous body, gray	20.00
Humidor, cov, 7″ h, green design on blue, artist A. E. Baggs	350.00
Planter, 3½″ d, round, turquoise orange peel glaze, sgd AEB 1934	190.00

Vases

4″, 7″ d, cylindrical base, extended outward flaring top, blue, sgd	50.00
4½″, flared base, straight cylinder body, green	45.00
6″, slender concave, waisted, slight inward tapered body, blue	65.00

MARY GREGORY TYPE GLASS

History: The use of enameled decoration on glass, an inexpensive imitation of cameo glass, developed in Bohemia in the late 19th century. The Boston and Sandwich Glass Co. copied this process in the late 1880s.

Mary Gregory (1856–1908) was employed for two years at the Boston Sandwich Glass Co. factory when the enameled decorated glass was being manufactured. Some collectors argue that Gregory was inspired to paint her white enamel figures on glass by the work of Kate Greenway and a desire to imitate pate-sur-pate. However, evidence for these assertions is very weak; and, a question can be raised whether or not Mary Gregory even decorated glass as part of her job at Sandwich.

The result is that "Mary Gregory Type" is a better term to describe this glass. Collectors should recognize that most examples are either European or modern reproductions.

Boxes

3″ h, 3⅝″ d, melon ribbed, lift off lid, emerald green, girl and foliage	125.00
4¾″ h, 6″ d, round, hinged, amber, 2 girls, flowers, foliage, ftd, brass rings on sides	500.00
Carafe and Tumbler, 8¼″ h, 4″ d, sapphire blue, boy, tree, foliage	225.00
Cologne Bottle, 7¼″, cranberry, applied gold lion's head each side, boy holding bunch of flowers, gold scalloped rim, gold trim stopper	135.00
Creamer and Sugar, 2¾″ creamer, 2½″ sugar, open, cranberry, pedestal	245.00
Cruets, amber, boy and girl, pr.	175.00
Dresser Tray, 10¾″ l, 8¾″ w, oval, emerald green, boy and girl dancing, girl playing mandolin	225.00
Ewer, 9½″, bulbous, cranberry, ribbed, scalloped top, applied twisted handle, open pontil	225.00
Miniature lamp, pale blue satin, dancing cherub	90.00
Mug, 3″, cranberry, boy	100.00

Perfume, royal blue, dec of young girl on glass, gold edging, SP stand mkd "Middletown Plate Co," 9¾″ h overall, $950.00.

Patch Boxes
2″ d, round, hinged, golden amber,
girl **165.00**
2″ d, round hinged, blue, boy **165.00**
Perfume Bottle, 4″, sapphire blue, ball
stopper, boy **175.00**
Pitchers
3¾″ h, 3½″ d, bulbous, round mouth,
cranberry, girl sitting, clear applied
handle. **175.00**
6″, melon ribbed, clear, girl catching
butterflies **125.00**
Plate, 6⅝″, cobalt blue, boy with hat . . **120.00**
Spa Glass, 4⅛″ h, 2⅜″ d, flattened oval
shape, amber, girl carrying
basket **100.00**
Stein, ladies, 4″, amber, ribbed top, girl
with hat **100.00**
Tankard, 12¾″, honey amber, girl in gar-
den, tinted features **225.00**
Tea Warmer, 3 scenic panels, ornate hp
brass holder, overhead handle **400.00**
Tumblers
3¾″, green, girl **60.00**
4¼″, cranberry, girl **65.00**
Urn, 14½″ h, 5½″ d, cov, teardrop fin-
ial, cobalt blue, girl with basket of flow-
ers, foliage **325.00**
Vases
2⅝″ h, 2¾″ d, bulbous, flared top,
cranberry, boy **100.00**
8⅜″ h, 4¼″ d, sq top, cranberry, girl. **165.00**
10¼″, bristol glass, pink, white cased,
girl with bird and blowing
horn **200.00**
11″, bulbous, collared neck with gold
trim, black amethyst, 2 boys playing
badminton, flesh tinted faces and
arms **275.00**
12″ h, 4⅝″ d, sapphire blue, girl getting
pitcher of water, white trim top and
bottom, applied handles **325.00**
13″ h, 5″ d, cranberry, scalloped top,
crystal reeded applied handles, girl
in apron with flowers **425.00**

MATCH HOLDERS

History: After 1850 the friction match achieved
popular usage. These early matches were packaged and sold in sliding cardboard boxes. To facilitate storage and to eliminate the clumsiness of
using the box, match holders were developed.

The first examples were cast iron or tin, the latter
often having advertising on them. A patent for a
wall hanging match holder was issued in 1849. By
1880 match holders also were being made from
glass and china. Match holders lost popularity in
the late 1930s and 1940s with the advent of gas
and electric heat and ranges.

**Advertising match holder, tin, 3⅜″ w,
5″ h, $55.00**

Advertising, china, Red Raven, crow
holding bottle, "Ask The Man" on
base, ashtray, mkd Warwick China . . **50.00**
Advertising, tin
Adams Express Co. **40.00**
Clover Brand Shoes **35.00**
DeLaval Separator. **80.00**
Dockash Stove Factory **60.00**
Dutch Boy, small boy dressed as
painter **95.00**
Topsy Hose **30.00**
Bisque, Victorian child with basket on
back, 6″ h **60.00**
Brass, wall, 7½″ h, hanging game, rabbit
and bird **55.00**
Cast Iron
Acorn, leaves, wall type **50.00**
Black boy, smiling face, holding large
round bowl (ashtray) and woven
match holder basket beside him . . **65.00**
High top shoe on base, old worn red
and black paint, striker on base,
5⅛″ h **20.00**
China and Porcelain
Boy kneeling beside basket, lamb
standing next to basket **70.00**
Boy, seated, grinning, monkey
scratching boy's head **77.50**
Pug and shepherd dogs staring at cat
peeking out of house **45.00**
Swans drinking from well **42.50**
Woodland scene dec, attached tray,
mkd Nippon. **200.00**
Glass
Hat, rings around hat for striking. . . . **25.00**
Paperweight base, rings for striking,
opening in center for matches. . . . **35.00**
Pattern glass, Daisy and Button, blue,
double, striker on front, 3″ h, 4″ w **85.00**
Majolica, figural, man and woman,
6½″ h, pr **95.00**

Satsuma, wall, orange and gold figure on
front of pocket **75.00**
Wall, figural, man standing with barrel on
back, SP, mkd James Tufts, Boston,
7″ h **65.00**

MATCH SAFES

History: Match safes are small containers used
to safely carry matches in one's pocket. They were
first used in the 1850s. Match safes are often figural
with a hinged lid and striking surface.

Note: While not all match safes have a striking
surface, this is one test, besides size, to distinguish
a match safe from a calling card case.

Advertising
  Arm and Hammer Soda, bakelite . . .   **40.00**
  Hardbutt Clothiers, silvered brass,
    shaped like a pair of men's pants.   **100.00**
  Prout's Best Flour, leather **25.00**
  Voigt Brewery Co., Detriot, emb Ger-
    man Silver, c1925 . . . .   **65.00**
  Waseco, Minnesota, farm animals,
    tin. **15.00**
  Zam-Zam, The Cure of Constipation,
    A Remedy For Indigestion, Head-
    aches, etc., silvered brass, emb adv
    on lift up cover, c1910 . . . .   **35.00**
Brass, figural
  Ale Bottle.   **85.00**
  Barrel, hinged at top, striker on base,
    ³/₄ x 1¹/₄ x 2⁵/₈″ h **65.00**
  Fox, painted **325.00**
  Hoof. **175.00**
  Owl, hinged top, striker on base, ³/₄ x
    1¹/₂″ x 2¹/₄″ h. **100.00**
  Violin Case. **125.00**
Chrome, pearlized trim, Irish Setter in
  center medallion **55.00**
Nickel Plated, figural
  Bean **95.00**
  Devil's Head **295.00**
  Elephant Head, ivory tusks. **285.00**

Scallop shell, brass, 2″ l, $125.00.

Mouse **225.00**
Owl **275.00**
Plated Metal, figural, pig, hinged at head,
  striker on base, 1 x 2³/₄ x 1¹/₂″ h. . . .   **80.00**
Silver Plated
  Figural, book, one side opens to hold
    coins, striker in center, ³/₄ x 1¹/₂ x 2″.   **35.00**
  Souvenir, St. Louis World's Fair, 1904,
    Electricity Building, portraits of Jef-
    ferson and Napoleon **60.00**
Sterling Silver
  Figural, cigar. **225.00**
  Rectangular, hunter with dogs, en-
    graved in medallion, photograph
    frame concealed on int. **200.00**

McCOY POTTERY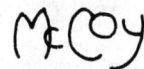

History: The J. W. McCoy Pottery Co. was established in Roseville, Ohio, in September, 1899.
The early McCoy Co. produced both stoneware and
some art lines, including Rosewood. In October,
1911, three potteries merged creating the Brush-
McCoy Pottery Co. This company continued to produce the original McCoy lines and added several
new art lines. Much of the early pottery is not
marked.

In 1910, Nelson McCoy and his father, J. W.
McCoy, founded the Nelson McCoy Sanitary Stoneware Co. In 1925, the McCoy family sold their
interest in the Brush-McCoy Pottery Co. and started
to expand and improve the Nelson McCoy Co. The
new company produced stoneware, earthenware
specialities, and artware. Most of the pottery
marked McCoy was made by the Nelson McCoy
Co.

Reference: Sharon and Bob Huxford, *The Collectors Encyclopedia of McCoy Pottery,* Collector
Books, 1980.

Additional Listings: *See Warman's Americana
& Collectibles* for more examples.

Baskets
  Bridal. **10.00**
  Green, basketweave **20.00**
Birdbath, 27″ h, Greystone finish **60.00**
Bowl, ftd, 3″ h, 7″ w, mkd Loynel. **135.00**
Candlesticks, 8″ h, onyz pattern glaze,
  Brush-McCoy **40.00**
Cereal Bowl, cov, grapes, large **75.00**
Cookie Jars
  Animal Crackers **25.00**
  Chef. **45.00**
  Old Woman's Shoe **55.00**
  Train, black. **45.00**
Ewer, 10″ h, dark brown glaze, grapes,
  leaves, mkd Rosewood, McCoy,
  1905 . . . .   **185.00**

Vase, 6¼" h, white ground, pink flowers, green leaves, brown twigs, $15.00.

Jardinieres
7", holly motif, green, c1935	**20.00**
9", dark brown with orange shading .	**75.00**
Mug, 3 handle, mkd Loy-Nel-Art.	**110.00**

Pitchers
Blue iris on yellow ground	**100.00**
Parrot, multicolored	**25.00**
W. C. Fields	**30.00**

Planters
Cowboy/Rodeo.	**25.00**
Fawn	**30.00**
Spinning Wheel, dog and cat	**20.00**
Punch Bowl, pedestal base, dark brown glaze, grapes, leaves, mkd Olympia, J. W. McCoy.	**375.00**
Teapot, cherries and leaf design, handle, cherry finial on cov, light green glaze	**25.00**

Vases
4", Zuniart, c1923	**65.00**
7", jug shape, mkd Olympia	**155.00**
10", blue, white, red and green squee-zebag design, mkd Brush-McCoy	**55.00**
10½", 2 handles, berries and leaves, mkd McCoy-Loy-Nel-Art	**215.00**
11", bulbous, handles, mkd Loy-Nel-Art	**135.00**
12", 2 handles, green ground, woman in white with flowing hair, ribbon, mkd Navarre, Brush-McCoy	**225.00**

MCKEE GLASS

History: The McKee Glass Co. was established in 1843 in Pittsburgh, Pennsylvania. In 1852 they opened a factory to produce pattern glass. In 1888 the factory was relocated to Jeannette, Pennsyl-vania, and began to produce many types of glass kitchenwares, including several patterns of Depres-sion Glass. The factory continued until 1951 when it was sold to the Thatcher Manufacturing Co.

McKee named its colors Chalaine Blue, Custard, Seville Yellow and Skokie Green. McKee glass may also be found with painted patterns, e.g., dots and ships. A few items were decaled. Many of the can-isters and shakers were lettered in black to show the purpose they were intended for.

Additional Listings: See *Warman's Americana & Collectibles* for more examples.

Animal Dish, cov, hen on nest, white, 6½" h	**120.00**
Birdhouse, white.	**125.00**
Bowls	
7" d, 9½" h, cut and pressed, pink, Snappy Apple, 3 feet	**60.00**
9", mixing	
Black Ship.	**12.00**
Green dots on custard	**18.00**
11", Laurel pattern, French Ivory . . .	**18.00**
Candy Dish, cov. Rock Crystal, cranberry	**115.00**
Canisters, cov, round	
Cereal, 48 oz, custard	**22.00**
Coffee, 48 oz, Skokie green.	**20.00**
Flour, 40 oz, Skokie green, decal . . .	**18.00**
Cinnamon Shaker, Skokie, "Cinnamon" on front	**12.00**
Coaster for Bottoms Up tumbler, jade	**75.00**
Drip Jar, cov, Red Ship.	**18.00**
Lamp, 12¾", crystal, prisms, mkd "Elec-trolier #407"	**145.00**
Measure, 2 cup, blue custard	**15.00**
Nappy, 4½", handle	
Custard	**6.00**
Skokie	**5.00**
Pitcher, 16 oz, mesuring marks, Red Ship.	**16.00**

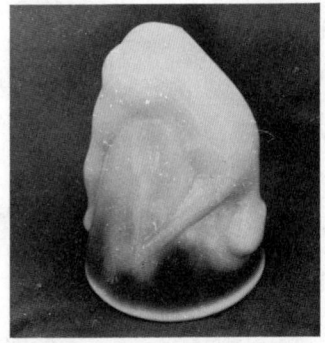

Bottoms Up glass, caramel opal, Pat. No. 77726, 3¼" h, $30.00.

Razor Hone, custard.	5.00
Reamers	
Chalaine blue, grapefruit	225.00
Skokie	30.00
Refrigerator Jar, lid, 4″ d, 5″ l, Red	
Ship.	10.00
Salt and Pepper Shakers, pr, Ruff N	
Ready, dark green.	16.00
Smoking Set, Stars and Stripes, custard,	
'1898".	250.00
Vase, 8¾″ h, tulip, silver overlay	100.00

MEDICAL AND APOTHECARY ITEMS

History: Medicine and medical instruments are well documented for the modern period. Some instruments are virtually unchanged since their invention. Others have changed drastically.

The concept of sterlization phased out decorative handles. Early handles of instruments were often carved and can be found in mother-of-pearl, ebony, and ivory. Today's sleekly designed instruments are not as desirable to collectors.

Apothecary items include items commonly found in an apothecary and pertain to the items used to store or prepare medications.

Reference: Don Fredgant, *Medical, Dental & Pharmaceutical Collectibles,* Books Americana, 1981.

Museum: Waring Historical Library, Medical University of South Carolina, Charleston, SC.

APOTHECARY

Chest, 9½ x 11 x 7″, mahogany veneer, int. has 2 dovetailed drawers, 19 compartments for bottles and jars, drawers with ivory knobs	465.00
Jars	
G. R. Benzoe, 11″, cov, light blue, gold trim, black letters	60.00
Herb, 7¾″ cov, off white, gold trim, florals, Latin inscription.	75.00
Laboratory Dome, 17″, clear blown glass	65.00
Mortar and Pestle, white ceramic, gold Rx, 7″	75.00
Prescription Book, "H. B. Glidden, Apothecaries, Hotel Claremont, New Hampshire," dated 1902–04.	75.00
Scales, brass pans, marble base, orig weights, 19th C.	200.00

DENTAL

Advertising mirror, "Crocker-Fels Dental Supplies," celluloid, 3½″	20.00
Cabinet, oak, floor model, restored, c1895.	850.00

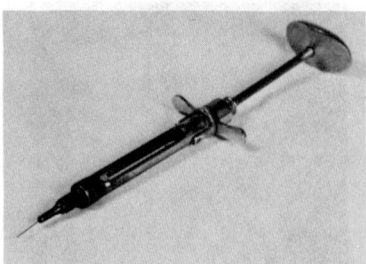

Dental syringe, $30.00.

Catalogs	
H. D. Justin & Son, Philadelphia, "Illustrated Catalogue and Price List of Dental Supplies," 1901, 400 pgs, 7½ x 11″, hard cover	40.00
L. D. Kaulk, "The L. D. Kaulk Dental Depot, Philadelphia," 1905, 800 pgs, 6 x 9″, illus. with dental furniture, instruments, and materials. . .	25.00
Chest, 16 x 7″, wooden, fitted with 137 solid steel forms of teeth and three iron tools to be used with forms, explanatory chart on cov, label "Made By Thomas S. White Dental Mfg Co.," 1910	200.00
Instruments, set of 4, ebony handles, orig fitted box	315.00
Scaling Kit, c1800.	1,200.00
Tooth Extractor, 5⅞″, ivory handle. . . .	75.00

MEDICAL

Bed Pan, 10½″ d, pewter, screw on handle, 2 oval eagle touch marks, Thomas Danforth Boardman	200.00
Bleeder, 2⅞″, brass and steel lancet, orig box	100.00
Ear Trumpet, ebony, telescoping	300.00
Electrocardiograph, Cambridge, 1930, portable	165.00
Electro-medical apparatus, Wappler, oak cabinet, 1898	175.00
Haemoglobinometer, 1920.	50.00
Hypodermic, 1¾ x 3⅜″, label "Codman & Shurtleff, Surgical and Dental Instruments, Boston," orig box	110.00
Instrument box, rosewood with brass inlay, oval medallion engraved "Dr. J. Brackin, Warren, O," int. label "Max Wocher & Son, Cincinnati, Ohio," fitted int. with partial set of orig instruments, 16½″ l.	400.00
Stethoscope, monaurel, c1840.	385.00
Surgeon's Kit, "Weiss & Son," complete, orig box, c1830.	645.00

OPTICAL

Cabinet, floor, lower portion 10 drawers, upper with slant front, sliding roll cover, over 200 orig lenses **475.00**

Case, 7½ x 9¼, optical lens for eye exams **50.00**

Sign, tin, 13″ w x 18″ h, "Wear 'Em," peeping eyes with round glasses, painted black, white, red, and green. **300.00**

MEDICINE BOTTLES

History: The local apothecary and his book of formulas played a major role in early America. In 1796 the first patent for a medicine was issued by the United States Patent Office. Anyone could apply for a patent. As long as the dosage was not poisonous, the patent was granted.

Patent medicines were advertized in newspapers and magazines and sold through the general store and by "medicine" shows. In 1907 the Pure Food and Drug Act, requiring an accurate description of contents of medicine on the label, put an end to the patent medicine industry. Not all medicines were patented.

Most medicines were sold in distinctive bottles, often with the name of the medicine and location in relief. Many early bottles were made in the glass manufacturing area of southern New Jersey. Later companies in western Pennsylvania and Ohio manufactured bottles.

References: Hugh Cleveland, *Bottle Pricing Guide*, Collector Books, 1980; Ralph & Terry Kovel, *The Kovels' Bottle Price List*, Crown Publishers, 1982, 6th ed.; Carlo & Dot Sellari, *The Illustrated Price Guide To Antique Bottles*, Country Beautiful Corp., 1975.

Periodicals: *Antique Bottle World*, 5003 West Berwyn, Chicago, IL 60630; *Old Bottle Magazine*, P. O. Box 243, Bend, OR 97701. Subscription: $10.00.

Additional Listings: See *Warman's Americana & Collectibles* for more examples.

Allen's, Mrs. S. A., World Hair Balsam, NY **35.00**

Armour & Co., Chicago, cathedral type panels, round corners, lady's leg neck, milk glass, 5½″ **20.00**

Baltzers Rheumatic Remedy, J. T. Baltzer Prop., New Orleans, rect, clear, 6″ **8.00**

Clickners Sugar Coated Vegetable Purgative Pills **35.00**

DeWitt's Soothing Syrup, Chicago, round, amethyst, 5″ **5.00**

Evans, Dr. W., Teething Syrup, flared lip, pontil, aqua, 2½″ **20.00**

Folger's, Dr. Robet B., Olosaopian, NY. **75.00**

Glovers Imperial Distemper Remedy, H. Clay Glover, NY, #412 on base, rect, amber **15.00**

Granular Citrate of Magnesia, rect, cobalt, 6½″ **12.00**

Humphreys' Homeopathic Veterinary Specifics, emb laughing horse, oval, clear, 3¼″ **10.00**

Indian Expectorant, Dr. D. Jaynes, Philadelphia **75.00**

Kilmer's, Dr., Ocean-Weed Heart Remedy, Binghamton, NY, USA **20.00**

Kilmer's, Dr., Swamp Root Kidney Remedy, Binghamton, NY, oval, aqua, sample, 4½″ **5.00**

Laird, Geo L. & Co., cathedral type, name emb in horseshoe shape, "Oleo-Chyle" vertically on back, ring top, blue, 6¾″ **50.00**

Newbros Herbicide, Kill The Dandruff Germ, ring top, amber **10.00**

Omega Oil, "It's Green," The Omega Chemical Co., Boston, emb leaf, slender cylinder, 6″ **6.00**

Pawnee Indian Ta-Ha, emb 25¢, Jos. Herman, Agt, aqua, 8½″ **20.00**

Perkes, Prof. W. H., Remedy, NY, sq, amber, 8¼″ **15.00**

Teasdale's Chlorodyne, 8 sided, cobalt, 5¾″ **8.00**

Tobias, Dr., Venetian Liniment, aqua, 5¾″ **25.00**

Wistar's, Dr., Balsam of Wild Cherry, 1848–1896, 6 panels, aqua, 3⅝″ . . . **35.00**

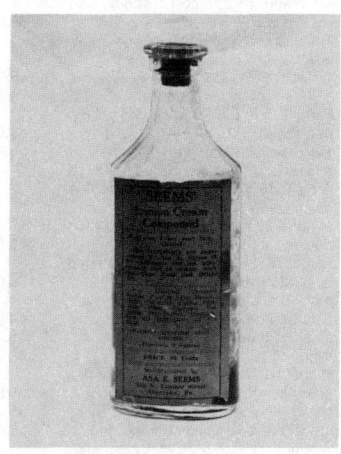

Medicine Bottle, cork stopper, graduated markings, 5¼″ h, 2″ w, $12.00.

MERCURY GLASS

History: Mercury glass is a light bodied, double-walled glass that was "silvered" by applying a solution of silver nitrate to the inside of object through a hole in the base of the formed object.

F. Hale Thomas, London, patented the method in 1849. In 1855 the New England Glass Co. filed a patent for the same type of process. Other American glass makers soon followed. The glass reached the height of its popularity in the early 20th century.

Tazza, 5³/₄" d, 2³/₄" h, etched birds and leaves, $50.00.

Bowl, 4³/₄", enameled floral design, gold int. **50.00**
Cake Stand, 8" d, emb floral dec, pedestal base **65.00**
Candlesticks
  9¹/₄", copperwheel engraved floral dec. **45.00**
  11", pr, enameled floral dec. **110.00**
Carafe, 12" h, 5¹/₂" d, mushroom stopper, dated 1909 . . . . **45.00**
Carafe, vacuum, stopper attached by chain, 12¹/₂" h, nickle plated, mkd Pat. June 1, 1909, Hotakold, Vacuum Specialty Co, NY. **25.00**
Compote, 8" d, 7¹/₂" h, engraved floral dec **125.00**
Creamer, 6¹/₂", grapevine dec, etched, applied clear handle **120.00**
Curtain Tiebacks, pr, 2¹/₂", emb floral dec, orig pewter shanks. **40.00**
Knobs, pr, grape design **45.00**
Rolling Pin **65.00**
Salt, master, 2⁵/₈", ftd, applied floral dec, gold gilt int.. . . . . **35.00**
Shaving Mug, emb fern dec. **35.00**
Spooner, white enameled floral dec . . . **28.00**
Sweetmeat Dish, 7¹/₂" h, 4" d, clear glass cov, pedestal base **38.00**
Tazza, 5¹/₂" d, 2¹/₂" h, etched floral and leaf dec **50.00**

Toothpick Holder, 3¹/₂", pedestal base, gold int. **32.00**
Tumbler, 4¹/₂" h, plain **22.00**
Vases, pairs
  10", enameled floral dec **135.00**
  12", urn shape, gold int., floral and foliage dec. **145.00**

METTLACH

History: In 1809 Jean Francis Boch established a pottery at Mettlach in Germany's Moselle Valley. His father had started a pottery at Septfontaines in 1767. Nicholas Villeroy began his pottery career at Wallerfanger in 1789.

In 1841 these three factories merged. They pioneered in underglaze printing on earthenware, using transfers from copper plates, and in using coal fired kilns. Other factories were developed at Dresden, Wadgassen, and Danischburg.

The castle and Mercury emblems are the two chief marks. Secondary marks are known. The base also contains a shape mark and usually a decor mark. Pieces are found in relief, etched, prints under the glaze, and cameo.

Prices are for print under glaze unless otherwise specified.

Reference: Gary Kusner, *The Mettlach Book*, privately printed, 1984, R. H. Mohr, *Mettlach Steins*, 9th edition, privately printed, 1982.

Additional Listings: Villeroy & Boch.

Advisor: Ron Fox.

Beakers
  2327/1050, ¹/₄ L, serving girl **75.00**
  2368/1092, ¹/₄ L, cavalier. **85.00**
  2368/1095, ¹/₄ L, cavalier at table. . . **85.00**
  2368/4241, ¹/₄ L, St. Augustine, FL. . **60.00**
Bowl, #353, relief, gray, white, blue, and silver **135.00**
Cigar Holder, #136, relief, 5", tree trunk, applied leaves. **65.00**
Compote, #1784, etched, 10¹/₂", faces, medallions, snake handles **625.00**
Goblet, #2954/1194, ¹/₄ L, cherubs. . . **115.00**
Jar, cov, 6¹/₂ L, relief. **100.00**
Lamp Base, 14", relief, dwarfs, bugs, snake handles **425.00**
Mugs
  1526/1098, ¹/₂ L, Uncle Sam and German soldiers **140.00**
  3095, 4", Hires Root Beer **125.00**
  3287, ¹/₂ L, Sons of the Revolution, Feb. 22, 1910 . . . . **70.00**

Plaques

    1044, 12″, hp bust of man, gold ground, sgd "Freida Kopperman Hannover 1882" **250.00**

    1044/95, 12″, Burg Eltz. **225.00**

    1044/162, 14″, Germania monument **140.00**

    1044/411, 12″, Alpine woman **185.00**

    1044/9032, 14″, pheasant **300.00**

    1365, 17″, castle scene **770.00**

    1387, 11″, etched, Warrior **325.00**

    1607, 11″, etched, autumn season, sgd "Warth" **575.00**

    2042, 15″, etched, English Riders, sgd "Stocke 91" **850.00**

    2113, 16″, etched, dwarf in nest, sgd "Schlitt" **1,525.00**

    2195, 17½″, etched, castle scene . . **770.00**

    2517, 17″, etched, town scene **1,125.00**

    2623, 7½″, etched, man with tray . . . **145.00**

    2898, 17½″, etched, spring scene . . **1,800.00**

Punch Bowls

    1158, 16 L, relief, vinework, lid of bearded man, orig pewter spout . . **900.00**

    1888, 6 L, relief, Imperial eagle with state shields **1,000.00**

    3088, 5 L, cov, underplate, etched, Noah's Ark perched on mountain with animals leaving, celebration, sgd "Heinr Schlitt" **1,500.00**

Shield, Great Britain, #3225/1290. . . . **425.00**

Steins

    675, ½ L, barrel, hopsbud inlay lid . . **150.00**

    1000, ¼ L, relief, 3 shields. **125.00**

Stein, 2373, scenes of St. Augustine, FL, alligator handle, ½L, $575.00.

    1163, ½ L, relief, Yale University . . . **220.00**

    1266, ¼ L, relief, 3 cavalier scenes . **125.00**

    1745, ¼ L, relief, leaves and verse. . **130.00**

    2069, ½ L, monkey holding fish **2,100.00**

    2140/895, ½ L, Inft. Regt. Friederich Der Niederlande NR 15 . . . . **600.00**

    2540, 1 L, etched, student and barmaid, sgd "H.S." **800.00**

    2721, ½ L, etched and glazed, cabinetmaker, occupational. **1,600.00**

    2936, ½ L, etched, Elks Club **425.00**

    3177, 2.2 L, cameo, woman in wreath, hunter on each side, sgd "ST" . . . **1,000.00**

    3236, ½ L, etched, Art Nouveau verse **245.00**

Sweetmeat Jar, cov, #1231, 4¾″ h, scenic with 6 cows, castle mark **525.00**

Tile, 3¼ x 5¾″, blue warrior **225.00**

Tray, 9 x 14″, wooden frame, barmaid with flowers **360.00**

Vases

    308, 3½″, relief. **60.00**

    1681, 9″, mosaic. **165.00**

    1899, 7½″, etched **220.00**

MILITARIA

History: Wars always have been part of history. Until the mid-19th century, soldiers often had to fill their own needs, including weapons. Even in the 20th century a soldier's uniform and some of his gear is viewed as his personal property, even though issued by a military agency.

Conquering armed forces made a habit of acquiring souvenirs from their vanquished foes. They brought their own uniforms and accessories home as badges of triumph and service.

Saving militaria may be one of the oldest collecting traditions. Militaria collectors tend to have their own special shows and view themselves outside the normal antiques channels. However, they haunt small indoor shows and flea markets in hopes of finding additional materials.

Additional Listings: Firearms and Swords. See World War I and World War II in *Warman's Americana & Collectibles* for more examples.

CIVIL WAR

Bayonnet, 19½″ l, 4 sided. **25.00**

Belt, waist, leather, brass bucket with eagle imprint, Union **100.00**

Boots, Cavalry, pr, black leather **150.00**

Cartridge Box, pistol, brown leather bill, brass insignia **125.00**

Casket Plate, silver on copper **40.00**

Cup, collapsible, orig japanned finish tin case. **75.00**

Discharge Papers, 1st Ohio, dated 1863 . . . . **85.00**

Field Glasses, 7½″, closed, brass, made by Lemaire Fabt., Paris **100.00**

Flag, 22 x 28″, 19th Corps, 159 New York State Volunteers, swallow tail, silk, two ties **1,000.00**
Mess Kit, knife, fork, and spoon, cast steel, mkd "Richards Patent July 23, 1861". **65.00**
Muster Roll, Confederate, Captain Wm. K. Bachman's Company of the German Artillery Regiment of the Hampton Legion, Aug. 31–Oct. 31, 1864, double folio, lists 141 soldiers and their status **125.00**
Orders Book, tall slim folio, tooled calf cov, 21½ pgs, contains "General and Special Orders of 12th Regiment, Pennsylvania Reserve Corps, August 6, 1861–March 17, 1862," contains 48 orders, directives, officer correspondence **70.00**
Razor, U. S. and eagle impressed in gutta percha handle **75.00**
Ribbons
  Portrait, J. B. Foraker, "No Rebel Flags Will Be Surrendered While I Am Governor," silk, Confederate . . **60.00**
  Reunion, "Army Of The Tennessee Reunion," 1881, Confederate **20.00**
Saddle, Calvary, McCullem and Militia types **300.00**
Saddle Bags
  Allegheny Arsenal, 1864 . . . . **250.00**
  Virginia, 1st Cavalry. **500.00**
Spy Glass, 16″, four sections, leather wrapped. **250.00**
Sword Belt Plate, Union, Non-Commissioned Officer **50.00**

FRANCO-PRUSSIAN WAR

Diorama, 32 x 30½ x 8¾″, artillery scene, metal, wood, papier mache, and natural materials, depicting a breech loading cannon on carriage, drawn by a team of 4 horses, 7 uniformed military figures. **1,500.00**
Helmet, Prussian General Officer, spiked, silver garde star, enameled black Eagle Order on breast of Heraldic Eagle, plain spike, gilt chinstrap and rosettes, silk lining **1,500.00**
Medal, "Order of the House of Hohenzollen Knight," badge with swords, silver gilt and enameled breast badge . **325.00**
Painting, 19 x 24½″, A. Balquet, artillery scene, oil on canvas, framed **500.00**

SPANISH AMERICAN WAR

Artillery Shell, brass, engraved "U. S. S. Boson, Manila Bay, May 1, 1898," wooden projectile **60.00**
Button, pinback, "Remember The Maine," battleship scene, patent 1896 . . . . **15.00**

Canteen. **20.00**
Cartridge Box, U. S. Army **120.00**
Models
  Spanish Battleship, *Almirante Oguendo,* wood and various metals, moveable cannons, 22″ l. (Ship was severly damaged at Battle of Santiago de Cuba on July 3, 1898) . . . **250.00**
  Torpedo, 17½″ l, brass, Austrian, mounted on brass and wood plinth, c1898 . . . . **450.00**

WORLD WAR I

Candle Lantern, folding, tin, mica panels, U. S. Medical Corps insignia. **75.00**
Cap, Ambulance Driver, insignia badge **75.00**
Dioramas
  11″ l, French Army General Brugere Staff Car, metal, wood, and canvas, mounted on a base supporting 9 papier mache military figures **1,400.00**
  16 x 10 x 8″, Russian 75 mm field gun and crew, brass, steel, and papier mache, 5 military gun crew standing ready at their artillery piece, officer prepares to give orders, naturalistic base **950.00**
Horse feed bag, canvas **20.00**
Iron Cross, 1st class, silver, orig case, 1914 . . . . **65.00**
Lithograph, 14 x 36″, French, colored, artillery scene, sgd, dated 1916, framed **100.00**

World War I, American, divisional helmet, orig liner, $48.00.

Medal, French, commemorative with bar, "Engage Volontaire". **15.00**
Painting, 7 x 10″, E. Presty, French battle cruiser at sea, oil on panel, sgd, framed **125.00**
Scale Model, mechanical, 17″ l, breech loading 75mm deck cannon, brass and steel, hand cranked rotating gun

rail, hand cranked trajectory and sighting mechanism, mounted on black marble plinth, together with a card engraving after J. O. Davidson, NY, 1891, depicting a similar deck gun in action, 8¼ x 10¾", framed **1,600.00**
Stickpin, Wound, black, German **10.00**
Uniforms
British Rifle Brigade, N.C.O., dark green tunic with braid around collar, pointed cuff, rank insignia sleeve with large crown **145.00**
U. S. Army, Captain, wool tunic, braid trim on cuff and 2 navy velvet hash marks, size 37–38 .... **150.00**

WORLD WAR II

Belt Buckle, DAK olive/drab paint, stamped 1942, leather tab **35.00**
Binoculars, Officer's, DAK, light tan camoflauge case, leather neck strap, line calibrations for artillery, mkd "Cag Dienstglass 6 x 30 #307755" **75.00**
Cigarettes, German, DAK package, tax stamps, mkd "Optima, Constantin". . **15.00**
Dagger, SS EM, full inscription, black handle with silver eagle insignia, silvered fittings. **285.00**
Field Telephones, pr, German, handpieces imp with Third Reich symbols, bakelite carrying cases **250.00**
Helmet, Luftwaffe fighter pilot, summer weight, leather padded fur earpieces, silk lining, leather chin strap **275.00**
Holster, SS officer, white parade leather, extra clip pouch, dated 1943, SS Rune Acceptance Stamp in 2 places. **75.00**
Scale Model, 30" l, Cargo Vessel *Cap Nord*, wood and various metals, half rigged, mounted on 2 brass supports (used as P-II boat, sunk off the North African coast by the Royal Air Force in 1944) **3,200.00**
Sighting Device for 88 mm cannon, 12" l, black paint, leather case, mkd "Fernrohrlage I, RIF". **45.00**
Stickpins
Red Cross, enameled **10.00**
SS, edelweiss, silver finish **25.00**
Uniforms
British
Captain, R.A.S.C. tunic and trousers, size 41–42 .... **125.00**
Major General A.M.F., tunic with medals and ribbons of O.B.E., D.S.O., 1939–45 Star, African Star, Pacific Star, War Medal, Australian war service medal, size 39–40 .... **250.00**
U.S., WAVES, complete uniform and hat **65.00**
Visor Cap, Army, rose piping for Armored

and Motor Personnel, green wool top, silvered metal eagle, dark green wool band, silvered wreath and metal rosette with red wool center, wide leather veneer visor, black leather chin strap **120.00**
Wrist Compass, Luft. Fighter Pilot **35.00**

MILK GLASS

History: Opaque white glass attained its greatest popularity at the end of the 19th century. American glass manufacturers made opaque white tablewares as a substitute for costly European china and glass. Other opaque colors, e.g., blue and green, were made. As the Edwardian era began, milk glass expanded into the novelty field.

The surge of popularity in milk glass subsided after World War I. However, milk glass continues to be made in the 20th century. Some modern products are reissues and reproductions of early forms. This presents a significant problem for collectors, although it is partially obviated by patent dates or company markings on the originals and by the tell tail signs of age.

Collectors favor milk glass from the pre-World War I era, especially animal covered dishes. The most prolific manufacturers of these animal covers were Atterbury, Challinor, Taylor, Flaccus, and McKee.

References: E. McCamley Belknap, *Milk Glass*, Crown Publishers, 1949, out-of-print; Regis F. and Mary F. Ferson, *Yesterday's Milk Glass Today*, privately printed, 1981; S. T. Millard, *Opaque Glass*, Wallace-Homestead, 1975, 4th edition.

Museum: Houston Antique Museum, Chattanooga, TN.

Notes: These are many so-called McKee animal covers. Prices given are for authentic items with either cover or base signed.

Reproductions are marked by an asterisk.

Pieces are cross referenced to the Ferson's book by the (F ---) marking at the end of a listing.

Additional Listings: See *Warman's Americana & Collectibles* for more examples.

Advisors: Regis and Mary Ferson.

Bird House, 5¼" d, green shingle roof, wood pattern white circular body, wren size opening, metal clip-on base, metal loop hanger, mkd on lower edge "MFG. BY McKEE G. CO. PAT. APPL'D FOR" (F 223) **52.00**
Bottles
Bear and Lamp Post, 11⅛" h, lifelike bear sits upright, forelegs around well detailed lamp post (F 435). . . **260.00**
Grant's Tomb, 8¼" h [with stopper, 10" h], patented figural tomb correctly closed by separate patented metal bust of Grant (F 472B, F 472C) **725.00**

Bowls

*Daisy, 8¼" d, pink and blue flowers among each quadrant, floral cluster inside, lacy scalloped edge, Challinor, Taylor (F 165) **80.00**

Maize, 7½" d, columns of corn kernels cover surface, broken by random blue foliage originating at base of concave mold, flint-like ring, patented 1889 by Locke for Libbey . . **100.00**

Butter Dishes

Family, 6⅛" h, china-like bust of father forms base, hat is cov, red glass eyes (F 269) **310.00**

Princess Feather, 4" h, diamond points enclosed by paired scrolls on stippled ground, three lobed finial, flint, Bakewell, Pears, c1865 (F 306) **140.00**

Candlestick, Crucifix, 8³/₁₆" h, stepped circular base, ivy twining below cross and climbing reverse side, reeded candle receptacle, Atterbury, c1881 (F 330) **45.00**

Candy Container, Suitcase, 4" l, decal of rifle and powder horn between gilt straps, tin base closure, wire handle, mkd on one end "PAT APL'D FOR," Westmoreland Specialty Company (F 566) **57.00**

Celery, Blackberry, 8⅛" h, scalloped edge bowl, lower ⅔ patterned, tall pedestal, Hobbs, Brockunier (F 314 . **125.00**

Child's Punch Set, scenes from Little Red Riding Hood on scalloped punch bowl and six cups, bowl: 4⅝" d, cup: 1⅝" d (F 198). **245.00**

Compotes

*Chick and Eggs, 6" d, stack of eggs, hatching chick in middle of stack forms finial, inside of cov mkd "PATᴰ AUG. 6, 1889," round base has lacy edge, Atterbury (F 49) **120.00**

Marquis and Marchioness, cov sweetmeat, 8" h, medallions portray Duke of Argyll and Princess Louise, "NOV. 28, 1878" and other historical data in shield (F 315) **160.00**

Condiment Set, Forget-Me-Not, cruet 5⅛" h, six lobed, floral patterned salt, pepper, and small cruet, matching trefoil tray, neck and handle of cruet plain, stopper reeded, blue, Challinor, Taylor (F 164). **190.00**

Creamers

Cobb, individual size, 3", surface resembles ear of corn, foliage rises from base, ear shaped handle, Challinor, Taylor (F 587) **40.00**

Sunflower, 4½" h, row of paneled sunflowers above row of paneled lillies-

of-the-valley, long lip, wide handle, Atterbury, c1880 (F 313). **37.00**

Dishes, covered

*Cat, lacy base. 6⅜" l, recumbent, glass eyed cat on rect pad, rest on typical Atterbury base, mkd on inside of cov "AUGUST 27, 1889" (F 55) **120.00**

*Cat, wide rib base, 5½" l, blue cat, white head and front, on correct blue base, Westmoreland Specialty Company (F 16). **52.00**

Couch, fainting, 5" l, tufted black surface, rolled headrest, red frame (F 386) **75.00**

Cow, basket base, 7¼" l, reclining cow cov, rope edge topping diamond finish basket, encircled "K" [Kemple] on bottom (F 213) **55.00**

Dog, Chow, 5½" l, tail curved over back, head turned to right, mkd on inner rim with script "McKee," typical McKee split rib base (F 71). . . **180.00**

Dog, Pekingese, 4¾" l, sits in rect base with beaded edge, diamond patterned sides, stippled ends, Sandwich (F 197). **240.00**

Fish, entwined, 6" d, domed cov with two glass eyed fish encircling shield finial, inside embossed "PATᴰ Aug. 1889," round lacy base, Atterbury. **145.00**

Hand and Dove, 6⅜" l, rect slab, hand with glass-set ring cradles eyed bird, mkd inside cov "PATᴰ AUG. 1889," lacy base, Atterbury (F 52) **110.00**

Lamb, 5½" l, detailed animal facing right, mkd under rim with script "McKee," split rib base (F 68) . . . **160.00**

*Owl Head, 5½" l, detailed head, crown to beak, prominent ears and molded eyes, split rib base, mkd on both parts with script "McKee" (F 71A) **550.00**

*Swan, raised wing, 9⅞" l, bird on ¼" rough surface, rect slab, inserted eyes, lace-like edge on base, int. basketweave surface (F 179). . **125.00**

*Turkey, Gobbler, 5½" l, detailed molding emphasizes fan tail, feathers, wattles, and surface cover, mkd under rim with script "McKee," split rib base (F 62). **165.00**

Dishes, Pickle

Bird, 10¾" l, detailed feather design covers sides, flange, and tail of bird shaped deep dish, lavender, Hemingray Glass Co. (F 176). **45.00**

Saloon, 12" l, basketweave bowl inside and out, thin glass panel divides bowl into two compartments, rope handle and trim, base mkd "PATᴰ JULY 21ˢᵀ 1874 & FEB 9ᵀᴴ 1875," Atterbury (F 338). **175.00**

Doorstop, 9" l, reclining lion on stepped oval slab, opening at end of fluted base for door chain, mkd on inside of base "PATENT PENDING" (F 119A)   **175.00**

Inkwells

Circular, 3¾" d, pear on leafy branch atop circular inkwell, brass closure, matte finish, mkd on vertical side "G. E. HATCH. PAT'D DEC. 27, 1875" (F 182) **85.00**

Snail, 4¼" h, snail shell container hinged on metal stand and pen rack, mkd on base "CLIPPER-PATENTED MAR. 12, 1878, OCT. 8, 1878" (F 535) **80.00**

Jars

*Mustard, Bull's Head, 4⅜" h, realistic, including old brown paint, figural container separates at mouth, tongue is ladle, base emb "PAT^T APL^D FOR," Atterbury (F 14) **125.00**

Rib and Bow, 5¾" h, ribbed surface bulges above and below narrow high waist surrounded by ribbon and bow, white ground with green, blue, and pink flecks, base mkd "PAT^T APL^D FOR," Atterbury (F 476). . . .   **60.00**

Lamps

Art Nouveau, 6" h, classical figure holding lyre seated by early electric lamp, fixture mkd "BRYANT PAT'D MAY 17–10" (F 452) **65.00**

Blackberry, 11¾" h, clear global font has wide band of pattern, attached to milk glass quatrefoil base by clinch connector, mkd "PAT. MAY 24, 1870," Hobbs, Brockunier (F 612) **100.00**

Matchholders

Bulldog, 2¼" h, lifelike head carries striking area on rear, thick glass, McKee & Brothers, c1899 (F 125).   **50.00**

Trilby Foot, 2¾" h, figural of woman's foot and lower leg, base impressed "TRIBLY," base bottom mkd "PATENTED AUG. 20, 1895" (F 684) . .   **80.00**

Paperweight, Washington Monument, 5½" h, sq base of obelisk imprinted with statistics and bust of Washington (F 389). **70.00**

Pitchers

Daisy, 9¼" h, alternating blue and red flowers in inverted beaded teardrops above beaded diamonds, yellow ground, Westmoreland Specialty Company (F 291). **85.00**

Raindrop, 7½" h, rows of alternately spaced drops cover body, handle and base have single row of smaller drops, blue (F 373) **100.00**

Plaque, Rabbit, 6" h, plump crouching figure, ears laid back, blue, Westmoreland Specialty Company (F 73).   **60.00**

Mustard, bull's head, 4⅜" h, tongue is ladle, base emb "PAT^T APL^D FOR," Atterbury, (F 14), $125.00

Plates

California Bear, 9" d, gilt bear in wreath of grains, fruit, and flowers, surrounded by "CALIFORNIA MIDWINTER FAIR," club and shell border (F 543) **100.00**

Three Dogs, 6" d, three half-grown dogs sit on top of plate, lower portion has open work border (F 397)   **95.00**

Platters

Liberty Bell, 11¼" l, "1776, 1876" and "DECLARATION OF INDEPENDENCE" surround bell inscribed "LIBERTY," duplicated on reverse plus "PAT^D SEPT 28, 1875," all in mirror image, shell handles, upper collar reads "100 YEARS AGO," lower collar reads "John Hancock" in script (F 571) **230.00**

Three Graces, 11⅝" d, platform imprinted "THREE GRACES," two dancing female figures crown a third, milk glass medallion center, clear border impressed "FAITH HOPE AND CHARITY," mkd on left handle "PAT^D NOV 23, 1875," Atterbury (F 570). **180.00**

Salts, Open

Basket, 3¾" l, two section basketweave container, rope handle, base mkd "JULY 21, 1874," Atterbury (F 352) **25.00**

Flying Fish, 4⅝" l, fins form container over back of lavender fish on aqua base (F 388) **40.00**

Salt Shakers

Dredge, 3⅜" h, Atterbury Twin, int. vertical divider separates salt and pepper chambers, handled octagonal body designated "SALT" and "PEPPER" sides, base mkd "PATD OCT. 28TH 1873," pewter closure (F 415) **48.00**

Owl Head, 2½" h, detailed, screwed metal closure (F 88).......... **60.00**

Shaving Mugs

Garfield, 2¾" h, separate brush compartment above ring handle, likeness of Pres. and Mrs. Garfield on opposite sides (F547)......... **95.00**

Hinge, 3½" h, sectioned int. separates soap and water, rim notch is brush rest above handle, patterned around hinge, base emb "PAT'D DEC. 26, 1876 AND DEC. 18, 1877" (F 184) **60.00**

Spooners

Oval Medallion, 5⅛" h, rect, narrowing at base, pansies baked on ovals in wide ends, narrow ends extend to form curved supports, scalloped top, Challinor, Taylor (F 245) **35.00**

Paneled Wheat, 5¼" h, six panels with stippled edge outline sheaves of wheat around lower half of mill edged spooner, upper portion plain, Hobbs, Brockunier (F 257) **35.00**

Statuettes

Dewey, 5½" h, details emphasize large nose, mustache, and goatee, admiral's naval uniform, bust mounted on circular base (F 542) . **80.00**

Lincoln, 6", head stands out from undraped shoulders on solid rect base, satin finish, front mkd "A. LINCOLN," back mkd "CENTENNIAL EXHIBITION GILLINDER & SONS" (F 563) **300.00**

Sugars

Diamond Point And Leaf, 7⅛" h, brilliant diamond point ground, interrupted by three leaf sprays, finial resembles diamond, flint, Sandwich (F 258) **55.00**

Paneled Flower, two eight petaled blossoms on each of six diamond point panels, sq finial, Challinor, Taylor (F 282) **55.00**

Sugar Shaker, Forget-Me-Not, six segments cov with floral sprays, green, mushroom shaped tin closure, Challinor, Taylor (F 481) **70.00**

Syrups

Bellflower, 5⅞", fine ribbed, single vine bellflower, applied handle (F 155C) .. **225.00**

Strawberry, 6⅝" h, jug's widest area banded by strip of leaves and fruit, applied handle, closure mkd beneath lip "PATD MAY 10, 1864," Bryce, Walker & Company (F 151) **120.00**

Toothpick, Alligator, 2¾" h, back supports receptacle, steadied by curved tail, wide spread feet (F 451) **75.00**

MILLEFIORI

History: Millefiori (thousand flowers) is an ornamental glass composed of bundles of colored glass rods fused to become canes. The canes were pulled while still ductile to the desired length, sliced, arranged in a pattern and again fused together. The Egyptians developed this technique in the first century B. C.; it was revived in the 1880s.

Note: Millefiori items, such as paperweights, cruets, toothpicks, etc., are being made by many modern companies.

Miniature Lamp, 12" h, cobalt, orange and ochre canes, brass trim, electrified, $600.00.

Ashtray **75.00**
Bowl, 2", pink, green, and white canes, applied handles............... **35.00**
Box, cov **165.00**
Cruet, matching stopper **135.00**
Cup and Saucer, c1915 .... **130.00**
Goblet, 7½", clear stem and base **175.00**
Lamps
10", table, mushroom shape, multicolored base and shade, electrified **424.00**

14″, kerosene, double gourd shaped
standard, domical shaped shade .. **150.00**
Pitcher, 4⅞″ **55.00**
Salt, master **90.00**
Sugar Shaker, handled **100.00**
Tie Tack, paperweight, green with multicolored canes **125.00**
Toothpick Holder, ruffled top, c1890 .. **145.00**
Tumbler, 4½″ **75.00**
Vases
5½″, handled, purple bands with white
oval lines, white bands with red
flowers and yellow centers **140.00**
7″, bulbous, long neck, fluted rim,
clambroth base and pontil **165.00**

MINIATURE LAMPS

History: Miniature oil and kerosene lamps, often
called "night lamps," are diminutive replicas of
larger lamps. Simple and utilitarian in design, miniature lamps found a place in the parlor (as "courting" lamps), hallway, children's rooms, and sick-
room.

Miniature lamps are found in many glass types
from Amberina to satin glass. Miniature lamps measure 2½ to 12 inches in height with the principal
parts being the base, collar, burner, chimney, and
shade. In 1877 both L. J. Atwood and L. H. Olmsted
patented burners for miniature lamps. Their burners
made the lamps into a popular household accessory.

Study a lamp carefully to make certain all parts
are original; married pieces are common. Reproductions abound.

References: Ann Gilbert McDonald, *Evolution of
the Night Lamp*, Wallace Homestead, 1979; Frank
R. & Ruth E. Smith, *Miniature Lamps*, Schiffer Publishing Ltd., 1981, 6th printing; Ruth E. Smith, *Miniature Lamps - II*, Schiffer Publishing Ltd., 1982.

Note: The numbers given below refer to the figure numbers found in the Smith books.

16-II, Jeweler's, cobalt **50.00**
20-II, Blue shade, Aladdin-type **265.00**
34-I, Cup and saucer **95.00**
36-II, Glow **150.00**
44-I, Little Jewel **80.00**
49-II, Little Banner **85.00**
58-I., Reflector **80.00**
70-I, Brass, finger **80.00**
78-I, Comet, nickel **100.00**
80-II, Beaded Ribs **40.00**
95-II, Clear, applied handle **75.00**
110-I, Green **110.00**
122-II, Ship's brass **50.00**
125-I, Christmas Tree, milk glass **135.00**
139-II, Luna, nickel plated **65.00**
143-I, Lincoln Drape, frosted amber ... **125.00**
144-I, Westmoreland, clear **125.00**
154-II, Brass, pedestal saucer **80.00**
161-II, Atterbury **125.00**

**Smith #231, Drape pattern, red satin,
8⅝″ h, $275.00.**

166-I, Greek Key **75.00**
183-I, Milk glass, emb beading, painted
flowers **275.00**
184-II, Swirl, reflector **35.00**
194-I, Apple Blossom, pink bands on
shade and base **185.00**
203-I, Gold trim **265.00**
204-I, Milk Glass **195.00**
219-II, Green, enamel decor **140.00**
228-I, Clear, black trim **325.00**
236-I, Milk glass, emb design trimmed
in gold, blue flowers, green leaves .. **300.00**
250-I, Diana, milk glass **100.00**
277-I, Milk glass, basketweave mold .. **175.00**
331-II, Bisque, cherub, butterfly **350.00**
390-I, Cased glass, yellow, glossy finish, nutmeg burner **500.00**
400-I, Satin, pink **460.00**
403-I, Beaded Drape, opal, ruby thumbprint **185.00**
467-I, Green **165.00**
508-I, Spanish Lace **345.00**
555-I, Vaseline and pink spatter **150.00**
628-I, Milk glass, painted design **115.00**
Fig. XXVIII-II, Satin glass, pink, DQ, MOP,
silver plated stem and foot, sq ruffled
shade, white lining **695.00**
Fig. XLIII-II, Amber, swirl pattern **340.00**

MINIATURES

History: There are three sizes of miniatures: doll
house scale (ranging from ½ to 1″), sample size,
and child's size. Since most earlier material is in
museums or extremely expensive, the most common examples are 20th century.

Many mediums were used for miniatures: silver, copper, tin, wood, glass, and ivory. Even books were printed in miniature. Prices are broad ranged, depending on scarcity and quality of workmanship.

The collecting of miniatures dates back to the 18th century. It remains one of the world's leading hobbies.

References: Flora Gill Jacobs, *Dolls Houses in America: Historic Preservation in Miniature*, Charles Schribner's Sons, 1974; Flora Gill Jacobs, *History of Dolls Houses*, Charles Schribner's Sons; Constance Eileen King, *Dolls and Dolls Houses*, Hamlyn; Von Wilckens, *Mansions in Miniature*, Tuttle.

Periodicals: Miniature Collector, Collector Communications Corp., 170 Fifth Ave, New York, NY 10010; Nutshell News, Clifton House, Clifton, VA 22024. Subscription: $26.00.

Collector's Clubs: International Guild Miniature Artisans, P.O. Box 842, Summit, NJ 07901. Dues: $25.00. Newsletter (biannual); National Association of Miniature Enthusiasts, 123 N. Lemon St., Fullerton, CA 92632. Dues: $15.00. *Miniature Gazette* (quarterly).

Museums: Kansas City Doll House Museum, Kansas City, MO; Margaret Woodbury Strong Museum, Rochester, NY; Mildred Mahoney Jubilee Doll House Museum, Fort Erie, Canada; Toy Museum of Atlanta, Atlanta, GA; Washington Dolls House and Toy Museum, Washington, DC.

Additional Listings: See Doll House Furnishings in *Warman's Americana & Collectibles* for more examples.

Advisor: Carolyn Sunstein.

Tea Service, Britannia, $65.00.

DOLL HOUSE SIZE

Bath
Tootsietoy set, c1930, MIB.	**150.00**
Wooden set, 4 pc, c1940.	**40.00**

Bedroom
Biedermeir
Bed, antique, elaborate gilt stencil on rosewood, c1850	**300.00**
Nightstand, marble top, oval mirror	**125.00**
Brass, bed, antique, 1″ scale, antique fittings.	**325.00**

Birdcages
Metal, 1″ scale, German, c1940	**25.00**
Tin, mechanical, 3″ h.	**90.00**

Bisque Figures
Lady standing, Japan.	**10.00**
Piano Baby, German, 1″ h, c1910. . .	**45.00**

Books
Almanac, English Bijou, engravings, Schloss, London, c1835, ¾ x ½″ .	**180.00**
New Testament, David Bryce, c1895.	**110.00**

Bronzes
Set of 3, Vienna, cats, modern.	**125.00**
Set of 8, Vienna bronzes, tiny, modern.	**225.00**
Set of 10, 1 to 2¼″ h, c1950	**800.00**
Vienna, figural, dogs pulling cat on stretcher, c1900.	**250.00**

Cabinets
Armoire, rosewood, 3 cupboard doors, 5 x 4″, c1870.	**325.00**
Biedermeir period, glass doors	**235.00**

Chairs
Biedermeir, set of 5, overscale, balloon back.	**300.00**
Fretwork, c1900	**30.00**
Ivory, en suite with sofa, ¾″ scale, c1850	**450.00**
Petite Princess, dining chairs, pr	**30.00**
Speilwaren, Germany, rococo design, c1960	**40.00**

Chests of Drawers
Biedermeir, gilt on rosewood, marble top, c1860.	**250.00**
Petite Princess, 3 drawers, plastic. . .	**25.00**
Wooden, grain painted, c1940	**45.00**

China
Figurine, horse with rider, Sitzendorf, early 20th C	**50.00**
Tea Set, patterned, English, with tray	**75.00**
Vase, antique Satsuma, 1½″ h	**45.00**

Clocks
China, Japan, c1920	**20.00**
Mantel, gilt, 1″ scale	**75.00**
Metal	
Horse with rider atop	**125.00**
Tall case, rare	**120.00**

Cradle, French, Brittany, c1900, 1″ scale **75.00**

Couches
Biedermeir, scrollback sofa, gilt floral design.	**135.00**
Fainting, antique, plain, velvet cover, 6½″ l	**90.00**
Petite Princess, sectional	**35.00**

Desks
Biedermeir, writing, marble top, gilt . .	**140.00**
Golden Oak, lift top, side drawers, 1910.	**125.00**

Dining Room
Biedermeir, rosewood and fine gilt dec.	**375.00**
Golden Oak, table, shaped, marble top	**75.00**

Wooden hutch, shelves, 2 cabinet doors, c1940 . . . . **40.00**

Fireplaces and Stoves

Andirons, SS, 2″ h, c1910 . . . . **160.00**

Fireplace tools with holder, bone, c1900 . . . . **50.00**

Scuttle, tin penny toy, painted **75.00**

Stove, soft metal, painted, c1890 . . . **125.00**

Living Room

Biedermeir

Library Table, silver stencil and scroll work, 1″ scale **125.00**

Sofa, love seat, 8 chairs (odd lot, fair to poor condition) **150.00**

French style, 6 pc set, c1900 . . . . . . **175.00**

Fretwork, chest, walnut, velvet lining, carving, c1900 . . . . **70.00**

Strombecker, 6 pc set, c1930 . . . . . **75.00**

Wood and cardboard stacking book-cases, mahogany finish, gilt sten-ciled, faux glass doors and leather books, antique **355.00**

Mirrors

Metal, corset mirror, antique, fine . . . **145.00**

Tin, painted, crude, c1860, old glass **45.00**

Pewter & Soft Metal

Candlesticks, pewter, 1½″ h, pr, c1895 . . . . **35.00**

Magazine Rack, lead, old **75.00**

Tea Set, 4 pcs plus tray, c1920 . . . . **65.00**

Pianos

Biedermeir, antique, 4 x 4″, hinged keyboard, silk cov speaker, work-able door **300.00**

Golden Oak, c1910, hinged paper cov keys **75.00**

Ivory, ¾″ scale, pierced top, 19th C, fine **190.00**

Petite Princess, orig box **45.00**

Rooms

Arcade

Bathroom, furnishings, some chips, c1920 . . . . **325.00**

Bedroom, 4 pcs, green, c1920 . . . **330.00**

French, folding, 10 pcs furniture, late 19th C **1,000.00**

Japanese, black lacquer, tableau set-ting with dolls and accessories . . . **225.00**

Silver

Candlesticks, pr, Jan Borduur, c1775 **800.00**

Carousel, Continental, c1900, 4½″ h. **385.00**

Salt, standing, silver gilt, 18th C **220.00**

Telephones

Desk, black, c1920 . . . . **25.00**

Gooseneck, metal, old **45.00**

Wall, tin, red, workable crank, 1 x 3″, old **90.00**

ACCESSORIES

Album, metal, old **45.00**

Candlesticks, ivory, 1″ h, attached can-dles, c1900 . . . . **75.00**

Compote, Bristol Glass, ½″ h, 19th C. . **40.00**

Croquet, set of 3, wood and ivory, ¾ x 1″, ¾″ wood box, instructions, French **350.00**

Cutlery, 10 pcs, Meissen handles, old . **85.00**

Cutlery Basket, ormolu, c1895 . . . . . . **30.00**

Chandeliers

Antique gilt, 3″, 6 arms **300.00**

Metal, 1″ scale, winged cupid center post, 3 arm gas light, late 19th C . **425.00**

Champagne bucket with bottle, glass . . **40.00**

Decanter, glass, old **45.00**

Easel, antique bone with reverse glass painting **50.00**

Frame, gilt, elaborate, late 19th C **55.00**

Iron, c1900, metal with cord, 1″ scale . **32.00**

Jugs Doulton, 19th C, 1″ h. **40.00**

Goss, ¾″ h **35.00**

Lamp, table, parlor, ormolu, gas with shaped base, white milk glass shade, 1″ scale **375.00**

Magnifying glass, ¾″, old **35.00**

Match holder, ormolu, c1910 . . . . **75.00**

Penknife, ¾″, faux tortoise, old **25.00**

Piano, Viennese, enamel, finely painted, 19th C **525.00**

Pipe Set, English, c1920 . . . . **35.00**

Scissors, metal, 1″, c1900, fine **50.00**

Sewing Machine, penny toy, early 20th C **105.00**

Toaster, metal, c1920, 1″ scale **25.00**

Vases, pr, gilt, c1910 . . . . **70.00**

Victrola, penny toy, tin, litho, large gilt horn, turns, produces music like tone **60.00**

Water Set, glass, 7 pc, c1900 . . . . **50.00**

Wringer washer, Arcade, c1920 . . . . . . **40.00**

SAMPLE SIZE

Cabinet, show, French, 19th C, shaped glass upper, inlaid woods, ormolu mount trim, unusual **575.00**

Chest, English, c1830, 3 drawer, secret lock **425.00**

Clock, Brittany, c1900, working **250.00**

Furniture set (love seat, chair, and table), Thonet doll size, c1890 . . . . **1,000.00**

Tankard, Viennese enamel, gilt top, 19th C, fine **275.00**

CHILD SIZE

Chair, American, painted dec, spindle back, 19th C **275.00**

Desks

Maple, CT, some restoration, not orig brass **5,400.00**

Walnut, early 19th C, orig. **2,200.00**

Dinner Service, porcelain, Fishers **150.00**

Range, German, spirit burner with pots and kettles, c1910. . . . . **300.00**

MINTON CHINA

History: In 1793 Thomas Minton and others formed a partnership and built a small pottery at Stoke-on-Trent, Staffordshire, England. Production began in 1798 with blue printed earthenware, mostly in the willow pattern. In 1798 cream colored earthenware and bone china were introduced.

A wide range of styles and wares was produced. Minton introduced porcelain figures in 1826, Parian wares in 1846, encaustic tiles in the late 1840s, and majolica wares in 1850. Many famous designers and artists in the English pottery industry worked for Minton.

Many early pieces are unmarked or have a Sevres type marking. The "ermine" mark was used in the early 19th century. Date codes can be found on tableware and majolica. Between 1873 and 1911 a small globe signed Minton with a crown on top was used.

In 1883 the modern company was formed and called Mintons Limited. The "s" was dropped in 1968. Minton still produces bone china tablewares and some ornamental pieces.

Bisquit Jar, blue willow pattern	140.00
Bowl, 10″, red dodo and winged creatures, John Pearson, 1880	95.00
Compote, 8½″ d, 3″ d, white ground, red roses, sgd	100.00
Cups and Saucers	
Demitasse, turquoise band, Birds of Paradise	32.00
Tea, tree leaf pattern, sgd	30.00
Jug, 10″, hinged pewter cov, majolica, cobalt blue ground, yellow florals, yellow mask spout, gray handle, dated, 1867	175.00
Pitcher, 7¾″, cream ground, white grapes at top, hunters and dog, 1840 mark	140.00
Plaque, Stokesay Castle, figures, horses, and dog by village pond, gilt frame, sgd J E in puce, c1880, rectangular, 11½″ h, 10″ w	1,540.00
Plates	
9″, dessert, red roses and flowers on wide border, artist sgd, set of 12	235.00
9″, hp, gold branches, green enamel flowers, 1893 mark, set of 12	225.00
9½″, scenic, English castle and land-	

scape, blue border with gilt band	85.00
9½″, pierced, Armorial, c1880	20.00
Platter, 15″ l, 18″ w, Indian Tree pattern	125.00
Sauce Tureen with Underplate, Indian Tree pattern	50.00
Soup Bowl, Japanese, c1880	20.00
Soup Tureen, spring bouquet pattern	120.00
Tiles	
Boadicea, 6 x 6″, brown ground, off white	50.00
Night and Day, 8 x 8″, white horse and girl flying through air, blue day, yellow sun, impressed mark on back	45.00

Teapot, gray, blossom dec, 2¾″ h, 7″ l, $165.00.

Vases	
10″ trophy shape, attached stand, pink ground, hp floral medallion	585.00
15½″, ovoid, scenic, 3 seated figures, cov with fruiting branch finial, 2 scroll handles, bun feet stand with molded key pattern panels, marked c1880	900.00
Vegetable Dish, cov, floral dec, 2 handled	55.00
Wash Bowl and Pitcher, amethyst ground, ruby and yellow floral design	175.00

MOCHA

History: Mocha decoration usually is found on utilitarian creamware and stoneware pieces and is produced through a simple chemical action. A color pigment of brown, blue, green, or black is made acidic by an infusion of tobacco or hops. When the acidic colorant is applied in blobs to an alkaline ground, it reacts by spreading in feathery, seaplant-like designs. This type of decoration usually is supplemented with bands of light colored slip.

Types of decoration vary greatly, from those done in a combination of motifs, such as "Cat's Eye" and "Earthworm," to a plain pink mug decorated with green ribbed bands. Most forms of mocha are hollow, e.g., mugs, jugs, bowls, and shakers.

English potters made the vast majority of the pieces. Marked pieces are extremely rare. Collectors group the ware into three chronological periods: 1780–1280, 1820–1840, and 1840–1880.

Bowls

  4½″, ftd, cream ground, uneven and
    wide blue bands. **130.00**
  5″, black seaweed on white band. . . **140.00**
  6½″, Earthworm, ochre ground, blue,
    black stripes **300.00**
  7¼″, white, dark brown, ochre, gray-
    green stripes **325.00**
  9″, seaweed on white band, yel-
    lowware ground **200.00**
  10½″, 5″ h, dark brown band with
    white slip dec, blue and tan stripes. **450.00**
Chamber Pot, miniature, blue seaweed
  on white slip band, yellow ware
  ground **65.00**
Creamers
  3″, marbleized brown, orange, tan, tan
    handle. **245.00**
  3⅞″ white and gray-blue, blue stripes. **100.00**
Cup and Saucer, Cat's Eye, ochre and
  brown, brown bands **150.00**
Flower Pots, underplates, pr, 5½″ h,
  beaded rim, blue, brown, marbleized
  mocha body, brown arrowhead shoul-
  der border **1,325.00**
Jar, cov, 6¼″, Earthworm, blue and white **230.00**
Jugs
  5″, blue seaweed on white center
    band, ochre ground **150.00**
  7½″, Earthworm, gray, black, and
    ochre **250.00**
  8½″, dark celadon green slip, brown
    bands, white zig-zag design, strap
    handle, foliate terminals, c1830. . . **365.00**
  9⅝″, central brown band of stylized
    leaves between orange and brown
    bands, Staffordshire, c1840 . . . . . **1,100.00**
Mugs
  3″, black seaweed on blue ground . . **175.00**
  4″, dark brown trees on green ground,
    blue and brown bands, crowned
    medallion, imp ½ Pint on front . . . **200.00**
  4½″, marbleized tones of blue, brown,
    and tan, zig-zag rim, dark brown
    band border, Staffordshire, c1830. **450.00**
  5⅞″, black seaweed on blue ground. **220.00**
Mustard Pot, 3⅛″, marbleized brown, SP
  hinged lid with thumb rest **130.00**
Pitcher, 5⅞″, Cat's Eye, chocolate
  brown ground, blue, black, and white
  stripes, Leeds type handle **400.00**
Salt, 3″ d, 2″ h, ftd, seaweed on white
  band, yellow ware ground **65.00**
Sauce Dish, 4½″, ftd, marbleized brown,
  black, gray, and white **150.00**

Jug, Seaweed, brown, ochre, and green,
$400.00.

Sugar Shakers
  3¾″, stripes, chocolate brown, blue,
    orange and white. **240.00**
  4½″, dark brown trees on blue ground. **185.00**
Tureen, cov, 10¼″, light brown, ochre,
  cream, blue sprig dec, alternating with
  brown dots and diamond design,
  brown bands, green incised line border, green leaf handles, white knob . **1,200.00**
Waste Bowl, 4¾″ d, 2¾″ h, brown sea-
  weed on orange band, emb green rim
  band **300.00**

MONART GLASS

History: Monart glass is a heavy, simple shaped art glass in which colored enamels are suspended in the glass during the glass making process. This technique was originally developed by the Ysart family in Spain in 1923. John Moncrief, a Scottish glassmaker, discovered the glass while vacationing in Spain, recognized the beauty and potential market, and began production in his Perth glassworks in 1924.

The name "Monart" is derived from the surnames Moncrief and Ysart. Two types of monart were manufactured: a "commercial" line which incorporated colored enamels and a touch of adventurine in crystal, and the "art" line in which the suspended enamels formed designs such as feathers or scrolls. Monart glass, in most instances, is not marked. The factory used paper labels.

Basket, 4″, mottled orange and green . **45.00**
Bowls
  4″, swirled blue, pink, and green. . . . **110.00**
  10½″ d, 4¾″ h, white, gray crackle,
    yellow, green flecks, oxblood red
    base, rim. **150.00**
  Finger, pink, Cluthra **40.00**

Vase, 8½" h, green pedestal, brown and clear body, green rim, $60.00.

Vases
5½", bulbous, mottled red-brown base
   shading to green **135.00**
6½", bulbous, blue, rose mottling . . .   **100.00**
8½", urn shape with flared top, clear
   with goldstone, Cluthra **110.00**
14", bulbous, tapered, extended neck,
   flared rim, blue shaded to pink, gold
   highlights, Cluthra **625.00**

MONT JOYE GLASS

History: Mont Joye is a type of glass produced by Saint-Hilaire, Touvier, de Varreaux & Company at their glassworks in Pantin, France. Most pieces were lightly acid etched to give them a frosted appearance and decorated with enameled floral decorations. All pieces listed are frosted, unless otherwise noted.

Perfume, 4½", acid etched, floral dec,
   gold trim. **125.00**
Rose Bowl, 5" d, 4½" h, carved violets,
   gold trim top **250.00**
Vases
4" h, 3" d, flared rim, internally ribbed,
   acid etched, hp flowers, gold
   stems **95.00**
7½", enameled daisies, ftd metal
   base, paper label, pr **225.00**
9½", pale green, enameled iris, sgd .   **250.00**
11", amethyst, enameled floral spray,
   not frosted **120.00**

13½", flared trumpet with ftd base,
   clear acid etched, painted silver and
   gold butterflies and dragonflies,
   sgd **350.00**
14", enameled iris, metal banded tops,
   pr **370.00**
16½", gold ground, floral and leaf dec,
   dec sq gold top **375.00**

MOORCROFT

History: William Moorcroft established the Moorcroft pottery in 1913 at Burselm, England. The company initially used an impressed mark, "Moorcroft, Burselm"; a signature mark, "W. Moorcroft," followed.

The majority of the art pottery wares were hand thrown, resulting in a great variation among similarly styled pieces. Color and marks are keys to determining age.

Walker, William's son, continued the business upon his father's death and made the same style wares. Modern pieces are marked simply "Moorcroft" with export pieces also marked "Made In England."

Jar, cov, anemones pattern, light blue ground, imp "Made In England" and, "Moorcroft," c1940, $100.00.

Ashtray, 5½" d, fish motif **360.00**
Bowls
3¼" d, blue-green, multicolored orchid
   inside, sgd. **65.00**
8", Grapes, c1930 . . . .   **60.00**

8″, Pansies, c1925	75.00
9″, Wisteria, c1915	70.00
11″, Poppies, raised foot, c1900	135.00
13″, Pomegranates, c1899	175.00
Box, cov, 3½″ w, 5″ l, flowers, blue ground, script gr	95.00
Butter pat, 3″, blue, red, Hibiscus	30.00
Candlesticks, pr, 7½″ h, Florian, blue carnation, dark blue ground	500.00
Creamer and Sugar, cov, red and ochre poppies	225.00
Goblet, 5 34″ h, blue ground, green, lilac, gold trim, sgd "MacIntyre Moorcroft"	550.00
Jar, cov, 3½″ h, paper label	75.00

Lamps
11″ h, blue ground, colored leaves, berries, script sgr	325.00
15″ h, green ground, colored leaves, berries, script sgr	400.00
Pitcher, 5″, stylized fruit, shaded ground, printed and imp marks	100.00

Vases
4″, Anemones, blue ground, squatty, c1900	200.00
6″, Peacock Eyes, Florian blue, c1900	200.00
8″	
Cornflowers, blue, c1920	275.00
Pomegranates, c1930	90.00
Tulips, sgd MacIntyre	175.00
10″, Wisteria	130.00
13″, Poppies, Florian blue, c1898, sgd	300.00

MORIAGE, JAPANESE

History: Moriage refers to applied clay (slip) relief motifs and decorations used on certain classes of Japanese pottery and porcelain.

This decorating was done by three methods: 1), handrolling and shaping, which was applied by hand to the biscuit in one or more layers; the design and effect required determined thickness and shape, 2), tubing, or slip trailing, which applied decoration from a tube, like decorating a cake, and 3), hakeme, which is reducing the slip to a liquid and decorating the object with a brush. Color was applied either before or after the process.

Ashtray, 5½″ d, round, brown, tan dragon dec, green M in wreath, Nippon mark	95.00
Basket, 8½″, h, ball shape, pale green ground, shaded pink stylized flowers, heavy beading	275.00

Bowls
10″, fruit, gold leaf medallions with gold beading	125.00
11″ d, 3″ h, 2″ border of raised pastel enameling, flowers inside	175.00
Chocolate Set, 10½″ cov pot, 5 cups and	

saucers, shaded green and beige, dragon dec	375.00
Creamer and Sugar, cov, flower finial, yellow-green ground, floral and leaf dec	160.00
Ewer, 7″, lavender-maroon, berries dec	145.00
Hatpin Holder, 4¾″, red flowers and green beading	75.00
Nut Bowl, clover shape, acorns, leaves, and thistles, 3 moriage jeweled handles	75.00
Powder Jar, cov, 4″ d, overall slip trail enameling jewels, scene on cov	45.00
Tankard, 12″, panels with large roses and trailing leaves, heavy enamel beading	275.00

Salt and pepper shakers, green ground on body, blue dots, top with white ground, gold dec, pr, $30.00.

Teapot, 6½″, green, bird, leaf, and berry dec	175.00

Vases
8¼″, bulbous, handled, 4 white dancing skeletons, holding fans, tambourines, and a lantern	285.00
9¼″, light green slip work, hp violets, 2 low handles	180.00
9½″, mint green slipwork, fuchsia and lavender flowers	185.00
10″, green, multicolored overall floral dec, handle	225.00

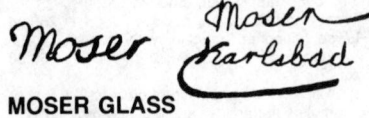

MOSER GLASS

History: Ludwig Moser (1833–1916) founded his polishing and engraving workshop in 1857 in Karlsbad (Karlovy Vary), Czechoslovakia. He employed many famous glass designers, e.g., Johann Hoffmann, Josef Urban, and Rudolf Miller. In 1900 Moser and his sons, Rudolf and Gustav, incorporated Ludwig Moser & Söhne.

Moser art glass included clear pieces with inserted blobs of colored glass, cut colored glass with classical scenes, cameo glass, and intaglio cut. Many inexpensive enameled pieces also were made.

In 1922 Leo and Richard Moser bought Meyr's Neffe, their biggest Bohemian rival in art glass. Moser executed many pieces for the Wiener Workstätte in the 1920s. The Moser glass factory continues to produce new items.

Reference: Mural K. Charon and John Mareska, *Ludvik Moser, King of Glass: A Treasure Chest of Photographs And History*, privately printed, 1984.

Tumbler, ftd, amber, 5⅜″ h, $70.00.

Ashtray, 4¼″ l, 2¾″ w, malachite glass floral dec, 4 feet	65.00
Bowls	
7¼″ d, 5⅝″ h, shaded pink opal, multicolored enamel oak leaves, applied acorns, 2 enameled bugs, sgd	375.00
8″ d, 5″ h, amber cut to clear, sgd	200.00
11″, oval, intaglio cut, emerald green shading to clear	250.00
Large, handled, crackle with seaweed dec	150.00
Boxes	
2½″ d, 1¾″ h, patch, cranberry, enameled butterflies, applied acorns on lift off cov, sgd	200.00
4⅜″ h, 4½″ d, hinged cov with applied amber salamander, enameled flowers and green foliage, 3 applied amber salamander feet, gold trim, unsigned	575.00
Compote, 5½″ h, 7¼″ d, tricorn, blue, enamel dec of acorn and ferns	400.00
Cordial, cranberry, heavy gold dec, applied opaque white snake on stem	85.00
Cruet, 8½″ h, 3¾″ d, flattened bulbous shape, pedestal foot, cranberry, heavy gold grape leaves and foliage, applied red, blue, green, and yellow grapes, applied clear gold trim handle, gold trim faceted stopper, unsigned	900.00
Cut and Saucer, large, cranberry, gold dec, white enameled flowers and gold foliage, clear applied handle covered with gold, sgd	325.00
Decanter, 11″, cranberry, lacy gold floral dec	225.00
Ewer, 5¾″ h, 2¾″ d, gold over crystal dec, multicolored enamel flowers, green leaves, pedestal base	135.00
Goblets	
4″, cranberry, heavy enamel foliage, dragonfly and ladybug	255.00
5½″ h, 3¼″ d, amber, green enameled oak leaves, applied acorns, 2 enameled bugs	375.00
Jar, 7″ h, 5″ d, cov, gold tracery and cranberry glass panels in 3 dimension	125.00
Mug, 3¼″ h, 2⅝″ d, green, applied green handle, enameled bee, multicolored oak leaves, applied lustre acorns, unsigned	295.00
Nightstand Set, 9½″ bottle, 5¾″ bottle, 4½″ h, 3⅞″ d bowl, cov 4⅜″ goblet, 11″ round tray, cranberry, heavy gold oak leaves, applied gold acorns dec, orig label on base	1,400.00
Perfume Bottles	
4¾″ h, 1⅞″ d, lime green, gold band with multicolored enameled leaves, gold top, clear trimmed stopper, unsigned	165.00
4¾″ h, 2″ d, amberina, blue enameled florals, gray panels with green applied jewels, gold band neck with applied jewels, amber cut stopper, sgd	250.00
5″, pink opalescent, gold enamel, trimmed with delicate red, white and blue enamel, sgd	350.00
Pitchers	
8″, crackle, fern dec	75.00
15″, blue, fern leaf dec, pedestal base	350.00
Pokal, cov, 12″, cranberry, dainty gold floral dec	300.00
Sweetmeat Dish, round, cranberry, engraved, gold base	225.00
Toothpick Holder, 2¼″ h, 3¼″ d, fan shape, cranberry with overall silver and gold foliage dec, gold scroll feet	300.00

Tumblers, juice
  3½″ h, 2¼″ d, melon sectioned, shaded yellow to clear, lacy enamel top, red and green jewels, sgd **200.00**
  3⅞″ h, 2¼″ d, rubena, multicolored oak leaves, applied lustre acorns .   **200.00**
Vases
  4⅛″, shaded apricot to pink, multicolored oak leaves, applied lustre acorns, sgd **245.00**
  5¾″ h, 2¼″ d sapphire blue, multicolored enamel grape leaves, applied yellow and red glass grapes, 4 applied amber rosette feet, unsigned **325.00**
  5⅞″ h, 2¾″ d, melon sectioned, blue, lacy gold foliage, multicolored enameled oak leaves with raised gold acorns, pedestal foot, unsigned **365.00**
  6″, pale amber, reticulated aqua and gold fish and floral dec **275.00**
  7½″ h, 7″ w, flat shape, electric blue, overall dec, blue and red jewels, 4 applied gold feet and rigaree up sides, sgd **1,450.00**
  8″ h, 7″ d, flattened oval shape, pink opalescent, multicolored oak leaves, applied lustred eagle and acorns, reeded gold feet, sgd **1,250.00**
  11″, footed, amethyst, enameled, knight in armor, gd **400.00**
  15″, enameled figures in court yard, printed on base, GUTENBERGUND-WIEN, dated 1895 . . . .   **575.00**
  21″, cov, pedestal base, cranberry, gold scroll dec, portrait of Empress Elizabeth **600.00**
Wine Glass, tall, amethyst, intaglio cut flowers **125.00**

Cup and saucer, mkd "Winterling/Bavaria/German," $12.00.

Cups & Saucers
  Edwards **25.00**
  Meakin **35.00**
Demitasse Set, 7½″ cov pot, pear shaped creamer and sugar, 6 cups and saucers, Japan **75.00**
Dinner Set, green and gold, marked Bavaria, 91 pcs **180.00**
Gravy Boat, Meakin **25.00**
Nappy, 4½″, Edwards **10.00**
Pitcher, 1 qt, Meakin Ironstone **40.00**
Plates
  8″, Edwards **10.00**
  8½″, Haviland, pink rim, double mark.   **25.00**
  9″, Meakin **20.00**
Shaving Mug, Ironstone China mark . . .   **25.00**
Sauce Boat on attached tray, green bands, Haviland, 8¼″ l, 5½″ h **75.00**
Tea Set, child's, orig box **100.00**
Tray, breakfast, lobed, hp over transfer, 15¾″ l **80.00**
Tureens, cov, with underplates
  Child's **30.00**
  Edwards, 8″ l, 5″ w, plus 7½″ ladle .   **180.00**
Wash Bowl and Pitcher, mkd Ironstone.   **200.00**

MOSS ROSE PATTERN CHINA

History: Several English potteries manufactured china with a moss rose pattern in the mid-1800s. Knowles, Taylor and Knowles, an American firm, began production of a moss rose pattern in the 1880s.

The moss rose was a common garden flower grown in English gardens. When American consumers tired of English china with oriental themes, they purchased the moss rose pattern as a substitute.

Bone Dish, Wilkinson Ironstone **10.00**
Bowl, 9″, sq, Meakin **60.00**
Butter Tub, Japan **25.00**
Coaster, SS rim, Rosenthal **10.00**
Creamer, 5½″, Meakin **30.00**

MOUNT WASHINGTON GLASS COMPANY

History: In 1837 Deming Jarves, founder of the Boston & Sandwich Glass Company, established for George D. Jarves, his son, the Mount Washington Glass Company in Boston, Massachusetts. In the following years the leadership and the name of the company changed several times as George Jarves formed different associations.

In the 1860s the company was owned and operated by Timothy Howe and William L. Libbey. In 1869 Libbey bought a new factory in New Bedford, Massachusetts. The Mount Washington Glass Company began operating again there under its original name. Henry Libbey became associated with the company early in 1871. He resigned in 1874 during the general depression; and, the glass works was closed. William Libbey had resigned in 1872 to work for the New England Glass Company.

The Mount Washington Glass Company opened again in the fall of 1874 under the presidency of A. H. Seabury and the management of Frederick S. Shirley. In 1894 the glass works became a part of the Pairpoint Manufacturing Company.

Throughout its history the Mount Washington Glass Company made a great variety of glass including: pressed glass, blown glass and art glass, lava glass, Napoli, cameo, cut glass, Albertine, and Verona.

References: George C. Avila, *The Pairpoint Glass Story,* Reynolds-DeWalt Printing, Inc., 1968; Leonard E. Padgett, *Pairpoint Glass,* Wallace Homestead, 1979.

Museum: The New Bedford Glass Museum, New Bedford, MA.

Additional Listings: Burmese, Crown Milano, Peachblow, and Royal Flemish.

Advisor: Ralph U. Saarinen.

Bowls
Melon shaped, 3½" d, white ground, pansy dec, gold dotted top **200.00**
Oval shaped, DQ, sq open top, pink to white ground, dotted flower dec. **235.00**
Condiment Set, tall ribbed salts, barrel ribbed mustard, satin finish, enamel dec, SP three-ring holder, sgd Pairpoint **230.00**
Cracker Jar, melon ribbed, squat, light green to white ground, yellow and white spider mums dec, SP rim, cover, and bail, sgd "MW" in cov. **300.00**
Creamer, tomato form, light green to white ground, floral and leaf dec, SP handle, spout **250.00**
Mustard Pots
Ribbed barrel, small, white ground, pink floral dec, SP bail and cov. . . **75.00**

Bowl, 4⅛" d, 2¼" h, rect top, DQ, white to apricot, painted and enamel floral dec, $140.00.

Ribbed form, large, 1¾" w, white ground, pink floral dec, SP cov and handle. **95.00**
Pickle Castor, DQ, pink to white ground, blue and white dotted floral dec insert, ornate SP frame and lid, sgd Pairpoint. **575.00**
Plates
8½" max width, two sides folded inward, glossy, pansy dec **150.00**
10½", satin finish, floral dec. **60.00**
Potpourri Pail, wooden pail form, glossy, pansy dec, SP cov and bail, sgd "MW" in cov. **150.00**
Salt, open, master, melon ribbed, light pink to white ground, firecracker flower dec, good dotted top **95.00**
Salt Shakers
Egg, enamel dec, orig top **65.00**
Fig, leaf dec, orig top **100.00**
Tomato, enamel dec, orig top. **70.00**
Sugar Shakers
Egg, yellow to white ground, pansy dec, orig top **185.00**
Fig, cranberry frosted, enamel floral dec, orig top **550.00**
Tomato, Burmese color ground, shasta daisy dec, orig dragonfly SP top **260.00**
Sweetmeat Jar, light green to white ground, holly and berry dec, SP top and cov, sgd "MW" in cov. **300.00**
Toothpick, melon ribbed base, straight neck, violet dec, blue dotted top. . . . **120.00**
Tumbler, white ground, brown oak leaf and coralene dec **55.00**
Vases
3¼" h, 4" w, scissor cut fingered top, light pink fingers, violet dec. **260.00**
7½" h, 4½" w, dark yellow to white ground, rose bud and green leaf dec, gold and gold dotted top **325.00**
10½", Napoli, clear ground, white lily dec inside, dec outlined outside with gold **500.00**
13", bulbous bottom, trumpet top, Burmese ground, shasta daisy dec. **300.00**

MULBERRY CHINA

History: Mulberry china, made primarily in the Staffordshire district of England between 1830 and 1850, is porcelain resembling the color of mulberry juice. The potters that manufactured flow blue also made mulberry china, the ware often having a flowing effect similar to flow blue.

Reference: Petra Williams, *Flow Blue China and Mulberry Ware-Similarity and Value Guide,* Fountain House East, 1981, revised edition.

Butter Dish, drainer, Tonquin, T. Heath, c1845. . . . . **125.00**

Creamers
  Corean, Podmore Walker & Co.,
    c1850 . . . . 95.00
  Manila, Ridgway, c1845 . . . . 60.00
Cup Plate, Jeddo, W. Adams & Son,
  c1845. . . . . 40.00
Cups and Saucers
  Athens, Wm. Adams & Son, c1849,
    handleless cup 85.00
  Damascus, Adams, handleless cup . . 100.00
  Jeddo, W. Adams & Son, c1845, han-
    dleless cup 45.00
  Washington Vase, Podmore & Walker,
    c1850, 5½" h, handle 80.00

**Cup and saucer, handleless, Bagshaw,
Meir, 1802–08, $75.00.**

Gravy Boat, Temple 95.00
Honey Dish, Beauties of China, Mellor,
  Venables & Co, c1845. . . . . 35.00
Pitcher, 12½" h, Marble pattern 95.00
Plates
  7"
    Alhambra. 25.00
    Cyprus, Ridgway, Bates & Co.,
      c1857 . . . . 30.00
    Genoa. 25.00
    Loreze, Edward Challinor, c1850 . . 25.00
    Vincennes 28.00
  7½"
    Beauties, J. B. 30.00
    Bosphorus, Marshall. 25.00
    Corean, Podmore Walker & Co.,
      c1850 . . . . 25.00
  8", Madras, W. & B. 25.00

  8½"
    Brush stroke 30.00
    Calcutta, E. Challinor, c1845 . . . . . 25.00
    Three Bouquets 20.00
  9¼"
    Cyprus, Ridgway, Bates & Co.,
      c1857 . . . . 45.00
    Jeddo, W. Adams & Son, c1845 . . 30.00
    Tonquin. 40.00
  9¾"
    Calcutta, E. Challinor, c1845 . . . . . 30.00
    Corean, Podmore Walker & Co.,
      c1850 . . . . 45.00
    Pelew, E. Challinor, c1840 . . . . . . 60.00
    Temple, Podmore Walker & Co. . . 30.00
  10½"
    Abbey Ruins, T. Mayer 35.00
    Adelaide's Bower 35.00
    Athens, W. Adams 30.00
Platters
  15¾", Rhone scenery 130.00
  18", Corean, Podmore Walker & Co. 250.00
Relish, Cologne, cameo head decor on
  handles 50.00
Sauce Dishes
  Bochara 25.00
  Cyprus 25.00
Sauce Tureen, cov, undertray, Susa. . . 200.00
Sauce Tureen Ladle 150.00
Shaving Mug, Ning Po 85.00
Soap, cov, Marble 60.00
Soup, 10¾" d, flange, Peru, Holdcroft . 40.00
Sugar, cov, Bochara 100.00
Tea Sets
  Avon, cov teapot, waste bowl, 4 han-
    dleless cups and saucers, 4
    8¾" plates 500.00
  Peru, cov teapot, cov sugar,
    creamer, tea bowl, 9 cups and sau-
    cers, 7 dessert plates. 800.00
Vegetable Dishes, cov
  Bochara 160.00
  Jeddo, octagonal. 135.00
  Washington Vase, octagonal 165.00
Waste Bowl, Corean. 45.00

MUSIC BOXES

History: Music boxes were invented in Switzerland around 1825. They cover a broad field of automatic musical instruments from a small box to a huge circus calliope.

A cylinder box consists of a comb with teeth which vibrate when stricking a pin in the cylinder and producing music from light tunes to opera and overtures.

The first disc music box was invented by Paul Lochmann of Leipzig, Germany, in 1886. It used an interchangeable steel disc with pierced holes bent to a point which hit the star-wheel as the disc revolved, and thus produced the tune. Discs were easily stamped out of metal, allowing a single music box to play an endless variety of tunes. It reached the height of its popularity from 1890 to 1910. The phonograph replaced it.

Music boxes also were put into many items, e.g., clocks, sewing and jewelry boxes, steins, plates, toys, perfume bottles, and furniture.

Collectors' Club: Musical Box Society, International, Rt. 3, Box 205, Morgantown, IN, 46160. Dues: $20.00.

Museums: Bellms Cars and Music of Yesterday, Sarasota, FL; Lockwood Matthews Mansion, Norwalk, CT.

Additional Listings: See *Warman's Americana & Collectibles* for more examples.

Regina, oak, coin operated, 15½″ disc, $2,200.00

Album, photograph, 4½″ disc, peripheral driven, 1 comb, key wind, 12 discs, 15″ l, c1900 . . . . **350.00**

Christmas Tree Stand, nickel plated, revolves on clock-work mechanism, small cylinder movement with 2 tunes, 10″ h, German, 1910 . . . . **300.00**

Cigarette Holder, revolving, gold, painted scenes of courting couple and flowers, 12″ h, French, c1910 . . . . **280.00**

Monkey Violinist, seated under arbor, head nods, blinking, knashing his teeth, raising arm, moves back and forth, wooden oval base contains music box, 26″ h **1,300.00**

Roller Organs
 Melodia, Mechanical Orguinette Co, New York, 2 rolls, side hand crank, gold stenciling and lettering, 12″ w, late 19th C **250.00**
 Orguinette, Gally Clariona, 14 note, paper roll, side hand crank, 10½″ mahogany case, American, c1880. **225.00**

Snuff Box, molded horn composition case, classical scene on lid, 2 control buttons on front and side, 3 tunes, French, late 19th C **400.00**

CYLINDER-TYPE

3½″ cylinder, Mermod Freres, 6 tunes, side crank wind, 13¾″ l wood case with foliate transfer, Swiss, c1900. . . **250.00**

6″ cylinder, 3 bells in view, 8 tunes, side lever wind, 17″ l rosewood veneer case with musical inlay, Swiss, c1890. **475.00**

6″ cylinder, "Two-Per-Turn", 12 tunes, side lever wind, 13½″ l rosewood veneer case with inlay musical cartouche, Swiss, c1860. . . . . **1,400.00**

6¼″ cylinder, 8 tunes, side lever wind, 17″ l rosewood veneer case, orig tune sheet, Swiss, c1890 . . . . **350.00**

7½″ cylinder, Paillard, 10 tunes, tune indicator, side lever wind, 18″ l wood case, orig tune sheet, Swiss, c1890 . **600.00**

8¼″ cylinder, Mermod Freres "Guitare", 6 tunes, zither attachment, side lever wind, 17″ l rosewood veneer case with foliate inlay, orig tune sheet, Swiss, c1900 . . . . **750.00**

10¾″ cylinder, "Overture," 4 overtures, listed on brass plaque, key wind, hinged side flap covers 3 control levers, 19½″ l rosewood case with boxwood stringing, brass inlay, red and blue enameled cartouche, Swiss, c1850. . . . . **2,800.00**

11″ cylinder, 6 tunes, key wind, 19″ inlaid rosewood case, orig program card, Swiss, c1845 . . . . **2,400.00**

11¼″ cylinder, Ducommun-Girod, 6 tunes, 3 side control levers, 19½″ l walnut case, Swiss, c1840 . . . . **675.00**

12½″ cylinder, 10 tunes, lever wind, start/stop and repeat/change levers, zither attachment, 23″ l rosewood case with floral dec, Swiss, c1880 . . **625.00**

13″ cylinder, Bruguier "Musique Expressive," 6 tunes, side lever wind, 22½″ l rosewood case with brass inlay, Swiss, c1860 . . . . **900.00**

13″ cylinder, 6 tunes, side lever wind, 22″ l rosewood case with flower sprays and leaves, Swiss, c1860. . . . . **2,200.00**

15″ cylinder, Bremond "Mandoline," 4 operatic airs, 2 piece comb, side lever wind, 24″ l burr-walnut case with boxwood stringing and fruitwood banding, orig tune sheet, Swiss, c1865. . . . . . **2,700.00**

17″ cylinder, Paillare "Harpe Harmonique Piccolo," 12 tunes, 2 piece comb, side crank wind, 28″ l rosewood veneer case with inlaid musical cartouche, orig tune sheet, Swiss, c1890. . . . . **1,900.00**

21" cylinder, 12 tunes, hidden bells, drum, and castanets, wind spring movement, 2 piece comb, 30" walnut case with floral marquetry, Swiss, c1870. . . . . **1,400.00**

DISC-TYPE

Abrahams, 11¾" disc, "The Britannia," peripheral driven, single comb, stop/start lever, side crank wind, 27" h walnut upright "smoking cabinet" case with mirrored doors, 7 discs, Swiss, c1905. . . . . **1,600.00**

Criterion, 11½" disc, double comb, side crank wind, 15" l mahogany decorated case. **2,100.00**

Lochmann, 24¾" disc, "Original," # 172, coin operated, peripheral driven, double comb, 12 bells, side crank wind, front coin slot, 86" h glazed walnut case with storage cabinet below, 11 discs, German, c1905 . . . . **10,200.00**

Mermod Freres, 15½" disc, "Mira," peripheral driven, double comb, start/stop, fast/slow levers, side crank wind, zither attachment, 27" l mahogany case, 15 discs, Swiss, c1905 . . . **2,700.00**

Otto & Sons, 8¾" disc, "The Olympia," center driven, single comb, side crank wind, 12" l oak case, 4 discs, American, c1915 . . . . **600.00**

Polyphon

15¾" disc, peripheral driven, single comb, side crank wind, 24½" l walnut case with inlay musical cartouche, 5 discs, German, c1905 . . . . **1,700.00**

19½" disc, Style 104, coin operated, peripheral driven, double comb, coin slots on each side, 38" h glazed walnut case, German, c1905 . . . . **1,800.00**

Regina

8½" disc, Style 22, center driven, single comb, top crank wind, 12" oak case, 10 discs, American, c1907 . . **700.00**

11" disc, Style 20, center driven, single comb, start/stop lever, top crank wind, 14½" l mahogany case, 6 discs, American, c1901 . . . . **1,300.00**

15½" disc, Style 11, peripheral driven, double comb, start/stop lever, side crank wind, 22" mahogany case with MOP inlay, 18 discs, American, c1900 . . . . **2,000.00**

27" disc, Style 6, peripheral driven, double comb, side crank wind, 34" l oak folding top case, 20 discs, American, c1897 . . . . **3,500.00**

Symphonion

15" disc, center driven, double comb, slow/fast lever, start/stop knob at front, 24" l oak case, 3 discs, American, c1900 . . . . **1,000.00**

19⅛" disc, coin operated, peripheral driven, double comb, side crank wind and coin slot, 38" h oak case, 13 discs, German, c1905 . . . . **1,700.00**

MUSICAL INSTRUMENTS

History: From the first beat of the prehistoric drum to the very latest in electronic music makers, musical instruments have provided popular modes of communication and relaxation.

The most popular antique instruments are violins, flutes, oboes, and other instruments associated with the classical music period of 1650 to 1900. Many of the modern instruments, such as trumpets, guitars, drums, etc., have value on the "used," rather than antique market.

The collecting of musical instruments is in its infancy. The field is growing very rapidly. Investors and speculators have played a role since the 1930s, especially in early string instruments. Sotheby's and Christie's hold annual auctions of fine musical instruments. Robert Doyle, Fishkill, NY, will hold the first absentee auction of musical instruments in the spring of 1985.

References: Tom and Mary Anne Evans, *Guitars: From the Renaissance To Rock;* Susan Gould and Robert Fredericks, *The Official Price Guide To Music Collectibles,* House of Collectibles, 1980.

Collectors' Club: Fretted Instrument Guild of America, 2344 South Oakley Avenue, Chicago, IL 60608.

Advisor: Glenn M. Kramer.

Banjo-mandolin, "Orpheum #1," MOP inlays, with case, $165.00.

Accordian, Hohner, fiber case, c1925. . **135.00**
Bagpipes, Scottish, c1850. . . . . **3,200.00**
Banjos
  Gibson, RB-250, c1955 . . . . **550.00**
  S. S. Stewart, 5 string, fancy, c1904. **425.00**
  Unknown maker, 5 string, c1910 . . . **95.00**
Bassoon, six key, c1810, fair cond. . . . **900.00**
Bugles
  American, Coleman, Philadelphia,
    c1912. . . . . **40.00**
  American, eight keyed, 19th C, bell en-
    graved "Klemm and Brother in Phil-
    adelphia," tube of brass with copper
    keys and fittings, tube extension
    with screw holder, pitched in high C,
    17″ l without mouthpiece **1,000.00**
  English, keyed, bell garland engraved
    "Wm. SHAW & SONS/LONDON,"
    copper body, six brass keys,
    17⅜″ l **550.00**
Clarinet
  French, boxwood, key of C **145.00**
  Selmer, wooden, c1945. . . . . **130.00**
Concertina
  Simpson, 48 bone buttons, c1870. . . **275.00**
  Wheatstone, 48 buttons, c1880 . . . . **625.00**
Cornet, Regent, case, c1935. . . . . **45.00**
Cymbals, American, 12″, leather han-
  dles, c1910. . . . . **80.00**
Drum, Ludwig, 16″ head, c1958. . . . . . **35.00**
Dulcimer, mahogany, c1944 . . . . **110.00**
Flutes
  A. R. Jollie, New York (1835–55),
    ebony, eight keyed, silver mounts,
    ivory headjoint with silver embou-
    chure sleeve, sounding length
    23⅛″ **275.00**
  Potter, boxwood, silver keys, c1815 . **85.00**
Guitars
  Fender, Stratocaster, c1959. . . . . . . **825.00**
  Gibson, acoustic, c1945. . . . . **375.00**
  Martin, D-18, c1957. . . . . **335.00**
  Unknown maker, acoustic, c1960 . . . **75.00**
Harp, Clark, Syracuse, NY, c1915 . . . . **750.00**
Harpsichord, American, Arnold Dol-
  metsch, 1910, inscribed on name-
  board "CHICKERING & SONS-BOS-
  TON-U.S.A.-MCMX No61" and on lid
  "ACTA VIRUM/PROBANT," lac-
  quered green case with wide gilt band-
  ing, five octave keyboard with ebony
  naturals and ebony accidentals faced
  with ivory, two 8 foot registers, one 4
  foot register, and one 16 foot register,
  trestle stand with turned legs, 94″ l,
  38½″ w **5,500.00**
Mandolins
  American, branded "BRIGGS SPE-
  CIAL/MADE BY/C. F. MARTIN &
  CO." on peghead and on the inside
  back, serial no. 6383, mahogany
  back and ribs, 21⅛″ l. **175.00**
  American, The Gibson, A-1, c1915 . . **145.00**

Unknown maker, bowl-back, c1900. . **55.00**
Oboe, Italian, c1835 . . . . **425.00**
Ocarina, European, soprano, key of E,
  c1905. . . . . **18.00**
Pianos
  Baldwin, upright, c1905 . . . . **425.00**
  Chickering, player, unrestored, c1915 **225.00**
Piccolo, English, cocus with six keys,
  c1855. . . . . **65.00**
Saxophones
  Dupont, tenor, brass **175.00**
  Selmer, MK-VI, alto, c1950. . . . . **650.00**
Tambourine, African, ivory and MOP
  inlays. **75.00**
Trombone, Marceau, nickle-plated **155.00**
Trumpet, Conn, Director, c1935 . . . . . . **85.00**
Tuba, Concertone, nickle-plated. **175.00**
Ukelele, S. S. Stewart, c1914 . . . . **95.00**
Ukelin, c1915. . . . . **35.00**
Viola, German, c1920 . . . . **375.00**
Violins
  Dutch [possibly], labeled "David Tec-
    cler Liutaro/Fecit Romae Anno
    1725," one piece back of bird's-eye,
    ribs and head of faint curl, table of
    fine grain broadening toward flanks,
    varnish light golden orange, 13
    13/16″ **935.00**
  French, labeled "Joseph Bassot, Lu-
    thier,/a Paris 1785," one-piece
    back of faint medium ascending
    from left to right, ribs similar, head
    nearly plain, table of broad grain,
    varnish a toast brown color, 14
    1/16″ l, case. **5,750.00**
  German, copy of Stradivarius, c1915. **35.00**
  Italian, labeled "Afredus Contino/Fre-
    miato al Concorso di Liuteria in
    Roma/unico di V. POSTIGLIONE/
    Fecit Napoli anno 1923," stamped
    on button "A. CONTINO, NAPOLI,"
    one piece back of irregular medium
    curl descending from left to right,
    ribs and head similar, table of me-
    dium grain broadening towards
    flanks,varnish an orange brown,13⅞″ **4,625.00**
  Italian, Lyall Stradivari, labeled "An-
    tonius Stradivarius Cremonensis/
    Faciebat Anno 1702," one piece
    back of medium curl descending
    slightly from left to right, ribs similar,
    head of less distinct medium curl,
    table of fine grain broadening to-
    wards flanks, varnish of an orange
    brown color, 14″ l, leather case by
    Hill **231,000.00**
Xylophone, Italian, c1860 . . . . **225.00**
Zither, Columbia, c1903 . . . . **110.00**

MUSIC-RELATED

Advertising
  Print, lithograph, Smith Piano Co.,
    c1903 . . . . **495.00**

Reverse Painting on Glass, Poole Pianos, C1895	750.00

Catalogs

Gibson, c1917	30.00
Miscellaneous music supplies, c1935	15.00
Display Case, Hohner harmonicas, c1928.	65.00
Photograph, child with trumpet, 5 x 7″, c1915.	10.00
Pin, banjo shaped, glass stones.	12.00

MUSTACHE CUPS AND SAUCERS

History: Mustache cups and saucers were popular in the late Victorian era, 1880–1900. They were made by many companies in porcelain and silver plate. The cups have a ledge across the top of the bowl of the cup to protect a gentleman's mustache from becoming soiled while drinking.

Silverplate, trimmed loop handle, made by James W. Tufts, Boston, $95.00.

PORCELAIN

Austrian, gold ivy borders, red berries .	35.00
Bavarian, shaded white to pink, transfer of pink and yellow chyrsanthemums	32.00

German

"Love The Giver", white, shaded green, gold letters and trim	50.00
"Papa", gold letters, white ground, mkd Germany	45.00
Haviland, hp, pink roses, blue forget-me-nots	65.00
Limoges, hp, lavendar floral dec, gold trim	55.00
Nippon, scenic, windmill, blue mark	175.00
R. S. Prussia, 3½″ h, flared top, molded feet, poppies in pink, orange.	245.00

Unmarked

Hand painted, roses, buds, leaves, wine bands, mkd 1847	40.00

White ground, ribbon of applied Dresden like flowers, gold inscription "For A Gift", mkd 1400 25	95.00

SILVER PLATED

Meridan, large stylized flowers engraved on large coffee cup, matching saucer, mkd	140.00
Reed & Barton, applied trim, embossed handle, mkd	55.00
Rockwell Silver Co., deep cut floral engraving across front extending to sides, gold wash, embossed handle, mkd	75.00

NAILSEA TYPE GLASS

History: Nailsea type glass is characterized by swirls and loopings, usually white, on a clear or colored ground. One of the first areas where this glass was made was Nailsea, England, 1788–1873, hence the name. Several other glass houses, including American factories, made this type of glass.

Barbar Bottle, red ground, white loopings	100.00
Bell, marriage, clear glass steeple handle, opaque white with pink loopings	200.00
Bowls, 7″, tricorn	
Chartreuse, ruffle edge	150.00
Cranberry, satin finish	350.00

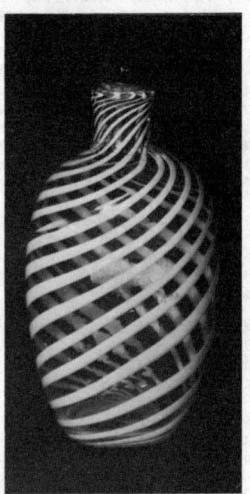

Flask, 7½″ h, white on clear, orig stopper, $85.00.

Condiment Set, 3 pc, pink ground **160.00**
Decanters
  Clear, opaque white and cranberry
    loops, matching bubble stopper,
    12¼" h, 4⅝" d **350.00**
  Rose ground, white loops **225.00**
Fairy Lamps
  Blue, matching trifold base, 6½" h . .   **450.00**
  Green, 2 applied glass leaves,
    mounted on silver plateau, 11½" h   **300.00**
Finger Bowl, 5½" d, clear, white
  loopings **100.00**
Flasks, reclining
  Emerald green, white loops, 6½" l . .   **150.00**
  Red opaque, white loops, 6½" l **100.00**
Gemel Bottle, clear with white loops, co-
  balt ringed mouth, double band of ri-
  garee where 2 halves are joined,
  8" l **150.00**
Lamp Shade, white and pink, pink ruffled
  edge **225.00**
Pickle Castor, blue ground, opal loops   **200.00**
Pitcher, 10", blue, white loops, applied
  handle **300.00**
Rolling Pin, light green, white loops,
  13" l. **125.00**
Tumbler, white ground, blue loops **100.00**
Vase, lily, pink ground, white loops . . .   **175.00**

NANKING

History: Nanking is a type of Chinese porcelain made in Canton, China, from the early 1800s into the 20th century for export to America and England. It often is confused with the Canton pattern.

Three elements help distinguish Nanking from Canton. Nanking has a spear and post border, as opposed to the scalloped line style of Canton. The blues may tend to be darker on the Nanking ware. Second, in the water's edge or Willow pattern, Canton usually has no figures. Nanking features a standing figure with open umbrella on the bridge. Finally, Nanking wares often are embellished with gold.

Green and orange variations of Nanking survive, although scarce. Copies of Nanking ware currently are being produced in China. They are of inferior quality and decorated in lighter rather than the darker blues.

Bowl, 15" d, oval, flat octagonal rim,
  c1800. . . . .   **750.00**
Cup and Saucer, loop handle **50.00**
Cup Plate, 5¼", lozenge shape **115.00**
Dishes
  10", early 19th C. **225.00**
  15", hot water, oval, blue and white,
    Inclined Pines, 1790–1810 . . . . . .   **750.00**
Ewer, 10", bulbous, early 19th C **275.00**
Ginger Jar, 6" **150.00**
Mugs
  5", pint, early 19th C **275.00**

Platter, 11½ x 14½", $340.00.

6⅛", water's edge scene **350.00**
Plates
  9½", octagonal, early 19th C **175.00**
  9½", water's edge scene, c1780–
    1800 . . . .   **185.00**
  10", oval, reticulated border, late 18th
    C **275.00**
Platter, 19", octagonal, c1890 . . . .   **375.00**
Tureens, cov
  10", rect, acorn knop finial, c1860 . .   **450.00**
  13½", oval, pinecone knop finial,
    c1800 . . . .   **850.00**

NAPKIN RINGS, FIGURAL

History: Gracious home dining during the Victorian era meant each household member had their personal napkin ring. Figural napkin rings were first patented in 1869. The remainder of the 19th century saw most plating companies, e.g., Cromwell, Eureka, Meriden, Reed and Barton, etc., manufacturing figural rings, many copying with slight variations the designs of other companies.

Values are determined today by the subject matter of the ring, the quality of the workmanship, and the condition.

Reference: Victor K. Schnadig, *American Victorian Figural Napkin Rings*, Wallace Homestead, 1971, out-of-print.

Additional Listings: See *Warman's Americana & Collectibles* for a listing of non-figural napkin rings.

Advisors: Paul and Paula Brenner.

Baby in cradle, foot sticks out from cov-
  erlet **375.00**
Baseball Player, bat on shoulder, stands
  next to ring, rect base **165.00**

Birds

Perched on leafy openwork ring, ornate rect base	85.00
Sits on ring, long tail	75.00
Boy, pulling on socks, sits next to ring	195.00
Boy and Begging Dog, next to ring, rect base	190.00
Butterfly, perched on chariot-shaped, wheeled ring	145.00
Camel on oval base, stands next to ring on pedestal	210.00

Cats

Harnessed to cart, ornate ring	220.00
Sits on haunches, ring attached to back	150.00
Cherries and Leaves next to ring, leaf-shaped base	95.00
Cherub, heart-shaped base, ring engraved "Best Wishes"	95.00
Chicken, defiant pose, stands with back to chased ring	120.00
Cow, standing on ornate round base, next to ring	190.00
Fans, support ring above butterfly, sqbase, ball feet	115.00
Giraffe, stands under palm tree, rect base	245.00
Goat, pulling wheeled cart	225.00
Horse, stands next to corral attached to ring	165.00

Boy lugging ring, Rogers Bros, #223, $245.00.

Kate Greenaway

Boy, carries school books, wears beret	185.00
Boy, kneels next to basket of eggs, oval base	215.00
Girl, faces ring, bulldog on top of ring	220.00
Girl, sits atop ring on cart pulled by cherub	245.00
Girl, pr, wearing bonnet and ear muffs, flank ring	190.00

Lamb, laying down next to ring, rect base, ball feet	190.00
Man and Woman, colonial costume, flank ring	245.00
Owl, sits on leaf dec base, smaller owls perched above	230.00

Rings

Lily Pad base, finger grip	50.00
Ornate base, ball feet, ring sits atop pedestal and wishbone.	65.00
Sailor (boy), holds anchor and cable, ornate base	225.00

Squirrels

Sits on branch-like base, eats nut, tail draped over ring	95.00
Sits on haunches next to ring, base with ball feet	85.00
Turtle, ring on back, ornate rect base. .	140.00
Wheelbarrow, supports plain ring	120.00

Women

Holds tennis racket, long dress	345.00
Stands next to cowering dog, ornate base	190.00

NASH GLASS

History: Nash glass is a type of art glass attributed to Arthur Nash and his sons, Leslie and A. Douglas. Arthur Nash, originally employed by Webb in Stourbridge, England, came to America and was employed in 1892 by Tiffany Furnaces at its Corona, Long Island plant.

While managing the plant for Tiffany, Nash designed and produced iridescent glass. In 1933 Tiffany withdrew support from the Corona plant and turned it over to the workers.

Nash applied for a patent on April 3, 1933, for a glass design process commonly called Chintz. The Nashes made Chintz between April 1933 and March 1934. Nash closed the Corona plant in 1934 and became a design consultant for Libbey Glass. The Chintz patent, finally granted on March 27, 1934, was assigned to Libbey, but never used by them.

Note: Those pieces marked with an "*" were sold by Sotheby's in November 1983 and represent Nash's first attempts to produce iridescent glass, done while he still was with Webb in England.

*Bottle, 4½" h, squat, pinched sides, amber irid, green and amber irid striated feather dec, inscribed "LCT B1", c1890.	1,000.00

Bowls

*2½" h, lobed, amber irid mirrored glass, ochre straited feather dec, inscribed "L.C.T. Favrile A.J. Nash", c1890	800.00
3¼" h, amber irid, shallow, ftd, inscribed "Nash 515"	200.00
4¾" d, underplate, opal rays, cranberry rims, sgd.	150.00

Candlesticks, pr, red Chintz, inscribed "#RD 652" 350.00
Compote, red Chintz, inscribed "#RD 89" 500.00
Creamer, 4¼" h, clear, pale orchid and green design, clear handle........ 300.00
Goblet, 6¼" h, clear glass, intaglio carved with putti frolicking in the grass, reverse monogram AN within a wreath of foliage, inscribed "L.C.T. Favrile AJN", fitted mohogany box 800.00
Perfume, 7⅞" h, orig pointed amber stopper with silvery blue irid, base with rays of blue, lilac, pale blue ft. 700.00
Plate, 6", Chintz, clear, orange 100.00

Vase, 9½" h, green-gold irid, clear irid base, unsigned, $275.00.

Vases
4¾" h, pedestal, bluish gold, inscribed "Nash 644". 300.00
5", gold irid, sgd 325.00
12", trumpet shape, vertical stripes of orange and yellow, inscribed "Nash 62AA". 400.00
Wine, Chintz, 5" h 100.00

NAUTICAL ITEMS

History: The seas that surround us have fascinated man since time began. The artifacts of sailors have been collected and treasured for years. Because of their environment, merchant and naval items, whether factory or hand made, must be of quality construction and long lasting. Many of these items are aesthetically designed as well.

Richard Bourne, Hyannis, Massachusetts, and Chuck DeLuca, York, Maine, regularly hold auctions of marine items.

References: Alan P. Major, *Maritime Antiques,* A. S. Barnes & Co., 1981; Jean Randier, *Nautical Antiques,* Doubleday and Co., 1977.

Periodical: *Nautical Brass etc.,* Box 744, Montrose, CA 91020. Subscription: $10.00.

Museums: Burgess Mariner's Museum, Newport News, VA; Museum of Science and Industry, Chicago, IL; Mystic Seaport Museum, Mystic, CT; National Maritime Museum, San Francisco, CA.

Advisor: Bill Wheeler.

Alarm or Signaling Gun, British, 19th C, wheels and barrel polished brass, carriage wooden, barrel 9½" l, carriage 12¾" 390.00
Barometer, cased, American mercury stick, c1800, mahogany case 38" h and 4" w, label "Simmons Portable Barometer," restored and refinished. 450.00
Belaying Pin, device for fastening lines onto rail of ship, cylindrical wood, carved handle, pin tapering toward blunt bottom, some old paint remaining, 20½" l, 2¼" d. 17.00
Bell, ship's, brass, 16" d, 16" h, 67 pounds, complete with clapper, "QUEEN ANNA MARIA 1965" cast in side 225.00
Bill of Lading, matted, from Steamer *Aris* of Philadelphia, 1872, sgd by master and customs, printed form with ship pictured at top, lists terms of shipping merchandise on a specific voyage and goods shipped with the rates charged 40.00
Binnacle, compass and it's housing, small yacht style, brass top, teak octagonal base, 26" h overall, 7½" compass mkd "Sewill, London," brass head (top) lacks the rear door and both burner covers (not uncommon) 850.00
Books
Brewington, M. V., *Peabody Museum Collection of Navigating Instruments,* Salem, MA: Peabody Museum: 1963, out-of-print 300.00
Bowditch, Nathaniel, *New American Practical Navigator,* Newburyport, MA: Blunt: 1802 (first edition), worn and scuffed, complete with folding chart..................... 1,200.00
Colcord, Capt. M. E., manuscript log book of Bark *Mignon* of Boston kept by her master, 1880s, freighting voyage through Caribbean, printed form book by Gilchrest White and Co., NY.................... 300.00
Flayderman, E. Norman, *Scrimshaw, Scrimshanders, Whales And Whalemen,* New Milford, CT: N. Flayderman Co.: 1972, out-of-print 350.00

Furlong, Lawrence, *American Coast Pilot*, Newburyport, MA: Blunt: 1798, 2nd edition, replaced spine label, otherwise fine **1,000.00**

Bos'n's Pipe, SP Boatswain's pipe or call, 6½" l overall, used to pipe commands to crew, exc. cond **25.00**

Chronometer, double cased clock for navigation timekeeping, full size Hamilton Model 21, double lidded case and carrying box, U. S. Navy, serial number 1815, fusee and spring detent rather than watch movement **1,600.00**

Clock, striking, Seth Thomas, "BottomBell," outside bell clock which strikes ship's watches rather than the hours, c1855, restored. **550.00**

Compass, small brass gimballed compass in mahogany box, 6" sq, brass presentation plate on cover "CYC Handicap Class Championship 1914 Won by Kotick". **70.00**

Deck Chair, folding wooden steamer chair, brown finish, solid but unrestored **140.00**

Figurehead, bearded man, possibly Stonewall Jackson, wearing gray coat and red vest, c24" h, well preserved, some cracks, repainted **4,000.00**

Helmet, Deep Sea Diver's, Siebe Gorman, maker's plate on breast plate, 12 bolt mount around the breast plate with brailes (plates held on the breast plate by the above bolts) and wing nuts, unpolished, usual dings, complete and solid **1,500.00**

Lantern, galvanized iron with brass fittings, 360° clear fresnel (ribbed) lens with large oil reservoir, 16" h overall, polished and restored **180.00**

Maker's Plate, curved brass, 1⅜ x 6¾" oval, mkd "Walsend Howden Pressure System of Oil Burning/Patent/ Walsend Slipway & Engineering Co. Ltd. Walsend-on-Tyne" **17.00**

Models

Cased, model of Danish ship, *Kristan*, 1884, made at sea by Capt. Soren Charles Nielson, 25 x 34", professionally restored in 1974. . . . . **600.00**

Half Hull, model split in two lengthwise, unrigged, used as a plan for the builder to take off the curves or lines, 8 lifts or laminations, pine, 43" l, good cond, traces of paint . . **250.00**

Shadow Box, 40½ x 25½ x 15½", Clipper *Great Republic*, sails set, eagle figurehead, great detail, ground repainted. **250.00**

Parallel Rulers, navigator's device for transferring a course line on a chart and making certain that it remains true, two linked straight edge rules,

12" l of ebony and brass, unsigned, c1900. . . . . **40.00**

Quarter Board, ship's name board, wooden, 78 x 19", black with white letters, routed with *ASMARI*, chipping paint but no rot, as salvaged **100.00**

Reverse Painting On Glass, *Lusitania* with a submarine lurking in the waves, framed 19½ x 15½", some chipping to paint, overall good to very good cond, frame fair. **200.00**

Sailing Card, an adv card seeking freight and passengers for a merchantman, Clipper *Mary Goodell* going to San Francisco, 6 x 3½", sewn over old tear, colors bright, framed **165.00**

Sand Glass, egg timer style device, wood, hand blown glass, times passage of ship against the log, used to derive speed from time and distance, 6¾" h, 2 minute duration, brown and white sand **175.00**

Sea Chest, 43" l, slant front, orig canvas covering and beckets (handles), belonged to Capt. Hallet of Hyannis, exc. cond **200.00**

Sea Letter, document sgd by President and Sec. of State, Great Seal attached, written in four languages parallel, request safe passage for ship, cargo, and crew, filled in by hand, John Adams and Timothy Pickering for Schooner *Alexander* out of Charleston for Madeira, dated Feb. 5, 1798, good crisp seals and signatures, some separation at old folds **1,000.00**

Sextant, instrument to measure angle between sun or star and horizon, made by C. Plath, Hamburg, c1938, serial number 15846, sighting card showing zero error and owner's card in lid, complete, cleaned, and adjusted, refinished case (Note: Plath is best, others half price). **700.00**

British signalling or saluting cannon, brass barrel and wheels, wooden carriage, 19th C, barrel 9½" l, 12¾" carriage, $425.00.

Ship Portrait, oil on canvas, 19 x 30″, Clipper *Loch Katrine,* fine detail including figurehead of woman and deck hands, good motion to ship, sgd in lower right, R. B. SPENCER (English, worked 1840–70). **4,250.00**

Steamship Menu, American President Lines *President Wilson,* large dinner menu for Lincoln's birthday **5.00**

Telescope, three draw brass spyglass, green leather cov barrel, 29″ l opened, 9½″ l closed, objective lens 1½″ d, fine optics, unsigned, leather is old replacement, c1900 . . . . **165.00**

Wheel (Helm), steering, 36″ from tip of spoke to tip of spoke, iron hub, wood solid but shows wear. **290.00**

Writing Desk, captain's, 30 x 17½ x 32″, burled walnut veneer, top folds over slanted writing surface which opens at the middle to provide stowage for writing instruments, etc., in one compartment, spyglass and sextant in larger compartment, three cubby holes under top, bottom opens with two doors to display shelves, restored. **1,300.00**

NAZI ITEMS

History: The National Socialist Party came to power in the 1920s during a period of severe economic depression in Germany. Under the leadership of Adolph Hitler, the party assumed first political control and then social control over Germany. National socialism dominated all aspects of German life. World War II was launched in 1939 to achieve a military conquest of Europe. The Nazi era ended in 1945 when Germany surrendered at the end of World War II.

References: John M. Kaduck, *World War II German Collectibles,* privately printed, 1978, 1983 price update; Robert H. Rankin, *The Official 1983 Price Guide To Military Collectibles,* House of Collectibles, 1983.

Periodicals: *Military Collectors News,* P. O. Box 7582, Tulsa, OK, 74105; *The MX Exchange,* P. O. Box 3, Torrington, CT 06790.

Additional Listings: See *Warman's Americana & Collectibles* for more examples.

Armband, NSDAP, 17″ l, 4½″ w, printed type **15.00**

Badges

Breast, large eagle with swastika, "Thur Gautreffen Erfurt 1.33″ **65.00**

Parachutist/Luftwaffe, breast, frosted silver wreath and golden eagle, back frosted with maker's mark, "G. H. Osanl, Dresden" **300.00**

Ribbon Bars

8 parades, green felt back, combination of (2) SS Long Service

Luftwaffe Pilot's Badge, white metal, silver wash, $95.00.

Awards, Westwall, Praque Miniature, 1939 Spange, Hindenburg 10 parades, green felt back, combination (2) SS Long Service, (3) NSDAP Long Service, Russian Front **90.00**

. . . . **75.00**

Banner, bugle, 18 x 19″, single large white Rune on one side on black ground, 4 black tie ropes, orig RZM paper tag, dated "23.5.43" **150.00**

Bayonet, dress, 7½″, bright blade, eagle handle with black checkered grips, DAF gear, black scabbard **100.00**

Belt Buckle, raised swastika and oak leaf, bright aluminum, brown leather tab, worn by Gendarmerie units **30.00**

Binoculars, Wehrmacht **85.00**

Books

Arbeitsmaidens Aw Wert (Work Maidens At Work) by H. Retzlaff, Leipszag, 1940, 136 pgs. **30.00**

Deutsches Jaschenbuch Fur 1937–38, 248 pgs of ads, photos of leaders **35.00**

Hitler Wie Ihn Keiner Kennt, Henrich Hoffman **50.00**

Kampf Um Berlin, Dr. J. Goebbels, 1936, Munich, 285 pgs, German text. **40.00**

Car Pennant, 8½ x 11½″, printed on both sides with white eagle on blue field, 2 tie strings **65.00**

China

Plates, 9″

"Reichsarbeitsdienst," white, dated 1938 . . . . **15.00**

SS Officer's, white, underglaze mkd "Bauscher-Weiden SS-Reich 1941" in green. **90.00**

Soup Bowl, 9½″, white, gear wheel and swastika in bottom. **20.00**

Vegetable Bowls, 8½″

Black NSDAP eagle on bottom . . . **25.00**

Blue rim, DAF insignia in green on bottom, mkd "KPM" **35.00**

Collar Tabs, pr, police, rank of "Unter-
wachtmeister," silver cord with green
and silver Bevo stripes **15.00**
Cross, Mother's, blue and white enamel,
"Der Deutschen Mutter," orig ribbon. **65.00**
Cuff Title, "SS Grossdeutschland", off
white embroidery with silver thread
borders on black wool, 17" l **200.00**
Door Plaque, bronze finish, large eagle
with clasped hands above swastika,
mkd "D & S" **20.00**
Flags
    34 x 70", Panzer Aerial Identification,
    metal eye rings **60.00**
    36 x 75", Republic, red, black, and
    white, brass hooks, Weimer **50.00**
    48 x 52", NSDAP, Dsitrict, identifica-
    tion in brown, blue, and white on red
    ground, tag "Marktsteft" in left cor-
    ner, 3 sided silver fringe **175.00**
Gas Mask, child's, hose attachment,
black eagle stamp, clear plastic front
face plate, white rubberized and cotton neck, chest and arm protector, all
one unit, mkd "Gasjackchen RL 1-39/
49 Vertrieb Gemass 58 Luftschute-
Gesete Genehmigt". **50.00**
Goggles, tanker's, amber lens, type used
in Africa **40.00**
Hat, SS, white Russian lamb's wool,
camoflauge, hidden black visor bill
tucked under quilted lining in front,
"SS RZM" marked eagle and skull insignia, leather adjustable strap, heavy
gray quilted interior **300.00**
Medals
    Shooting, silver finish, "Kreisschies-
    sen Kofstein, 1942" **30.00**
    1939 Knights Cross of the Iron Cross,
    neck ribbon, "800" mkd on double
    loop ring, magnetic center, bright sil-
    ver finish, ribbon in mint condition. **875.00**
    25 Year Faithful Service Cross, large
    black enameled swastika, frosted
    silver devices, cornflower blue
    ribbon **15.00**
Overcoat, Custom's Officer, doe skin, sil-
ver pebbled buttons, French sleeve
cuffs, dark green collar, silver shoulder
boards with gold letters, white leather
dagger strap, Berlin maker on
label **200.00**
Parade Flag Pole Top, 8¼", nickel plated
swastika and gear **40.00**
Passbook, DAF Arbeits, red front, large
gold swastika and gear **15.00**
Photo Album of 1936 Olympics, 3 x 4",
17 photos showing events, stadium,
SS leaders **50.00**
Stationery, unused folio, Hitler's person-
nel letterhead, emb NSDAP eagle
above "Der Fuhrer" in raised gold
letters. **45.00**

Stickpins
    Party, NSDAP, silver swastika within
    brass circle **10.00**
    Veteran's Association, silver eagle,
    black enamel, hallmarked "Ges
    Gesch," frosted metal back **5.00**
Whistle, pewter, concentration camp . . **15.00**

NETSUKES

History: The traditional Japanese kimono has no
pockets. Daily necessities such as money, tobacco
supplies, etc., were carried in leather pouches or
inros which hung from a cord with a netsuke toggle.
Netsuke comes from "ne" (to root) and "tuske" (to
fasten).

Netsukes originated in the 14th century and initially were associated with the middle class. By the
mid-18th century all levels of Japanese society
used them. Some of the most famous artists, e.g.,
Shuzan and Yamada Hojitsu, worked in the netsuke
form.

Netsukes average 1 to 2 inches and are made
from wood, ivory, bone, ceramics, metal, horn, nut-
shells, etc. The subject matter is broad based, but
always portrayed in a lighthearted, humorous manner. A netsuke must have no sharp edges and balance so it hangs correctly on the sash.

Value depends on artist, region, material, and
skill of craftsmanship. Western collectors favor *ka-
tabori*, pieces which represent an identifiable object.

Note: Recent reproductions are on the market.
Many are carved from African ivory.

SIGNED

Bat, resting on one wing, other outstretched, wood with soft metal inlaid
eyes, Terumasa, 19th C. **200.00**
Father, reading to son who is holding toy
doll, ivory, Gyokubun, 19th C **450.00**
Fisherman and son, octopus coming
from basket, ivory, Homin, 19th C. . . **725.00**
God, performing New Year's exorcism,
flings beans from box at *oni* cowering
at his feet, ivory, Tomochika, 19th C. **475.00**
Immortal, long head, leaning forward bal-
ancing stained ivory ball on joined
sleeves, wood, Meikeisai Hojitsu, 19th
C. **675.00**
Mermaid with suckling young amid
curved tail, wood, Hosen, 19th C . . . **2,750.00**
Monkey, seated, holding persimmon
branch between paws, ivory, Tatei,
19th C **900.00**
Mushroom cluster, wood, Ichiriki, 19th
C. **625.00**
Ox, recumbent, wearing rope harness,
calf at her side, pale ivory with inlaid
eyes, Mitsuharu, c1781 . . . . **1,200.00**

Carved ivory, 19th C, $95.00.

Rat, clutching bean pod between paws,
wood with ivory teeth, inlaid dark horn
eyes, Kano Tomokazu, 19th C **2,750.00**
Shishi, standing, raised head, wood with
inset MOP eyes, Kazuo **975.00**
Skull, coiling snake on top, tail through
eye socket, wood, Shoko, 19th C . . . **875.00**
Tobosaku, standing, smiling, holding
peach branch in one hand, basket in
the other, ivory with dark horn inlaid
eyes, Yoshimasa, 18th C **1,500.00**
Wolf, holding monkey, ivory with inlaid
eyes, script sgd Tomatoda, 19th C . . **1,100.00**
Workman, seated cross-legged, holding
mallet and plane, head tied with inlaid
ivory cloth, wood, Miyasaki Joso, late
19th C **1,800.00**

UNSIGNED

Coins, on string, round and rect shapes,
heavy cord through centers, 2 tone
wood, c1900. . . . . **625.00**
Dragon, caught in a hoop, ivory, c1890. **400.00**
Fox, in kimono with an *obi*, fox child in
kimono at her feet, wood with ivory
inlaid eyes, 19th C **575.00**
Immortal, reclining on table, rect base,
ivory, 18th C **375.00**
Lotus pod with 3 wasps, pale boxwood,
19th C **775.00**
Monkeys, 3 playing with gourd, ivory,
20th C **250.00**
Octopus, humorous, sits on top of fishing
pot, scratching head with tentacle,
wood with inlaid ivory eyes, 19th C . . **675.00**
Puppy, shaggy coat, reclining on cushion
in rattan basket, ivory with dark horn
inlaid eyes, 19th C **950.00**
Shojo, sleeping, holds head in one hand,
sake ladle in the other, empty pot by
her side, wood, 19th C **500.00**
Woman holding baby and comforting 2
small children by her side, ivory,
19thC. **225.00**

NEWCOMB POTTERY

History: William and Ellsworth Woodward, two
brothers, were the founders of a series of businesses which eventually merged into the Newcomb
pottery effort. In 1885 Ellsworth Woodward, a pro-
ponent of vocational training for women, organized
a school from which emerged the Ladies Decorative Art League. In 1886 the brothers founded the
New Orleans Art Pottery Company with the ladies
of the league serving as decorators. The first two
potters were Joseph Meyer and George Ohr. The
pottery closed in 1891.

William Woodward was on the faculty at Tulane.
Ellsworth taught fine arts at the Sophie Newcomb
College, a woman's school which eventually
merged with Tulane. In 1895 Newcomb College
developed a pottery course in which the wares
could be sold. Some of the equipment came from
the old New Orleans Art Pottery.

Mary G. Sheerer joined the staff to teach decoration. In 1910 Paul E. Cox solved many of the
technical problems connected with making pottery
in a southern environment. Other leading figures
were Sadie Irvine, Professor Lota Lee Troy, and
Kathrine Choi. Pottery was made until the early
1950s.

Students painted a quality art pottery with a distinctive high glaze. Designs have a decidedly southern flavor, e.g., myrtle, jasmine, sugar cane, moss,
cypress, dogwood, and magnolia motifs. Later
matte glazed pieces usually are decorated with
carved back floral designs. Pieces depicting murky,
bayou scenes are most desirable.

References: Ralph and Terry Kovel, *The Kovels'
Collector's Guide To American Art Pottery,* Crown
Publishers, Inc., 1974; Jessie Poesch, *Newcomb
Pottery: An Enterprise for Southern Women,* Schif-
fer Publishing, Ltd, 1984.

Collectors' Club: American Art Pottery Association, P.O. Box 714, Silver Springs, MD 20901.

Museum: Newcomb College, Tulane University,
New Orleans, LA.

Bowls
5", blue, pink buds at top, artist Cyn-
thia Littlejohn. **475.00**
5½", artist Anna Frances Simpson,
potter's mark JM **400.00**
9½ x 3", blue with raised pink trumpet
flowers, artist Anna F. Simpson. . . **675.00**
Candlestick, 9¾", blue ground, pink dogwood on base, artist Sadie Irvine, pot-
ter's mark JM, paper label **625.00**
Flower Frog, 1⅝ x 4", 9 holes, blue and
pink, artist Sadie Irvine **150.00**

Bowl, tricorn top, 6¼″ d, 3¾″ h, Joseph Meyer potter, stamped, "63/MJ 40," artist sgd "Sadie Irvine," $675.00.

Pitcher, 8½″, blue and tan, high glaze,
artist Martin L. LeBlanc **1,300.00**
Vases
  3¼ x 3″, ultramarine blue, pink dec
  and green leaves, artist Sadie Irvine,
  potter's mark JM **375.00**
  5½″, maroon matte **450.00**
  6″, lavender with raised geometric de-
  sign, artist Jonathan Hunt **375.00**
  6½″, blue, moon shining through
  Spanish moss, artist Julia Michel . . **600.00**

NILOAK POTTERY

History: Niloak Pottery was made near Benton, Arkansas. Charles Dean Hyten experimented with native clay, trying to preserve its natural colors. By 1911 he perfected mission ware, marbelized pottery in which the creme and brown colors predominate. The pieces were marked Niloak (kaolin spelled backwards).

After a devastating fire, the pottery was rebuilt and named Eagle Pottery. This factory included the space to add a novelty pottery line which was introduced in 1929. This line usually was marked Hywood-Niloak, until 1934 when the name Hywood was dropped from the mark. Mr. Hyten left the pottery in 1941. In 1946 operations ceased.

Additional Listings: See *Warman's Americana & Collectibles* for more examples, especially the novelty pieces.

Note: Prices listed below are for Mission Ware pieces.

Advisor: Robert Berman.

Lamp base, $165.00.

Ashtray, 1½ x 4″ **35.00**
Bowls
  5 x 2″ **40.00**
  10½ x 4″, fruit **70.00**
Clock, 4 x 5″ **165.00**
Cup, drinking, 4 x 3″ **40.00**
Jar, cov, 6″ **85.00**
Pitcher, 10″, long handle **125.00**
Umbrella Stand, 22″ **350.00**
Vases
  4″, cylindrical body **35.00**
  4″, flared body, narrower neck and
  collar **40.00**
  6″, cone shaped, ftd **65.00**
  8″, bud vase **65.00**
  8″, cylindrical body, ftd **100.00**
  14″, hour glass shape **165.00**
  18″, slight flared body, medium lip . . **235.00**
Wall Pocket, dark red and brown glaze
  [early colors] **100.00**
Water Bottle, cup cover, 8″ **145.00**

NIPPON CHINA, 1891-1921

History: Nippon, the Japanese word for Japan, first was used on export items in 1891, when the McKinley tariff act proclaimed that all items of foreign manufacture be stamped with their country of origin. Japan chose to use "Nippon." In 1921 the United States decided the word "Nippon" no longer was acceptable and required that all Japanese wares be marked with "Japan." The Nippon era ended.

There are over 166 recorded Nippon backstamps or marks. The three most popular are the wreath, maple leaf, and rising sun marks. Wares with variations of all three marks are being reproduced today. A knowledgeable collector can easily spot the reproductions by the mark variances.

The majority of the marks are found in three different colors: green, blue, and magenta. Colors indicate the quality of the porcelain used: green for first grade porcelain, blue for second grade, and magenta for third grade. Marks were applied by two methods, decal stickers under glaze and imprinting directly on the porcelain.

References: Gene Loendorf, *Nippon Hand Painted China*, McGrew Color Graphics, 1975; Joan Van Patten, *The Collector's Encyclopedia Of Nippon Porcelain, Series One*, Collector Books, 1979; Joan Van Patten, *The Collector's Encyclopedia Of Nippon Porcelain, Series Two*, Collector Books, 1982.

Periodical: *The Nippon Chronicle*, 129 Bathurst Street, Toronto, Ontario, Canada M5V. 2R2. Subscription: $10.00.

Collectors' Clubs: Canadian Nippon Collectors Association, Box 759, Alliston, Ontario, Canada L0M 1A00; International Nippon Collectors Club, P. O. Box 617, Jericho, NY 11753. Dues: $15.00.

Advisor: Kathy Wojciechowski.

Ashtrays
   5½" d, moriage dragon, slate gray
     ground, Royal Moriage mark **125.00**
   Relief molded, yellow and orange
     grape leaves, dark brown ground,
     Wreath mark **250.00**
Baskets
   4" l, pale blue tiny flowers outlined in

Urn, 17", large medallion of Queen Louise, heavy gold overlay design, multicolored jewels, turquoise ground dome lid, Maple Leaf mark, $950.00.

    gold, gold handle, Rising Sun
    mark **45.00**
   7" l, bisque scene of lake, trees, and
    cottage, beaded handle, Wreath
    mark **75.00**
Berry Set, large master bowl & 7 matching small bowls, large pink and blue flowers traced with green foliage, fancy scalloped edges, Shinzo Nippon mark **95.00**
Biscuit Jar, round, melon ribbed, heavy red florals, cobalt and gold trim, Cherry Blossom mark. **135.00**
Bowls
   6½" d, 6½" h, bunches of purple violets, cream ground, Wreath mark   **45.00**
   7" w, 2" h, huge mums, green foilage ground, flutted edges, Maple Leaf mark. **115.00**
   Octagonal, gold maple leaf medallions surrounded by gold lattice work, dark green and white ground, large center medallion, Maple Leaf mark   **75.00**
Cake Set, master plate with pierced handles, 10¾" w, five small serving plates, swans swimming in lake, cobalt, heavy gold trim, Maple Leaf mark **350.00**
Candlestick, bisque scenic, one large sailing ship, shades of pastel blue . .   **95.00**
Candlesticks, 6" h, Wedgewood blue and white, Wreath mark, pr **375.00**
Candy Dish, 7" h, ftd, large red roses with gold tracings, cobalt and gold trim, Wreath mark **65.00**
Celery Dish, 13½" l, shallow, bisque scenic, large sailboat in lake, shades of pale yellow, Wreath mark. **60.00**
Celery Set, master celery, 13½" l, six small salts, hp stalk of celery in center, Wreath mark. **175.00**
Child's Feeding Dish, 8" d, child playing with dog, Rising Sun mark **65.00**
Chocolate Pot, 9½" h, melon ribbed, groups of red and pink roses, cream ground **75.00**
Chocolate Set
   9½" h scalloped edge pot, 5 scalloped edge cups, bands of pink and blue flowers, green foliage **135.00**
   9½" h pot, 6 cups and saucers, paper thin porcelain, white with heavy gold design, Wreath mark **225.00**
Chocolate Set, demi, 12½" d tray, 6½" h pot, creamer, sugar bowl, & 2 cups and saucers, Egyptian sailing ships, large black palm trees, all outlined in gold, Wreath mark. **425.00**
Cigarette Box, 4½" l, farm scene on lid, floral dec on base, Wreath mark. . . .   **175.00**
Compote, pedestal base, fruits and foliage, gold rim, Wreath mark. **65.00**
Condensed Milk Container, 6" h, tiny pink and white roses, white beaded

scrolling, mauve tones, hole in bottom for pushing milk container out, R. C. mark **135.00**

Condiment Set, 4½" d tray, individual mustard, salt, and pepper, top band of tiny pink and mauve flowers, white ground, Crown mark **45.00**

Cup and Saucers

Bisque scenic of cottage and forest, Shinzo mark **35.00**

Gold overlay design, gold beading, forest green ground, pedestal base cup with saucer, Maple Leaf mark **85.00**

Desk Set, triangular shaped ink well, rocking blotter, two section standing envelope rack, standing calendar holder, stamp box, and two blotter corners, bisque, Indian in canoe scene, pale yellow ground, Wreath mark . . . **550.00**

Dishes

4¾" sq, lavender and blue bisque scenic of house and trees, Wreath mark **23.00**

8 x 5½", gaudy floral, mauve, green, and gold design with roses, open pierced handles, unmarked **45.00**

Dolls

3½", girl, jointed arms and legs, painted blue shoes, blonde hair with blue ribbon, blue eyes, incised Nippon **75.00**

5", jointed arms and legs, long brown hair, blue eyes, painted on shoes and socks, incised Nippon **125.00**

5", pincushion, green satin dress trimmed with lace and pink roses, molded blonde hair with blue ribbon, incised Nippon **200.00**

24", girl, long dark hair, bisque head, sleep eyes, open mouth with four teeth, leather body, F Y Nippon mark **475.00**

Dresser Sets

3 pcs, ftd hair receiver, ftd powder box, and hat pin holder with attached tray, medallions of lady's portrait on front, flowers on back, heavy gold overlay design, blue Maple Leaf mark **450.00**

5 pcs, 11" tray, ftd hair receiver, ftd powder box, pedestal base pin tray, and hat pin holder, bands of pink and white flowers, white ground, green foliage traced in gold, Rising Sun mark **125.00**

Egg Warmer, panels of pink roses, green and gold trim, white ground, Rising Sun mark **110.00**

Ewers

9", ftd, moriage bird in flight and flowers, Hand Painted Nippon mark. . . **200.00**

10", large red and pink roses, heavy gold overlay, solid cobalt ground, Maple Leaf mark **350.00**

10¾", Halloween scene, tapestry, Maple Leaf mark **700.00**

Ferners

7½" w, four ftd, beaded design, heavy gold overlay, green and cream ground, Maple Leaf mark **225.00**

Rectangular, 3 ftd, trees and sailing ships, moriage flowers, gold trim, E. E. Nippon mark **95.00**

Hair Receivers

4½" h, four narrow legs, green, gold, and mauve geometric design, Maple Leaf mark **95.00**

Short and fat shape, medallion of bust portrait of lady, heavy gold overlay and beading, Maple Leaf mark . . . **185.00**

White ground, single blue band on lid. **35.00**

Hat Pin Holders

4¾" h, sq shape, tiny top and bottom bands of lavender violets, Wreath mark. **35.00**

Medallions of pink and white roses, heavy gold overlay, turquoise ground, four graceful feet, Maple Leaf mark **125.00**

Humidors

6¼" h, bisque scenic, large windmill, pale blue ground, Wreath mark . . . **300.00**

6½" h, Indians on charging horses, molded in relief, Wreath mark **1,300.00**

Inkwell, 2¾" w, scenic, man on camel, Wreath mark. **125.00**

Lamp, 17" h, medallion of sailing ships, cobalt, heavy gold beading, mark unknown. **325.00**

Lemonade Set, pitcher and 6 mugs, large red and white roses, green foliage, cream ground, Torii Nippon mark **150.00**

Mayonnaise Set, 3 pcs, ftd bowl, underplate, ladle, all match, orange poppies outlined in gold, cream ground, R. C. mark **95.00**

Mug, gold enameled dragons, forest green ground, Wreath mark **235.00**

Mustache Cup, scenic, large windmill, earth tones, matching underplate, Rising Sun mark **175.00**

Mustard Jar, bisque scenic, sailing ships, shades of orange, brown beaded rim, Wreath mark. **56.00**

Napkin Ring, multicolored jewels, heavy gold dec over turquoise ground, Maple Leaf mark **65.00**

Nut Set, 7 pcs, master bowl, 6" w, 3" d, six small bowls, orange floral dec outlined in gold, gold fluted rims, R. C. mark **95.00**

Pin Box, 2" d, Geisha girls and pagodas, Royal Nishiki mark. **45.00**

Pitchers
7", medallion of red roses, cobalt, gold
trim, Maple Leaf mark **275.00**
7½", squat shape, long stemmed
green stalks with orange poppies,
gold handle and trim, Torii mark . . **125.00**
Plaques, pierced to hang
9", center medallion of dog's head,
moriage border, Maple Leaf mark . **350.00**
10", lion and lioness, relief molded,
Wreath mark **850.00**
10", river and forest scene, Wreath
mark **175.00**
10", roses (multicolored pastels) in a
wicker basket, Wreath mark **275.00**
10½", eagle perched on branch and
ready for flight, relief molded,
Wreath mark **5,000.00**
Plates
7" h, 3" w, bisque scenic, cottage,
TEOH mark. **28.00**
9", heavy red florals, Wreath mark . . **65.00**
Punch Set, bowl, 16" d, separate ftd
base, bunches of grapes, dark ground,
6 matching pedestal cups, Wreath
mark **950.00**
Ring Tree, shallow dish, attached gold
hand, purple violets, gold trim, Maple
Leaf mark. **70.00**
Salt and Pepper Shakers
Cottage, bisque scenic. **22.00**
Floral **15.00**
Floral, red and white, heavy
moriage **65.00**
Red roses, cobalt, heavy gold **65.00**
Smoke Sets
6¾" sq tray, humidor, match holder,
cigarette holder, woodland scene,
Wreath mark **600.00**
7½" d tray, humidor, ashtray, match
holder, cigar and matches motif,
Wreath mark **395.00**
Spitoon, 3¼" d, lady's [hand held], pink
roses, gold trim, Wreath mark **145.00**
Stamp Box, geometric black stripes, inside tray has two compartments,
Wreath mark. **85.00**
Stein, 7" h, Galle scene with brown mor-
iage trees, pale orange ground, white
enamel flowers, Maple Leaf mark . . . **400.00**
Sugar Shakers
Geometric designs with salmon col-
ored flowers, E. E. mark. **90.00**
Floral, green, white moriage beaded
crisscrosses, fancy gold handle,
pleated body, Wreath mark. **120.00**
Talcum Powder Flask, 5" h, pink and
blue floral, gold trim, Wreath mark . . **135.00**
Tankard, 12½" h, gaudy design of heavy
large red roses and gold overlay and
beading, Royal Kinran mark **185.00**
Tankard Set, 11" tankard, 6 mugs, large
blue owl on tree branch, pale blue

ground, moriage trim and handle,
Wreath mark. **1,500.00**
Teapot, Lake, trees, and cottage scene,
earth tones, TEOH mark **45.00**
Tea Sets
11 pcs, teapot, creamer, sugar, 4 cups
and saucers, large yellow and turquoise flowers in full bloom, green
ground, Pagoda mark. **135.00**
15 pcs, ftd teapot, creamer, sugar, 4
ftd cups and saucers, 4 salad
plates, large pink and red roses covering entire body, cobalt and gold
trim, Pagoda mark **500.00**
Tea Strainer, 2 pcs, pink and red roses,
heavy gold ground, Wreath mark . . . **75.00**
Tea Tile, 5¼" d, large windmill, cottage,
and lake, shades of brown, Wreath
mark **65.00**
Toast Rack, sections for 3 slices of
toast, gold raised bunches of grapes
and grape leaves, white ground,
Spoke mark **135.00**
Toothpick Holder, 2½" h, fruit and floral,
Rising Sun mark **65.00**
Urn, 14", middle band of pastel orange
ruins scene, top and bottom sections
of white enameled flowers, solid gold
handles, Wreath mark **750.00**
Vases
6¼", floral, pink and burgundy roses,
all outlined in gold, blue ground, bisque and glossy finish, Wreath
mark. **55.00**
6½", relief molded, forest scene with
two dogs chasing stag, stand up
handles with beaded trim, Wreath
mark. **800.00**
8½", large clipper ship, earth tones,
wide jeweled and enameled top and
bottom bands, gold loop handles,
Wreath mark **195.00**
9½", large moriage snow geese in
flight, light to slate gray ground,
beaded handles, Wreath mark. . . . **220.00**
10" h, 9" d, large gaudy roses, deep
green and gold dec, solid gold ring
and loop handles, Cherry Blossom
mark. **210.00**
12½", forest scene in center, laven-
der and purple ground, Imperial
mark. **145.00**
16", three sections of Art Deco dec,
moriage beaded rim, ruffled rim,
large solid gold handles, Royal Kin-
ran mark **350.00**
Wall Pocket, figural and floral, shades of
brown, pink, and white, Cherry Blos-
som mark **135.00**
Whiskey Jug, 7" h, forest scene, shades
of yellows and browns, gloss finish,
moriage beaded neckband, handle,
and stopper, Wreath mark **400.00**

NODDERS

History: Nodders are figurines with heads and/or arms attached to the body with wires to enable them to move. Nodders are made in a variety of materials - bisque, celluloid, papier mache, porcelain, and wood.

Most nodders date from the late 19th century with Germany being the principal source of supply. Among the American made nodders, those of Disney and cartoon characters are most eagerly sought.

Advisor: Caroline E. Edleman.

Brownie, 10", cop, blue, Palmer Cox . .	265.00
Choir Boy, 7", papier mache	25.00
Couple, 6", seated, china bodies, bisque heads.	500.00
Daddy Warbucks, bisque.	100.00
Donkey, 7 x 6", celluloid, mkd "Occupied Japan".	110.00
Elephant, 10", papier mache	145.00
Girl, 4 x 2¾", bisque, seated, pink tiara, fan, fancy dress of peach, white, and pink, emb dec, gold, and beading, German	155.00
Indian, 5½", bisque, sitting, with basket of fruit	125.00
Kayo, bisque, mkd "Germany".	125.00
Mandarin, 6¼", china, blue, matchsafe	165.00
Men	
5½ x 2½ x 3¼", bisque, sitting under tree by fence, hat on tree, gray, white, and tan	125.00
9", papier mache, seated in twig chair	100.00

Girl in white dress, yellow basket,
4½" h, unmarked, $130.00.

Orientals	
Ladies	
4½", sitting, holding fan, enamel dec, blue pants, red blouse	185.00
7¼ x 3 x 5", French bisque, dressed in pink, yellow, and blue, pulling cart, gold dot trim	145.00
Men	
4½ x 3¾", leaning over strapped bale, head and hand moves, white beard, cobalt robe, black hat and boots.	165.00
5¾ x 4¼", seated, blue and white robe, matching skull cap with gold knob, gold buttons and dec, holds dagger & sheath.	110.00
6 x 6", bisque, seated, holds large pink fan behind head, gold trim, and beading, German	175.00
Rabbit, 8", papier mache, sitting, light brown.	75.00
Santa Claus, 9½", papier mache, red and blue, Germany	180.00

NORITAKE CHINA

History: Morimura Brothers founded Noritake China in 1904 in Nagoya, Japan. They made high quality chinaware for export to the United States and also produced a line of china blanks for hand painting. In 1910 the company perfected a technique for the production of high quality dinnerware and introduced streamlined production.

During the 1920s Larkin Company, Buffalo, New York, was a prime distributor of Noritake China. Larkin offered Azalea, Briarcliff, Linden, Modjeska, Savory, Sheridan, and Tree In The Meadow patterns as part of their premium line.

The factory was heavily damaged during World War II; production was reduced. Between 1946 and 1948 the company sold their china under the "Rose China" mark, since the quality of production did not match the earlier Noritake China. An 1948 expansion saw the resumption of quality production and the use of the Noritake name once again.

There are close to 100 different marks for Noritake, the careful study of which can determine the date of production. Most pieces are marked "Noritake" and have a wreath, "M," "N," or "Nippon." The use of the letter "N" was registered in 1953.

References: Lou Ann Donahue, *Noritake Collectibles*, Wallace Homestead, 1979; Joan Van Patten, *Collector's Encyclopedia of Noritake*, Collector Books, 1984.

Additional Listings: See *Warman's Americana & Collectibles* for price listings of the Azalea attern.

Ashtray, 3½", figural yellow bird, red int., black ext.	50.00
Basket, 7", handled, multicolored florals.	30.00

Bowl, 3 ftd, 7¾" d, 2⅛" h, chestnuts in browns, orange, and yellow, $95.00.

Bon Bon, florals in red, green, and yellow, gold trim, green mark 35.00
Bowls
  8", medallions of roses, black and gold geometric borders 25.00
  8½", sq, 2 handles, multicolored bird of paradise, yellow flowers, pale lavender lustre border, green mark . . 35.00
  9", pierced gold handles, lemon swags framed with black, numerous floral medallions. 35.00
Bread Tray, 12" l, 2 gold handles, 2 brown horseheads, green trees in background, gold trim 75.00
Cake and Ice Cream Set, 7 pcs, (bowl, underplate, sq cake plate, four 8½" plates), colorful parrot on plum branch on black ground, gold rims. 80.00
Candlesticks, pr, 5½", blue, orange, and black butterflies on gold lustre ground 95.00
Celery Set, 7 pcs, (12" handled serving dish, six 3¾" individual salts), hp naturalistic celery stalk and black olives on tan ground, gold border, gold rim 85.00
Cheese and Cracker Dish, cov int. dish with girl finial, red dress, blue lustre and orange triangular border design 165.00
Cigarette Holder, bell shaped, blue lustre, colorful bird finial. 85.00
Compote, 11½" d, rose scallops with gold design, center floral medallion, gold handles, rim, and foot bands, green mark. 60.00
Creamer and Sugar, cov, deep pink hp flowers, gold trim. 35.00
Demitasse Set, 17 pc, Rosamor 55.00
Egg Warmer, 5½" d, 4 egg cups, purple iris dec, gold trim on handle. 75.00
Fruit Set, 12 x 7½" tray, 6 handled dishes, dec with strawberries, cherries, lemons, blue lustre, and gold trim 125.00
Gravy Boat, attached underplate, matching ladle, hp, fish swimming under-

water, blue ground, lacy gold trim and beading 65.00
Jam Set, cov jar, underplate, spoon, yellow bird finial, blue lustre 40.00
Napkin Rings, pr, Art Deco, orig box . . 70.00
Nappy, 5", white and pink roses, green shaded leaves, gold rim and ring handle, green mark. 25.00
Powder Puff Box, 4", round, lady in yellow sunbonnet, green and white dress, floral trim, lustre ground. 100.00
Relish, 9", hp sailboat and palm trees . 35.00
Spooner, 8" l, 2 handles, white and gold lustre trim, red mark 40.00
Vases
  6½", fan shape, multicolored floral medallion, green and white scalloped edge, green band on circular foot, red mark 65.00
  8½", bud, deep orange lustre ground, Art Deco girl in white on front, red mark. 125.00
  11¼", cylindrical, 2 gold trimmed handles, hp white and pink poppies, green leaves, gold foliate design on shoulder and base 150.00
Wall Pockets
  5 x 2¼", colorful floral design blown out on top, black ground, applied figural bumblebees. 45.00
  8", scenic band of swans swimming, trees against sunset background, lustre 75.00

NORITAKE: TREE IN THE MEADOW PATTERN

History: Tree In The Meadow is one of the most popular patterns of Noritake china. Since the design is hand painted, there are numerous variations of the scene. The basic scene features a large tree (usually in the foreground), a meandering stream or lake, and a peasant cottage in the distance. Principal colors are muted tones of brown and yellow.

The pattern is found with a variety of backstamps and appears to have been imported into the United States beginning in the early 1920s. The Larkin Company distributed this pattern through its catalog sales in the 1920–1930 period.

Reference: Joan Van Patten, *Collector's Encyclopedia of Noritake,* Collector Books, 1984.

Ashtrays, pr, nested 35.00
Basket. 50.00
Berry Set, master bowl with pierced handles, 6 sauce dishes 65.00
Bowls
  5¾" 10.00
  9" 35.00

Vase, fan shape, Noritake mark, $120.00.

Bread Tray	40.00
Butter Tub, open handles, insert, cov	65.00
Cake Plate, 10″, open handles	35.00
Candlestick, 5½″	50.00
Candy Jar, cov, gold ball finial	75.00
Compote	100.00
Condiment Set, 5 pc	35.00
Creamer and Sugar, cov	45.00
Cruet, double, gold spouts and handles	45.00
Cup and Saucer	15.00
Demitasse Pot	180.00
Lemon Dish, 5½″, ring handle	15.00
Mustard Jar, 2½″ h, attached underplate, cov, orig spoon	50.00
Plates	
6½″	8.00
7½″	10.00
8½″	15.00
Platter, 14″	35.00
Playing Card Holder, 3¾″ h	95.00
Salt and Pepper Shakers, pr, bulbous	25.00
Sugar Shaker	25.00
Syrup Jug, cov, underplate	50.00
Teapot	100.00
Vase, 8¾″, baluster form	100.00
Vegetable Dish, 9¾″, oval	40.00
Waffle Set	50.00
Wall Pocket, 8¼″, blue lustre ground, pattern in wide band at top	55.00

NORTH DAKOTA SCHOOL OF MINES

History: The North Dakota School of Mines was established in 1890. Earle J. Babcock, an instructor in chemistry, was impressed with the high purity of North Dakota potter's clay. In 1898 Babcock received funds to develop his finds. He tried to interest commercial potteries in North Dakota clay, but had limited success.

In 1910 Babcock persuaded the school to establish a Ceramics Department. Margaret Cable, who studied under Charles Binns and Frederick H. Rhead, was appointed head. She remained until her retirement in 1949.

Decorative emphasis was placed on native themes, e.g., flowers and animals. Art Nouveau, Art Deco, and fairly plain pieces were made.

The pottery is marked in cobalt blue underglaze with "University of North Dakota/Grand Forks, N.D./Made at School of Mines/N.D. Clay" in a circle. Some earlier pieces only were marked "U.N.D." or "U.N.D./Grand Forks, N.D." Most pieces are numbered (they can be dated with University records) and signed by both the instructor and student. Cable signed pieces are most desirable.

Reference: *University Of North Dakota Pottery, The Cable Years*, Knight Publishing Company, 1977.

Advisor: Robert Berman.

Ashtray, KEM design, seal 1930	135.00
Bowls	
3″, plain blue	85.00
4½″, bison design, brown, sgd Cable	175.00
Figurines	
Donkey, pale gray glaze	60.00
Horse, blue matte, 6″	70.00
Ginger Jar, cov, 8½″, blue and white Oriental design	250.00
Paperweight, prairie rose design, brown	120.00
Vases	
4″, blue and white, antelopes	160.00
6¼″, cov wagon design, brown, sgd Cable	175.00

Vase, 4″ h, 4½″ d, white to light green ground, imp circular dec, imp leaf dec, stamp mark, inscribed 95A Huck in circle, $165.00.

7", sgd Huch

Aqua, wheat design **185.00**
Blue drip glaze. **80.00**

10"

Red to purple glaze, plain. **100.00**
Yellow glaze **100.00**

11½", carved Art Deco design, brown
to red glaze, red in carved areas. . **250.00**

OCCUPIED JAPAN

History: At the end of World War II, the Japanese economy was devasted. To secure needed hard currency, the Japanese pottery industry produced thousands of figurines and other knick-knacks for export. From the beginning of the American occupation until April 28, 1952, these objects were marked "Japan," "Made in Japan," "Occupied Japan," and "Made in Occupied Japan." Only pieces marked with the last two designations are of strong interest to Occupied Japan collectors. The first two marks also were used at other time periods.

The variety of products is endless—ashtrays, dinnerware, lamps, planters, souvenir items, toys, vases, etc. Initially it was the figurines which attracted the largest number of collectors; today many collectors focus on non-figurine material.

References: Gene Florence, *The Collector's Encyclopedia Of Occupied Japan Collectibles,* Collector Books, 1976, 1982 edition; Gene Florence, *The Collector's Encyclopedia Of Occupied Japan Collectibles,* 2nd series, Collector Books, 1979, 1982 revision.

Collectors' Club: Occupied Japan Collectors Club, 18309 Faysmith Avenue, Torrance, CA 90504.

Additional Listings: See *Warman's Americana & Collectibles* for more examples.

Figurine, 7¼" h, female, rose dress, brown base, mkd, $25.00.

Bisque, unglazed

Cornucopia, 7 x 8", model of chariot
with rearing horse and 2 cherubs,
multicolored beading and gold trim **65.00**

Figurines

Seated gentleman with arm around
waist of lady, book on lap **35.00**
Small boy dressed as fisherman,
shelf sitting type **10.00**

Flower Frog, 6" h, figural, girl with bird
on shoulder, pastel highlights, gold
trim **40.00**

Match Holder, 7 x 4½", Colonial man
and woman, each holding baskets,
striker on side **45.00**

Planter, Cupid and shell, sphinx
base **35.00**

Toothpick Holder, 3", nude girl, foot
on book, lustre trim **12.00**

Wall Pocket, 4 x 2¾ x 1½", Colonial
lady on balcony **20.00**

Celluloid, 2½ x 3½", donkey **8.00**

Cloth, 4 pc sheet set, (2 sheets, 2 pillow
cases), double, embroidered label on
pillowcases. **35.00**

Metal

Ashtray, 5 x 3", bronze type, emb filigree on sides and top. **18.00**

Desk Set, 3 pc, ornate leaf shaped
tray. **35.00**

Lighter, table, shaped like Aladdin's
lamp. **20.00**

Pin, butterfly shape, cloisonne type. . **5.00**

Pin Cushion, tin, red velvet top opens
to reveal mirror inside. **15.00**

Pliers, orig box, mkd "High Quality,
NKK, Made In Occupied Japan" . . **20.00**

Toy, tin windup, man on horseback,
MIB **40.00**

Tray, 9¾ x 5½", SP over copper, emb
and etched flowers. **30.00**

Vase, 6", SP, double ftd, stylized flowers and leaves, Art Deco style . . . **25.00**

Papier mache, tray, 8¼ x 5", hp roses,
mkd "Alcohol Proof/SS/Made In Occupied Japan" **15.00**

Porcelain, glazed

Busts, pr, Napolean and Josephine,
ceramic lace around hat **45.00**

Child's play dishes, 20 pcs, Mickey
Mouse dec **100.00**

Clock, china case, pink roses, pale
green leaves, 2 applied bluebirds,
scrollwork, Sessions clock **50.00**

Condiment Set, red tomato on green
leaf tray **25.00**

Creamer and sugar, cov, beehive
shape **25.00**

Cups and Saucers

Demitasse, ftd cup, yellow leaf and
stem dec, gold outlines, light blue
ground. **35.00**

Tea, bellflower dec, shaded green

and yellow leaves, gold trim, mkd
GZL **30.00**
Dinnerware, 40 pcs, (6 pc place set-
ting for 6, 4 serving pcs), Wild Rose
pattern, mkd "Yamaka China, Oc-
cupied Japan" **235.00**
Figurines
Collie, reclining, 5½ x 3" **18.00**
Lady, 7½", holding skirt up slightly
with one hand **20.00**
Scottie, 4½ x 7½" **25.00**
Flower Frog, 7½", penquin shape,
black and white **30.00**
Lamp, 10½", Colonial lady, flowers ex-
tend from neck and hat **40.00**
Match Holder, hanging, figural boy and
girl, striker on base **110.00**
Planter, 6", goose **15.00**
Plate, 4", autumn lake scene, mkd
"Tainshashi, Made in Occupied
Japan" **10.00**
Salt and Pepper Shakers, holder, 2
pink pigs in sty, standing with paws
on railing of holder **15.00**
Tea Sets
5 pc, (cov teapot, creamer, cov
sugar), cottage shape, multicolored, shaped windows, doors,
and thatched roofs, mkd "T" in a
circle **50.00**
23 pc, (cov teapot, creamer, cov
sugar, 6 cups and saucers, 6
7¾" plates), rose design, gold
trim, mkd "Noritake, Made in Oc-
cupied Japan" **135.00**
Toby Mug, 7½", street vendor **50.00**
Toothpick Holder, boy playing accordian, dog seated beside him **20.00**
Urn, 2½", 2 handles, blue and white,
pattern similar to Wedgwood **10.00**
Wall Plaque, 6", Dutch boy, basket of
flowers **18.00**

G. E. OHR,
OHR POTTERY   BILOXI.

History: Ohr pottery was produced by George
E. Ohr in Biloxi, Mississippi. There is some dis-
crepancy as to when he actually established his
pottery. Some suggest 1878; but, Ohr's autobiography indicates 1883. In 1884 Ohr exhibited 600
pieces of his work, indicating that he had been
working for some time.

Ohr's techniques included twisting, crushing,
folding, denting, and crinkling thin walled clay into
odd, grotesque, and sometimes graceful forms.
Much of his early work is signed with an impressed
stamp of his name and location in block letters. His
later work, often marked with the flowing script designation "G E Ohr," was usually left unglazed.

In 1906, Ohr closed the pottery and stored over
6,000 pieces as his legacy to his family. He hoped
it would be purchased by the U.S. Government,
which never happened. The entire collection remained in storage until it was rediscovered in 1972.

Today Ohr is recognized as one of the leading
potters in the American Art Pottery movement.
Some greedy individuals have taken the latter unglazed pieces and covered them with poor quality
glazes, in hopes of making them more valuable.
These pieces, usually with the flowing script mark,
do not have "stilt marks" on the bottom.

**Puzzle Mug, 3½" h, mottled green high
glaze, pressed rope and leaf handle,
screw under handle script sgd "G.E.
OHR", $365.00.**

Bowls
4", round, mustard glaze, blue, green,
and brown streaks **160.00**
5" d, 2½" h, crimped rim, mahogany
glaze, imp mark **125.00**
Chamberstick, 2½", cylindrical, gun
metal glaze, script sgd **150.00**
Cup, 2½", green to violet glaze, written
homily on ext., imp mark, 1896 . . . . . **135.00**
Jug, 4½" h, 3" d, swollen cylindrical
shape, gun metal glaze, script sgd . . **275.00**
Mug, 5", green glaze, one rectangular
handle and one scroll handle, script
sgd **225.00**
Pitcher, 4¾", bulbous, shaped rim, speck-
led green glaze, rect handle **250.00**
Pot, 4½" h, 5" d, crumpled, gun metal
glaze, orange int., imp mark **390.00**
Teapot, 4½" h, 8" d, circular lid, speckled
pink glaze with moss highlights, in-
cised mark **850.00**
Top Hat, 2⅝", blue glaze, imp mark . . . **140.00**
Vases
4", pitcher shape, crimped neck,
brown speckled glaze, imp mark . . **350.00**
4¾", crimped waist, green speckled
ochre glaze, imp mark **210.00**
5¾", crimped open mouth and neck,
pale white glaze, green speckled
int., imp mark **150.00**

6", bulbous shape, inverted lip, dark green glaze, gun metal int., imp mark... 250.00
6¼", double flared neck, brown glaze, imp mark... 250.00
6½", baluster shape, crimped elongated neck, dark green glaze, imp mark... 175.00
9", cylindrical, ruffled mouth, brown spotted glaze, imp mark... 275.00
10½", baluster shape, mottled red, gray, blue, and green, imp mark... 275.00
Whistle, 3⅔", cylindrical, figural bird on top, green-black glaze, imp mark... 175.00

OLD IVORY
84

OLD IVORY CHINA

History: Old Ivory derives its name from the background color of the china. It was made in Silesia, Germany, during the second half of the 19th century. Marked pieces usually have a pattern number (pattern names are not common) and the crown Silesia mark.

Plate, 8", floral dec, mkd "VIII," $50.00.

Berry Sets, 9½" master bowl, 4 small bowls
  Englantine... 150.00
  No. 73... 135.00
Biscuit Jar, cov, No. 16... 175.00
Bowls
  5¼" d, 3" h, No. 84, waste, dec inside and outside... 75.00
  6", tab handle, No. 84... 55.00

9½" d, No. 16... 55.00
10" d, No. 16... 60.00
Cake Plate, 10" d, No. 16, pierced handles... 60.00
Cake Set, 7 pcs, 10¼" pierced handle plate, six 6" d plates, No. 84... 175.00
Celery Tray, 9¼" l, No. 78... 60.00
Cups and Saucers
  No. 15... 42.00
  No. 200... 40.00
  No. 202... 35.00
Pickle Tray, 8½" l, 5" w, No. 16... 55.00
Plates
  7½", No. 16... 25.00
  7¾"
    No. 28, Ohme mark and Silesia mark... 25.00
    No. 75, Ohme mark and Silesia mark... 25.00
  8½", No. 11... 30.00
Platter, 11½", No. 22, Holly... 100.00
Relish, 6¼" l, 4½" w, No. 84... 55.00
Salt and Pepper, No. 16... 75.00
Saucer, No. 84... 20.00
Sugar, cov, No. 84... 45.00
Toothpick, No. 75... 85.00

OLD PARIS CHINA

History: Old Paris china is fine quality porcelain, made by various French factories during the 18th and 19th centuries. Some pieces were marked, but the majority was not. Characteristics of this type of china include fine porcelain, beautiful decorations and gilding. Favorite colors were dark maroon, deep cobalt blue, and a deep green.

Additional Listing: Continental China and Porcelain (General).

Apothecary Jars, pr, 10¼", hp florals and eagles, gold striping, made for "Drogueria Belga, Mexico"... 325.00
Bowl, basketweave, open, paw feet, gold floral dec... 200.00
Cache Pots, pr, 9½", green ground, floral scene on one side, courting scene on reverse, gilding... 1,450.00
Calling Card Tray, 6", floral dec on maroon ground... 65.00
Cup and Saucer, magenta floral on white ground shading to sea green, gold trim, c1890... 75.00
Figurine, 6½", lady seated on reclining camel, palm trees, mkd "Asia"... 300.00
Gravy Boat, cov, blue bird dec, anchor and rope finial... 125.00
Inkstand, 15 x 11 x 11", figural, reclining man, polychrome dec... 450.00
Patch Box, scalloped, emb gold dec, white ground... 50.00
Plate, 9½", floral center, scalloped border, sgd "Boyer"... 35.00

Plate, 8⅛" d, pale blue-gray border, multicolored boy and girl, $50.00.

Snuff Box, cobalt blue ground, enameled
floral dec, sgd................ **225.00**
Tureen, 11½ x 13", cobalt blue on white,
hp floral dec.................. **275.00**
Vases
   4½", spill, portrait dec........... **100.00**
   10¾", rose ground, 4 large gilded
    leaves, maroon open bug, gold
    trim...................... **100.00**
   11 x 8½", pillow shape, birds and fol-
    iate, 4 gold paw feet.......... **325.00**
   12½", hp classical scenes in re-
    serves.................... **350.00**

OLD SLEEPY EYE

History: Sleepy Eye, a Sioux Indian chief who
reportedly had a droopy eye, gave his name to
Sleepy Eye, Minnesota, and one of its leading flour
mills. In the early 1900s Old Sleepy Eye Flour offered four Flemish gray heavy stoneware premiums, decorated in cobalt blue: a straight-sided butter crock, curved salt bowl, stein, and vase. The
premiums were made by Weir Pottery Company,
later to become Monmouth Pottery Company, and
finally to emerge as the present-day Western
Stoneware Company of Monmouth, Illinois.

Additional pottery and stoneware pieces were issued. Forms included five sizes of pitchers (4,
5½, 6½, 8, and 9 inches), mugs, steins, sugar
bowls, and tea tiles (hot plates). Most were cobalt
blue on white; but, other glaze hues, such as
browns, golds, and greens, were used.

Old Sleepy Eye also issued many other items,
including baker's caps, lithographed barrel covers,

beanies, fans, multicolored pillow tops, postcards,
trade cards, etc. Production of Old Sleepy Eye
stoneware ended in 1937.

In 1952 Western Stoneware Company made a
22 and 40 ounce stein in chestnut brown glaze with
a redesigned Indianhead. From 1961 to 1972 gift
editions, dated and signed with a Maple Leaf mark,
were made for the Board of Directors and others
within the company. Beginning in 1973, Western
Stoneware Company issued an annual limited edition stein, marked and dated, for collectors.

Collectors' Club: Old Sleepy Eye Collectors
Club, Box 12, Monmouth, IL 61462. Dues: $5.00.
Sleepy Eye Newsletter (bimonthly).

Reproduction Alert: Blue and white pitchers,
crazed, weighted, and often with a stamp or the
word "Ironstone" are the most copied. The stein
and salt bowl also have been made. Many reproductions come from Taiwan.

A line of fakes, new items which never existed,
includes an advertising pocket mirror with miniature
flour barrel label, small glass plates, fruit jars, toothpick holders, glass and pottery miniature pitchers,
and salt and pepper shakers. One mill item has
been made, a sack marked as though it were old
but of a size that could not possibly hold the amount
of flour indicated.

Advisors: David and Betty Hallam.

MILL ITEMS

Barrel Label, "Hummer Flour," litho-
  graph, round, two hummingbirds
  around flowers, 196 lbs.......... **250.00**
Cookbook, loaf of bread, "Sleepy Eye
  Milling Co." and portrait of chief.... **125.00**
Dough Scraper, tin blade, wood handle
  with "Sleepy Eye Flour"........... **250.00**
Letter Opener, bronze, Indian head on
  handle, mkd "Sleepy Eye Milling Co.,
  Sleepy Eye, Minn."............. **750.00**
Pillow Top, head of chief in center,
  framed...................... **500.00**
Pinback button, "Old Sleepy Eye For
  Me," bust portrait of chief........ **150.00**
Sheet Music, "Sleepy Eye," music by
  Hall Parks, lyrics by Mark Hawkins.. **200.00**
Spoons
  Demitasse, roses (not Indian) in
   bowl...................... **135.00**
  Teaspoon, Indian on handle, Unity
   SP....................... **85.00**
Trade Cards, set of 10, framed...... **1,500.00**

OLD SLEEPY EYE CLUB CONVENTION ITEMS

1976, mug..................... **210.00**
1977, membership pin............. **50.00**
1982, barrel.................... **55.00**
1983, pitcher.................. **90.00**

Advertising Sign, 13⅝ x 19″, litho tin over cardboard, New York Metal Sign Works, $1,400.00.

POTTERY AND STONEWARE

Mugs
Blue banded, 4¼″	170.00
Cobalt	395.00

Pitcher, blue on yellow 5¼″, small Indian head on handle 700.00

Pitchers, blue on white
4″	150.00
9″	230.00

Steins
Blue on white, 7¾″, 1906–37	260.00
Brown on white, 7¾″	825.00
Chestnut brown, 1952	210.00
Director's, blue on white, 1968 to 1973	175.00

Sugar Bowl, cobalt blue on white, 1906–37, 4″ h 360.00

Tea Tile (hot plate), cobalt blue on white 1,000.00

Vase, blue on white 170.00

ONION MEISSEN

History: The blue onion or bulb pattern is of Chinese origin and depicts peaches and pomegranates, not onions. It was first made in the 18th century by Meissen, hence the name Onion Meissen.

Factories in Europe, Japan, and elsewhere copied the pattern. Many still have the pattern in production, including the Meissen factory now located in East Germany.

Note: Prices given are for pieces produced between 1870 and 1930. Many pieces are marked with a company's logo; after 1891 the country of origin is indicated on imported pieces. Early Meissen examples bring a high premium.

Bowls
7½″	45.00
9″	40.00
10½″, oval	50.00
Bread Board	45.00
Candleholders, 4½″, pr	65.00
Cheese Dish, cov	150.00
Coffee Pot, 9½″	160.00

Compotes
8½″ h	165.00
9″ h, 9″ d, reticulated rim	350.00
Creamer and Sugar	135.00

Cups and aucers
Coffee	45.00
Demitasse	35.00
Dinner Set, 54 pcs, imp marks, c 1860	1,875.00

Dishes
7″, leaf shape, handles	40.00
10½″, round, deep, imp mark	55.00

Funnels
4″	78.00
4¾″	95.00
5½″	110.00

Gravy Boat, attached underplate, 2 handles 160.00

Ladle, 4″ l, 2″ d, wooden handle 135.00

Masher, wooden handle 135.00

Napkin Ring 23.00

Plates
8″	35.00

Soup Plate, 9¾″ d, scalloped edge, mkd Meissen with star, late, $45.00.

9″	50.00
9¾″	55.00
14″, scalloped edge.............	85.00
Platters	
10″	75.00
11½″	150.00
12″, round	175.00
19″	300.00
Relish Dishes	
6½″ l, 4¾″ w, oblong, octagonal ...	45.00
11¾″ l, 7¼″ w, scalloped edge	85.00
Rolling Pin.....................	155.00
Salt and Pepper.................	65.00
Salt Box	135.00
Sauce Dish, 4¾″	30.00
Scoop, 9″ l	45.00
Shoe, 7″ l, 2½″ w...............	95.00
Soup Bowl, 9½″.................	70.00
Strainer, wooden handle...........	90.00
Sugar, cov.....................	65.00
Tea Strainer, wooden handle........	65.00
Tea Tile.......................	75.00
Tenderizers, wooden handles	
2½″	125.00
3″	135.00
Tureen, soup	200.00
Vase, 6½″	75.00
Vegetable Dishes, covered	
7¾″, oval	125.00
9½″, round, dome cov...........	175.00
10″ sq	150.00

OPALESCENT GLASS

History: Opalescent glass is a clear or colored glass with milky white decorations which show a fiery or opalescent quality when held to light. The effect was achieved by applying bone ash chemicals to designated areas while a piece was still hot and then refiring it at tremendous heat.

There are three basic categories of opalescent glass: (1) Blown (or mold blown) patterns, e.g., Daisy & Fern and Spanish Lace; (2) Novelties, pressed glass patterns made in limited pieces which often included unusual shapes such as Corn or Trough; and (3) Pattern (pressed) glass.

Opalescent glass was produced in England in the 1870s. Northwood began the American production in 1897 at its Indiana, Pennsylvania, plant. Jefferson, National Glass, Hobbs, and Fenton soon followed.

Reference: William Heacock, *Encyclopedia of Victorian Colored Pattern Glass: Book II, Opalescent Glass from A to Z*, Antique Publications, 2nd ed., 1977.

Additional Listings: See Pattern Glass for pressed opalescent patterns.

BLOWN

Barber Bottle, Hobb's Hobnail, blue ...	125.00
Bowl, Poinsettia, clear, ruffled, tripod ..	50.00

Bride's Basket, Bubble Lattice, cranberry	165.00
Butter Dish, cov, Chrysanthemum Base Swirl, cranberry...............	275.00
Celeries	
Daffodil, blue	60.00
Drapes, white to clear, cranberry edge, ruffled top	60.00
Creamer, Swirl, blue, miniature.......	65.00
Cruets	
Daisy & Fern, clear to white, cut glass stopper....................	60.00
Hobb's Hobnail, vaseline, orig stopper....................	210.00
Dish, Coin Spot Paneled, canary, 4¾″ d	25.00
Fairy Lamp, Swirl, amber, pyramid shape top, clear Clarke base, 3¾″ h......	90.00
Finger Bowl, Chrysanthemum Base Swirl, cranberry...............	45.00
Pitchers, water	
Buttons & Braids, green..........	95.00
Coin Spot, cranberry	135.00

Tankard pitcher, 13⅜″ h, blue, Poinsetta pattern, Hobbs, Bruckunier & Co., $225.00.

Fern, blue, applied blue handle, petal form rim, tankard.............	275.00
Hobb's Hobnail, cranberry	225.00
Ribbed Opal Lattice, cranberry, amber handle, 6″.................	125.00
Swirl	
Cranberry, square top, Burlington mark	235.00
Vaseline, bulbous, round top, vaseline reeded applied handle, pink and white enamel flowers, gold foliage and branches, 7¼″ h.	150.00

Punch Cup, Chrysanthemum Base Swirl, white	35.00
Rose Bowl, Daisy & Fern, cranberry, ruffled rim	45.00
Spooner, Spanish Lace, blue	75.00
Sugar Bowl, cov, Bubble Lattice, blue	85.00

Sugar Shakers

Daisy & Fern, cranberry, orig lid	135.00
Windows, white	85.00
Sweetmeat Jar, Opal Stripe, blue, fluted, vaseline scalloped applied edge and ruffles around rim, SP basket frame, 5¾" d	110.00

Syrups

Bulbous Base Coin Spot, green	135.00
Coin Spot & Swirl, white	65.00
Daisy & Fern, cranberry	245.00
Toothpick, Ribbed Opal Lattice, cranberry, satin finish	95.00

Tumblers

Button & Braids, blue	35.00
Daisy & Fern, cranberry	30.00
Reverse Swirl, vaseline	45.00
Swirl, cranberry	35.00

NOVELTIES

Bowls

Beaded Cable, green, ruffled, 7" d	45.00
Grape & Cherries, blue	65.00
Greek Key & Scale, blue, ftd	40.00
Poinsettia Lattice, white	70.00
Winter Cabbage, blue	55.00
Curtain Tiebacks, pewter posts, pr	85.00
Ewer, Striped Opal, vaseline, flattened bulbous, pink applied flowers, amber applied leaves and handle, 8¼" h	135.00
Plate, Wishbone & Drape, green	20.00
Spooner, Leaf with Basketweave, blue	115.00
Tumbler, Arabian Nights, blue	55.00

Vases

Aurora Borealis, blue	35.00
Jefferson Spool, green	20.00
Piasa Bird, blue	50.00
Tree Trunk, green, 10¾" h	25.00

OPALINE GLASS

History: Opaline glass was a popular mid to late 19th century European glass. The glass has a certain amount of translucency and often is found decorated in enamel designs and trimmed in gold.

Basket, deep blue body, gold trim, clear handle	145.00

Bowls

9", cov, ftd, enamel floral dec	50.00
15", 2 pc, standard, poppy dec outlined in gold	110.00
Cologne Bottle, ftd, green, enamel beading, gilt scrolls dec, matching topper	75.00

Jack-in-the pulpit vase, 5½" h, robin's egg blue body, applied amber feet, $75.00.

Cruet, pink, quilted body, alabaster handle	155.00
Epergne, 3 trumpet vases, blue	200.00
Jewel Box, 6⅜ x 5", hinged lid, painted medallion of lovers on lid, Norse warrior on body, ormolu mount	160.00

Lamps

Kerosene, pink reservoir and blue stem, orig chimney	400.00
Marriage type, blue, patent "D. C. Ripley & Co."	1,500.00
Oil, 20½", opaque white ground, polychrome enameling with stylized floral design, ormolu grotesque mask feet, French, c1890	200.00

Mantle Lustres

12", pr, white satin body, green fold over top, gold trim	225.00
13", pr, blue, white snakes entwined around stem	220.00
Mug, white, enameled floral dec, gold trim	60.00
Perfume Bottle, 7", blue, gold trim, Art Nouveau metal holder	85.00
Pickle Castor, cov, green insert, SP ormolu frame, c1880	175.00

Pitchers

Milk, pink, floral dec	175.00
Miniature, 1¾", blue, gold ec	45.00
Powder Box, cov, 3¼" d, sapphire blue, enameled florals on lid, c1850	225.00
Ring Tree, 2½", blue, gold trim	55.00
Rose Bowl, pale pink	85.00

Vases

6¾", pr, mauve with gold trim	175.00
10", bud, pink, gold enamel dec	100.00
12¼", pr, pale green ground, figural reserves, metal base	200.00

14″, pr, baluster shape, polychrome dec of linnets perched on flowering branches, fitted as electric table lamps **300.00**

ORIENTAL RUGS

History: The history of oriental rugs or carpets dates back to 3,000 B.C.; but, it was in the 16th century that they became prevalent. The rugs originated in the regions of Central Asia, Iran (Persia), Caucasus, and Anatolia. Early rugs can be classified into basic categories: Iranian, Caucasian, Turkoman, Turkish, and Chinese. Later India, Pakistan, and Iraq produced rugs in the oriental style.

The pattern name is derived from the tribe which produced the rug, e.g., Iran is the source for Hamadan, Herez, Sarouk, Tabriz, and others.

When evaluating an oriental rug, age, design, color, weave, knots per square inch, and condition determine the final value. Silk rugs and prayer rugs bring higher prices.

Note: Beware! There are repainted rugs on the market.

Reference: Ivan C. Neff and Carol V. Maggs, *Dictionary of Oriental Rugs*, Van Nostrand Reinhold Company, 1979.

Anatolian, prayer, 3′10″ x 2′11″, red mihrab below pea-green prayer arch, tan main border, blue and violet guard borders. **475.00**
Bakhtiari
  6′7″ x 5′2″, indigo field in symetrical design with radiating flowerheads . **950.00**
  11′ x 6′7″, navy field, 2 rows of connecting beige medallions, shield devices, beige main border of rosettes, flowers, and vines, 3 guard borders **1,550.00**
Chinese, 6′9″ x 4′1″, toffee field, central floral medallion and butterflies with key-fret spandrels, toffee main border with vine and symbols, 2 guard stripes, late 19th C **600.00**
Daghestan, prayer, 4′11″ x 4′, ivory field, diagonal rows of flowers leading to prayer arch, main border of leaf and flower design, 2 navy floral borders, trefoil guard stripe **925.00**
Heriz
  6′6″ x 4′8″, brick red field, navy floral medallion and ivory floral spandrels, dark brown main border with leaves and rosettes, 2 floral guard borders **950.00**
  10′8″ x 8′3″, salmon field, navy and salmon petal shape center medallion with floral sprays and medium blue spandrels, dark blue main border of rosettes and vine, 2 gold guard borders **3,100.00**

11′3″ x 9′8″, brick red field, 2 concentric floral poled medallions, large floral spandrels, floral brick main border, 2 floral guard borders. **1,820.00**
Karabagh, 7′1″ x 3′8″, brick red field, 2 ivory and 1 brown octagonal medallion with leaves, rosettes, and geometric devices, Prussian blue main border of octagons, 2 guard borders, shows wear. **920.00**
Karagashli, 5′5″ x 3′7″, dark blue field, 3 brick red medallions with stylized leaves and rosettes, gold main border with connecting leaves, 2 narrow guard borders, c1880. . . . . **2,500.00**

Sarouk, ivory field woven with directional floral motifs, midnight blue main border, 4′2″ x 6′4″, $725.00.

Kashan, 15′3″ x 12′1″, medium blue field, allover floral arrangements, rose main border with palmettes and leaves, 2 pairs floral guard borders . . **5,000.00**
Kazak, 4′3″ x 6′2″, deep red field, 2 navy, medium blue, and green medallions, shaded blue main border **875.00**
Khorrasan, 11′6″ x 8′6″, navy field, allover Herati pattern, red main border with palmettes and rosettes, 3 pairs of floral ground borders **1,075.00**

Khotan, 7'2" x 4'5", salmon field, octagonal key-fret center medallion, 2 floral medallions, stylized waves main border, c1875 . . . . **925.00**

Konagend Shirvan, 6'5" x 4'6", ivory field, horizontal rows of stylized botehs, narrow brick red main border of leaf and wine glass design, 5 guard borders. **1,450.00**

Koshan, prayer, 6'9" x 4'4", navy field, flowering vases leading to multiple arch, brick red main border of palmettes and rosettes, 2 guard borders **1,800.00**

Krabagh, 4'7" x 7'3", 2 rows of 6 compartments, red, gold, ivory, and medium blue **950.00**

Kudish, 6'9" x 4'8", diagonal rows of alternating brown, brick red, and blue with flowers and devices, ivory main border with stars, 2 guard borders **625.00**

Kurd Bedjar, runner, 17'6" x 3', navy field, allover diagonal rows of floral arrangements, ivory floral border, 2 floral guard borders **1,050.00**

Mahal, 12'2" x 8'9", navy field, allover repeating leaf scrolls, brick red floral main border, 2 narrow guard stripes **1,800.00**

Mudjar, prayer, 4'9" x 3'9", brick red field, lamp leading to apple-green prayer arch, tangerine main border with rosettes and lilies, 2 guard borders, some wear, late 19th C **900.00**

Oushak, 7'9" x 7'9", inscribed ivory field framed by linked red spandrels, blue-gray main border, 14 narrow guard stripes **1,300.00**

Sarouk, 6'5" x 4'2", wine-red field, flowering branches around openwork floral medallion, vases of flowers at either end, dark blue palmettes and vine border **750.00**

Shiraz, 4'10" x 3'8", rust field, large shield shape medallion enclosing rust poled medallion, ivory medallions in corners, main border of repeating diamonds, 6 guard borders **1,200.00**

Talish, 7'10" x 3'1", brick red oblong center panel, ivory main border with crabs, 2 vine borders, 4 floral guard stripes **800.00**

Tekke Turkoman Mafrash, 3'2" x 1', claret field, 5 oblong ivory panels, 3 narrow guard borders **375.00**

Turkish, 6'9" x 4'1", honey field, 2 salmon petal shape medallions, floral sprays, medium blue main border with palmettes, 2 claret floral guard borders, early 19th C **1,700.00**

Yomud Turkoman, prayer, 4'9" x 4', brick red field, vertical rows of stylized latch-hook vines alternating with stepped cruciform devices, 2 ivory cruciform design borders, 4 checkerboard guard borders, late 19th C **1,000.00**

Yuruk, 6'5" x 4'1", brick red field, allover pattern of diagonal rows of connecting diamonds enclosing smaller hooked diamonds, ivory main border of multicolored crosses **1,100.00**

Ziegler Mahab, 14'3" x 10'8", navy field, compartmented gardern sprays, red main border of alternating rosettes and palmettes, 2 pairs of floral guard borders. **2,750.00**

ORIENTALIA

History: Orientalia is a term used to apply to ojbects made in the Orient, which encompasses the Far East, Asia, China, and Japan. The diversity of cultures produced a variety of objects and styles.

Reference: Sandra Andacht, Nancy Garthe, and Robert Mascarelli, *Price Guide to Oriental Antiques, Second Edition,* Wallace-Homestead, 1984.

Periodical: *The Orientalia Journal, P. O. Box 94, Little Neck, NY 11363. Bimonthly newsletter. Subscription: $12.00.*

Additional Listings: Canton, Celadon, Cloisonne, Fitzhugh, Nanking, Netsukes, Rose Medallion, Japanese Prints, and other categories.

Belt Hook, Chinese, Warring States Period, spatula shape, cast in high relief with animal masks at each end joined by entwined chilongs with grooved bodies, inlaid glass beads, brightly gilded dragon head hook, reverse with button, 5¼" l **3,300.00**

Brush Pots

5½", Kangxi, cylindrical, finely mottled powder blue underglaze **1,400.00**

13⅞", Japanese, 19th C, cylindrical, blue and white, mountain landscape, scholars standing on bridge, waterfall **1,000.00**

Brushes, pr, Chinese, carved bamboo handles carved with dragons, phoenix, and foliate scrolls, removable end cap with MOP applique, incised with four character Wanli makr, sq Quanlong period inkcake, molded with inscriptions. **2,000.00**

Bowls

8½", Muramachi Period, alms, gilt bronze, flared sides, high foot **600.00**

9⅜", Junyas, early Ming Dynasty, gray-green glaze **1,400.00**

Ceramics

Chinese, Tang Dynasty

Apple Jar, 3¾" d, compressed globular form, incurved rim with grooved line, upper part cov with chestnut, green, and cream glazes in uneven scalloped line, pale buff body, 3¾″ d **3,500.00**

Bowl, 7″ d, brown and white glazed stoneware **2,750.00**

Ewer, 2½″ h, globular body, short trumpet neck, bright green glaze dotted with white spots, deep blue splashes, strap handle, short spout, white slip ground over pinkish ware **8,000.00**

Figures

4″ h, dog, seated, broad muzzle, droopy ears, long slender neck, amber glaze over buff ware . . **900.00**

9⅜″ h, attendant wearing long coat tied at neck, hands clasped beneath folds, face well molded, painted brows, eyes, and mustache, framed by hood, traces of white pigment **2,750.00**

Pillow, 9¾″ l, slightly concave ruyi shaped top, engraved with pattern of stippled waves, horizontal bands of green and chestnut-brown shaded to cream, deep sides fluted and molded with frieze of formal lotus blossoms splashed in green and amber, restored **2,250.00**

Korean, Koryo Dynasty

Bowl, 7¾″ d, inlaid celadon, white slip int. with four lychee clusters, triple ring border, central floret, ext. inlaid in black and white slip with four floret medallions, thick ring foot, crackled blue-green glaze **8,250.00**

Dish, 4½″ d, flared sides, ring foot, int. inlaid in white slip, gray-green glaze with thick pooling on ext. . **550.00**

Costumes

Chinese

Aprons, pr, 19th C, 36½″ l, yellow gauze, bats and emblems, black and blue applique borders **275.00**

Ceremonial Robe, Kesi, 19th C, 55½″ l, bright yellow ground, woven with dragon medallions, four clutching flaming pearls in red, blue, green, and white **10,000.00**

Coat, gentleman's, 58″ l, royal blue silk, dragon medallions, goat and rabbit fur lining **400.00**

Robe, 19th C, 58½″ l, dark blue ground brocaded with metallic gold dragons holding single and triple pearls amid blue, yellow, green, and red silk clouds, orig saffron color silk gift cov **4,200.00**

Japanese, ainu robe, 19th C, 49½″ l, cotton, dark blue, appliqued white and tan stylized floral patterns, dark blue stitching, red borders, floral medallions **1,400.00**

Tibetan, jacket, Ming Dynasty, 22½″ l, pieced, olive ground, silk brocade with metallic gold, blue, red, and white dragons, fur cuffs **850.00**

Cup, Chinese, Tang Dynasty, 2 ⁹⁄₁₆″ h, engraved silver, meandering foliate scrolls, bands of petal lappets on base, wide band of detached foliate scolls between raised borders, ring punched ground, knopped hollow pedestal foot **18,000.00**

Cup and Saucer, Chinese, Kangxi, 2½″ cup, 4″ saucer, octagonal, blue and white, panels of flowering branches **550.00**

Figures

Chinese

4⅝″ h, 18th/19th C, carved dark brown horn, Guanyin (goddess of Mercy) seated, holding ruyi sceptre **550.00**

11″ h, carved coral, Meiren, elegantly robed maiden and attendant seated on tree stump, finely incised details, carved wood stand **3,500.00**

Japanese, 11¾″ h, bronze, peddler, holding straw hat in one hand, wares in box in front, umbrella slung across back **400.00**

Kannon, Heian Period, 11th C, 17½″ wood, trace of gilt, standing on columnar double lotus base, hands raised, loose robes, conical headdress **1,700.00**

Fish Bowls, pr. Famille-Noire, 19″, globular, enamel birds and butterflies, and flowering trees, glossy black ground, iron-red lotus blossom border, false gadroon band base, wood stands . . . **5,000.00**

Furniture

Altar Coffer, Chinese, Huang Huali, 17th C, 60½ x 32 x 19½″, rect top, three drawers flanked by carved brackets of foliate dragons, apron

Teapot, 3¾″ h to finial, Banko ware, $75.00.

carved with two confronting scroll dragons, cut down, restored **8,000.00**

Chair, Japanese, late 19th C, 34″ h, carved wood, dragon back and arms, semi-circular shaped seat, 4 cabriole legs **450.00**

Stand, Chinese, late 19th C, 33″ h flower form top inset with pink marble panel, 5 slender cabriole legs carved with monster masks, openwork apron of flowering prunus, dragon form feet **375.00**

Table, Chinese, Huang Huali, 31½ x 11¾ x 18″, rect top, metered frame above beaded apron of barbed and lobed outline, curved legs, scrolled toes **5,000.00**

Garden Seats, pr, 19″ h, studded barrel shape, turquoise ground, iron-red and famille verte enamels, scene of mandarin ducks on lotus pond, pierced cash emblems top and sides **1,550.00**

Ginger Jar, Chinese, Kangxi, 10″, oviform, white, trellis ground, underglaze blue, four roundels with leaping carp, wide fluted bands of Davist symbols, carved wood cov and stand **1,100.00**

Inro, 19th C, three case, dec with inlaid metal and aogai of boy picking flower **175.00**

Jar, Chinese, Ming, 16–17th C, 8″, high shoulder, low cylindrical neck, stoneware, blue glaze **350.00**

Lacquer

Box, storage, Japanese, 19th C, 20″ h, black and gold, circular section with four supports, gilt bronze mounts **1,400.00**

Cupboard, Chinese, late 19th C, gilt dec, red, top, sides, and doors painted in green, black, and brown with court ladies and attendants, 35 x 19¼ x 34⅝″ **2,400.00**

Tables, console, Chinese, 19th C, pr, gilt dec, black, demi-lane tops, landscape reserve, wan fret and foliate border, shaped apron, 34½ x 17¼ x 31⅞″ **8,000.00**

Lamp, Chinese, Han Dyansty, 11¾″ h, dark green glazed red pottery, hollow modeled in form of large figure holding four smaller figures in front, tall cylindrical vessel, minor chipping, restored **4,125.00**

Lantern, Japanese, Meiji, 31½″ h, bronze, reticulated globular shape, domed peaked cov with monster head corners, flaming pearl finial, supported on lotus blossom, raised on 4 cabriole legs, low relief plinth with karashishi panels **600.00**

Mirror, Chinese, Tang Dynasty, 3¾″ d, silvery bronze with traces of green en-

crustation, pierced knop, band of songbirds in flight between insects hovering over flower sprigs, trefoil border rim **800.00**

Panel, Japanese, Kelsi, 19th C, 83¾ x 50½″, eight immortals, multicolored, gold thread details. **1,700.00**

Pin, Chinese, Tang Dynasty, 10⅞″ l, gilt bronze, tapering triangular shaft, circular flanged terminal, openwork finial of scrolling foliate vines and lotus . . . **1,550.00**

Plaque, Chinese, Han Dynasty, 4″ l, crescent shape, gilt bronze, cast chimera, head with ferocious expression, twisted neck, pr of wings, surrounded by clouds, lower recessed flange pierced for attachment, extensive gilding and green encrustation on reverse **4,700.00**

Plate, Chinese, Kanxi, 10″, maiden poling boat on river, scroll rim band . . . **500.00**

Seals

1″, Chinese, Han Dynasty, gilt bronze, sq, cast with tortoise on top, head raised, clawed feet, carpace incised with realistic markings, four characters (hou guan nei yin) on base. **6,150.00**

4⅜″, Chinese, 18th C, carved soapstone, mountain shaped, yellowish-white, russet streaks, carved scaly dragon emerging from clouds **1,800.00**

Shrine, Chinese, Northern Wei Dynasty, gilt bronze, petal shaped back cast with the Buddha Sakyamuni and the Buddha Prabhutarantna, each framed by incised flame mandoila, reverse deeply incised with figure of Buddha in monastic robes, raised on narrow plinth supported by four legged rect base incised with lengthy inscription and cylical date (503 A.D.). **18,800.00**

Tapestry, Buddhist, Edo Period, 61 x 43″, gold chased and colored silk threads, congregation of deities in grove of Bodhi trees, swirling clouds with lotus blossoms, Sanskrit characters, framed **725.00**

Teapot, Chinese, Kangxi, 6¾″, Famille-verte, petal molded panels each with different flower, upright handle painted to resemble rattan, flared cov, blue bird finial **1,100.00**

Vases

4″, Guanyao Yenyen, Yongzheng Period, ovoid, tall trumpet neck, lustrous, crackled mushroom glaze . . **200.00**

7³⁄₁₆″, rock crystal, cov, pear form, carved in low relief, 2 millet sprays beneath elephant head handles, band of cross-hatching, circular pedestal foot **1,450.00**

14½″, Quin, Sang de Bouex, early 19th C, pear shape, tall flared neck,

red glaze to ochre, streaked lavender rim, brown slip base **1,000.00**
22½", Japanese, late 19th C, bronze, oviform, cast with low and high relief, karashishi gamboling by frogs, red patination, copper overlay **1,550.00**
Wine Cup, Dehua Kangxi, 3⅝" h, translucent white glaze, relief molded, pr of dragons amid clouds **325.00**

OVERSHOT GLASS

History: Overshot glass was developed in the mid 1800s. A gather of molten glass was rolled over the marver upon which had been placed crushed glass to produce overshot glass. The piece then was blown into the desired shape. The finished effect was a glass that was frosted or iced in appearance.

Early pieces mainly were made in clear; but, as the demand for colored glass increased, color was added to the base piece and occasionally to the crushed glass.

Pieces of overshot generally are attributed to the Boston and Sandwich Glass Co., although many other companies also made it as it grew in popularity.

Server, clear, flint glass, possibly sandwich, 7¾" d, 5⅞" h, $150.00.

Basket, 4" sq, light green overshot, applied vaseline flower, clear handle . . **135.00**
Cruet, rubena, applied clear reeded handle, clear faceted cut stopper **175.00**
Ewer, 9¼", metallic overshot **235.00**
Fairy Lamps
Crown, cranberry, sgd Clarke base . . **85.00**
Ribbed, clear vertical ribs on opal dome, sgd Clarke base **95.00**
Pitchers
6 x 5½", rubena, melon rib body, clear reed handle **125.00**
7", clear, applied ribbed handle **100.00**
7⅜ x 5¼", bulbous, 3 way ruffled top, overshot on pink and white spatter, clear reeded applied handle **165.00**

7¾ x 5½", blue, amber reeded handle **125.00**
Rose Bowl, 3¾", rubena, applied flower and pale green leaves **120.00**
Sugar Castor, pink **90.00**
Tumbler, rubena **100.00**

OWENS POTTERY

History: J. B. Owens began making pottery in 1885 near Roseville, Ohio. In 1891 he built a plant in Zanesville and in 1897 began producing art pottery. Not much art pottery was produced by Owens after 1907, when most of their production centered on tiles.

Owens Pottery, employing many of the same artists and designs of its two crosstown rivals, Roseville and Weller, can appear very similar to that of its competitors (i.e. Utopian—brown glaze; Lotus—light glaze; Aqua Verde—green glaze, etc.).

There were a few techniques used exclusively at Owens. These included Red Flame ware (slip decoration under a high red glass) and Mission (overglaze, slip decorations in mineral colors) depicting Spanish Mission scenes. Other specialities included Opalesce (semi-gloss designs in lustred gold and orange) and Coralene (small beads affixed to the surface of the decorated vases).

References: Paul Evans, *Art Pottery of the United States*, Everybodys Press, Inc., 1974; Ralph and Terry Kovel, *The Kovels' Collector's Guide to American Art Pottery*, Crown Publishers, Inc., 1974.

Jardiniere, 9 x 7½", orange tulips, brown glaze **115.00**
Jug, handled, tomato dec **160.00**
Lamp, 13½", red flowers, gold dec, gold bands at top and base, black high glaze, Sudanese **250.00**
Mug, 5¼", yellow berry dec, brown glaze, artist initials **100.00**
Pitcher, 12", orange berry dec, Utopian glaze, sgd "T. Stelle" **185.00**
Umbrella Stand, 20½", large brown iris dec, brown and green leaves, matte **250.00**
Urn, 7 x 7", 3 handles, 3 feet, vines and berries, Utopian glaze **165.00**
Vases
2½", miniature, abstract floral dec, brown high gloss, mkd "Z/Owens/Utopia/103", artist Mae Timberlake **150.00**
8¼", dark brown, lady's face and red roses dec, mkd "Owens/Henri Deaux" **325.00**

Vase, 5″ h, 3¾″ w, 2 handles, dark blue ground, crackled green glaze, imp "J.H. Owens" in circle, $55.00.

9″, 4 feet, band with floral design, matte green. **100.00**
10¼″, cream to tan shading, large branch of brown and cream leaves, matte, mkd "Owens/Utopia". **175.00**
Wallpocket, green, sgd "Owensart" . . . **120.00**

PAIRPOINT

History: The Pairpoint Manufacturing Co. was organized in 1880 as a silverplating firm in New Bedford, Massachusetts. The company merged with Mt. Washington Glass Co. in 1894 and became the Pairpoint Corporation. The new company produced speciality glass items, often accented with metal frames.

Pairpoint Corp. was sold in 1938; and, Robert Gunderson became manager. He operated it as the Gunderson Glass Works until his death in 1952. From 1952 until the plant closed in 1956, operations were maintained under the name Gunderson-Pairpoint. Robert Bryden reopened the glass manufacturing business in 1970, moving it back to the New Bedford area.

Reference: Leonard E. Padgett, *Pairpoint Glass*, Wallace Homestead, 1979.

Additional Listings: See *Warman's Americana & Collectibles* for listings of modern Pairpoint Cup Plates.

Basket, 11 x 9 x 6″, intaglio grapes, cherries, peaches **165.00**
Biscuit Jars
5¼ x 6½″, Delft scene with windmill, blue and white, SP frame, mkd "Pairpoint #2769 Delft". **200.00**

6 x 7″, Burmese, enamel floral dec, scroll base, mkd "Pairpoint" on lid **375.00**
Bowl, 9⅜ x 4½″, intaglio berry and leaf dec, c1910 . . . . **275.00**
Box, 2½″, round, SS hinged lid, controlled bubble body **225.00**
Bride's Basket, 9″, ftd SP holder, Greek warriors heads in medallions on holder, peppermint stick type bowl . . **135.00**
Candlesticks
4½ x 5″, pr, mushroom tops, green with clear controlled bubbles. **110.00**
6″, pr, vaseline, intaglio grape pattern. **85.00**
Candy Dish, cov, controlled bubbles on cov, finial, clear foot **145.00**
Compotes
7″, ruby, clear bubble base **70.00**
7½ x 8½″, black ground, intricate SS overlay on top and base, bubble ball connector to black foot **285.00**
10¼″, cov, Mansfield pattern, mint green **225.00**
13″, cov, amethyst, paperweight stem and finial. **250.00**
Cornucopias
6″, light green, clear bubble ball base **115.00**
8″, ruby, clear bubble ball base **85.00**

Cake basket, 13¾″, handle to handle, relief cherries in center, pierced bird handles, four pierced feet in floral design, SP, $125.00.

Decanter, 12″, stopper, quart size, basket pattern **1,250.00**
Ewer, 6¼ x 9″, football shape, wide triangular spout, applied handle in shape of 2 lotus branches, molded ridges and lotus leaves, gold enamel dec of lotus blossoms and leaves, light green enamel on leaf portions, and dark green in areas between leaves, mkd "Pairpoint Limoges 2028/56″, imp "2028". **750.00**

Fairy Lamp, blue, coralene floral dec,
sgd Clarke base 350.00
Goblet, Adelaide pattern, cobalt. 25.00
Jewel Box, sq, blown out and molded
roses, ribbon dec, applied gold dec . 210.00
Lamps
8½″ d reverse painted shade with Oriental pheasant, 15″ bronzed base,
sgd base and shade, c1910 . . . . . 650.00
12″, shade with green Murano glass
inserts, base with etched water lilies, good patina on base, sgd. . . . 500.00
15″, reverse painted teepee shade,
frosted, SP acorn finial, marble and
SP base, SP cherubs leaning
against SP pole stem, sgd 800.00
Meat Platter, 16½ x 11½″, ftd 45.00
Mug, 5″, engraved sailing ship, sgd
"Bryant Silvia," orig label. 100.00
Nut Bowl, leaf shape, figural cherries and
twig feet, c1894 . . . . 65.00
Perfume Bottle, 10¾″, paperweight
style, globular base, regular set air
traps, high bird finial 65.00
Pickle Castor, pink satin glass insert, SP
frame. 375.00
Salt, master, ftd, cobalt blue dish, reticulated SP frame 35.00
Syrup, 4½″, SP, bright cut flowers, flowers in relief on cov 45.00
Tobacco Jar, brass, rooster finial, mkd
"40th Anniv. Rooster Guard, 1870–
1910". 85.00
Vases
10″, trumpet, bubble ball connector,
Canaria, grape and leaf dec 110.00
11″, bubble ball stem, pedestal base,
green 85.00
12″, trumpet, bubble ball connector,
ruby 160.00
13″, Jack in the pulpit, burmese,
c1940. 150.00
Wine, Rouge Flambe 50.00

PAPERWEIGHTS

History: Although paperweights had their origin
in ancient Egypt, it was in the mid-19th century that
this art form reached its zenith. The classic period
for paperweights was 1845–55 in France where the
Clichy, Baccarat, and Saint Louis factories produced the finest examples of this art. Other weights,
made in England, Italy, and Bohemia during this
period rarely match the quality of the French
weights.

The earliest American factories to make paperweights were the New England Glass Co. in Cambridge, Massachusetts, and the Boston and Sandwich Glass Co. in Sandwich, Massachusetts, about
1852.

Popularity peaked during the classic period and

faded toward the end of the 19th century. Paperweights were rediscovered nearly a century later in
the mid-1900s. Contemporary weights still are
made by Baccarat, Saint Louis, Perthshire, and by
many studio craftsmen in the U.S. and Europe.

Reference: L. H. Selman Ltd, *Collector's Paperweights: Price Guide and Catalogue*, Paperweight
Press, 1983.

Additional Listings: See *Warman's Americana
& Collectibles* for examples of advertising paperweights.

**Gillinder, World's Columbian Exposi-
tion, 1492–1892, $85.00.**

ANTIQUES

Baccarat
Buttercup, miniature, 1⅞″, clear, white
flower, yellow center, short green
stalk, 5 green leaves, sunburst
base 2,000.00
Butterfly, 3⅛″, deep purple body and
antennae, black eyes, multicolored
wings, alternating white and mille-
fiori garland, star cut base 2,000.00
Clematis bud, 5¼″, spray with 6 white
buds, 7 leaves, stalk 1,210.00
Dogrose, 2⅞″, clear, 5 blue and white
cupped petals, white and red center, long green stalk, green leaves,
star cut base 1,210.00
Millefiori, close, 2½″, clear, tightly
packed canes including cockerel,
squirrel, monkey, and 2 pelicans,
dated and sgd, B 1847. . . . . 1,100.00
Millefiori, close, mushroom, 2⅞″, multicolored tight canes within torsade
of white cable and blue thread with
mercury band, star cut base 950.00

Pansy, 2½″, clear, 2 purple and 3 yellow petals, curved green stalk, green leaves and bud, star cut base.................................. **525.00**

Primrose, miniature, 2″, clear, 5 white outlined pink petals, pink and white center, curved green stalk, 5 green leaves, star cut base **900.00**

Bacchus, millefiori, close, 3⅛″, clear, set in basket of elongated blue canes lined in white and red **700.00**

Bohemian

Horse, miniature, faceted, 2″, amber flash base, engraved horse galloping across field **550.00**

Millefiori, concentric, 2⅝″, clear, 2 rows of large canes, central red and white canes, upset muslin ground . **350.00**

Boston and Sandwich Glass Company

Buttercup, 2⅞″, 5 white petals, white star center with pink and white cane, white bud, 5 leaves, green stalk, shaded pink and white jasper ground **850.00**

Floral, 2⅝″, single yellow and white flower, 1 bud, 5 leaves, green stem, red and white jasper ground **1,400.00**

Fruit, 2½″, 5 pears, 4 cherries, green leaves, latticinio ground **950.00**

Poinsettia, 2½″, single red poinsettia, 3 green leaves, stem, latticinio ground **1,100.00**

Clichy

Checker, 3¼″, clear, 2 circles of multicolored canes including large pink and green rose, central, claret, yellow, pink, blue, and white canes, white latticinio ground, bed of horizontal cable................. **1,325.00**

Millefiori, 2⅛″, 19 canes including 2 rose canes, strips of white filigree. **850.00**

Millefiori, patterned, 3″, clear, 8 multicolored garlands, 2 circlets of green, white, and pink canes, large central deep pink, green, and white florette **625.00**

Millefiori, scattered, 3″, clear, large multicolored canes, deep opaque pink ground................ **1,500.00**

Miniature, 1¾″, multicolored canes, white filigree, one red rose **550.00**

Pansy, 2⅝″, 3 pale yellow petals with brown markings, 2 purple petals, curved green stalk, green leaves, purple bud.................. **2,300.00**

Swirl, 2¼″, clear, alternating opaque white and turquoise threads radiating from central purple, claret, white, and yellow pastry mold center cane **975.00**

New England Glass Company

Apple, 2¾″ h, 3¼″ d base, natural color with stem, mounted on clear circular foot................ **1,250.00**

Flower, miniature, 1¾″, pale pink petals with white stripes, 3 green leaves, green stalk............ **850.00**

Fruit, 2⅜″, 5 pears, 4 cherries, 4 green leaves..................... **400.00**

Millefiori, concentric, 2¾″, 3 rings surrounding single red and white cane, white latticinio ground.......... **350.00**

Quince with stem, 2⅞″, figural, golden brown................... **1,500.00**

St. Louis

Bouquet, upright, faceted, 2⅝″, cobalt blue flower, yellow center, 2 pink and white buds, 2 millefiori canes, many green leaf tips, white latticinio spiral ground............... **2,000.00**

Crown, 3¼″, red and green ribbons edged in white alternating with white latticinio threads radiating from green, blue, pink, and white central **975.00**

Dahlia, faceted, 3¼″, clear, 2 rows of overlapping blue ridged petals, yellow and blue center, short green stalk, 3 leaves, swirling white latticinio ground **1,400.00**

Fruit, 2⅝″, 2 pears, 1 green and 3 red cherries, 6 green leaves, white latticinio basket................ **900.00**

Lizard, 3½″, green translucent glass, molded and gilded reptile, coiled on bulbous base................ **1,900.00**

Millefiori, close, 3″, central salmon, white and green canes with white dog, 6 multicolored rows, outer circle lime green and white hollow canes with turquoise centers..... **1,800.00**

Nicolas I, sulfide, 3¼″, clear, garland of alternating pink, yellow, green and white millefiori canes at edge. **400.00**

Pelargonuim, miniature, 1¾″, clear, 5 deep pink petals, white and black markings, yellow, black, and green center, short green stem, 2 green leaves, 5 leaf tips............ **1,250.00**

Pompon, 2⅝″, clear, white flower, pale yellow center, curved green stalk, white bud, 2 green leaves, swirling pink latticinio ground **1,430.00**

MODERN

Ayotte, Rick

Goldfinch, 2¾″, clear, sgd near base **275.00**

Scarlet Tanager, faceted, 2⅜″, sgd near base **300.00**

Baccarat

Hunter and dog, sulfide, cut diamond facets, 3½″, hunter and dog in woodland scene, translucent ruby red ground **1,875.00**

Jefferson, sulfide, 1955 .... **250.00**

Roosevelt, Eleanor, sulfide, commemorative, 3⅛", overlay, cut lavender to white to clear, sgd 150.00

Wilson, Woodrow, sulfide, 3¼", overlay, cut yellow to white to clear, swirl pattern, sgd. 125.00

Del Tarsitano, clear, 2¾", 3 ripe cherries hanging from yellow stalk, brown branches, shaded green leaves, sgd cane 475.00

Hacker, Harold J., lizard, 2⅜", black and yellow, mottled ground, sgd, 1964 .. 450.00

Kazuin, Charles
Crocus, pedestal, 3⅜" h, single yellow crocus, 3 green leaves, sgd blue and white cane in bottom 1,300.00

Millefiori, pedestal, miniature, 1⅝", 8 blue, green, and white canes with blue hearts around edge, pink, white, and green central cane with 4 leaf clover, yellow outer twist ring, dark blue ground shot with gold .. 750.00

Pansy, 2", multicolored, 3 green leaves, green stalk, white ground, sgd with gold K on bottom 775.00

Rose, 2⅛", single open red rose and another blossom, 7 green leaves, gold bee, blue ground, sgd with gold K on bottom 1,200.00

Stankard, Paul J.
Lady slipper, 2¾", yellow flower, cobalt blue ground, #58/75/29277, c1975 .... 700.00

Meadowreath, 2⅜", yellow flower, amethyst ground, sgd, c1974 .... 675.00

White Dogwood, 2½", white blossom, 3 green leaves, cobalt ground, #A99175/7375, sgd cane, c1975 500.00

Tarsitano, D, bouquet, 2½", 13 pink rosebuds, white berry type flowers, green leaves, sgd cane DT 550.00

Val St Lambert, sulfide, faceted, 2⅞", hand holding bouquet, mottled and multicolored ground 275.00

Whitefriar, millefiori, concentric, magnum size, 6 rows pastel canes, row of yellow canes with red rose center. 400.00

MISCELLANEOUS

Empress Eugenie of France, 3⅞", gilt metal, relief molded, head and shoulders, Pinchbeck 775.00

Fish, bronze, figural, emblem with Gloucester, Mass. 40.00

Franklin Fire Ins. Co. of Philadelphia, commemorative, bronze, heavy emb pictures, 1919 .... 75.00

Lincoln, 5¼ x 4⅞", oval, frosted, intaglio cut head of Lincoln 150.00

Queen Victoria, head and shoulders, 3⅛", glass, enamel painted, set in metal mount 975.00

Washington, 3⅛", round, frosted intaglio bust, clear ground, frosted sides, made for 1876 centennial .. 145.00

PAPIER MACHE

History: Papier Mache is made from a mixture of wood pulp, glue, resin, and fine sand which is subject to great pressure and then dried. The finished product is tough, durable, and heat resistant. Various finishing treatments are used, such as enameling, japanning, lacquering, mother of pearl inlaying, and painting.

During the Victorian era papier mache articles such as boxes, trays, and tables were in high fashion. Papier mache also found use in the production of banks, candy containers, masks, toys, and other children's articles.

Additional Listings: Russian Items.

Cup, 2½" h, gold ground, black on base, red band at top, floral dec, made in USSR, $40.00.

Banks
Charlie McCarthy, sitting on chest, 6" 65.00

Mickey Mouse, standing beside chest, 6" 75.00

Bulldog, glass eyes, growler, 19th C. ... 375.00

Candy Containers
Santa, holding sack over chimney. .. 50.00
Witch, 5" 100.00

Chest, 17¾ x 7½ x 9½", 3 drawers, doors, top, and sides dec with panels of lily-of-the-valley and snow drops, gilt borders 150.00

Doll, Bess Truman, 9", hp, inaugural gown, label Kimcraft, Independence, MO 90.00

Figures
Lion, 7", hp, c1910 .... 25.00
Mr. Pickwick, 13", "Ale That is Ale" . 40.00
Tiger, 12", hp, c1910. .... 65.00

Lantern, owl, wings extended, 10½" w	**185.00**

Masks
Man, full beard and head of hair,
13½" **65.00**
Skull, 10" **95.00**
Nodder, fat man, white beard, hat, and
cane, 4¼" **50.00**
Plate, 10", hp, floral dec **18.00**
Roly Polys
Foxy Grandpa, 4" **100.00**
German man, 6½", suit and bow tie. **60.00**
Rooster, pip squeak base, 9", orig
paint, red, green, yellow, and maroon **155.00**
Sewing Box, 7 x 12½ x 10", hinged lid,
inlaid MOP grapes and leaves,
painted flowers, leaves, and vines,
sgd Tiffany, Young & Ellis (1848–52). **395.00**
Snuff Box, shoe shape, 3" **45.00**
Squeak Toy, 3 birds in cage, 8½" h,
round, wire cage **220.00**
Trays
12 x 10", rectangular, grape dec,
handled................... **150.00**
22¾ x 17½", oval, brushed gilt border, 19th C **95.00**
Whistle, rooster, 5½" l, white, red trim **35.00**

PARIAN WARE

History: Parian ware is a creamy white, translucent, marble-like porcelain. It originated in England in 1842 and was first know as "Statuary Porcelain." Minton and Copeland have been credited
with its development. Wedgwood also made it. In
America, parian ware was manufactured by Chis-
topher Fenton in Bennington, Vermont.

At first parian ware was used only for figures and
figural groups. By the 1850s it became so popular
a vast range of wares were turned out.

Bank, 5½", cow standing on base **35.00**
Bottle, 13¼" h, 3½" d, sq base, figural
Venus De Milo, on back "Perfect Love
Goddess of Liqueurs" **60.00**
Box, 4½", oval, emb scrolls on base,
emb florals on cov **85.00**
Busts
Grecian lady with laurel wreath, 10½" **60.00**
Lincoln, sq base, 8"............. **65.00**
Robespierre, Sevres, 1925, 10" **125.00**
Schiller, waisted socle, imp mark, Ro-
binson and Leadbetter, 20½" **175.00**
Scott, draped, imp J. & T. B., 10½" . **75.00**
Shakespeare, 21½"............. **150.00**
Sumner, Charles, 19th C political
statesman for civil rights, imp on
back, "Take Care of My Civil Rights
Bill," 11¾" **70.00**
Wagner, waisted socle, Robinson and
Leadbetter, imp mark, 23½" **275.00**
Woman, long hair, lace headdress,
roses draped over shoulder, 10¾" **155.00**

**Bust, 6½" h, John Bright, (English Or-
ator, Statesman, Quaker) 1811–1889, by
Robinson Leadbetter, $90.00.**

Creamers
4⅝", children playing cards **95.00**
4⅝", emb design, emb argyle, W. B.
Cobridge **25.00**
Ewer, 10", emb flowers and grapes, reticulated scroll base............ **90.00**
Figurines
Colonial boy, seated long haired dog,
arm raised clutching a bone, 9"... **75.00**
Girl with basket of flowers, pastel pink
and white, mkd Robinson and
Leadbetter.................. **300.00**
Little Red Riding Hood, wrapped in
cloak with basket at her feet, Minton
imp date mark 1853 .... **115.00**
Lurline, nude, seated on rock forma-
tion, lyre beside her, large fish, long
flowing hair, green and gilt scroll
trim, imp Copeland, 12" h, 7¾" d . **240.00**
Owls, matchmaking, pair on branch,
dated March, 1871, 7½" h, 4½" w,
5½" l **275.00**
Psyche, Greek goddess, seated holding Cupid's quiver and arrows,
Cupid floating behind her reaching
for his tools, 9" **165.00**
Woman, draped, partially nude, holds
flame aloft, winged Cupid over left
arm, sq ftd base, garland draped pillar at her side, 9" h, 6" w....... **145.00**
Woman seated on vine covered
stump, bird perched on upper arm,
draped gown, pearl necklace, oval
base, imp Copeland, 13¼" h, 7" w **285.00**
Jugs
9" h, 4⅜" d, Naomi and her daughters-
in-law, women emb in lavender, lavender top and handle trim, date
mark 1847.................. **150.00**
9", 3 loop handles, sloping body,
pierced flower heads **165.00**

Lamp, 3⅞", 3 faces with glass eyes and
  enameling, owl, cat, and bulldog. . . .   **125.00**
Pitchers
  6", ribbed, stippling, relief ivy, twisted
    rope handle. **32.00**
  6¼", emb cherubs and vines, mkd
    Copeland. **55.00**
  6⅜", high emb musical instruments,
    mkd Copeland. **85.00**
  8¾", emb floral dec, English registry
    mark and W.B. in rope **85.00**
Plaque, 13" d, round, 3 winged Cupids,
  nude, self framed, pierced for hanging,
  imp on back Enorette B&G **160.00**
Ring Holder, 4", figural hand **40.00**
Spill Vase, sage green, stipple ground,
  scenic, babes in woods, T.J. Mayer,
  c1850. . . . .   **85.00**
Sugar Shaker, figural owl **50.00**
Syrup Jug, 6¾", emb lilies, hinged pew-
  ter lid **45.00**
Vases
  5½", bust of Grecian woman with leaf
    crown each side of vase. **35.00**
  8", figural hand holding scalloped top
    vase with scroll dec **150.00**
  9", baluster shape, scalloped rim, emb
    grapes, vines and leaves **45.00**

PATE-DE-VERRE

History: Pate-de-Verre can be translated simply
as glass paste. It is manufactured by grinding lead
glass into a powder or crystal form, making it into
a paste by adding a 2 or 3% solution of sodium
silicate, molding, firing, and carving. The Egyptians
discovered the process as early as 1500 B.C.
  In the late 19th century, the process was rediscovered by a group of French glassmakers. Amalric
Walter, Henri Cros, Georges Despret, and the
Daum brothers were leading manufacturers. Contemporary sculptors are creating a second renaissance, lead by the technical research of Jacques
Daum.

Ashtrays
  3½" sq, mottled turquoise and mid-
    night blue, 2 rectangular compart-
    ments, molded with bumblebee with
    black and orange body, green
    wings, deep brown head, sgd A Wal-
    ter/Nancy and Berge/SC, c1925. .   **700.00**
  4½" d, round, mottled, streaked yel-
    low-green, molded with upright leaf-
    age, molded sgd G. Argy-Rousseau,
    c1925 . . . .   **750.00**
Bookend, 5¾" h, yellow fox leaping from
  leaf molded green ground to trellis
  hung with green and purple grapes,
  leaves, sgd A Walter Nancy, c1925 .   **800.00**
Bowl, 4¼" d, straight gray sides streaked
  with violet and raspberry, molded with

a band of purple and raspberry blossoms, sgd G. Argy- Rousseau, c1925   **550.00**
Box, cov, circular, 3½" d, mottled dusty-
  rose sides, purple accents, pine
  boughs and cones in shades of avocado, yellow, emerald green, cover
  with pine bough and cone finial, dish
  sgd A Walter Nancy, Berge sc, cov
  sgd AW/N & B, c1925. . . . .   **750.00**
Clock, 4¾" l, circular dial in pale yellow
  arched surround flanked by foliate
  panels, rectangular base, dish compartment, sgd A Walter/Nancy,
  c1920. . . . .   **1,150.00**
Dish, 6½" d, trefoil contour, gray
  splashed with yellow, molded at one
  side with large bee, sienna head, aqua
  green wings, sgd A Walter/Nancy and
  Berge/Sc **1,800.00**
Figurines
  2⅞" l, scarab, pale turquoise shading
    to gray, sgd Despret/877, c1900. .   **275.00**
  6½" h, sea lion, seated, resting on
    front flippers, pale to deep sea
    green, sgd A Walter/Nancy, h. mer-
    cier, c1925 . . . .   **550.00**

**Bowl, 4" d, 1⅝" h, pedestal foot, purple
grape relief inside and out, Gargy-Rous-
seau, $850.00.**

Inkstand, 4¾" l, rectangular, yellow,
  molded on 3 sides with rust fruits and
  green leaves, large rust and blue
  green bee, sgd A Walter/Nancy and
  Berge Sc, c1900 . . . .   **450.00**
Paperweight, 3¼" l, tiny mouse foraging
  among leafy branches, shades of olive
  green, mustard, emerald green, sgd
  Daum/Nancy **450.00**
Pendants
  2⅝" l, oval, white dahlia, yellow high-
    lights, deep gold base, green stalks,
    gray ground, sgd G.A.R., c1925. . .   **550.00**
  2¾" l, oval, high relief, rust and black
    beetle against mottled ochre and
    yellow ground, sgd AW/N and LB   **575.00**
Tray, 6⅝" l, oval, shaped rim cast with
  scrolling green foliage, 2 rust and
  black beetles, yellow center, sgd A.
  Walter/Nancy and J. Cayette, c1925   **1,350.00**

Vase, 9¾" h, flaring cylindrical, pale ochre walls, mustard, white, coral, and deep brown, orange low relief of 2 kneeling female figures, brown harp, cut ground of concentric circles and zig-zags, sgd G. Argy-Rousseau, imp France, c1925. . . . . **8,000.00**

PATE-SUR-PATE

History: Pate-sur-Pate, paste on paste, is a 19th century porcelain form featuring relief designs achieved by painting successive layers of thin pottery paste one on top of the other.

About 1880 Marc Solon and other Sevres artists, inspired by a Chinese celadon vase in the Ceramic Museum at Sevres, experimented with this process of porcelain decoration. Solon migrated to England at the outbreak of the Franco-Prussian War and worked at Minton, where he perfected the pate-sur-pate process.

Box, triangular shape, seated nude on stream bank, sgd "Gol/F.M. Barbotine/ Limoges, France," 5½ x 5½ x 2¼", $1,500.00.

Boxes, covered
5" sq, blue ground, mythical lovers in relief on cover, mkd Limoges **160.00**
7 x 5", green ground, white cupids and girl's head on lid **120.00**
Flasks
10½" h, pr, flattened bodies, one dec with nude putti fishing, other dec with nude putti seated on branch holding bird's nest, reverse of both with panels of pate-sur-pate of fruit, flowers on black ground, gilt foliage band, neck and foot dec in gilt band of stylized foliage and zig-zag de-

sign, sgd T. R. (Thomas Rice), crowned Minton mark, c1874 . . . . **2,000.00**
14¼" h, deep green ground, dec in white slip, 2 figures, one Sunrise, one Sunset, two female figures wearing diaphanous gowns perched on shoulders, sgd Schenk, mkd George Jones **1,100.00**
Plates
9" d, raised gold arabesque motif on white glazed ground, rectangular raised gold center of white slip on coral ground, small boy playing flute for birds, sgd Birks, mkd Minton, c1875 . . . . **800.00**
9½", turquoise ground, 2 birds on branch, blossoms, leaves, Greek key border, sgd Desire Leroy, mkd Minton, c1876 . . . . **700.00**
10¼", dinner, set of 15, each with 3 medallions of classical profiles in white slip on deep teal ground, white center ground, pale yellow panels, printed Minton crowned globe mark, sgd Albonie Birks, retailer's mark "Tiffany & Co/New York/Made in England/Pattern No. H2877", dated 1916 . . . . **1,800.00**
Vases
6" h, pr, flat oval, handled, apricot ground, mkd Autumn and Summer **250.00**
8½", pilgrim type, 2 handles, celadon green ground, white relief of Eros and Venus, colored trim around neck, sgd L. Solon, mkd Minton . . **3,800.00**
10", celadon green ground, flowers and leaves in relief, sgd **240.00**
13½", Persian style, sgd C. Toft, c1870 . . . . **1,700.00**
15", pr, glazed parian body dec in white slip, classical maiden and cupid on reserve of cobalt blue, pale blue borders, cream ground, gilded, mounted as table lamps, sgd Birks, mkd Minton, c1900 . . . . **1,650.00**
20½", glazed deep chocolate brown Parian body, white slip frieze of manacled couple flanked by putti constructing brick walls between green, gray, melon, yellow, and teal blue borders of scrolling flowers, foliage, mounted on sq wood base, sgd L. Solon, 1877. . . . . **3,500.00**
25⅜", glazed deep olive green Parian body, white slip dec of court maidens, cupid judge, reverse with cupids surrounding justice trophies, shoulder and base dec in polychrome flowers, foliage, mask handles, rim and base with gilt and silvered details, fleur-de-lis mark of Paris 1878 Exhibition, sgd L. Solon, mkd Minton **4,000.00**

PATTERN GLASS

History: Pattern glass is clear or colored glass pressed into one of hundreds of patterns. Deming Jarves of the Boston and Sandwich Glass Co. invented the first successful pressing machine in 1828. By the 1860s glass pressing machinery had been improved, and mass production of good quality matched tableware sets began. The idea of a matched glassware table service (including goblets, tumblers, creamers, sugars, compotes, cruets, etc) quickly caught on in America. The number of pieces in certain patterns became numerous, with pieces serving specific functions, e.g., a banana stand or molasses can.

Early pattern glass (flint) was made with a lead formula, giving it a ringing quality. During the Civil War lead became too valuable to be used in glass manufacturing. In 1864 Hobbs, Bruckunier & Co., West Virginia, developed a soda lime (non-flint) formula. Pattern glass also was produced in many colors, milk glass, opalescent glass, slag glass, and custard glass.

The hundreds of companies which produced pattern glass have varied and involved histories of development, expansions, personnel problems, material and supply demands, fires, and mergers. In 1899 the National Glass Co. was formed as a combine of nineteen glass companies in Pennsylvania, Ohio, Indiana, West Virginia, and Maryland. U. S. Glass, another consortium, was founded in 1891. These combines resulted as attempts to save small companies by pooling talents, resources, and patterns. Because of this pooling, patterns can be attributed to several companies.

Sometimes the pattern name of a piece was changed from one company to the next, often to reflect current fashion trends. U. S. Glass created the States series by issuing patterns named for a particular state. Several of these patterns were new issues, others were former patterns renamed.

References: Richard Carter Barret, *Popular American Ruby Stained Pattern Glass,* Forward's Color Productions, Inc., 1968; Bob H. Batty, *A Complete Guide to Pressed Glass,* Pelican Publishing Co., Inc., 1978; E. M. Belnap, *Milk Glass,* Crown Publishers, Inc., 1949; Regis F. and Mary F. Ferson, *Yesterday's Milk Glass Today,* privately printed, 1981; William Heacock, *Encyclopedia of Victorian Colored Pattern Glass, Book I, Toothpick Holders from A to Z,* Antique Publications, 1981; William Heacock, *Old Pattern Glass,* Antique Publications, 1981; William Heacock, *Opalescent Glass from A to Z,* Antique Publications, 1981; William Heacock, *Syrups, Sugar Shakers & Cruets,* Antique Publications, 1981; William Heacock, *1000 Toothpick Holders: A Collector's Guide,* Antique Publications, 1977, William Heacock, *Rare and Unlisted Toothpick Holders,* Antique Publications, 1984; William Heacock and Fred Bickenheuser, *U. S. Glass from A to Z,* Antique Publications, 1981.

Minnie Watson Kamm, *Pattern Glass Pitchers, Books 1 through 8,* privately printed, 1970, 4th printing; Ruth Webb Lee, *Early American Pressed Glass,* Lee Publications, 1966, 36th edition; Ruth Webb Lee, *Victorian Glass,* Lee Publications, 1944, 13th edition; Bessie M. Lindsey, *American Historical Glass,* Charles E. Tuttle Co., 1967; Mollie H. McCain, *Pattern Glass Primer,* Lamplighter Books, 1979; Mollie H. McCain, *The Collector's Encyclopedia of Pattern Glass,* Collector Books, 1982; George P. and Helen McKearin, *American Glass,* Crown Publishers, 1941; James Measell, *Greentown Glass,* Grand Rapids Public Museum Association, 1979; Alice Hulett Metz, *Early American Pattern Glass,* privately printed, 1958; Alice Hulett Metz, *Much More Early American Pattern Glass,* privately printed, 1965.

S. T. Millard, *Goblets I,* privately printed, 1938, reprinted Wallace Homestead, 1975; S. T. Millard, *Goblets II,* privately printed, 1940, reprinted Wallace Homestead, 1975; Arthur G. Peterson, *Glass Salt Shakers: 1,000 Patterns,* Wallace-Homestead, 1970; Jane Shadel Spillman, *American and European Pressed Glass in the Corning Museum of Glass,* Corning Museum of Glass, 1981; Jane Shadel Spillman, *The Knopf Collectors Guides to American Antiques, Glass Volumes 1 and 2,* Alfred A. Knopf, Inc., 1982, 1983; Doris and Peter Unitt, *American and Canadian Goblets,* Clock House, 1970; Doris and Peter Unitt, *Treasury of Canadian Glass,* Clock House, 1969, 2nd edition; Peter Unitt and Anne Worrall, *Canadian Handbook, Pressed Glass Tableware,* Clock House Productions, 1983; Dina von Zweck, *The Woman's Day Dictionary of Glass,* The Main Street Press, 1983.

Periodicals: *Collecting Glass: Research, Reprint and Reviews,* Antique Publications, P.O. Box 553, Marietta, OH 45750. Subscription: $25.00; *Glass Review,* P. O. Box 542, Marietta, OH 45750. Subscription: $12.50.

Museums: Corning Museum of Glass, Corning, NY. National Museum of Man, Ottawa, Ontario, Canada.

Additional Listings: Bread Plates, Children's Toy Dishes, Cruets, Custard Glass, Milk Glass, Sugar Shakers, Toothpicks, and specific companies.

Abbreviations:

GUTDODB—Give Us This Day Our Daily Bread
hs—high standard
ls—low standard
os—original stopper

For this edition of Warman's, pattern glass dealers from across the United States were invited to participate in a survey to determine the 50 most popular patterns of pattern glass which were being sold. The enthusiastic response has determined what patterns are listed as well as resulting in other changes made in this edition. The most requested patterns were members of U. S. Glass's States series. We thank these dealers for their time and efforts.

Dori Miles, Crown Point, New York, went far beyond the call of volunteer duty to ensure the accuracy in listings and prices in this section. Her dedication is symbolic of a select group of dealers and collectors who view price guides as useful market tools and contribute their expertise and time to make them better.

Research in pattern glass is continuing. As in the past, we have tried to present patterns with correct names, histories, and pieces. Catagories have been changed to reflect the most current thinking.

Another change in this edition is the arrangement of all patterns alphabetically. Colored, opalescent, and clear patterns now are included in one listing, avoiding duplication of patterns and colors.

Pattern glass has been widely reproduced. We have listed reproductions with an *. These markings are given only as a guide and clue to the collector that some reproductions may exist in a given pattern.

Advisor: Dori Miles.

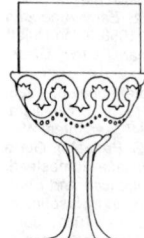

ABERDEEN

Non-flint, maker unknown, c1870.

	Clear		Clear
Butter, cov	40.00	Goblet	20.00
Compotes		Pitcher, water	50.00
Cov	40.00	Sauce, flat	15.00
Open	25.00	Sugars	
Creamer	35.00	Cov	35.00
Egg Cup	25.00	Open	20.00

ACTRESS (Theatrical)

Made by LaBelle Glass Co., Bridgeport, Ohio, and Crystal Glass Co., c1870.

	Clear and Frosted		Clear and Frosted
Bowl, 6″, ftd	40.00	Creamer	65.00
Bread Plates		Dresser Tray	60.00
Motto, H.M.S. Pinafore	65.00	Goblet	65.00
Maggie Mitchell	65.00	Marmalade Jar, cov.	85.00
Butter, cov	85.00	Mug, H.M.S. Pinafore	50.00
Cake Stand, 10″	150.00	Pickle Dish, Love's Request	
Candlesticks, pr	250.00	Is Pickles	40.00
Celery Vases		Pitchers	
Actress Head	110.00	Milk, H.M.S. Pinafore	210.00
H.M.S. Pinafore, ftd	165.00	Water, Miss Neilson	225.00
Cheese Dish, cov, The Lone		Salt, master	68.00
Fisherman on cov, 2		Salt & Pepper Shaker, pr, orig	
Dromios on base	225.00	pewter top	80.00
Compotes		Sauce, ftd	17.50
Cov, hs, 8″ d	145.00	Spooner	70.00
Open, hs, 10″	80.00	Sugar, cov	85.00
Open, hs, 12″	100.00		
Open, ls, 7″	65.00		

ADONIS (Pleat and Tuck, Washboard)

Pattern made by McKee Bros. of Pittsburgh, Pennsylvania in 1897.

	Canary	Clear	Deep Blue
Bowl, 5″, berry	13.50	12.00	15.00
Butter, cov	65.00	47.50	75.00
Cake Plate, 10″	20.00	18.00	22.00

	Canary	Clear	Deep Blue
Cake Stand, 10½"..	45.00	40.00	50.00
Celery Vase	35.00	30.00	38.00
Compotes,			
Cov, hs	34.00	30.00	36.00
Open, hs, 8"	27.50	35.00	30.00
Open, jelly, 4½"..	40.00	35.00	45.00
Creamer	28.00	22.50	32.00
Pitcher, water	54.00	50.00	60.00
Relish	17.00	15.00	20.00
Salt & Pepper Shak			
ers, pr	40.00	35.00	45.00
Sauce, flat, 4".....	10.00	8.50	12.00
Spooner	35.00	30.00	38.00
Sugar, cov	40.00	35.00	45.00
Syrup	50.00	40.00	52.00
Tumbler	22.00	20.00	24.00

ALABAMA (Beaded Bull's Eye and Drape)

Made by U. S. Glass Co., c1898. One of the States patterns. Also found in green (rare).

	Clear	Ruby Stained		Clear	Ruby Stained
Butter, cov	55.00	—	Nappy	25.00	—
Celery Vase	35.00	—	Relish...........	18.00	—
Compote, open, 5",			Salt & Pepper		
jelly...........	60.00	—	Shaker	28.00	—
Creamer	35.00	55.00	Spooner	25.00	—
Cruet. os.	55.00	—	Sugar, cov	48.00	—
Dish, rect	20.00	—	Syrup	65.00	—
Honey Dish, cov ...	65.00	—	Toothpick	60.00	145.00

ALASKA (Lion's Leg)

Non-flint opalescent made by Northwood Glass Co. from 1897 to 1910. Forms are square except cruet, tumblers, salt and pepper shakers. Some pieces are found with enamel decoration. Sauces can be found in clear ($30.00); the creamer ($110.00) and spooner ($95.00) are known in clear blue.

	Clear Green	Blue Opal	Vaseline Opal	White Opal
Banana Boat.	100.00	275.00	250.00	75.00
Bowl, berry, ftd	125.00	75.00	70.00	45.00
Butter, cov	—	250.00	250.00	150.00
Celery Tray.......	—	125.00	110.00	85.00
Creamer	40.00	65.00	75.00	40.00
Cruet	260.00	250.00	225.00	135.00
Pitcher, water	65.00	420.00	350.00	175.00
Salt Shaker, dec ...	—	60.00	50.00	45.00
Sauce...........	—	35.00	30.00	20.00
Spooner	50.00	60.00	50.00	45.00
Sugar, cov	—	150.00	140.00	100.00

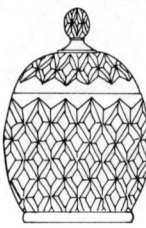

ALL-OVER DIAMOND (Diamond Splendor, Diamond Block #3)

Made by George Duncan and Sons, Pittsburgh, Pennsylvania, c1891 and continued by U.S. Glass Co. It was occasionally trimmed with gold, and had at least 65 pieces in the pattern.

	Clear		Clear
Biscuit Jar, cov	50.00	Ice Tub, handles	35.00
Bowl, berry	16.00	Lamp, Banquet, tall stem	125.00
Cake Stand	35.00	Nappy	15.00
Candelabrum, very ornate, 4		Pickle Dish, long	15.00
arm with lustres	150.00	Pitcher, water, bulbous, 6	
Celery	22.00	sizes	42–60.00
Claret Jug	50.00	Spooner	18.00
Compote, cov	40.00	Sugars	
Condensed Milk Jar	25.00	Cov	35.00
Cruets, patterned stopper		Open	18.00
4 oz	42.50	Syrup	55.00
6 oz	25.00	Tumbler	15.00
Decanter	45.00	Tray, water or wine	30.00
Egg Cup	18.50	Wine	20.00
Goblet	22.00		

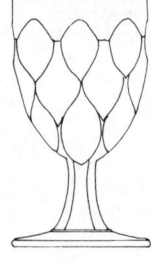

ALMOND THUMBPRINT (Pointed Thumbprint, Finger Print)

An early flint glass pattern with variants in flint and non-flint. Pattern has been attributed to Bryce, Bakewell, and U. S. Glass.

	Flint	Non-Flint		Flint	Non-Flint
Butter, cov	80.00	47.50	Decanter	70.00	—
Celery Vase	62.50	—	Egg Cup	45.00	35.00
Champagne	60.00	35.00	Goblet	30.00	15.00
Compotes			Salts		
Cov, hs, 4¾", jelly	60.00	40.00	Flat, large	25.00	—
Cov, hs, 10"	80.00	45.00	Ftd, cov	45.00	—
Cov, ls, 4¾"	55.00	30.00	Ftd, open	25.00	18.00
Cov, ls, 7"	45.00	25.00	Sugar, cov	60.00	40.00
Cordial	35.00	37.50	Sweetmeat Jar, cov	75.00	—
Creamer	65.00	40.00	Tumbler	40.00	—
Cruet, ftd, os	55.00	—	Wine	20.00	15.00

AMAZON (Sawtooth Band)

Non-flint; made by Bryce Brothers, Pittsburgh, Pennsylvania, late 1870s–1880 and also by the U. S. Glass Co., c1890. Mostly found in clear, either etched or plain. Heacock notes pieces in amber, blue, and vaseline. Over 65 pieces made in this pattern, including a toy set. Add 200% for color, e.q., pedestalled amber cruet with maltese cross stopper ($165.00) and pedestalled blue cruet with hand and bar stopper ($200.00).

	Etched	Plain		Etched	Plain
Banana Stand	95.00	65.00	Butter, cov	65.00	50.00
Bowls			Cake Stands		
6"	—	25.00	Large	—	50.00
6½", cov, oval	—	50.00	Small	—	40.00

	Etched	Plain		Etched	Plain
Celery Vase	35.00	30.00	Pitcher, water	60.00	50.00
Champagne	—	35.00	Salt & Pepper Shak-		
Claret.	35.00	25.00	ers, pr	50.00	40.00
Compotes			Salts		
Open, 4½", jelly . .	45.00	35.00	Individual	—	15.00
Open, hs, 9½",			Master.	—	18.00
sawtooth edge .	—	50.00	Sauce, ftd	—	10.00
Cordial	40.00	—	Spooner	25.00	25.00
Creamer	30.00	28.00	Sugar, cov	45.00	35.00
Cruet, os.	50.00	45.00	Syrup	45.00	40.00
Egg Cup	—	10.50	Tumbler	25.00	21.00
Goblet	35.00	30.00	Wine	30.00	20.00

ANTHEMION (Albany)

Non-flint made by Model Flint Glass Co., Findlay, Ohio, c1890–1900, and by Albany Glass Co. Also found in amber and blue.

	Clear		Clear
Bowl, 7", sq, turned-in edge	20.00	Pitcher, water	55.00
Butter, cov	65.00	Plate, 9½"	25.00
Cake Plate, 9½"	35.00	Sauce	10.00
Cake Stand	40.00	Spooner.	25.00
Celery Vase	20.00	Sugar, cov	40.00
Creamer	30.00	Tumbler	30.00
Marmalade Jar, cov.	25.00		

APOLLO

Non-flint, first made by Adams and Co., Pittsburgh, Pennsylvania, c1870, and later by U. s. Glass Co., c1891. Frosted increases price 20%. Also found in ruby stained and engraved.

	Clear		Clear
Bowl, 9"	25.00	Lamp, 10"	55.00
Butter, cov	45.00	Pickle Dish	15.00
Cake Stand	40.00	Pitcher, water	45.00
Celery Tray, rect.	15.00	Sauce, ftd, 5"	10.00
Celery Vase	40.00	Spooner.	24.00
Cheese Dish, cov	—	Sugar, cov	40.00
Compotes		Sugar Shaker	40.00
Cov, hs	50.00	Syrup.	—
Open, hs.	35.00	Tray, water.	40.00
Creamer.	30.00	Tumbler	—
Egg Cup.	18.00	Wine	—
Goblet	32.00		

ARCHED FLEUR DE LIS (Late Fleur De Lis)

Made by Bryce, Higbee and Co., in 1897–1898. Also gilded.

	Clear	Ruby Stained		Clear	Ruby Stained
Banana Stand	40.00	60.00	Butter, cov	40.00	60.00
Bowl, 9", oval	18.00	—	Cake Stand.	40.00	—

	Clear	Ruby Stained		Clear	Ruby Stained
Compote, jelly, cov .	18.00	—	Sauce.	8.00	25.00
Creamer	30.00	45.00	Spooner, double		
Dish, shallow, 7″ . . .	12.50	25.00	handled	20.00	38.00
Mug, 3¼″	—	20.00	Sugar, cov, double		
Olive, handle.	15.00	—	handled	35.00	48.00
Pitcher, water	125.00	150.00	Toothpick	30.00	45.00
Plate, 7″, sq	15.00	27.50	Tumbler	15.00	28.00
Relish, 8″	15.00	—	Vase, 10″	46.00	50.00
Salt Shaker.	9.00	38.00	Wine	25.00	35.00

ARCHED GRAPE

Flint and non-flint made by Boston and Sandwich Glass Co., c1880.

	Non-Flint		Non-Flint
Butter, cov	45.00	Sauce, flat	8.00
Celery Vase	35.00	Spooner.	30.00
Compote, cov, hs	50.00	Sugar, cov	45.00
Creamer.	45.00	Wine	35.00
Goblet	25.00		
Pitcher, water, applied			
handle	65.00		

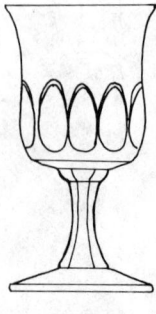

ARCHED OVALS

Made by U. S. Glass Co., c1908. Found in rose flashed and rarely in cobalt blue. Popular pattern for souvenir wares.

	Clear	Cobalt	Green	Ruby Stained
Bowl, berry	12.50	—	18.00	—
Butter, cov	45.00	—	50.00	—
Celery Vase	15.00	40.00	20.00	—
Compotes				
Cov, hs, 8″, belled	42.00	—	—	—
Open, hs, 8″	30.00	—	—	—
Cruet	35.00	—	45.00	—
Goblet	20.00	—	30.00	35.00
Mug	18.00	30.00	20.00	25.00
Pitcher, water	30.00	—	40.00	—
Plate, 9″	20.00	—	25.00	—
Salt & Pepper Shak				
ers, pr	45.00	—	50.00	—
Spooner	20.00	—	25.00	—
Sugar, cov	35.00	—	40.00	—
Toothpick	18.00	50.00	25.00	—
Tumbler	12.00	60.00	18.00	35.00
Wine	10.00	—	25.00	25.00

ARGONAUT SHELL (Nautilus)

Made by Northwood Glass Co., c1897. Also made in carnival glass. Heavily reproduced in blue and custard.

	Blue Opal.	Custard	Vaseline Opal.
Bon Bon	50.00	—	—
Bowls			
Berry, large	150.00	325.00	125.00
Small	35.00	65.00	35.00
Butter, cov	250.00	280.00	225.00
Compote, Jelly	120.00	125.00	250.00
Creamer	200.00	125.00	175.00
Cruet, os.	250.00	475.00	175.00
Pitcher, water	300.00	350.00	325.00
Salt & Pepper Shakers, pr	100.00	350.00	100.00
Spooner	75.00	100.00	95.00
Sugar, cov	250.00	225.00	225.00
Toothpick	—	275.00	—
Tray	20.00	—	30.00
Tumbler	275.00	125.00	250.00

ARGUS

Flint, thumbprint type pattern made by Bakewell Pears & Co. in Pittsburgh, Pennsylvania, in the early 1870s.

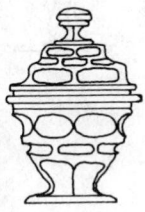

	Clear		Clear
Ale Glass	75.00	Lamp, ftd	75.00
Bitters Bottle	60.00	Mug, applied handle	75.00
Bowl, 5½"	50.00	Pitcher, water, applied	
Butter, cov	90.00	handle	175.00
Celery Vase	85.00	Salt, master, open	30.00
Champagne	35.00	Spooner	45.00
Creamer, applied handle	70.00	Sugar, cov	50.00
Decanter, qt	70.00	Tumbler, bar	45.00
Egg Cup	25.00	Whiskey, applied handle	55.00
Goblet	40.00	Wine	40.00

ART (Job's Tears)

Non-flint produced by Adams and Co., Pittsburgh, Pennsylvania, in the 1870s. Reissued by U. S. Glass Co. in the early 1890s.

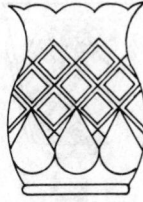

	Clear	Ruby Stained		Clear	Ruby Stained
Banana Stand	95.00	150.00	Celery Vase	35.00	50.00
Biscuit Jar	65.00	150.00	Compotes		
Bowls			Cov, hs, 7"	70.00	—
6" d, 3¼" h, ftd	30.00	—	Open, hs, 9", flared scalloped		
7", low, collar base	30.00	—	edge	50.00	—
8", berry, one end pointed	40.00	55.00	Creamers		
Butter, cov	55.00	75.00	Hotel, large, round shape	45.00	—
Cake Stand, 10"	60.00	—	Regular	50.00	—

	Clear	Ruby Stained			Clear	Ruby Stained
Cruet, os.	65.00	—	Pointed at one			
Goblet	30.00	—	end	12.50	—
Mug	25.00	—	Spooner	28.00	—
Pitchers			Sugar, cov	45.00	40.00
Milk	145.00	—	Tumbler	25.00	—
Water, 2½ qt	55.00	—	Vinegar Jug, 3 pt	50.00	—
Plate, 10″	35.00	—	Wine	30.00	—
Relish	25.00	—			
Sauces					
Flat, round, 4″	8.00	—			

ASHBURTON

A popular pattern produced by Boston and Sandwich Glass Co. and McKee Brothers from the 1850s to the late 1870s with many variations. Originally made in flint by New England Glass Co. and others and later in non-flint. Prices are for flint. Also reported is an amber handled whiskey mug and a scarce emerald green wine glass ($200.00).

	Clear		Clear
Ale Glass, 5″	70.00	Honey Dish	10.00
Bitters Bottle	55.00	*Jug, qt	90.00
Bowl, oval	35.00	Lamp	75.00
Carafe	175.00	*Lemonade Glass	55.00
Celery Vase, scalloped top	85.00	Mug, 7″	100.00
Champagne, cut	70.00	Pitcher, water	450.00
Claret, 5¼″ h	50.00	Plate, 6⅝″ d	75.00
Compote, open, ls.	65.00	Sauce	15.00
Cordial, 4¼″ h	50.00	Spooner	30.00
Creamer, applied handle	175.00	*Sugar, cov	55.00
Decanter, qt, bar lip	70.00	Tumbler, ftd	80.00
Egg Cup		Whiskey, applied handle	75.00
Double	95.00	Wine Bottle, tumble up	65.00
Single	25.00	*Wine	
Flip Glass, handled	100.00	Cut	65.00
Goblet	40.00	Pressed	40.00

ASHMAN

Non-flint, c1880. Pieces are square in shape. There are frequent variations within pieces. Also made in blue.

	Amber	Clear		Amber	Clear
Bread Tray, motto	—	55.00	Open, hs	—	37.50
Bowl	—	20.00	Creamer	45.00	35.00
Butter, cov			Goblet	—	32.00
Conventional finial	50.00	38.00	Pitcher, water	—	60.00
Large ball-type finial, sometimes with flowers within the ball	—	50.00	Relish	—	15.00
			Spooner	—	35.00
			Sugar, cov	—	45.00
Cake Stand, 9″	—	40.00	Tray, water	50.00	40.00
Compotes			Tumbler	—	25.00
Cov, hs, 12″	—	65.00	Wine	—	25.00

ATLANTA (Square Lion, Clear Lion Head)

Produced by Fostoria Glass Co., Moundsville, West Virginia, c1895. Pieces are square in shape.

	Clear	Frosted		Clear	Frosted
Bowls			Marmalade Jar	65.00	85.00
7″, scallop rim . . .	60.00	—	Pitcher, water	110.00	—
8″, low collar			Relish, oval.	35.00	—
base	55.00	—	Salt & Pepper Shak-		
Butter, cov	60.00	110.00	ers, pr	90.00	—
Cake Stand, 10″ . . .	85.00	—	Salts		
Celery Vase	40.00	75.00	Individual	30.00	—
Compotes			Master.	50.00	70.00
Cov, hs, 7″	75.00	—	Spooner	45.00	—
Open, hs, 5″, jelly	50.00	—	Sugar, cov	50.00	—
Creamer	45.00	60.00	Toothpick	40.00	60.00
Goblet	45.00	60.00	Tumbler	35.00	—

ATLAS

Non-flint glass pattern occasionally ruby stained and etched. Made by Adams and Co., U. S. Glass Co. in 1891, and Bryce Brothers, Mt. Pleasant, Pennsylvania, in 1889.

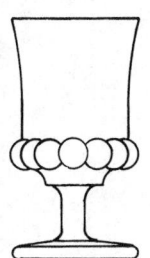

	Clear	Ruby		Clear	Ruby
Bowl, 9″	20.00	—	Salt & Pepper Shak-		
Butter, cov, regular .	45.00	75.00	ers, pr	20.00	—
Cake Stand, 9″	30.00	—	Salt, master	15.00	—
Celery Vase	28.00	—	Sauces		
Champagne, 5½″ h	32.00	—	Flat.	8.00	—
Compotes			Footed	12.00	20.00
Cov, hs, 8″	65.00	—	Spooner	28.00	35.00
Cov, hs, 5″, jelly. .	45.00	65.00	Sugars		
Open, ls, 7″	35.00	—	Cov.	38.00	65.00
Creamers			Open.	20.00	—
Table, applied			Syrup (molasses		
handles	30.00	55.00	can)	45.00	—
Tankard.	25.00	—	Tray, water	75.00	—
Goblet	20.00	—	Tumbler, ½ pt	18.00	—
Marmalade Jar	45.00	—	Whiskey	20.00	45.00
Pitcher, water	45.00	—	Wine	20.00	—

AURORA (Diamond Horseshoe)

Made in 1888 by the Brilliant Glass Works, which only existed for a short time. Taken over by the Greensburgh Glass Co. who continued the pattern. Also found etched.

	Clear	Ruby Stained		Clear	Ruby Stained
Bread Plate, 10″,			Compote, cov, hs . .	65.00	95.00
round, large star in			Creamer	30.00	50.00
center	30.00	35.00	Decanter, os	—	145.00
Butter, cov	45.00	90.00	Goblet	25.00	42.00
Cake Stand.	40.00	80.00	Mug, handle	50.00	65.00
Celery Vase	18.00	36.00	Olive, oval.	18.00	35.00

	Clear	Ruby Stained		Clear	Ruby Stained
Pitcher, water	40.00	100.00	Sugar, cov	45.00	65.00
Relish Scoop,			Tray, water or wine .	45.00	65.00
handle.	12.00	25.00	Tumbler	30.00	45.00
Salt & Pepper			Waste Bowl	30.00	45.00
Shakers, pr	45.00	80.00	Wine	25.00	40.00
Sauce, flat	8.00	18.00	Wine Tray.	35.00	45.00
Spooner	25.00	48.00			

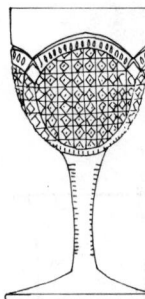

AUSTRIAN (Finecut Medallion)

Made by Indiana Tumbler and Goblet Co., Greentown, Indiana, 1897. Experimental pieces were made in cobalt blue, nile green, and opaque colors.

	Amber	Canary	Clear	Emerald Green
Bowls				
8″, round	—	150.00	50.00	—
8¼″, rect.	—	145.00	50.00	—
Butter, cov	85.00	250.00	90.00	—
Compote, open, ls . .	—	140.00	75.00	—
Cordial	145.00	100.00	50.00	150.00
Creamer	120.00	80.00	40.00	120.00
Goblet	—	125.00	45.00	—
Nappy, cov	—	135.00	55.00	—
Pitcher, water	—	325.00	100.00	—
Plate, 10″	—	—	40.00	—
Punch Cup	150.00	85.00	20.00	125.00
Rose Bowl	—	150.00	50.00	—
Sauce, 4⅝″ d	—	50.00	20.00	—
Spooner	—	95.00	40.00	—
Sugar, cov	—	135.00	45.00	—
Tumbler	175.00	85.00	30.00	—
Wine	175.00	110.00	30.00	150.00

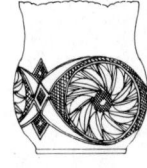

AZTEC

Made by McKee Glass Co., 1900 to 1910. Late imitation cut pattern, often marked "PRES-CUT" in circle base; about 75 items in pattern.

	Clear		Clear
Bowl, berry	15.00	Finger Bowl, underplate	20.00
Butter, cov	45.00	Goblet	35.00
Cake Plate, trilobed	20.00	Pitcher, applied handle, ½ gal.	35.00
Cake Stand	30.00	Plate	20.00
Carafe, water	40.00	Punch Bowl, stand, and 12	
Celery Tray.	15.00	handled cups.	125.00
Celery Vase	18.00	Punch Cup	8.00
Champagne	28.00	Salt & Pepper Shakers, pr . .	35.00
Compote, open	30.00	Sauce	10.00
Condensed Milk Jar	18.00	Soda Fountain Accessories	
Cordial	20.00	Crushed Fruit Jar.	55.00
Cracker Jar, cov	50.00	Straw holder, glass lid . . .	65.00
Creamer	20.00	Spooner	15.00
Cruet	35.00	Sugar, cov	25.00
Cup	8.00	Syrup	50.00
Decanter, cut stopper	32.50	Toothpick	18.00

	Clear		Clear
Tumbler		Whiskey......	12.00
Iced Tea....	18.50	Wine	25.00
Water......	15.00		

BABY FACE

Non-flint made by George Duncan & Sons, c1870.

	Clear		Clear
Butter, cov....	165.00	Goblet........	85.00
Celery Vase....	75.00	Pitcher, water..	275.00
Compotes		Salt	50.00
Cov, hs, 5¼".....	140.00	Spooner.......	95.00
Open, ls, 8".....	55.00	Sugar, cov....	150.00
Creamer.......	110.00	Wine	160.00

BALTIMORE PEAR (Gipsy)

Non-flint, originally made by Adams and Company, Pittsburgh, Pennsylvania, in 1874. Also made by U. S. Glass Company in 1890s. There are 18 different size compotes. Given as premiums by different manufacturers and organizations. Heavily reproduced.

	Clear		Clear
Bowl, 9"........	30.00	Water........	90.00
*Butter, cov....	75.00	Plates	
*Cake Stand, 9"....	35.00	8½"	28.00
*Celery Vase....	47.00	10"..........	30.00
Compotes		*Sauces	
Cov, ls, 8½"	45.00	Flat.........	15.00
Open, hs.....	30.00	Footed	18.00
*Creamer.......	25.00	Spooner.......	40.00
*Goblet	30.00	*Sugar	
Pickle........	18.50	Cov	50.00
*Pitchers		Open	25.00
Milk	60.00	Tray, 10½"....	35.00

BANDED PORTLAND (Virginia #1, Maiden's Blush)

States pattern, originally named Virginia, by U. S. Glass Co. Painted and fired green, yellow, blue, and possibly pink, ruby stained, and rose-flashed (which Lee notes is Maiden's Blush referring to the color, rather than the pattern, as Metz lists it). Double flashed refers to color above and below the band, single flashed refers to color above or below band only.

	Clear	Color Flashed	Ruby Stained
Bowl..........	16.50	—	35.00
Butter, cov	50.00	150.00	—
Cake Stand......	55.00	—	—
Candlesticks, pr. ...	95.00	—	—
Carafe	55.00	—	90.00
Celery Tray......	30.00	—	—
Celery Vase	25.00	—	45.00
Cologne Bottle	65.00	—	—

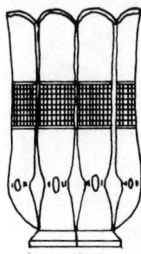

	Clear	Color Flashed	Ruby Stained
Compotes			
Cov, hs, 7″	85.00	—	—
Cov, jelly, 6″	40.00	65.00	—
Creamers			
Individual, oval . . .	25.00	—	32.00
Regular, 6 oz. . . .	35.00	—	50.00
Cruet, os.	60.00	90.00	125.00
Decanter, handled . .	50.00	—	—
Dresser Tray	50.00	—	—
Goblet	40.00	—	70.00
Lamps			
Flat	45.00	—	—
Tall	50.00	—	—
Nappy	18.00	—	—
Olive	18.00	—	—
Pin Tray	16.00	—	
Pitcher, water,			
tankard	50.00	90.00	250.00
Pomade Jar, cov . . .	30.00	45.00	—
Powder Jar	20.00	35.00	—
Punch Bowl, hs	110.00	—	300.00
Punch Cup	20.00	—	30.00
Ring Holder, gold rim and post, scarce	80.00	—	—
Salt & Pepper Shakers, pr	55.00	—	75.00
Sardine Box	55.00	—	
Sauce, round, flat, 4 or 4½″	12.00	—	20.00
Spooner	28.00	—	45.00
Sugars			
Cov, large	45.00	—	75.00
Open, individual, oval	18.00	—	32.00
Sugar Shaker, orig top	45.00	—	85.00
Syrup	45.00	—	135.00
Toothpick	25.00	45.00	—
Tumbler	27.00	—	45.00
Vases			
6″	20.00	—	38.00
9″	35.00	—	50.00
Wine	40.00	—	75.00

BARBERRY (Berry)

Non-flint made by McKee Glass Co. and the Boston and Sandwich Glass Co. in the 1860s and 1880s. 6″ plates are found in amber, pale green, and pale blue; they are considered scarce.

	Clear		Clear
Bowls		Butters	
6″, oval	15.00	Cov	50.00
7″, oval	15.00	Cov, flange, pattern on	
8″, oval	20.00	edge	100.00
8″, round, flat	22.50	Cake Stand	150.00
9″, oval	25.00	Celery Vase	40.00

	Clear		Clear
Compotes		Salt, master, ftd	20.00
Cov, ls, 8″	38.00	Sauce, ftd	12.00
Open, hs, 8″	36.00	Spooner, ftd	30.00
Creamer...............	30.00	Sugar	
Egg Cup...............	20.00	Cov	45.00
Goblet	24.00	Open, buttermilk type....	30.00
Pickle................	10.00	Syrup...............	125.00
Pitcher, water, applied		Tumbler, ftd	30.00
handle	85.00	Wine	25.00
Plate, 6″...............	20.00		

BARLEY

Non-flint, originally made by Campbell, Jones and Co., c1882, in clear; possibly by others in varied quality. Add 100% for color which is hard to find.

	Clear		Clear
Bowls		Pitcher, water	45.00
8″, berry	15.00	Plate, 6″...............	35.00
10″, oval............	20.00	Platter, 13″ l, 8″ w	25.00
Bread Tray, oval	35.00	Relishes	
Butter, cov	35.00	Flat, 8″ l, 6″ w.........	20.00
Cake Stand, 10″	32.00	Wheelbarrow, 8″, pewter	
Celery Vase	25.00	wheels.............	60.00
Compotes		Salt, master, wheelbarrow,	
Cov, hs, 6″	30.00	pewter wheels.........	75.00
Cov, hs, 8½″..........	50.00	Sauces	
Open, hs, 8½″.........	35.00	Flat.................	7.50
Creamer...............	25.00	Footed	10.00
Goblet	25.00	Spooner.............	20.00
Marmalade Jar	30.00	Sugar, cov	35.00
Pickle Castor, SP frame and		Vegetable Dish, oval	18.00
tongs	85.00	Wine	25.00

BARRED FORGET-ME-NOT

Made by Canton Glass Co., Canton, Ohio, c1883. There are two goblet styles; the larger has a coarser pattern.

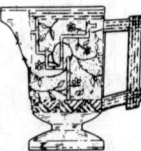

	Amber	Apple Green	Blue	Clear	Milk or Vaseline
Butter, cov	45.00	60.00	48.00	35.00	45.00
Cake Stand.......	55.00	75.00	60.00	45.00	55.00
Celery Vase	50.00	60.00	55.00	30.00	50.00
Compotes					
Cov, hs	45.00	65.00	55.00	45.00	50.00
Open, ls	40.00	45.00	50.00	30.00	45.00
Creamer	40.00	50.00	45.00	30.00	40.00
Goblet	45.00	60.00	40.00	30.00	55.00
Pitchers					
Milk..........	55.00	60.00	55.00	40.00	55.00
Water	65.00	80.00	65.00	45.00	60.00
Plate, 9″, handles .	45.00	40.00	50.00	30.00	45.00
Relish...........	26.00	25.00	25.00	15.00	25.00
Sauce, flat	20.00	20.00	25.00	12.00	20.00
Spooner	30.00	40.00	30.00	20.00	30.00
Sugar, cov	40.00	60.00	45.00	30.00	40.00
Wine	50.00	40.00	35.00	25.00	30.00

BASKETWEAVE

Non-flint, c1880. Some covered pieces have a stippled cat's head finial.

	Amber or Canary	Apple Green	Blue	Clear	Vaseline
Bread Plate, handled, 11″	—	—	22.00	10.00	—
Butter, cov	35.00	60.00	40.00	35.00	40.00
Cordial	25.00	40.00	28.00	25.00	30.00
Creamer	30.00	50.00	35.00	28.00	36.00
Cup & Saucer	35.00	60.00	35.00	30.00	38.00
Dish, oval	12.00	20.00	15.00	10.00	16.00
Egg Cup	18.00	30.00	20.00	15.00	25.00
*Goblet	30.00	50.00	30.00	25.00	30.00
Mug	25.00	40.00	25.00	15.00	30.00
Pickle	18.00	30.00	20.00	15.00	22.00
Pitchers					
Milk	45.00	65.00	45.00	60.00	50.00
*Water	50.00	75.00	50.00	75.00	45.00
Plate, 11″, handled .	25.00	38.00	25.00	20.00	30.00
Sauce	10.00	10.00	12.00	8.00	12.00
Spooner	30.00	36.00	25.00	20.00	25.00
Sugar, cov	35.00	60.00	35.00	30.00	40.00
Syrup	50.00	75.00	50.00	45.00	55.00
Tumbler	18.00	30.00	20.00	15.00	20.00
*Tray, water, scenic center	35.00	48.00	48.00	30.00	48.00
Waste Bowl	21.00	36.00	25.00	18.00	25.00
Wine	28.00	50.00	30.00	25.00	30.00

BEADED BAND

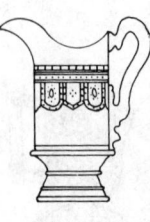

Attributed to Burlington Glass Co., Hamilton, Ontario, Canada, c1884. Limited production and scarce pattern. May have been made in light amber and other colors.

	Clear		Clear
Butter, cov	45.00	Single	15.00
Cake Stand	30.00	Sauce, ftd	10.00
Compote, cov	55.00	Spooner	25.00
Creamer	30.00	Sugar, cov	40.00
Goblet	28.00	Syrup	55.00
Pickle, cov	45.00	Wine	20.00
Pitcher, water	60.00		
Relishes			
Double	30.00		

BEADED GRAPE MEDALLION

Non-flint made by Boston Silver Glass Co., Cambridge, Massachusetts, c1868. Also found in flint; add 100%.

	Clear		Clear
Bowl, 7″	35.00	Celery Vace	35.00
Butter, cov, acorn finial	50.00	Castor Set, 4 bottles	110.00

	Clear			Clear
Compotes			Plate, 6″.	24.00
Cov, collared base.	60.00		Relish, mkd "Mould Pat'd	
Cov, hs.	75.00		May 11, 1868	40.00
Creamer, applied handle . . .	55.00		Salt, master, ftd	20.00
Goblet	30.00		Spooner.	40.00
Egg Cup.	20.00		Sugar, cov, acorn finial	60.00
Honey Dish, 3½″	10.00		Wine	75.00
Pitcher, water, applied				
handle	100.00			

BEADED SWIRL (Swirled Column)

Made by George Duncan & Sons, c1890. The dual names are for the two forms of the pattern. Beaded Swirl stands on flat bases and is solid in shape. Swirled Column stands on scrolled (sometimes gilded) feet, and the shape tapered towards the base. Some pieces trimmed in gold and also in milk white.

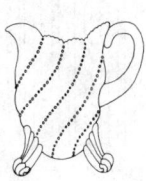

	Clear	Emerald Green		Clear	Emerald Green
Bowls			Goblet	35.00	40.00
Berry, 7″	12.00	20.00	Mug	10.00	12.00
Flat.	18.00	25.00	Pitcher, water	40.00	85.00
Footed, oval	18.00	24.00	Sauces		
Footed, round . . .	18.00	24.00	Flat.	8.00	12.00
Butter, cov	35.00	45.00	Footed	10.00	14.00
Cake Stand.	35.00	45.00	Spooners		
Celery Vase	30.00	55.00	Flat.	30.00	45.00
Compotes			Footed	30.00	45.00
Cov, hs	42.00	52.00	Sugars, cov		
Open, hs	38.00	45.00	Flat.	35.00	45.00
Creamers			Footed	35.00	45.00
Flat.	30.00	40.00	Syrup	48.00	—
Footed	30.00	40.00	Tumbler	20.00	30.00
Dish	12.00	18.00	Wine	28.00	35.00
Egg Cup	14.00	15.00			

BEADED TULIP (Andes)

Non-flint made by McKee Brothers, Pittsburgh, Pennsylvania, c1894.

	Clear	Emerald Green		Clear	Emerald Green
Butter, cov	45.00	125.00	Footed	12.00	—
Cake Stand.	50.00	—	Spooner	30.00	—
Compote, cov, hs . .	55.00	—	Sugar, cov	48.00	80.00
Creamer	35.00	75.00	Trays		
Goblet	35.00	—	Water	50.00	—
Marmalade Jar	40.00	—	Wine	50.00	—
Pickle, oval	18.00	—	Wine	32.00	—
Pitcher, water	65.00	—			
Plate, 6″	25.00	—			
Sauces					
Flat, leaf shape					
edges.	10.00	—			

BEATTY HONEYCOMB (Beatty Waffle)

Non-flint made by Beatty Glass Co., Tiffin, Ohio, c1888. Reproduced by Fenton Glass in green opalescent (basket, rose bowl, and vases) and milk glass.

	Blue Opal	White Opal		Blue Opal	White Opal
Bowl, berry	100.00	50.00	Salt & Pepper Shakers, pr	150.00	100.00
Butter, cov	115.00	90.00	Sauce	35.00	25.00
Celery Vase	95.00	75.00	Spooner	40.00	30.00
Creamers			Sugars, cov		
Individual	35.00	20.00	Individual	65.00	55.00
Regular	30.00	25.00	Regular	70.00	65.00
Cruet, os.	100.00	85.00	Toothpick	50.00	45.00
Mug	35.00	25.00	Tumbler	50.00	45.00
Mustard	60.00	45.00			
Pitcher, water	—	150.00			

BEATTY RIB OPALESCENT (Rib Opal)

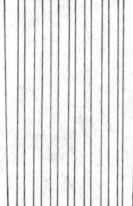

Made by Beatty and Sons Glass Co., Tiffin, Ohio, c1888. May have been made in vaseline opalescent.

	Blue Opal	Clear Opal		Blue Opal	Clear Opal
Bowls, berry			Salt & Pepper Shakers, pr	150.00	100.00
Rect	60.00	55.00	Salt, individual	30.00	25.00
Round	65.00	50.00	Sauces		
Butter, cov	85.00	75.00	Rect	30.00	15.00
Celery Vase	65.00	50.00	Round	30.00	15.00
Cracker Jar, cov	300.00	120.00	Spooner	45.00	35.00
Creamers			Sugars		
Individual	45.00	30.00	Individual	30.00	25.00
Regular	60.00	35.00	Regular, cov	60.00	40.00
Dish, oblong, 4⅞ x 3⅝"	25.00	15.00	Toothpick, 2⅞"	45.00	35.00
Finger Bowl	45.00	30.00	Tumbler	45.00	35.00
Matchholder, 1¹⁵⁄₁₆"	50.00	45.00			

BEATTY SWIRLED OPALESCENT (Swirled Opal)

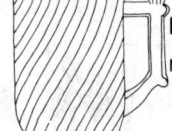

Made by Beatty and Sons Glass Co., Tiffin, Ohio, c1889.

	Blue Opal.	Vaseline Opal	White Opal.
Bowl, berry	80.00	85.00	70.00
Butter, cov	115.00	175.00	100.00
Celery Vase	50.00	55.00	45.00
Creamer	40.00	50.00	30.00
Cruet, os.	120.00	—	—
Mug	35.00	40.00	30.00
Pitcher, water	150.00	160.00	125.00
Sauce	35.00	35.00	30.00
Spooner	50.00	55.00	40.00
Sugar, cov	55.00	100.00	50.00
Syrup	125.00	150.00	115.00
Toothpick	50.00	—	45.00
Tray, water	120.00	125.00	110.00
Tumbler	50.00	55.00	35.00

BEAUTIFUL LADY

Made by Bryce, Higbee and Co. in 1905.

	Clear		Clear
Banana stand, hs	30.00	Pitcher, water	45.00
Bowls		Plates	
8″, low collared base	15.00	7″, sq	15.00
9″, flat	18.00	8″.	15.00
Bread Plate	15.00	9″.	25.00
Cake Plate, 9″	25.00	11″.	25.00
Cake Stand, hs.	35.00	Salt and Pepper	40.00
Compotes		Spooner.	15.00
Cov, hs.	35.00	Sugar, cov	25.00
Open, hs.	25.00	Tumbler	12.00
Creamer.	24.00	Vase, 6½″	15.00
Cruet	30.00	Wine	25.00
Goblet	35.00		

BELLFLOWER

A fine flint glass pattern first made in the 1830s and attributed to Boston and Sandwich. Later produced by McKee Glass Co. and other firms for many years. There are many variations of this pattern - single vine and double vine, fine and coarse rib, knob and plain stems, and rayed and plain bases. Type and quality must be considered when evaluating. Prices are for high quality flint.

Abbreviations: DV - double vine; SV - single vine; FR - fine rib; CR - coarse rib.

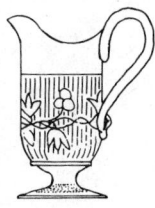

	Clear		Clear
Bowls		SV-CR, straight sides	40.00
6″ d, 1¾″ h, SV.	75.00	SV-FR, knob stem, barrel	
8″, all types.	65.00	shape	55.00
Butter, cov, SV-FR	75.00	*SV-FR, plain stem, rayed	
Castor Set, 5 bottle, pewter		base, barrel shape	30.00
stand	225.00	Hat, SV-FR, made from tum-	
Celery Vase, SV-FR	115.00	bler mold, rare.	350.00
Champagnes		Honey Dish, SV-FR, 3″	30.00
DV-FR, cut bellflowers . . .	250.00	Lamp, whale oil, SV-FR,	
SV-FR, knob stem, rayed		brass stem, marble base .	175.00
base, barrel shape	115.00	Mug, SV-FR	125.00
Compotes		Pitchers	
Cov, hs, 8″ d, SV-FR	375.00	Milk, DV-FR.	400.00
Open, ls, 7″, DV-FR, scal-		Milk, SV-CR, quart	125.00
loped top.	125.00	*Water, SV-FR	285.00
Open, ls, 9″, SV-CR.	100.00	Plate, 6″, SV-FR	50.00
Cordial, SV-FR, knob stem,		Salt, master, SV-FR, ftd. . . .	45.00
rayed base, barrel shape .	115.00	*Sauce, flat, V-FR.	12.00
Creamer, SV-FR	140.00	Spooner, SV-FR	35.00
Decanter, qt, SV-FR, bar		Sugars	
top	150.00	Cov, SV-CR.	90.00
Dish, SV-FR, 8″, round, flat,		Open, SV-FR.	50.00
scalloped top.	65.00	Syrup, SV-FR, applied	
Egg Cups		handle	410.00
DV, cut bellflowers.	200.00	Tumblers	
SV-FR	40.00	DV-CR	95.00
Goblets		SV-FR, ftd.	90.00
DV-FR, cut bellflowers . . .	230.00	SV-FR, cut bellflowers . . .	250.00
SV-CR, barrel shape	45.00	Whiskey, 3½″, SV-FR	120.00

	Clear			Clear
Wines			SV-FR, plain stem, rayed	
DV-FR, cut bellflowers,			base, straight sides. . . .	**65.00**
barrel shape.	**250.00**			
SV-FR, knob stem, rayed				
base, barrel shape	**90.00**			

BELMONT'S ROYAL (Royal, Royal Lady)

Made by Belmont Glass Co., Bellaire, OH, about 1881. Some pieces have ball feet. A light amber bread plate ($75.00) is known.

	Clear			Clear
Bread Plate, crying child in			Creamer.	**95.00**
center.	**55.00**		Dish, cov, oval	**110.00**
Butter, cov, 6 sided skirted			Salt, master, 6 sided skirted	
base.	**140.00**		base.	**20.00**
Celery Vase	**80.00**		Spooner.	**95.00**
Cheese Dish, cov, base has			Sugar, cov	**95.00**
portrait center, large dome			Tray, ice cream.	**120.00**
lid.	**150.00**			
Compote, cov, hs, 9″, mkd				
"Fox" in lid design.	**150.00**			

BERKELEY (Blocked Arches)

Made by U. S. Glass Co. in 1893.

	Clear	Frosted		Clear	Frosted
Biscuit Jar, cov	**55.00**	**60.00**	Finger Bowl.	**25.00**	**30.00**
Bowl, berry	**20.00**	**25.00**	Goblet	**35.00**	**38.00**
Butter, cov	**45.00**	**50.00**	Plate, 6″.	**16.00**	**20.00**
Cake Stand.	**50.00**	**55.00**	Sugar, cov	**35.00**	**40.00**
Creamer	**30.00**	**35.00**	Syrup	**40.00**	**45.00**
Cruet, os.	**60.00**	**70.00**	Tumbler	**30.00**	**35.00**
Cup and Saucer . . .	**50.00**	**60.00**	Wine	**38.00**	**42.00**

BETHLEHEM STAR

Made by Indiana Glass Co., Dunkirk, IN, c1907.

	Clear			Clear
Butter, cov	**35.00**		Relish	**15.00**
Celery Vase	**15.00**		Sauce, flat	**10.00**
Compote, cov, jelly	**35.00**		Spooner.	**25.00**
Creamer.	**28.50**		Sugar, cov	**40.00**
Goblet	**25.00**		Wine	**25.00**
Pitcher, water	**52.00**			

BIGLER

Flint, made by Boston and Sandwich Glass Co. and by other early factories. A scarce pattern in which goblets are most common and vary in height, shape and flare.

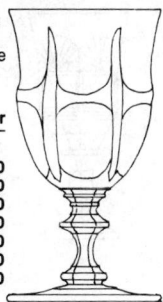

	Clear		Clear
Bar Bottle, qt	80.00	Lamp, whale oil, monument	
Bowl	65.00	base.	155.00
Celery Vase	115.00	Mug, applied handle	45.00
Champagne	85.00	Plate, toddy	30.00
Creamer.	75.00	Salt, master	20.00
Egg Cup, double.	50.00	Tumbler, water	50.00
Goblets		Whiskey, handled	75.00
Regular.	40.00	Wine	45.00
Short Stem	45.00		

BIRD AND STRAWBERRY (Bluebird)

Non-flint, c1890. Made by Beatty and Indiana Glass Co., Dunkirk, IN. Pieces occasionally highlighted by the coloring of birds blue, strawberries pink, and leaves green, plus the addition of gilting.

	Clear	Colors		Clear	Colors
Bowls			Creamer	45.00	125.00
5"	25.00	35.00	Cup	25.00	—
9½", ftd, oval. . . .	45.00	75.00	Goblet	70.00	90.00
10½", flat	50.00	65.00	Nappy, heart shape	40.00	—
Butter, cov	95.00	200.00	Pitcher, water	160.00	275.00
Cake Stand, 10" . . .	50.00	110.00	Plate, 12"	75.00	—
Celery Tray.	35.00	—	Spooner	40.00	125.00
Celery Vase	45.00	—	Sugar, cov	60.00	125.00
Compotes			Tumbler	50.00	80.00
Cov, hs, 6½"	85.00	—	Wine	45.00	—
Open, ls, 6", ruffled					
top.	80.00	110.00			

BLEEDING HEART

Non-flint, originally made by King & Son, Pittsburgh, PA, c1870, and by U. S. Glass Co., c1898. Also found in milk glass. Goblets are found in six variations. Note: A goblet with a tin lid, containing a condiment (mustard, jelly, or baking powder) was made. It is of inferior quality compared to the original goblet.

	Clear		Clear
Bowls		Mug, 3¼".	65.00
7¼", oval	15.00	Pitcher, water, applied han-	
9¼", oval	25.00	dle	125.00
Butter, cov	58.00	Plate	35.00
Cake Stand, 10"	75.00	Platter, oval	65.00
Compotes		Relish, oval	35.00
Cov, hs, 9"	70.00	Salt, master	40.00
Open, ls, 8½"	25.00	Sauce, flat	10.00
Creamer, applied handle . . .	50.00	Spooner.	35.00
Dish, cov, 7".	48.00	Sugar	
Egg Cup.	40.00	Cov	50.00
Goblet, knob stem	35.00	Open	20.00
Honey Dish	15.00	Tumbler, ftd	75.00

BLOCK AND FAN

Non-flint made by Richard and Hartley Glass Co., Tarentum, PA, late 1880s. Continued by U. S. Glass Co. after 1891.

	Clear	Ruby Stained		Clear	Ruby Stained
Biscuit Jar, cov	65.00	92.00	Ice Tub	45.00	50.00
Bowls			Orange Bowl	50.00	—
8", ftd	20.00	—	Pitchers		
10 x 6", rect	45.00	—	Milk	35.00	—
Butter, cov	45.00	60.00	Water	45.00	—
Cake Stand, 10" . . .	35.00	—	Plates		
Carafe	50.00	—	6"	20.00	—
Celery Tray	25.00	—	10"	22.00	—
Celery Vase	30.00	—	Relish, rect	25.00	—
Condiment Set, salt,			Salt & Pepper	45.00	—
pepper & cruet on			Sauces		
tray	75.00	—	Flat, 5	5.00	—
Creamer			Ftd, 3¾"	8.00	15.00
Individual	—	35.00	Spooner	25.00	—
Regular	25.00	35.00	Sugar, cov	45.00	—
Cruets, os			Sugar Shaker	45.00	—
Large	25.00	55.00	Syrup	60.00	90.00
Small	35.00	—	Tray, Ice Cream,		
Dish, large, rect . . .	25.00	—	rect	75.00	—
Finger Bowl	55.00	—	Tumbler	30.00	—
Goblet	55.00	—	Wine	45.00	—

BOSWORTH (Star Band)

Non-flint, Indiana Glass Co., c1907.

	Clear		Clear
Bowl, berry	12.00	Pitcher, water	30.00
Butter, cov	25.00	Relish	10.00
Celery Vase, handles	18.00	Spooner	15.00
Compote, jelly	15.00	Sugar, cov	30.00
Creamer	15.00	Tumbler	12.00
Goblet	25.00	Wine	18.00

BOW TIE

Non-flint made by Thompson Glass Co., Uniontown, PA, c1889.

	Clear		Clear
Bowls		Orange Bowl, ftd, hs, 10" . .	75.00
8"	35.00	Pitcher, water	70.00
10¼ d, 5" h	65.00	Punch Bowl	100.00
Butter, cov	70.00	Relish, rect	25.00
Butter Pat	15.00	Salts	
Cake Stand, large, 9" d	60.00	Individual	12.00
Compotes, open		Master	35.00
hs, 5½"	60.00	Sauce, flat	18.00
hs, 9¼"	65.00	Spooner	35.00
ls, 6½"	45.00	Sugars	
Creamer	45.00	Cov	55.00
Goblet	42.50	Open	40.00
Honey, cov	55.00	Tumbler	40.00
Marmalade Jar	55.00		

BRITTANIC

Non-flint, c1898. Also made in emerald green in a finger or waste bowl.

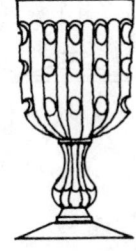

	Clear	Ruby Stained		Clear	Ruby Stained
Banana Stand	75.00	110.00	Lamps		
Bowl, berry	20.00	—	7½″	65.00	—
Butter, cov	40.00	55.00	8½″	75.00	—
Cake Stand	45.00	—	Pitcher, water	50.00	—
Castor Set, 4 bottles	65.00	—	Rose Bowl	20.00	—
Compote, cov	55.00	75.00	Salt and Pepper . . .	45.00	50.00
Creamer	30.00	50.00	Spooner	25.00	35.00
Cruet, os.	35.00	—	Sugar, cov	40.00	—
Goblet	30.00	45.00	Tumbler	20.00	—
Honey Dish, cov, sq	50.00	—	Wine	20.00	35.00

BROKEN COLUMN (Irish Column, Notched Rib, Rattan)

Made in Findlay, Ohio, c1891, by Columbia Glass Co., c1892, and later made by U. S. Glass Co. May also have been made at Portland, ME. Notches can be ruby stained. A solid, cobalt blue cup is known.

	Clear	Ruby Stained		Clear	Ruby Stained
Banana Stand	110.00	—	Creamer	40.00	125.00
Basket, applied han-			Cruet, os.	65.00	150.00
dle, 12″ h, 15″ l . .	150.00	—	*Goblet	50.00	—
Biscuit Jar	85.00	110.00	Pickle Castor, sp		
Bowls			frame	85.00	375.00
6″, berry	20.00	45.00	Pitcher, water	85.00	200.00
9″	35.00	—	Plates		
Butter, cov	85.00	200.00	5″	35.00	—
Cake Stands			7½″	40.00	75.00
9″	65.00	—	Relish, 8″ l, 5″ w . . .	20.00	—
10″	75.00	—	Salt & Pepper	75.00	125.00
Carafe, water	65.00	—	Sauce, flat	18.00	35.00
Celery Tray, oval . . .	35.00	—	Spooner	40.00	100.00
Celery Vase	45.00	110.00	Sugar, cov	65.00	150.00
Compotes			Sugar Shaker	60.00	90.00
Cov, hs, 5¼″ d,			Syrup	80.00	400.00
10½″ h	65.00	180.00	Tumbler	40.00	55.00
Cov, hs, 10″.	—	350.00	Wine	45.00	—
Open, hs, 8″ d . . .	75.00	200.00			
Open, ls, 5″ d, 6″					
h, flared	65.00	—			

BUCKLE

A flint and non-flint made by Gillinder and Sons in Philadelphia, PA, in the late 1870s. Possibly made by Sandwich Glass Co. in Massachusetts.

	Flint	Non-Flint		Flint	Non-Flint
Bowls			Compotes		
8″, berry, orig had			Cov, hs, 6″ d	40.00	40.00
wire basket frame.	60.00	50.00	Open, hs, 8½″,		
10″	60.00	50.00	fluted	45.00	40.00
Butter, cov	68.00	60.00	Open, ls	40.00	35.00

	Flint	Non-Flint		Flint	Non-Flint
Creamer, applied handle	45.00	40.00	Spooner	35.00	25.00
Egg Cup	35.00	30.00	Sugar		
Goblet	45.00	28.00	Cov	75.00	55.00
Pickle	40.00	15.00	Open, buttermilk type	45.00	30.00
Pitcher, water, applied handle	500.00	75.00	Tumbler	55.00	30.00
Salt, flat, oval	30.00	15.00	Wine	100.00	75.00

BUCKLE WITH STAR (Orient)

Non-flint made by Bryce, Walker and Co. in 1875, U. S. Glass Co. in 1891.

	Clear		Clear
Bowls		Sauces	
6″, cov	25.00	Flat.	5.00
10″, oval	18.00	Footed	8.00
Butter, cov	40.00	Spooner	20.00
Cake Stand	30.00	Sugars	
Celery Vase	20.00	Cov	35.00
Compotes		Open	20.00
Cov, hs, 7″	55.00	Syrups	
Open, hs, 9½″.	30.00	Applied handle, pewter or Brittania top, man's head finial	85.00
Creamer.	35.00		
Goblet	30.00		
Mug.	60.00	Molded handle, plain tin top	60.00
Pitcher, water	80.00		
Relish	15.00	Tumbler	45.00
Salt, master, ftd	25.00	Wine	35.00

BULLET EMBLEM (Shield In Red, White And Blue)

Made by U. S. Glass Co., c1898. Made to commemorate the Spanish-American War.

	Clear		Clear
Butter, cov	150.00	Spooner.	100.00
Creamer.	145.00	Sugar, cov	200.00
Goblet	100.00		

BULL'S EYE

Flint made by the New England Glass Co. in the 1850s. Also found in colors and milk glass, which doubles the price.

	Clear		Clear
Butter, cov	175.00	Mug, 3½″, applied handle . .	110.00
Castor Bottle	35.00	Pitcher, water	85.00
Celery Vase	70.00	Relish, oval	25.00
Champagne	85.00	Salts	
Cologne Bottle	85.00	Individual.	40.00
Creamer.	125.00	Master, ftd	100.00
Decanter, qt, bar lip	110.00	Spooner.	40.00
Egg Cups		Sugar, cov	115.00
Cov	165.00	Tumbler	80.00
Open	48.00	Water Bottle with tumble up	100.00
Goblet	65.00	Whiskey.	70.00
Lamp.	100.00	Wine	50.00

BULL'S EYE AND DAISY

Made by U. S. Glass Co., 1909. Also made with amethyst, blue, green, and pink stains in eyes. Prices close to ruby stained pieces.

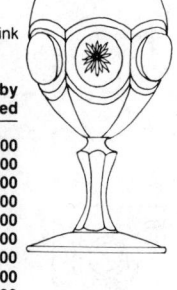

	Clear	Emerald Green	Ruby Stained
Bowl.	12.00	12.00	15.00
Butter, cov	24.00	25.00	30.00
Celery Vase	15.00	20.00	28.00
Creamer	20.00	22.00	20.00
Goblet	20.00	22.00	25.00
Pitcher, water	35.00	40.00	40.00
Salt Shaker.	20.00	20.00	20.00
Sauce.	18.00	20.00	24.00
Spooner	15.00	20.00	20.00
Sugar, open	25.00	25.00	30.00
Tumbler	12.00	14.00	18.00
Wine	15.00	20.00	30.00

BULL'S EYE AND FAN (Daisies in Oval Panels)

Made by U.S. Glass, c1910.

	Amethyst Stain	Clear	Emerald Green	Pink Stain	Sapphire Blue Stain
Bowls					
5″, pinched ends .	—	—	18.00	—	—
8″, berry	—	15.00	20.00	—	30.00
Butter, cov	—	50.00	65.00	—	—
Cake Stand.	—	25.00	—	—	—
Creamers					
Individual.	—	14.00	—	—	—
Regular	—	25.00	30.00	—	35.00
Custard Cup	—	10.00	—	—	—
Goblet	25.00	20.00	45.00	25.00	45.00
Lemonade Mug. 5″ .	—	20.00	—	—	—
Pitchers					
Lemonade, ftd . . .	—	55.00	—	—	—
Water, tankard . . .	55.00	45.00	100.00	20.00	100.00
Relish.	20.00	18.00	36.00	20.00	36.00
Sauce.	25.00	16.00	20.00	24.00	30.00
Spooner	25.00	20.00	45.00	25.00	45.00
Sugar, cov	40.00	50.00	60.00	30.00	35.00
Toothpick	—	35.00	45.00	65.00	—
Tumbler	55.00	15.00	45.00	40.00	35.00
Wine	20.00	18.00	40.00	40.00	25.00

BULL'S EYE WITH DIAMOND POINT (Union)

Made in flint by New England Glass Co., c1869.

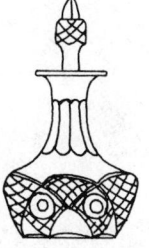

	Clear		Clear
Butter, cov	225.00	Egg Cup.	90.00
Celery Vase	150.00	Goblet	115.00
Champagne	145.00	Lamp, finger, applied handle	125.00
Cologne Bottle, os	90.00	Pitcher, water, 10¼″, tan-	
Creamer.	200.00	kard	275.00
Decanter, qt, os	200.00	Sauce	20.00

	Clear		Clear
Spooner	100.00	Tumble-Up	165.00
Sugar, cov	175.00	Whiskey	125.00
Syrup	155.00	Wine	135.00
Tumbler	125.00		

BULL'S EYE WITH FLEUR DE LIS

Flint, c1850.

	Clear		Clear
Bowl, fruit	85.00	Lamp, marble base	175.00
Butter, cov	175.00	Mug, handle	100.00
Celery Vase	85.00	Pitcher, water	275.00
Creamer	250.00	Salt, master	50.00
Decanter, qt, bar lip	110.00	Spooner	50.00
Egg Cup	50.00	Sugar, cov	115.00
Goblet	75.00	Wine	50.00

BUTTON ARCHES

Non-flint, made by Duncan and Miller Glass Co. in 1885. Pieces have frosted band. Some pieces, known as "Koral," usually souvenir type, are also seen in clambroth, trimmed in gold. In the early 1970s souvenir ruby stained pieces, including a goblet and table set, were reproduced.

	Clambroth	Clear	Ruby Stained
Bowl, 8"	—	20.00	—
Butter, cov	—	45.00	100.00
Cake Stand, 9"	—	35.00	—
Compote, jelly	—	35.00	50.00
Creamer	25.00	20.00	40.00
Cruet, os.	—	55.00	165.00
Cup	20.00	15.00	20.00
*Goblet	35.00	25.00	38.00
Mug, small	30.00	25.00	30.00
Pitchers			
Milk	—	35.00	40.00
Water, tankard	—	130.00	115.00
Plate, 7"	—	10.00	25.00
Salt Shaker, three types	—	15.00	30.00
Sauce, flat	—	10.00	22.00
Spooner	—	20.00	50.00
Sugar, cov	—	35.00	90.00
Syrup	—	—	140.00
Toothpick	30.00	18.00	35.00
Tumbler	20.00	20.00	27.00
Wine	25.00	10.00	30.00

BUTTON BAND (Umbilicated Hobnail, Wyandotte)

Non-flint made by Ripley and Co. in 1880s and U. S. Glass Co. in 1890s. Can often be found engraved, priced the same.

	Clear		Clear
Butter, cov	45.00	Pitcher, water, tankard.	50.00
Cake Stand, 10″	65.00	Spooner.	20.00
Castor Set, 5 bottles in glass		Sugar, cov	30.00
stand	95.00	Tray, water.	40.00
Compote, open, 1s	45.00	Tumbler	20.00
Creamer.	30.00	Wine	38.00
Goblet	30.00		

CABBAGE ROSE

Non-flint made by Central Glass Co, Wheeling, WV, c1870.

	Clear		Clear
Basket, handled, 12″.	100.00	Pitcher, water	125.00
Bowl, 8½″, oval, berry.	30.00	Relish, 8½″ 1, 5″ w, rose-	
Butter, cov	60.00	filled horn of plenty center	35.00
Cake Stand, 11″ and 12½″ .	60.00	Salt, master, ftd	25.00
Celery Vase	45.00	Sauces, six sizes	10–20.00
Compotes, cov, rose finials		Spooner.	30.00
hs, 7½″.	115.00	Sugars	
hs, 11″	125.00	Cov	55.00
Creamer, applied handle . . .	55.00	Open, buttermilk type. . . .	30.00
Egg Cup.	35.00	Tumbler	40.00
*Goblet	45.00	Wine	45.00
Mug.	60.00		

CABLE

Flint, c1850. Made by Boston and Sandwich Glass Co. to commemorate the laying of Atlantic Cable. Also found with amber stained panels and in opaque colors (rare).

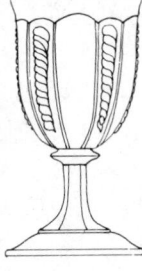

	Clear		Clear
Bowl	35.00	Lamps, 8¾″	
Butter, cov	100.00	Glass Base	135.00
Cake Stand	55.00	Marble Base	100.00
Celery Vase	90.00	Pitcher, water, rare	500.00
Champagne	135.00	Plate, 6″.	100.00
Compotes, open		Salts, ind	
ls, 7″, 8″, and 9″	55.00	Flat.	45.00
ls, 11″.	75.00	Footed	20.00
Creamer.	350.00	Sauce, flat	10.00
Decanter, qt, ground stopper.	150.00	Spooner.	40.00
Egg Cups		Sugar, cov	85.00
Cov	225.00	Syrup.	137.50
Open	60.00	Tumbler, ftd	175.00
Goblet	65.00	Wine	165.00

CACTUS

Non-flint made by Indiana Tumbler and Goblet Co. c1895. Made in clear and chocolate. Pattern made in opalescent vaseline by Fenton Art Glass in 1950.
Additional Listings: Greentown Glass (chocolate pieces).

	Clear		Clear
Bowls		Plate, 7½″	80.00
7¼″ d	50.00	Sauces	
8¼″	70.00	Flat, 5¼″	30.00
Butter, cov	125.00	Footed	45.00
Cake stand	165.00	Spooner	50.00
Celery Vase	80.00	Sugar, cov	80.00
Compote, cov, hs, 8¼″	125.00	Syrup	75.00
Creamer, cov	80.00	*Toothpick	50.00
Cruet, os	100.00	Tumbler	45.00
Nappy	50.00	Vase, 6″	60.00
Pitcher, water	175.00		

CADMUS

Non-flint made by Beaumont Glass Co., Grafton, WV, in mid-1880s.

	Clear		Clear
Bowl	15.00	Goblet	15.00
Butter, cov	30.00	Spooner	15.00
Compote, jelly	20.00	Sugar, cov	25.00
Creamer	20.00	Wine	16.00

CALIFORNIA (Beaded Grape)

Non-flint made by U. S. Glass Co., Pittsburgh, PA, c1890. Also with gold trim.

	Clear	Emerald Green		Clear	Emerald Green
Bowl, 8″	25.00	35.00	*Goblet	35.00	50.00
Bread Plate, 10¼ x			Olive, handle	20.00	35.00
7¼″	25.00	40.00	Pickle	20.00	30.00
Butter, cov	50.00	80.00	Pitchers, water	85.00	110.00
Cake Stand, 9″	50.00	85.00	*Plate, 8¼″, sq	22.50	35.00
Celery Tray	30.00	45.00	*Sauce, 4″	12.00	15.00
Celery Vase	45.00	65.00	Salt & Pepper	45.00	75.00
Cov, hs, 6½″	65.00	95.00	Spooner	30.00	45.00
Open, hs, 7″	40.00	60.00	Sugar, cov	35.00	55.00
Open, hs, 4¾″,			Sugar Shaker	55.00	85.00
jelly	30.00	45.00	*Tumbler	25.00	35.00
Creamer	40.00	50.00	*Wine	35.00	55.00
Cruet, orig swirled					
stopper	65.00	95.00			

CANADIAN

Non-flint, made by Burlington Glass Works, Hamilton, Ontario, Canada, c1870.

	Clear		Clear
Bread Plate, 10″	45.00	Celery Vase	45.00
Butter, cov	75.00	Compotes	
Cake Stand, 9¼″	95.00	Cov, hs, 7″	70.00

	Clear		Clear
Cov, hs, 8″	85.00	Plate, 6″, handles	30.00
Open, ls, 7″.	35.00	Sauces	
Creamer.	55.00	Flat.	12.00
Goblet	50.00	Footed	18.00
Pitchers		Spooner.	45.00
Milk	65.00	Sugar, cov	65.00
Water	75.00	Wine	45.00

CANE

Non-flint made by Gillinder Glass Co. and McKee Glass Co., c1885. Goblets and toddy plates with inverted "buttons" known.

	Amber	Apple Green	Blue	Clear	Vaseline
Butter, cov	45.00	60.00	75.00	40.00	60.00
Celery Vase	35.00	40.00	50.00	32.50	40.00
Compote, open, ls, 5¾″	25.00	30.00	35.00	25.00	35.00
Creamer	35.00	40.00	50.00	25.00	30.00
Finger Bowl.	20.00	30.00	35.00	15.00	30.00
Goblet	30.00	50.00	45.00	20.00	35.00
Match holder, kettle	16.00	—	35.00	30.00	35.00
Pickle	25.00	20.00	25.00	15.00	20.00
Pitcher, water	50.00	55.00	65.00	40.00	55.00
Plate, toddy, 4½″. . .	20.00	25.00	30.00	14.00	18.00
Salt & Pepper	60.00	50.00	80.00	30.00	70.00
Sauce, flat	—	—	—	7.00	—
Slipper	25.00	—	25.00	15.00	—
Spooner	35.00	25.00	30.00	20.00	25.00
Sugar, cov	45.00	50.00	55.00	45.00	55.00
Tray, water	35.00	35.00	45.00	30.00	40.00
Tumbler	20.00	25.00	35.00	18.00	25.00
Waste Bowl, 7½″ . .	30.00	30.00	35.00	20.00	30.00
Wine	35.00	50.00	55.00	25.00	40.00

CANE AND ROSETTE (Flower Paneled Cane)

Non-flint, attributed to Portland Glass, c1885.

	Clear		Clear
Bowl, cov, octagonal	45.00	Goblet	25.00
Butter, cov, ftd	40.00	Pickle Jar, cov	45.00
Cake Stand, large	40.00	Pitcher, water	45.00
Celery Vase	30.00	Sauce, ftd	10.00
Champagne . . . . . . ˙.	30.00	Spooner.	25.00
Compote, cov, hs, 8″.	40.00	Sugar, cov	40.00
Creamer.	30.00	Wine	35.00

CANE HORSESHOE (Paragon)

Made by U. S. Glass Co., 1909. Prices are for pieces with gold trim.

	Clear		Clear
Bowl	15.00	Pitcher, water	40.00
Butter, cov	25.00	Relish	15.00
Cake Stand	30.00	Sauce	8.00
Celery Vase	25.00	Spooner	20.00
Compote, cov, hs	45.00	Sugar, cov	30.00
Creamer	30.00	Syrup	35.00
Cruet, os	30.00	Tumbler	15.00
Goblet	20.00	Wine	18.00

CAPE COD

Non-flint, attributed to Boston and Sandwich Glass Co., c1870.

	Clear		Clear
Bowl, 6″, handled	40.00	Pitcher, water	65.00
Butter, cov	55.00	Plates	
Celery Vase	45.00	5″, handles	30.00
Compotes		10″	40.00
Cov, hs, 8″ d	100.00	Platter, open handles	45.00
Open, hs, 7″	50.00	Sauce, ftd	20.00
Creamer	45.00	Spooner	35.00
Goblet	45.00	Sugar, cov	65.00
Marmalade Jar, cov	65.00	Wine	45.00

CARDINAL

Non-flint, c1875, attributed to Ohio Flint Glass Co., Lancaster, OH. There were two butter dishes made, one in the regular pattern and one with three birds in the base - labeled in script cardinal (red bird), pewit, and titmouse. The later is less common.

	Clear		Clear
Butters, cov		Sauces	
Regular	60.00	Flat, 4″	10.00
Three birds in base	100.00	Footed, 4½″ or 5½″	15.00
Cake Stand	75.00	Spooner	35.00
Creamer	50.00	Sugars	
Goblet	35.00	Cov	65.00
Pitcher, water	95.00	Open	35.00

CAROLINA (Inverness)

Made by Bryce Brothers and later by U. S. Glass Co., as part of the States series, c1903. Ruby stained pieces often are souvenir marked. Some clear pieces found with gilt or purple stain.

	Clear	Ruby Stained		Clear	Ruby Stained
Bowl berry	18.00	—	Compotes		
Butter, cov	50.00	—	Open, hs, 8″,		
Cake Stand	35.00	—	beaded	50.00	—

	Clear	Ruby Stained		Clear	Ruby Stained
Open, hs, 9½"...	24.00	—	Salt Shaker.......	15.00	35.00
Open, jelly	12.00	—	Spooner	25.00	—
Creamer	20.00	—	Sugar, cov	30.00	—
Goblet	35.00	45.00	Tumbler	20.00	—
Mug	30.00	35.00	Wine	22.50	35.00
Pitcher, milk	35.00	—			

CATHEDRAL

Non-flint pattern made by Bryce Bros., Pittsburgh, PA., in the 1880s and by U. S. Glass Co. in 1891. Also found in ruby stained, add 50%.

	Amber	Amethyst	Blue	Clear	Vaseline
Bowl, berry, 8"	35.00	50.00	40.00	25.00	40.00
Butter, cov	60.00	110.00	62.00	45.00	60.00
Cake Stand.......	42.00	75.00	48.00	40.00	45.00
Celery Vase	33.00	60.00	40.00	30.00	35.00
Compotes					
Cov, hs, 8"	80.00	125.00	100.00	60.00	55.00
Open, hs, 9½"...	50.00	75.00	65.00	40.00	—
Open, ls, 7".....	40.00	75.00	35.00	25.00	30.00
Creamers					
Flat, sq	50.00	82.00	—	45.00	48.00
Tall	45.00	80.00	50.00	30.00	45.00
Cruet, os.	80.00	—	—	—	—
Goblet	50.00	70.00	45.00	30.00	50.00
Lamp, 12¾" h.....	—	—	185.00	—	—
Pitcher, water	60.00	110.00	65.00	60.00	60.00
Relish, fish shape ..	—	35.00	50.00	—	35.00
Salt, boat shape ...	15.00	20.00	15.00	10.00	20.00
Sauces					
Flat...........	16.00	30.00	20.00	12.00	16.00
Footed	18.00	35.00	22.00	15.00	20.00
Spooner	40.00	65.00	50.00	30.00	45.00
Sugar, cov	70.00	100.00	45.00	45.00	40.00
Tumbler	32.50	40.00	35.00	25.00	40.00
Wine	45.00	60.00	50.00	30.00	50.00

CHAIN AND SHIELD (Shield and Chain)

Non-flint, attributed to Portland Glass Co., c1875.

	Clear		Clear
Bread Plate, handled......	30.00	Pitcher, water	30.00
Butter, cov	45.00	Sauce, flat	10.00
Cordial................	20.00	Spooner...............	20.00
Creamer...............	30.00	Sugar, cov	40.00
Goblet	32.50	Wine	35.00

CHAIN WITH STAR

Non-flint, made by U. S. Glass Co., c1890.

	Clear		Clear
Bread Plate, 11", handles ..	35.00	Compotes	
Butter, cov	40.00	Cov, hs.............	45.00

	Clear			Clear
Open, ls	30.00	Sauces		
Creamer.	35.00	Flat.		10.00
Goblet	25.00	Footed		12.00
Pickle, oval.	12.00	Spooner.		20.00
Pitcher, water	50.00	Sugar, cov		40.00
Plate, 7″.	25.00	Wine		30.00

CHAMPION (Greentown #11)

Made by McKee Bros. and Indiana Tumbler and Goblet Co., 1894–1917. Pieces are often found with gold trim.

	Amber Stained	Clear	Emerald Green	Ruby Stained
Bowl.	—	18.00	—	—
Butter, cov	—	45.00	—	—
Cake Stand.	—	35.00	—	90.00
Compotes				
Cov.	—	55.00	—	—
Open, fluted top. .	80.00	40.00	—	—
Creamer	—	25.00	—	—
Goblet	—	25.00	—	—
Ice Bucket	—	40.00	—	—
Marmalade Jar	—	25.00	—	—
Pickle Dish, 8″.	—	15.00	—	—
Pitcher, water	—	70.00	—	—
Plate, 8″ or 10″. . . .	—	25.00	—	—
Rose Bowl	—	20.00	45.00	—
Spooner	—	20.00	—	45.00
Sugar, cov	—	40.00	—	85.00
Syrup	—	75.00	—	—
Toothpick	50.00	20.00	40.00	45.00
Tray, water	—	45.00	—	—
Tumbler	—	15.00	—	—
Wine	—	15.00	—	—

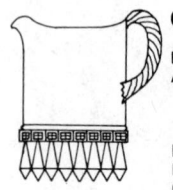

CHANDELIER (Crown Jewel)

Non-flint, O'Hara Glass Co., Pittsburgh, PA, c1880, continued by U. S. Glass Co. Also attributed to Canadian manufacturer.

	Etched	Plain		Etched	Plain
Bowl, 8″ d, 3¼″ h . .	35.00	37.50	Pitcher, water	80.00	80.00
Butter, cov	85.00	65.00	Salt & Pepper	75.00	50.00
Celery Vase	40.00	40.00	Sauce, flat	—	15.00
Compotes			Sponge Dish.	—	30.00
Cov, hs	75.00	60.00	Spooner	35.00	30.00
Open, hs, 9½″. . .	55.00	45.00	Sugar, cov	70.00	60.00
Creamer	65.00	55.00	Sugar Shaker	75.00	55.00
Finger Bowl.	40.00	30.00	Tray, water	70.00	50.00
Goblet	65.00	50.00	Tumbler	40.00	35.00
Inkwell, dated hard			Wine	75.00	60.00
rubber top	—	60.00			

CHECKERBOARD (Bridle Rosette)

Made by Westmoreland Glass Co., early 1900s. Reproduced earlier in milk glass and in recent years with pink stain. The Cambridge "Ribbon" pattern, usually marked Nearcut, is similar.

	Clear		Clear
Bowl, 9", shallow	18.00	Water	35.00
Butter, cov	45.00	Plates	
Celery Tray	15.00	7"	20.00
Celery Vase	28.00	10"	25.00
Compote, open, ls, 8"	25.00	Salt and Pepper	45.00
Creamer	20.00	Sauce, flat	6.00
Cruet, os	40.00	Spooner	20.00
Cup	10.00	Sugar, cov	35.00
Goblet	35.00	Tumblers	
Honey, cov, sq, pedestal	45.00	Iced Tea	15.00
Pitchers		Water	18.00
Milk	40.00	Wine	15.00

CLASSIC

Clear and frosted non-flint produced by Gillinder and Sons, Philadelphia, PA, in the late 1870s. Pieces with log feet instead of a flat or collared base are worth more.

	Clear		Clear
Bowl, 8", hexagonal, ftd	150.00	Thomas H. Hendricks	165.00
Butter, cov, log feet	175.00	John A. Logan	165.00
Celery Vase	100.00	Warrior	120.00
Compote, cov, log feet	250.00	Sauces	
Creamer	125.00	Flat	30.00
Goblet	175.00	Log Feet	40.00
Pitcher, water	285.00	Spooner	95.00
Plates		Sugar, cov	175.00
Jas G. Blaine	165.00	Sweetmeat Jar	175.00
Pres. Cleveland	180.00		

CLASSIC MEDALLION (Cameo #1)

A pattern of 1870–1880, maker unknown.

	Clear		Clear
Bowl, 8", straight sides	25.00	Creamer	30.00
Butter, cov	50.00	Pitcher, water	125.00
Celery Vase	30.00	Spooner	25.00
Compote, cov, hs	50.00	Sugar, cov	40.00

CLEAR DIAGONAL BAND

Non-flint, c1880. Also has been found in light amber.

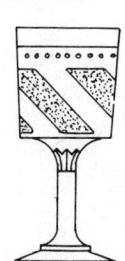

	Clear		Clear
Bread Plate, Eureka	40.00	Cov, ls	30.00
Butter, cov	40.00	Creamer	25.00
Celery Vase	25.00	Dish, oval	10.00
Compotes		Goblet	20.00
Cov, hs	45.00	Marmalade Jar	25.00

	Clear			Clear
Pitcher, water	40.00	Spooner		20.00
Plate	18.00	Sugar, cov		40.00
Relish, oval	8.00	Wine		25.00
Salt & Pepper	30.00			

CLEAR RIBBON

Made by George Duncan & Sons, c1880.

	Clear		Clear
Bread Plate, motto, GUT-DODB, ftd	40.00	Dish, cov, oblong	
Butter, cov	50.00	6″	25.00
Cake Stand, 9″	35.00	8″	30.00
Celery Vase	18.00	Goblet, fancy foot	32.00
Compotes		Pickle	10.00
Cov, hs	65.00	Pitcher, water	50.00
Open, ls	25.00	Sauce, ftd	8.00
Creamer	28.00	Spooner	20.00
		Sugar, cov	40.00

COLORADO (Lacy Medallion)

Non-flint States pattern made by U. S. Glass Co. in 1897. Made in amethyst stained, ruby stained, and opaque white with enamel floral trim, all of which are scarce. Some pieces found with ornate silver frames or feet. Purists consider these two separate patterns, with the lacy medallion restricted to souvenir pieces.

	Blue	Clear	Green
Banana Stand	45.00	25.00	40.00
Bowls			
6″	35.00	15.00	30.00
7½″, ftd	40.00	20.00	35.00
8½″, ftd	65.00	45.00	60.00
Butter, cov	200.00	65.00	115.00
Cake Stand	70.00	55.00	65.00
Celery Vase	50.00	25.00	45.00
Compotes			
Open, ls, 6″	45.00	20.00	40.00
Open, ls, 9¼″	50.00	35.00	45.00
Creamers			
Individual	35.00	20.00	30.00
Regular	55.00	35.00	50.00
Mug	40.00	20.00	30.00
Nappy	40.00	15.00	35.00
Plate, 6″	50.00	25.00	45.00
Punch Cup	30.00	15.00	25.00
Salt Shaker	65.00	30.00	40.00
Sauce	30.00	15.00	18.00
Spooner	40.00	20.00	25.00
Sugar, cov	60.00	35.00	55.00
Toothpick	65.00	25.00	30.00
Tray, Calling Card	35.00	25.00	30.00
Tumbler	35.00	18.00	25.00
Vase, 12″	100.00	35.00	55.00
Violet Bowl	55.00	—	—
Wine	—	25.00	30.00

CONNECTICUT

Non-flint. One of the States patterns made by U. S. Glass Co., c1898. Found in plain and engraved.

	Clear		Clear
Biscuit Jar	25.00	Open, hs, 7″	22.50
Bowls		Creamer.	18.00
4″.	10.00	Dish, 8″, oblong	16.00
8″.	15.00	Lemonade, handled.	20.00
Butter, cov	30.00	Pitcher, water	30.00
Cake Stand	30.00	Relish	10.00
Celery Tray.	15.00	Salt & Pepper.	35.00
Celery Vase	15.00	Tumbler, water	15.00
Compote			
Cov, hs.	37.50		

CORD AND TASSEL

Non-flint, made by La Belle Glass C., Bridgeport, OH, and patented by Andrew Baggs in 1872. Also made by Central Glass Co. and other companies.

	Clear		Clear
Butter, cov	65.00	Mug, applied handle	75.00
Cake Stand, 9½″	57.50	Mustard Jar, cov.	45.00
Celery Vase	45.00	Pitcher, water, applied han-	
Compotes		dle	80.00
Cov, hs, ...	75.00	Salt & Pepper.	45.00
Open, ls	35.00	Spooner.	30.00
Creamer.	50.00	Sugar, cov	55.00
Egg Cup.	35.00	Syrup.	100.00
Dish, oval, vegetable.	25.00	Tumbler, water	50.00
Goblet	45.00	Wine	40.00
Lamp, applied handle, ped-			
estal.	100.00		

CORD DRAPERY

Made by National Glass Co., Greentown, IN, from 1899 to 1903; later by Indiana Glass at Dunkirk, IN, after 1907.

	Amber	Blue	Clear	Emerald Green
Bowl, 7½″.	25.00	25.00	20.00	30.00
Butter, cov	75.00	75.00	65.00	125.00
Cake Stand.	50.00	55.00	35.00	75.00
Compotes				
Open, 6″	45.00	60.00	40.00	85.00
Open, 7″	75.00	75.00	60.00	95.00
Open, jelly	—	55.00	40.00	—
Creamer	45.00	50.00	40.00	60.00
Cruet, os.	200.00	75.00	70.00	90.00
Cup	18.00	18.00	15.00	25.00
Goblet	50.00	50.00	55.00	65.00
Pickle, 9¼″, oval . . .	40.00	—	25.00	—
Pitcher, water	50.00	50.00	50.00	75.00
Plate	35.00	40.00	25.00	40.00
Relish.	25.00	25.00	20.00	30.00

	Amber	Blue	Clear	Emerald Green
Sauce, flat	10.00	12.00	10.00	15.00
Spooner	30.00	35.00	30.00	45.00
Sugar, cov	55.00	60.00	45.00	75.00
Sweetmeat cov, 6½″ d, 5¼″ h	165.00	—	—	—
Tumbler	30.00	30.00	27.50	45.00
Wine	45.00	45.00	40.00	60.00

CORDOVA

Non-flint made by the O'Hara Glass Co., Pittsburgh, Pa. It was exhibited for the first time at the Pittsburgh Glass Show, December 16, 1890. A toothpick has been identified in ruby stained.

	Clear	Emerald Green		Clear	Emerald Green
Bowl, Berry, cov . . .	30.00	—	Pitcher, water	40.00	—
Butter, cov, handled	45.00	—	Punch Bowl.	87.50	—
Cologne Bottle	20.00	—	Punch Cup	15.00	30.00
Compotes			Nappy, handled, 6″d	12.00	—
Cov, hs	40.00	—	Salt & Pepper	35.00	—
Open, hs	30.00	—	Spooner	30.00	40.00
Creamer	35.00	40.00	Sugar, cov	40.00	80.00
Finger Bowl.	16.00	—	Toothpick	15.00	—
Inkwell, metal lid . . .	85.00	—	Tumbler	18.00	—
Mug, handled	15.00	30.00	Vase	15.00	—

COTTAGE (Dinner Bell)

Non-flint made by Adams and Co., Pittsburgh, PA, in the late 1870s and U. S. Glass Co. in the 1890s. Known to have been made in emerald green, amber, light blue, and amethyst.

	Clear	Ruby Stained		Clear	Ruby Stained
Banana Stand	55.00	—	Pitchers		
Bowl, 9½, oval	20.00	—	Milk.	28.00	—
Butter, cov	40.00	—	Water	47.00	—
Cake Stand, 9″	30.00	—	Plates, 8″	22.00	—
Celery Vase	35.00	—	Relish	10.00	—
Champagne	35.00	49.00	Salt Shaker.	25.00	—
Compotes			Saucer	15.00	25.00
Cov, hs 8¼″	65.00	—	Spooner	20.00	—
Jelly	24.00	45.00	Sugar, cov	47.00	—
Creamer	25.00	50.00	Syrup	55.00	—
Cruet, os.	37.00	—	Tray, water	30.00	—
Dish, oval, deep . . .	22.00	—	Tumbler	25.00	—
Finger Bowl.	16.00	—	Waste Bowl	20.00	—
Goblet	30.00	—	Wine	35.00	—

CROESUS

Made in clear by Riverside Glass Works, Wheeling, WV, in 1897. Produced in amethyst and green by McKee Glass in 1899. Pieces trimmed in gold; prices are for examples with gold in very good condition.

	Amethyst	Clear	Green
Bowls			
6¼″, ftd.	225.00	75.00	125.00
8″	175.00	—	125.00
10″, ftd	180.00	—	—
*Butter, cov	215.00	100.00	170.00
Celery Vase	325.00	65.00	135.00
Compote, jelly	250.00	25.00	215.00
Condiment Set (cruet, salt & pepper on small tray). . . .	250.00	200.00	200.00
Creamers			
Individual	110.00	—	200.00
Regular	160.00	65.00	75.00
Cruet, os.	275.00	75.00	200.00
Pitcher, water	310.00	90.00	250.00
Relish, boat shaped	75.00	35.00	65.00
Salt & Pepper	150.00	50.00	145.00
Sauces			
Flat.	45.00	18.00	36.00
Footed	—	—	40.00
Spooner	90.00	40.00	75.00
Sugar, cov	200.00	75.00	140.00
*Toothpick	100.00	25.00	80.00
Tray, condiment . . .	85.00	35.00	40.00
*Tumbler	75.00	30.00	50.00

CRYSTAL WEDDING

Non-flint made by Adams Glass Co., Pittsburgh, PA, in the late 1880s and U. S. Glass Co. in 1891. Also found in frosted, amber stained, and cobalt blue (rare). Heavily reproduced in clear and milk with enamel trim.

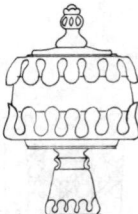

	Clear	Ruby Stained		Clear	Ruby Stained
Banana Stand	100.00	—	Goblet	50.00	—
Bowl, Berry, 8″	35.00	—	Pitchers		
Butter, cov	50.00	75.00	Milk.	110.00	—
Cake Plate	45.00	85.00	Water, sq.	165.00	—
Cake Stand, 10″ . . .	60.00	—	Plate, 10″	25.00	40.00
Celery Vase	32.50	—	Relish.	25.00	—
Compotes			Salt, individual	30.00	—
Cov, hs, 6″, sq. . .	65.00	—	Spooner	35.00	60.00
Cov, ls, 4″ sq. . . .	32.00	—	Sugar, cov	70.00	85.00
Open, hs, 7″ sq . .	55.00	—	Toothpick	50.00	—
Open, ls, 5″ sq . .	42.00	—	Tumbler	30.00	45.00
Creamer	50.00	68.00	Wine	42.00	—

CUPID AND VENUS

Non-flint made by Richards and Hartley Glass Co., Tarentum, PA, in the late 1870s. Also made in vaseline.

	Amber	Clear		Amber	Clear
Bowls			Marmalade Jar, cov	—	50.00
8", cov, ftd	—	124.00	Mugs		
9", oval	—	32.00	Miniature	—	40.00
10", ftd, scalloped			Medium, 2½"	—	35.00
rim	—	124.00	Large, 3½"	—	40.00
Bread Plate	75.00	45.00	Pitchers		
Butter, cov	—	65.00	Milk	150.00	60.00
Cake Plate	—	45.00	Water	190.00	50.00
Celery Vase	—	40.00	Plate, 10", round	75.00	40.00
Champagne	—	90.00	Sauces		
Compotes			Flat	—	10.00
Cov, 8", hs	—	100.00	Footed, 3½", 4"		
Open, 9¼", hs	—	45.00	and 4½"	—	14.00
Cordial, 3½"	—	110.00	Spooner	—	35.00
Creamer	—	35.00	Sugar, cov	—	65.00
Cruet, os	—	75.00	Wine, 3¾"	—	100.00
Goblet	—	65.00			

CURRANT

Non-flint, made by Campbell, Jones and Co., and patented in 1871.

	Clear		Clear
Bowl, 7", vegetable	18.00	Plates, oval	
Butter, cov	55.00	5" x 7"	25.00
Cake Stand, 9½"	65.00	6" x 9"	30.00
Celery Vase	50.00	Salt, ftd	30.00
Compotes		Sauce, ftd, 4"	10.00
Cov, hs, 8"	55.00	Spooner	30.00
Cov, ls, 8"	45.00	Sugar	
Cordial	45.00	Cov	55.00
Creamer, applied handle	60.00	Open, buttermilk type	35.00
Egg Cup	25.00	Tumbler, ftd	27.50
Goblet	30.00	Wine	37.50
Pitcher, water, applied han-			
dle	75.00		

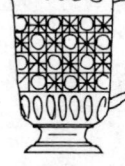

CURRIER AND IVES

Non-flint made by Bellaire Glass Co. in Findlay, OH, in 1890. Known to have been made in colors, but rarely found.

	Clear		Clear
Bowl, oval, 10", canoe		Dish, oval, boat shaped, 8"	27.50
shaped	30.00	Goblet, knob stem	26.00
Butter, cov	50.00	Lamp, 9½", hs	75.00
Compotes		Pitchers	
Cov, hs	55.00	Milk	50.00
Open, hs, 7½"	48.00	Water	60.00
Creamer	30.00	Plate, 10"	20.00
Cup and saucer	35.00	Relish	8.50

	Clear		Clear
Salt Shaker	20.00	Trays	
Sauce, oval	10.00	Water, Balky Mule	65.00
Spooner	30.00	Wine, Balky Mule	50.00
Sugar, cov	35.00	Water Bottle, 12″h, os	50.00
Syrup	45.00	Wine, 3¼″	18.00

CUT LOG (Cat's Eye and Block, Ethol)

Non-flint, made by Greensburg Glass Co., 1888. Also reported in camphor glass, but rare.

	Clear		Clear
Biscuit Jar	50.00	Creamer, ind.	15.00
Bowl, 10″, deep, ftd, scalloped	40.00	Cruet, os	50.00
		Goblet	45.00
Butter, cov	60.00	Mug	16.00
Cake Stand, 9″	70.00	Mustard Jar	35.00
Celery Tray	20.00	Olive Dish	18.00
Celery Vase	40.00	Pitcher, water, applied han-	
Compotes		dle	85.00
Cov, hs, 7¼″	85.00	Relish	20.00
Cov, hs, 12½″	95.00	Spooner	30.00
Cov, jelly, 6¼″	45.00	Sugar, cov	55.00
Open, hs, 8″	55.00	Sugar, cov, ind	35.00
Open, hs, 10″	67.50	Tumbler	30.00
Creamer, 5″	45.00	Wine	25.00

DAHLIA

Non-flint, made by Canton Glass Co., c1880. Also attributed to Portland and Canadian manufacturer.

	Amber	Apple Green	Blue	Clear	Vaseline
Bowl	30.00	25.00	24.00	15.00	30.00
Bread Plate	55.00	50.00	50.00	35.00	55.00
Butter, cov	80.00	70.00	70.00	40.00	80.00
Cake Plate	60.00	45.00	45.00	24.00	60.00
Cake Stand, 9″	75.00	50.00	48.00	25.00	75.00
Champagne	80.00	65.00	65.00	55.00	80.00
Compotes					
Cov, hs, 7″	100.00	85.00	85.00	55.00	80.00
Open, hs, 8″	60.00	45.00	45.00	30.00	60.00
Cordial	55.00	50.00	48.00	30.00	55.00
Creamer	40.00	30.00	35.00	20.00	40.00
Egg Cups					
Double	80.00	65.00	65.00	45.00	80.00
Single	55.00	40.00	40.00	20.00	55.00
Goblet	65.00	55.00	55.00	30.00	65.00
Mugs					
Large	55.00	55.00	55.00	35.00	55.00
Small	50.00	45.00	40.00	30.00	50.00
Pickle	35.00	30.00	30.00	20.00	35.00
Pitchers					
Milk	70.00	55.00	55.00	40.00	70.00
Water	110.00	100.00	100.00	85.00	100.00

	Amber	Apple Green	Blue	Clear	Vaseline
Plates					
7″	45.00	40.00	40.00	15.00	45.00
9″, handles	35.00	45.00	50.00	18.00	60.00
Platter	50.00	45.00	45.00	30.00	50.00
Relish, 9½″ l.	20.00	20.00	20.00	15.00	25.00
Salt, ind, ftd	35.00	30.00	30.00	5.00	35.00
Sauces					
Flat.	15.00	12.00	12.00	10.00	12.00
Footed	20.00	15.00	15.00	10.00	20.00
Spooner	50.00	40.00	50.00	30.00	50.00
Sugar, cov	75.00	60.00	60.00	40.00	75.00
Syrup	75.00	—	—	55.00	—
Wine	65.00	50.00	55.00	35.00	65.00

DAISY AND BUTTON

Non-flint pattern made in the 1870s by several companies in many different forms. In continuous production since inception.

	Amber	Apple Green	Blue	Clear	Vaseline
Bowl, triangular	30.00	40.00	40.00	24.00	50.00
Bread Plate, 13″ . . .	30.00	60.00	30.00	20.00	40.00
Butter Chip	10.00	24.00	15.00	8.00	25.00
Butters, cov					
Round.	70.00	80.00	70.00	65.00	80.00
Square	110.00	115.00	110.00	100.00	120.00
Butter Pat	30.00	40.00	35.00	25.00	35.00
Canoes					
4″	10.00	24.00	15.00	8.00	24.00
8½″	18.00	35.00	25.00	20.00	30.00
12″	40.00	35.00	28.00	20.00	40.00
14″	30.00	40.00	35.00	25.00	40.00
Castor Sets					
4 bottle, glass std	90.00	85.00	95.00	80.00	75.00
5 bottle, metal std	105.00	100.00	110.00	100.00	95.00
Celery Vase	30.00	45.00	35.00	30.00	45.00
Compotes					
Cov, hs, 6″	35.00	50.00	45.00	25.00	50.00
Open, hs, 8″	75.00	65.00	60.00	40.00	65.00
Creamer	35.00	40.00	40.00	18.00	35.00
Cruet, os.	95.00	55.00	50.00	40.00	50.00
Egg Cup	20.00	30.00	25.00	15.00	30.00
Finger Bowl.	25.00	50.00	30.00	20.00	42.00
Goblet	40.00	50.00	40.00	25.00	40.00
Hat, 2½″.	25.00	35.00	40.00	20.00	35.00
Ice Tub.	—	—	—	—	75.00
Inkwell	40.00	50.00	45.00	30.00	45.00
Parfait.	25.00	35.00	30.00	20.00	35.00
Pickle Castor.	125.00	90.00	150.00	75.00	150.00
Pitchers, water					
Bulbous, reed					
handle	125.00	95.00	90.00	65.00	90.00
Tankard.	45.00	65.00	55.00	40.00	60.00
Plates					
5″, leaf shape . . .	20.00	24.00	16.00	18.00	25.00
6″, round.	10.00	22.00	15.00	6.50	24.00
7″, square	20.00	35.00	18.00	15.00	35.00
Punch Bowl, stand. .	90.00	100.00	95.00	85.00	100.00

	Amber	Apple Green	Blue	Clear	Vaseline
Sauce, 4″	15.00	25.00	15.00	18.00	25.00
Salt & Pepper	30.00	40.00	30.00	20.00	35.00
Slippers					
5″	30.00	35.00	45.00	35.00	35.00
11½″.	40.00	50.00	30.00	35.00	50.00
Spooner	35.00	35.00	45.00	35.00	30.00
Sugar, cov	40.00	50.00	40.00	35.00	50.00
Syrup	45.00	50.00	45.00	30.00	45.00
Toothpicks					
Round	40.00	55.00	25.00	40.00	45.00
Urn	20.00	25.00	20.00	10.00	35.00
Tray	40.00	65.00	50.00	35.00	55.00
Tumbler	15.00	30.00	25.00	15.00	25.00
Vase, wall pocket . .	125.00	—	—	—	—
Wine	15.00	25.00	20.00	10.00	45.00

DAISY AND BUTTON WITH CROSSBARS

Non-flint pattern made by Richards and Hartley, Tarentum, PA, c1888.

	Amber	Blue	Clear	Vaseline
Bowls				
6″	26.00	30.00	20.00	28.00
9″	40.00	40.00	25.00	35.00
Bread Plate	30.00	45.00	25.00	35.00
Butters, cov				
Flat	55.00	55.00	45.00	55.00
Footed	—	75.00	25.00	60.00
Celery Vase	35.00	40.00	30.00	40.00
Compotes				
Cov, hs, 8″	55.00	65.00	45.00	55.00
Open, hs, 8″	45.00	50.00	30.00	45.00
Open, ls, 7″	30.00	—	—	—
Creamers				
Individual	25.00	35.00	20.00	30.00
Regular	40.00	50.00	35.00	40.00
Cruet, os.	75.00	55.00	37.50	45.00
Goblet	40.00	40.00	25.00	35.00
Pitchers				
Milk	45.00	50.00	35.00	50.00
Water	85.00	70.00	40.00	65.00
Salt & Pepper	40.00	45.00	30.00	40.00
Sauces				
Flat	15.00	20.00	10.00	15.00
Footed	18.00	25.00	15.00	24.00
Spooner	35.00	35.00	24.00	35.00
Sugars, Cov				
Individual	25.00	35.00	10.00	25.00
Regular	50.00	65.00	25.00	55.00
Syrup	50.00	60.00	35.00	50.00
Toothpick	40.00	40.00	28.00	35.00
Tumbler	20.00	30.00	15.00	25.00
Wine	30.00	35.00	27.50	30.00

DAISY AND BUTTON WITH NARCISSUS (Daisy and Button with Clear Lily)

Non-flint made in late 1890s. Later made by Indiana Glass Co. Dunkirk, IN, into 1920s. Sometimes found with flowers flashed with cranberry flashing and pieces trimmed in gold. Many pieces have been reproduced.

	Clear	Flashed Color		Clear	Flashed Color
Bowl, 6″ w, 9¼″ l, oval, ftd	30.00	—	Sauces		
			Flat	8.00	—
Butter, cov	40.00	—	Footed, 4″	12.00	—
Celery Vase	20.00	—	Salt & Pepper	35.00	—
Compote, open, ls . .	35.00	—	Spooner	25.00	—
Creamer	25.00	—	Sugar, cov	32.00	42.50
Decanter, os	40.00	62.50	Tray, water or wine,		
Goblet	20.00	—	10″	25.00	40.00
Pitcher, water	47.50	70.00	Tumbler	15.00	—
Punch Cup	10.00	18.00	Wine	12.00	20.00

DAISY AND BUTTON WITH V ORNAMENT (Van Dyke)

Made by A. J. Beatty & Co., 1886–1887.

	Amber	Blue	Clear	Vaseline
Bowls				
9″	35.00	42.00	37.50	55.00
10″	40.00	45.00	40.00	45.00
Butter, cov	85.00	80.00	65.00	90.00
Celery Vase	45.00	50.00	30.00	50.00
Creamer	35.00	50.00	28.00	50.00
Goblet	35.00	45.00	25.00	50.00
Mug	20.00	30.00	18.00	35.00
Pickle Castor	120.00	120.00	85.00	100.00
Pitcher, water	65.00	90.00	40.00	60.00
Punch Cup	12.00	20.00	12.50	25.00
Sauce, flat	20.00	20.00	10.00	30.00
Spooner	40.00	35.00	25.00	45.00
Sugar, cov	60.00	50.00	40.00	75.00
Toothpick	30.00	40.00	25.00	35.00
Tray, water	55.00	65.00	35.00	55.00
Tumbler	25.00	28.00	15.00	35.00

DAKOTA (Baby Thumbprint, Thumbprint Band)

Non-flint made by Ripley and Co., Pittsburgh, PA, in the late 1880s and early 1890s. Later reissued by U. S. Glass Co. as one of the States patterns. Prices listed are for etched fern and berry pattern; also found with fern and no berry and oak leaf etching. Sometimes ruby stained with souvenir markings.

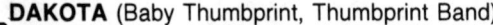

	Clear Etched	Clear Plain		Clear Etched	Clear Plain
Basket, 10 x 2″	165.00	—	tles, and salt & pepper shakers . .	165.00	—
Bowl, berry	45.00	30.00			
Butter, cov	75.00	55.00	Compotes		
Cake Stand, 10½″ . .	65.00	50.00	Cov, hs, 12″	75.00	—
Castor Set, 2 oil bot-			Cov, ls, 6″, jelly . .	60.00	50.00

	Clear Etched	Clear Plain		Clear Etched	Clear Plain
Open, hs, 7″	55.00	40.00	Sauces		
Creamer.........	55.00	30.00	Flat...........	20.00	12.50
Cruet...........	70.00	40.00	Footed	25.00	15.00
Finger Bowl......	60.00	45.00	Spooner.........	40.00	30.00
Goblet	35.00	30.00	Sugar, cov, hotel...	60.00	55.00
Pitchers			Tray, water	125.00	80.00
Milk..........	100.00	—	Tumbler	35.00	30.00
Water	90.00	65.00	Wine	37.50	25.00
Salt & Pepper	—	90.00			

DEER AND PINE TREE (Deer and Doe)

Non-flint pattern, made by Belmont Glass Co., and McKee Glass Co. 1883. Souvenir mugs with gilt found in clear and olive green.

	Amber	Apple Green	Blue	Clear
Bread Plate.......	65.00	55.00	57.50	38.00
Butter, cov	110.00	90.00	105.00	70.00
Celery Vase	—	—	—	45.00
Compotes				
Cov, hs, 8″, sq...	—	—	—	62.00
Open, hs, 7″	—	—	—	40.00
Open, hs, 9″	—	—	—	55.00
Creamer.........	95.00	85.00	90.00	60.00
Goblet	—	—	—	52.50
Marmalade Jar	—	—	—	65.00
Pickle...........	—	—	—	24.00
Pitchers				
Milk..........	—	—	—	70.00
Water	110.00	90.00	105.00	70.00
Sauces				
Flat...........	—	—	—	16.00
Ftd	—	—	—	24.00
Spooner.........	—	—	—	35.00
Sugar, cov	—	—	—	60.00
Tray, water	100.00	—	90.00	60.00

DELAWARE (Four Petal Flower)

Non-flint pattern made by U. S. Glass Co. c1899. Also found in amethyst (scarce), clear with rose trim, custard, and milk glass.

	Clear	Green With Gold	Rose With Gold
Banana Bowl......	40.00	50.00	60.00
Bowls			
8″............	30.00	35.00	50.00
9″............	25.00	45.00	55.00
Bride's Basket, SP frame	—	110.00	165.00
Butter, cov	60.00	125.00	145.00
Claret Jug, tankard shape	—	175.00	200.00
Celery Vase, flat ...	40.00	80.00	95.00
Creamer.........	25.00	55.00	70.00
Cruet, os.........	90.00	145.00	150.00

	Clear	Green With Gold	Rose With Gold
Finger Bowl	25.00	50.00	45.00
Pin Tray	35.00	—	65.00
Pitcher, water			
Bulbous	50.00	—	100.00
Tankard	110.00	200.00	185.00
Puff Box, bulbous,			
jeweled	—	200.00	350.00
Punch Cup	15.00	40.00	40.00
Sauce, 5½″, boat . .	15.00	35.00	30.00
Spooner	48.00	50.00	55.00
Sugar, cov	55.00	85.00	95.00
Toothpick	45.00	80.00	110.00
Tumbler	20.00	45.00	50.00

DEWDROP WITH STAR

Non-flint made by Campbell, Jones and Co., Pittsburgh, PA, in 1877. There was no goblet made in this pattern.

	Clear		Clear
Bread Plate, sheaf of wheat		Lamp, patented 1876	100.00
center	35.00	Pitcher, water, applied	
Bowl, 7″, collared base	20.00	handle	125.00
Butter, cov, dome lid	50.00	*Plate, 9″	25.00
Cake Stand	40.00	Relish	15.00
Cheese Dish, cov, dome lid	115.00	*Salt, ftd	20.00
Compotes		Sauces	
Cov, hs	75.00	Flat	10.00
Cov, ls, 5″	60.00	Footed	12.00
Open, hs	45.00	Spooner	35.00
Creamer, applied handle . . .	40.00	Sugar, cov, domed lid	50.00

DEWEY (Flower Flange)

Made by Indiana Tumbler & Goblet Co., Greentown, IN, 1894. Later by U. S. Glass Co. until 1904. Some experimental colors were made including a nile green opaque mug ($75.00).

	Amber	Caramel	Clear	Green	Vaseline
Bowl, 8″, ftd	35.00	—	—	45.00	45.00
Butter, cov	70.00	150.00	45.00	65.00	95.00
Creamer, cov	40.00	150.00	30.00	50.00	55.00
Cruet, os	115.00	155.00	75.00	145.00	125.00
Mug	45.00	155.00	35.00	48.00	55.00
Parfait	35.00	—	—	—	—
Pitcher, water	90.00	175.00	55.00	175.00	175.00
Plate, 7½″, ftd	35.00	130.00	30.00	40.00	65.00
Relish	35.00	145.00	20.00	45.00	45.00
Sauce, flat	20.00	—	—	25.00	30.00
Spooner	40.00	130.00	25.00	40.00	50.00
Sugar, cov					
Individual	45.00	—	25.00	45.00	65.00
Regular	50.00	150.00	35.00	55.00	75.00
Tumbler	55.00	150.00	50.00	45.00	60.00

DIAGONAL BAND

Made in c1875-1885, maker unknown.

	Amber	Apple Green	Clear
Bread Plate.......	35.00	40.00	30.00
Butter, cov	60.00	80.00	35.00
Cake Stand.......	40.00	55.00	30.00
Celery Vase	45.00	50.00	25.00
Compotes			
Cov, hs, 7″	65.00	80.00	50.00
Cov, ls, 8″......	62.50	70.00	45.00
Open, hs, 7½″ ...	45.00	50.00	20.00
Creamer.........	40.00	50.00	20.00
Goblet	30.00	45.00	20.00
Pitchers			
Milk...........	—	—	32.00
Water	65.00	95.00	40.00
Relish, 6⅞″ oval ...	14.00	18.00	10.00
Sauces			
Flat...........	—	—	6.00
Footed	—	—	10.00
Spooner........	24.00	40.00	20.00
Sugar, cov	40.00	50.00	30.00
Wine	35.00	45.00	20.00

DIAGONAL BAND WITH FAN

Non-flint, made by Ripley & Co., Pittsburgh, PA, and continued by U. S. Glass after 1891.

	Clear		Clear
Butter, cov	40.00	Pitcher, water	45.00
Celery Vase, scalloped top .	25.00	Plates	
Champagne, 5¼″	25.00	6″..................	12.00
Compotes		8″..................	18.00
Cov, hs, 6″	40.00	Sauce, ftd	6.00
Open, ls, 6¾″	35.00	Salt & Pepper..........	45.00
Creamer...............	30.00	Spooner..............	20.00
Goblet	25.00	Sugar, cov	35.00
Marmalade Jar, cov.......	35.00	Wine	18.00
Pickle................	18.00		

DIAMOND POINT

Flint, originally made by Boston and Sandwich Glass Co., in the 1830-1840 period, and by the New England Glass Co. Many other companies manufactured this pattern throughout the 19th century.

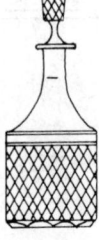

	Flint	Non-Flint		Flint	Non-Flint
Bowls			Candlesticks, pr....	145.00	—
7″, cov	60.00	20.00	Celery Vase	65.00	30.00
8″, cov	60.00	20.00	Champagne	70.00	—
8″, open	45.00	15.00	Claret...........	60.00	—
Butter, cov	95.00	50.00	Compotes		
Cake Stand, 14″ ...	185.00	—	Cov, hs, 8″	75.00	—

	Flint	Non-Flint		Flint	Non-Flint
Open, ls, 7½″ ...	50.00	40.00	Salt & Pepper	45.00	—
Creamer, applied			Salt, master, cov ...	50.00	—
handle.........	115.00	—	Sauce, flat	12.00	—
Decanter, qt, os ...	100.00	—	Spillholder........	40.00	—
Egg Cup	35.00	18.00	Spooner	40.00	25.00
Goblet	45.00	35.00	Syrup	75.00	—
Honey	15.00	—	Sugar		
Mustard, Brittania			Cov..........	65.00	—
cov	25.00	—	Open, buttermilk		
Pitchers			type	25.00	18.00
Pink	60.00	—	Tumbler, bar	65.00	35.00
Quart.	180.00	—	Whiskey, applied		
Plates			handle	75.00	—
6″	30.00	—	Wine	75.00	30.00
8″	50.00	—			

DIAMOND PYRAMIDS

Non-flint made by Fostoria Glass Co., Moundsville, WV, c1902.

	Clear		Clear
Bowl, berry.............	12.50	Salt & Pepper...........	25.00
Butter, cov	35.00	Spooner.............	12.00
Creamer................	18.00	Sugar, cov	22.00
Cruet, facetted stopper	30.00	Toothpick.............	20.00
Pitcher, water	45.00	Tumbler...............	12.50

DIAMOND QUILTED

Non-flint, c1880.

	Amber	Amethyst	Blue	Clear	Vaseline
Bowls					
6″	10.00	20.00	—	—	—
7″	18.00	—	—	—	25.00
Butter, cov	50.00	100.00	100.00	40.00	80.00
Celery Vase	35.00	75.00	45.00	40.00	40.00
Compotes					
Cov, hs, 8″	140.00	120.00	120.00	45.00	90.00
Open, ls, 9″	—	—	—	15.00	35.00
Creamer..........	45.00	40.00	70.00	25.00	55.00
*Goblet	35.00	40.00	40.00	30.00	40.00
Mug	—	—	40.00	—	—
Pitcher, water	75.00	85.00	80.00	50.00	75.00
Sauces					
Flat............	12.00	—	16.50	8.00	18.00
Footed	16.00	18.00	18.00	12.00	20.00
Spooner	34.00	40.00	40.00	30.00	55.00
Sugar, cov	50.00	75.00	55.00	40.00	45.00
Tray	55.00	70.00	70.00	30.00	65.00
*Tumbler	45.00	40.00	40.00	25.00	32.50
Wine	25.00	42.00	40.00	15.00	30.00

DIAMOND SPEARHEAD

Made by Northwood-Dugan Glass Co., Indiana, PA, around 1900. No cruet reported
A cake stand has been found, but it was not listed in early catalogues.

	Clear	Cobalt Blue Opal	Green Opal	Sapphire Blue Opal	White Opal
Bowl, berry	20.00	—	40.00	35.00	32.00
Butter, cov	40.00	150.00	85.00	75.00	—
Carafe	—	—	180.00	—	—
Celery Vase	18.00	—	40.00	35.00	32.00
Compotes					
Cov, hs	—	—	35.00	30.00	32.00
Cov, ls, jelly	—	—	60.00	50.00	—
Creamer	20.00	70.00	35.00	30.00	32.00
Cup and Saucer . . .	—	—	60.00	60.00	—
Goblet	—	—	90.00	35.00	—
Mug	20.00	—	55.00	35.00	—
Pitcher, water	50.00	200.00	85.00	75.00	—
Plate, 10″	—	—	80.00	—	—
Relish	—	—	25.00	20.00	—
Sauce	—	—	15.00	10.00	—
Spooner	20.00	—	50.00	35.00	—
Sugar, cov	30.00	—	50.00	45.00	—
Syrup	—	230.00	75.00	65.00	—
Toothpick	—	125.00	30.00	100.00	—

DIAMOND THUMBPRINT

Flint, attributed to Boston and Sandwich Glass Co., and other factories from 1840
to 1850s.

	Clear		Clear
Butter, cov	200.00	*Goblet	450.00
Celery Vase, scalloped top .	185.00	Honey Dish	25.00
Champagne	285.00	Pitcher, water	500.00
Compote, Open, ls, scal-		Saucer, flat	25.00
loped, 8″	55.00	Spooner	85.00
Creamer	225.00	Sugar, cov	150.00
Decanters		Tumbler	150.00
Pint, ns	175.00	Whiskey, applied handle . . .	300.00
Quart, os	225.00	Wine	250.00

DICKINSON

Made by the Boston and Sandwich Glass Co., c1860s.

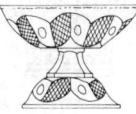

	Clear		Clear
Butter, cov	60.00	Pitcher, water, applied	
Creamer, applied handle . . .	55.00	handle	130.00
Compotes		Sauce	10.00
Open, hs, 5½″	65.00	Spooner	40.00
Open, ls, 7¼″	55.00	Sugar, cov	65.00
Goblet	45.00		

DOLLY MADISON (Jefferson's #271)

Made by Jefferson Glass Co., Follansbee, WV, c1907.

	Clear	Blue Opal	Clear	Clear Opal	Green Opal
Bowl, berry, 9¼″ . . .	35.00	50.00	30.00	35.00	45.00
Butter, cov	40.00	110.00	25.00	65.00	120.00
Creamer	35.00	65.00	30.00	80.00	90.00
Pitcher, water	45.00	150.00	45.00	125.00	140.00
Sauce	20.00	45.00	15.00	45.00	50.00
Spooner	30.00	75.00	25.00	75.00	85.00
Sugar, cov	45.00	65.00	55.00	45.00	100.00
Tumbler	30.00	40.00	30.00	40.00	60.00

DRAPERY (Lace)

Non-flint made by Doyle and Co., Pittsburgh, PA, in the 1870s. Reportedly made by Sandwich Glass Co. at an earlier period. Pieces with fine stippling have applied handles; pieces with coarse stippling have pressed handles.

	Clear		Clear
Butter, cov	45.00	Plate, 6″	30.00
Creamer, applied handle . . .	35.00	Spooner	30.00
Egg Cup	25.00	Sugar, cov	30.00
Goblet	32.50		
Pitcher, water, applied handle	60.00		

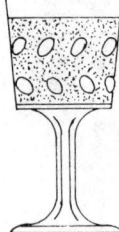

EGG IN SAND (Bean)

Non-flint, c1880. Has been reported in colors, but rare.

	Clear		Clear
Bread Plate, octagonal	25.00	Sauce	12.00
Butter, cov	45.00	Spooner, flat rim	20.00
Creamer	32.00	Sugar, cov	38.00
Goblet	30.00	Tray, water	35.00
Pitcher, water	42.00	Tumbler	36.00
Relish	12.50	Wine	32.50
Salt and Pepper	30.00		

EGYPTIAN

Non-flint, attributed to Boston and Sandwich Glass Co., c1870.

	Clear		Clear
Bowl, 8½″	50.00	Creamer	55.00
Bread Plates		Goblet	50.00
Cleopatra	90.00	Honey	14.00
Mormon Temple	350.00	Pickle, oval	20.00
Butter, cov	75.00	Pitcher, water	150.00
Celery Vase	60.00	Plate, 12″, handle, Pyramids	75.00
Compotes		Relish	20.00
Cov, hs, 7″, Sphinx base .	180.00	Sauce, ftd, 4½″	18.00
Open, hs, 7½″, Sphinx base	69.00	Spooner	30.00
		Sugar, cov	70.00

EMPRESS (Double Arch #2)

Made by Riverside Glass Works, Wellsburg, WV, c1898. Also found in amethyst (rare). Clear and emerald green pieces trimmed in gold; prices are for pieces with gold in very good condition.

	Clear	Emerald Green		Clear	Emerald Green
Breakfast Set, ind creamer and sugar	40.00	—	Pitcher, water	65.00	135.00
Butter, cov	50.00	100.00	Salt Shaker	30.00	50.00
Celery Vase	55.00	—	Spooner	30.00	45.00
Creamer	32.00	62.00	Sugar, cov	45.00	85.00
Cruet	50.00	100.00	Sugar Shaker	45.00	110.00
Oil Lamp, atypical	60.00	—	Toothpick	—	125.00
			Tumbler	30.00	55.00

ESTHER (Tooth and Claw)

Non-flint made by Riverside Glass Works, Wellsburg, WV, c1896. The green has gold trim. Also found in ruby stained and amber stained with enamel decoration.

	Clear	Green		Clear	Green
Bowl, 8″	35.00	—	Pitcher, water	65.00	135.00
Butter, cov	65.00	100.00	Salt & Pepper	50.00	100.00
Cake Stand, 10½″	45.00	80.00	Spooner	35.00	50.00
Celery Vase	40.00	62.00	Sugar, cov	55.00	85.00
Creamer	45.00	70.00	Syrup	—	150.00
Cruet, os.	45.00	120.00	Toothpick	45.00	110.00
Goblet	40.00	95.00	Tumbler	25.00	50.00

EVERGLADES (Carnelian)

Made by Harry Northwood Co., Wheeling, WV, c1903. Add 200% for green opalescent.

	Blue Opal	Canary Opal	Custard	White Opal
Banana Dish	175.00	170.00	—	150.00
Bowl, berry	135.00	100.00	150.00	80.00
Butter, cov	250.00	150.00	300.00	125.00
Compote, jelly	75.00	90.00	350.00	67.50
Creamer	90.00	75.00	145.00	45.00
Cruet, os.	375.00	385.00	700.00	175.00
Pitcher, water	350.00	375.00	600.00	200.00
Sauce	35.00	35.00	50.00	25.00
Spooner	75.00	65.00	125.00	45.00
Sugar, cov	175.00	145.00	165.00	75.00
Tumbler	65.00	65.00	110.00	25.00

EXCELSIOR

Flint made by several firms, including Sandwich and McKee, from 1850s-1860s. Quality and design vary. Prices are for high quality flint.

	Clear		Clear
Bar Bottle	50.00	Bitters bottle	25.00
Bowl, 10″, open	125.00	Butter, cov	100.00

	Clear		Clear
Candlestick	125.00	Goblet, Maltese Cross	52.50
Celery Vase, scalloped top	50.00	Lamp, hand	95.00
Claret	45.00	Pickle Jar, cov	45.00
Compotes		Pitcher, water	325.00
Cov, ls	125.00	Salt, master	22.00
Open, hs	85.00	Spillholder	75.00
Cordial	40.00	Spooner	65.00
Creamer	60.00	Sugar, cov	90.00
Egg Cups		Tumbler, bar	60.00
Double	50.00	Whiskey, Maltese Cross	65.00
Single	40.00	Wine	40.00

EYEWINKER

Non-flint made in Findlay, OH, in 1889. Reportedly made by Dalzell, Gilmore and Leighton Glass Co., who were organized in 1883 in West Virginia, moved to Findlay in 1888. Made only in clear glass; colors have been reproduced. A goblet and tooth-pick originally were not made in this pattern.

	Clear		Clear
Banana Dish	85.00	Lamp, Kerosene	85.00
Bowl, 9"	75.00	Nappy, folded sides, 7¼"	22.50
*Butter, cov	70.00	Pitcher, water	85.00
Cake Stand	85.00	Plate	
Celery Vase	55.00	10", upturned sides	65.00
Compotes		Square, upturned rims	30.00
Open, 7¼", with fluted		Syrup, pewter top	110.00
edge	65.00	Salt Shaker	35.00
Open, 4½", jelly	45.00	Spooner	35.00
Creamer	50.00	Sugar, cov	65.00
Cruet	65.00	Tumbler	35.00

FAN WITH DIAMOND (Shell)

Non-flint, made by McKee Glass Co., c1880.

	Clear		Clear
Bowl, flat, oval	25.00	Pitcher, water	45.00
Butter, cov	50.00	Sauce	12.00
Compote, cov, hs	65.00	Spooner	25.00
Creamers		Sugars	
Applied handle	45.00	Cov	50.00
Pressed handle	30.00	Open, buttermilk type	20.00
Egg Cup	30.00	Syrup, applied handle, bird	
Goblet	25.00	finial	100.00

FEATHER (Doric)

Non-flint made in Indiana in 1896 and by McKee Glass. Later the pattern was reissued with variations and quality differences. Also found in amber stain (rare).

	Clear	Emerald Green		Clear	Emerald Green
Banana Dish	65.00	75.00	Cake Plate	30.00	—
Bowl, 8", sq	15.00	—	Cake Stand, 9½"	35.00	—
Butter, cov	50.00	125.00	Celery Vase	35.00	—

	Clear	Emerald Green		Clear	Emerald Green
Champagne	40.00	—	Pitchers		
Compotes			Milk	55.00	—
Cov, hs, 8½″	125.00	—	Water	50.00	200.00
Cov, ls, 4¼″, jelly	25.00	—	Plate, 10″	30.00	—
			Salt Shaker	30.00	70.00
Cov, ls, 8¼″	35.00	—	Spooner	25.00	60.00
Cordial	95.00	—	Sugar, cov	45.00	80.00
Creamer	45.00	65.00	Syrup	90.00	—
Cruet, os.	46.50	85.00	Toothpick	70.00	125.00
Dishes, nest of 3: 7″, 8″, and 9″	40.00	—	Tumbler	30.00	75.00
Goblet	50.00	75.00	Wine		
Marmalade Jar	45.00	—	Scalloped border	40.00	—
			Straight border	30.00	—

FEATHER DUSTER (Rosette Medallion, Huckel)

Made by United States Glass Co. in 1898, and probably by another company around 1895.

	Clear	Emerald Green		Clear	Emerald Green
Bowl, Berry, 8″	22.00	—	Plate, 9″	22.00	—
Butter, cov	45.00	—	Relish	18.00	—
Cake Stand, 10″	35.00	—	Spooner, plain form	20.00	—
Celery Vase	22.00	—	Sugar, cov	35.00	—
Compote			Tray, "Gold Standard Tray", full-length portrait of McKinley, Feather Duster border, 1896	200.00	—
Cov, hs, 8″	50.00	—			
Open, ls, shallow bowl, 9″	25.00	—			
Creamer	25.00	—			
Goblet	30.00	—	Tumbler	18.00	—
Pitcher, water, ½ gallon	45.00	55.00	Waste Bowl	20.00	—

FESTOON

Non-flint, 1890-1894. No goblet or wine were made in this pattern.

	Clear		Clear
Bowls		Relish	15.00
8″, Berry	20.00	Sauce, flat	7.50
9″, rect	25.00	Spooner	25.00
Butter, cov	55.00	Sugars	
Cake Stand, 10″	45.00	Cov	40.00
Creamer	30.00	Open	15.00
Pickle Castor, cov	110.00	Tray, water, 10″	30.00
Pitcher, water	50.00	Tumbler, five sizes	25.00
Plate, 8¼″	30.00	Waste Bowl	30.00

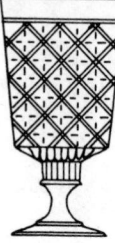

FINECUT

Non-flint made by Bryce Bros., Pittsburgh, PA, c1879, and by U. S. Glass Co. in 1891.

	Amber	Blue	Clear	Vaseline
Bowl, 8¼".	15.00	20.00	12.00	15.00
Bread Plate.	50.00	60.00	25.00	50.00
Butter, cov	55.00	75.00	45.00	60.00
Cake Stand.	—	—	30.00	—
Celery Tray	—	45.00	25.00	40.00
Celery Vase, SP holder	—	—	—	115.00
Creamer	35.00	40.00	16.00	75.00
Goblet	45.00	55.00	20.00	42.00
Pickle	—	—	12.00	—
Pitcher, water	45.00	80.00	35.00	55.00
Plates				
6"	—	20.00	8.00	—
7"	18.00	40.00	12.50	20.00
10"	25.00	50.00	15.00	45.00
Relish.	35.00	40.00	18.00	35.00
Sauce, flat	14.00	15.00	10.00	14.00
Spooner	30.00	45.00	18.00	40.00
Sugars				
Covered	45.00	55.00	35.00	45.00
Open.	40.00	45.00	25.00	40.00
Tray, water	50.00	55.00	20.00	50.00

FINECUT AND BLOCK

Made by King Glass Co., Crystal Glass Co. in c1890, and by McKee Glass Co. c1894. Also attributed to Portland Glass Co. Made in clear, solid colors of amber, blue, and yellow (all comparable in price), and in clear with color blocks.

	Clear	Solid Colored Pieces	Color Block: Amber	Color Block: Blue	Color Block: Yellow or Pink
Bowl, berry	35.00	—	—	—	—
Butters, cov					
Flat.	65.00	—	—	—	—
Footed	75.00	165.00	—	—	—
Cake Stands					
Large	40.00	—	—	—	—
Small.	35.00	—	—	—	—
Celery Tray	30.00	—	50.00	45.00	60.00
Compotes					
Cov, ls.	35.00	—	—	—	—
Open, ls, 8½" . . .	30.00	—	45.00	40.00	45.00
Open jelly	18.00	50.00	75.00	75.00	75.00
Creamer	35.00	—	70.00	60.00	65.00
Goblet	25.00	—	60.00	65.00	65.00
Pitcher, water	45.00	85.00	85.00	95.00	125.00
Plate, 5¾"	12.50	—	—	—	—
Punch Cup	12.00	—	—	—	—
Relish, rect	12.00	—	55.00	50.00	55.00
Salt, individual	12.00	—	—	—	—
Sauces					
Flat.	8.00	—	16.00	16.00	16.00
Footed	10.00	—	—	—	

	Clear	Solid Colored Pieces	Color Block: Amber	Color Block: Blue	Color Block: Yellow or Pink
Spooner	—	20.00	55.00	65.00	50.00
Sugar, cov	40.00	—	125.00	135.00	125.00
Trays					
Ice Cream	55.00	—	—	—	—
Water	60.00	—	—	—	—
Tumbler	20.00	50.00	50.00	45.00	45.00
Wine	25.00	—	45.00	45.00	45.00

FINECUT AND PANEL

Non-flint pattern made by many Pittsburgh factories in the 1880s. Reissued in the early 1890s by U. S. Glass Co.

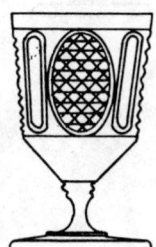

	Amber	Blue	Clear	Vaseline
Bowls				
7″	28.00	35.00	15.00	25.00
9″	—	—	—	30.00
Bread Plate.	32.50	40.00	25.00	—
Butter, cov	45.00	75.00	40.00	60.00
Cake Stand, 10″ . . .	50.00	55.00	30.00	50.00
Compotes				
Cov, hs	125.00	135.00	50.00	130.00
Open, hs	65.00	60.00	35.00	60.00
Creamer	35.00	50.00	25.00	40.00
Goblet	50.00	50.00	20.00	35.00
Pitchers				
Milk.	—	—	—	50.00
Water	85.00	65.00	50.00	45.00
Plate	25.00	30.00	18.00	25.00
Platter	30.00	50.00	25.00	30.00
Relish.	20.00	30.00	16.00	18.00
Sauce, ftd	14.00	25.00	8.00	15.00
Spooner	35.00	45.00	25.00	28.00
Sugar, cov	37.50	42.50	30.00	32.50
Tray, water	60.00	55.00	50.00	60.00
Tumbler	25.00	30.00	18.00	35.00
Wine	30.00	35.00	20.00	25.00

FINE RIB

Flint made by New England Glass Co. in the 1860s. Later made in non-flint, which has limited collecting interest.

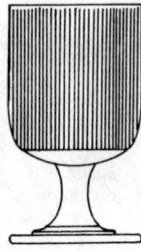

	Clear Flint		Clear Flint
Bitters Bottle	50.00	Pitcher, water, applied handle	95.00
Bowl, 7″, cov	85.00	Plates, 6″ & 7″	20.00
Butter, cov	75.00	Salts	
Castor Set	200.00	Cov, ftd.	85.00
Celery Vase	50.00	Individual.	37.50
Champagne	68.00	Spooner.	65.00
Compote, open, 9″, ls	55.00	Sugar, cov	75.00
Cordial	45.00	Tumbler, bar	45.00
Creamer, applied handle . . .	125.00	Tumble-up	125.00
Egg Cup.	45.00	Whiskey, handled	70.00
Goblet	50.00	Wine	38.00
Lamp	150.00		
Mug.	45.00		

FISH SCALE (Coral)

Non-flint made by Bryce Brothers, Pittsburgh, PA, in the mid-1880s and by U. S. Glass Co. in 1891.

	Clear		Clear
Bowls		Water	55.00
Cov, 9½″	45.00	Plates	
Open, 8″	16.50	7″, round	15.00
Butter, cov	45.00	9″, square	27.50
Cake Plate	55.00	Salt & Pepper	65.00
Cake Stand, 9″	30.00	Sauce	5.00
Celery Vase	30.00	Spooner	24.00
Compote, Jelly	25.00	Sugar, cov	50.00
Creamer	35.00	Tray, condiment, rect.	35.00
Goblet	28.00	Tumbler	45.00
Lamp, Finger	75.00	Waste Bowl	25.00
Mug, large	25.00		
Pitchers			
Milk	35.00		

FLAMINGO HABITAT

Maker unknown, etched pattern.

	Clear		Clear
Bowl, 10″, oval	40.00	Open, 6″	35.00
Celery Vase	45.00	Creamer	50.00
Champagne	40.00	Goblet	40.00
Cheese Dish, blown, folded		Sauce, ftd	20.00
rim, dome lid	75.00	Spooner	25.00
Compotes		Sugar, cov	50.00
Cov, 4½″	75.00	Wine	45.00
Cov, 6½″	95.00		

FLEUR DE LIS AND DRAPE (Fleur de Lis and Tassel)

Non-flint made by U. S. Glass Co., c1892. Clear and emerald green pieces often trimmed with gilt. Also made in milk glass (rare).

	Clear	Emerald Green		Clear	Emerald Green
Bowl	15.00	30.00	Water	50.00	60.00
Butter, cov	45.00	55.00	Plates, 8″	20.00	35.00
Cake Stand	35.00	55.00	Spooner	21.00	35.00
Compote, cov	35.00	60.00	Sugar, cov	30.00	55.00
Creamer	25.00	42.00	Syrup, metal top	50.00	85.00
Cruet, os.	45.00	85.00	Tumbler	20.00	32.00
Goblet	32.50	40.00	Water Tray, 11½″	24.00	50.00
Mustard Jar, cov	35.00	50.00	Wine	25.00	45.00
Pitcher					
Milk	40.00	—			

FLORIDA (Green Herringbone)

Non-flint made by U. S. Glass Co., late 1880s-1890s. One of States patterns.

	Clear	Emerald Green		Clear	Emerald Green
Bowl, 9″	18.00	24.00	9¼″	15.00	28.00
Butter, cov	40.00	50.00	Relishes		
Cake Stand	27.00	38.00	6″, sq	10.00	15.00
Celery Vase	28.00	35.00	8½″, sq	15.00	22.00
Compote, open, hs,			Salt Shakers	25.00	50.00
6½″, sq.	—	40.00	Sauce.	8.00	15.00
Creamer	25.00	40.00	Spooner	20.00	35.00
Goblet	25.00	40.00	Sugar, cov	32.00	40.00
Mustard Pot, attach-			Syrup	40.00	175.00
ed underplate,			Tumbler	20.00	30.00
plate, cov	25.00	45.00	Wine	25.00	50.00
Pitcher, water	50.00	75.00			
Plates					
7½″	10.00	18.00			

FLUTED SCROLLS

Made by Harry Northwood & Co., Indiana, PA, c1898. Sometimes with burnished gold trim.

	Blue Opal	Custard	Vaseline Opal	White Opal
Bowl, berry	100.00	100.00	75.00	
Butter, cov	135.00	200.00	185.00	65.00
Creamer	75.00	100.00	45.00	45.00
Cruet. os.	100.00	175.00	85.00	—
Pitcher, water	210.00	190.00	175.00	—
Puff Box	50.00	—	50.00	—
Sauce.	30.00	45.00	25.00	—
Spooner	100.00	100.00	85.00	65.00
Sugar, cov	95.00	115.00	150.00	80.00
Tray	40.00	—	30.00	25.00
Tumbler	75.00	—	65.00	—

FRANCESWARE

Made by Hobbs, Brockunier & Co., Wheeling, WV, c1880. A clear frosted hobnail or swirl pattern glass with amber stained top rims. It may be pressed or mold blown. Swirl pieces are noted, otherwise they are hobnail.

	Clear	Frosted/ Amber Stain		Clear	Frosted/ Amber Stain
Bowl, 7½″.	50.00	75.00	11″	150.00	200.00
Box, 5¼″, round,			Salt & Pepper		
cov	45.00	65.00	Hobnail	50.00	65.00
Butter, cov	80.00	110.00	Swirl	60.00	—
Creamer	50.00	70.00	Sauce, 4″, sq	20.00	32.00
Finger Bowl, 4″	40.00	50.00	Spooner	45.00	50.00
Pitchers			Sugars		
8½″	90.00	150.00	Cov.	60.00	55.00

	Clear	Frosted/Amber Stain		Clear	Frosted/Amber Stain
Open.........	40.00	60.00	Toothpick........	65.00	85.00
Sugar Shaker, swirl .	65.00	70.00	Tray, leaf shape, 12″.	75.00	100.00
Syrup, swirl.......	65.00	75.00	Tumbler.........	35.00	45.00

FROSTED CIRCLE

Produced by Bryce Bros., Pittsburgh, PA, from 1876 to c1885. Later by U. S. Glass Co. in the late 1890s.

	Clear Circle	Frosted Circle		Clear Circle	Frosted Circle
Bowls, cov			Pitcher, water.....	—	50.00
7″............	—	25.00	Plates		
8″............	—	30.00	4″............	10.00	22.00
Butter, cov.......	40.00	60.00	9″............	12.00	17.00
Cake Stand, 8″....	—	35.00	Sauce, ftd........	8.00	12.00
Compotes			Salt & Pepper.....	—	60.00
Cov, hs			Spooner.........	—	35.00
7″.........	20.00	35.00	Sugar, cov.......	37.50	50.00
8″.........	35.00	45.00	Sugar Shaker.....	—	60.00
Open, 10″, hs ...	42.50	55.00	Syrup...........	—	125.00
Creamer.........	—	38.00	Tumbler.........	20.00	30.00
Cruet, os.........	45.00	65.00	Wine...........	—	35.00
Goblet..........	27.50	35.00			

FROSTED LEAF

Flint, c1850. Listed as being produced by Portland Glass Co. between 1873 and 1874.

	Flint		Flint
Butter, cov............	150.00	Sauce, flat.............	25.00
Celery Vase............	145.00	Spooner..............	95.00
Champagne............	175.00	Sugars	
Compote, cov...........	275.00	Cov................	195.00
Creamer..............	300.00	Open, buttermilk type....	90.00
Decanter, os............	275.00	Tumbler	
Egg Cup..............	130.00	Ftd................	140.00
Goblet...............	150.00	Regular.............	200.00
Pitcher, water...........	450.00	Wine................	200.00

GALLOWAY (Virginia #2)

Non-flint made by U. S. Glass Co., 1904. Clear glass with and without gold trim; also known with cranberry flashing and ruby stain.

	Clear w/ Gold	Cranberry Flashed		Clear w/ Gold	Cranberry Flashed
Bowl, berry.......	26.00	50.00	Creamer.........	30.00	40.00
Butter, cov.......	65.00	125.00	Cruet...........	45.00	—
Cake Stand.......	55.00	—	Goblet..........	65.00	—
Carafe, water.....	48.00	75.00	Mug............	35.00	50.00
Celery Vase......	35.00	65.00	Olive, 6″........	20.00	30.00

	Clear w/ Gold	Cran- berry Flashed		Clear w/ Gold	Cran- berry Flashed
Pitcher, water, ice lip	55.00	—	Salt & Pepper	30.00	—
Plate, round 8″	12.00	30.00	Sugar, cov	35.00	75.00
Punch Bowl, 15¼″	125.00	—	Syrup	50.00	—
Punch Cup	12.00	25.00	Tumbler, handled	35.00	50.00
Relish	20.00	30.00	Waste Bowl	25.00	—
			Wine	45.00	—

GARFIELD DRAPE

Non-flint pattern issued in 1881 by Adams & Co., Pittsburgh, Pennsylvania, after the assassination of President Garfield.

	Clear		Clear
Bread Plates		Creamer	40.00
Memorial, portrait of Garfield	65.00	Goblet	40.00
"We Mourn Our Nation's		Pitchers	
Loss", portrait	75.00	Milk	65.00
Butter, cov	60.00	Water	75.00
Cake Stand, 9½″	75.00	Relish, oval	18.00
Celery Vase	50.00	Sauce, ftd	10.00
Compote, cov, hs, 8″	90.00	Spooner	30.00
		Sugar, cov	50.00

GEORGIA (Peacock Feather)

Probably Richards and Hartley, but reissued by several glass companies, including U. S. Glass Co. in 1902 as part of their States series. Rare in blue. No goblet known in pattern.

	Clear		Clear
Bowl, 8″	30.00	Lamps	
Butter, cov	45.00	Chamber, pedestal, blue	275.00
Cake Stand, 11″	40.00	Hand, oil, 7″	65.00
Compotes		Pitcher, water	55.00
Cov, hs, 8″	50.00	Plate, 5¼″	18.00
Open, jelly	20.00	Salt & Pepper	60.00
Condiment Set, tray, oil cruet,		Spooner	28.00
salt and pepper	75.00	Sugar, cov	40.00
Creamer	35.00	Syrup, metal lid	55.00
Cruet, os	55.00	Tumbler	25.00

GIANT BULL'S EYE (Bull's Eye and Spearhead)

Made by Bellaire Glass Co., Findlay, Ohio, and continued by U. S. Glass Co. after 1891.

	Clear		Clear
Brandy bottle, os, tall, narrow	55.00	Lamp, handled	75.00
Claret Jug, tankard shape	60.00	Pitcher, water	65.00
Compote, cov	50.00	Tumbler	30.00
Cruet, os	60.00	Vase	35.00
Decanter, os	50.00	Wine	30.00
Goblet	35.00	Wine Tray, 7¼″	25.00

GOOSEBERRY

Non-flint of the 1880s. Made by Boston and Sandwich Glass Co. and others in clear and milk glass. Reproduced in milk glass.

	Clear	Milk Glass		Clear	Milk Glass
Butter, cov	50.00	50.00	Sauce	12.00	15.00
Compote, cov, hs,			Spooner	24.00	30.00
8"	75.00	65.00	Sugar, Cov	45.00	55.00
Creamer	30.00	50.00	Syrup, applied han-		
Goblet	35.00	45.00	dle	75.00	90.00
Mug	40.00	40.00	Tumbler	35.00	40.00
Pitcher, water, ap-					
plied handle	85.00	100.00			

GOTHIC

Flint made by Boston and Sandwich Glass Co., c1860s.

	Clear		Clear
Bowl, 7"	60.00	Egg Cup	45.00
Butter, cov	85.00	Goblet	45.00
Celery Vase	115.00	Sauce, flat	18.00
Champagne	125.00	Spooner	45.00
Compotes		Sugar, cov	75.00
Cov, hs, 8"	110.00	Tumbler	95.00
Open, ls, 7"	65.00	Wine	60.00
Creamer	75.00		

GRAND (Diamond Medallion)

Non-flint, made by Bryce, Higbee and Co. 1885. Stemware comes in plain and ringed stems.

	Clear		Clear
Bread Plate, 10"	20.00	Goblet	25.00
Butter, cov		Pitcher, water	50.00
Flat	35.00	Relish, 7½", oval	8.00
Footed	40.00	Salt & Pepper	45.00
Cake Stands		Spooner	25.00
8"	30.00	Sugar, cov	35.00
10"	35.00	Syrup, metal top	55.00
Celery Vase, pedestal	25.00	Waste Bowl, collared	20.00
Compote, open, hs, 9"	35.00	Wine	35.00
Creamer	25.00		

GRAPE BAND

Issued in flint by Bryce, Walker and Co. in the late 1850s; non-flint in 1869.

	Flint	Non-Flint		Flint	Non-Flint
Butter, cov	75.00	50.00	Creamer, applied		
Compotes			handle	—	48.00
Cov, hs	—	50.00	Egg Cup	—	18.00
Open, hs	—	25.00	Goblet	40.00	25.00

	Flint	Non-Flint		Flint	Non-Flint
Pickle	—	14.00	Open, buttermilk		
Pitcher, water	—	60.00	type	—	35.00
Plate, 6″	—	15.00	Wine	35.00	25.00
Spooner	—	30.00			
Sugars					
Cov.	—	45.00			

GRASSHOPPER (Long Spear)

Maker unknown; over 40 pieces documented. Pieces without the grasshopper bring 30% less. Goblet is modern.

	Amber	Clear		Amber	Clear
Bowls			Pickle	—	20.00
Covered	—	35.00	Pitcher, water	125.00	—
Open, ftd	—	25.00	Salt, master, ftd.	—	16.00
Butter, cov	—	60.00	Spooner	75.00	50.00
Celery Vase	90.00	80.00	Sugar, cov	—	65.00
Creamer	—	45.00			
Marmalade Jar, cov,					
insert	—	125.00			

HAMILTON

Flint, c1869. Some attribute pattern to Boston and Sandwich Glass Co. Other companies also may have made it.

	Clear		Clear
Butter, cov	65.00	Pitcher, water	150.00
Celery Vase	60.00	Plate, 6″	45.00
Compotes		Salt, ftd	30.00
Cov, hs	75.00	Spooner	38.00
Open, ls, 6″, scallop rim	77.50	Sweetmeat Dish, hs, cov	75.00
Creamer, applied handle	75.00	Sugar, cov	75.00
Egg Cup, frosted leaf	50.00	Tumbler, water or bar	85.00
Goblet	45.00	Whiskey, applied handle	95.00
Lamp, hand	85.00	Wine	90.00

HAND (Pennsylvania #2)

Made by O'Hara Glass Co., Pittsburgh, Pennsylvania, c1880. Covered pieces have a hand holding bar finial, hence the name.

	Clear		Clear
Bowl, 10″	25.00	Creamer	40.00
Bread Plate	35.00	Goblet	45.00
Butter, cov	85.00	Marmalade Jar, cov.	50.00
Cake Stand	55.00	Pickle	20.00
Celery Vase	45.00	Pitcher, water	75.00
Compotes		Sauce, ftd	15.00
Cov, hs, 8″	95.00	Spooner	30.00
Open, hs, 7¾″	45.00	Sugar, cov	85.00
Cordial, 3½″	65.00	Wine	45.00

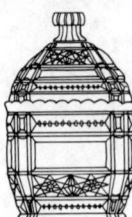

HANOVER (Block With Stars #2, Blockhouse)

Originally made by Richards and Hartley, of Tarentum, Pennsylvania, in 1888 and possibly earlier. Made in many pieces.

	Clear	Dark Amber		Clear	Dark Amber
Bowl, 10″, berry. . . .	20.00	40.00	Goblet	25.00	55.00
Bread Plate, 10″ . . .	20.00	30.00	Ketchup Bottles, pr .	50.00	75.00
Butter, cov	40.00	80.00	Mugs		
Cake Stand, 10″ . . .	42.00	62.00	Large	22.00	48.00
Celery Vase	27.00	38.00	Small.	18.00	40.00
Cheese Dish, cov,			Pitcher, water	50.00	85.00
10″	50.00	95.00	Plate, 6″.	25.00	40.00
Compotes			Sauce, ftd.	10.00	15.00
Cov, hs	45.00	90.00	Spooner	25.00	37.00
Open, ls	40.00	45.00	Sugar, cov	45.00	55.00
Creamer	30.00	45.00	Tumbler	25.00	30.00

HARP (Lyre)

Flint glass made by Bryce Bros., Pittsburgh, Pennsylvania, in the late 1840s and early 1850s. Also found in McKee catalog of 1859.

	Clear		Clear
Butter, cov	150.00	Nappy	100.00
Compote, cov, ls, 6″	200.00	Salt, master	75.00
Goblet, rare	1,000.00	Spooner	95.00
Lamp, handle	125.00	Sweetmeat Jar, cov	200.00

HARTFORD

Made by Fostoria Glass Co., Moundsville, West Virginia, until about 1930.

	Clear	Emerald Green		Clear	Emerald Green
Basket, flat, handle,			Olive, flat, 5½″ sq,		
turned up sides . .	18.00	28.00	turned up sides . .	15.00	25.00
Bowls			Relish, oval	15.00	22.00
6″, sq, collared			Salt & Pepper	45.00	65.00
base	8.00	12.00	Salt, individual.	10.00	20.00
7″ and 8″	9.00	15.00	Sauces		
Butter, cov, sq.	40.00	55.00	4½″, flat	5.00	8.00
Celery Vase	32.50	40.00	4½″, footed	8.00	12.00
Creamer	25.00	35.00	Sugar, cov	35.00	45.00
Dish, 9″, rect.	14.50	21.00	Syrup, metal top . . .	45.00	75.00
Finger Bowl.	10.00	15.00	Tumbler, small.	15.00	20.00

HARTLEY (Paneled Diamond Cut With Fan)

Made by Richards and Hartley in 1880s, later by U. S. Glass Co. Trilobed form has either plain or engraved panels. Twenty-three pieces documented.

	Amber	Blue & Vaseline	Clear
Bowls, berry			
7″, ftd	35.00	40.00	18.00
9″	30.00	40.00	20.00
Bread Plate, trilobed	30.00	40.00	20.00
Butter, cov	50.00	60.00	40.00
Cake Stand, 10″ . . .	45.00	50.00	40.00
Celery Vase	32.00	40.00	25.00
Compotes			
Cov, ls, 7¾″.	68.00	75.00	45.00
Open, 7″ and 8″. .	30.00	40.00	18.00
Creamer	20.00	35.00	25.00
Dish, centerpiece. . .	40.00	45.00	20.00
Goblet	35.00	40.00	25.00
Pitchers			
Milk, qt	75.00	85.00	40.00
Water, ½ gal	85.00	85.00	60.00
Plate	45.00	50.00	30.00
Relish.	18.00	20.00	15.00
Spooner	28.00	30.00	18.00
Sugar, cov	40.00	50.00	30.00
Tumbler	30.00	35.00	20.00
Wine	40.00	48.00	35.00

HARVARD YARD (Harvard # 1)

Made by Tarentum Glass Co., 1896. Also found in clear with gold, emerald green, and pink.

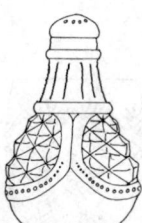

	Clear		Clear
Butter, cov	32.00	Plate, 10″	15.00
Cake Stand	30.00	Spooner	18.00
Creamer	18.00	Sugar, cov	25.00
Goblet	25.00	Tumbler	15.00
Pitcher, water	30.00	Wine	12.00

HAWAIIAN LEI

Made by Higbee Bryce and Co. during 1900s. Also may have been made in Canada. Colors reported in child dish reproductions. Some pieces are marked with company trademark—a small bee embossed in glass with HIG/bee, but similar fake trademark reproduced from the 1970s to present.

	Clear		Clear
Basket, small, applied			
handle	40.00	Dish.	15.00
Bowls		Goblet	35.00
7″.	18.50	Pickle Castor, SP lid and	
9″.	19.00	frame	75.00
Butter, cov	50.00	Pitcher, water	60.00
Cake Stand, 7½″	35.00	Rose Bowl	18.00
Celery Vase, handled	15.00	Salt & Pepper.	45.00
Champagne	35.00	Tumbler	14.00
Compote, open, hs, 8″	35.00	Vase, tall, flared rim	18.00
Creamer.	45.00	Wine	35.00

HEART WITH THUMBPRINT (Bull's Eye in Heart)

Non-flint, made by Tarentum Glass Co. 1898. Emerald green pieces have gold highlights. Made experimentally in custard, opaque nile green and cobalt.

	Clear	Emerald Green		Clear	Emerald Green
Banana Boat	75.00	—	Nappy, turned up edges	30.00	—
Barber Bottle	65.00	—	Pitcher, water	58.00	—
Bowl, 9″	35.00	—	Plates		
Butter, cov	60.00	110.00	6″	30.00	—
Cake Stand	125.00	—	10″	45.00	—
Carafe, water	50.00	—	Punch Cup	22.00	—
Card Tray	20.00	—	Rose Bowl	30.00	—
Celery Vase	50.00	—	Sauce, 4½″	15.00	—
Compote, open, hs, 8½″	48.00	—	Sugars		
Creamers			Ind	25.00	35.00
Ind	20.00	45.00	Regular, cov	55.00	60.00
Regular	32.50	50.00	Syrup	60.00	—
Cruet	75.00	—	Tray, 8¼″ l, 4¼″ w .	35.00	—
Goblet	55.00	65.00	Tumbler	50.00	—
Hair Receiver, metal lid	30.00	—	Vase, 10″	60.00	—
Ice Bucket	60.00	—	Wine	45.00	—

HICKMAN (La Clede)

Non-flint pattern made by McKee Glass Co., Pittsburgh, Pennsylvania, c1897.

	Clear	Emerald Green		Clear	Emerald Green
Bon bon, 9″, sq.	12.00	—	Olive, 4″, handle . . .	10.00	20.00
Bowl, berry	20.00	35.00	Pickle	15.00	20.00
Butter, cov	35.00	58.00	Pitcher, water	55.00	—
Cake Stand, 9½″ . . .	30.00	—	Plate, 9¼″	15.00	—
Champagne	25.00	—	Punch Cup	10.00	15.00
Cologne Bottle, faceted stopper	30.00	—	Punch Glass, ftd . . .	30.00	—
Compotes			Relish	18.00	15.00
Cov, hs, 7″	55.00	—	Rose Bowl	22.00	—
Open, hs, 8″	45.00	—	Salt Shaker, single		
Open, ls, 4½″, jelly	25.00	45.00	Round, long cut neck	15.00	—
Creamer	25.00	28.00	Round, squat	20.00	30.00
Cruet, os.	45.00	—	Salt, individual, flat, sloping sides	8.00	—
Dish, 4″ sq	16.00	—	Spooner	27.00	—
Goblet	35.00	50.00	Sugar, cov	40.00	50.00
Ice Bucket	50.00	—	Sugar Shaker	45.00	—
Mustard Jar, attached underplate, cov	45.00	—	Toothpick	45.00	75.00
			Tumbler	30.00	—
Nappy, 5″	10.00	—	Vase, 10¼″	45.00	12.00
			Wine	30.00	—

HIDALGO (Frosted Waffle)

Non-flint made by Adams and Co., Pittsburgh, Pennsylvania, in the early 1880s. This pattern comes etched and clear, and also with part of pattern frosted. Add 20% for frosted.

	Amber Stained	Clear		Amber Stained	Clear
Bowl, 10″, sq	—	20.00	Plate, 10″	—	25.00
Bread Boat, large . .	—	58.00	Salt & Pepper	—	40.00
Butter, cov	—	50.00	Salt, master, sq. . . .	—	15.00
Celery Vase	32.50	15.00	Sauce, handled. . . .	—	10.00
Compote, cov, hs . .	—	40.00	Spooner	—	20.00
Cruet	—	65.00	Sugar, cov	—	35.00
Cup and Saucer . . .	—	40.00	Sugar Shaker	—	45.00
Goblet	38.00	18.00	Syrup	—	50.00
Nappy, handled, sq .	—	18.00	Tray, water	—	55.00
Pickle, boat shaped.	—	12.00	Tumbler	—	25.00
Pitcher, water	—	45.00			

HOBNAIL OPALESCENT

Made by several companies with variations in forms of pieces, c1880–1900. Pieces are found round in shape, with frilled tops, pieces on three feet, pieces on four feet, square in shape or octagonal in shape.

	Blue Opal	Cranberry Opal	Vaseline Opal	White Opal
Butters, cov				
Flat	100.00	110.00	105.00	85.00
Four Feet	110.00	115.00	110.00	90.00
Celery Vase	85.00	120.00	100.00	85.00
Creamers				
Flat	95.00	115.00	110.00	85.00
Four Feet	100.00	120.00	115.00	98.00
Cruet, os.	—	—	125.00	50.00
Mug	35.00	55.00	50.00	30.00
Pitcher, water	100.00	125.00	120.00	95.00
Sauce, flat	25.00	35.00	30.00	20.00
Spooners				
Flat	25.00	40.00	30.00	20.00
Four Feet	35.00	40.00	30.00	25.00
Sugars, cov				
Flat.	40.00	60.00	55.00	30.00
Four Feet	45.00	65.00	60.00	35.00
Toothpick	30.00	50.00	50.00	30.00
Tumbler	40.00	55.00	50.00	30.00

HOBNAIL, POINTED

Non-flint c1880. Also found in apple green, dark green, and vaseline.

	Amber	Blue	Clear
Bone Dish........	25.00	30.00	20.00
*Bowl...........	25.00	30.00	20.00
Butter, cov.......	45.00	48.00	40.00
Cake Stand, 10".. .	40.00	45.00	35.00
Celery Vase......	30.00	35.00	20.00
Compote, open, hs, 8"...........	40.00	45.00	35.00
Cordial..........	25.00	30.00	20.00
Creamer.........	30.00	35.00	25.00
Goblet..........	30.00	35.00	25.00
Inkwell.........	30.00	35.00	25.00
Pickle..........	15.00	20.00	12.00
*Pitcher, water.....	40.00	45.00	35.00
Plate, 7"........	14.00	16.00	12.00
Salt, individual.....	10.00	15.00	5.00
*Sauce, flat.......	15.00	12.00	10.00
Spooner.........	25.00	30.00	20.00
*Sugar, open.......	20.00	25.00	15.00
Tray, water, 11½"..	35.00	40.00	30.00
*Wine...........	20.00	25.00	15.00

HOBNAIL WITH FAN

Non-flint, made by Adams and Co., c1880.

	Amber	Blue	Clear
Bowl, berry.......	35.00	40.00	25.00
Butter, cov.......	55.00	60.00	40.00
Celery Vase......	35.00	40.00	30.00
Creamer.........	40.00	45.00	25.00
Dish, oblong......	—	—	24.00
Goblet..........	35.00	40.00	20.00
Salt, ind.........	15.00	15.00	10.00
Sugar, cov.......	45.00	50.00	30.00
Tray, 12" l........	30.00	35.00	20.00

HOLLY

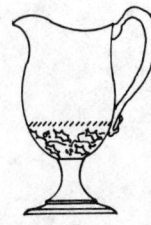

Non-flint made by Boston and Sandwich Glass Co., late 1860s, early 1870s.

	Clear		Clear
Butter, cov.............	150.00	Salt, ftd...............	60.00
Cake Stand, 11".........	125.00	Spooner...............	60.00
Celery Vase...........	80.00	Sugars	
Compote, cov, hs........	165.00	Cov...............	150.00
Creamer, applied handle ...	140.00	Open, buttermilk.......	60.00
Egg Cup..............	50.00	Tumbler..............	125.00
Goblet...............	95.00	Wine................	135.00
Pitcher, water applied handle................	185.00		

HONEYCOMB

A popular pattern made in flint and non-flint glass by numerous firms, c1850–1900, resulting in many minor pattern variations.

	Flint	Non-Flint		Flint	Non-Flint
Ale Glass	60.00	—	Egg Cup	—	20.00
Barber Bottle	—	25.00	Goblet	25.00	18.00
Bowls			Honey, cov	—	25.00
7¼", oval, base mkd "Mould pat'd May 11, 1869," acorn finial on cov	—	35.00	Lamps		
			All Glass	—	45.00
			Marble base	—	40.00
10"	—	40.00	Lemonade	40.00	20.00
Butter, cov	—	60.00	Mug, half pint	—	15.00
Cake Stand	—	35.00	Pitcher, water, applied handle	100.00	50.00
Castor Bottle	25.00	15.00	Plate, 6"	—	12.50
Celery Vase	35.00	18.00	Pomade Jar	—	15.00
Champagne	65.00	—	Salt & Pepper	—	40.00
Compotes			Salt, master, cov, ftd	—	40.00
Cov, hs	65.00	45.00	Sauce	12.00	7.50
Open, hs	55.00	25.00	Spooner	25.00	20.00
Cordial, 3½"	20.00	—	Sugar, cov	75.00	45.00
Creamer, applied handle	25.00	18.00	Tumblers		
Decanter			Flat	—	12.50
Pint	—	18.50	Footed	—	15.00
Quart, os	—	65.00	Wine	35.00	18.00

HONEYCOMB WITH STAR (Starred Honeycomb)

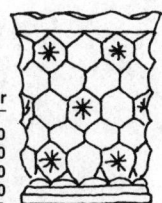

Non-flint made by Fostoria Glass Co., c1905. Clear and gold trimmed.

	Clear		Clear
Butter, cov	30.00	Cup	10.00
Cake Stand	30.00	Nappy, handled	10.00
Celery Vase	15.00	Salt Shaker	12.00
Compote, cov, hs	35.00	Spooner	15.00
Creamer	20.00	Sugar, cov	30.00
Cruet	40.00	Tumbler	15.00

HORN OF PLENTY

A fine flint glass pattern reputed to have been first made by Boston and Sandwich Glass Co. in the 1850s. Later made in flint and non-flint by other firms.

	Clear Flint		Clear Flint
Bowl, 8½"	145.00	Champagne	160.00
Butters, cov		Compotes	
Conventional finial	125.00	Cov, hs, 6¼"	175.00
Head of Washington	400.00	Open, hs, 7"	125.00
Shape of Acorn	130.00	Open, hs, 8"	100.00
Cake Stand	350.00	Open, hs, 9¼"	200.00
Celery Vase	165.00	Open, hs, 10½"	135.00

	Clear Flint		Clear Flint
Cordial	95.00	Relish, 7″ l, 5″ w	45.00
Creamer, applied handle . . .	235.00	Salt, master, oval, flat	75.00
Decanters		Sauce, 5¼″	25.00
Pint	100.00	Spillholder	65.00
Quart, os	130.00	Spooner	45.00
Egg Cup	40.00	Sugars	
*Goblet	75.00	Cov	120.00
*Lamp	200.00	Open	65.00
Mug, small, applied handle .	155.00	*Tumbler, water	100.00
Pepper Sauce Bottle, pewter		Whiskey	
top	200.00	Applied handle	135.00
Pitcher, water	575.00	Shot glass, 3″	100.00
Plate, 6″	110.00	Wine	130.00

HORSESHOE (Good Luck, Prayer Rug)

Non-flint made by Adams & Co. and others in the 1880s.

	Clear		Clear
Bowls, cov, oval		Cordial	150.00
7″	150.00	Creamer, 6½″	95.00
8″, horseshoe finial	165.00	Goblet, knob stem	35.00
Bread Plate, 14 x 10″, double		Marmalade Jar, cov	35.00
horseshoe handles	55.00	Pitcher, water	85.00
Butter, cov	60.00	Plates	
Cake Stands		7″	30.00
9″	75.00	10″	35.00
10″	95.00	Relish, 5 x 7″	10.00
Celery Vase, knob stem	40.00	Salts	
Cheese, cov, woman		Individual, horseshoe	
churning	275.00	shape	18.00
Compotes		Master, horseshoe shape .	50.00
Cov, hs, 7″, horseshoe		Spooner	30.00
finial	50.00	Sugar, cov	55.00
Cov, hs, 11″	85.00	Vegetable Dish, oblong	35.00
Open, hs, 8″	70.00	Wine	150.00

HUMMING BIRD (Flying Robin)

Non-flint, c1880.

	Amber	Blue	Canary	Clear
Butter, cov	110.00	110.00	85.00	60.00
Celery Vase	90.00	90.00	65.00	45.00
Compote, hs, open .	95.00	95.00	65.00	40.00
Creamer	90.00	90.00	60.00	45.00
Goblet	75.00	75.00	55.00	40.00
Pitchers				
Milk	—	—	—	50.00
Water	150.00	150.00	100.00	70.00
Sauce, ftd	60.00	60.00	30.00	18.00
Spooner	80.00	80.00	45.00	30.00
Sugar, cov	100.00	100.00	65.00	55.00
Tray, water	110.00	120.00	80.00	60.00
Tumbler, bar	75.00	75.00	45.00	30.00
Waste Bowl, 5¼″ . .	—	—	—	35.00

ILLINOIS

Non-flint. One of the States patterns made by U. S. Glass Co., c1897. Most forms are square.

	Clear	Emerald Green		Clear	Emerald Green
Basket, applied handle, 11½″	80.00	—	Tankard, round, SP rim	75.00	160.00
Bowl, 8″	35.00	—	Plate, 7″, sq	21.00	—
Butter, cov	45.00	—	Salt and Pepper		
Candlesticks, pr.	90.00	—	Shakers, pr	35.00	—
Celery Tray, 11″	22.00	—	Spooner	20.00	—
Cheese, cov	50.00	—	Straw Holder, metal		
Creamers			top	150.00	—
Ind	30.00	—	Sugars		
Regular	40.00	—	Ind	25.00	—
Cruet	55.00	—	Regular, cov	55.00	—
Lamp, tall, banquet,			Syrup, pewter top	95.00	—
matching shade	500.00+	—	Toothpick	30.00	—
Marmalade Jar	135.00	—	Tumbler	25.00	40.00
Olive	12.00	—	Vase, 6″, sq	35.00	45.00
Pitchers, water					
Square	65.00	—			

INTAGLIO (Flower Spray with Scroll)

Made by Northwood Co., Indiana, Pennsylvania, c1899. Also reported in custard trimmed in green and gold. Creamers in blue opalescent were used as premiums in 1901 by Arbuckle Coffee.

	Blue Opal	Custard	Vaseline Opal	White Opal
Bowl, berry or large.	150.00	185.00	150.00	75.00
Butter, cov	200.00	175.00	210.00	150.00
Compote, jelly	45.00	75.00	65.00	35.00
Creamer	70.00	125.00	90.00	40.00
Cruet, os.	125.00	—	110.00	95.00
Pitcher, water	200.00	—	225.00	125.00
Sauce	35.00	75.00	40.00	25.00
Spooner	75.00	115.00	80.00	50.00
Sugar, cov	150.00	100.00	100.00	85.00
Tumbler	50.00	70.00	55.00	45.00

INVERTED FAN AND FEATHER

Made by Northwood Co., Wheeling, West Virginia, c1900. Also known in carnival and canary opalescent. See Pink Slag.

	Blue Opal	Clear Opal	Custard	Green With Gold
Bowl, berry	125.00	100.00	200.00	110.00
Butter, cov	275.00	195.00	245.00	195.00
Compote, jelly	200.00	195.00	175.00	195.00
Creamer	100.00	65.00	175.00	85.00
Cruet	200.00	195.00	600.00	195.00
Pitcher, water	325.00	200.00	500.00	200.00

	Blue Opal	Clear Opal	Custard	Green With Gold
Rose Bowl	150.00	—	—	—
Salt Shaker, single. .	—	—	95.00	—
Spooner	95.00	75.00	100.00	75.00
*Sugar, cov.	145.00	95.00	125.00	100.00
*Toothpick	125.00	100.00	550.00	100.00
*Tumbler	80.00	25.00	80.00	35.00

INVERTED FERN

Flint, c1860. Attributed to Boston and Sandwich Glass Co.

	Clear			Clear
Butter, cov	95.00		Pitcher, water	200.00
Champagne	115.00		Salt, master, ftd	35.00
Compote, open, hs, 8″	55.00		Saucer, flat.	10.00
Creamer, applied handle . . .	125.00		Spooner.	40.00
Egg Cup.	30.00		Sugar, cov	75.00
Goblet, rayed base	40.00		Tumbler	90.00
Plate, 6″.	100.00		Wine	60.00

INVERTED STRAWBERRY

Non-flint, made by Cambridge Glass Co., c1908. Ruby stained also found in souvenir types. No original toothpick made.

	Clear	Ruby Stained		Clear	Ruby Stained
Bowl, 9″	25.00	—	Punch Cup	12.00	—
Celery Tray, handled	27.50	—	Relish, 7″	12.00	—
Compote, open, hs,			Rose Bowl	30.00	—
5″	38.00	—	Salt, individual.	20.00	—
Cruet	45.00	—	Sauce, flat, 4″	18.00	—
Goblet	25.00	—	Sugar, cov	45.00	—
Mug	20.00	30.00	*Toothpick	25.00	—
*Pitcher, water	45.00	—	Tumbler	—	45.00
Plate, 10″	22.00	40.00			

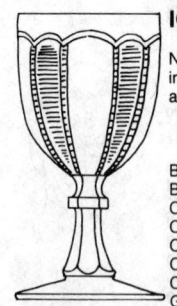

IOWA (Paneled Zipper)

Non-flint made by U. S. Glass Co. c1902. Part of the States pattern series. Available in clear glass with gold trim (add 20%) and pink or cranberry stained. Also found in amber (goblet $65.00), green, and blue. Add 50% for color.

	Clear			Clear
Bowl, berry.	12.00		Pitcher, water	50.00
Butter, cov	40.00		Punch Cup	12.00
Cake Stand	35.00		Salt Shaker, single	20.00
Compote, cov, 8″	40.00		Spooner.	20.00
Creamer.	30.00		Sugar, cov	35.00
Cruet, os	30.00		Table Set, 4 pc.	125.00
Cup	18.00		Toothpick	25.00
Goblet	28.00		Tumbler	12.00
Olive	18.00		Wine	25.00

IRIS WITH MEANDER (Iris)

Made by Jefferson Glass Co., Steubenville, Ohio, c1903. Available in gold trim in clear, apple green, amethyst (toothpick $50.00), and blue. Also found in amber, opalescent (rare) and green opalescent (usually found in berry sets and toothpicks).

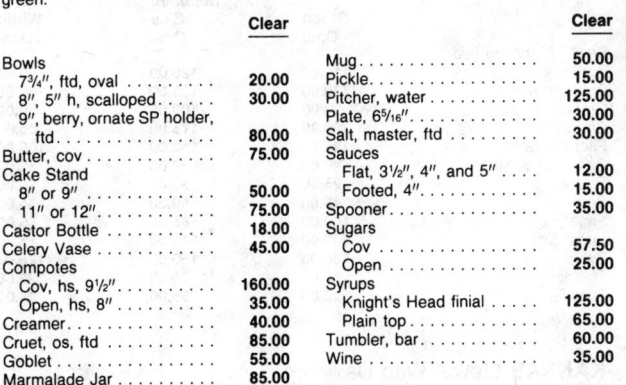

	Blue Opal	Canary Opal	White Opal
Bowl, berry	95.00	80.00	50.00
Butter, cov	240.00	190.00	125.00
Compote, jelly, 5″ . .	85.00	75.00	50.00
Creamer	125.00	100.00	60.00
Cruet, os.	200.00	150.00	100.00
Pickle	30.00	30.00	20.00
Pitcher, water	225.00	200.00	125.00
Plate, 7″	50.00	60.00	35.00
Salt & Pepper	100.00	100.00	85.00
Sauce.	30.00	30.00	30.00
Spooner	75.00	65.00	50.00
Sugar, cov	150.00	100.00	80.00
Toothpick	85.00	62.50	50.00
Tumbler	60.00	45.00	30.00
Vase, 11″	60.00	35.00	25.00

JACOB'S LADDER (Maltese)

Non-flint made by Bryce Bros., Pittsburgh, Pennsylvania, in 1876 and U. S. Glass Co. in 1891. A few pieces found in amber or yellow. A salt dip is known in pale green.

	Clear		Clear
Bowls		Mug.	50.00
7¾″, ftd, oval	20.00	Pickle.	15.00
8″, 5″ h, scalloped.	30.00	Pitcher, water	125.00
9″, berry, ornate SP holder,		Plate, 6⁵⁄₁₆″.	30.00
ftd.	80.00	Salt, master, ftd	30.00
Butter, cov	75.00	**Sauces**	
Cake Stand		Flat, 3½″, 4″, and 5″	12.00
8″ or 9″	50.00	Footed, 4″.	15.00
11″ or 12″.	75.00	Spooner.	35.00
Castor Bottle	18.00	**Sugars**	
Celery Vase	45.00	Cov	57.50
Compotes		Open	25.00
Cov, hs, 9½″.	160.00	**Syrups**	
Open, hs, 8″	35.00	Knight's Head finial	125.00
Creamer.	40.00	Plain top	65.00
Cruet, os, ftd	85.00	Tumbler, bar.	60.00
Goblet	55.00	Wine	35.00
Marmalade Jar	85.00		

JERSEY SWIRL (Swirl)

Non-flint pattern made by Windsor Glass Co., Pittsburgh, Pennsylvania, c1887. Heavily reproduced in color. The clear goblet also reproduced.

	Amber	Blue	Canary	Clear
Bowl, 9¼″.	55.00	55.00	45.00	35.00
Butter, cov	55.00	55.00	50.00	40.00

	Amber	Blue	Canary	Clear
Cake Stand, 9″	60.00	60.00	45.00	30.00
Celery Vase	42.00	42.00	35.00	30.00
Compote, hs, 8″ . . .	50.00	50.00	45.00	35.00
Creamer	45.00	45.00	40.00	30.00
*Goblets				
Buttermilk	40.00	40.00	35.00	30.00
Water	40.00	40.00	35.00	30.00
Pickle Castor, SP frame and lid	—	—	—	125.00
Pitcher, water	50.00	50.00	45.00	35.00
Plates, round				
6″	25.00	25.00	20.00	15.00
8″	30.00	30.00	25.00	18.00
10″	32.00	32.00	28.00	20.00
Salt, Ind	18.00	18.00	15.00	12.00
Sauce, 4½″, flat . . .	20.00	20.00	15.00	10.00
Spooner	30.00	30.00	25.00	20.00
Sugar, cov	40.00	40.00	35.00	30.00
Tumbler	30.00	30.00	25.00	20.00
Wine	50.00	50.00	40.00	30.00

JEWELED HEART

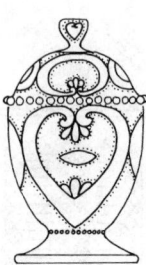

Made by Northwood Glass Co., Indiana, Pennsylvania, and others, 1898–1910. Also made in clear, blue, and apple green. A clear creamer is valued at $20.00 and a clear green toothpick at $45.00. The pattern originally had no goblet or wine.

	Green Opal	Sapphire Blue Opal	White Opal
Bowl, berry, ruffled edge	110.00	125.00	50.00
Butter, cov	130.00	135.00	100.00
*Creamer	90.00	100.00	50.00
Cruet	200.00	175.00	85.00
Pitcher, water	135.00	150.00	100.00
Salt Shaker, single. .	40.00	50.00	35.00
Sauce.	25.00	30.00	20.00
Spooner	45.00	50.00	35.00
*Sugar, cov.	100.00	85.00	55.00
Sugar Shaker	100.00	110.00	75.00
Syrup	130.00	150.00	125.00
*Toothpick	35.00	35.00	30.00
Tumbler	25.00	35.00	25.00

KANSAS (Jewel With Dewdrop)

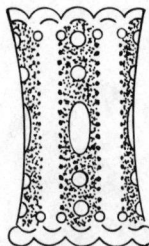

Non-flint originally produced by Cooperative Flint Glass Co., Beaver Falls, Pennsylvania. Later produced as part of the States pattern series by U. S. Glass Co. in 1901. Also known with jewels stained in pink or gold.

	Clear		Clear
Bowls		Butter, cov	55.00
7″, oval.	25.00	Cake Plate	45.00
8½″	40.00	Cake Stands	
Bread Plate, ODB	60.00	7⅝″	65.00

	Clear			Clear
9″	45.00	Pitcher, water		55.00
10″	60.00	Relish, 8½″, oval		20.00
Celery Vase	35.00	Salt Shaker		50.00
Compotes		Sauce, flat, 4″		15.00
Open, hs, 9½″	60.00	Sugar, cov		50.00
Open, ls, 6½″	45.00	Toothpick		45.00
Creamer	40.00	Tumbler		40.00
Goblet	50.00	Wine		60.00
Mug, regular	40.00			

KENTUCKY

Non-flint made by U. S. Glass Co., c1897, as part of the States pattern series. The goblet is found in ruby stained ($50.00). A footed, square sauce ($30.00) is known in cobalt blue with gold.

	Clear	Emerald Green		Clear	Emerald Green
Butter, cov	50.00	—	Pitcher, water	45.00	—
Cake Stand, 9½″	40.00	—	Salt Shaker, single	20.00	—
Cruet, os	45.00	—	Sauce, ftd, sq	8.00	16.00
Cup	10.00	30.00	Toothpick, sq	35.00	60.00
Goblet	20.00	50.00	Tumbler	—	40.00
Nappy	8.50	—	Wine	25.00	45.00

KING'S CROWN (Ruby Thumbprint; X.L.C.R.)

Known as Ruby Thumbprint when pieces are ruby stained. A non-flint pattern made by Adams and Co., Pittsburgh, Pennsylvania, in the 1890s and later. Made in clear and with the thumbprints stained amethyst, gold, green, and yellow, and in clear with etching and trimmed in gold. It became very popular after 1891 as ruby stained souvenir ware. Cobalt blue· pieces reported as very rare. Approximately 87 pieces documented.

    NOTE: Pattern has been copiously reproduced for the gift-trade market. New pieces are easily distinguished: in the case of Ruby Thumbprint, the color is a very pale pinkish red; green and blue pieces have an off-color. Reproduced in milk glass.

    Available in amethyst stained in goblet ($30.00) and wine ($10.00) and in green stained in goblet ($25.00) and wine ($15.00). Add 30% for etched pieces.

	Clear	Ruby Stained		Clear	Ruby Stained
Banana Stand, ftd	100.00	135.00	Regular	60.00	70.00
Butter, cov	45.00	90.00	Cup & Saucer	68.00	—
Cake Stands			Goblet	15.00	45.00
9″	35.00	50.00	Mustard, cov	36.00	—
10″	90.00	110.00	Pickle, lobed	12.00	—
Castor Bottle	45.00	70.00	Pitchers		
Castor Set, glass			Milk	60.00	75.00
stand, 4 bottles	400.00	—	Water, bulbous	—	285.00
Celery Vase	75.00	50.00	Water, tankard	140.00	200.00
Claret	48.00	—	Salt & Pepper	40.00	65.00
Compotes			Salt, master, oblong	25.00	—
Cov, ls, 12″	90.00	225.00	Sauce, 4″	12.00	20.00
Open, hs, 5½″	55.00	95.00	Spooner	40.00	60.00
Open, hs, 8¼″	75.00	95.00	Sugar, cov	22.00	45.00
Open, ls, 5¼″	30.00	45.00	Toothpick	25.00	25.00
Creamers			Tumbler	18.00	36.00
Ind	24.00	40.00	Wine	18.00	30.00

KING'S #500

Made by King Glass Co. of Pittsburgh, Pennsylvania in 1899. It was made in clear, frosted, and a rich, deep blue, known as Dewey Blue, both trimmed in gold. Continued by U. S. Glass Co. in 1891 and made in a great number of pieces. A clear goblet with frosted stem ($50.00) is known.

	Clear w/Gold	Dewey Blue w/Gold		Clear w/Gold	Dewey Blue w/Gold
Bowls			Cup	15.00	35.00
7"	10.00	30.00	Decanter, locking		
8"	12.00	35.00	top	100.00	—
9"	14.00	40.00	Pitchers, water,		
Butter, cov	50.00	125.00	round	55.00	200.00
Cake Stand	40.00	60.00	Relish	20.00	—
Celery Vase	25.00	—	Salt Shaker, single. .	15.00	40.00
Compotes			Sauce	15.00	30.00
Covered	45.00	—	Spooner	20.00	45.00
Open	30.00	—	Sugar, cov	45.00	75.00
Creamer	30.00	50.00	Syrup	55.00	175.00
Cruet	45.00	135.00	Tumbler	20.00	35.00

KLONDIKE (Amberette, English Hobnail Cross)

This pattern reported to have been made originally by A. J. Beatty And Co., c1885. It was also made by Hobbs, Brockunier Co., and Dalzell, Gilmore and Leighton Co. Made in colors other than clear and amber stained, which are the original colors.
Made to commemmorate the Alaskan Gold Rush. The frosted panels depict snow; the amber bands, gold. Found clear and frosted, with or without scrolls, depending on the maker. Prices are listed for frosted; clear panels, approximately 30% less.

	Frosted w/ Amber Stain		Frosted w/ Amber Stain
Bowl, berry, 8"	175.00	Spooner	100.00
Butter, cov	400.00	Sugars	
Cake Stand, 8", sq	500.00	Cov	285.00
Celery Vase	200.00	Open	225.00
Creamer	200.00	Syrup, pewter lid	650.00
Cruet, os	550.00	Toothpick	375.00
Goblet	350.00	Tray, 5½", sq	200.00
Pitcher, water	450.00	Tumbler	135.00
Punch Cup	85.00	Vases, trumpet shape	
Sauce, flat	75.00	8"	275.00
Salt Shaker, single	200.00	10"	265.00

KOKOMO (Bar and Diamond, R and H Swirl Band)

Made in clear glass by Richards and Hartley, Tarentum, Pennsylvania in the late 1880s to 1891. Found in ruby stained and etched. About 54 pieces manufactured.

	Clear	Ruby Stained		Clear	Ruby Stained
Bread Tray	30.00	45.00	Compotes		
Butter, cov	35.00	—	Cov, ls, 7½"	30.00	45.00
Cakestand	55.00	—	Open, ls, 8"	20.00	—
Celery Vase	15.00	45.00	Condiment Set, ob-		

	Clear	Ruby Stained		Clear	Ruby Stained
long tray, shakers, cruet	80.00	100.00	Salt & Pepper in holder	45.00	—
Creamer	35.00	60.00	Sauce, ftd, 5″	7.00	20.00
Cruet	25.00	—	Spooner	25.00	45.00
Decanter, 9¾″, wine	45.00	75.00	Sugar, cov	40.00	65.00
Finger Bowl	25.00	35.00	Sugar Shaker	45.00	85.00
Goblet	24.00	40.00	Syrup	45.00	130.00
Lamp, hand, atypical—has no diamonds	50.00	100.00	Tray, water	50.00	90.00
			Tumbler	20.00	35.00
Pitcher, water, tankard	65.00	95.00	Wine	30.00	40.00

LEAF AND DART (Pride)

Made by Boston and Sandwich Glass Co., Sandwich, Massachusetts, and Richards and Hartley Flint Glass, Pittsburgh, Pennsylvania, c1860. Shards have been found at Burlington Glass Works, Hamilton, Ontario.

	Clear		Clear
Butter, cov	50.00	Salt, master, ftd	
Celery Vase	40.00	cov	75.00
Creamer, applied handle	50.00	open	30.00
Cruet, pedestal, applied handle	110.00	Sauce, 4″, flat	8.00
Egg Cup	35.00	Spooner	35.00
Goblet	30.00	Sugar, cov	50.00
Pitcher, water, applied handle	125.00	Tumbler, ftd	30.00
		Wine	40.00

LEAF AND STAR (Tobin)

Made by New Martinsville Glass Co. between 1910–1915. A toothpick, valued at $45.00, has been found in orange iridescent. Also found in ruby stained (add 40 to 50%).

	Clear with Gold		Clear with Gold
Bowl, berry	18.00	Pitcher, water	50.00
Butter, cov	35.00	Sauce, flat	8.00
Creamer	28.00	Spooner	25.00
Dresser Jar, metal top	15.00	Sugar, cov	30.00
Goblet	22.00	Tumbler	20.00
Hair Receiver, metal top	15.00		

LENS AND STAR (Star and Oval)

Made by O'Hara Glass Co., Pittsburgh, Pennsylvania, in 1880; in 1891 and after by U. S. Glass Co. It comes in clear with plain or etched panels. No colors are known.

	Frosted		Frosted
Butter, cov	45.00	Pitcher, water, barrel shape, applied reeded handle	50.00
Celery	30.00	Sauce	8.00
Creamer	30.00		

	Frosted		Frosted
Spooner	20.00	Tumbler	25.00
Sugar, cov	45.00	Waste Bowl	20.00
Syrup	45.00		

LIBERTY (Cornucopia #2)

Made by McKee Glass Co., in 1892. Sometimes found with engraving.

	Clear		Clear
Butter, cov	45.00	Tankard, ½ gal, tall	60.00
Champagne, 4½ oz	35.00	Sauce, flat	10.00
Cordial	25.00	Spooner	25.00
Creamer	30.00	Sugar, cov	45.00
Goblet	40.00	Tray, water	45.00
Pitchers, water		Tumbler	30.00
Regular, ½ gallon jug	50.00	Wine	25.00

LIBERTY BELL (Centennial)

Made by Gillinder and Co., Philadelphia, Pennsylvania for the Centennial Exposition, 1876. Reproduced.

	Clear		Clear
Bowl, 8″, ftd	100.00	Pitcher, water, applied reed-	
Bread Plates, 13⅜ x 9½″		ed handle	350.00
Clear, no signatures	85.00	Plate, 6″, dated	75.00
Milk glass, sgd John Han-		Relish, oval	45.00
cock	200.00	Salt & Pepper, dated 1876	250.00
Butter, cov	150.00	Salt Dip, ind, oval	30.00
Creamer, applied handle	130.00	Sauce, ftd	30.00
Goblet	50.00	Spooner	95.00
Mug, snake handle	335.00	Sugar, cov	110.00

LINCOLN DRAPE WITH TASSEL

Flint pattern made originally by Boston & Sandwich Glass Co., probably continued by other companies, c1865. Commemorative of Lincoln's death. Some very rare pieces in cobalt blue are 200% more.

	Clear		Clear
Butter, cov	100.00	Lamp, Marble base	125.00
Compotes		Pitcher, water, applied han-	
Cov, hs, 8½″	150.00	dle	350.00
Open, ls, 6″	65.00	Plate, 6″	80.00
Creamer, applied handle	125.00	Salt, ftd	45.00
Egg Cup	50.00	Sauce, 4″	20.00
Goblets		Spooner	50.00
Lady's	165.00	Sugar, cov	125.00
Water	100.00	Syrup, applied handle	125.00
Honey	20.00	Wine	135.00

LION

Made by Gillinder and Sons, Philadelphia, Pennsylvania, in 1876. Available in clear (50% less), but not eagerly sought by collectors. Many reproductions.

	Frosted		Frosted
Bread Plate, 12″ including lion handles, GUTDODB. .	100.00	Goblet	70.00
Butters, cov		Marmalade Jar, rampant finial	85.00
Lion's head finial	90.00	Paperweight, lion head	175.00
Rampant finial	125.00	Pitchers	
Celery Vase	75.00	Milk	350.00
Champagne	175.00	Water	200.00
Cheese, cov, rampant lion finial	400.00	Relish, lion handles.	50.00
Compotes		Salt, master, rect lid	250.00
Cov, hs, 7″, rampant finial	150.00	Sauce, 4″, ftd	25.00
Cov, 9″, rampant finial, oval, collared base	200.00	Spooner.	75.00
Open, ls, 8″.	75.00	Sugars, cov	
Creamer.	65.00	Lion head finial	65.00
Egg Cup, 3½″ h	50.00	Rampant finial	85.00
		Syrup, orig top	325.00
		Wine	200.00

LOG CABIN

Non-flint made by Central Glass Co. Wheeling, West Virginia, c1875. Also available in color, but rare.

	Clear		Clear
Bowl, cov, 8 x 5¼ x 3⅝″. . .	250.00	Pitcher, water	300.00
Butter, cov	275.00	Sauce, flat	40.00
Compote, hs, 10½″.	225.00	Spooner.	130.00
Creamer.	130.00	Sugar, cov	300.00
Marmalade Jar	275.00		

LOOP (Seneca Loop)

Flint, c1850s–1860s; later in non-flint. Made by several firms. Sandwich produced fiery opalescent pieces. Yuma Loop is a contemporary with comparable values.

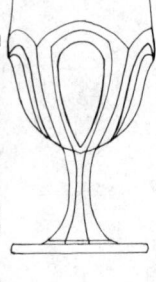

	Flint	Non-Flint		Flint	Non-Flint
Bowl, 9″	40.00	25.00	Goblet	25.00	18.00
Butter, cov	60.00	40.00	Pitcher, water, applied handle.	145.00	—
Cake Stand.	125.00	—	Salt, master, ftd	25.00	18.00
Celery Vase	45.00	20.00	Spooner	30.00	20.00
Compotes			Sugar, cov	60.00	—
Cov, hs, 9½″	100.00	—	Tumblers		
Open, hs, 9″	75.00	40.00	Footed	25.00	15.00
Cordial, 2¾″ h.	40.00	20.00	Water	40.00	20.00
Creamer, applied handle.	70.00	35.00	Wine	30.00	12.00
Egg Cup.	30.00	20.00			

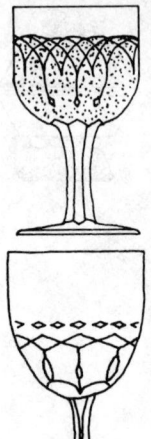

LOOP AND DART

Clear and stippled pattern in flint and non-flint of the 1860s with many variants: Loop and Dart with Diamond Ornament, Loop and Dart with Round Ornament, Double Loop and Dart, and others. Prices for all are comparable. Flint add 25%. See Leaf and Dart.

	Non-Flint		Non-Flint
Bowl, 9″, oval	20.00	Plate, 6″	25.00
Butter, cov	45.00	Relish	25.00
Cake Stand, 10″	40.00	Salt, ftd	35.00
Celery Vase	35.00	Spooner	35.00
Compote, cov, hs, 8″	65.00	Sugar, cov	50.00
Creamer, applied handle	45.00	Tumblers	
Cruet	75.00	Footed	30.00
Egg Cup	25.00	Water	45.00
Goblet	30.00	Wine	40.00
Pitcher, water, applied handle	85.00		

LOOP AND JEWEL (Jewel and Festoon; Venus)

Non-flint made by Beatty Glass and National Glass Co. then continued by Indiana Glass Co. Made until 1915. About 40 pieces known. A few rare pieces available in milk white.

	Clear		Clear
Bowl, 7″	12.00	Salt, ftd, 3 handled	30.00
Butter, cov	40.00	Salt Shaker, single	15.00
Compote, 6½″	20.00	Sauce, flat, 4″	5.00
Creamer	25.00	Spooner	15.00
Dish, 5″ sq	15.00	Sugar, cov	40.00
Pickle, 8″, rect	15.00	Syrup	55.00
Pitcher, water	45.00		

LOOP WITH DEWDROP

Early maker unknown. Reissued by U. S. Glass Co. in 1892 and later in 1898.

	Clear		Clear
Bowl, 8″	12.50	Marmalade Jar	30.00
Butter, cov	35.00	Pitcher, water, ½ gal	40.00
Cake Stand, 10″	42.00	Salt & Pepper	40.00
Celery Vase	25.00	Spooner	18.00
Compote, cov, hs, 8″	45.00	Sugar, cov	32.00
Condiment Set, tray	70.00	Syrup	47.50
Creamer	25.00	Tray, two handles	35.00
Cruet	45.00	Tumbler	20.00
Cup and Saucer	25.00	Wine	25.00
Goblet	28.00		

LOUISIANA (Sharp Oval and Diamond, Granby)

Made by Bryce Bros., Pittsburgh, Pennsylvania in 1870s, continued later (about 1892) by U. S. Glass Co. as one of the States patterns. Also available with gold and frosted.

	Clear		Clear
Bowl, 9″, berry	15.00	Mug, handled, gold top	25.00
Butter, cov	55.00	Nappy, 4″, cov	30.00
Celery Vase	25.00	Pitcher, water	45.00
Compotes		Relish	15.00
Cov, hs, 8″	50.00	Spooner	25.00
Open, hs, 5″, jelly	30.00	Sugar, cov	45.00
Creamer	35.00	Tumbler	20.00
Goblet	30.00	Wine	35.00
Matchholder, attached			
saucer	30.00		

MAGNET AND GRAPE (Magnet and Grape with Stippled Leaf)

Flint first made by Boston and Sandwich Glass Co., c1860. Later non-flint versions have grape leaf in either clear or stippled. Reproduced by Metropolitan Museum, New York.

	Flint Frosted Leaf	Non-Flint Stippled or Clear Leaf		Flint Frosted Leaf	Non-Flint Stippled or Clear Leaf
Butter, cov	185.00	40.00	Pitcher, water, applied handle.	350.00	70.00
Celery Vase	175.00	25.00	Relish, oval	35.00	15.00
Champagne	125.00	35.00	Salt, ftd	60.00	25.00
Compote, open, hs,			Sauce, 4″	15.00	8.00
7½″	110.00	37.50	Spooner	95.00	25.00
Creamer	200.00	40.00	Sugar, cov, ...	150.00	40.00
Decanter, os			Syrup	125.00	55.00
Pint.	150.00	75.00	Tumbler, water	125.00	30.00
Quart.	200.00	85.00	Whiskey	140.00	25.00
Egg Cup	100.00	25.00	Wine	85.00	35.00
*Goblets					
American Shield. .	300.00	—			
Low Stem	75.00	—			
Regular stem	70.00	30.00			

MAINE (Paneled Stippled Flower)

Non-flint made by U. S. Glass Co., Pittsburgh, Pennsylvania c1890. Researchers dispute if goblet was made originally. Sometimes found with enamel trim.

	Clear	Emerald Green		Clear	Emerald Green
Bowl, 8″	30.00	40.00	Pitchers		
Bread, oval, 10 x			Milk.	—	85.00
7¾″	30.00	—	Water	—	110.00
Butter, cov	48.00	—	Relish.	15.00	—
Cake Stand.	40.00	75.00	Salt Shaker, single. .	30.00	—
Compote, open, hs,			Sauce.	12.00	—
8″	30.00	—	Sugar, cov	45.00	—
Creamer	30.00	—	Syrup	60.00	210.00
Mug	35.00	—			

MANHATTAN

Non-flint with gold, made by U. S. Glass Co., c1902. A depression glass pattern also has the "Mahattan" name; don't confuse the two.

	Clear	Rose Stained		Clear	Rose Stained
Basket,..........	80.00	—	Punch Cup	10.00	—
Bowl, 10″	20.00	—	Salt Shaker, single..	20.00	35.00
Butter, cov	38.00	—	Sauce...........	10.00	—
Cake Stand, 10″ ...	40.00	35.00	Spooner	20.00	—
Celery Vase	25.00	—	Straw Holder, cov ..	65.00	—
Cheese, cov, 8⅜″ d.	—	115.00	Sugar, cov	40.00	65.00
Compote, cov, hs, 9½″	45.00	—	Syrup	48.00	—
Creamer	30.00	60.00	Toothpick	30.00	—
Cruet			Tumblers		
Large	50.00	110.00	Ice Tea	30.00	—
Small.	40.00	—	Water	20.00	—
Goblet	25.00	—	Vase, 6″	18.00	—
Olive, Gainsborough	30.00	—	Water Bottle	40.00	—
Pitcher, water, tankard, ½ gal	60.00	—	Wine	18.00	—

MARDI GRAS (Duncan and Miller #42, Paneled English Hobnail with Prisms)

Made by Duncan and Miller Glass Co., c1898. Available in gold highlights and ruby stained (open jelly compote at $55.00 and creamer at $47.50).

	Clear		Clear
Bowl, 8″, berry	18.00	Pitchers	
Butter, cov	45.00	Milk	50.00
Cake Stand, 10″.........	65.00	Water...............	75.00
Celery Tray, curled edges ..	25.00	Punch Cup	10.00
Champagne, saucer	32.00	Relish	12.50
Claret...............	35.00	Sherry, flared or straight ...	20.00
Compotes		Spooner	25.00
Cov, hs.............	55.00	Sugar, cov	35.00
Open, jelly, 4½″.........	30.00	Syrup, metal lid..........	45.00
Cordial	35.00	Tumblers	
Creamers		Bar.................	25.00
Ind, oval	18.00	Champagne...........	20.00
Regular............	35.00	Water	30.00
Finger Bowl	20.00	Vase, trumpet shape, 3 sizes................	20.00
Goblet	37.50		
Lamp Shade...........	35.00	Wine	30.00

MARQUISETTE

Non-flint made by Cooperative Glass Co., Beaver Falls, Pennsylvania, c1880.

	Clear		Clear
Butter, cov	50.00	Creamer, applied handle ...	55.00
Celery Vase	40.00	Goblet	30.00
Compotes		Spooner	25.00
Cov, hs..............	60.00	Sugar, cov	55.00
Open, ls	35.00		

MARSH PINK (Square Fuchsia)

Made in Ohio, c1880s. Pieces are square shaped. Some amber examples have been reported. Round Marsh Pink goblet not of this pattern, probably made in Nova Scotia.

	Clear		Clear
Bowl, 9″	20.00	Pickle Castor, sp frame	100.00
Butter, cov, handles	45.00	Pitcher, water	75.00
Cake Stand	45.00	Plate, 10″, sq	35.00
Compotes		Salt & Pepper	70.00
Cov, hs, 7½″	50.00	Sauces	
Cov, jelly, 5½″	30.00	Flat, handle	10.00
Creamer	32.50	Footed	12.00
Dish, 5″, cov	30.00	Spooner	25.00
Honey Dish, ftd, cov	50.00	Sugar, cov	35.00

MARYLAND (Inverted Loop and Fan; Loop and Diamond)

Made originally by Bryce Brothers, Pittsburgh, Pennsylvania. Continued by U. S. Glass Co. as one of their States patterns.

	Clear w/gold	Ruby Stained		Clear w/gold	Ruby Stained
Bowl, berry	15.00	—	Olive, handled	12.00	—
Bread Plate	20.00	—	Pitcher, water	40.00	85.00
Butter, cov	45.00	—	Plate, 7″, round	25.00	—
Celery Tray	20.00	—	Relish, oval	12.00	—
Celery Vase	25.00	—	Salt Shaker, single	30.00	—
Compotes			Sauce, flat	8.00	—
Cov, hs	65.00	85.00	Spooner	22.00	—
Open, hs, 7½″	30.00	—	Sugar, cov	45.00	60.00
Open, jelly	12.00	—	Toothpick	45.00	65.00
Creamer	28.00	55.00	Tumbler	25.00	—
Goblet	35.00	48.00	Wine	40.00	60.00

MASCOTTE (Minor Block)

Non-flint made by Ripley and Co., Pittsburgh, Pennsylvania, in the 1870s. Reissued by U. S. Glass Co. in 1898. The butter dish shown on Plate 77 of Ruth Webb Lee's *Victorian Glass* is said to go with this pattern. It has a horseshoe finial and was named for the famous "Maude S," "Queen of the Turf" trotting horse during the 1880s. Many containers, including commercial apothecary jar, made in this pattern.

	Clear	Etched		Clear	Etched
Bowl, 9″	25.00	35.00	Pyramid Jar, 7″ d,		
Butter Pat	8.00	18.00	one fits into other		
Butters, cov			and forms tall jar-		
"Maude S"	100.00	—	type container with		
Regular	50.00	65.00	lid, three sizes with		
Cake Basket, handle	80.00	65.00	flat separators	40.00	—
Celery Vase	35.00	38.00	Salt Shaker, single	15.00	25.00
Cheese, cov	55.00	75.00	Sauce, ftd, 4″	8.00	12.00
Compotes			Spooner	22.00	28.00
Cov, hs, 8″	60.00	75.00	Sugar, cov	40.00	45.00
Open, ls, 8″	30.00	45.00	Tray, water	40.00	55.00
Creamer	35.00	35.00	Tumbler	20.00	30.00
Goblet	24.00	30.00	Wine	25.00	30.00
Pitcher, water	50.00	70.00			
Plate, turned in sides	38.00	—			

MASSACHUSETTS (Geneva #2, M2-131)

Made in 1880s, maker unknown, and continued in 1898 by U. S. Glass Co. as one of the States series. The vase ($35.00) and wine ($45.00) are in emerald green. Some pieces reported in cobalt blue.

	Clear		Clear
Bar Bottle, metal shot glass for cover	70.00	Plate, 8″	32.00
		Relish, 8½″	15.00
Bowl, 9″, berry, sq	16.00	Rum Jug	75.00
Butter, cov	60.00	Spooner	22.00
Celery Tray	22.00	Sugar, cov	40.00
Compote, open	35.00	Tumblers	
Creamer	25.00	Champagne or Juice	25.00
Cruet, os	40.00	Water	30.00
Goblet	45.00	Whiskey (shot)	15.00
Mug	24.00	Vase, 7″	25.00
Pitcher, water	68.00	Wine	40.00

MEDALLION (Hearts & Spades, Spades)

Non-flint, c1880.

	Amber and Canary	Apple Green and Blue	Clear
Butter, cov	40.00	50.00	35.00
Cake Stand, 9¼″	40.00	55.00	25.00
Celery Vase	30.00	40.00	20.00
Compote, cov, hs	50.00	60.00	40.00
Creamer	35.00	45.00	25.00
Egg Cup	25.00	40.00	20.00
Goblet	35.00	45.00	25.00
Pickle	20.00	25.00	15.00
Pitcher, water	50.00	65.00	45.00
Sauces			
Flat	10.00	15.00	8.00
Footed	12.00	20.00	10.00
Spooner	30.00	40.00	18.00
Sugar, cov	40.00	50.00	25.00
Tumbler	25.00	35.00	15.00
Wine	30.00	40.00	20.00

MICHIGAN (Loop & Pillar)

Non-flint made by U. S. Glass Co., c1893. One of the States pattern series. The 10¼″ bowl ($42.00) and punch cup ($12.00) are found with yellow or blue stain. Also painted carnations made in "Sunrise," gold, and ruby stained.

	Clear	Rose Stained		Clear	Rose Stained
Bowl, 10¼″	25.00	50.00	Cruet, os	55.00	100.00
Butter, cov	60.00	90.00	Crushed Fruit Bowl	75.00	—
Celery Vase	35.00	75.00	Goblet	32.00	50.00
Creamers			Nappy, Gainsboro		
Ind, 602 tankard	20.00	40.00	handle	35.00	—
Regular	30.00	50.00	Olive, two handles	—	25.00

	Clear	Rose Stained		Clear	Rose Stained
Pickle	12.00	—	Sugar, cov	48.00	60.00
Pitcher, water, 3 pt	45.00	80.00	Syrup	55.00	—
Salt Shaker, single, 3 types	20.00	30.00	*Toothpick	40.00	55.00
			Tumbler	28.00	40.00
Sherbert, handled	7.00	15.00	Vase, bud	25.00	35.00
Spooner	35.00	45.00	Wine	37.50	50.00

MINERVA

Non-flint made by Boston and Sandwich Glass Co. and other companies in 1870s. There are two forms.

	Clear		Clear
Bowls		Pitcher, water, 9½"	100.00
Footed	40.00	Plates	
Rectangular		8"	55.00
7"	25.00	10"	60.00
9"	40.00	Platter, oval, 13"	70.00
Butter, cov	65.00	Sauces	
Cake Stand, 11"	135.00	Flat	12.00
Compote, cov, hs, 7"	90.00	Footed, 4"	18.00
Creamer	50.00	Spooner	40.00
Goblet	85.00	Sugar, cov	70.00
Marmalade Jar, cov	100.00		
Pickle, inscribed "Love's Request is Pickles"	30.00		

MINNESOTA

Non-flint made by U. S. Glass Co., late 1890s. One of the States patterns. A two-piece flower frog has been found in emerald green ($46.00).

	Clear	Ruby Stained		Clear	Ruby Stained
Basket	65.00	—	Hair Receiver	30.00	—
Biscuit Jar, cov	55.00	115.00	Mug	20.00	—
Bowl, 8½", flared	30.00	—	Pitcher, water, tankard	85.00	200.00
Butter, cov	45.00	—	Relish	15.00	—
Celery Tray, 13"	25.00	—	Spooner	25.00	—
Compotes			Sugar, cov	40.00	—
Open, hs, 10", flared	60.00	—	Syrup	55.00	—
Open, ls, 9", sq	55.00	—	Toothpick, 3 handles	30.00	—
Creamer	30.00	—	Tumbler	15.00	—
Cruet	35.00	—	Wine	30.00	—
Goblet	25.00	50.00			

MISSOURI (Palm and Scroll)

Non-flint made by U. S. Glass Co. c1899, one of the States pattern series. Also made in amethyst and canary.

	Clear	Emerald Green		Clear	Emerald Green
Bowl, berry, 8"	18.00	30.00	Cake Stand, 9"	50.00	—
Butter, cov	55.00	65.00	Cordial	35.00	—

	Clear	Emerald Green		Clear	Emerald Green
Creamer	25.00	35.00	Pitcher, water	45.00	85.00
Cruet	55.00	125.00	Salt Shaker, single. .	25.00	40.00
Goblet	45.00	60.00	Sauce, flat, 4″	10.00	14.00
Mug	35.00	45.00	Spooner	25.00	35.00
Pickle Dish, rectangular	18.00	27.50	Sugar, cov	50.00	65.00
			Wine	30.00	50.00

MOON AND STAR (Palace)

Non-flint and frosted (add 30%). First made by Adams & Co., Pittsburgh, Pennsylvania, in 1874 and later by several manufacturers, including Pioneer Glass who made ruby stained examples. Six different type compotes documented. Heavily reproduced in clear and color.

	Clear		Clear
Bowls		Egg Cup	35.00
Berry, 8″	25.00	Goblet	40.00
Round, 12½″	40.00	Lamp	140.00
Bread Plate [Tray], rectangular	45.00	Pickle, oval	18.00
Butter, cov	60.00	Pitcher, water, applied handle	140.00
Cake Stand, 9″	55.00	Salt & Pepper Shakers, pr	65.00
Celery Vase	60.00	Salt, ind	12.00
Champagne	40.00	Sauces	
Claret	47.50	Flat	8.00
Compotes		Footed	12.00
Cov, hs, 10″	95.00	Spooner	40.00
Cov, ls, 6½″	45.00	Sugar, cov	65.00
Open, hs, 9″	30.00	Syrup	100.00
Open, ls, 7½″	25.00	Tray, water	65.00
Creamer, applied handle	50.00	Tumbler, ftd	45.00
Cruet	125.00	Wine	50.00

NAILHEAD (Gem)

Non-flint, made by Bryce, Higbee, and Co., in 1880s. Also found in ruby stained (goblet at 30.00, wine at 35.00).

	Clear		Clear
Butter, cov	45.00	Plates	
Cake Stand, 9½″	25.00	Round, 9″	20.00
Celery	35.00	Square, 7″	15.00
Compotes		Sauce, flat	12.00
Cov, 8″, hs	47.50	Sugar, cov	35.00
Open, 9½″, hs	35.00	Spooner	21.00
Creamer	23.00	Tumbler	30.00
Goblet	25.00	Wine	18.50
Pitcher, water	40.00		

NEVADA

Non-flint made by U. S. Glass Co. as a States Pattern. Pieces are sometimes partly frosted and have enamel decoration. Add 20% for frosted.

	Clear		Clear
Biscuit Jar	45.00	Salts	
Butter, cov	50.00	Ind	8.00
Cake Stand, 10″	35.00	Master	14.00
Celery	27.50	Salt Shaker, single, two	
Compote, cov, 8″, hs	45.00	types	15.00
Creamer	32.00	Sauce	10.00
Cruet	35.00	Spooner	25.00
Cup, custard	12.00	Sugar, cov	35.00
Pickle, oval	10.00	Syrup, tin top	45.00
Pitcher, water, tankard, ½		Toothpick	25.00
gal	40.00	Tumbler	15.00

NEW ENGLAND PINEAPPLE

Flint made by Boston and Sandwich Glass Co. in early 1860s. Rare in color. The footed sherbert which is reproduced was not made originally.

	Flint	Non-Flint		Flint	Non-Flint
Castor Bottle	50.00	—	Pitcher, water	295.00	—
Castor Set, 4 bottles,			Salts		
complete	300.00	—	Ind	24.00	—
Champagne	165.00	—	Master	45.00	—
Compote, open, hs,			Sauce, flat	15.00	10.00
8½″	125.00	80.00	Spooner	40.00	35.00
Creamer, applied			Sugar, cov	120.00	55.00
handle, 2 sizes	150.00	70.00	Tumblers		
Decanter, qt, os	225.00	—	Bar	100.00	—
Egg Cup	40.00	—	Water	85.00	—
*Goblet, 2 sizes	60.00	22.00	Whiskey, handled	145.00	—
Mug	95.00	—	*Wine	140.00	—

NEW HAMPSHIRE (Bent Buckle, Modiste)

Non-flint made by U. S. Glass Co. in the States Pattern series. There is a large ruby mug known.

	Clear w/gold	Cran-berry Stained		Clear w/gold	Cran-berry Stained
Bowls			Goblet	25.00	50.00
Flared, 8½″	15.00	25.00	Mug, large	15.00	45.00
Round, 8½″	17.50	30.00	Pitcher, water, tank-		
Square, 8½″	25.00	35.00	ard	50.00	70.00
Butter, cov	65.00	70.00	Sugars		
Carafe	60.00	—	Cov	45.00	60.00
Celery Vase	35.00	50.00	Ind, open	20.00	25.00
Compote, open	37.00	42.00	Toothpick	25.00	38.00
Creamers			Tumbler	18.50	32.00
Ind	10.00	30.00	Vase	20.00	35.00
Regular	25.00	45.00	Wine	18.00	35.00
Cruet	55.00	75.00			

NEW JERSEY (Loops and Drops)

Non-flint made by U. S. Glass Co. in States Pattern Series. Collectors insist gold highlights are perfect.

	Clear w/gold	Ruby Stained		Clear w/gold	Ruby Stained
Bowls			Plates		
8″, flared	25.00	50.00	8″		
10″, oval	30.00	—	Flat	12.00	—
Butter, cov	65.00	75.00	Footed	22.00	—
Cake Stand, 8″	65.00	—	12″	30.00	—
Celery Tray, rectan-			Salt & Pepper	50.00	—
gular	25.00	—	Sauce.	10.00	30.00
Compotes			Spooner	27.00	—
Cov, hs, 5″, jelly. .	45.00	55.00	Sugar, cov	40.00	—
Cov, hs, 8″	75.00	—	Sweetmeat, 8″, open,		
Creamer	35.00	42.00	ftd.	40.00	—
Cruet	55.00	—	Syrup, no gold.	90.00	—
Goblet	35.00	—	Toothpick	55.00	—
Olive, pointed, flared	18.00	—	Tumbler	22.00	38.00
Pickle, rectangular . .	8.50	—	Wine, straight or		
Pitcher, water, ap-			flared	35.00	—
plied handle.	55.00	—			

O'HARA DIAMOND (Sawtooth and Star)

Non-flint, made by O'Hara Glass Co. in 1928 and by U. S. Glass Co. in 1898.

	Clear	Ruby Stained		Clear	Ruby Stained
Bowl.	25.00	60.00	Plates		
Butter, cov, ruffled			7″	20.00	—
base	45.00	125.00	8″	30.00	—
Compotes			10″	40.00	—
Cov, hs	40.00	—	Salt, master	12.00	—
Open, hs, jelly . . .	46.00	—	Spooner	20.00	48.00
Creamer	30.00	60.00	Sugar, cov	35.00	75.00
Cruet	55.00	110.00	Sugar Shaker	55.00	—
Cup and Saucer . . .	38.00	60.00	Syrup	55.00	145.00
Goblet	25.00	50.00	Tumbler	30.00	40.00
Lamp, Oil	47.00	—			

ONE HUNDRED ONE

Non-flint made by the Bellaire Goblet Co., Findlay, Ohio, in the late 1870s.

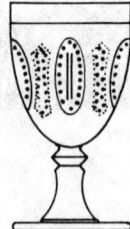

	Clear		Clear
Bread Plate, 101 border, Farm implement center, 11″	75.00	Lamp, hand, oil, 10″	80.00
		Pitcher, water	115.00
Butter, cov	60.00	Plate, 7″ or 8″	20.00
Cake Stand, 9″	65.00	Relish	15.00
Celery Vase	50.00	Spooner.	25.00
Compote, cov, ls.	60.00	Sugars	
Creamer.	35.00	Cov	45.00
Goblet	40.00	Open	15.00
		Wine	60.00

OPEN ROSE

Non-flint, c1870. Attributed to Boston and Sandwich Glass Co.

	Clear		Clear
Bowl, oval, 9″ x 6″	25.00	Pitcher, water, applied handle	150.00
Butter, cov	55.00	Relish	15.00
Compotes		Spooner	25.00
Cov, hs, 9″	60.00	Sugars	
Open, ls, 7½″	35.00	Cov	50.00
Creamer	40.00	Open, buttermilk	30.00
Egg Cup	25.00	Tumbler	50.00
Goblet	25.00		

OREGON #1 (Beaded Loop)

Non-flint. First made in the 1880s. Reissued in 1907 as one of the States series.

	Clear		Clear
Bowls		Goblet	32.00
7″	15.00	Pickle Dish, boat shape	15.00
8″	18.50	Pitchers	
Berry, cov	25.00	Milk	35.00
Bread Plate	35.00	Water	55.00
Butter, cov	35.00	Sauces	
English	65.00	Flat, 3½ to 4″	10.00
Flanged	50.00	Footed, 3½″	15.00
Flat	40.00	Spooner	
Cake Stand	28.00	Flat	20.00
Carafe, water	35.00	Footed	22.50
Celery Vase	28.00	Sugar, cov	
Compotes		Flat	25.00
Open, hs, 8″	50.00	Footed	30.00
Open, ls, 9″	22.00	Syrup	55.00
Creamer		Toothpick	35.00
Flat	30.00	Tumbler	25.00
Footed	35.00	Wine	40.00
Cruet	50.00		

PALMETTE

Non-flint, late 1870s. Syrup known in milk glass.

	Clear		Clear
Bowls		Egg Cup	35.00
8″	25.00	Goblet	35.00
9″	15.00	Lamp, 8½″, all glass	80.00
Bread Plate, handled, 9″	30.00	Pickle, scoop shape	18.00
Butter, cov	48.00	Pitcher, water	85.00
Cake Stand	65.00	Salt, master, ftd	22.00
Castor Bottle	20.00	Sauce, flat, 6″	10.00
Castor Set, 5 bottles	125.00	Shaker, saloon, oversize	60.00
Celery Vase	40.00	Spooner	35.00
Compotes		Sugar, cov	55.00
Cov, hs, 8½″	65.00	Syrup, applied handle	100.00
Cov, hs, 9¾″	75.00	Tumblers	
Open, ls, 7″	25.00	Bar	57.50
Creamer, applied handle	50.00	Water, ftd	35.00

PANAMA (Finecut Bar, Viking #2)

Made by U. S. Glass Co., in 1890s, in clear; but there could be other colors. A 1907 trade catalog shows 56 pieces.

	Clear		Clear
Bowl, Berry	25.00	Goblet	27.00
Butter, cov	40.00	Pickle	15.00
Cake Stand	25.00	Pitcher	
Celery Tray	18.00	Milk	32.00
Creamer		Water	42.00
Ind	18.00	Sugar, cov :	35.00
Regular	25.00	Spooner	18.00
Compotes		Tumbler	20.00
Cov, hs	45.00	Wine	18.00
Cov, ls	30.00		
Dish flaring edges, called a "Sweet Pea" bowl	18.00		

PANELED DAISY (Brazil)

Non-flint made by Bryce Bros., Pittsburgh, Pennsylvania, in the late 1870s and by U. S. Glass Co. in 1891. Also found in amber (sugar shaker for $125.00) and blue (sugar shaker for $145.00).

	Clear	Milk		Clear	Milk
Bowls			Pitcher, water	60.00	—
5″ x 7″, oval	15.00	—	Plates		
9″, square	18.00	—	Round, 7″	22.00	37.00
Butter, cov, 2 types	50.00	—	Square, 9″	30.00	45.00
Cake Stands			Relish, 5 x 7″, fish-shaped, wider at		
10¼″	45.00	—	one end	15.00	—
11″	50.00	—	Sauce, flat, sq	6.00	—
Celery Vase	27.00	—	Spooner	25.00	—
Compotes			Sugar, cov	40.00	—
Cov, hs, 6″, jelly	45.00	—	Sugar Shaker	45.00	80.00
Cov, hs, 10″	60.00	—	Tray, water	45.00	—
Open, hs, 11″	42.00	—	*Tumbler	26.00	—
Creamer	45.00	—	Waste Bowl	15.00	—
*Goblet	25.00	—			
Mug	30.00	—			

PANELED FORGET-ME-NOT (Regal)

Non-flint, made by Bryce Bros., Pittsburgh, Pennsylvania, c1870. Made in limited production in amethyst and green.

	Amber	Blue	Clear
Butter, cov	45.00	60.00	30.00
Cake Stand, 10″	67.50	90.00	45.00
Celery Vase	45.00	70.00	30.00
Compotes			
Cov, hs, 8″	80.00	100.00	55.00
Open, hs, 8½″, scalloped rim	—	—	55.00
Creamer	45.00	60.00	30.00

	Amber	Blue	Clear
Goblet	52.50	70.00	35.00
Marmalade Jar, cov.	60.00	80.00	40.00
Pickle, boat shape..	27.00	35.00	18.00
Pitcher, water	90.00	110.00	60.00
Sauce, ftd.	18.00	25.00	12.00
Spooner	37.50	50.00	25.00
Sugar, cov	60.00	80.00	40.00
Wine	52.50	70.00	35.00

PANELED "44" (Athenia, Reverse "44")

Non-flint made by U. S. Glass Co., c1912. Most pieces bear intertwined U. S. Glass Co. mark in base. Forms include pedestals and handles. Comes trimmed in gold and untarnishable platinum. Lemonade set ($45.00) and covered butter ($95.00) in rose or green staining. Some pieces in plain blue.

	Clear w/ platinum		Clear w/ platinum
Bon Bon, trifid ftd, cov.	35.00	Olive, flat, handless.	30.00
Bowls, 8″, flat.	50.00	Pitchers, water	
Butter, cov, flat	55.00	Flat, bulbous, ½ gal	85.00
Candlestick, 7″	50.00	Footed tankard.	90.00
Cruet	65.00	Salt & Pepper.	75.00
Creamers		Sugar, cov, flat, handled . . .	60.00
Flat.	45.00	Sugar, powdered, flat, no	
Footed	55.00	handles.	55.00
Finger Bowl	30.00	Toothpick.	45.00
Goblet	45.00	Tumbler, water	30.00
Lemonade Set, pitcher, 6		Wine	50.00
tumblers	275.00		

PANELED THISTLE

Non-flint made by J. P. Higbee Glass Co., Bridgeville, Pennsylvania, in the early 1900s. The Higbee Glass Co. often used a bee as a trademark. This pattern has been heavily reproduced with a similar mark. Occasionally found with gilt. A covered sugar in ruby stained is known.

	Clear		Clear
Basket, small size.	40.00	Plates	
Bowl, 8″, bee mark	18.00	7″.	18.00
Butter, cov,.	55.00	10″, bee mark	22.00
Cake Stand, 9″	35.00	Punch Cup, bee mark	25.00
Celery Tray.	20.00	Relish, bee mark.	15.00
Celery Vase	25.00	Rose Bowl, 5″	45.00
Compotes		Salt, ind	10.00
Open, hs, 8″	25.00	Sauces	
Open, hs, 5″, jelly	30.00	Flared, bee mark	14.00
Creamer, bee mark	35.00	Footed	12.00
Cruet, os	55.00	Spooner.	25.00
Doughnut Stand, 6″.	25.00	Sugar, cov	45.00
Goblet	35.00	Toothpick, bee mark	50.00
Honey, cov, sq, bee mark . .	50.00	Tumbler	20.00
Pitchers		Vase, 5″.	15.00
Milk	40.00	Wine, bee mark	40.00
Water	50.00		

PAVONIA (Pineapple stem)

Non-flint made by Ripley and Co. in 1885 and by U. S. Glass Co. in 1891. This pattern comes plain and etched.

	Clear	Ruby Stained		Clear	Ruby Stained
Bowl, 9″	20.00	—	Goblet, etched	35.00	50.00
Butter, cov	65.00	110.00	Pitcher, water, 12″, tankard	65.00	125.00
Cake Stand, large, etched.	40.00	—	Salt, master	27.50	—
Celery Vase, etched	35.00	—	Sauce, ftd, 3½″ or 4″	15.00	—
Compotes			Spooner, pedestal . .	30.00	48.00
Cov, hs, 6″	45.00	—	Sugar, cov	55.00	75.00
Open, jelly, etched.	38.00	—	Tumbler, etched, bellflowers	30.00	40.00
Creamer, etched . . .	45.00	50.00	Wine, etched.	30.00	40.00
Finger Bowl, ruffled underplate	48.00	65.00			

PENNSYLVANIA (Balder)

Non-flint issued by U. S. Glass Co., 1898. Also known in ruby stained. A ruffled jelly compote documented in orange carnival.

	Clear w/gold	Emerald Green		Clear w/gold	Emerald Green
Biscuit Jar, cov	55.00	100.00	Cruet, os.	48.00	—
Bowls			Decanter, handle, os.	85.00	—
8″, berry	30.00	35.00	Goblet	25.00	—
8″, sq	20.00	82.00	Pitcher, water	50.00	—
Butter, cov	55.00	85.00	Punch Bowl.	175.00	—
Carafe	45.00	—	Spooner.	24.00	32.00
Celery Vase	35.00	—	Sugar, cov	40.00	55.00
Compote, hs, ruffled, jelly.	50.00	—	Syrup	50.00	—
Creamers			Tumbler	24.00	40.00
Ind	18.00	35.00	Whiskey	12.00	—
Regular	35.00	50.00	Wine	18.00	—

PEQUOT

Made by Portland Glass Co., Portland, Maine, between 1863 and 1873. Shards found at Burlington Glass Works, Hamilton, Ontario.

	Clear		Clear
Bowl, 6″, pedestal.	20.00	Marmalade Jar	50.00
Butter, cov	45.00	Pitcher, water, reeded, hollow, applied handle	275.00
Celery Vase	50.00		
Champagne	45.00	Spooner.	40.00
Compote, open, hs, 7½″ . . .	50.00	Sugar, cov	55.00
Creamer.	45.00	Wine	35.00
Goblet	45.00		

PICKET

Non-flint made by the King Glass Co., Pittsburgh, Pennsylvania in the 1870s. Pattern has five different size compotes.

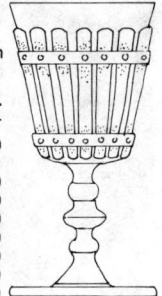

	Clear		Clear
Bread Plate	55.00	Master	25.00
Butter, cov	50.00	Sauces	
Celery Vase	40.00	Flat	8.00
Compotes		Footed	10.00
Cov, hs, 8″	75.00	Spooner	28.00
Open, hs, 8″	35.00	Sugar, cov	45.00
Open, ls, 7″	40.00	Toothpick	35.00
Creamer	35.00	Tray, water	50.00
Goblet	35.00	Waste Bowl	30.00
Pitcher, water	50.00		
Salts			
Ind	10.00		

PINEAPPLE AND FAN #1 (Heisey's #1255)

Made by A. H. Heisey and Co., Newark, Ohio, c1897, before the Heisey trademark was used. Came in about 70 pieces. Pieces often trimmed in gold. Also known in custard and ruby stained (toothpick at $125.00).

	Clear	Emerald Green		Clear	Emerald Green
Biscuit Jar, cov	55.00	85.00	Custard Cup	12.00	30.00
Bowl	30.00	45.00	Pitcher, water	60.00	225.00
Butter, cov	50.00	175.00	Rose Bowl	35.00	75.00
Cake Stand	45.00	75.00	Spooner	35.00	65.00
Celery Tray, flat	25.00	—	Sugar, cov	45.00	125.00
Compotes			Syrup	60.00	145.00
Open, hs, 8″	30.00	225.00	Toothpick	75.00	125.00
Open, jelly, 5″	32.00	—	Tumbler	25.00	60.00
Creamer	35.00	95.00	Vase, 10″, trumpet	25.00	45.00

PINEAPPLE AND FAN #2 (Czarina)

Non-flint made by Adams & Co., Pittsburgh, Pennsylvania. Later made by U. S. Glass Co. in 1891. Also found in emerald green, ruby stained, and white milk glass trimmed in gold.

	Clear		Clear
Bowl, 8″	25.00	Punch Bowl, 12″	60.00
Butter, cov	40.00	Rose Bowl	18.00
Cake Stand, 9″	35.00	Spooner	20.00
Creamer	25.00	Sugar, cov	30.00
Cruet, os	55.00	Syrup	50.00
Decanter	40.00	Tumbler	12.00
Finger Bowl	25.00	Waste Bowl	15.00
Goblet	24.00	Whiskey	15.00
Pitcher, water, tankard	45.00	Wine	16.00
Plate, 6½″	15.00		

PLEAT AND PANEL (Derby)

Non-flint made by Bryce Bros., Pittsburgh, Pennsylvania, c1870–1880 and by U. S. Glass Co. in 1891. Found in square and rectangular forms. Rare in blue, canary, and amethyst.

	Clear		Clear
Bowl, 8", cov	35.00	Marmalade Jar, cov	50.00
Bread Plate	35.00	Pitcher, water	50.00
Butter, cov	48.00	Plates	
Butter Pat	25.00	6"	20.00
Cake Stand, 10"	40.00	8"	24.00
Celery Vase	30.00	Relish, 8½"	18.00
Compotes		Salt, master	20.00
Cov, hs, 8"	48.00	Spooner	35.00
Open, hs, 8"	35.00	Sugar, cov	40.00
Creamer	30.00	Tray, water	60.00
*Goblet	30.00	Wine	50.00
Lamp	65.00		

PLUME

Non-flint made by Adams Glass Co., Pittsburgh, Pennsylvania, c1874 and by U. S. Glass Co. in 1891. Has both horizontal and vertical plumes. Also found etched. Pattern contains 46 pieces.

	Clear	Ruby Stained		Clear	Ruby Stained
Bowls, 8"			er with engraved		
Scalloped rim	25.00	—	vertical plumes, 6		
Square	20.00	—	tumblers, 12½"		
Butter, cov	50.00	135.00	tray	200.00	—
Cake Stand, 10"	40.00	—	Pitcher, water, applied handle	50.00	140.00
Celery Vase	30.00	65.00	Sauce, flat, 4"	15.00	—
Compote, open, hs, 9", crimped rim	38.00	—	Spooner	25.00	40.00
Creamer	35.00	55.00	Sugar, cov	45.00	60.00
Goblet	35.00	55.00	Syrup	60.00	—
Lemonade Set, pitch-			Tumbler	25.00	35.00

PLUTEC

Made by McKee Glass Co., c1900. Some pieces trademarked "Pres-Cut"

	Clear		Clear
Bowl	12.00	Plates	
Butter, cov	25.00	10¾"	25.00
Cake Stand	25.00	11"	25.00
Celery Vase	20.00	Sauce, flat	8.00
Compotes, open, hs	25.00	Spooner	20.00
Creamer	25.00	Sugar, cov	25.00
Decanter	45.00	Toothpick	20.00
Goblet	18.00	Tray, wine	30.00
Pickle	15.00	Tumbler	15.00
Pitcher, water	45.00	Wine	20.00

POPCORN

Non-flint, attributed to Boston and Sandwich Glass Co., late 1860s. Pieces were made with handles resembling an ear of corn, a flat oval which was filled with lines. Pieces with an outstanding ear should read "with ear" and the others "lined ear". The ear of corn motif probably was continued by another company.

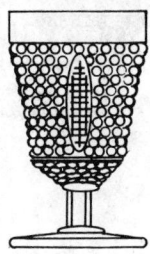

	Clear		Clear
Butter, cov	65.00	Pitcher, water, applied handle	100.00
Cake Stand, 11″	80.00	Sauce	12.00
Creamer	55.00	Spooner	30.00
Goblets		Sugar, cov	45.00
Lined ear	30.00	Wine, with ear	65.00
With ear	50.00		

PORTLAND

Non-flint pattern made by several companies and also by U. S. Glass Co. in the early 1900s. An oval pintray in ruby souvenir ($20.00) is known.

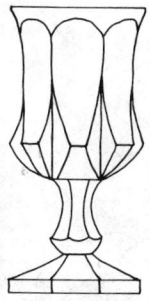

	Clear w/gold		Clear w/gold
Basket, handled	85.00	Goblet	35.00
Bowls		Lamp base, 9″	65.00
Berry	20.00	Pitcher, water, straight sides	55.00
Small, flat, cov.	20.00	Puff Box, glass lid	25.00
Bureau Jar, sp top	30.00	Relish	15.00
Butter, cov	50.00	Spooner	35.00
Cake Stand, 10½″	45.00	Sugar, cov	45.00
Carafe, water	45.00	Sugar Shaker	40.00
Celery Tray	25.00	Syrup	50.00
Compote, cov, 6″	55.00	Toothpick	20.00
Creamer	30.00	Tumbler	18.00
Cruet, os	55.00	Wine	25.00

POWDER AND SHOT

Flint, made by Boston & Sandwich Glass Co., c1870s. Finial of covered pieces is flattened upright fan. Although Metz claims it was produced in non-flint, examples have not been found.

	Flint		Flint
Butter, cov	95.00	Egg Cup	50.00
Castor Bottle	40.00	Goblet	65.00
Celery Vase	85.00	Salt, master, ftd	45.00
Compotes		Spooner	55.00
Cov, hs	100.00	Sugars	
Open, ls	50.00	Cov	90.00
Creamer, applied handle	95.00	Open	35.00

PRIMROSE

Non-flint made by Canton Glass Co., Canton, Ohio, c1880. Apple green is scarce.

	Amber and Yellow	Blue and Green	Clear
Bowl, 8″	32.00	35.00	24.00
Butter, cov	50.00	60.00	35.00
Cake Stand, 10″ . . .	50.00	65.00	40.00
Celery Vase	35.00	40.00	25.00
Compote, cov, ls, 6″	40.00	45.00	30.00
Creamer	35.00	48.00	30.00
Egg Cup	30.00	35.00	20.00
Goblets			
Knob Stem	40.00	45.00	30.00
Plain Stem	35.00	40.00	24.00
Pickle	18.00	20.00	14.00
Pitchers			
Milk.	45.00	55.00	35.00
Water	55.00	50.00	40.00
Plates			
4½″	18.00	20.00	15.00
9″, handled	30.00	35.00	20.00
Platter, 12 x 8″	35.00	45.00	30.00
Sauce, ftd	15.00	20.00	12.00
Spooner	25.00	30.00	20.00
Sugar, cov	40.00	55.00	35.00
Tray, water	50.00	60.00	35.00
Waste Bowl	30.00	35.00	20.00
Wine	35.00	45.00	30.00

PRINCESS FEATHER (Rochelle)

Non-flint made by Bakewell, Pears & Co. in the late 1870s. Occasional pieces made in flint. Later by U. S. Glass Co. in the 1890s. A rare blue opaque tumbler has been reported.

	Clear		Clear
Bowl, 7″, cov, pedestal	35.00	Pitcher, water	65.00
Butter, cov	50.00	Plates	
Cake Plate, handled	35.00	6″.	30.00
Celery Vase	40.00	7″.	35.00
Compotes		8″.	40.00
Cov, hs, 8″	50.00	9″.	45.00
Open, ls, 8″.	35.00	Spooner.	25.00
Creamer, applied handle . . .	55.00	Sugars	
Dish, oval.	20.00	Cov	55.00
Egg Cup.	40.00	Open, buttermilk	25.00
Goblet	30.00		

PRISCILLA #1 (Findlay's)

Non-flint made by Dalzell, Gilmore & Leighton, Findlay, Ohio, in the late 1890s and continued by National Glass Co. Fenton reproduced pattern in clear, colors, and opalescent in 1951. Also introduced many forms different from the original such as 12½″ plate, goblet, wine, 6″ handled bonbon, and sugar and creamer.

	Clear		Clear
Banana Stand.	90.00	Butter, cov	70.00
Bowl, 10¼″, straight sides . .	50.00	Cake Stand, 9½″	50.00

	Clear			Clear
Celery Vase	55.00		Plate	25.00
Compotes			Spooner	30.00
Cov, hs, 9″	75.00		Sugar, open	20.00
Open, hs, 7″	45.00		Syrup	75.00
Creamer	25.00		Toothpick	50.00
Cruet, os	60.00		Tumbler	25.00
Goblet	35.00		Wine	35.00
Pitcher, water, tankard	75.00			

PRISCILLA #2 (Fostoria's 676)

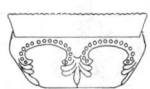

Made by Fostoria Glass Co., Moundsville, West Virginia, in 1898. Also made in custard with green or gold trim and white milk glass.

	Clear	Emerald Green		Clear	Emerald Green
Bowl, 8½″, berry	15.00	35.00	Marmalade Jar, cov.	45.00	115.00
Butter, cov	65.00	95.00	Pickle	15.00	25.00
Cake Stand	35.00	70.00	Pitcher, water	30.00	65.00
Carafe, water	40.00	65.00	Salt Shaker	12.00	30.00
Compotes			Sauce, flat, 4½″	10.00	15.00
Cov	55.00	75.00	Sherbet Cup	8.00	15.00
Open	40.00	55.00	Spooner	30.00	50.00
Creamer	35.00	70.00	Sugar, cov	45.00	80.00
Cruet, os.	65.00	250.00	Syrup, nickel top	55.00	150.00
Egg Cup	18.00	35.00	Toothpick, 4½″	35.00	65.00
Finger Bowl	12.00	20.00	Tumbler	25.00	35.00

PRISM WITH DIAMOND POINTS

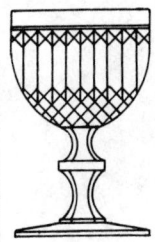

Flint made by Bryce Brothers and also attributed to Boston and Sandwich Glass Co. A flint milk glass spooner is known.

	Clear		Clear
Butter, cov	60.00	Pitcher, water	100.00
Compote, cov, hs, 6″	90.00	Salt, master	30.00
Creamer	75.00	Spooner	35.00
Egg Cups		Sugar, cov	50.00
Double	55.00	Tumbler	40.00
Single	35.00	Wine	50.00
Goblet	45.00		

PSYCHE AND CUPID

Non-flint, c1880, maker unknown

	Clear		Clear
Butter, cov	60.00	Sauce, ftd, 4½″	15.00
Celery Vase	40.00	Spooner	45.00
Creamer, 7″	50.00	Sugar, cov	55.00
Goblet	40.00	Wine	45.00
Pitcher, water	85.00		

QUARTERED BLOCK (Duncan & Miller #55)

Made by Duncan & Miller Co. c1903.

	Clear		Clear
Bowl	12.00	Pitcher, water	25.00
Butter, cov	25.00	Sauce	6.00
Celery Vase	18.00	Spooner	15.00
Compote, open, hs	30.00	Sugar, cov	20.00
Creamer	20.00	Toothpick	15.00
Goblet	18.00	Tumbler	12.00
Lamp	35.00	Wine	15.00

QUEEN ANNE (Bearded Man)

Non-flint made by LaBelle Glass Co., Bridgeport, Ohio, c1879. Finials are Maltese cross. AT least 28 pieces documented.

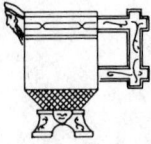

	Clear		Clear
Butter, cov	45.00	Water	50.00
Celery Vase	30.00	Spooner	25.00
Compote, cov	45.00	Sugar, cov	40.00
Creamer	35.00	Syrup	90.00
Egg Cup	35.00		
Pitchers			
Milk	45.00		

QUESTION MARK (Oval Loop)

Made by Richards and Hartley in 1895 and later by U. S. Glass Co., 1891. An 1888 catalog lists 32 pieces.

	Clear		Clear
Bowl, oblong		Pitchers	
7″	15.00	Milk	40.00
10″	25.00	Water	45.00
Butter, cov	30.00	Salt Shaker	15.00
Candlestick, chamber, finger		Sauce, 4″, collared	10.00
loop	45.00	Spooner	20.00
Celery Vase	25.00	Sugar, cov	25.00
Compote, open, hs, 7″	25.00	Tumbler	15.00
Creamer	30.00	Wine	20.00
Goblet	20.00		

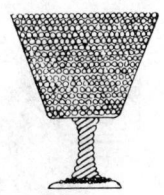

RAINDROP

Non-flint, c1880. An apple green hat ($75.00) and opaque blue milk glass pitcher are known. Also may have been made in white milk glass.

	Amber and Canary	Blue	Clear
Cake Plate	40.00	50.00	30.00
Compote, open, ls, 8″	35.00	45.00	20.00

	Amber and Canary	Blue	Clear
Creamer	35.00	45.00	20.00
Cup and Saucer . . .	40.00	50.00	25.00
Egg Cup, double . . .	35.00	45.00	25.00
Finger Bowl.	25.00	35.00	15.00
Lamp, miniature. . . .	95.00	—	—
Pickle	25.00	35.00	16.00
Pitcher, water	45.00	55.00	35.00
Sauces			
Flat.	12.00	14.00	8.00
Footed	15.00	18.00	10.00
Syrup	50.00	60.00	35.00
Tray, water	45.00	55.00	35.00

RED BLOCK (Late Block)

Non-flint with red stain made by Doyle and Co.; later made by five companies plus U. S. Glass Co. in 1892.

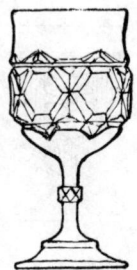

	Clear		Clear
Bowl, 8".	60.00	Sauce, flat, 4½"	22.50
Butter, cov	95.00	Salt Dip, ind	50.00
Celery Vase, 6½"	85.00	Salt Shaker, single	60.00
Creamer.	70.00	Spooner.	38.00
Decanter, 12", os, variant . .	175.00	Sugar, cov	70.00
*Goblet	35.00	Tumbler	32.50
Mug.	35.00	*Wine	35.00
Pitcher, water, 8" h	115.00		

REVERSE TORPEDO (Bull's Eye Band, Bull's Eye with Diamond Point #2, Pointed Bull's Eye)

Made by Dalzell, Gilmore & Leighton Glass Co., Findlay, Ohio, c1888–1890. Also attributed to Canadian factories.

	Clear		Clear
Banana Stand, 9¾".	135.00	Open, hs, jelly	55.00
Biscuit Jar, cov	165.00	Open, ls, 9¼", ruffled	
Bowls		edge	90.00
8½", shallow	30.00	Goblet	85.00
9", fruit, pie crust rim	65.00	Pitcher, water, tankard,	
Butter, cov	75.00	10¼"	140.00
Cake Stand	100.00	Sauce, flat, 3¾"	18.00
Celery Vase	55.00	Sugar, cov	85.00
Compotes		Syrup.	165.00
Cov, hs, 10"	125.00	Tumbler	35.00
Cov, hs, 6"	80.00		

RIBBED IVY

Flint, late 1850s. Attributed to Boston and Sandwich Glass Co.

	Clear		Clear
Bowl, 6″	15.00	Salts, master	
Butter, cov	110.00	Cov	115.00
Castor Bottle	35.00	Open, scalloped rim	40.00
Celery Vase	350.00	Sauce	10.00
Champagne	110.00	Spooner	40.00
Compotes		Sugar, cov	85.00
Cov, hs, 6″, jelly	125.00	Sweetmeat, cov, on stand	165.00
Open, hs, 9″, scalloped		Tumbler	
edge	85.00	Bar	75.00
Creamer	125.00	Water	75.00
Decanter, quart, os	150.00	Whiskey	
Egg Cup	30.00	Handled	100.00
Goblet	40.00	Plain	65.00
Hat	385.00	Wine	85.00

RIBBED PALM (Sprig)

Flint made by McKee Glass Co., Pittsburgh, Pennsylvania, 1868.

	Clear		Clear
Bowl, 7″, pedestal, scalloped		Plate, 6″	35.00
rim	40.00	Salt, ftd	32.00
Butter, cov	85.00	Sauce, flat	15.00
Champagne	95.00	Spooner	45.00
Compote, open, ls, 7″	60.00	Sugar, cov	75.00
Creamer, applied handle	175.00	Sweetmeat, cov, 6″	125.00
Egg Cup	35.00	Tumbler	75.00
Goblet	30.00	Wine	40.00
Lamp, all glass	85.00		
Pitcher, water, applied han-			
dle, ½ gal	150.00		

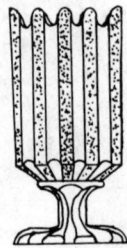

RIBBON

Non-flint, usually frosted, made by Bakewell, Pears, Pittsburgh, Pennsylvania, in the late 1860s. It has been erroneously called "Frosted Ribbon" at times, which can be confusing. Other Ribbon patterns are Clear Ribbon, Frosted Ribbon, Double Ribbon, Fluted Ribbon, and Grated Ribbon.

	Frosted		Frosted
Butter, cov	75.00	Pitcher, water	75.00
Cake Stand, 8½″	45.00	Platter, 9″ x 13″, oblong, cut	
Celery Vase	40.00	corners	62.50
Cologne Bottle, os	65.00	Sauces	
Compotes		Footed	18.00
Cov, hs, 8″	75.00	Tab-handled	18.00
Cov, ls, 7″	45.00	Spooner	28.00
Open, hs, 10½″, SP, Dol-		Sugar, cov	65.00
phin stand	225.00	Tray, water, 15″	100.00
Creamer	30.00	Waste Bowl	35.00
*Goblet	37.50	Wine	92.50

RIBBON CANDY (Bryce)

Non-flint, made by Bryce Brothers, Pittsburgh, Pennsylvania, 1880s. Reissued by U. S. Glass Co. in 1890s. Bowls come in a variety of sizes: open or with lids; flat or with a low collared foot. Also known in emerald green.

	Clear		Clear
Butter, cov, 2 types.	45.00	Plates	
Cake Stands		6″.	18.00
8″.	30.00	8″.	25.00
10½″	45.00	Relish	12.00
Claret.	40.00	Salt & Pepper.	42.00
Cordial	45.00	Sauce, flat, 4″.	10.00
Creamer.	25.00	Spooner.	18.00
Cruet, os	55.00	Sugars	
Cup and Saucer	35.00	Cov	35.00
Goblet	35.00	Open	20.00
Honey, cov, sq	60.00	Syrup.	65.00
Lamp, oil	75.00	Tumbler	25.00
Pitcher, water	65.00	Wine	25.00

RISING SUN (Sunshine)

Made by Ripley and Co., then continued by U. S. Glass Co. in 1908 at Glassport, Pennsylvania. Also found in carnival.

	Clear w/gold	Rose or Green Deco- rated		Clear w/gold	Rose or Green Deco- rated
Bowl, berry	12.00	—	Pitcher, water	40.00	—
Butter, cov	32.50	45.00	Relish.	15.00	—
Cake Plate, 10½″ . .	22.50	—	Sauce, flat	6.50	—
Cake Stand.	35.00	—	Spooner	18.00	—
Celery Vase	25.00	30.00	Sugar, cov		
Compotes			Regular or Hotel,		
Cov, hs	45.00	—	three-handled . .	40.00	—
Open, hs	30.00	—	Tall, ftd, no han-		
Creamer			dle.	35.00	—
Regular or Hotel. .	25.00	—	Toothpick, triple-han		
Tall, ftd	22.50	—	dled	18.00	35.00
Cruet, os.	40.00	—	Tumbler	15.00	25.00
Dish, ruffled edge . .	15.00	—	Whiskey (shot)	12.00	16.00
Goblet	20.00	25.00	Wine	25.00	30.00

ROMAN KEY

Flint glass pattern of the 1860s made Union Glass Co. and by others in several variants. Available in clear but of little value. Sometimes erroneously called "Greek Key."

	Flint Frosted		Flint Frosted
Bowl, 8″.	45.00	Goblet	60.00
Butter, cov	80.00	Pitcher, water	225.00
Celery Vase, ftd	80.00	Salt, ftd	45.00
Champagne	75.00	Sauce, 4″	18.00
Compote, open, hs, 7″	95.00	Spooner.	45.00
Creamer, applied handle . . .	125.00	Sugar, cov	90.00
Decanter, os.	160.00	Wine	85.00
Egg Cup.	50.00		

ROMAN ROSETTE

Non-flint made by Bryce, Walker and Co. 1875–1885. Reissued by U. S. Glass Co. in 1892 and 1898. Also attributed to Portland Glass Co. and seen with English registry mark.

	Clear	Ruby Stained		Clear	Ruby Stained
Bowl, 8½″	22.00	—	Pitchers		
Bread Plate	30.00	—	Milk	40.00	—
Butter, cov	48.00	—	Water	50.00	—
Cake Stand, 9″	45.00	—	Plate, 7½″	35.00	—
Celery Vase	18.00	—	Relish, oval, 9″	20.00	—
Compotes			Salt & Pepper, SP . .	55.00	80.00
Cov, hs, 4½″, jelly	50.00	—	Spooner	25.00	—
Cov, hs, 6″	65.00	—	Sugar, cov	43.00	—
Creamer	28.00	45.00	Wine	35.00	55.00
*Goblet	33.00	—			

ROPE BANDS (Argent, Clear Panels with Cord Band)

Made by Bryce Bros., Pittsburgh, Pennsylvania, c1870s; later made by U. S. Glass Co.

	Clear		Clear
Bowl	15.00	Pitcher, water	40.00
Bread Plate, medallion center	30.00	Plates, medallion center	
		6″	15.00
Butter, cov	40.00	7″	18.00
Cake Stand	35.00	Relish	12.00
Celery Vase	22.00	Sauce, ftd	10.00
Compotes, double knob stem		Spooner	18.00
Cov	35.00	Sugar, cov	30.00
Open	22.50	Tumbler	18.00
Creamer	25.00	Wine	27.50
Goblet, double knob stem . .	25.00		

ROSE-IN-SNOW

Non-flint made by Bryce Bros., Pittsburgh, Pennsylvania in the square form, c1880. Also made in the more common round form by Ohio Flint Glass Co. and after 1891 by U. S. Glass Co.

	Amber and Canary	Blue	Clear
Butters, cov			
Round	50.00	125.00	40.00
Square	60.00	150.00	50.00
Cake Stand, 9″	—	—	90.00
Compotes			
Cov, hs, 8″	75.00	175.00	55.00
Cov, ls, 7″	60.00	150.00	45.00
Open, ls, 5¾″ . . .	35.00	120.00	25.00

	Amber and Canary	Blue	Clear
Creamers			
Round.........	45.00	100.00	40.00
Square	40.00	120.00	40.00
*Goblet...........	35.00	100.00	30.00
*Mug, "In Fond Remembrance"..	45.00	110.00	32.00
*Pickle Dishes			
Double, 8½" x 7"	45.00	110.00	100.00
Single, oval, handles at end....	25.00	95.00	20.00
Pitcher, water, applied handle.....	175.00	200.00	125.00
Plate, 6" or 7".....	25.00	80.00	25.00
Platter, oval.......	—	—	125.00
Sauces			
Flat..........	15.00	40.00	12.00
Footed	8.00	48.00	15.00
Spooners			
Round.........	25.00	80.00	25.00
Square	35.00	100.00	35.00
Sugar, cov			
Round.........	40.00	120.00	40.00
Square	45.00	140.00	45.00
Tumbler, bar......	45.00	100.00	50.00

ROSE SPRIG

Non-flint made by Campbell, Jones & Co., Pittsburgh, Pennsylvania 1888.

	Amber and Canary	Blue	Clear
Biscuit Jar, dome lid	—	—	100.00
Cake Stand, 9"....	75.00	90.00	60.00
Celery Vase	50.00	60.00	40.00
Compotes			
Open, 7".......	67.50	—	55.00
Open, 8", oval...	70.00	—	—
Creamer	42.00	52.50	35.00
Goblet	52.50	67.50	45.00
Mug	—	—	40.00
Pitcher, water	60.00	70.00	50.00
Plate, 8".........	37.50	45.00	30.00
Relish, boat shape..	30.00	35.00	25.00
*Salts			
Patent Date 1888	62.50	75.00	50.00
Sleigh	30.00	37.50	25.00
Spooner	30.00	35.00	25.00
Sugar, cov	52.50	67.50	45.00
Tray, water	55.00	70.00	45.00
Tumbler	37.50	45.00	30.00
Wine	52.50	67.50	45.00

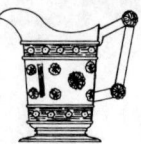

ROSETTE (Magic)

Non-flint made by Bryce Bros., Pittsburgh, Pennsylvania, in the late 1870s. Continued by the U. S. Glass Co. Later made in Ohio in 1898.

	Clear		Clear
Bowl, 7¼", cov	30.00	Pitchers	
Bread Plate, 9", handles	25.00	Milk, qt	35.00
Butter, cov	35.00	Water, ½ gal	40.00
Cake Stand, 11"	35.00	Plate, 7"	12.00
Compotes		Relish, fish shape	15.00
Cov, hs, 6"	40.00	Sauce, flat, handled	8.00
Open, hs, 7"	30.00	Spooner	20.00
Open, hs, 4½", jelly	25.00	Sugar, cov	35.00
Creamer	25.00	Wine	20.00
Goblet	25.00		

ROSETTES AND PALMS

Non-flint, made by J. B. Higbee Co., c1910.

	Clear		Clear
Banana Stand	40.00	Pickle Dish	30.00
Biscuit Jar, cov	42.00	Pitcher, water	45.00
Butter, cov	45.00	Plate, 10"	25.00
Cake Stand, 9½"	28.00	Sauce, flat	18.00
Celery Vase, flat	18.00	Spooner	22.00
Creamer	35.00	Sugar, cov	35.00
Goblet	30.00	Wine	24.00

ROYAL IVY ("New" Jewel)

Non-flint made by Northwood Glass Co. in 1889. Made in cased spatter, clear and frosted rainbow cracquelle, clear with amber, stained ivy, and clambroth opaline. These last mentioned were experimental pieces, not made in sets.

	Clear Frosted	Rubena Clear	Rubena Frosted
Butter, cov	100.00	150.00	275.00
Creamer, applied handle	60.00	150.00	200.00
Cruet	90.00	—	325.00
Marmalade Jar, SP cov	125.00	—	—
Pickle Castor, SP frame	—	—	375.00
Pitcher, water, applied handle	100.00	175.00	300.00
Rose Bowl	55.00	70.00	85.00
Spooner	45.00	70.00	95.00
Sugar, cov	150.00	165.00	180.00
Sugar Shaker	65.00	135.00	150.00
Syrup	120.00	225.00	300.00
Toothpick	—	—	125.00
Tumbler	35.00	50.00	75.00

ROYAL OAK (Acorn)

Non-flint made by Northwood Glass Co., Martins Ferry, Ohio, c1899. In early 1900s, it was made in opaque, white with colored tops and colored acorns and leaves. Milk-white pieces are rare.

	Clear Frosted	Rubena Clear	Rubena Frosted
Butter, cov	195.00	—	235.00
Creamer	150.00	—	—
Cruet, os.	215.00	425.00	480.00
Mustard Jar, cov . . .	90.00	—	—
Pickle Castor Insert	—	—	235.00
Pitcher, water	100.00	400.00	350.00
Salt Shaker, single. .	40.00	—	—
Spooner	120.00	—	100.00
Sugar, cov, acorn finial	65.00	—	—
Sugar Shaker	75.00	—	—
Syrup	135.00	—	—
Tumbler	65.00	—	85.00

SAWTOOTH (Mitre Diamond)

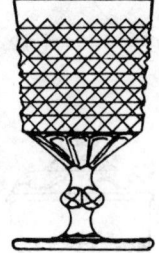

An early clear flint-glass pattern made in the late 1850s by the New England Glass Co., Boston and Sandwich Glass Co., and others. Later made in non-flint by Bryce Brothers and U. S. Glass Co. Also known in milk glass and clear deep blue.

	Flint	Non-Flint		Flint	Non-Flint
Butter, cov	75.00	45.00	Plain Stem.	—	20.00
Cake Stand, 10″ . . .	85.00	55.00	Pitchers, water		
Celery Vase, 10″ . . .	60.00	30.00	Applied handle. . .	125.00	—
Champagne	55.00	32.00	Pressed handle . .	—	55.00
Compotes			Plate, 6½″	45.00	30.00
Cov, hs, 9½″ . . .	85.00	48.00	Pomade Jar, cov . . .	50.00	35.00
Open, ls, 8″, saw-tooth edge	45.00	30.00	Salts		
Creamers			Cov, ftd	65.00	40.00
Applied handle. . .	65.00	40.00	Open, smooth edge	25.00	20.00
Pressed handle . .	—	30.00	Spooner	40.00	14.00
Cruet, acorn stopper	100.00	—	Sugar, cov	65.00	35.00
Egg Cup	45.00	25.00	Tumbler, flat	35.00	25.00
Goblets			Wine, knob stem . . .	35.00	25.00
Knob Stem	40.00	25.00			

SCALLOPED DIAMOND POINT (Late Diamond Point Band, Panel with Diamond Point, Diamond Point With Flute)

Non-flint pattern. Not to be confused with early, flint Diamond Point. Made by Central Glass Co., Wheeling, West Virginia. Also made by U. S. Glass Co. after 1891. A wine ($75.00) is known in electric blue.

	Clear		Clear
Bowl, oval, 9″	20.00	Cake Stands	
Butter Dish, cov	35.00	8″	25.00

	Clear		Clear
12″.	55.00	Plates	
Cheese Dish, cov, 8″.	50.00	5″.	10.00
Creamer.	35.00	9″.	25.00
Goblet	30.00	Sauce, ftd, 4″	10.00
Mustard Jar, cov.	30.00	Spooner.	25.00
Pickle Dish, oval	18.00	Sugar, cov	35.00
Pickle Jar, cov	45.00		

SCALLOPED TAPE (Jewel Band)

Non-flint, c1880. Maker unknown. Occasionally found in amber, blue, canary, and light green.

	Clear		Clear
Bread Plate, oval, "Bread Is		Pitchers	
The Staff of Life".	45.00	Milk	35.00
Butter, cov	35.00	Water	50.00
Cake Stand	35.00	Plate, 6″.	15.00
Compotes		Sauces	
Cov, hs, 8″	55.00	Flat, 4″	8.00
Open, hs.	40.00	Ftd.	10.00
Creamer.	30.00	Spooner.	20.00
Dish, rect, cov, 8″	45.00	Sugar, cov	35.00
Egg Cup.	25.00	Wine	25.00
Goblet	30.00		

SCROLL (Stippled Scroll)

Non-flint, made by Duncan Glass Co., c1870s.

	Clear		Clear
Butter, cov	40.00	Salt, ftd	20.00
Celery	30.00	Spooner.	25.00
Compotes		Sugars	
Cov, hs.	45.00	Cov	40.00
Open, hs.	35.00	Open, buttermilk	30.00
Creamer, applied handle . . .	35.00	Tumbler, ftd	18.00
Goblet	25.00	Wine	25.00
Pitcher, water, applied han-			
dle	75.00		

SCROLL WITH ACANTHUS

Made by Northwood Glass Co., after 1903, at Wheeling, West Virginia. There is sometimes enameled decoration on the transparent pieces. Transparent colors are 20% less, purple slag 50% higher.

	Blue Opal	Canary Opal	White Opal
Bowl, berry	60.00	65.00	35.00
Butter, cov, ftd	125.00	110.00	50.00
Compote, jelly, 5″ . .	50.00	45.00	30.00
Creamer	100.00	85.00	40.00
Pitcher, water	285.00	255.00	100.00
Sauces, berry	25.00	25.00	20.00

	Blue Opal	Canary Opal	White Opal
Spooner	45.00	50.00	30.00
Sugar, cov	85.00	75.00	45.00
Tumbler	40.00	35.00	25.00

SCROLL WITH FLOWERS

Non-flint. Attributed to Central Glass Co. in the 1870s and Canton Glass Co. Occasionally found in amber, apple green, and blue.

	Clear		Clear
Butter, cov	40.00	Pitcher, water	45.00
Cake Plate, 10½″, handled .	25.00	Plate, double-handled, 10½″	30.00
Creamer.	30.00	Sauce, double-handled	10.00
Egg Cup, handled	18.00	Spooner.	25.00
Goblet	25.00	Sugar, cov	40.00
Mustard Jar, cov	35.00	Wine	30.00
Pickle, handled	18.00		

SHELL AND JEWEL (Victor, Nugget)

Non-flint made by Westmoreland Glass Co., c1893. Also made in Canada and called "Nugget."

	Amber	Blue	Clear	Cobalt Blue	Iridescent Green
Banana Stand, 10″ .	—	—	65.00	—	—
Bowl, 8″	35.00	—	20.00	—	—
Butter, cov	—	—	60.00	—	—
Cake Stand, 10″ . . .	—	—	50.00	—	—
Compote, open, hs, 7″	—	—	35.00	—	—
Creamer	—	—	40.00	—	75.00
Pitcher, water	50.00	60.00	40.00	100.00	—
Spooner	—	—	20.00	—	—
Sugar, cov	—	—	47.50	—	75.00
Tumbler	35.00	40.00	45.00	—	45.00
Water Set, 8 pcs . . .	300.00	350.00	200.00	—	—

SHELL AND TASSEL (Shell and Spike)

Non-flint made by George A. Duncan & Sons, Pittsburgh, Pennsylvania, in the 1880s. It was patented by Augustus Heisey on July 26, 1881. Two forms were issued: square with shell shaped finials and later, round with frosted dog finials. Also made in azure blue, amber, and canary, but extremely rare.

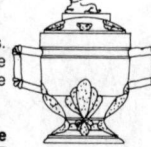

	Round	Square		Round	Square
Bowl, 12″, oval	55.00	—	Compotes		
Bread Plate.	50.00	65.00	Open, hs, 10″ . . .	—	65.00
Butter, cov	45.00	75.00	Open, jelly, 4½″ . .	—	45.00
Butter Pat, shell shaped	25.00	—	Creamer	40.00	55.00
Cake Stand, 12″ . . .	—	90.00	*Goblet.	40.00	—
Celery Vase	45.00	55.00	Ice Cream Tray	45.00	—
			Oyster Plate	—	110.00

	Round	Square		Round	Square
Pitcher, water	65.00	75.00	Spooner	32.50	35.00
Salt Shakers, single.	30.00	—	Sugar, cov, dog fin-		
Sauces			ial	100.00	85.00
Flat	—	10.00	Vase, 7½", scalloped		
Ftd	10.00	15.00	rim	135.00	—

SHERATON (Ida)

Non-flint made by Bryce, Higbee & Co., Pittsburgh, Pennsylvania, c1880. Also made in Canada.

	Amber	Blue	Clear
Bowl, 8"	35.00	40.00	15.00
Bread Plate	45.00	50.00	25.00
Butter, cov	40.00	50.00	25.00
Celery Vase	30.00	35.00	20.00
Compote, open, ls,			
7"	25.00	30.00	20.00
Creamer	40.00	45.00	30.00
Goblet	40.00	50.00	35.00
Pitchers			
Milk	40.00	50.00	30.00
Water	45.00	55.00	30.00
Relish, handled	25.00	30.00	15.00
Sauce, flat	15.00	18.00	10.00
Spooner	22.00	25.00	15.00
Sugar, cov	45.00	55.00	30.00
Wine	30.00	40.00	25.00

SHRINE (Jewel with Moon and Star)

Non-flint made by Beatty & Indiana Glass Co., Dunkirk, Indiana, c. late 1880s.

	Clear		Clear
Bowl		Pitcher, water	48.00
6½"	25.00	Platter	35.00
9½"	30.00	Relish	15.00
Butter, cov	45.00	Sauce	35.00
Cake Stand, 8½"	30.00	Spooner	30.00
Creamer	35.00	Sugar Bowl, cov	40.00
Goblet	45.00	Tumbler	25.00
Lemonade	35.00		

SHUTTLE (Hearts of Loch Haven)

Made by Indiana Tumbler and Goblet Co., Greentown, Indiana, between 1894 and 1903.

	Clear w/gold	Cara-mel		Clear w/gold	Cara-mel
Bowl, berry	25.00	—	Pitcher, water	50.00	—
Butter, cov	50.00	150.00	Spooner	18.00	—
Cordial	30.00	—	Sugar, cov	37.00	—
Creamer	30.00	—	Tumbler	25.00	80.00
Cruet, os.	75.00	—	Wine	15.00	50.00
Mug	22.00	95.00			

SKILTON (Oregon #2)

Made by Richards and Hartley of Tarentum, Pennsylvania. This is not one of the U. S. Glass States pattern series and should not be confused with Beaded Loop, which is Oregon #1, named by U. S. Glass Co. It is better known as Skilton and was named by Millard to avoid confusion with Beaded Loop.

	Clear	Ruby Stained		Clear	Ruby Stained
Bowl	20.00	—	Pickle	15.00	—
Butter, cov	45.00	—	Pitchers		
Cake Stand	35.00	—	Milk	45.00	—
Celery Vase	25.00	—	Water	50.00	125.00
Compotes			Salt & Pepper Shakers, pr	45.00	—
Cov, hs, 8"	45.00	—	Spooner, flat	25.00	40.00
Open, ls	30.00	—	Sugar, cov	35.00	—
Creamer	30.00	47.50	Tray, water	45.00	—
Dish, oblong, sq	25.00	—	Tumbler	25.00	40.00
Goblet	35.00	—	Wine	35.00	45.00
Olive, handled	20.00	—			

SNAIL (Compact, Idaho)

Non-flint made by George Duncan & Sons, Pittsburgh, Pennsylvania, c1880, and by U. S. Glass Co. in the States Pattern series. Ruby-flashed pieces date after 1891.

	Clear	Ruby Stained		Clear	Ruby Stained
Banana Stand	165.00	—	Pitcher, water, tankard	100.00	—
Bowls			Plate, 7"	35.00	—
8", oval	28.00	35.00	Punch Cup	38.00	—
9"	28.00	—	Relish, 7", oval	25.00	—
Butter, cov	85.00	—	Salt, master	18.00	—
Cake Stand	75.00	—	Salt & Pepper	65.00	—
Celery Vase	48.00	65.00	Spooner	32.00	—
Cheese, cov	65.00	—	Sugars		
Compotes			Ind, cov	35.00	—
Cov, hs, 10"	50.00	—	Regular, cov	70.00	—
Open, hs, 8"	35.00	—	Syrup	85.00	225.00
Creamer	30.00	—	Tumbler	55.00	—
Cruet, os	57.00	175.00	Vase	50.00	—
Finger Bowl	25.00	—	Wine	75.00	—
Goblet	65.00	—			

SPANISH-AMERICAN

Made in the late 1890s in commemoration of Admiral Dewey and the Spanish-American war. Two pitchers were made by the Beatty-Brady Glass Co., Dunkirk, Indiana. The only known matching pieces are listed below.

	Clear		Clear
Water Pitcher, Admiral Dewey, Flagship Olympia, flags, cannon, balls around base	70.00	Water Pitcher, Captain Gridley, "You may fire when ready", bullets around base	85.00
Tumbler, portrait of Dewey, matches pitcher	50.00	Tumbler to match	80.00

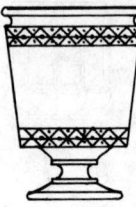

SPIREA BAND

Non-flint made by Bryce, Higbee & Co., Pittsburgh, Pennsylvania, c1885.

	Amber	Blue	Clear	Vaseline
Bowl, 8″	25.00	40.00	24.00	30.00
Butter, cov	45.00	55.00	32.00	44.00
Cake Stand, 11″ . . .	42.00	55.00	50.00	42.00
Celery Vase	40.00	50.00	25.00	40.00
Compote, cov, hs, 7″	44.00	50.00	40.00	44.00
Cordial	32.00	42.00	20.00	32.00
Creamer	34.00	44.00	24.00	35.00
Goblet	34.00	44.00	20.00	32.00
Pitcher, water	50.00	60.00	35.00	50.00
Platter, 10½″.	32.00	42.00	18.00	32.00
Relish.	30.00	40.00	16.00	30.00
Sauce, ftd	15.00	18.00	8.00	14.00
Spooner	25.00	30.00	15.00	24.00
Sugar, open	30.00	40.00	18.00	30.00
Tumbler	24.00	35.00	15.00	30.00
Wine	30.00	35.00	20.00	30.00

SPRIG

Non-flint made by Bryce, Higbee & Co., Pittsburgh, Pennsylvania, mid-1880s.

	Clear		Clear
Bread Plate	40.00	Pitcher, water	45.00
Butter, cov	45.00	Sauces	
Cake Stand, 10″	35.00	Flat.	10.00
Celery Vase	35.00	Ftd	14.00
Compotes		Spooner	22.00
Cov, hs.	48.00	Sugar, cov	48.00
Open, hs.	30.00	Tumbler	17.50
Creamer.	25.00	Wine	35.00
Goblet	35.00		

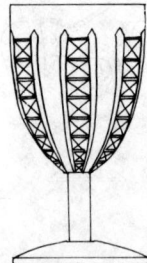

STARS AND STRIPES (Brilliant)

Made by Jenkins Glass Co., Kokomo, Indiana, in 1899. Appeared in 1899 Montgomery Ward catalog as "Brilliant."

	Clear		Clear
Bowl, berry	15.00	Pitcher, water	20.00
Butter, cov	20.00	Salt Shaker	15.00
Celery Vase	15.00	Sauce	6.00
Cordial	15.00	Spooner	15.00
Creamer.	18.00	Sugar, cov	20.00
Cup, sherbert, handled	8.00	Tumbler	10.00
Goblet	15.00	Wine	10.00

STATES, THE (Cane and Star Medallion)

Non-flint made by the U. S. Glass Co. in 1908. Also found in emerald green; add 50%.

	Clear w/ gold		Clear w/ gold
Bowls		Punch Bowl, 8 cups	110.00
7″, rd, w/ 3 handles.	25.00	Salt & Pepper.	40.00
9¼″, rd	28.00	Sauce, flat, 4″, tub shape . .	10.00
Butter, cov	65.00	Spooner.	25.00
Celery Tray.	18.00	Sugar, cov	40.00
Compote, open, hs, 7″	30.00	Syrup.	65.00
Creamers		Toothpick, flat, rectangular,	
Ind, oval	15.00	curled lip.	45.00
Regular, round.	28.00	Tray, 7¼″ l, 5½″ w	18.00
Goblet	35.00	Tumbler	25.00
Pitcher, water	45.00	Wine	30.00
Plates, 10″	35.00		

STIPPLED FORGET-ME-NOT

Non-flint made by Findlay Glass Co. in the 1880s, and after 1891 by the Model Flint Glass Co., Findlay, Ohio. Also found in amber and white.

	Clear		Clear
Bread Plate	35.00	7″, Star center.	30.00
Butter, cov	50.00	9″, Kitten center, handles.	45.00
Cake Stand, 12″	45.00	9″, Star center.	35.00
Celery	30.00	Relish, oval	14.00
Compotes		Salt, master, oval	35.00
Cov, hs, 8″	50.00	Sauce, ftd	15.00
Cov, ls, 6″.	37.50	Spooner.	25.00
Creamer.	30.00	Sugar, cov	35.00
Goblet	35.00	Toothpick, hat shaped.	75.00
Mug.	30.00	Tray, water, aquatic scene. .	50.00
Pitcher, water	50.00	Tumbler	30.00
Plates		Wine	35.00
7″, Baby in Tub reaching			
for ball.	55.00		

STIPPLED STAR

Non-flint made by Gillinder & Sons in the 1870s. Reproductions in color.

	Clear		Clear
Butter, cov	50.00	Goblet	30.00
Celery vase	40.00	Pitcher, water	75.00
Compotes		Sauces	
Cov, hs, 12″	65.00	Flat.	10.00
Open, hs, 8″	45.00	Footed	15.00
Creamer, applied handle . . .	50.00	Spooner.	25.00
Egg Cup.	35.00	Sugar, cov	45.00

STRAWBERRY (Fairfax)

Non-flint pattern first made in 1870 and patented by John Bryce. Attributed to Boston and Sandwich Glass Co. by Lee. Later made by Bryce, Walker & Co.

	Clear	Milk		Clear	Milk
Bowl, oval, 9¼" x 6"	30.00	—	Pitcher, water, applied handle	125.00	135.00
Butter, cov	55.00	50.00	Sauce, flat	14.00	—
Compotes			Spooner	40.00	40.00
Cov, hs, 8"	75.00	—	Sugar		
Cov, ls, 8"	65.00	—	Cov	65.00	65.00
Creamer, applied			Open, buttermilk	40.00	45.00
handle	65.00	75.00	Tumbler, bar	45.00	—
*Egg Cup	37.50	32.00	Wine	95.00	—
*Goblet	38.00	56.00			

STRAWBERRY AND CURRANT (Multiple Fruits)

One of a non-flint series of fruit patterns which has become known as Multiple Fruits (Cherry and Fig, Loganberry and Grape, Blackberry and Grape, and Cornucopia with Sprig of Cherries). They were made by Dalzell, Gilmore, and Leighton in Findlay, Ohio. A Loganberry and Grape jelly goblet, with "U" shaped bowl; is of inferior quality and not part of the pattern.

There are matching pieces in all forms, although whether or not all forms were made in all four patterns is not known. Reproduction goblets found in clear, opalescent, and colors.

	Clear		Clear
Butter, cov	50.00	Water	50.00
Celery Vase	35.00	Sauce, ftd	12.00
Cheese, cov	50.00	Spooner	30.00
Creamer	40.00	Sugar, cov	40.00
*Goblet	35.00	Syrup	80.00
Mug	40.00	Tumblers	25.00
Pitchers			
Milk	40.00		

SWAG WITH BRACKETS

Made by Jefferson Glass Co., Steubenville, Ohio, c1904. Also found in non-opalescent, gold trimmed, amethyst, blue, and vaseline.

	Blue and Canary Opal	Green Opal	White Opal
Butter, cov	175.00	150.00	—
Compote, Jelly	45.00	55.00	30.00
Creamer	90.00	75.00	55.00
Cruet, os	125.00	110.00	—
Pitcher, water	275.00	200.00	130.00
Salt Shaker, single	50.00	40.00	35.00
Spooner	75.00	65.00	40.00
Sugar, cov	165.00	90.00	50.00
Tumbler	75.00	50.00	35.00

TEARDROP AND TASSEL (Sampson)

Non-flint made by the Indiana Tumbler & Goblet Co., Greentown, Indiana, c1890, to celebrate Admiral Sampson's victory in the Spanish-American War.

	Clear	Dark Blue	Green	Green Opaque
Bowl, 7½"........	36.00	55.00	45.00	75.00
Butter, cov	55.00	95.00	65.00	125.00
Celery Vase	40.00	—	—	—
Compotes				
Cov, hs, 7"	75.00	90.00	80.00	125.00
Open, ls, 8".....	30.00	45.00	35.00	65.00
Creamer	50.00	70.00	45.00	90.00
Goblet	60.00	95.00	75.00	95.00
Pickle...........	15.00	30.00	25.00	35.00
Pitcher, water	70.00	110.00	80.00	140.00
Salt Shaker, single..	50.00	75.00	60.00	70.00
Spooner	30.00	45.00	35.00	65.00
Sugar, cov	60.00	80.00	70.00	95.00
Tumbler	40.00	50.00	45.00	65.00
Wine	65.00	80.00	70.00	110.00

TENNESSEE (Jewel and Crescent; Jeweled Rosette)

Made by King Glass Co., Pittsburgh, Pennsylvania, and continued by U. S. Glass Co., in 1899, as part of the States series.

	Clear	Colored Jewels		Clear	Colored Jewels
Bowl, berry	20.00	45.00	Creamer	22.50	—
Bread Plate.......	40.00	75.00	Goblet	30.00	—
Butter, cov	55.00	—	Mug	35.00	—
Cake Stands			Pitcher, water	55.00	—
9½"	35.00	—	Relish...........	20.00	—
10½"..........	45.00	—	Spooner	30.00	—
Celery Vase	25.00	—	Sugar, cov	45.00	—
Compotes			Toothpick	45.00	50.00
Cov, 5", jelly	40.00	55.00	Tumbler	25.00	—
Open, hs, 9"	45.00	—	Wine	35.00	—

TEXAS (Loop with Stippled Panels)

Non-flint made by U. S. Glass Co., c1900, in the States Pattern series. Occasionally pieces found in ruby stained.

	Clear w/gold	Rose Flashed		Clear w/gold	Rose Flashed
Bowls			Pickle, 8½".......	26.00	—
8½"	25.00	40.00	Pitcher, water	75.00	—
7", scalloped	25.00	50.00	Plate, 9"	35.00	—
Butter, cov	55.00	—	Sauce, ftd........	15.00	—
Cake Stand, 9½"..	60.00	80.00	Spooner	35.00	—
Celery Tray.......	30.00	—	*Sugar, cov........	55.00	—
Celery Vase	40.00	—	Toothpick	45.00	95.00
Compotes			Tumbler	25.00	—
Cov, hs, 8"	65.00	—	Vases		
Open, hs, 5"	40.00	—	6½"	25.00	—
Creamer, regular ...	28.00	35.00	9"..........	35.00	—
Cruet, os.	55.00	165.00	Wine	45.00	100.00
Goblet	45.00	85.00			

TEXAS BULL'S EYE (Filley, Bull's Eye Variant)

Originated by Bryce Bros., Pittsburgh, Pennsylvania, and continued by Findlay Glass, Findlay, Ohio. Also made in Canada. Originally made in semi-flint (no bell tone, but some lead content).

	Clear		Clear
Butter, cov	55.00	Sugars	
Creamer	35.00	Cov	45.00
Egg Cup	30.00	Open, buttermilk	40.00
Goblet	30.00	Tumblers, regular	50.00
Pitcher, water	55.00	Wine	40.00
Spooner	25.00		

THISTLE

Non-flint, made by Bryce, Walker & Co. in 1872.

	Clear		Clear
Bowl, 8″	30.00	Relish	25.00
Butter, cov	50.00	Salt, ftd	30.00
Cake Stand, large	75.00	Sauce, flat	15.00
Compotes		Spooner	30.00
Cov, hs	70.00	Sugars	
Cov, ls	40.00	Cov	65.00
Cordial	60.00	Open, buttermilk type	35.00
Creamer, applied handle	65.00	Tumbler	45.00
Egg Cup	40.00	Wine	55.00
Goblet	40.00		
Pitcher, water, applied handle	85.00		

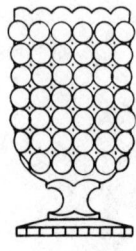

THOUSAND EYE

Non-flint made by Adams Glass Co., Tarentum, Pennsylvania, 1875, by Richards and Hartley, c1888, and by New Brighton Glass Co., New Brighton, Pennsylvania, 1889. It was made in two forms: Richard, and Hartley with the plain stem and Adams with a three-knob stem. Covered pieces of this type have three knob finials. Three-knob variation should be 35% more than plain.

	Amber	Apple Green	Blue	Clear	Vaseline
Butter, cov	65.00	90.00	70.00	45.00	65.00
Celery, hat shaped	50.00	70.00	50.00	35.00	45.00
Cologne Bottle	30.00	55.00	35.00	20.00	30.00
Compote, cov, hs, 6″	50.00	95.00	65.00	60.00	50.00
Cordial	30.00	55.00	35.00	20.00	30.00
Creamer	45.00	72.00	50.00	30.00	35.00
*Cruet	35.00	60.00	40.00	25.00	35.00
Egg Cup	60.00	90.00	70.00	45.00	60.00
*Goblet	35.00	60.00	40.00	25.00	35.00
Inkwell	45.00	—	75.00	35.00	45.00
*Hat	20.00	45.00	25.00	15.00	20.00
Lamps					
Handle, ls	60.00	85.00	65.00	50.00	60.00
Plain stem, hs	90.00	115.00	95.00	75.00	90.00

	Amber	Apple Green	Blue	Clear	Vaseline
Pitcher, water	75.00	95.00	80.00	65.00	75.00
*Plates					
6", ABC plate, clock center . . .	—	—	—	40.00	—
8"	25.00	50.00	30.00	20.00	25.00
10"	30.00	55.00	35.00	25.00	30.00
Platter, 11", oval . . .	40.00	65.00	45.00	35.00	40.00
Sauce, ftd	12.00	35.00	15.00	10.00	12.00
Spooner	25.00	50.00	30.00	20.00	25.00
Sugar, cov	45.00	70.00	50.00	40.00	45.00
Syrup, pewter top . .	85.00	90.00	65.00	50.00	60.00
Toothpick	20.00	50.00	35.00	18.00	20.00
Trays					
12½"	55.00	80.00	60.00	50.00	55.00
14", oval	60.00	85.00	60.00	55.00	60.00
*Tumbler	25.00	50.00	30.00	20.00	25.00
*Twine holder	30.00	55.00	35.00	25.00	30.00
*Wine	35.00	50.00	30.00	20.00	25.00

THREE-FACE

Non-flint made by George E. Duncan & Son, Pittsburgh, Pennsylvania, c1872. Designed by John E. Miller, a designer with Duncan, who later became a member of the firm. Companies in the Pittsburgh area produced many patterns in expectation of the 1876 Philadelphia Centennial Exposition. It has been heavily reproduced.

	Clear			Clear
Butter, cov	150.00	Open, ls, 6"		65.00
Cake Stands		Creamer		100.00
9"	110.00	Goblet		95.00
11"	150.00	Lamp, Oil		140.00
Celery Vase	95.00	Marmalade Jar		200.00
Champagnes		Pitcher, water		295.00
Hollow stem	250.00	Salt Dip		35.00
Saucer type	150.00	Sauce, ftd		25.00
Claret	85.00	Salt & Pepper		75.00
Compotes		Spooner		70.00
Cov, hs, 10"	175.00	Sugar, cov		110.00
Cov, ls, 4"	150.00	Wine		45.00
Open, hs, 9"	100.00			

THREE PANEL

Non-flint made by Richards & Hartley Co., Tarentum, Pennsylvania, c1888, and by U. S. Glass Co. in 1891.

	Amber	Blue	Clear	Vaseline
Bowls				
8½"	25.00	40.00	20.00	40.00
10"	30.00	50.00	35.00	45.00
Butter, cov	45.00	50.00	40.00	50.00
Celery Vase, ruffled top	—	—	35.00	—
Compote, open, ls, 7"	35.00	40.00	25.00	40.00
Creamer	40.00	50.00	30.00	30.00
Goblet	40.00	50.00	30.00	40.00

	Amber	Blue	Clear	Vaseline
Lamp, kerosene . . .	135.00	—	—	—
Mug	30.00	45.00	25.00	35.00
Pitcher, water	90.00	65.00	40.00	60.00
Spooner	40.00	45.00	30.00	40.00
Sugar, cov	50.00	60.00	40.00	65.00
Tumbler	35.00	40.00	20.00	30.00

TOKYO

Made by Jefferson Glass Co., Steubenville, Ohio, c1905. Also found in clear, blue, and apple green —all with gold trim.

	Blue Opal	Green Opal	White Opal
Bowl, berry	60.00	50.00	40.00
Butter, cov	135.00	100.00	70.00
Compote, jelly	40.00	45.00	35.00
Creamer	70.00	55.00	50.00
Cruet	185.00	140.00	90.00
Dish, 6½″	40.00	45.00	40.00
Pitcher, water	200.00	165.00	100.00
Salt Shaker, single. .	50.00	40.00	30.00
Sauce.	30.00	25.00	20.00
Spooner	45.00	40.00	30.00
Sugar, cov	90.00	80.00	60.00
Toothpick	110.00	80.00	50.00
Tumbler	50.00	45.00	35.00
Vase	60.00	60.00	45.00

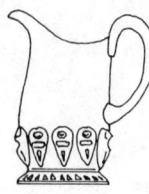

TORPEDO (Pigmy)

Non-flint made by Thompson Glass Co., Uniontown, Pennsylvania, c1889. A open 9″ bowl ($45.00), goblet ($85.00), and tumbler ($50.00) found in ruby stained. Black amethyst master salt ($150.00) also known.

	Clear		Clear
Banana Stand.	75.00	Marmalade Jar, cov.	55.00
Bowls		Pitchers	
Cov, 8″	40.00	Milk, 8½″	75.00
Open, 8″	20.00	Water, 10½″	85.00
Open, 9½″, flared rim. . . .	35.00	Punch Cup	25.00
Butter, cov	85.00	Salt Shaker, single, 2 types. .	50.00
Cake Stand, 10″	55.00	Salt, master	30.00
Celery Vase, scalloped top .	35.00	Sauce, 4½″, collared base. .	15.00
Compotes		Spooner, scalloped top	35.00
Cov, hs, 13¾″	165.00	Sugars	
Cov, hs, 4″, jelly	75.00	Cov	65.00
Open, hs, 8½″.	60.00	Open	30.00
Creamer.	55.00	Syrup.	65.00
Cruet, os, applied handle. . .	90.00	Trays, water	
Cup and Saucer	65.00	10″, round.	85.00
Decanter, os, 8″	65.00	11¾″, clover shaped	75.00
Goblet	50.00	Tumbler	30.00
Lamps		Waste Bowl	40.00
3⅜″, handled	75.00	Wine	65.00
8″, plain base, pattern on			
bowl	85.00		

TREE OF LIFE (Portland's)

Made flint and non-flint by Portland Glass Co., 1864–1874. Originally made in red or deep pink, green, purple, yellow, and light and dark blue, but color is rare today.

	Flint		Flint
Bowl, berry, oval shape	30.00	Goblets	
Butter, cov	55.00	Clear shield on side	50.00
Celery Vase, SP frame	55.00	Plain.	35.00
Cologne bottle, facetted		Regular, mkd P. G. flint . .	65.00
stopper	48.00	Ice Cream Tray.	47.50
Champagne	55.00	Lemonade	25.00
Compotes		Pitcher, water	75.00
Open, hs, 8½″.	125.00	Plate, 6″.	25.00
Open, ls, 10″	50.00	Sauces	
Creamers		3¾″	12.00
Glass throughout	60.00	Leaf shaped	15.00
Silverplated holder	75.00	Spooner, flint	35.00
Dish, fruit, large, silver-		Sugars	
frame	90.00	Glass throughout	70.00
Egg Cup.	30.00	Silverplated holder	75.00
Epergne, signed, P.G. Co.		Toothpick.	30.00
Pat'd.	125.00	Tray, water.	90.00
Finger bowl, underplate	50.00		

TRIPLE TRIANGLE

Made by Doyle and Co. of Pittsburgh, Pennsylvania, in 1890. Continued by U. S. Glass Co. after 1891. Also found in clear (50% less).

	Ruby Stained		Ruby Stained
Butter, cov, handled	80.00	Sauce, flat	20.00
Celery Tray.	45.00	Spooner, handled	40.00
Creamer.	55.00	Sugar, handled, cov	60.00
Cup	30.00	Table Set, 4 pc.	265.00
*Goblet	40.00	Tumbler	35.00
Mug.	35.00	*Wine	40.00
Pitcher, water	135.00		

TRUNCATED CUBE (Thompson's #77)

Non-flint made by Thompson Glass Co., Uniontown, Pennsylvania, c1892. Also found with engraving.

	Clear	Ruby Stained		Clear	Ruby Stained
Butter, cov	45.00	60.00	Spooner	27.50	45.00
Celery Vase	35.00	40.00	Salt Shaker, single. .	15.00	25.00
Creamers			Sugar, cov	30.00	45.00
Ind	20.00	30.00	Syrup	40.00	65.00
Regular	30.00	45.00	Toothpick	30.00	45.00
Decanter, os, 12″ h	60.00	145.00	Tumbler	22.50	30.00
Goblet	20.00	30.00	Wine	20.00	35.00
Pitcher, water, tank-					
ard	45.00	70.00			

TULIP WITH SAWTOOTH

Originally made in flint glass by Bryce Bros., Pittsburgh, Pennsylvania, c1860. Later made in non-flint.

	Flint	Non-Flint		Flint	Non-Flint
Bottle, bar	70.00	—	Egg Cup	40.00	—
Butter, cov	125.00	82.00	Goblet	65.00	27.50
Celery Vase	60.00	22.50	Mug	80.00	—
Champagne	75.00	32.50	Pitcher, water	150.00	—
Compotes			Plate, 6″	60.00	—
Cov, hs, 6″	90.00	—	Pomade Jar	45.00	—
Cov, hs, 8½″	95.00	—	Salt, master, plain		
Cov, ls, 8½″	85.00	—	edge	25.00	15.00
Open, ls, 9″	60.00	—	Spooner	35.00	—
Creamer	85.00	—	Sugar, cov	95.00	—
Cruets			Tumblers		
Applied handle	60.00	—	Bar	85.00	28.00
Pressed handle	—	40.00	Footed	50.00	—
Decanters, os, handled	150.00	—	*Wine	55.00	20.00

TWO PANEL

Non-flint in oval forms made by Richards and Hartley Glass Co., Tarentum, Pennsylvania, 1880–1886, and by U. S. Glass Co. in 1891.

	Amber	Apple Green	Blue	Clear	Vaseline
Bowls					
5½″	35.00	40.00	40.00	15.00	25.00
8″	35.00	40.00	40.00	20.00	35.00
Butter, cov	50.00	55.00	55.00	30.00	40.00
Celery Vase	45.00	50.00	50.00	25.00	40.00
Compote, cov, hs, 6½″, oval	35.00	—	—	—	85.00
Creamer	40.00	45.00	45.00	20.00	35.00
*Goblet	30.00	35.00	35.00	25.00	40.00
Lamp, high standard	85.00	125.00	100.00	45.00	115.00
Mug, 2 sizes	30.00	35.00	40.00	20.00	30.00
Pitcher, water	60.00	60.00	65.00	35.00	50.00
Platter	25.00	—	—	—	—
Salts					
Ind	15.00	15.00	15.00	5.00	15.00
Master	18.00	25.00	18.00	10.00	12.00
Sauces					
Flat, oval	10.00	12.00	10.00	8.00	10.00
Footed	12.00	14.00	15.00	10.00	12.00
Salt Shakers, single	40.00	45.00	40.00	25.00	30.00
Spooner	45.00	50.00	45.00	25.00	35.00
Sugar, cov	50.00	55.00	55.00	30.00	40.00
Tray, water	45.00	55.00	55.00	35.00	45.00
Tumbler	35.00	40.00	35.00	15.00	25.00
Waste Bowl	40.00	45.00	40.00	20.00	30.00
*Wine	40.00	45.00	40.00	20.00	30.00

U. S. COIN

Non-flint frosted, clear, and gilted pattern made by U. S. Glass Co. in 1892 for three or four months. Production was stopped by U. S. Treasury because real coins, dated as early as 1878, were used in the molds. 1892 coin date is the most common.

	Clear	Frosted
Bowls		
6″	175.00	225.00
9″	225.00	350.00
Bread Plate	200.00	300.00
Butter, cov, dollars and halves	275.00	525.00
Cake Stand, 10″	250.00	450.00
Celeries		
Tray	200.00	—
Vase, quarters	135.00	375.00
Champagne	—	425.00
Compotes		
Cov, hs, 7″	350.00	550.00
Open, hs, 7″, quarters and dimes	200.00	350.00
Open, hs, 7″, quarters and halves	225.00	375.00
Creamer	375.00	525.00
Cruet, os.	400.00	575.00
Epergne	500.00	1,200.00

	Clear	Frosted
Goblet	250.00	400.00
Goblet, dimes	—	550.00
Lamps		
Round font	300.00	475.00
Square font	350.00	—
Mug, handled	200.00	350.00
Pickle	205.00	—
Pitcher, water, dollars	425.00	850.00
Sauce, ftd, 4″, quarters	100.00	200.00
Spooner, quarters	250.00	350.00
Sugar, cov	250.00	375.00
Syrup, dated pewter lid		550.00
*Toothpick	180.00	300.00
Tray, water, 8″, rect	300.00	—
Tumbler	135.00	235.00
Waste Bowl	250.00	—
Wine	250.00	400.00

UTAH (Frost Flower, Twinkle Star)

Non-flint made by U. S. Glass Co. in 1901 in the States Pattern series. Add 25% for frosting.

	Clear
Bowls	
Cov, 6″	20.00
Open, 8″	18.00
Butter, cov	35.00
Cake Plate, 9″	20.00
Cake Stands	
8″	20.00
10″	30.00
Celery Vase	20.00
Compotes	
Cov, ls, 6″, jelly	25.00
Open, ls, 6″, jelly	18.00

	Clear
Creamer	30.00
Goblet	25.00
Pickle	12.00
Pitcher, water	42.50
Sauce, 4″	7.50
Salt & Pepper Shakers, pr	40.00
Salt & Pepper Shakers, in holder	45.00
Spooner	15.00
Sugar, cov	35.00
Tumbler	15.00
Wine	35.00

VALENCIA WAFFLE (Block and Star #1)

Made by Adams & Co., c1885–1895; continued by U. S. Glass after 1891.

	Amber	Apple Green	Blue	Clear	Vaseline
Bowl, berry	15.00	25.00	20.00	12.00	15.00
Bread Tray	30.00	—	30.00	25.00	35.00
Butter, cov	55.00	65.00	45.00	40.00	42.50
Cake Stand, 10″	60.00	40.00	45.00	35.00	40.00
Celery Vase	20.00	30.00	25.00	18.00	20.00

	Amber	Apple Green	Blue	Clear	Vaseline
Castor set, complete	60.00	—	65.00	50.00	60.00
Compotes					
Cov, hs	50.00	75.00	55.00	45.00	50.00
Cov, ls.	35.00	50.00	65.00	30.00	35.00
Creamer	30.00	—	45.00	30.00	30.00
Dish	20.00	—	25.00	10.00	20.00
Goblet	35.00	—	35.00	30.00	35.00
Pitchers					
Milk	35.00	—	40.00	35.00	40.00
Water	65.00	—	50.00	40.00	45.00
Relish or Pickle	30.00	20.00	18.00	15.00	15.00
Sauce, ftd, 4″, sq . .	15.00	—	15.00	18.00	15.00
Spooner	25.00	—	25.00	20.00	25.00
Sugar, cov	40.00	—	45.00	35.00	40.00
Syrup	95.00	80.00	—	—	—
Tumbler	20.00	—	20.00	18.00	20.00

VERMONT (Honeycomb with Flower Rim; Inverted Thumbprint with Daisy Band)

Non-flint made by U. S. Glass Co., 1899–1903. Also made in custard (usually decorated), chocolate, caramel, and novalty slag, milk glass, and blue.
Note: Toothpick has been reproduced in clear and opaque colors.

	Clear w/gold	Green w/gold		Clear w/gold	Green w/gold
Basket, handle	30.00	45.00	Pitcher, water	40.00	90.00
Bowl, berry	25.00	45.00	Sauce.	15.00	25.00
Butter, cov	40.00	75.00	Spooner	25.00	45.00
Celery Tray	27.50	35.00	Sugar, cov	35.00	60.00
Creamer	30.00	55.00	*Toothpick	35.00	60.00
Goblet	40.00	60.00	Tumbler	20.00	45.00

VIKING (Bearded Head)

Non-flint, made by Hobbs, Brockunier, and Co. in 1876 as their centennial pattern. No tumbler of goblet originally made.

	Clear		Clear
Bowls		Creamer, 2 types	60.00
Cov, 8″, oval	45.00	Egg Cup	35.00
Cov, 9″, oval	55.00	Marmalade Jar	105.00
Bread Plate	75.00	Mug, applied handle	50.00
Butter, cov	75.00	Pitcher, water	100.00
Celery Vase	45.00	Relish	25.00
Compotes		Salt, master	40.00
Cov, hs, 9″	80.00	Sauce	15.00
Cov, ls, 8″, oval	95.00	Spooner	35.00
Open, hs	60.00	Sugar, cov	65.00

WAFFLE AND THUMBPRINT

Flint made by the New England Glass Co. and Boston & Sandwich Glass Co., c1850. Later by Bryce, Walker & Co., Pittsburgh, Pennsylvania.

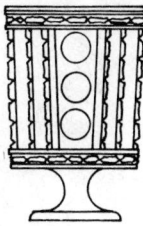

	Clear		Clear
Bowl, 5 x 7″	30.00	11″, whale oil	175.00
Butter, cov	95.00	Pitcher, water	300.00
Celery Vase	110.00	Spooner	45.00
Champagne	70.00	Sugar, cov	125.00
Compote, cov, hs	150.00	Sweetmeat, cov, hs, 6″	150.00
Creamer	125.00	Tumblers	
Decanter, os	100.00	Flip Glass	135.00
Egg Cup	45.00	Water, ftd	75.00
Goblet, knob stem	60.00	Whiskey	95.00
Lamps		Wine	60.00
9½″	115.00		

WASHINGTON (Early)

Flint made by New England Glass Co., c1869.

	Clear		Clear
Bowl, 6 x 9″, oval	45.00	Egg Cup	75.00
Bottle, bitters	85.00	Goblet	85.00
Butter, cov	175.00	Lamp	145.00
Celery Vase	95.00	Pitcher, water	250.00
Champagne	125.00	Plate, 6″	60.00
Compotes		Salt, master	55.00
Cov, hs, 6″	125.00	Sauce	25.00
Cov, hs, 10″	175.00	Spooner	50.00
Cordial	150.00	Sugar, cov	125.00
Creamer	200.00	Tumbler	85.00
Decanter, os	150.00	Wine	100.00

WASHINGTON CENTENNIAL (Chain with Diamonds)

Non-flint made by Gillinder & Co., Philadelphia, Pennsylvania, for centennial celebration.

	Clear		Clear
Bread Plates		Open, hs, 8″	45.00
"Carpenter's Hall"	100.00	Creamer, applied handle	90.00
"George Washington"	100.00	Egg Cup	45.00
"Independence Hall"	100.00	Goblet	50.00
Butter, cov	80.00	Pitcher, water, applied handle	125.00
Cake Stands		Relish, claw handle, dated	30.00
8½″	45.00	Salt, master, oval, flat	35.00
10″	65.00	Sauce, flat	15.00
Celery Vase	60.00	Spooner	35.00
Champagne	65.00	Sugar, cov	70.00
Compotes		Syrup, metal lid	150.00
Cov, hs, 9″	75.00	Wine	55.00

WATER LILY AND CATTAILS

Made by Fenton Glass Co., Williamstown, West Virginia; Northwood Glass Co., Wheeling, West Virginia, c1900; and Diamond-Dugan Co. Found in carnival glass.

	Amethyst Opal	Blue Opal	Clear Opal	Green Opal
Bowl, berry, 8″, ruffled	50.00	75.00	35.00	45.00
Butter, cov	100.00	90.00	65.00	80.00
Creamer	75.00	60.00	45.00	50.00
Dish, bonbon, tricorn.	50.00	45.00	30.00	35.00
Pitcher, water	200.00	175.00	65.00	125.00
Plate	35.00	35.00	25.00	30.00
Relish, handle	40.00	35.00	30.00	35.00
Sauce	35.00	30.00	20.00	25.00
Spooner	40.00	40.00	35.00	40.00
Sugar, cov	65.00	60.00	45.00	50.00
Tumbler	40.00	40.00	30.00	35.00

WEDDING RING (Double Wedding Ring)

Flint, c1860; non-flint, c1870s. Toothpick, frequently seen in muddy purple, not originally made.

	Flint		Flint
Butter, cov	100.00	Pitcher, water	165.00
Celery Vase	80.00	Relish	60.00
Champagne	95.00	Sauce	30.00
Cordial	75.00	Spooner	80.00
Creamer	80.00	Sugar, cov	110.00
Decanter, os	125.00	Tumbler	85.00
Goblet	85.00	Wine	95.00

WESTWARD HO (Pioneer)

Non-flint, usually frosted, made by Gillinder & Sons, Philadelphia, Pennsylvania, late 1870s. Molds made by Jacobus who also made Classic. Has been reproduced.

	Clear		Clear
Bread Plate	150.00	Marmalade Jar, cov	175.00
Butter, cov	185.00	Mugs	
Celery Vase	125.00	2″	200.00
Compotes		3½″	150.00
Cov, hs, 5″	200.00	Pitcher, water	200.00
Cov, hs, 9″	235.00	Sauce, ftd, 4½″	35.00
Cov, ls, 5″	175.00	Spooner	85.00
Open, hs, 8″	125.00	Sugar, cov	165.00
Creamer	125.00	Wine	225.00
Goblet	100.00		

WHEAT AND BARLEY (Duquesne)

Non-flint made by Bryce Bros., Pittsburgh, Pennsylvania, in the late 1870s. Later made by U. S. Glass Co., 1891.

	Amber	Blue	Clear	Vaseline
Bowl, 8″, cov	35.00	40.00	25.00	35.00
Butter, cov	45.00	60.00	35.00	55.00
Cake Stands				
8″	30.00	45.00	20.00	30.00
10″	40.00	50.00	30.00	40.00
Compotes				
Cov, hs, 7″	45.00	55.00	35.00	45.00
Cov, hs, 8″	45.00	55.00	35.00	45.00
Open, hs, jelly . . .	30.00	40.00	20.00	35.00
Creamer	30.00	40.00	25.00	35.00
Goblet	35.00	47.50	25.00	40.00
Mug	30.00	40.00	20.00	35.00
Pitchers				
Milk	40.00	60.00	30.00	50.00
Water	55.00	65.00	45.00	65.00
Plates				
7″	20.00	30.00	15.00	25.00
9″, closed han-				
dles	25.00	35.00	20.00	40.00
Sauces				
Flat, handle	12.00	15.00	10.00	15.00
Footed	15.00	15.00	10.00	15.00
Spooner	30.00	40.00	20.00	30.00
Sugar, cov	40.00	50.00	30.00	40.00
Tumbler	25.00	35.00	18.00	30.00

WILDFLOWER

Non-flint made by Adams & Co., Pittsburgh, Pennsylvania, c1874, and by U. S. Glass Co., c1898. This pattern has been heavily reproduced.

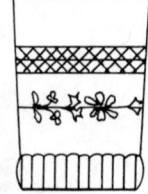

	Amber	Apple Green	Blue	Clear	Vaseline
Bowl, 8″, sq	25.00	35.00	35.00	18.00	25.00
Butters, cov					
Collared base. . . .	40.00	50.00	50.00	40.00	45.00
Flat.	35.00	45.00	45.00	35.00	40.00
Cake Stand, 10½″. .	50.00	75.00	60.00	45.00	50.00
Champagne	40.00	55.00	50.00	35.00	45.00
Celery Vase	55.00	60.00	55.00	35.00	55.00
Compote, cov, hs, 8″,					
oblong.	60.00	75.00	75.00	50.00	70.00
Creamer	30.00	35.00	35.00	25.00	45.00
*Goblet	35.00	40.00	40.00	25.00	40.00
Lamp, hand.	65.00	70.00	75.00	50.00	70.00
Pitcher, water	50.00	75.00	45.00	35.00	65.00
Plate, 10″, sq	25.00	30.00	45.00	25.00	25.00
Platter, 10″, oblong .	40.00	45.00	40.00	30.00	30.00
*Salt, turtle	45.00	50.00	50.00	40.00	40.00
Sauce, ftd, 4″,					
round	12.00	18.00	15.00	12.00	15.00
Salt Shaker.	20.00	55.00	35.00	20.00	45.00
Spooner	30.00	35.00	30.00	20.00	35.00
Sugar, cov	45.00	45.00	50.00	30.00	45.00

	Amber	Apple Green	Blue	Clear	Vaseline
Syrup	125.00	150.00	140.00	65.00	150.00
Tray, water, oval . . .	50.00	60.00	60.00	40.00	55.00
Tumbler	25.00	30.00	35.00	20.00	30.00
Wine	40.00	45.00	45.00	30.00	35.00

WILLOW OAK (Wreath)

Non-flint made by Bryce Bros. Pittsburgh, Pennsylvania, c1880, and by U. S. Glass Company in 1891.

	Amber	Blue	Canary	Clear
Bowl, 8″	25.00	40.00	48.00	20.00
Butter, cov	50.00	65.00	77.50	40.00
Cake Stand, 8½″ . . .	40.00	55.00	66.00	35.00
Celery Vase	45.00	60.00	72.00	35.00
Compotes				
Cov, hs, 7½″	50.00	65.00	77.50	40.00
Open, 7″	30.00	40.00	48.00	25.00
Creamer	35.00	50.00	60.00	30.00
Goblet	40.00	50.00	60.00	35.00
Mug	35.00	45.00	54.00	30.00
Pitcher				
Milk.	50.00	60.00	72.00	40.00
Water	50.00	60.00	72.00	40.00
Plates				
7″	35.00	45.00	54.00	30.00
9″, closed handles	30.00	35.00	42.00	25.00
Sauces				
Flat, handle, sq . .	15.00	20.00	24.00	10.00
Footed, 4″	20.00	25.00	30.00	15.00
Salt Shaker.	25.00	40.00	48.00	20.00
Spooner	35.00	40.00	48.00	30.00
Sugar, cov	45.00	50.00	60.00	35.00
Tray, water, 10½″ . .	35.00	50.00	60.00	30.00
Tumbler	30.00	35.00	42.00	25.00
Waste Bowl	35.00	40.00	48.00	30.00

WINDFLOWER

Non-flint, late 1870s, unknown maker.

	Clear		Clear
Bowl, 8″, oval	30.00	Pitcher, water, applied handle	65.00
Butter, cov	50.00	Salt, master, ftd	25.00
Celery Vase	40.00	Spooner.	30.00
Compotes		Sugars	
Cov, hs.	65.00	Cov	60.00
Open, ls, 7″.	35.00	Open, buttermilk	35.00
Creamer, applied handle . . .	40.00	Tumbler	40.00
Egg Cup.	35.00	Wine	45.00
Goblet	40.00		

WISCONSIN (Beaded Dewdrop)

Non-flint made in Pittsburgh, Pennsylvania, in the 1880s. Later made by U. S. Glass Co. in Indiana, 1903. One of States patterns.

	Clear		Clear
Banana Stand.	75.00	Goblet	50.00
Bowls		Marmalade Jar, straight	
6″, oval, handled, cov . . .	25.00	sides, glass lid.	125.00
7″, round.	30.00	Mug.	35.00
8″, oblong, preserve.	35.00	Pitchers	
Butter, flat flange	50.00	Milk	55.00
Cake Stand, 10″	45.00	Water	70.00
Celery Tray.	35.00	Plate, 6¾″	25.00
Celery Vase	45.00	Relish	20.00
Compotes		Salt Shaker, single	30.00
Cov, hs, 7″	45.00	Spooner.	30.00
Open, hs, 10½″.	35.00	Sugar, cov	55.00
Open, jelly.	20.00	Sugar Shaker	60.00
Condiment Set, SP, horse-		Sweetmeat, 5″, ftd, cov	35.00
radish on tray	100.00	Syrup	75.00
Creamer.	50.00	*Toothpick	55.00
Cruet, os	55.00	Tumbler	40.00
Cup & Saucer.	50.00	Wine	55.00

WYOMING (Enigma)

Made by U. S. Glass Co., in the States Pattern series, 1903.

	Clear		Clear
Butter, cov	50.00	Mug.	40.00
Cake Plate	55.00	Pitcher, water, ½ gal	90.00
Cake Stand	70.00	Sugar, cov	45.00
Creamer.	35.00	Spooner.	30.00
Goblet	55.00	Wine	60.00

X-RAY

Non-flint made by Riverside Glass Works, Wellsburgh, West Virginia, 1896 to 1898. Prices are for pieces with gold trim. An amethyst toothpick ($125.00) is known.

	Clear	Emerald Green		Clear	Emerald Green
Bowl, berry, 8″,			Salt & Pepper Shak-		
beaded rim	25.00	50.00	ers, pr	20.00	35.00
Butter, cov	55.00	55.00	Sauce, flat	—	18.00
Celery Vase	—	45.00	Spooner	40.00	45.00
Compote, cov, hs . .	35.00	60.00	Sugar, cov	25.00	50.00
Creamer	35.00	60.00	Syrup	—	185.00
Cruet	—	125.00	Toothpick	35.00	60.00
Pitcher, water	50.00	75.00	Tumbler	10.00	15.00

YALE (Crow-foot, Turkey Track)

Non-flint made by McKee and Brothers Glass Co., Jeannette, Pennsylvania, patented, 1887.

	Clear		Clear
Butter, cov	40.00	Pitcher, water	55.00
Cake Stand	48.00	Syrup	65.00
Celery Vase	35.00	Salt Shaker, single	30.00
Compotes		Sauce, flat	10.00
Cov	48.00	Spooner	25.00
Open, scalloped rim	25.00	Sugar, cov	35.00
Creamer	30.00	Tumbler	20.00
Goblet	35.00		

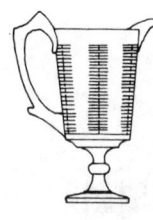

ZIPPER (Cobb)

Non-flint made by Richards & Hartley, Tarentum, Pennsylvania, c1880.

	Clear		Clear
Bowl, 7"	15.00	Pitcher, water, ½ gal	40.00
Butter, cov	40.00	Relish, 10"	15.00
Celery Vase	25.00	Sauces	
Cheese, cov	55.00	Flat	5.00
Compote, cov, ls, 8"	45.00	Footed	10.00
Creamer	25.00	Spooner	25.00
Cruet, os	42.00	Sugar, cov	35.00
Goblet	27.50		

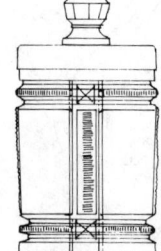

ZIPPERED BLOCK (Cryptic, Nova Scotia Ribbon & Star, Duncan #90)

Non-flint made by George A. Duncan & Sons, Pittsburgh, Pennsylvania, in the late 1870s and later by U. S. Glass. Also made in Canada. Comes frosted and frosted with cut stars. Add 20% for frosting.

	Clear	Ruby Stained		Clear	Ruby Stained
Butter, cov	100.00	150.00	Salt Shaker	50.00	80.00
Compote, cov, hs . .	125.00	—	Sauce	15.00	25.00
Creamer	75.00	100.00	Spooner	30.00	60.00
Goblet	40.00	60.00	Sugar, cov	60.00	115.00
Pickle, oblong	25.00	40.00	Tumbler	30.00	45.00
Pitcher, water	125.00	185.00			

S.E.G.

PAUL REVERE POTTERY

History: Paul Revere Pottery, Boston, Massachusetts, was an outgrowth of a club known as "The Saturday Evening Girls." The S.E.G. was a group of young female immigrants who met on Saturday night for reading and crafts such as ceramics.

Regular production began in 1908. The name Paul Revere was adopted because the pottery was located near the Old North Church. In 1915 the firm moved to Brighton, Massachusetts. Known as the "Bowl Shop," the pottery grew steadily. In spite of popular acceptance and technical advancements, the pottery required continual subsidies. It finally closed in January 1942.

Items produced ranged from plain and decorated vases to tablewares to illustrated tiles. Many decorated wares were incised and glazed either in an Art Nouveau matte finish or an occasional high glaze.

In addition to the impressed mark, paper "Bowl Shop" labels were used prior to 1915. Pieces also can be found dated with P.R.P. or S.E.G. painted on the base.

References: Paul Evans, *Art Pottery of the United States,* Everybodys Press, Inc., 1974, Ralph and Terry Kovel, *The Kovel's Collector's Guide to American Art Pottery,* Crown Publishers, Inc., 1974.

Bowls
```
  2 x 5½", blue glaze, incised "P.R.P."        80.00
  2¼ x 5½", child's blue tones, yellow
    duck and green accents in center,
    "Johan" on rim . . . . . . . . . . . . . .   175.00
  2¾ x 6¼", blue semi-gloss glaze, mkd
    "S.E.G." . . . . . . . . . . . . . . . . . . .  65.00
Butter, cov, hen and chick dec, twig han-
  dles, mkd "S.E.G.," c1918 . . . . . . . .   325.00
Creamer, 3¼", chick dec on cream
  ground, mkd "S.E.G." . . . . . . . . . . .   100.00
Hat Pin Holder, blue daisy motif, gold
  trim, mkd "S.E.G." . . . . . . . . . . . . .   130.00
Inkwell, 2½ x 4", blue high glaze . . . . .   75.00
Paperweight, 5" d, 6 colors, Paul Revere
  on horseback mark . . . . . . . . . . . . .   225.00
Plates
  8½", landscape dec of hills and trees,
    5 colors, mkd "S.E.G." . . . . . . . . .   260.00
```

Vase, 5¾", tapered cylinder, band rim, light blue, high glaze, $45.00.

```
9", stylized water lily on green ground,
  mkd "S.E.G.". . . . . . . . . . . . . . . .   150.00
Sugar, cov, 4", geese design, sgd
  "P.R.P" . . . . . . . . . . . . . . . . . . . .   145.00
Tea Tile. . . . . . . . . . . . . . . . . . . . . .   200.00
Vases
  6¼", scenic band in blue and green,
    outlined in black, brown high glaze,
    mkd "S.E.G. 11-21-04". . . . . . . . .   250.00
  6½", mustard yellow, mkd . . . . . . . .    65.00
  11", blue-green high glaze, sgd
    "S.E.G., 6-15" . . . . . . . . . . . . . .    85.00
```

PEACHBLOW

History: Peachblow, an art glass which derives its name from a fine Chinese glazed porcelain, resembles a peach or crushed strawberries in color. Three American glass manufacturers and two English firms produced peachblow glass in the late 1880s. A fourth American firm renewed the process in the 1950s. The glass from each firm has its own identifying characteristics.

Hobbs, Brockunier & Co., Wheeling peachblow: Opalescent glass, plated or cased with a transparent amber glass; shading from yellow at the base to a deep red at top; glossy or satin finish.

Mt. Washington "Peach Blow": A homogeneous glass, shading from a pale gray-blue to a soft rose color. Pieces may be enhanced with glass appliques, enameling, and gilding.

New England Glass Works, New England peachblow [advertised as "Wild Rose," but called "Peach Blow" at the plant]: Translucent, shading from rose to white; acid or glossy finish. Some pieces enameled and gilded.

Thomas Webb & Sons and Stevens and Williams, England: Around 1888 these two firms made a peachblow style art glass marked "Peach Blow" or "Peach Bloom." A cased glass, shading from yellow to red. Occasionally found with cameo-type designs in relief.

Gunderson Glass Co.: About 1950 produced peachblow type art glass to order; shades from an opaque faint tint of pink, which is almost white, to a deep rose.

Note: All pieces listed below are satin finish unless otherwise noted.

GUNDERSON

Cup and saucer, white reeded handle .	200.00
Decanter, 9½", pedestal base, deep rose top to white base	500.00
Goblet, 5⅜"	225.00
Plate, 8"	165.00
Rose Bowl, 3½" h, 4¼" d, pinched ruffled top, ...	125.00
Vases	
4½", wide ruffled rims, shiny finish, pr	175.00
7¾", lily	190.00

MT. WASHINGTON

Bon-bon dish, tricon shape	600.00
Bottle, condiment, 5¼", fine ribbed, floral decor, faceted, blue stopper . .	600.00
Vase, 7¾", stick	850.00

NEW ENGLAND

Bowl, 7½" d, 2¾" h, ruffle top, glossy finish	425.00
Celery Vase, crimped top	795.00
Cup and saucer, matte finish	290.00
Finger bowl, shiny finish	200.00
Juice glass, shiny finish.	125.00
Pear, whimsey, 6".	350.00
Pitcher, water, shiny finish, applied amber thorn handle	575.00
Spooner, 4⅝", sq ruffled top, Wild Rose	425.00
Tumbler, 3¾", Wild Rose	250.00
Vases	
5½", lily	475.00
6", sq top, DQ	375.00
Whiskey glass, acid finish	160.00

WEBB

Biscuit jar, 7½", enameled, SP cov . . .	620.00
Bowl, 8", star shape, ruffled top, dainty white flowers, cream lining	525.00
Cologne bottle, acid finish, metal top . .	275.00
Compote, 7" d, 5⅝" h, SP screw on base	200.00

Ewer, 5½", miniature, floral branch decor, cased, applied ribbed handle painted yellow	325.00
Jar, cov, 4½", gold prunus	650.00
Scent bottle, 4¾" h, 3⅝" d, heavy gold prunus and branches, gold butterfly, hallmarked silver top	500.00
Sweetmeat jar, 4½" h, 3¾" d, acid finish, gold prunus decor, cream lining, silver top, rim and handle	400.00
Vase, 8" h, 3" d, bulbous, narrow neck, gold florals and butterfly decor, acid finish, cream lining	500.00

Wheeling, Vase, 7¾", acid finish, $1,000.00.

WHEELING

Clarets, shiny finish, SS neck bands, faceted amber stoppers, twisted amber handles, pr	500.00
Creamer and sugar, 4", sq mouth, shiny finish	1,250.00
Cruet, petticut, frosted amber handle and stopper	825.00
Mustard, 3⅛", SP top, SS spoon	500.00
Pear, whimsey, shiny finish	650.00
Pitcher, 5½", shiny finish, amber handle	750.00
Salt, shiny finish	155.00
Toothpick, shiny finish.	350.00
Tumbler, 3¾" h, 2¾" d	300.00
Vase, 9", stick, shiny finish	550.00

PEKING GLASS

History: Peking glass is a type of cameo glass of Chinese origin. Its production began in the 1700s and continued well into the 19th century. The background color of Peking glass may be a delicate shade of yellow, green, or white. One style of white background is so delicate and transparent that it often is referred to as the "snowflake" ground. The overlay colors include a rich garnet red, deep blue, and emerald green.

Bottle, 9⅜", globular body, cylindrical neck, snowflake ground, deep red overlay carved in relief with stylized lotus meander, Qianlong mark, c1780–1850 .... **2,450.00**

Goblet, 6¼", white ground, amethyst carving, thick stem, sgd "China" ... **185.00**

Jar, cov, 4", white ground, blue overlay **200.00**

Snuff Bottles
   2", flattened ovate body, opaque white ground, meandering green, yellow, pink, and blue vertical stripes **225.00**
   2½", flattened pear shape body, shoulders molded with lion head handles, translucent yellow ground, swirling splashes of mustard yellow, green, and black **300.00**
   3", flattened pear shape body, carved at sides with mock ring handles, snowflake ground, emerald green overlay, frog finial stopper. **275.00**

Urns, 12½", pr, cov, ovoid form, snowflake ground overlaid in garnet carving of 3 women in garden, prunus tree, cov dec with blossoming prunus branch surrounding flower form knop, 19th C **8,000.00**

Vases
   5½", 8 sided, bright yellow ground, black overlay, sgd, teakwood stand **375.00**
   6¼", baluster, white ground, blue overlay in floral design, teakwood base **350.00**
   7⅛", pr, baluster, white ground, brownish red overlay in florals, butterfly. **475.00**

Snuff bottle, 2⅜" h, pastel colored leaves, green jade top, $200.00.

7½", faceted bottle form, milky white ground, mazarine blue overlay carved in reserves enclosing birds and flowering trees, 19th C. **550.00**

12", urn shape, snowflake ground, emerald green overlay of cranes flying over foliage **750.00**

PELOTON

History: Wilhelm Kralik of Bohemia patented Pelaton art glass in 1880. It also was patented later in America and England.

Peloton glass is found with both transparent and opaque grounds with opaque being more common. Opaque colored glass filaments (strings) are applied by dipping or rolling the hot glass. Generally, the filaments (threads) are pink, blue, yellow, and white (rainbow colors) or a single color. Items also may have a satin finish and enamel decorations.

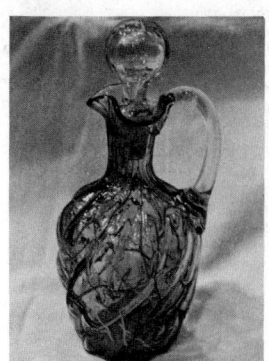

Cruet, 7" h, clear with multi-colored filaments, $275.00.

Bowl, boat shape, rainbow **325.00**

Plate, 7⅞" d, blue on clear ground, enamel floral dec **100.00**

Rose Bowl, 3½" d, 3⅞" h, opaque white ribbed ground, multicolored rainbow filaments, crystal shell feet........ **300.00**

Sweetmeat Jar, opaque ground, rainbow filaments, SP bail and lid **600.00**

Vases
   3½", pleated top, opaque, rainbow filaments **175.00**
   4½", scalloped top, opaque, ribbed, rainbow filaments. **150.00**
   4⅝", squatty, bulbous, opaque white, ribbed, rainbow filaments **325.00**
   5", fan top, ruffled, lavendar pink ground, rainbow filaments....... **300.00**

6", lavendar pink ground, cased, ribbed, white filaments, clear wafer foot. **350.00**

7½", ftd, clear, cranberry filaments . . **150.00**

PERFUME, COLOGNE, AND SCENT BOTTLES

History: Decorative bottles to hold scents have been made in various shapes and sizes. They reached a "golden age" during the second half of the 19th Century.

An atomizer is a perfume bottle with a spray mechanism. Cologne bottles usually are larger and have stoppers which also may be used as applicators. A perfume bottle has a stopper that often is elongated and designed as an applicator.

Scent bottles are small bottles used to hold a scent or smelling salts. A vinaigrette is an ornamental box or bottle with a perforated top used to hold aromatic vinegars or smelling salts. Fashionable women of the late 18th and 19th centuries carried them in purses or slipped them in to gloves in case of a sudden fainting spell.

Reference: Hazel Martin, *A Collection Of Figural Perfume & Scent Bottles*, privately printed, 1982.

ATOMIZERS

Art Deco, 3" h, opaque black with gold design **50.00**

Baccarat, 6" h, amberina swirl glass . . **75.00**

Cambridge Glass, 6¼", gold stippled opaque jade, silk lined box. **145.00**

Atomizer, Czechosolvakian, clear blue glass stem, enameled floral top on gold ground, $140.00.

Continental, 8" h, pear shaped cut glass with fluted middle section, starburst base, monogrammed, SS lid formed as a semi-clad youth standing on a shell, holding dolphin, c1900 . . . . . . **825.00**

DeVilbiss, 7", goldstone mounted on black blass, sgd **175.00**

COLOGNE BOTTLES

Cut Glass, 8⅜" h, 3⅝" d, green cut to crystal, SS top, hallmarked, dated 1905, London, orig cut crystal stopper. **175.00**

French, 4¾", clear, 6 raised panels, overall gold dec **100.00**

Opaque blue, 6¾" h, applied coraline dec, matching stopper. **220.00**

Orrefors, gray-green ground, amethyst seaweed design on side, sgd #214, 1938 . . . . **200.00**

Ruby, 6¾" h, 2⅝" d, sanded gold, enameled green foliage, pink roses, 3 opal jewels, orig ruby ball stopper. . . **125.00**

Sandwich, Ellipse, fiery opal, hexagonal **450.00**

Webb, 5⅞", cameo, amberina over green, white lining, satin finish, SS top. **445.00**

PERFUMES

Baccarat, 6⅝" h, 2½" d, amberina swirl. **65.00**

Cameo, English, 1⅞" h, 1¼" d, morning glory blossom, white cut to deep blue to powder blue body, white lining, hallmarked SS top **700.00**

Cased, 5½" h, 2⅛" d, lemon yellow, sanded gold leaves and ribbon, studded with red and green applied jewels, clear ball stopper cov in gold **90.00**

Cranberry, 5¼" h, 3" d, silver panels with gold scrolls, gold dots and flowers, clear cut faceted stopper. **110.00**

Figurals
3⅜" h, 1¼" d, china, lady and parrot, multicolored, metal and cork stopper **75.00**

4½", monkey, felt, green, jointed with removable head to reveal perfume bottle **185.00**

9¼", ruby glass, young boy feeding birds **245.00**

Lalique, 3¼" h, heart shaped, "Cour Joie," made by Nina Ricci, MIB **225.00**

Lithyalin, 5", Frederick Eggerman, Bohemia, dark brick red, c1830 . . . . **1,250.00**

Moser, enameled flowers on gold irid ground, sgd **100.00**

Orrefors, 5" h, bulbous, etched Eve and serpent, dark glass base, inscribed "Orrefors L 1398.2/A2," c1936 . . . . **250.00**

Paperweights, Charles Kazuin
$3^{1}/_{4}''$ h, $1^{1}/_{2}''$ d, stopper and body with yellow flower, red center, 4 green and white leaves on blue ground, 6 round facets on body, 6 round facets around perimeter of stopper, sgd "K" in gold **1,250.00**
$6^{1}/_{2}''$ h, red rose in base and elongated flame stopper, sgd in cane in base **1,900.00**
Sterling Silver Overlay, emerald green bottle, stopper. **160.00**
Tortoise Shell, 5'', bulbous base, very thin neck, turned over rim, 4'' steeple shape dauber **100.00**

SCENTS

Burmese, $4^{3}/_{4}''$ h, $3^{3}/_{8}''$ d, acid finish, salmon pink to yellow, heavy gold leaves and birds, silver gilt screw on top, hallmarked **800.00**
Lalique, $6^{3}/_{4}''$ h, opal, Sirenes, bulging baluster walls molded in medium relief with dancing maidens, domed cov in wave motifs, inscribed "R. Lalique, France, No. 2651," c1930 . . . . **880.00**
Porcelain, "Girl In A Swing" type, finely modeled, form of lovers standing by a rose tree, young boy attempting to embrace the girl, enameled in rose, turquoise, blue, green, and pink, finial of 3 pink roses with green leaves, c1755. . . . . **2,000.00**
Rock Crystal, $5^{1}/_{2}''$ h, flattened pear form, fan terminal, cut with fans and scrolls, applied gold lattice work pendants of rosettes set with diamonds, sapphire, rubies, fire opal, crown form lid dec with gold, diamonds and rubies **2,000.00**
Satin Glass, $4^{1}/_{2}''$ h, $2^{5}/_{8}''$ d, blue, DQ, MOP, white lining, SS top **250.00**
Stevens & Williams, yellow-green with white loopings, SS cap, collar and chain **150.00**
Webb, Thomas
$3^{1}/_{4}''$ h, $2^{3}/_{8}''$ d, gold prunus dec, gold butterfly, ivory satin ground, hallmarked SS top **450.00**
5'' h, $2^{1}/_{2}''$ d, sq, blue satin, 4 panels with carved opaque white flowers, hallmarked SS screw on top. **1,400.00**

VINAIGRETTES

Glass, $5^{1}/_{2}''$, emerald green, ribbed, ground stopper, pointed end **50.00**
Porcelain
Heart shape, flat, scene of lovers on front and florals on back, orig glass dauber, hinged lid and finger chain **125.00**
Heart shape, puffy, emb with cherubs and flowers, hinged opening, c1880 . . . . **200.00**

Sterling Silver, emb flowers and leaves, lift off lid, fancy open work, emb dec, oval **175.00**

PETERS AND REED POTTERY

History: J. D. Peters and Adam Reed founded their pottery company in South Zanesville, Ohio, in 1900. Common flower pots, jardinieres and cooking wares comprised their early major output. Occasionally art pottery was attempted; but, it was not until 1912 that their Moss Aztec line was introduced and widely accepted. Other art wares included Chromal, Landsun, Montene, Pereco and Persian.

Peters retired in 1921 and Reed changed the name of the firm to Zane Pottery Company. Marked pieces of Peters and Reed Pottery are unknown.

Additional Listings: See *Warman's Americana & Collectibles* for more examples.

Vase, $11^{3}/_{8}''$, yellow with brown drip glaze, $75.00.

Basket, $7^{1}/_{2}''$ d, hanging, moss green glaze, relief molded roses, Moss Aztec **35.00**
Bowl, 5'' d, Moss Aztec. **45.00**
Cuspidor, $8^{1}/_{4}''$ d, pine cone dec, Moss Aztec **52.00**
Jar, cov, $5^{1}/_{2}''$, high glaze, sgd Zanesware **55.00**
Jardiniere, 11'' h, 9'' d, brown high glaze, grapes and leaves. **200.00**
Jugs
$5^{1}/_{2}''$, applied lion, flowers. **45.00**
$6^{1}/_{4}''$ h, $5^{1}/_{2}''$ d, ball shape, handled, grape and vine dec **70.00**
Pitcher, $4^{1}/_{4}''$, brown with wreath **35.00**

Tankard, 12″, brown glaze, grape and
  vine dec **75.00**
Vases
  4½″ h, 8½″ w, pedestal base, 2 turned
    up handles, garlands of flowers on
    each side on flat shoulders **50.00**
  9″, tan ground, blue and brown drip,
    Shadow Ware **45.00**
  9¾″, terra cotta with green wash, pine
    cone and needles **60.00**
  12½″, wreath and cherubs **55.00**
Wall Pocket, 10½″, cone shape, sgd Fer-
  rell, Moss Aztec **65.00**

PEWTER

History: Pewter is a metal alloy, consisting
mostly of tin with small amounts of lead, copper,
antimony, and bismuth added to improve formability
and hardness. The metal can be cast, formed
around a mold, spun, easily cut, and soldered to
form a wide variety of utilitarian articles.

Pewter ware was known to the ancient Chinese,
Egyptians, and Romans. English pewter supplied
the major portion of the needs of the American
colonies for nearly 150 years before the American
Revolution. The Revolution ended the embargo on
raw tin and allowed the small American pewter industry to flourish. This period lasted until the Civil
War.

The listing concentrates on the American and
English pewter forms most often encountered by
the collector.

Reference: Donald L. Fennimore, *The Knopf
Collectors' Guides to American Antiques, Silver &
Pewter*, Alfred A. Knopf, Inc., 1984.

Collectors' Club: Pewter Collector's Club of
America, P. O. Box 239, Saugerties, NY 12477.
Pewter Bulletin.

Basins
  Austin, Richard, Boston, MA, 1792–
    1817, 8″ d **525.00**
  Brunstrom, John A., 11¾″ **875.00**
  Lightner, George, 10″ **625.00**
  Towsend & Compton, London, 1780–
    1811, 10½″ **325.00**
Beakers
  Dixon, James, Sheffield, England,
    4½″ h **245.00**
  Griswold, Ashbil, Meriden, CT, 1802–
    42, 3″ **225.00**
  Yale, Hiram and Charles, Wallingford,
    CT, 1820–25, 3″ **300.00**
Candlesticks, pr
  Graves, J. & H, Middletown, CT, 1850,
    9¾″ **450.00**
  Hopper, Henry, 10″ **625.00**
  Morey and Ober, Boston, MA, 1852–
    55, 8″ **500.00**

Teapot, 9½″ h, G. Richardson, $325.00.

Putnam, James, Malden, MA, 1830–
  35, 8½″ **550.00**
Unmarked American, 4⅛″ **225.00**
Castor Sets
  Smith, Eben, holder with 4 bottles . .   **350.00**
  Trask, Israel, Beverly, MA, 1807–56,
    holder with 4 blown bottles **475.00**
Chalice, Young, Peter, New York and Al-
  bany, NY, 1771–1800, 8½″ **3,250.00**
Chargers
  Austin, Nathaniel, Charleston, MA,
    1783–1800, 13½″, repaired **425.00**
  Boardman & Co., NY, 19th C **275.00**
  Hamlin, Samuel, Hartford, CT, 1767–
    1801, 13½″ **675.00**
  Leffer, Samuel, London, 15″ **300.00**
  Towsend & Compton, London, 1780–
    1811, 12¾″ **275.00**
  Weldon & Feltman, 13½″ **400.00**
  Yates, Lawrence, London, 1740–74,
    14″ **300.00**
Coffee Pots
  Boardman, Thomas D., Hartford, CT,
    1805–50, 12″ h **475.00**
  Dunham, Rufus, Westbrook, ME,
    1837–61, urn shape, 11½″ **275.00**
  Palethrop, John, 12″ **500.00**
  Porter, Freeman, 12″ **350.00**
  Savage, William, Middletown, CT,
    1830, touch reads "SAVAGE/MIDD
    CT/NO. 2″, 10″ **400.00**
Communion Flagons
  Kirchen, Georg, German, 1763,
    hinged cov, oval finial, heart motifs
    dec **725.00**
  Leonard, Reed & Barton, Tauton, MA,
    1835–40, cov, 10½″ **300.00**
Compote, unmarked, 7¾″ d, 4¾″ h . . .   **225.00**
Cuspidor, Curtis, Daniel, Albany, NY,
  1822–40, 9″ **325.00**
Dishes, deep
  Curtis, Daniel, Albany, NY, 1822–40,
    11″ d **450.00**

Danforth, Edward, Hartford, CT, 1786–
99, 13¼″. **350.00**
Danforth, William, Middletown, CT,
1791–94, 13¼″ **400.00**
Flagons
Boardman, Thomas D, Hartford, CT,
1805–50, cov, 14″ **1,400.00**
Calder, William, Providence, RI, 1817–
56, cov, 11″. **750.00**
Trask, Israel, Beverly, MA, 1807–56,
cov, 10½″ **675.00**
Hot Water Dish, Nicholson, Robert, Lon-
don, 1690, 2 post handles, 16¾″ . . . **350.00**
Inkwell
Unmarked, domed lid, china insert,
3¾″ d, 3″ h **200.00**
Whitcomb, George, school desk type,
2″ **115.00**
Ladle, Palethrop, John H. Jr., Phila., PA,
1820–45, 13″ l **400.00**
Lamps
Chamber, unmarked American, sau-
cer base, ring handle, double diver-
gent camphene burners with caps,
cylinder font with turned moldings,
7⅜″ **275.00**
Sparking, Dunham, Rufus, Westbrook,
ME, 1837–61, single drop whale oil
burner, 4¼″ **220.00**
Whale Oil
Morey & Smith, Boston, double font,
handle, 6″ h **300.00**
Reed & Barton, Tauton, MA, 1850,
double drop burner, 7⅛″ **400.00**
Unmarked, American, pr, 1830, sau-
cer base, double drop burner with
brass fittings, 4¾″. **450.00**
Unmarked, American, saucer base,
molded handle on stem, double
drop burner with brass fittings,
6⅝″. **300.00**
Measures
English, Set of 8, 1/24 pint to 1 qt, early
19th C **900.00**
French, set of 8, "Double Litre" to
"Centrilitre", 1⅝ to 9″ h **250.00**
Mug, Danforth, Samuel, Hartford, CT,
1795–1816, pt. **600.00**
Pitchers
Boardman, Thomas, D., Hartford, CT,
1805–50, 10″. **900.00**
Gleason, Roswell, Dorchester, MA,
1822–71, cov, 9″ **645.00**
Richardson, George, Sr., Boston, MA,
1818–28, cov, 10″ **725.00**
Strumple, E., 13½″ **600.00**
Unmarked American, 9″. **475.00**
Plates
Austin, Nathaniel, Charlestown, MA,
1763–1800, 8″. **300.00**
Austin, Richard, Boston, MA, 1792–
1817, 8″ **300.00**
Barns, Blakslee, Phila., PA,1812–17, 8″ **275.00**

Boardman, Thomas D., Hartford, CT,
1805–50, 9¾″. **375.00**
Calder, William, Providence, RI, 1817–
56, 9½″. **450.00**
Danforth, Samuel, Hartford, CT, 1795–
1816, 7⅞″. **175.00**
Gleason, Roswell, Dorchester, MA,
1822–71, 9″. **345.00**
Jones, Gershom, Providence, RI,
1774–1809, 8″. **350.00**
Kilbourn, Samuel, 11″ **300.00**
Melville, David, Newport, RI, 1755–83,
8¼″ **300.00**
Towsend & Compton, London, 1780–
1811, 8½″. **125.00**
Unidentified English
Hallmarked, 1670, multiple reed
border, 8⅝″ **200.00**
Semper Eadem & London scroll
touch, 18th C, 8¼″. **350.00**
Weldon & Feltman, 12″ **275.00**
Yates, Lawrence, London, 1740–74,
10″. **250.00**

Plate, 8¾″ d, Thomas Danforth, Philadelphia, $350.00.

Porringers
Danforth, Samuel, Hartford, CT, 1795–
1816, old English handle, 4¼″ . . . **350.00**
Gleason, Roswell, Dorchester, MA,
1822–71, crown handle, 3¾″ **425.00**
Hamlin, Samuel, Providence, RI,
1767–1801, flower handle, 5⅜″. . . **350.00**
Lewis, I. C. & Co., Meriden, CT, 1839–
52, wine taster, solder repairs to
base of handle, 2⅛″ **125.00**
Melville, David, Newport, RI, 1755–93
Crown handle, 4¼″ **1,000.00**
Geometric handle, 3¾″. **250.00**
Whitmore, Jacob, flower handle, 5″. . **850.00**
Sugars, cov
Boardham & Hall, Phila., PA, 1840, 2
handles. **175.00**
Unmarked American, circular border
dec of acorn and 2 oak leaves,
5⅜″ **150.00**

Tankards
- Austin, Richard, Boston, MA, 1792–1817, qt, cov with finial, 7″ **4,000.00**
- Smith & Co., 8″ **300.00**
- Yates, Lawrence, London, 1740–74, 7″ **200.00**
- Tappit-hen, Scottish, 1780–1800, crested, "ILAW" engraved on front, 11¼″ h **350.00**

Teapots
- Gleason, Roswell, Dorchester, MA, 1822–71
  - Inverted mold form, 9¼″ h **225.00**
  - Queen Anne pear shape, straight line touch, 7⅛″. **1,200.00**
- McQuillkin, William, Phila., PA, 1845–53, inverted mold form, 8¼″ **250.00**
- Porter, Freeman, 9″. **325.00**
- Savage, William, Middletown, CT, 1830, 8″ **350.00**

PHOENIX BIRD CHINA

History: Phoenix Bird pattern is a blue and white china exported from Japan during the 1920s to 1940s. A limited amount was made during the occupation of Japan.

Initially it was available at Woolworth's 5 & 10, through two wholesale catalog companies, or by selling subscriptions to Needlecraft magazines. Myott Son & Co., England, also produced this pattern under the name "Satsuma," c1936. These earthenware items were for export only.

Once known as "Blue Howo Bird China," the Phoenix Bird pattern is the most sought after of seven similar patterns in the Hō-ō bird series. Other patterns are: Flying Turkey (head faces forward with a heart-like border); Howo (only pattern with name on base); and, Twin Phoenix (border pattern only, center white). The Howo and Twin Phoenix patterns are by Noritake and are occasionally marked "Noritake". Flying Dragon (bird-like), an earlier pattern, comes in green and white as well as the traditional blue and white and is marked with six oriental characters. A variation of Phoenix Bird pattern has a heart-like border and is called Hō-ō.

Phoenix Bird pattern has over 350 different shapes and sizes. Also varying is the quality found in the execution of design, shades of blue, and shape of the ware itself. All these factors must be considered in pricing. The maker's mark tends to add value; over 80 marks have been cataloged.

Post 1970 pieces are being produced in limited shapes with precise detail, but are on a milk white ground and usually don't have a maker's mark. When a mark does appear on a modern piece, it appears stamped in place.

Reference: Joan Collett Oates, *Phoenix Bird Chinaware, Book One*, privately printed, 1984. (Note: Numbers listed below refer to items illustrated in this book.)

Collectors' Club: Phoenix Bird Collectors of America, 5912 Kingsfield Drive, West Bloomfield, MI 48033. Dues: $8.00 *Phoenix Bird Discoveries* quarterly).

Additional Listings: See *Warman's Americana & Collectibles* for more examples.

Advisor: Joan Oates.

Tumbler, 2¾″ h, $22.00.

Batter Jug, cov.	**45.00**
Berry Set, 7 pcs, sq, scalloped, hp, sgd	**150.00**
Candy Tub.	**15.00**
Chamberstick, repaired	**35.00**
Cheese and Cracker, tiered.	**60.00**
Chocolate Pot, #1.	**95.00**
Cover, for boullion	**15.00**
Cup, Farmer's, cup 4¼″ d, saucer 6″ d	**20–30.00**
Cup and Saucer, Ho-o, #2-B	**15.00**
Demitasse (After Dinner)	
Cup and Saucer, #4-B	**12.50**
Saucer	**7.00**
Mayonnaise Bowl, 3 ball feet.	**25.00**
Mustard Pot, attached plate, no cov. . .	**45.00**
Pitcher, cider, large.	**125.00**
Plates	
6″, bread and butter, scalloped, Ho-o	**10.00**
8½″.	**10–15.00**
9″, breakfast.	**15.00**
9¾″, dinner.	**20–30.00**
Platter, oval, 7¾″, mark #17.	**18.00**
Reamer	
Pitcher	**55.00**
Top, chipped.	**45.00**
Rice Bowl, #1.	**10.00**
Salt Dip, #2	**10.00**
Salt Shaker, #12.	**15.00**
Salt and Pepper, scalloped, set #6. . .	**20.00**
Spoon Holder, oval.	**35.00**
Sugar and Creamer, #20-A	**35.00**
Sugar Shaker, handled, Flying Turkey .	**45.00**

Tea Set, 3 pcs, teapot, creamer, and sugar, child's #5	**65.00**
Tea Strainer, stand	**55.00**
Tea Tile, round	**35.00**
Teapot, large, #18	**45.00**

Tureens
Gravy, attached plate, oval, cover has hole for ladle	**75.00**
Vegetable, cov, round	**75.00**

PHOENIX GLASS

History: Phoenix Glass Company, Beaver, Pennsylvania, was established in 1880. Known primarily for commercial glassware, the firm also produced a molded, sculptured, cameo-type line from the 1930s until the 1950s.

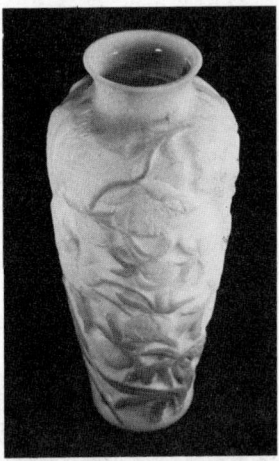

Vase, 12½", ivory ground, yellow flowers, green leaves, $200.00.

Ashtray, triangular, Praying Mantis	35.00
Banana Boat, 5 x 8 x 14", lovebirds in gold, white ground	275.00

Bowls
8", boat shape, lemons and leaves in green on white ground	75.00
13½", blue lovebirds, opal ground	325.00
14", diving nudes, 3 colors	185.00
Candlestick, glossy smoked glass, oval base, hummingbird and flower	50.00
Creamer and Sugar, Catalonia, yellow	25.00

Lamps
6½", lavender peonies on white ground	75.00
11", yellow ferns and foliage on gray ground	115.00

14", red berries, green leaves, brown stems, bronze plated base	135.00
Planter, 3¼ x 8½", green lion, white ground	50.00

Plates
8¼", dancing nudes, yellow	50.00
8½", kumquats, green	35.00
Powder Box, cov, hummingbird and roses in white on blue ground	75.00
Rose Bowl, white star flowers and white bands on rose pink ground	175.00
Tumbler, nudes dancing, yellow	35.00

Vases
6¼", pink peonies, green leaves, white ground	75.00
7", Praying Mantis, amethyst ground	110.00
7 x 8", molded brown grasses, blue grasshoppers, frosty white ground	85.00
8", white cosmos, salmon ground	85.00
9 x 8 x 3½", blue fish with large tails, yellow ground	250.00

9½"
Baluster shape, bittersweet on custard	80.00
Pillow shape, wild geese in white on raspberry ground	160.00
Urn shape, glossy mint green, white cased interior, raised scrolls and flowers	110.00

10"
Classical shape, frosted and clear, blown out berries on vine	65.00
Figural, Madonna, white	125.00
11", dogwood blossoms, paper label	125.00
12", dancing nudes, frosted	200.00

PHONOGRAPH RECORDS

History: With the advent of the more sophisticated recording materials, such as 33⅓ RPM long playing records, 8-track tapes, and cassettes, earlier phonograph records became collectors' items. Most have little value. The higher priced examples are rare (limited production) recordings. Condition is critical.

Periodical: *Goldmine*, 700 E. State Street, Iola, WI 54990. Subscription: $35.00.

Andrew Sisters, Beer Barrel Polka, Decca, 1939	3.00
Armstrong, Louis, Basin Street Blues, Okeh, 1928	25.00
Astaire, Fred, A Fine Romance, Brunswick, 1936	5.00
Barnet, Charlie, Baby, Take A Bow, Banner, 1934	4.00
Basie, Count, One O'Clock Jump, Okeh, 1942	4.00
Carmichael, Hoagy, Georgia on My Mind, Victor, 1930	20.00
Cole, Nat "King", Honeysuckle Rose, Decca, 1940	5.00

Crosby, Bing, Sweet Georgia Brown,
Brunswick, 1933 . . . . **9.00**
Dorsey, Tommy, I'm Getting Sentimental
over You, theme song, Victor, 1939 . **4.00**
Ellington, Duke, Animal Crackers, Gen-
nett, 1926. . . . . **30.00**
Fitzgerald, Ella and the Ink Spots, I'm
Beginning to See the Light, Decca,
1945 . . . . **3.00**
Goodman, Benny, Let's Dance, theme
song, Columbia, 1939 . . . . **3.00**
Holiday, Billie, Them There Eyes, Vo-
calion, 1939 . . . . **6.00**
Horne, Lena, The Man I Love, Victor,
1941 . . . . **3.00**
James, Harry, You Made Me Love You,
Columbia, 1941. . . . . **3.00**
Jolsen, Al, Swanee, Columbia, 1920. . . **10.00**
Lewis, Ted, When My Baby Smiles at
Me, theme song, Columbia, 1926 . . . **5.00**
Lombardo, Guy, Auld Lang Syne, theme
song, Decca, 1939 . . . . **4.00**

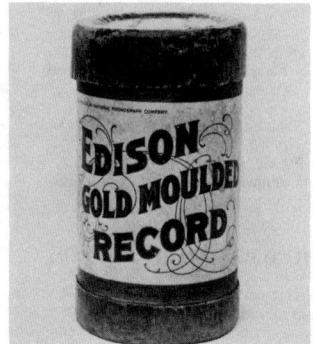

**Edison Gold Moulded Records, picture
of Thomas A. Edison on reverse, copyright 1904, Nat. Phonograph Co,
$5.00.**

Lopez, Vincent, The Sheik of Araby,
Black Swan, 1921 . . . . **8.00**
Martin, Mary, My Heart Belongs to
Daddy, Brunswick, 1938. . . . . **5.00**
Mercer, Johnny, Small Fry, Bing Crosby
vocal, Decca, 1938 . . . . **5.00**
Miller, Glenn, Peg O' My Heart, Decca,
1937 . . . . **8.00**
Nichols, Red, Five Pennies, Victor,
1928 . . . . **8.00**
Shaw, Artie, Begin the Beguine, Blue-
bird, 1938. . . . . **5.00**
Sinatra, Frank, You'll Never Know, Co-
lumbia, 1943. . . . . **4.00**

Smith, Kate, When the Moon Comes
over the Mountain, Columbia, 1931. . **8.00**
Vallee, Rudy, My Time Is Your Time,
theme song, Victor, 1929 . . . . **3.00**
Whiteman, Paul, Serenade in Blue, Cap-
ital, 1942 . . . . **3.00**

PHONOGRAPHS

History: Early phonographs were commonly
called "talking machines." Thomas A. Edison invented the first successful phonograph in 1877.
Other manufacturers followed with their variations.

Collectors' Club: Antique Phonograph Collectors Club, 502 E. 17th Street, Brooklyn, NY 11226.
Dues: $10.00 *The Antique Phonograph Monthly* (10
issues).

Brunswick, disc, mahogany table model,
sq case, 11¾" turntable, c1921 . . . . **225.00**
Busy Bee, disc, oak table model, 8 petal
Morning Glory horn **400.00**
Cameraphone, disc, 78 RPM, portable,
leather covered case. **135.00**
Columbia
Concert Grand AG, cylinder, oak case,
plays both regular and grand cylinders, nickel plated, black and gold
dec. **1,000.00**
Peerless BF, cylinder, oak case, 14"
brass bell horn, ribbon decal,
c1906 . . . . **575.00**
Royal BV, cylinder, oak case, nickel
plated, ribbed Morning Glory horn,
ribbon decal, c1907 . . . . **350.00**

**Edison Home, cover, brass plated,
c 1897–1903, $450.00.**

Edison
Amberola, VI, cylinder, mahogany table model, 32 cylinders in boxes,
c1913 . . . . **750.00**
Diamond Disc, A-80, oak table model,
12" turntable, nickel plated, c1915 **250.00**

Diamond Disc, B-60, oak table model, 12″ turntable, nickel plated, c1913 . . . 300.00
Standard, G. cylinder, oak case and cov, plays only Blue Amberol cylinders, 4 minute, cygnet flowered horn, c1912 . . . 375.00
Parlograph, electric, cylinder, black metal case, 14″ brass bell horn . . . 200.00
Pathe "Duplex" Grand Concert, cylinder, oak case, handles, aluminum bell horn, plays both regular and Salon size cylinders . . . 450.00
Sonora Gothic Deluxe, disc, walnut console case, triple spring, automatic stop, storage for 80 records, c1920 . 250.00
Standard Talking Machine, Model X, disc, oak table model, nickel ribbed Morning Glory horn, 10″ turntable, c1908 . . . 450.00
Triumph A . . . 575.00
Victor
Junior, disc, oak case, Morning Glory horn, brake and speed regulator, 8″ turntable . . . 650.00
Model 11, disc, oak case, 23″ rear mounted ribbed horn, brake and speed regulator, 10″ turntable . . . 550.00
School House, disc, floor model, oak cabinet and horn, nickel plated, storage shelf . . . 1,675.00
Zon-O-Phone, Concert Grand, disc, table model, oak case, 10″ turntable, 27″ Morning Glory horn, double spring . . . 500.00

PHOTOGRAPHS

History: A vintage print is a positive image developed from the original negative by the photographer or under the photographer's supervision at the time the negative is made. A non-vintage print is a print made from an original negative at a later date. It is quite common for a photographer to make prints from the same negative over several decades. Changes between the original printing and subsequent prints usually can be identified.

Limited edition prints must be clearly labeled.

Reference: John F. Maloney, *An Identification And Value Guide To Vintage Cameras And Images*, Books Americana, 1981.

Collectors' Club: American Photographic Historical Society, P. O. Box 1775, Grand Central Station, New York, NY 10163. Dues: $22.50. *Photographica.*

Additional Listings: See *Warman's Americana & Collectibles* in the categories of Carte de Visite and Cabinet Cards and Stereographs.

Abbott, Berenice
Frame House, Bedford & Grove Streets, silver print, 10⅛ x 7¾″, handstamped on back "Abbott/Federal Art Project," caption and negative information hand written, 1936 . . . 300.00
Snuff Shop, silver print, 9½ x 7⅝″, sgd in pencil on the mount, Commerce Street Stamp on back, 1938 . . . 500.00
Aubert Francois, (1839–1906), *Corpse of Emperor Maximillian*, albumen print, 8¾ x 6½″, 1867 . . . 1,775.00
Bernhard, Ruth, *Two Leaves*, silver print, 9¾ x 7⅜″, sgd in pencil on mount, title on back, 1953 . . . 350.00
Bing, Idse, *Ballanchine's Errante, Staged by Pavel Tchelitchev, Paris, 1933*, silver print, 11¼ x 8½″, sgd and dated on back, title and date in pencil . . . 600.00
Blumenfeld, Erwin, (1897–1969), *Nude*, silver print, 13¼ x 9⅝″, Blumenfeld estate stamp and sgd by assistant Marina Schinz in pencil on back, late 1930s . . . 950.00
Bodine, A. Aubrey, (1906–1970), *Landos & Kampher*, Bromoil print, 12⅝ x 9⅞″, sgd, titled and dated in pencil on orig overmat, 1934 . . . 1,000.00
Braun, Adolphe, (1811–1877), *Mont Rose*, carbon print, 14 x 17¾″, blindstamped on back, c1860 . . . 2,000.00
Bruguiere, Francis, (1879–1945), untitled, experimental nude of Rosalinde Fuller, silver print montage, 9¼ x 7⅛″, sgd and various pencil notations, c1926 . . . 950.00
Cameron, Julia Margaret, (1815–1879), *The Adversary—Love In Idleness*, albumen print, 11½ x 11¼″, circular, sgd and titled in ink on Colnaghi blindstamped mount, gold border, inscribed "For The Paris Exhibition, Study No. 1 of Love in Idleness" in pencil on mount, c1866 . . . 2,900.00
Cartier-Bresson, Henri, *Canaries for Sale*, silver print, 8¼ x 11¾″, photographer's magnum handstamp and typed described label, c1940 . . . 250.00
Cunningham, Imogen, (1883–1976), *The Unmade Bed, 1957*, silver print, 10½ x 13½″, sgd and dated in pencil, Green Street label with title and date 2,500.00
Curtis, Edward S., *Eskadi-Apache*, sepia toned photogravure on Holland Van Gelder paper, 14½ x 10¼″, Seattle, 1907 . . . 200.00
Dates, Judy, *Portrait of Minor White*, silver print, 13¾ x 10½″, sgd, titled and copyrighted by photographer in pencil, 1975 . . . 80.00
Dodgson, Rev. Charles L. (Lewis Carroll) (1832–1898), *Alexander Kitchin*, albumen print, 8⅛ x 5⅞″, c1870 . . . 3,300.00
Edgerton, Harold, *Tennis Player*, silver print, 15¾ x 19½″, sgd in ink, c1954 4,000.00

Eickemeyer, Rudolf, Jr., *Forest Land-scape With Stream*, platinum print, 9 x 7″, initialed and dated in red ink on mount, 1906. . . . .   **300.00**

Evans, Walker, *Subway Study, 2 Women on Pelham Bay Park Line*, silver print, 4¾ x 7″, Evans estate stamp on back. **275.00**

Feininger, T. Lux, *Work of J. Schmidt's Experimental Sculpture Class*, silver print, 3¼ x 4½″, sgd and titled in pencil, c1930 . . . .   **500.00**

Gilpin, Laura, (1891–1979), *Temple of the Three Lintels*, silver print on gravelux paper, 14 x 9⅞″, sgd in pencil with printed title on overmat, 1940 . . . .   **550.00**

Haviland, Paul B., (1880–1950), *Portrait of Annie Brigman in a Spanish Shawl*, platinum print, 6½ x 4⅝″, monogram in red ink on back, c1910 . . . .   **800.00**

Hausmann, Raoul, (1886–1970), *Tulipes* (sic.), silver print, 6¼ x 4½″, sgd, titled, and dated in ink and notations in pencil, 1939 . . . .   **1,550.00**

Hill, David Octavius, (1802–1870) and Adamson, Robert (1821–1848), *Finlay Deerstalker*, colotype, 8 x 5⅜″, title in pencil on mount, sgd, 1845 . . . .   **2,000.00**

Hine, Lewis W., *Joseph Severio, Peanut Vendor, Wilmington, Del*, silver print, 4½ x 3½″, description of boy and his life on back, 1910 . . . .   **375.00**

Kertez, Andre, *Versailles*, silver print, 9¾ x 7⅛″, sgd, titled, and dated in pencil and stamped, 1926 . . . .   **1,000.00**

Mantz, Werner, *Row of Sacks*, silver print, 5⅝ x 8⅝″, sgd and dated in pencil on mount, stamped on back, 1929 . . . .   **800.00**

Mohaly-Nagy, Laszlo, (1895–1946), *Photoplastik*, silver print, 7⅜ x 6⅜″, sgd in ink on back, 1925 . . . .   **2,875.00**

O'Doyle, Paul, *Cecile Sorel*, platinum print, 8⅝ x 6⅜″, sgd, inscribed on mount "Pour le Baron de Meyer avec toute mon admiration, Cecile Sorel," c1920. . . . .   **225.00**

Outerbridge, Paul, Jr., (1896–1958)
  Box, Bottle, Can, platinum-palladium print, 4⅝ x 3½″, Outerbridge estate stamp on back. **7,200.00**
  Nude With Rockette's Jacket, carbocolor print, 18¼ x 10⅜″, one of two existing prints, c1936 . . . .   **13,200.00**
  Seashell Abstraction, bleached and toned silver print, 4⅜ x 3⅜″, c1928 . . . .   **3,500.00**

Ray, Mann, *Self Portrait, 1945*, silver print from *Les Treize Cliche Vierges*, 9½ x 7″, sgd and #33/50 in white ink, 1968 . . . .   **600.00**

Sander, August, *Two Couples*, silver print, 9 x 6¾″, photographer's Koeln blindstamp lower left, 1910 . . . .   **350.00**

Skeen & Co., *Coffee Blossoms*, albumen print, 11¾ x 8¼″, sgd and #1455 in negative, c1880. . . . .   **25.00**

Steichen, Edward, (1879–1973), *Nude Torso, New York*, toned silver print, 13¾ x 10¾″, stamped "Photograph by Edward Steichen, printed from orig negative," 1934. . . . .   **4,000.00**

Stieglitz, Alfred, *Equivalent*, silver print, 3⅝ x 4⅝″, sgd, titled, and dated in pencil on mount, cloud images, 1924   **9,000.00**

Strand, Paul, (1890–1976), *The Beach, Percé, Gaspé, Quebec*, silver print, 3½ x 4½″, sgd and titled in ink with red pencil highlights, c1936 . . . .   **7,775.00**

Struss, Karl, (1896–1982), *Maytime* (Harrison Ford), platinum print, 9¼ x 7¼″, sgd, titled, and dated in pencil and emb stamp on mount, Struss's Hollywood stamp on back **750.00**

Watkins, Carlton, E., (1829–1916), *Further Up The Valley, The Three Brothers*, albumen print, 15¼ x 21″, title in ink on mount, c1861 . . . .   **800.00**

Weston, Edward (1886–1958)
  Oregon Coast, silver print, 7½ x 9½″, sgd and dated in pencil, Beaumont Newhall Collection stamp, 1939 . .   **2,250.00**
  Tracks on Sand, Oceano, silver print, 7 x 8½″, sgd, dated, and #10-40 in pencil, 1935. . . . .   **1,100.00**

PICKARD CHINA

History: The Pickard China Company was founded by Wilder Pickard in Chicago, Illinois, in 1897. Originally the company imported European china blanks, principally from the Havilands at Limoges, which they then hand painted. The firm presently is located in Antioch, Illinois.

Bowls
  6½″, gold floral dec. **45.00**
  9″, hp poppies, water lilies, gold trim, 1896. . . . .   **125.00**

Cake Plates
  10″, handled, Woodland Path-Edgelong Woods, artist Challinor **300.00**
  11½″, shaded rose ground, hp pink, white, and rose roses, gold scalloped rim and ribbon handles **125.00**

Candlestick, 7¼″, irid, hp floral dec . . .   **225.00**

Chocolate Pot, 9½″, pink clover, heavy gold, artist sgd Reuvy **325.00**

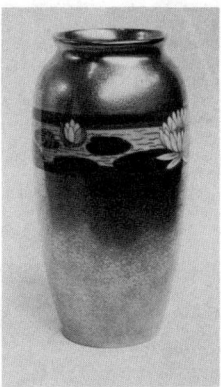

**Vase, gold etched effect, blue band
containing water lily dec, artist sgd
"James," mkd "Pickard: Etched China,"
blank mkd "R.S. Tillowitz," $225.00.**

Coffee Pot, 8", gold scroll, inset band
with basket.................... **80.00**
Compote, 6" d, 3" h, gold etched **40.00**
Condiment Set with spoon, gold **200.00**
Creamers and Sugars
   Currants, heavy gold trim, artist sgd
    O. Goess **225.00**
   Deserted Garden, wide gold band,
    artist sgd Marker **245.00**
   Stylized red leaves and green foli-
    age, cream ground, heavy gold,
    artist sgd Lind, 1898 mark **200.00**
Dishes
   4 x 7", oval, irid, rose dec, sgd **65.00**
   8½" 1, leaf shape, floral
    dec, gold etched **50.00**
Jug, 6", corn painting, artist sgd **190.00**
Mayonnaise Dish with underplate, floral
   dec, gold etched **55.00**
Mug, 6⅞", poinsettias, gold banding
   and trim, oil style edge on white
   ground, artist sgd **200.00**
Nappy, currants dec, dark red and
   purple...................... **95.00**
Perfume with Stopper, 6½", violets,
   artist sgd H. Reuvy, c1905........ **300.00**
Pitchers
   4½", small pink and blue flowers,
    Nippon blank................ **60.00**
   6" h, 8" d, cider, cream ground,
    raised flowers, artist sgd Fisher,
    1905...................... **225.00**
   8", water, floral dec, wide gold band,
    sgd Rean, c1898 .... **300.00**

10½", tankard, poppy dec, tinted
   ground, heavy gold, artist sgd
   Fuchs, 1905 mark **465.00**
Plates
   8¾", hp violets, light green ground,
    artist sgd.................. **45.00**
   9", center large pink blossom and
    green leaves, multicolor floral and
    gold reserves rim, artist sgd **85.00**
   10½", scenic view of Yosemite Val-
    ley, pastel, gold rim, Nippon blank,
    orig paper label "Pickard Studios/
    Chicago/3/Cake Tray/Yosemite
    Valley," artist sgd E. Challinor,
    maple leaf Pickard mark........ **400.00**
   10¾", service, gold over blue bor-
    der, floral center **35.00**
Salt and Pepper, Ora Logenta, artist
   sgd Hess **34.00**
Sugar Shaker, 4½", poppies, artist sgd
   Gasper, c1910 .... **235.00**
Tankard, 15", purple shaded to brown,
   large clusters of purple grapes,
   green leaves, gold border, artist sgd,
   1895–1898 .... **425.00**
Teapot, 5½", floral dec, gold etched .. **95.00**
Tray, 16¾ x 10½", oval, hp purple
   grapes, green leaves, gold band, artist sgd **185.00**
Vases
   7", handled, scenic, lake, trees,
    sunset.................... **175.00**
   9", black, purple grapes, heavy gold,
    artist sgd Hessler, c1898 .... **285.00**
   10", handled, gold dec, acid etched,
    sgd...................... **125.00**
   12", pastel, scenic, sgd **375.00**
Wall Plaque, 12", Edge of Budlong
   Woods, artist sgd Challinor **575.00**

PICKLE CASTORS

History: A pickle castor is a table accessory used
to serve pickles. It generally consists of a silver
plated frame fitted with a glass insert, matching
silver plated lid, and matching tongs. Pickles castors were very popular during the Victorian era. Inserts are found in pattern glass and colored art
glass.

Amethyst, applied enamel floral dec,
   SP frame, lid................. **275.00**
Cane pattern, amber, SP frame **90.00**
Daisy & Button pattern, apple green,
   SP frame, glass lid **185.00**
Daisy & Fern, blue, opal, apple blos-
   som mold, ornate ftd SP frame, orig
   tongs **250.00**
Double, green glass inserts, Pairpoint
   silver frame, fork.............. **175.00**

Pattern glass, Daisy and Button with V Ornament, blue, SP frame, matching lid and tongs, mkd Wilcox, $235.00.

Double, paneled crystal inserts, floral cutting, ornate ftd SP frame, tongs . .	300.00
Flute Panels, SP frame, tongs, finial lid, emb Wm. Rogers	70.00
IVT, cranberry, white enameled daisies, yellow centers, green leaves, SP frame, lid, tongs, 12″ h	325.00
New England Glass, cased satin swirl insert, mottled rose-mauve, SP frame	225.00
Rubina, Ribbed Optic pattern, hp enamel sprays of white daisies and blue forget-me-nots, gold leaves, ftd 4½″ d base, ornate SP lid, bail, side trim, mkd Colonial Silver Plate Co., Portland, ME.	400.00
Satin, cranberry, leaf mold insert, ornate SP frame, tongs.	350.00

PIGEON BLOOD GLASS

History: Pigeon blood refers to the deep orangish-red colored glass ware produced around the turn of the century. Do not confuse it with the many other red glass wares of that period. Pigeon blood has a very definite orange glow.

Biscuit Jar, 8½″ to top of finial, SP rim, cov, and bail handle	250.00
Bottle, 9½″, clear, maker, Victor Durand	50.00
Bowl, 9″, beaded rim	150.00
Creamer, Bulging Loop, clear applied handle	165.00
Cruet, 7″, enameled floral dec	100.00
Pickle Castor with fork, 8″, Bulging Loop, ftd, SP, Empire Mfg. Co.	280.00
Pitchers	
8″, clear applied handle	175.00
10″, water, Bulging Loop	350.00
Rose Bowl, 5½″ d, 4″ h, bulbous, enameled floral dec.	75.00
Salt and Pepper Shakers, Bulging Loop	100.00
Sugar Shaker, Bulging Loop	220.00

Salt and pepper shakers, 2¾″ h, metal tops, $110.00.

Syrup Jar, cov, Torquay	190.00
Tankard, 10″, DQ	165.00
Toothpick Holder, 2½″, ribbed	65.00
Tumbler, 3½″, alternating panels and ribs	75.00
Vases	
4½″, urn shape, 2 clear applied handles	80.00
7″, cylindrical, enamel dec	125.00

PINK SLAG

History: True pink slag is found only in the molded Inverted Fan and Feather pattern. Quality pieces shade from pink at the top to white at the bottom.

Recently pieces of pink slag, made from molds of the now defunct Cambridge Glass Company, have been found in the Inverted Strawberry and Inverted Thistle pattern. This is not considered "true" pink slag and brings only a fraction of the Inverted Fan and Feather pattern prices.

The glass auctions of Early Auction Company, Milford, Ohio, annually feature several pieces of pink slag.

Bowl, berry, master.	500.00
Butter, cov.	650.00
Creamer	425.00

Cruet	**1,400.00**
Pitcher, water	**800.00**
Spooner	**350.00**

Punch cup, footed, $325.00.

Sugar
Cov	**550.00**
Open	**300.00**
Toothpick	**400.00**
Tumbler	**410.00**

PIPES

History: The history of pipe making dates as early as 1575. Almost all types of natural and man made materials, some which retained smoke and some that did not, were used to make pipes. Among the materials were amber, base metals, clay, cloisonné, glass, horn, ivory, jade, meerschaum, parian, porcelain, pottery, precious metals, precious stones, semi-precious stones, assorted woods, *iner alia*. Chronologically the four most popular materials and their generally accepted introduction dates are: c1575, clay; c1700, woods; c1710, porcelain; and, c1725, meerschaum.

National pipe styles exist around the globe, wherever tobacco smoking is custom or habit. Pipes reflect a broad range of themes and messages, e.g., figurals, important personages, commemoration of historical events, mythological characters, erotica and pornographica, the bucolic, the bizarre, the grotesque, and the graceful.

Pipe collecting began in the mid-1880s; William Bragge, F.S.A., Birmingham, England, was an early collector. Although firmly established through the efforts of free-lance writers, auction houses, and museums (but not the tobacco industry), the collecting of antique pipes is an amorphous, maligned, and misunderstood hobby. It is amorphous because there are no defined collecting bounds; maligned because it is conceived as an extension of pipe smoking, now socially unacceptable [many pipe collectors are avid non-smokers]; and, misunder-

stood because of its association with the "collectibles" field.

1983 marked the sixth consecutive year that major collections from estates and private parties entered the market in America and abroad. The most prominent collection was the Metromedia Collection of Duke University Art Museum, Durham, NC, which was auctioned by Christie's in New York on December 13, 1983.

References: R. Fresco-Corbu, *European Pipes*, Lutterworth Press, 1982; E. Ramazzotti and B. Mamy, *Pipes et Fumeurs des Pipes. Un Art, des Collections, Sous le Vent*, 1981; Benjamin Rapaport, *A Complete Guide To Collecting Antique Pipes*, Schiffer Publishing, 1979, 1st edition.

Periodicals: *Pipe Smoker*, Pipe Collectors International, Inc., P. O. Box 22085, 6172 Airways Boulevard, Chattanooga, TN 37422. Subscription: $15.00. Quarterly, occasional article on antique pipes; *Smokeshop*, BMT Publications, Inc., 254 W. 31st Street, New York, NY 10001. Subscription: $24.00. Monthly, occasional article on antique pipes.

Museums: Museum of Tobacco Art and History, Nashville, TN; National Tobacco-Textile Museum, Danville, VA; U.S. Tobacco Museum, Greenwich, CT.

Ceramic [Porcelain, etc.]
African, Ashanti, red pottery bowl, modeled as seated male figure, 7" l, late 19th C	**155.00**
English, Staffordshire, Pratt-type, bowl molded with four male masks, stem modeled with dog and snake, painted in brown, blue, and green, 10" l, early 19th C	**305.00**

European
Lot of 3, porcelain, 1) bisque, bowl in form of skull, 2) bowl painted with bust of "Der Blinde Tobias," face composed of pornographic elements; 3) plain; all 19th C, lot	**275.00**
Student, en suite set of bowl and reservoir, matched theme of view of Heidelberg, hp in chromolithographic colors, cherrywood stem, silk tasseled retaining cord, 24" l overall	**270.00**
German, porcelain bowl painted with soldier and gentleman standing below crossed flags [early representation of reservisten (regimental) pipe], carved wood, horn, and stag antler stem, flexible mouthpiece, 40" l overall, German Empire, c1865	**90.00**

Clay, lot of 3, 1) French, modeled bowl in form of knight in armor, painted eyes, 4" l; 2) Gambier, bowl in form of young man with long curled hair, wood push stem, 18″ overall; 3) bowl in form of bearded Arab head, painted in glazed colors, 3″ w; all mid-19th C, lot **185.00**

Meerschaum

Floral Stem, scrolling, tendril-like leaves, amber mouthpiece, 11″ l, case stamped WDC [William De-Muth, NYC], c1900. . . . . **500.00**

Richard Wagner, figural, amber mouthpiece, 7½″ l, fitted case, French, 1880. . . . . **285.00**

Wolves, family of 3, carved in high relief, standing, two in costume, cheroot holder, amber mouthpiece, fitted case, Vienna, c1875. . . . . **145.00**

Miscellaneous

Argillite, Haida, model totem pole, carved with three stylized figures, 6″ h, mid-19th C, slightly damaged . . **90.00**

Elkhorn, Lapland, carved in form of tree trunk with two bowls, relief carving of hunter and medieval musician, bone carved with figure of wild boar, 9½″ l, c1910 . . . . **90.00**

Gourd, Thai, incised silver lotus bowl and tip, brass mouthpiece, 7″ l, late 19th C **130.00**

Silver, miniature, hookah, chased with scrolling foliage on the foot, spherical body, bowl, and pierced cov, cov hung with small bells on chain, 7″ h, early 20th C **135.00**

Silver and Enamel, Russian, bowl in Turkish chibouque style with cylindrical tapering top into a lobed circular bowl, bright painted enamels of stylized foliage, long stem, fitted with a short brass chain suspending a prika, 10″ l, late 19th C **160.00**

Soapstone, Eskimo, carved as man skinning an animal, 9″ h, late 19th C **140.00**

Stone, American Indian, tomahawk type, wood shaft, iron head, attached beaded pendant with paired eagle claws, feathers, and teeth on chains, another length with yellow beads, seed pods, and orange dyed teeth, 49″ l, late 19th C **500.00**

Oriental

Opium Pipe, Sri Lanka, four bowl, long lacquered wood stem carved with raised bands of geometric ornaments which divides into four pottery dampers with incised ornaments, 60″ l, late 19th C **125.00**

Smoking set, dry, Japanese tonkotsu, silver and bamboo pipe, walrus ivory pipecase carved in form of emaciated man, complete with wood inro, 9½″ l, c1875 . . . . **400.00**

Water Pipe, cloisonne, Qing Dynasty

[Chinese], colored flowering plants on blue and turquoise grounds, hexagonal section bowl and stem, brush and pricker, 15″ h, c1890 . . **155.00**

Wood [Briar, etc.]

African, lot of 2, Mangbetu wood, sheet tin bowls, one with wood stem bound with copper and brass with applied upholstery nails, 12½″ l, other of curved form and bound with brass and copper wire, 17″, seedpod pipe bowl from the Ubangi-Welle region, early 20th C, lot. . . . **165.00**

Austrian, Debrecen-style, boxwood, carved in bas-relief, scene of William Tell shooting arrow at blindfolded boy with apple on head, forest backdrop, push stem of eichhorn and antler horn, silver retaining chains with acorn tassels, 8½″ l, Viennese, c1860 . . . . **265.00**

Meerschaum, bulldog, figural, studded muzzle, colored bowl, amber mouthpiece, 6½″ l, case stamped Ludwig and Elidam Hartmann, Vienna, c1890, $350.00.

European, cherrywood, figural, French legionnaire's head, kepi as wind cover, push stem of cherrywood, horn mouthpiece, 18½″ l overall, c1875 . . . . **125.00**

German, carved wood cigarillo holder, boar hunt, carved beneath the bowl with foliate scrolls and a hunter on a rearing horse, boar flanked by a hound, meerschaum bowl, amber mouth piece, 6″ l, fitted case, c1880 . . . . **400.00**

POCKET KNIVES

History: Alcas, Case, Colonial, Ka-Bar, Queen, and Schrade are the best of the modern pocket knife manufacturers, with top positions enjoyed by Case and Ka-Bar. Knives by Remington and Winchester, firms no longer in production, are eagerly sought.

Form is a critical collecting element. The most desirable forms are folding hunters (1 and 2 blades), trappers, peanuts, Barlows, elephant toes, canoes, Texas toothpicks, Coke bottles, gun stocks, and Daddy Barlows. The decorative aspect also heavily influences prices. Values are for pocket knives in mint condition.

Reference: James F. Parker and Bruce Voyles, *The Official Price Guide to Collector Pocket Knives*, House of Collectibles, 1979.

Periodicals: *The American Blade*, 112 Lee Parkway Drive, Stonewall Building, Suite 104, Chattanooga, TN 37421; *Knife World*, P. O. Box 3395, Knoxville, TN 37917.

Collectors' Clubs: American Blade Collectors, 112 Lee Parkway Drive, Stonewall Building, Suite 104, Chattanooga, TN 37421; The National Knife Collectors Association, P. O. Box 21070, Chattanooga, TN 37421.

Museum: National Knife Museum, Chattanooga, TN.

Additional Listings: See *Warman's Americana & Collectibles* for more examples.

Advisor: Roy C. Repsher.

CASE

Case uses a numbering code for its knives. The first number (1–9) is the handle material; the second number (1–5) designates the number of blades; the third and fourth number (0–99) the knife pattern. Stage (5), pearl (8 or 9), and bone (6) are most sought in handle materials. The most desirable patterns are 5165—folding hunters, 6185—doctors, 6445—scout, muskrat—marked muskrat with no number, and 6254—trappers.

In the Case XX series a symbol and dot code is used to designate a year.

1920–1940
5111½ L	600.00
5452	300.00
6245, dog groomer	200.00
8265	1,000.00

1940–1965
4200, melon taster, serated blade. . .	150.00
5265	200.00
61093	175.00
62009, Barlow.	100.00
Muskrat	90.00

1965–1970, XX series
32095, fisherman's	100.00
5254	85.00
5172, bulldog	150.00
6111½	100.00
6143, Daddy Barlow	40.00

1970–1980 (number of dots indicates year)
2137, sod buster.	25.00
52131, canoe	100.00
6246R, rigger	45.00
P13755, stag, Kentucky Bicentennial.	50.00

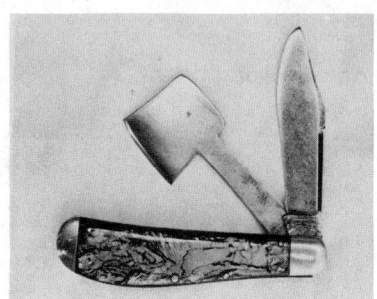

K-Bar, mottled, gold stone, Imperial, Providence, RI, $125.00.

KA-BAR (Union Cut. Co., Olean, NY)

The company was founded by Wallace Brown at Tidioute, PA in 1892. It was relocated in Olean, NY, in 1912. The products have many stampings including Union [inside shield], U-R Co. Tidioute [variations], Union Cut Co., Olean, NY, Alcut Olean, NY, Keenwell, Olean, NY, and Ka-Bar. The larger knives with a profile of a dog's head on the handle are most desirable. Pattern numbers rarely appear on a knife prior to the 1940's.

1154, leg knife	150.00
21107, Grizzly	2,000.00
2217, rigger	70.00
61161, composition handle	125.00
6191, knife, forks, spoon.	625.00
6250, elephant toe	300.00
6260 KF	100.00
Cigar Cutter	150.00

KEEN KUTTER (Simons Hardware, St. Louis, MO)

K1771¾, Daddy Barlow	150.00
K1898¾, toothpick	100.00
K8464¼, Kattle	50.00

REMINGTON, Last made in 1940.

R 1123, bullet	600.00
R 1173, bullet	1,200.00
R 1253, bullet	1,000.00
R 1263, bullet	1,100.00
3333, scout	125.00
4235, red, white, and blue.	200.00
Bullet, authorized reproduction.	60.00

WINCHESTER

1050, Texas toothpick.	300.00
1701, Barlow	100.00

2380, doctor's	**350.00**
3376	**250.00**

OTHER MANUFACTURERS

Folding Hunter

Baker, U.S.A.	**100.00**
Cattarangus Cut. Co.	**350.00**
Marbles Arms Co.	**350.00** ·
Naponock Knife Co., Naponock, NY, combination tool set.	**200.00**
C. Platts & Sons, Eldred, PA	**100.00**+
Queen Cut. Co., Titusville, PA	**100.00**
Union Razor Co., Titusville, PA.	**100.00**+
Valley Forge Cut. Co., NJ.	**200.00**
Western States Cut. Co., Boulder, CO, buffalo skull mark.	**300.00**
Geo. Wosterholm & Son Cut. Co., General Taylor.	**1,500.00**
Elephant Toe	
Cattaraugus Cut. Co.	**300.00**
N.Y. Knife Co.	**350.00**

POISON BOTTLES

History: Poison bottles were designed to warn and prevent accidental intake or misuse of their poisonous substances, especially in the dark. Poison bottles generally were made of colored glass, embossed with "Poison" or a skull and crossbones, and sometimes were coffin shaped.

John H. B. Howell of Newton, New Jersey, designed the first safety closure in 1866. The idea did not become popular until the 1930s when bottle designs became simpler and the user had to read the label to identify the contents.

References: Hugh Cleveland, *Bottle Pricing Guide,* Collector Books, 1980; Ralph & Terry Kovel, *The Kovels' Bottle Price List,* Crown Publishers, Inc., 1982, 6th ed.; Carlo & Dot Sellari, *The Illustrated Price Guide to Antique Bottles,* Country Beautiful Corp., 1975.

Periodicals: *Antique Bottle World,* 5003 West Berwyn, Chicago, IL 60630; *Old Bottle Magazine,* P. O. Box 243, Bend, OR 97701. Subscription: $10.00.

A.B.M., Tinct Iodine, emb skull and crossbones, stopper, amber	**10.00**
Clarke Fluid Co., Cincinnati, "Poison" on side, 8 to 64 oz graduated measure on other side, amethyst, quart size	**25.00**
E.R.S. & S. Acid Arsenous	**5.00**
Ferris & Co., Ltd, Bristol, emb near base, "Poison" in center, vertical ribbing, aqua, 7½"	**15.00**
Frost, John M., Buffalo, NY, round, clear, 2½"	**5.00**
Grasselli Arsenate of Lead, "Poison" emb on shoulder	**50.00**

Amber, 3⁹⁄₁₆″ h, embossed "Poison," blown, $8.00.

Ikey Einstein, "Poison" on each side, rect, clear, 3¾"	**20.00**
McCormick & Co., Baltimore, Laundunum, 3 sided, 4"	**25.00**
Millings, R. C., Bed Bug Poison, Charleston, SC, clear, 6½", side shoulder strap	**20.00**
Mulford, skull and crossbones, cobalt.	**18.00**
Quick Death Insecticide	**5.00**
Wyeth Poison, name vertical on back, round ring handle, cobalt, 2¼"	**15.00**

POLITICAL ITEMS

History: Since 1800 the American presidency always has been a contest between two or more candidates. Initially souvenirs were issued to celebrate victories. Items issued during a campaign to show support for a candidate were actively being distributed in the William Henry Harrison election of 1840.

Campaign items cover a wide variety of materials—buttons, bandannas, tokens, pins, etc. The only limiting factor has been the promoter's imagination. The advent of television campaigning has reduced the emphasis on individual items. Modern campaigns do not seem to have the variety of materials which were issued earlier.

References: Herbert Collins, *Threads of History,* Smithsonian Institution Press, 1979; Theodore L. Hake, *Encyclopedia of Political Buttons, United States, 1896–1972,* Dafron House, 1974; Theodore L. Hake, *Political Buttons, Book II, 1920–1976,* Americana & Collectible Press, 1977; Theodore L. Hake, *Political Buttons, Book III, 1789–1916,* Americana & Collectible Press, 1978; Edmund B. Sullivan, *American Political Badges and Medalets,*

1789–1892, Quarterman Publications, Inc., 1981.
Note: Theodore L. Hake issued a revised set of prices for his three books in 1984.

Collectors' Club: American Political Items Collectors, 1054 Sharpsburg Drive, Huntsville, AL 35803.

Museum: Smithsonian Museum, Washington, D.C.

Additional Listings: See *Warman's Americana & Collectibles* for more examples.

Advisor: Theodore L. Hake.

Ballot, Sample, 1960, NY, election for president and vice president, listing Nixon, Kennedy, and Farrel Dobbs . .   **10.00**
Bandanna, 1904, Parker Davis, red, white, and blue flag design, "Good Government For The People," jugate portraits, 22 x 25" **80.00**
Banners
  1928, Smith, 3½ x 6", "Al Smith," paper, blue and white **15.00**
  1932, Roosevelt, 9 x 12", "Win With Franklin D. Roosevelt Our Next President," red, white, and blue fabric, gold braid. **20.00**
Buttons
  1896, Bryan, jugate, "Bryan-Sewall 16 to 1," black, white, and blue **25.00**
  1896–1900, McKinley, 1¼", jugate, "Commercial Travelers Sound Money League—Tried and True—McKinley & Hobart Our Choice," black, white, and blue. **50.00**
  1904, Roosevelt, 2⅛" celluloid, full figure of Liberty, portraits of Theodore Roosevelt and Fairbanks, multicolored. **150.00**
  1908, Bryan, 1¼", sepia jugate, "Bryan & Kern" **75.00**
  1908, Taft, ⅞", gray and white **10.00**

Plate, 9½", William Howard Taft, James Schoolcraft Sherman, "Grand Old Party/Standard Bearers," 1908, $85.00.

1912, Wilson, 1½", "For President Woodrow Wilson," gray and white   **75.00**
1920, Harding, ⅞", litho, "Harding & Coolidge," blue and white. **15.00**
1924, Smith, 1¾", "For President Alfred E. Smith," gray. **125.00**
1928, Hoover, jugate, "Hoover and Curtiss," black, white, red, and blue **65.00**
1936, Roosevelt, ⅞", celluloid, "Franklin D. Roosevelt For President," black and white **15.00**
1940, Willkie, 1", litho, "Wings For America—Willkie," red, white, and blue, fighter planes. **12.00**
1948, Truman, 1¾", "For President, Harry S. Truman," black and white   **18.00**
1956, Eisenhower, 2", "The Garden State Salutes Ike, Our Man of the Hour," red, white, and blue. **25.00**
1956, Stevenson, 1⅜", "Stevenson President," red, white, and blue . .   **8.00**
1968, Reagan, 1⅝", "I'm For Reagan," black, white, and blue **20.00**
1976, Ford, 1⅝", "Re-Elect Ford In '76," black, white, and red **5.00**
Charm, 1884, Cleveland-Hendricks, ⅞" d, brass, sepia cardboard photos under glass **100.00**
Cigar Box, late 1800s, Henry Clay, 2 x 4 x 8", wood, color portrait **25.00**
Compact, lady's, 1940, Willkie, "We Want Willkie," 2¾", brass, red, white, and blue. **18.00**
Convention Badges
  1900, National Republican Convention, Philadelphia, June 19, 1900, blue fabric, medallion with brown and white celluloid portraits of Lincoln, Grant, and McKinley. **50.00**
  1912, National Progressive Party NY State Convention, Syracuse, 1912, brass fob emb with bull moose, blue ribbon **30.00**
  1912, Republican National Convention Chicago, 1912, Iowa, ear of corn at top of red, white, and blue ribbon, bright gold medallion with state capital. **45.00**
  1916, District Delegate Texas, National Democratic Convention, St. Louis, June 1916, brass with red, white, and blue enamel. **40.00**
Fan, 1936, Landon, 8½" d, cardboard, "Landon For President," brown and yellow. **35.00**
Fobs
  1912, Wilson, ⅞", black and white celluloid, leather strap. **40.00**
  1916, Hughes, 1¾" sepia, "Charles E. Hughes," and portrait on celluloid   **65.00**
  1920, Cox-Roosevelt, "Our Choice," silvered brass **90.00**

Glass, 1896, McKinley, 4", clear, portrait, "Protection and Plenty" emb on base **50.00**

Hat, 1888, Benjamin Harrison, beige felt, dark blue and white paper label on inside with portraits, eagle with olive branch and flags, leather headband **300.00**

Badge, William McKinley, 1896, 1900, $65.00.

Inaugural Items
- 1909, Taft, pin, brass, heart shape, red, white, and blue hanger **20.00**
- 1933, Roosevelt, fob, brass, emb "Our President Franklin D. Roosevelt, March 3, 1933" **50.00**
- 1953, Eisenhower, medal, 2³⁄₄", brass **20.00**
- 1961, Kennedy, button, 3¹⁄₂", red, blue, black, white, and gold. **12.00**

Lantern, paper, 1872, Grant-Wilson, 12" h, 7¹⁄₂" d, dark blue and light purple stars above and below names **175.00**

License Plates
- 1928, Al Smith, 2¹⁄₂ x 10", blue and white litho in tin **20.00**
- 1968, Wallace, 6¹⁄₂ x 12", "Wallace For President," red, white, and blue **8.00**

Mirror, 1908, Taft, color portrait inscribed "Oh My!—The Souvenir Popcorn, Made by National Candy Co" **60.00**

Parasol, 18" d, 22" l, bamboo handle, red, white, and blue paper stars and stripes design, c1900. . . . . **35.00**

Pennants
- 1940, Roosevelt, 5 x 6", "FDR," red, white, and blue, wood stick at top, gold braid **20.00**
- 1960, Kennedy-Johnson, 30" l, red, white, and blue felt. **15.00**

- 1968, Humphrey, 30" l, red, white, and blue felt. **10.00**

Pins
- 1840, Harrison, reverse painting on glass of log cabin, brass rim **350.00**
- 1896, McKinley, diecut brass, mechanical, elephant head, "G.O.P." on forehead, cov raises to black and yellow paper label with lady's pantaloons and padlock "For Protection" **175.00**
- 1896, McKinley, brass shell, goldbug, 1¹⁄₂" **40.00**
- 1928, Hoover, bar, red, white, and blue porcelain on brass, orig card. **20.00**
- 1936, Landon, diecut emb brass, sunflower shape, emb "Landon Knox" **20.00**

Pipe, mid-1800s, Henry Clay, white pottery, 2¹⁄₂" h, 1" d, name and portrait on front **100.00**

Pocket Knife, 1904, Theodore Roosevelt, celluloid, 3¹⁄₂" l, one side shows Lincoln, Garfield, and McKinley, obverse with Theodore Roosevelt and advertising from Titusville, PA, mkd "Canton Cuttery" **45.00**

Postcard
- 1908, Bryan, "Two of America's Great Essentials (Bryan & Corn) To Peace & Prosperity" **20.00**
- 1909, Suffragette Series, No. 12, woman holding "Official Ballot," slogan "I Love My Husband, but— Oh You Vote," multicolored **20.00**
- 1960, Kennedy, full color, "Vote For John F. Kennedy President Nov. 8, 1960," unused. **8.00**

Ribbons
- 1884, Blaine, 2¹⁄₂ x 5¹⁄₂", sepia cardboard photo, shield, flags and knight helmet, gold imprint on red "For President 1884 Hon. Jas. G. Blaine" **40.00**
- 1884, Cleveland, 2¹⁄₂ x 6", sepia paper portraits on shields, black and white, imprinted "Grover Cleveland—Thomas A. Hendricks" **50.00**
- 1896, McKinley, 2¹⁄₂ x 6¹⁄₂", McKinley standing on box labeled "Our Standard" with farmer and mechanic at side, large eagle and flag, gilt brass hanger, black and white silk **100.00**
- 1901, McKinley Mourning, 3¹⁄₄ x 9¹⁄₂", inscribed with portrait and "Republican Invincibles of Philadelphia September 19, 1901". **30.00**

Sheet Music
- 1924, Al Smith, "We'll All Go Voting For Al," Irving Berlin, published by the New York State Committee For The Nomination of Gov. Alfred E. Smith, red, white, and blue **35.00**

1924, Wilson, "We'll Link His Name With Lincoln," black and white . . .	**10.00**
1936, Landon, "Our Landon," red, white, and blue	**15.00**
Stereo Cards	
1896, McKinley and Hobart	**12.00**
1902, President Roosevelt in the Cabinet Room of the White House . . .	**10.00**
Stickpins	
1888, Harrison, diecut brass shell. . .	**30.00**
1896, McKinley, paper photo	**25.00**
1900, Roosevelt, "Mack & Teddy," diecut emb Rough Rider's hat. . . .	**50.00**
1904, Roosevelt, eyeglass shape, sepia portraits of T. Roosevelt and Fairbanks	**90.00**
Studs	
1892, Harrison, ⅝″ d, sepia celluloid	**25.00**
1920, Cox, diecut metal, rooster center, "I Will Crow In November" . . .	**20.00**
1936, Landon, brown and yellow enamel sunflower.	**10.00**
Tabs	
1928, Hoover, brass	**10.00**
1940, Roosevelt, red, white and blue, "FDR/For/President/ILGWU". . . .	**12.00**
Tietack, 1940, Eleanor Roosevelt, portrait on silvered metal, "Democratic Party of Michigan" on back	**12.00**
Tokens	
1844, Henry Clay, brass, "The Noble and Patriotic Supporter of Protection"	**25.00**
1888, Cleveland, octagonal, portrait on obverse, "Cleveland—Our Whole Country, Now & Forever". .	**35.00**
Trade Cards	
1880, Electoral Vote of 1880, Garfield & Arthur—Hancock & English, obverse with advertisement for Morse's Yellow Dock Blood Purifier, 3 x 5½″	**15.00**
1884, Hood's Sarsaparilla Presidential Campaign Card, brown and white portrait of Blaine	**20.00**

POMONA GLASS

History: Pomona glass, produced only by the New England Glass Works and named for the Roman goddess of fruit and trees, was patented in 1885 by Joseph Locke. It is a delicate lead, blown art glass which has a pale, soft beige ground and a top one inch band of honey amber.

There are two distinct types of backgrounds. First ground, made only from late 1884 to June 1886, was produced by fine cuttings through a wax coating followed by an acid bath. Second ground was made by rolling the piece in acid resisting particles and acid etching. Second ground was made in Cambridge until 1888 and until the early 1900s in Toledo where Libbey moved the firm after pur-

chasing New England Glass works. Both methods produced a soft frosted appearance, with fine curlicue lines more visible on first ground pieces. Designs are used on some pieces, which were etched and then stained in color. The most familiar design is blue cornflowers.

Do not confuse Pomona with "Midwestern Pomona," a pressed glass with a frosted body and amber band.

Bowl, 5½″ d, 3″ h, first grind, flint, ruffled amber ribbon, crimped foot, ground pontil, $115.00.

Bowls	
4½″ d, 2nd ground, crimped rim	**50.00**
8″ d, 3½″ h, 2nd ground, cornflower, crimped rim	**275.00**
Celeries	
1st ground, cornflower	**300.00**
2nd ground, berries, gold leaves dec	**75.00**
Cruet, 2nd ground, clear handle, stopper, crimped ftd, thumbprint	**85.00**
Finger Bowl, 1st ground, frosted stripes	**150.00**
Nappy, 1st ground, handle	**225.00**
Pickle Castor, 1st ground, cornflower dec, SP frame.	**425.00**
Pitcher, 2nd ground, 8″ h, trefoil handle, Diamond Optic, gold stain top . .	**350.00**
Punch Cups	
1st ground, Acanthus leaf, bubble in bottom	**100.00**
1st ground, 2½″ h, gold stain, blue cornflower, 6 rows of hobnails . . .	**175.00**
Rose Bowl, 2nd ground, 4¼″ d, 2½″ h, crimped top	**150.00**
Toothpick, 1st ground, 2¼″ h	**175.00**
Tumbler, 2nd ground, cornflower	**85.00**
Vase, 5″, 2nd ground, ruffled top, scalloped base	**185.00**
Water Set, 1st ground, gold stain, pitcher 6¾″ h, tankard shape, 6 tumblers.	**750.00**

PORTRAIT WARE

History: Plates, vases, and other articles with portraits on them were popular in the second half of the 19th century. Although male subjects, such as Napoleon or Louis XVI, were used, the ware usually depicted a beautiful woman, often unidentified.

A large number of English and Continental china manufactures made portrait ware. Because most ware was hand painted, an artist's signature often is found.

Additional Listings: KPM and Royal Vienna.

Cup, child's, 2½″ h, brown dog with blue bonnet, small boy, picnic hamper, bowl, umbrella, "On Tour" printed on top, mkd Germany. **40.00**

Cup and Saucer, 5″ cup, 7″ saucer, int. of cup with 3 small round portraits of men and women in 18th C attire, large center portrait of Louis XVI, saucer with 3 different portraits, dark rose, teal blue, gold, mkd N with Crown, artist sgd **90.00**

Dresser Tray, 12″ l, white ground, gold design, 2 portrait medallions, 4 floral medallions, mkd Nippon. **225.00**

Jewel Box, 10½″ d, 5″ h, elaborate blown-out florals, ribbons on cover, base, beige bround, gold highlights, center portrait of seated woman in 18th C attire, mkd Mt. Washington . . **950.00**

Plates
8¼″ d, two maidens and cupid in wooden glen, cobalt border, gilt dec, gold rim, Germany **45.00**

8½″, bare shouldered woman, long brown hair, maroon and white drape, maroon and gold border, mkd Royal Vienna, beehive. **80.00**

8½″, lady with lilacs in background, gold scalloped edge, gold tracery, hp, Austria. **65.00**

8½″, Victorian lady, gold, beading, Limoges **125.00**

9½″, bust of woman, large brim hat with plumes, burgundy, red border, lacy gold, white jewels, mkd Schwarzburg **60.00**

9½″, Louis XIV, blue and cream ground, gold tracery, Serves 1846 mark. **295.00**

10″, pr, blonde woman on one, bru nette on other, artist sgd Constance, mkd Austria **110.00**

10¾″, Victorian lady in rose dress, gold trim, irregular edge with heavy gold flowers, trim, white and green shaded ground, mkd Royal Crown Bavaria. **110.00**

11¾″, Marie Theresa, Marie Antoinette, Louis XV, 5 portraits, gold trim, blue ground, pierced for hanging. **135.00**

12″, Geronimo, Indian in full head dress, milk glass, hp. **65.00**

Tiles
Lady's head, mounted in leather case **55.00**
Lady wearing large hat, round **40.00**

Tray, 11″ l, 7½″ w, portraits of George and Martha Washington, Mt. Vernon, mkd Germany **40.00**

Vases
6″ h, tapestry, three ladies, mkd Germany. **165.00**

7½″, 2 handles, blue ground, MOP, gold, young woman, mkd E S Germany. **85.00**

10″, gold scroll handles, blonde lady with daisies in hair, angel, colorful flowers **250.00**

17″, cov, green glass, gilt, hp overlay portrait of woman, portrait 5½″ h, 4″ w **350.00**

POSTERS

History: The poster was an extremely effective and critical means of mass communication, especially in the period before 1920. Enormous quantities were produced, helped in part by the progaganda role played by posters in World War I.

Print runs of two million were not unknown. Posters were not meant to be saved. Once they served their purpose, they tended to be destroyed. The paradox of high production and low survival is one of the fascinating aspects of poster history.

The posters of the late 19th century and early 20th century represent the pinnacle of American lithography printing. The advertising posters of

8½″, **Melle La Vallreie, blue mark "L.S. & S./Carlsbad/Austria,"** $35.00.

firms such as Strobridge or Courier are true classis. Philadelphia was one center for the poster industry.

Europe pioneered in posters with high artistic and aesthetic content. Many major artists of the 20th century designed posters. Poster art still plays a key role throughout Europe today.

References: John Barnicoat, *A Concise History of Posters*, Harry Abrams, Inc., 1976; George Theofiles, *American Posters of World War I: A Price and Collector's Guide*, Dafram House Publishers, Inc.

Additional Listings: See *Warman's Americana & Collectibles* for more examples.

Advisor: George Theofiles.

ADVERTISING

"Blue Anchor Inn", 13 x 19", Coles Phillips, c1905, "fade-away" girl steps into the water from a sailboat	145.00
"Century Cookbook," 12 x 27", E. Potthast, Century Publishing, 1897, Victorian woman samples steaming pot on ornate iron stove	200.00
"Ferry's Seeds," 22 x 28", 1916, flowers in vase in front of full moon in window.	175.00
"Galakton Infant Food," 13 x 21", c1897, nanny feeds baby formula	575.00
"Golden West Compound, Leaves/Herbs/Bark Tonic, World's Mildest Laxative," c1915, detailed image of looming Indian chief	300.00
"Hartman Luggage," 26 x 33", c1925, sporty couple in pith helmets and white clothes stand in Moroccan setting with gleaming Hartman luggage.	175.00
"Marchand's Golden Hair Wash," 11 x 21", George Evans, 1934, blonde woman in yellow swimsuit, male admirer, jet black ground	95.00
"No Dope In Vinco Herb Tablets," 10 x 18", c1920, placard, black and white	60.00
Strawbridge and Clothier, "Christmas Pleasure Is Assured . . . ," 21 x 40", c1905, young woman hangs wreath in window.	100.00
"Victor Cycles," 17 x 22", Will Bradley, 1899, two sided window type	425.00

CIRCUS, SHOWS AND ACTS

"Brown's Shows," 20 x 30", Donaldson, c1895, men dressed in Harlequinn-like attire support all female balancing act atop long poles	150.00
"Clyde Beatty The Jungle King," 28 x 40", Hagenbeck-Wallace, c1935, Beatty in center with whip and chair, panthers, lions, and tigers in huge cage	125.00
"Ringling Bros. Circus. Kings Of The Circus World," 19 x 29", Strobridge,	
1908, litho vignettes of the five Ringling Bros.	225.00
"Tiger Bill's Wild West," 28 x 40", c1910, Riverside, CA, panorama of Indian attack on buckskinned settlers	225.00

Circus poster, 17 x 24", Quebec, Canada, c1970,

MOVIE

European

"Camille," 1930s, 14 x 22", Belgian, Robert Taylor embracing a swooning, bare shoulder Greta Garbo . . .	125.00
"Charlot," Everest Films, c1916, 48 x 62", Charlie Chaplin	1,250.00
"La Belle Menuniere, 1937, 47 x 62", J. Van Caulaert, showing Jacqueline Pagnol looking seductively at viewer, clear blue eyes filled with passion and understanding	225.00
"Lolita," 1962, 23 x 32", France, Sue Lyon image, licking a lollipop, wearing huge heart shaped sunglasses	50.00

Insert Posters, 14 x 36", American

"Last Outpost, The," 1951, Ronald Reagan in Civil War uniform, embracing Rhonda Fleming, wielding sabre	125.00
"O'Malley Of The Mounted," Fox,	

1937, George O'Brien protects female star, brilliant red Mountie outfit, pistol ready **75.00**

One Sheets, 27 x 41", American

"Affairs of Annabel, The," c1937, Lucille Ball, Jack Oakie **85.00**

"Californian, The," 1937, R. Cortez with whip. **80.00**

"Laura," Tooker litho, Tierney looming over trenchcoated Dana Andrews **325.00**

"Merry Go Round of 1938," Bert Lahr, other character actors in great caricatures around semi-nude female chef, dancing girls **75.00**

"Mummy's Ghost, The," Universal, 1944, Lon Chaney, Jr., and John Carradine **125.00**

"Paradise For Three," MGM, 1934, Tooker litho, Robert Young, Mary Astor, Edna Mae Oliver, and Reginald Owen in circle **85.00**

"Professor Creeps, Mantan Moreland," Dixie Films, c1945, Moreland in funny pose with pretty girl on his lap **95.00/**

"Rings On Her Fingers," 1942, Tooker litho, Gene Tierney and Henry Fonda. **150.00**

"Should Husbands Work?", Republic, c1938, James Gleason. **80.00**

"Thief of Bagdad, The," 1940, classic Korda film, looming man with hairlock separates mountains **325.00**

"Whispering Smith Speaks," Fox, 1935, Tooker litho, George O'Brien as detective in multicolored clouds with rail engineer pointing something out as locomotive whizzes past **75.00**

THEATRICAL, OPERA, MUSIC HALL, BRITISH, 1930s

"Aladdin," 20 x 30", lovely woman rubs urn while surrounded by brilliantly colored looming genie **65.00**

"Babes In The Wood," 20 x 30", lovely woman discovers the babes in classic scene, golden light glowing through the background. **50.00**

"Cinderella," 20 x 30", "pin-up" starry eyed blonde woman swoons into arms of prince. **50.00**

"Dick Wittington," 20 x 30", tantilizing woman with huge, smiling cat. **65.00**

"Robinson Crusoe," 20 x 30", personified as woman with parrot on shoulder, caricatured Friday frying eggs. **75.00**

TRAVEL, TRANSPORTATION AND RELATED ITEMS

Automobiles

"Exposition Citroen," 32 x 45", c1925,

Citroen design logo diagonally across center, panorama of massive C type sedans, cabriolets, etc. across top. **330.00**

"Peter's Union Pneumatic Tires," 28 x 36", Ludwig Hohlwein, c1915, sailor walking toward distant cabriolet and waving people, carrying tube in one hand, tire in other, bottom reads "The Lifesaver" **675.00**

"Peugeot," 24 x 35", Rene Vincent, c1923, black and white, showing lovely woman receiving packages from delivery boy before entering hugh limo **450.00**

Aviation

"Aviation Meet/PAU France, 1911," 32 x 46", blue eagle flies in front of silhouettes of airships and planes **450.00**

"Flying Irishman, The," 27 x 41", film poster, 1939, starring Douglas, "Wrong Way" Corrigan. **135.00**

"Gordon Bennett Cup, 1912," 28 x 38", Diem, Stuttgart, "Germania" balloon hoisted by crewmen in foreground while "Amerika" balloon is admired by well dressed spectators. **1,250.00**

"Revolving Airship Scene, The," musical comedy, c1896, 28 x 40", night scene of people rolling around inside ornate Victorian "Air Line Sleeping Car" as it comes loose from looming motorized airship **225.00**

Bicycling,

"Rocket Cycles," 28 x 51", c1900, Pichet, French Army officer whizzes about on cycle, minor restoration to borders **200.00**

"Velodrome Madeline," 37 x 50", A. Dagnaux, c1896, woman in orange dress shoots through Paris streets, disrupting wagons, and carrying text banner in her upraised hand **175.00**

Steamship

Atlantic Transport Line, London-New York, 26 x 40", c1925, *MINNE-TONKA* coming to pier with cheering crowd **375.00**

Hamburg America Line, 26 x 40", Anton, c1935, sleek liner looms in sea over map of west coast of South America **375.00**

Red Star Lines, 27 x 35", C. Saltzmann, 1893, Anvers to New York and Philadelphia, steamer riding silver waves towards Statue of Liberty and Brooklyn Bridge. **450.00**

"*S.S.FRANCE*, A New Concept In Luxury For All," 34 x 45", Bob Peak litho, night image for 1962 launching. **225.00**

WORLD WAR I—AMERICAN

"All Together. Enlist In the Navy," 29 x 40", Reuterdahl, sailors of all nations beckon. **165.00**

"Columbia Calls," 28 x 40", Halstead, Columbia beckons on globe with banner, Army. **85.00**

"Gee! If I Were A Man, I'd Join The Navy," Christy, 1918, young girl in sailor uniform, chamois background, "Naval Reserve or Coast Guard" on bottom. **500.00**

"Here He Is Sir! U.S. Navy," 29 x 40", Charles Dana Gibson litho, mother shakes hand with Uncle Sam, Horatio Alger-like son waiting beside her . . .   **285.00**

"Marines. First To Fight For Democracy," 30 x 40", L. A. Shaefer image of Marine gun crew aboard ship firing away at hugh Zeppelin in sky. **165.00**

"Over There," 38 x 56", Albert Sterner, stone litho, sailor holding banner, looking to stormy sea aside pointing Columbia **300.00**

"To-Day. Buy That Liberty Bond," 16 x 23", orange sun peeks over blue horizon. **35.00**

WORLD WAR I—EUROPEAN

France

"Africa and Colonial Troops Day," 34 x 43", Charles Fourqueray, 1917, stone litho, shows determined Colonial soldiers being led by ghostly Moroccan on rearing white horse .   **425.00**

"Brave Little Hen/She Gives Much and Asks Little," 15 x 22", G. Duanne, Paris schoolgirl conservation poster, deep blue/black hen sitting on pile of eggs, blue border . .   **275.00**

"By The Light of Flares, The Soldier Dreams of Home and Victory," 32 x 46", Jean Droit, grizzled French soldier looking out from trench, eerie orange light **125.00**

"Campagne Algerienne/Souscrive," 31 x 36", Jonas, c1915, Algerian soldier in full field pack leaving his family in village square. **125.00**

"Soldier's Day," 32 x 46", Poulbot litho of two children holding trays needing funds for their father in the army. **150.00**

Germany

"Exhibition of Work By German Internees," 17 x 24", Ludwig Holhwein, 1918, seated POW with saw, before white Helvetian cross. **550.00**

"Fund For German Soldier's Home," 24 x 36", Frick, c1920, nurse gives soup to vet, another vet smoking pipe **110.00**

"Ludendorff Fund For War Injured," 19 x 26", Hanns Anker, c1917, mythological nude warrior rests against spear to feed eagle, "Help Your Friends" at bottom. **150.00**

"The 9th Arrow," 37 x 56", F. Erier, 1917, nude male archer pulling bow to fire while kneeling near a rock, earthy colored background, for 9th War Loan **975.00**

"War Exhibition of Captured Relics, Posen, 1917," 33 x 48", H. Wobbeking, design of death's head Hussar riding Hohlwein-like horse **475.00**

WORLD WAR II—AMERICAN

"Buy War Bonds," 29 x 40", N. C. Wyeth, classic allegory of Uncle Sam, enveloped in flag, leading soldiers and planes into battle and billowing black clouds **150.00**

"Give Him Enough And On Time," 27 x 41", Norman Rockwell, Army Ordinance, 1942, machine gunner in tattered uniform, firing Browning watercooled gun, illuminated by light of battle. **550.00**

"Let's Go, U. S. Marines," 28 x 40", 12/30/41, one of 5,000, powerful image of Marine marching across image afront orange background **200.00**

"Marines Have Landed, The," James Montgomery Flagg, 1940, one of 7,500, Marine holds rifle high, wades ashore **165.00**

"Quick Action/United States Coast Guard, Remember Pearl Harbor," Coast Guard poster, c1943, Japanese Zeros fly over PT boat as it fires wildly, silk screen **165.00**

"Wanted For Murder, Her Careless Talk Cost Lives," 20 x 30", Victor Keppler photo in "wanted" poster design . . .   **50.00**

WORLD WAR II—NAZI

"Gymnastic Competition. Dresden, 1937," 24 x 34", Max Wislicenaus, litho of joisting knight charging on ornately blanketed steed. **300.00**

"New Architecture/Germany," 26 x 41", Klein, image of looming silver eagle and swastika over panorama of Speer's architecture **450.00**

"To The Olympics Time And Again With AGFA Film," 31 x 53", charcoal like blacks of bird's eye view of 1936 stadium, runners **250.00**

"Volunteers Come Forward! Youth Needed For Land Service In The Hitler Youth," 24 x 33", Mjolnir, recruiting, c1935, youth cries to viewer in front of farmer baling wheat.......... **375.00**

"Young Lady, Come To the German Nurse Corps," 33 x 45", Havemann, large portrait of smiling Aryan nurse in color against blue background **150.00**

POT LIDS

History: Pot lids are the lids from pots or small containers which originally held ointments, pomades or soap. Although a complete set of pot and lid is desirable to some collectors, lids are the most collectible. The lids frequently were decorated with multicolored underglaze transfers of rural and domestic scenes, portraits, florals, and landmarks.

The majority of the containers with lids were made between 1845–1920 by F. & R. Pratt, Fenton, Staffordshire, England. In 1920, F. & R. Pratt merged with Cauldon LTD. Several lids were reissued by the firm using the original copper engraving plates. They were used for decoration and never served as actual lids. Reissues by Kirkhams Pottery, England, generally have two holes for hanging and often are marked as reissues. Cauldon, Coalport, and Wedgwood were other firms making reissues.

Reference: A. Ball, *The Price Guide to Pot-Lids And Other Underglaze Multicolor Prints On Ware*, Antique Collectors Club, 1980.

Note: Sizes are given for actual pot lids; size of any framing not included.

Albert Memorial with carriage, framed, 4" **100.00**

**Pratt, Whimbleton, July 2nd, 1880, 4",
$185.00.**

Battle Of The Nile, Pratt, ebonized oak frame, 4" **250.00**

Belle Vue Pegwell Bay, Pratt, ebonized frame, 5¼"................... **250.00**

Bellevue Tavern, Pratt, 4¾"......... **140.00**

Chapel Royal Savoy **100.00**

Church Of The Holy Trinity, Stratford on Avon, 4¾"................ **450.00**

Dangerous Skating, Jesse Austin drawing, Pratt, 2⅞"................. **325.00**

Dr. Johnson, 4⅛"................ **375.00**

Enthusiast, The, from a drawing by Jesse Austin, 4⅛"............. **470.00**

False Move, A, T. J. & J. Mayer **300.00**

Farriers, The, several inner rim chips, 4¾"....................... **300.00**

Great Exhibition of 1851, The, Opening Ceremony, T. J. & J. Mayer **375.00**

Holborn Viaduct, framed, 4" **150.00**

Lady with Guitar................. **125.00**

Landing The Catch, framed, 4⅛" **100.00**

Lobster Sauce, Pratt.............. **265.00**

Pair, A, 4" **575.00**

Peace, orig drawing by Jesse Austin, sgd, 4".................... **600.00**

Pegwell Bay Established 1760, Pratt, walnut frame, 3⅝".............. **250.00**

Pegwell Bay, flat, 3½".............. **425.00**

Philadelphia Exhibition 1876, orig drawing by Jesse Austin, framed, 4¼"... **400.00**

Residence of Anne Hathaway, Shakespeare's Wife, Shottery Nr Stratford on Avon, framed, 4" **100.00**

Room In Which Shakespeare Was Born, 1594 Stratford on Avon, framed, 3⅞"................. **325.00**

Royal Harbour Ramsgate, mahogany frame, 4" **350.00**

Sanderingham, The Seat of H.R.H. The Prince of Wales, framed, 4⅛" .. **300.00**

Seven Ages of Man, The, orig drawing by Jesse Austin, framed, 4⅛"...... **225.00**

Shakespeare's House Henley St Stratford on Avon, orig drawing by Jesse Austin, pearl dot border, 4³⁄₁₆" **600.00**

Shrimpers At Pegwell Bay, Pratt, ebonized frame, 3⅞".............. **320.00**

Strasburg, 4⅝".................. **475.00**

Strathfieldsaye The Seat of The Duke of Wellington, 4¾" **425.00**

Tam O'Shanter and Souter Johnny, framed, 4" **275.00**

Thames Embankment, framed, 3¾"... **300.00**

Times, The, framed, 3¾"........... **300.00**

Trafalgar Square, orig drawing by Jesse Austin, framed, 4¼"........ **500.00**

Transplanting Rice, framed, 4⅛" **375.00**

Walmer Castle Kent, with sentry, marked on back "Tatnell & Son Manufacturers Pegwell Bay Nr Ramsgate, framed, 4½"......... **200.00**

War, 17th C battle scene, Jesse Austin, Fenton, oblong, 5½" **200.00**

PRATT

PRATT WARE

PRATT
FENTON

History: The earliest Pratt earthenware was made in the late 18th century by William Pratt, Lane Delph, Staffordshire, England. In 1810–1818, Felix and Robert Pratt, William's sons, established their own firm, F. & R. Pratt, in Fenton in the Staffordshire district. Potters in Yorkshire, Liverpool, Sunderland, Tyneside, and Scotland copied the ware.

The wares consisted of relief molded jugs, commercial pots and tablewares with transfer decoration, commemorative pieces, and figure and animal groups.

Much of the early ware is unmarked. The mid-19th century wares bear several different marks in conjunction with the name Pratt, including "& Co."

Reference: John and Griselda Lewis, *Pratt Ware 1780–1840,* Antique Collectors' Club, 1984.

Additional Listing: Pot Lids

Plaque, 13″, "Christ in the Wheat Field," sgd J. Austin, multicolored, out turned rim, c1851, $100.00.

Box, cov, animal dec, transfer print . . .	70.00
Candlestick, 4⅞″, emb, classical dec . .	125.00
Charger, 13″, floral dec, blue, ochre, and yellow, green leaves, brown stems, blue feather border, c1790.	475.00
Compote, 12½″ oval, handled, classical dec	300.00
Cottage, 3½″ h, small white bricks, doors and window outlined in blue, panes and roof in yellow, c1820.	275.00

Creamer, 5″, emb, enameled peacocks in round reserve	150.00
Cup and Saucer, child's Prince of Wales and Princess Royal riding in open carriage drawn by goat, Windsor Castle in background, blue-green leaf border, yellow lustre rim, c1850	150.00
Dessert Set, 18 pcs, Mountain Stream, c1860.	400.00
Figurines	
Man with basket of flowers, long coat, floral base, 5⅜″.	150.00
Woman with fan, long dress, green base, 5¼″.	175.00
Flasks	
5½″, round, portrait of King George and family, reverse with portrait of Admiral Jarvis, c1790	475.00
6½″, molded busts of George Augustus Eliott, c1790.	260.00
Goblet, 5⅜″ h, 3½″ d, purple, lake scene with horses, reverse with donkey and 3 people resting by ruins, gold trim . .	150.00
Inkwell, classical dec, 1830	150.00
Jars	
4″, The Hunt, blue, registry date mark, 1851	40.00
4¼″, polychrome transfer lid scene, fish seller	65.00
Jugs	
5¾″, molded heart shape panels with children, imp "Sportive Innocence" and "Mischivious Sport," green, ochre, and blue, scroll handle, c1789	225.00
6½″, hunting scene, blue, gold dec, mask handle, dated 1856	190.00
7″, waterfall, malachite ground	125.00
Meat Paste Jar, 3¼″, Pegwell Bay, Kent, Clarke #69	35.00
Mug, 4⅞″, figural, satyr face, ochre, brown, blue, and green, int. frog, pedestal base	135.00
Mush Cup, pastoral scenes	55.00
Mustard Jar, Boar Hunt, blue transfer. .	35.00
Pitchers	
4¾″, floral dec, green, brown, and gold, green leaf border	155.00
5½″, classical figures, Juno, Minerva and Patroclus, horses, gold trim . .	100.00
6″, hunting scene, green, yellow, and blue, leaf border	125.00
Plaque, 8 x 9″, oval, emb, blacksmith shoeing horse, lady, gentleman, and groom	250.00
Plates	
3½″, woman dancing, 3 colors	75.00
3½″, woman in fancy hat, ochre, brown and blue	80.00
8½″, Philadelphia Exposition 1876 . .	125.00
9″, Long Live The Queen.	45.00
9″, Haddon Hall, Chatsworth, brown and green, classic figure border . .	125.00

Platter, 4⅛″, oval, miniature, emb fish . **140.00**
Pomade Jar, 4″, terra cotta, boar hunt
scene, blue **25.00**
Serving Dish, 9½″, ftd, landscape scene,
19th C **120.00**
Snuff Box, Constantinople **70.00**
Tea Caddies
4¾″, flask shape, each side molded
with 2 figures from contemporary
theater, finished in colored glazes,
late 18th C **275.00**
4¾″, figural, man and servant on one
side, lady and maid on reverse,
c1780 . . . . **325.00**
5″, emb, comical figures of 2 men and
woman, 18th C attire **350.00**
Teapot, 5″, floral dec, late 18th C **240.00**
Vase, 4½″, urn shape, handled, classical
figures, orange with gold **100.00**

PRINTS

History: Prints serve many purposes. They can
be a reproduction of an artist's paintings, drawings,
or designs. Prints themselves often are an original
art form. Finally, prints can be developed for mass
appeal as opposed to aesthetic statement. Much
of the production of Currier & Ives fits this latter
category. Currier & Ives concentrated on genre,
urban, patriotic, and nostalgia scenes.

Prints are beginning to attract a wide following.
This is partially because prices have not matched
the rapid rise in oil and other paintings.

Reproductions are a problem, especially of The
Currier & Ives prints. Check the dimensions before
buying any print.

References: Frederic A. Conningham and Colin
Simkin, *Currier & Ives Prints*, Crown Publishers, Inc.,
1970, revised edition; Michael Ivankovich, *A Price
Guide to Wallace Nutting Pictures*, Cheetah Prints,
1984; Denis C. Jackson, *The Price & Identification
Guide to J. C. Leyendecker & F. X. Leyendecker*,
privately printed, 1983; Carl F. Luckey, *Collector
Prints Old and New*, Books Americana, 1982; Ruth
M. Pollard, *The Official Price Guide to Collector
Prints*, House of Collectibles, 1979; Roger B. Stein,
American Naval Prints; International Exhibitions
Foundation, 1976; Marian S. Sweeney, *Maxfield
Parrish Prints*, privately printed, 1974; Willis B.
White, Jr., *Wallace Nutting Pictures*, privately
printed, 1980.

Collectors' Clubs: American Historical Print Collectors Society, Inc., 555 Fifth Avenue, Suite 504,
New York, NY 10017. *Imprint* (quarterly); Prang-
Mark Society, Century House, Old Irelandville, Watkins Glen, NY 14891. *Prang-Mark Society Newsletter* (annual).

Audubon, J. J.
American Flamingo, 1838, Havell
engr, 38 x 25¾″, Plate 441 . . . . . . **9,500.00**
Artic Tern, 1835, Havell engr, 19⅝ x
12⅜, Plate 250 . . . . **2,500.00**
Canada Lynx, J. T. Bowen, 1843,
21¼ x 27⅛″, Plate 61 . . . . **1,750.00**
Crested Grebe, 1836, Havell engr,
20⅞ x 30⅝″, Plate 262 . . . . **650.00**
Red Duck, 1836, Havell engr, 21 x
29⅞″, Plate 332 . . . . **1,200.00**
Bodmer, Carl, The Interior Of The Hut
Of A Mandan Chief, hand colored
etching and aquatint, by Desmadryl,
17⅞ x 24⅝, Plate 19 . . . . **3,875.00**
Currier and Ives
Ambuscade, The, hand colored litho-
graph, 11⅜ x 15½″ **850.00**
American Choice Fruits, 1869, 17 x
24″ **950.00**
American Railroad Scene. Snow
Bound, 1871, 8½ x 12⅝″ **1,600.00**
Cares Of A Family, The, A. F. Tait,
1856, 18¾ x 23⅞″ **1,500.00**
Chance For Both Barrels, A, 1857,
18⅞ x 27″ **3,500.00**
Check, A, "Keep Your Distance," A.
F. Tait, 1853, 14¼ x 20⅝″ **800.00**
Express Train, The, 1870, 8 x 12″ . . **1,100.00**
Fast Trotters on Harlem Lane, NY, J.
Cameron, DE, 1870, 18½ x 28½″ **3,000.00**
Flower Vase, The, hand colored lith-
ograph, 21 x 16½″ **500.00**
Last War Whoop, The, L. Maurer after
A. F. Tait, 1856, 18½ x 25¾″ **4,500.00**
Mill Stream, The, F. F. Palmer, DE,
1864, small **3,000.00**
Niagara Falls, hand colored litho-
graph, 14¾ x 19¾″ **850.00**
Night By The Campfire, 1861, 10½ x
15″ **600.00**
Prairie Hunter, The, "One Rubbed
Out," A. F. Tait, 1852, 14¼ x 21″ **1,500.00**
Shooting on the Beach, hand colored
lithograph, 8½ x 12½″ **750.00**
"Trotting Cracks" On The Snow, L.
Maurer, 1858, 16¾ x 28″ **3,500.00**
Wayside Inn, The, F. F. Palmer, DE,
1864, 16 x 23⅜″ **3,000.00**
Winter Morning, F. F. Palmer, DE,
1861, 11½ x 15½″ **2,500.00**
Doolittle, Amos, Display of the United
States of America, hand colored stip-
pled and line engraving, 1794, 20⅞ x
17¼″ **6,500.00**
Endicott & Co., Sperm Whaling, No. 2–
The Capture, lithograph, 1862, 16⅜ x
25¾″ **2,750.00**
Endicott, William & Co., Atlantic's Re-
turn, hand colored lithograph, 7¾ x
12″ **200.00**
Foreman, E. W. & E. Brown, Jr., New
York and Environs from Williams-

burgh, hand colored lithograph, printed by Sarony & Major, 1848, 19⅞ x 32½" **800.00**

Helleu, Paul Cesar, La Femme Au Chapeau, drypoint, c1900, 22⅜ x 13⅞" . **2,500.00**

Henderson, P (after), The American Cowslip, aquatint, stipple and engraving in colors, J. Whatman, 1799, 19⅝ x 14¾" **750.00**

Hill, John W., New York With The City of Brooklyn In The Distance, hand colored etching and aquatint, 1855, 27⅞ x 34⅛" **1,000.00**

Icart, Louis, etching and drypoint in colors, pencil sgd
  Attic Room, The, 1940, 17 x 40" ... **1,000.00**
  Coup De Vent–Gust of Wind, copyright 1925 by les Graveurs Modernes, Paris, #151, framed, 22 x 18½" .. **600.00**
  Delilah, copyright 1929 by L. Icart, Paris, #172, framed, 21½ x 14" .. **625.00**
  Don Juan, copyright 1928 by L. Icart, Paris, edited by Editions d'Art Devambez, Paris, #E325, framed, 21 x 14" **700.00**
  Kittens, 1925, 22 x 17", oval **2,225.00**
  Mardi Gras, 19 x 19" **750.00**
  Pink Slippers, The, 25 x 12" **1,750.00**
  Sleeping Beauty, edited 1927 by les Artistes Modernes, Paris, framed, 14¾ x 18½" **1,225.00**
  White Lilies, 20 x 24" **1,500.00**

Kent, Rockwell, The Oarsman, wood engraving, 1931, sgd in pencil, edition of 150, 5½ x 7" **450.00**

Lehman & Duval, A View of The Butte Des Morts Treaty Ground in 1827, chromolithograph, James Otto Lewis, 7⅛ x 12" **150.00**

Mucha, Alphonse, La Poesie, full color lithograph, 1898, 22⅜ x 14" **3,000.00**

Newell, J. Perry, The Battle of Lake Erie, Commodore O. H. Perry's Victory,

Louis Icart, Love's Blossom, unframed, $1,750.00.

Gained September 10th 1813, hand colored lithograph, printed by J. H. Bufford's Sons, Boston, 1878, 13¾ x 28⅜" **950.00**

Nutting, Wallace
  Almost Ready, 13 x 16" **75.00**
  Belle of the Olden Days, A, 14 x 17" **50.00**
  Canal in Sunshine, A, Italy, 13 x 17" **75.00**
  Chair for John, A, 11 x 14" **50.00**
  Franconia Brook, A, 7 x 11" **40.00**
  Good Night, 18 x 22" **135.00**
  Morning Errand, A, California, 13 x 17" **100.00**
  Path of Roses, A, 7 x 9" **25.00**
  Sea Captain's Daughter, 11 x 17" ... **150.00**
  Thanksgiving Landscape, A, 7 x 9".. **25.00**
  Vermont Spring, 10 x 12" **30.00**
  Wayside Inn, The, 13 x 17" **70.00**

Parrish, Maxfield
  Magazine Covers
    1895, *Harper's Bazaar* **50.00**
    1899, Dec., *Life* **45.00**
    1904, Dec. 3, *Collier's* **35.00**
    1907, Dec. 14, *Harper's Weekly* .. **30.00**
    1914, June, *Ladies Home Journal* **25.00**
    1917, Jan., *Metropolitan Magazine* **50.00**
  Prints
    Book Lover, 1910, 8 x 10" **75.00**
    Dream Garden, 1915, 14 x 24½" .. **275.00**
    Forest Princess, 1916, 11 x 14" .. **100.00**
    Humpty Dumpty, 1973, 40 x 32".. **15.00**
    Pied Piper, 1914, 7 x 21" ... **350.00**
    Royal Gorge, Colorado, The, 1925, 16½ x 20" **230.00**
    Spirit of Transportation, The, 1923, 16 x 20". **250.00**
    Thanksgiving, 1909, 9 x 11" **75.00**

Prang, Louis
  Partridge, Selmar Hess, publisher, 4¾ x 7¾" **20.00**
  Trillium, 1886, 7½ x 10½" **25.00**

Rockwell, Norman, see ROCKWELL, NORMAN in this book and "Rockwell, Norman" in *Warman's Americana & Collectibles*

Russell, Benjamin, Sperm Whaling With its Varieties, lithograph, J. H. Bufford, 1870, 16⅝ x 32¾" **600.00**

Vanderlyn, John, A View of the Western Branch of the Falls of Niagara, hand colored aquatint, F. C. Lewis, 1804, 24⅛ x 33¼" **2,500.00**

Wall, William Guy, View Near Sandy Hill, hand colored aquatint, 1822, 18 x 24" **1,000.00**

West, Benjamin, Battle of New Orleans and Death of Major General Packenham On The 8th of January, 1815, hand colored, Joseph Yeager, engr, 16 x 20⅞" **750.00**

Whitefield, Edwin, View of Brooklyn, L.I. From U. S. Hotel, NY, lithograph, 1846, 15¼ x 36¼" **625.00**

PRINTS-JAPANESE

History: Buying Japanese woodblock prints requires attention to detail and skilled knowledge of the subject. The quality of the impression (good, moderate, or weak), the color, and condition are critical. Various states and strikes of the same print cause the price to fluctuate. Knowing the proper publisher and censor's seals is helpful in identifying an original print.

Most prints were recopied and issued in popular versions. These represent the vast majority of the prints found in the marketplace. These popular versions should be viewed solely as decorative since they have little value.

A novice buyer should seek expert advice before buying. Talk with a specialized dealer, museum curator, or auction division head.

The listings below concentrate on details to show the depth of data needed for adequate pricing. Condition and impression are good, unless indicated otherwise.

O = Oban, 10 x 15″
Ot = Oban tat-e, large in width
Oy = Oban yoko-e, large in length
C = Chuban,
7 x 10″
H = Hosoban,
5½ x 13″
T = Triptyck

Eisen, evening snow on Skinobu Hill, view of the island in Lake Shinobu on which stands Benton Temple, from Edo Hakkei series, published by Yamamoto-Heikichi, c1846, censor's seal, sgd Keisai Eisen ga, Oy 275.00

Eishi
  Ladies and children in landscape, sgd Eishi ga, Ot 800.00
  Three bijin under pines and wisteria, sgd Eishi ga, repaired, Ot 600.00
Harunobu, man adjusting a woman's sandal, sgd Harunobu ga, C 600.00
Hasui
  Bridge and boat in the moonlight, from Tabimiyage Dai-ni-shu series, sgd Hasui with diamond seal Kawase, Watanabe publisher's seal, dtd August Taisho 10 (1921), Ot 1,400
  Man walking with pack horse, down mountain road at sunset, sgd Hasui, red seal, dtd Taisho 7 (1918), Nagaban tate-e 2,500.00
  Snowfall at Zojoji Temple, sgd Hasui, circular red seal, dtd Taisho 14 (1925), Ot 900.00
Hiroshige
  Cooling at Ryugoku and fireworks, 3 beauties on pleasure boat Kawaichimaru, published by Fujikei, 1848–49, sgd Hiroshige ga, Ot 650.00
  Koto Shokei series (Fine View of Edo), published by Kawasho, early 1840s, Oy
    Outside Hibiya 450.00

    View of Shinsenza at Shiba 775.00
    Within Yamashita Gate......... 300.00
    Yoroi Ferry 450.00
Hiroshige II
  Figure in a temple complex in the snow from Toto Sanjurokusho series, sgd Hiroshige ga, Ot 400.00
  Ice fishing, Shinano Province from Shokoko meisho hyakkei series, sgd Hiroshige ga, Ot 675.00
Hokusai
  Bunya no Asayasu, the poem speaking of dew sparkling on the grass like brilliant jewels, black manji, Oy 4,000.00
  Cranes at foot of Fuji, sgd Zen Hokusai Iitsu hitsu, Oy. 2,000.00
  Inume Pass in Kai Province, 3 pack horses following 2 figures, blue outline, Oy 3,000.00
Kunisada
  Bijin in gray checked kimono, sgd Kunisada, Ot 475.00
  Two ladies helping child to climb drum bridge at Kameido shrine, sgd Gototei Kunisada ga, Oy 600.00
Kuniyoshi
  Buyu Mitate series (Selected Warriors for the Twelve signs of the Zodiac), sgd Ichiyusai Kuniyoshi ga, Toshidama seal, publisher's mark Minatoya Kohii
    Emperor Yuryaku catching wild boar in stand of bamboo.......... 700.00
    Goat with General Kan U drinking wine under full moon. 700.00
    Monkey................... 325.00

Kunisada, Utgawa, 1786–1868, 13½ x 9½″, $900.00.

Samurai shining flare in the night, from
set of Ten Brave Retainers of Oguri,
sgd Ichiyusai Kuniyashi ga, C **150.00**

Shunei, assault on the imperial palace in
a storm, sgd Shunei ga, Oy **450.00**

Shunsho
  Actor, Malsumoto Koshiro II as samurai before a freize of bamboo,
  sgd Shusho ga, H **600.00**
  Actor, Uzaemon VIII as dancing sa-
  murai, sgd Shunsho ga, repaired,
  H **375.00**
  Ichikawa Monnosuke III in samurai
  role, sgd Shunko ga, H. **825.00**

Toyohiro, 3 ladies conversing before entrance to house, sgd Toyohiro ga, re-
paired, Ot **375.00**

Toyokuni, portrait of Hiroshige, green
robes, yellow at top border, sgd To-
yokuni, ga, Ot **925.00**

Uramaro, Yomauba holding chestnut
above Kintoki, published by Murataya
Jirobei, sgd Uramaro hitsu, some
creasing and stained, Oy **3,200.00**

Yoshida, Ugo no Yube (evening after
rain), sgd Yoshida, round seal, jizuri
seal, dtd Taisho 15 (1926), Oy **550.00**

Yoshinobu, 2 bijin in an interior, sgd
Yoshinobu ga, C **4,500.00**

Yoshitora, city folk watching start of balloon race, published by Kagaya Ki-
chibei, 1865, sgd Yoshitora ga, Ot . .   **1,300.00**

PURPLE SLAG (MARBLE GLASS)

History: Challinor, Taylor & Co., Tarantum, Pennsylvania, c1870s-80s, was the largest producer of
purple slag in the United States. Since the quality
of pieces varies considerably, there is no doubt
other American firms made it as well.

Purple slag also was made in England. English
pieces are marked with British Registry marks.

Other color combinations, such as blue, green,
or orange, were made, but are rarely found. Purple
slag has been heavily reproduced over the years
and still is reproduced at present.

Additional Listings: Greentown Glass (chocolate slag) and Pink Slag.

Bowls
  8", Dart Bar **45.00**
  8⅜", Raindrops. **40.00**
Creamers
  Scroll with Acanthus **55.00**
  Sunflower **55.00**
Dish, cov, 6" l, 4½" w, 6" h, Beaded
  Rib. **70.00**
Master Salt, 4" d, 2½" h **30.00**
Match Holder, 5" h, 5" d, dolphin
  heads. **65.00**

Tumbler, 3¼", $40.00.

Mug, Singing Birds	**38.00**
Soap Dish, ribbed.	**55.00**
Spooner, Flower and Panel	**45.00**
Toothpick Holder, Ringed Urn	**30.00**
Vase, 7", Maple Leaf	**45.00**
Water Pitcher, Dart Bar.	**95.00**

QUEZAL   *Quezal*

History: The Quezal Art Glass Decorating Company, named for the "quetzal," a bird with brilliant
colored feathers, was organized in 1901 in Brooklyn, New York, by two disgruntled Tiffany workers,
Martin Bach and Thomas Johnson. They soon hired
two more Tiffany workers, Percy Britton and William
Wiedebine.

The first products, unmarked, were exact Tiffany
imitations. In 1902 the "Quezal" trademark was first
used. Quezal pieces differ from Tiffany pieces in
that they are more defined and the decorations
more visible and brightly colored. No new techniques came from Quezal.

Johnson left in 1905. T. Conrad Vahlsing, Bach's
son-in-law, joined the firm in 1918, but left with Paul
Frank in 1920 to form Lustre Art Glass Company
which copied Quezal pieces. Martin Bach died in
1924; and, by 1925 Quezal ceased operations.

Wares are signed "Quezal" on the base of vases
and bowls and rims of shades. The acid-etched or
engraved letters vary in size and may be found in
amber, black, or gold. A printed label of a quetzal
bird was used briefly in 1907.

Bowls
  7½" d, fluted, flat rim, irid blue, gold   **300.00**
  12" d, peacock blue, hammered silver
  base, mkd Oscar B. Bach, NY . . .   **450.00**
Candlesticks, 7¾", irid blue, sgd, pr . . .   **525.00**
Candy Dish, 5¾" d, 2¼" h, irid gold,
  folded foot, sgd. **275.00**

Vase, 12″, gold Aurene ground, light green draping vines, heart shaped leaves, $1,250.00.

Lamp, table, 17″, gold vined, green leaves, sgd.	1,300.00
Nut Dish, 3″, gold irid, sgd	135.00
Salts	
2¾″, gold with blue, sgd	150.00
Ribbed, irid gold, sgd.	195.00
Shades	
6¼″ h, 5″ d, ruffled rim, yellow pulled feather, opal ground, calcite interior, pr.	225.00
6¾″, green, gold King Tut decor, gold lining.	750.00
8″, white, gold criss-cross design, white interior, sgd.	300.00
Vases	
5″, cabinet, wide bottom, thin body, flared top, pulled green feather, pink highlights, sgd	900.00
6½″, trumpet shape, pulled green feather, gold border, rainbow irid base, gold irid interior.	1,250.00
6½″ h, 5″ d, green, blue and ruby lattice design, ivory cased, SS overlay	2,950.00
7¼″, irid blue, sgd.	400.00
9″, jack-in-the-pulpit shape, green, gold and white feather	550.00
10½″, opaque white with irid gold and orange designs	1,200.00
12½″, opal, orange-gold King Tut design.	1,150.00

QUILTS

History: Quilts have been passed down as family heirlooms for many generations. Each is an individual expression. The same pattern may have hundreds of variations in both color and design.

The advent of the sewing machine increased, not decreased the number of quilts which were made. Quilts still are being sewn today.

The key considerations for price are age, condition, aesthetic beauty, and design. Prices are now at a level position. The exception is the very finest examples which continue to bring record prices.

References: John Finley, *Kentucky Quilts, 1800–1900*, Phantheon Books, 1982; Phyllis Harders, *The Warner Collector's Guide To American Quilts*, Main Street Press, 1981; William C. Ketchum, Jr., *The Knopf Collectors' Guides to American Antiques: Quilts*, Albert A. Knopf, Inc., 1982; Rachel and Kenneth Pellman, *The World of Amish Quilts*, Good Books, 1984.

Album, pieced and appliqued calico, brightly colored red, green, yellow, and blue in squares with a floral motif including cornucopia, central arrow pierced heart, compote filled with fruit, trapunto, white cotton field with herringbone and scallop stitching, swag borders, squares inscribed with stitchers' names, dated 1849, PA, 112 x 112″.	3,520.00
Amish	
Cross and Square, pieced cotton, bright purple, jade green, pink, black, navy blue, and orange, field of star and circle quilting, 20th C, 80 x 60″	500.00
Double Monkey Wrench, pieced cotton, maroon, gray, blue, and gold, flowerhead and cable stitch quilting, PA, 19th C, 64 x 64″	800.00

Log Cabin, 82″ sq, $200.00.

Grandmother's Flower Garden, pieced wool, pink, red, olive green, multicolored prints, and black, olive green border, red binding, outline quilting, IN, c1880, 77½ x 76¾" . . **750.00**

Pine cone, pieced wool and cotton, aubergine, blue, brown, and green, blue, and brown borders, outline quilting, PA, late 19th C, 88 x 88" **1,550.00**

Bachelor's Puzzle, pieced, mustard yellow on white, yellow border, IL, c1910, 82 x 96" **500.00**

Birds in Air, pieced, multicolored print triangles on unbleached muslin, red lattice, finely stitched quilting, MA, c1880, 73 x 74" **550.00**

Blossom and Bud, pieced and appliqued cotton, printed and solid red, green, yellow, and pink calico, white cotton field, elaborate feather and wreath quilting, PA, 19th C, 84 x 87" **800.00**

Cross Leaf, pieced and appliqued calico, printed red and green patches, red buds with trapunto, on white cotton field with finely stitched cube and seed quilting, PA, 19th C, 84 x 84" **1,325.00**

Diamond Patch, pieced calico, printed and solid red, yellow, green, blue, and white patched, diagonal line quilting, NY, 19th C, 76 x 88" **700.00**

Double Star, pieced cotton, jade green, yellow, and maroon, flowerhead, diagonal, and cable quilting, PA, late 19th C, 76 x 76" **900.00**

Flower Applique, red and pink calico flowers, yellow centers, green calico leaves and stems, white ground, sgd and dated 1830, OH **650.00**

Johnny In The Corner In A Garden Maze, pieced cotton, tweed type red, field of slate blue, back and binding of bright solid marigold, IN Mennonite, early 20th C **375.00**

Ocean Waves, pieced cotton, prints of browns, yellows and deep red ground, IN, c1900, 81 x 83" **625.00**

Peony, appliqued cotton, 24 stylized peonies and buds in red, yellow, and green-blue calico, border of trailing vine of leaves in green-blue, white ground, floral and concentric diamond quilting, NY, c1855, 78 x 72" **850.00**

President's Wreath, pieced and appliqued cotton, red and green, white cotton ground with heart, leaf, and cable quilting, PA, 19th C, 80 x 76" **725.00**

Star and Cable, pieced cotton, red, yellow, and green, red central panel, sawtooth borders, outer dark green border with meandering feather quilting, central wreath and diagonal line quilting, PA, late 19th C, 80 x 76" **1,650.00**

Star and Octagon, pieced calico, red,

maroon, green, and pink, cube quilting, red and white borders, Midwestern, 19th C, 76 x 88" **500.00**

Star of Bethlehem, pieced calico, yellow, red, green, and brown, Stars of LeMoyne on corners, white cotton field, fine scallop quilting, pierced diamond borders, PA, 19th C, 108 x 100" **1,210.00**

Star of Bethlehem, pieced and appliqued calico and chintz, red, green, yellow, and blue calico in feathered Star of Bethlehem pattern, corners appliqued with floral printed chintz cut outs, white cotton ground, red sawtooth border, cube quilting, reverse stamped "Granite Co. Wire Twist Cottons", PA, 19th C, 120 x 120" **3,300.00**

Streak of Lightning, pieced, red, white, and blue, red binding, OH, early 20th C, crib size **350.00**

QUIMPER

History: Quimper faience, dating back to the 17th century, is named for Quimper, a French town where several potteries were located. Several mergers resulted in the evolution of two major houses - the Jules Henriot and Hubaudière-Bousquet factories.

The peasant design first appeared in the 1860s, and many variations exit. Florals and geometrics, equally popular, also were produced in large quantities. During the 1920s the Hubaudière-Bousquet factory introduced the Odetta line which utilized a stone body and Art Deco decorations.

The two major houses merged in 1968, each retaining its individual characteristics and marks. The concern suffered from labor problems in the 1980s and recently was purchased by an American group.

Marks: The HR and HR Quimper marks are found on Henriot pieces prior to 1922. The HenRoit Quimper mark was used after 1922. The HB mark covers a long span of time. The addition of numbers or dots and dashes refers to inventory numbers and are found on later pieces. Most marks are in blue or black. Pieces ordered by department stores, such as Macy's and Carson Pirie Scott, carry the store mark along with the factory mark, making them less desirable to collectors. A comprehensive list of marks is found in Bondhus's book.

References: Sandra V. Bondhus, *Quimper Pottery: A French Folk Art Faience*, privately printed, 1981; Millicent Mail, *Quimper Faience*, Airon, Inc., 1979; Marjatta Taburet, *La Faience de Quimper*, Editions Sous le Vent, 1979, French text.

Museums: Musee des Faiences de Quimper, Quimper, France; Victoria and Albert Museum, French Ceramic Dept., London, England.
Advisors: Susan and Al Bagdade.

Advertising Sign, front with male peasant and mkd "H.B. Quimper," back with prop	95.00

Ashtrays

H.B. Quimper mark, circular, three cigarette rests, bust of male peasant in center, raised painted dots in orange and white, tan and cobalt ground	45.00
Unmarked, 5″ d, stoneware, geometric tan and brown design in center, blue-green edge.	65.00

Bookends, pr

Male peasant playing flute on one, female holding distaff on other, native dress, full molded figures, glossy colors, tan bases, sgd Maillard, c1920s	250.00
Man on one, female holding fish on other, modern movement colors, mkd H.B. Quimper	465.00

Bowls

H.B. Quimper mark, 6″ d, peasant woman, floral wreath border	38.00
HenRiot Quimper mark, double handled, rich border decor, marriage dance scene	500.00
Box, Sardine, cov, rect, 4½″ w, attached underplate, 8½″ w, male and female peasants, mkd HenRiot Quimper . . .	300.00

Boxes

5″ d, stoneware, Art Deco motif, dark colors of browns, black, and tans, mkd H.B. Quimper-Odetta.	175.00

Basket, gray glaze, blue handle, Henriot Mark, $125.00.

6½″, sq with cut corners, two Breton men with horns, rich border decor, four small legs, mkd HenRiot Quimper	150.00
Chamberstick, 6½″, oval shape, ring handle, female peasant, yellow ground, mkd HenRiot Quimper	265.00
Chambersticks, pr, man on one, female on other, pale coloring, mkd H.R. Quimper	550.00
Condiment Jar, cov, 2½″ h, bold coloring in bands and crosshatching, two raised pierced tabs for wire handle, mkd HenRoit Quimper	65.00
Cup and Saucer, octagonal form, floral and peasant figure, mkd H.B. Quimper	45.00
Dejeuner Set, oval plate with depression for matching cup, male peasant with pipe, shell tab on plate, mkd H.R. Quimper	175.00
Door Plaque, 9″ l, female figure carries bucket, florals, mounting holes outlined in blue starbursts, border outlined in blue and orange-yellow, mkd H.B. Quimper	175.00
Egg Cup, typical peasant decor, mkd H.R. Quimper	65.00

Figurines

Child bouncing ball, yellow and brown colors, red and blue highlights, sgd "Sevellec" under base, mkd H.R. Quimper	300.00
Male Peasant, 9″, bright colors, mounted on base, "Yann" on front of base, mkd HenRiot Quimper	145.00
Male and Female Peasants, male: standing, arms folded, cobalt coat, tan pantaloons, oval base in marbleized earth tones, orange and green raised painted dots for trim, female: hands in pocket of white apron with trim in four red dots, cobalt dress with raised orange and green painted dots, mkd H.B. Quimper	570.00
Man playing bagpipe, miniature, "Yann" on front of base, mkd HenRiot Quimper	65.00
St. Meen, 9″, multicolored, mkd H.B. Quimper	400.00
Ste. Barbe du Froël, 9″, multicolored, mkd HenRoit Quimper	400.00
Swan, small size, shades of blues, mkd HenRiot Quimper	175.00
Inkstand, 13½″ l, double cov wells, crest of Brittany on base, sculptured border and backplate, four feet.	250.00
Inkwell, single, 3 pcs [body, well, cov], heart shaped, peasant decor, mkd H.B. Quimper	165.00
Lamps, pr, 13″ h, female peasant holding jug, male peasant, modern move-	

ment colors of blue and tan shades, orig fixtures, artist sgd "Maillard" ... **575.00**

Menu Holder, 5½", "Menu" printed at top, man with horn in lower left corner, blue-gray glaze, mkd Porquier-Beau . **300.00**

Mustard Pot, pale blue, gray ground, cov notched for spoon, mkd on front H.B. Quimper **255.00**

Pitchers
  5¾", bagpipe shape, brown pipe handle, blue bow and peasant decor, mkd HenRiot Quimper **130.00**
  10", figural, duck, beak forms spout, mkd H.B. Quimper **250.00**

Planter, 7½" l, swan shape, multicolored feathers, molded into body, mkd HenRiot Quimper. **300.00**

Plates
  Cup, hexagonal, single native flower in center, floral wreath border, unmarked **30.00**
  7", salad, woman dressed in orange and blue on apple-green ground, orange band at border with blue inner stripes, mkd HenRiot Quimper. . . . **50.00**
  7¾", luncheon, blue rooster, orange and green flowers, yellow ground, mkd H.B. Quimper **75.00**
  9", male peasant, blue and yellow banded border, mkd H.R. Quimper **125.00**
  9¼", decorative, peasant in traditional costume, detailed, country scene in background, blue acanthus border with crest of Brittany, soft, runny glaze, scalloped edge, mkd H.R. Quimper **250.00**
  9½", octagonal, male peasant, mkd HenRiot Quimper **48.00**
  Square, cut corners, female peasant in center, floral border, ermine tail in back in each corner, mkd HenRiot Quimper **65.00**

Porringer, geometric int., leaf handles, mkd HenRiot Quimper **65.00**

Quintal, 6½", woman on front, florals in orange, blue, and green, yellow ground, mkd HenRiot Quimper **130.00**

Relish Dish, 13" w, two joined, shaped seashells, floral and geometric motif, green painted double dolphin handle in center, mkd H.B. Quimper **165.00**

Tureen, cov, 9½" h, man on base, woman on cov, footed, mkd AP **500.00**

Vases
  5½", tulip shaped, peasant with pail, mkd HenRiot Quimper **95.00**
  7½" h, bud, bulbous body, narrow neck with flared rim, full frontal view of peasant woman, open floral on back, band of green and orange geometrics on yellow ground at neck, c1930s, mkd HenRiot Quimper **75.00**

8", clock imitation, sq form, pr, man on one, woman on other, yellow border **350.00**

8", tulip, three tiered, soft, pale colors, mkd H.B. Quimper **400.00**

10", double handled, rich decor border **225.00**

11", flared top, pr. girl with parasol on one, man with bagpipe on other, white ground, mkd H.R. Quimper. . **1,100.00**

12", bagpipe shape, woman on front, florals on back, blue-gray ground, c1900, mkd H.B. Quimper. **500.00**

14½", three joined horns, tricorn form, peasant on one horn, florals on other two, rich decor border **550.00**

Vegetable, cov, oval, 14" handle to handle, ftd, peasant on each side, floral sprays between, blue sponged open handles and finial, soft glaze, mkd HenRiot Quimper. **200.00**

Wall Pockets
  6½", man with pipe on front, pierced for hanging, mkd on front H.R. Quimper **150.00**
  7½", bagpipe shaped, woman peasant and florals, white ground, mkd H.B. Quimper. **125.00**

Wine Set, tray: 9" d, server: 6½" h, six small cups: 1½" d, tray and cups in florals and blue and orange band, server with female peasant, tan handle, mkd HenRiot Quimper. **220.00**

RADIOS

History: The radio was invented 100 years ago. Marconi was the first to assemble and employ the transmission and reception instruments that permitted sending electric messages without the use of direct connections. Between 1905 and the end of World War I many technical advances were made to the "wireless," including the invention of the vacuum tube by DeForest. By 1920 technology progressed. Radios filled the entertainment needs of the average family.

Changes in design, style, and technology brought the radio from the black boxes of the 1920s to the styled furniture pieces and console models of the 1930s and 1940s, to midget models of the 1950s, and finally to the high-tech radios of the 1980s.

References: David and Betty Johnson, *Antique Radios: Restoration and Price Guide,* Wallace Homestead, 1982; Morgan McMahon, *Vintage Radio,* privately printed, 1972.

Periodical: *Radio Age,* 636 Cambridge Road, Augusta, GA 30909.

Collectors' Clubs: Antique Wireless Association, 17 Sheridan Street, Auburn, NY 13021; Antique Radio Club of America, 81 Steeplechase Road, Devon, PA 19333.

Museums: Antique Wireless Museum, East Bloomfield, NY; Caperton's Radio Museum; Louisville, KY; Muchow's Historical Radio Museum, Elgin, IL; Museum of Wonderful Miracles, Minneapolis, MN; New England Museum of Wireless and Steam, East Greenwich, RI; Voice of the Twenties, Orient, NY.

Additional Listings: See *Warman's Americana & Collectibles* for more examples.

Atwater Kent, #318, table model, dome, $75.00.

Admiral, table model, Art Deco, wood .	75.00
Atwater Kent, Model 20, mahogany case, 3 dials	100.00
Crosley	
Art Deco, table model, ivory case. . .	50.00
"Fivers"	45.00
Dick Tracy wrist radio, orig box	75.00
Federal, crystal set	110.00
Philco	
Cathedral	100.00
Transitone, maroon plastic case	20.00
RCA, Model #16	90.00
Radiola, Model X, Regenoflex, WD11 tubes	155.00
Silver Marshall, Cathedral	275.00
Silvertone, Century of Progress, shaped like building, veneered	40.00
Westinghouse, Aerolia, Senior	100.00
Wings, Cathedral	200.00
World Crystal Set	100.00
Zenith, Zephr, 6-S-147, multiband	75.00

RAILROAD ITEMS

History: Railroad collectors have existed for decades. The merger of the rail systems and the end of passenger service made many objects available for private collections. The Pennsylvania Railroad sold its archives at public sale.

Railroad enthusiasts have organized into regional and local clubs. Join one if interested. Your local hobby store can probably point you to the right person. The best pieces pass between collectors and rarely make it into the general market place.

References: Stanley L. Baker, *Railroad Collectibles: An Illustrated Value Guide*, Collector Books, 1981, 2nd ed.; Richard Luckin, *Dining On Rails*, privately printed, 1983.

Museums: Baltimore and Ohio Railroad, Baltimore, MD; Museum of Transportation, Boston, MA; New York Museum of Transportation, Albany, NY; California State Railroad Museum, Sacramento.

Periodicals: Key, Lock and Lantern, P.O. Box 15, Spencerport, NY 14559. Subscription: $12.00; Railroad Collectors Association, Inc. (RCAI), Box 365, St. Ignatins, MT 59865. Annual subscription: $10.00.

Additional Listings: See *Warman's Americana & Collectibles* for more examples.

Ashtray and Match Holder, 6″ d, Missouri Pacific, blue glass	35.00
Bell, engine, 26″ h, metal in cast iron frame, mounted on wooden base . . .	235.00
Blanket, Union Pacific R R, gray, black stripes, logo in center	80.00
Builder's Plate, steam, Balwin, BLW #55470, 8/1922, Northwestern Pacific 4-6-0 #183, 9¼″, round, brass.	150.00
Calendar, 1940, Burlington Route, Zephyr observation car pictured	50.00
China	
Bouillon cup, New York Central, De Witt-Clinton, 1925–51	50.00
Bowl, 6⅛″, AT&SF, Black Chain, backstamp, 1930	100.00
Butter Chips	
C & O, Silhouette, black Martha	

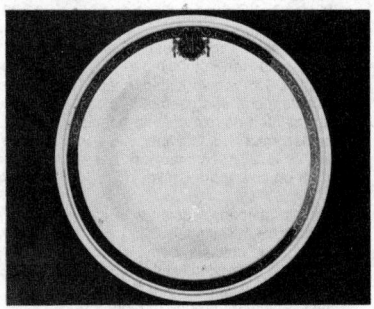

China, soup bowl, 9″, Northern Pacific, mkd "Ivory, Lamberton, Scammel," $25.00.

Washington on white ground, Syracuse China 50.00

SP, Imperial, Buffalo China, backstamp 50.00

Celery Trays

Baltimore & Ohio, Centennial, flow blue transfer, Scammel-Lamberton, 1927–54 . . . . 65.00

Santa Fe, 12¼" l, 6" d, Bleeding Blue 100.00

Cereal Bowl, 5", GNRR, Rocky, goat logo, Syracuse China, side mkd . . 80.00

Compote, Penn RR, Purple Laurel, backstamp 65.00

Creamer, Canadian Pacific, logo, c1910 . . . . 25.00

Cup, Chesapeake & Ohio, Chessie logo 75.00

Cups and Saucers

AT&SF, Mimbreno, backstamp . . . 130.00

Olympian, gold Greek key border, Limoges 100.00

Mug, New York Central, cream with rust brown design, Shenango China, New Castle, Pa, ... 30.00

Pitcher, 4", Mt. Tom Railroad Co, Holyoke, Mass 30.00

Plates

8¼", Texas & Pacific RY, The Eagle, Syracuse China, backstamp 90.00

9", AT&SF, Adobe, no backstamp. 75.00

9½", Northern Pacific, goat overlooking mountains, "Glory to the West" 85.00

9¾", AT&SF, Mimbreno, backstamp 70.00

10", NYC, pacemaker, green and white, top mark. 75.00

10¼", oval, Missouri Pacific, The Eagle, Syracuse China, backstamp 80.00

10½", Southern RY, Peach Blossom 90.00

Platters

10½", B&O, Centennial 65.00

12½", oval, SP, sunset logo, green floral border, Onandaga Pottery. 85.00

Sauce Boat, SP, Prairie Mt. Wildflower, backstamp. 80.00

Saucer, dessert, 5¼" Atlantic Coast Line, Flora of the South, Buffalo China, backstamp 65.00

Soup Plate, 9", UP, Desert Flower . . 35.00

Teapots

B&O, Centennial, blue and white . . 350.00

Missouri Pacific Lines, cobalt blue, gold trim, Hall Pottery 150.00

Vegetable Dishes

Atlantic Coast Line, Palmetto, 1926 . . . . 100.00

C&O, George Washington, Bicentennial, Buffalo Pottery, 1932. . . 100.00

Decanter, vacuum, Pullman, chrome, plated. 85.00

Glassware

Goblet, 8", Great Northern, clear, etched logo 38.00

Ice Tea, 12 oz, AT&SF, etched 35.00

Juice, 8 oz, C&O, emb emblem 15.00

Hardware

Torch, PW&BRR, iron, screw top . . . 45.00

Wrench, Rock Island 8.00

Hat, conductor's, Rock Island 75.00

Lanterns, hand

Dressel, 3½", globe, WE-MKT 50.00

Handlan, 4¼", PRR, keystone logo, clear etched 75.00

Lighter, cigarette, Long Island Railroad, c1950. . . . . 25.00

Napkin, New York, New Haven & Hartford Railroad, 21 x 21", linen 18.00

Oil Lamp, club car, NY Central, tin, repainted base. 45.00

Paperweight, Santa Fe, brass, c1940 . . 35.00

Silver

Bottle holder, PRR, mkd top and bottom 100.00

Bouillon spoon, UPRR, Meriden 15.00

Coffee pot, cov, 14 oz, UP 60.00

Cover, meat, NYC, Int'l Silver, backstamp, c1950. . . . . 100.00

Creamer, cov, T&P, backstamp 80.00

Pickle fork, PRR, Kings pattern, 1888 25.00

Sugar tongs, Missouri Pacific Lines, Empire, Int'l Silver, 1921 . . . . 60.00

Tray, change, Missouri Pacific, Int'l Silver, 1925. . . . . 50.00

Vase, bud, 7"h, T&P, The Eagle, side logo, I S Co, backstamp, 1953 . . . 125.00

Spittoon, 6½" d, NYC, Sleeping Car Co, SP, Homes & Wessell Metal Co 200.00

Station Agent's Blue Book, 523 pgs, c1925. . . . . 18.00

Step Stool, conductor's, UP. 130.00

Switch Keys (See Keys in *Warman's Americana and Collectibles*)

Table Cloth, 34½ x 34½", Frisco Lines, St Louis-San Francisco RY beneath logo in center, white on white. 38.00

Tallow Pot, 7" h, 13" l, Oregon, Wash RR & Navigation Co, side emb 45.00

Tender Number Plates

Grand Trunk Western, #3406, 6⅞ x 28½", rect, painted steel, slide into pocket on tender 45.00

Jersey Central, #929, 7 x 18", rect, painted steel, slide into pocket on tender. 50.00

Uniform Button, New Haven, large, gold 5.00

Wall Lamp, caboose, Adams & Westlake, metal, 10" chimney 60.00

Water Can, 14" h, NP, side emb 30.00

Whistle, caboose back-up, 4½" h, Missouri Pacific, brass 55.00

RAZORS

History: Razors date back several thousand years. Early man used sharpened stones. The Egyptians, Greeks, and Romans had metal razors.

Razors made prior to 1800 generally were crudely stamped WARRANTED or CAST STEEL, with the maker's mark on the tang. Until 1870 almost all razors for the American market were manufactured in Sheffield, England. Most blades were wedge shaped; many were etched with slogans or scenes. Handles were made of natural materials: various horns, tortoise shell, bone, ivory, stag, silver, and pearl. All razors were handmade.

After 1870 razors were machine made with hollow ground blades and synthetic handle materials. Razors of this period usually were manufactured in Germany (Solingen) or in American cutlery factories. Hundreds of molded celluloid handle patterns were produced.

Cutlery firms produced boxed sets of two, four, and seven razors. Complete and undamaged sets are very desirable. Most popular are the 7-Day sets with each razor etched with a day of the week.

The fancier the handle or more intricately etched the blade, the higher the price. Rarest handle materials are pearl, stag, sterling silver, pressed horn, and carved ivory. Rarest blades are those with scenes etched across the entire front. Value is increased by certain manufacturer's names, e.g., H. Boker, Case, M. Price, Joseph Rogers, Simmons Hardware, Will & Finck, Winchester, and George Wostenholm.

hgb = hollow ground blade
wb = wedge blade

Reference: Robert A. Doyle, *Straight Razor Collecting, An Illustrated Price Guide*, Collector Books, 1980, out-of-print [but, available from author].

Periodical: *Blade Magazine*, 112 Lee Parkway, Stonewall Building, Suite 104, Chattanooga, TN 37421. Subscription: $10.00

Additional Listings: See *Warman's Americana & Collectibles* for more examples.

Advisor: Robert A. Doyle.

AMERICAN

Case, W. R. & Sons, Bradford, PA, hgb, green celluloid handle	30.00
Christiansen, H. M., Brockton, MA, hgb, imitation ivory handle with emb whale on front	22.00
Clauss, Fremont, OH, hgb, aluminum chased handle, fancy engraved pattern on both sides	70.00
Electric Cutlery Co., Newark, NJ, hgb, fancy celluloid handle, raised scene of windmill, rowboat in water, fence, and trees, all in color	42.50
King, M. & J. W., New York, wb, black horn handle, c1890	45.00
Maher & Grosh, Toledo, OH, hgb, real ivory handle	37.50

Torrey, J. R., Worcester, MA, hgb etched with trademark, tortoise shell handle	25.00
Winchester trademark, hgb, hand hammered tang, imitation tortoise shell handle, rare mark and desirable	75.00

ENGLISH

Clark & Hall, Sheffield, wb, clear horn handle, c1810	55.00
Joseph Fenton & Sons, Cutlers, Sheffield, wb, black horn handle, c1870	21.00
John Heiffor, Paradise Square, Sheffield, wb, back of tang stamped "Made For The Army," black horn handle	60.00
John S. Holler, hgb, SS fancy handle	250.00
J. Nowill & Sons, Sheffield, wb, black horn handle stamped "Celebrated Boston Razor"	85.00
Oak Razor Works, Sheffield, hgb etched with spread American eagle and words "American Razor," black horn handle	20.00
Frederick Reynolds, Sheffield, blade etched "The Champion of Liberty" with full length scene of George Washington, clear horn handle, c1860s	45.00
Frederick Reynolds, Sheffield, wb, mottled horn handle	17.00
Southington Cutlery Co., Sheffield, hgb, imitation ivory molded to resemble carved ivory	22.50
Wade & Butcher, Sheffield, hgb, etched "Celebrated Razor," pearl handle, two panels each side, tang end of pearl is carved	275.00
Wade & Butcher, Sheffield, wb, etched with patriotic motif "The Union Must and Shall Be Preserved," c1860s	125.00

GERMAN

H. Boker & Co., blade etched "Finest Cast Steel," imitation ivory handle with inlaid metal decoration	32.50
Ern, hgb, imitation ivory handle, raised touring car with driver and passenger	150.00
Hamburg Concave, blade etched "Quick Cutter," black celluloid handle	12.50
Hope Cutlery Co., hgb, imitation ivory handle, raised nude woman picking grapes on lower portion of front side	85.00
Imperial Razor Warranted, hgb, etched "Imperial Safety," picture of two cyclists on double bycicle, black celluloid handle	27.50
Rolka Klein, hgb, imitation ivory handle, shape of bamboo shoot	16.00
J. F. McCoy Co., hgb, etched "Monarch," plain black celluloid handle	12.50
Oxford Razor Works, hgb, imitation tortoise shell handle	8.00
Puma, hgb, etched in gold across top	

Joseph Rodgers Sheffield, matched pr, ivory handles, flat leather cov wood presentation case, c1860, $250.00.

| half, top of blade deeply engraved "Solingen," black horn handle . . . . . | 36.00 |

SETS OF RAZORS

Pair, Wade & Butcher, wb, ivory handles, flat leather cov wood presentation case.	155.00
Pair, J. R. Torrey, Worcester, MA, hgb, black celluloid handles, upright leather cov wood case	32.00
Four, A. Barrett & Co., London, top of each blade numbered "1" to "4," black horn handles, upright wood case emb with same name as the razors .	225.00
7-Day Set, English, Sheffield, wb, ivory handles, felt lined walnut case trimmed in brass, c1860.	375.00
7-Day Set, German, gold washed blades, "Souvenir Of Germany," different German city etched on each razor, imitation tortoise shell handles, wood case cov in paper	200.00
7-Day Set, Unknown maker, one carved tortoise shell handle with locking device, 7 different interchangeable blades, c1820-30, rare.	750.00

RED WING POTTERY

History: The Red Wing pottery category covers several potteries from Red Wing, Minnesota. In 1868 David Hallem started Red Wing Stoneware Co., the first pottery, with stoneware as its primary product and with a red wing stamped under the glaze as its mark. The Minnesota Stoneware Co. started in 1883. The North Star Stoneware Co. opened its factory in 1892, closed it in 1896, and used a raised star and the words Red Wing as its mark.

The Red Wing Stoneware Co. and the Minnesota Stoneware Co. merged in 1892. The new company, the Red Wing Union Stoneware Co., made stoneware until 1920 when it introduced a pottery line which it continued until the 1940s. In 1936 the name was changed to Red Wing Potteries, Inc. During the 1930s it introduced several popular lines of hand painted pattern dinnerware which was distributed through department stores, Sears, and gift stamp centers. Dinnerware declined in the 1950s, being replaced with hotel and restaurant china in the early 1960s. The plant closed in 1967.

References: David A. Newkirk, *A Guide To Red Wing Markings*, Monticello Printing, 1979; Dolores Simon, *Red Wing Pottery With Rumrill*, Collector Books, 1980; Lyndon C. Viel, *The Clay Giants, The Stoneware of Red Wing, Goodhue County, Minnesota*, Book 2, Wallace Homestead, 1980.

Additional Listings: See *Warman's Americana & Collectibles* for more examples.

Vase, 8⅛", light blue glaze, imp mark, #1151, $50.00.

Ashtray, 7¼" d, mkd Red Wing Pottery	25.00
Beater Jar, advertisement for H. L. Sander, Arlington, MN, mkd Red Wing Saffron Ware	85.00
Bowls	
7", 4 blue stripes, advertisement for T. C. Johnson, Latimer, IA	45.00
9½", saffron sponge dec, "Pochahontas, Iowa"	75.00
10", 2 blue stripes, mkd "10 Red Wing USA"	65.00

10″, blue sponge band	75.00
11″, paneled, blue sponge dec.	85.00
11″, stoneware, paneled, rust and blue sponge dec on ext.	95.00
Casserole, cov, 7″, Grayline	100.00
Churn, 4 gallon, target dec	80.00
Cookie Jar, cov, brown, cattails dec. . .	120.00

Crocks
15 gallon, large wing dec	100.00
20 gallon, mkd Red Wing Union Stoneware.	225.00

Dog Food Crock, 7½″ d, 2½″ h, setter dec, brown	35.00
Fruit Jar, quart, stoneware, mkd Stone Mason, Red Wing, 1899	90.00
Jug, miniature, 1½″ d, 4″ h, paper label.	50.00

Pitchers
6″, Brushware.	50.00
8″, Grayline	90.00
10″, sponge band, "Titonka, Iowa". .	135.00

Poultry Drinking Fount, stoneware, 2 pcs	45.00
Toothpick, gopher and log, "The Gopher State, FTDA, St. Paul, 1932".	125.00
Urn, 6½″, handled, Brushware.	55.00

Vases
7½″ h, 3″ d, yellow, peacock in relief, pr	125.00
10″, Brushware	85.00
11″, bulbous, Brushware, emb flower strays, mkd Union Stoneware	55.00

Water Cooler, "5" imp on bottom, orig spigot.	90.00

REDWARE

History: The availability of clay, the same used to make bricks and roof tiles, accounted for the great production of red earthenware pottery in the American colonies. Redware pieces are mainly utilitarian—bowls, crocks, jugs, etc.

Lead glazed redware retained its reddish color, but a variety of colored glazes were obtained by the addition of metals to the basic glaze. Streaks and mottled splotches in redware items resulted from impurities in the clay and/or uneven firing temperatures.

"Slipware" is a term used to describe redwares decorated by the application of slip, a semi-liquid paste made of clay. Slipwares were made in England, Germany, and elsewhere in Europe for decades before becoming popular in the Pennsylvania German region and elsewhere in colonial America.

Bank, 5¾″, frog, brown glaze	165.00

Bowls
8¼ x 3″, clear glaze int., brown splotches	185.00
8½ x 2¾″, rope tooled handles, greenish amber glaze with streaks of brown	200.00

Flower Pot, I.S. Stahl, attached base, crimped edges, green and brown glaze, 4½″ d, 2¼″ h, c1938, $85.00.

8½ x 5″, double ear handles, greenish glaze with orange spots	155.00
9⅞ x 3¼″, clear glaze, brown spots.	315.00
18 x 12 x 3¾″, oval, coggled edge, clear glaze with speckles of brown, 3 line yellow slip dec	700.00
Butter Tub, mottled orange and brown glaze, mkd "John Bell, Waynesboro"	1,200.00
Candlestick, 5″, brown glaze, mkd "M.A. & A.A. #22-1866"	250.00

Chargers
11½ x 1⅝″, coggled-edge, 4 line yellow slip dec.	825.00
12¼ x 2″, coggled edge, 3 line yellow slip dec	775.00
12½ x 1⅞″, coggled edge, yellow slip in wavy line	925.00
13¼″, notched rim, cross comb trailings of yellow slip, PA, 19th C. . . .	500.00
13¼″, finely notched rim, combed trailings of yellow slip, 6 stylized yellow slip flowers	800.00

Creamer, 3¼″, clear glaze, brown speckles.	260.00

Crocks
5″, green glaze in spots and stripes .	175.00
12½″, cov, brown glaze, green and yellow slip	300.00

Figurines
Dog, sitting, basket around neck, mottled glaze, attributed to John Bell .	2,125.00
Lion, 8½″, brown speckled glaze, Shenandoah	4,500.00
Rabbit, 5¾″, mottled reddish amber glaze, made in tin chocolate mold.	175.00

Flower Pots
3¾″, mottled cream glaze, attached saucer.	175.00

5", green and brown glaze, attached
saucer. 100.00
Hot Plate, brown with manganese
splash, emb urn of flowers, mkd "John
Bell, Waynesboro" 575.00
Inkwell, 3⅜", dark brown glaze 75.00
Jars
5⅞", side handle, clear glaze, brown
splotches 250.00
6", side handle, brown mottled glaze 185.00
7¾", clear greenish glaze, mottled orange and green, imp label "Solo-
mon Bell, Strasburg, VA" 250.00
Jugs
6⅜", ovoid, applied handle, black
speckled metallic glaze. 110.00
8", ovoid, strap handle, dark green-
ish glaze. 125.00
Loaf Dish, crow's feet in yellow slip . . . 425.00
Milk Pan
7½ x 2¼", finger crimped edge, clear
int. glaze. 145.00
12½ x 2½", greenish olive glaze . . . 100.00
13¼, molded lip, clear glaze, trailings
of green and brown slip, sponge dec
on red-brown ground 1,210.00
14¼, molded lip, trailings of manganese glaze on orange-brown . . . 1,320.00
Mold, fish, curved, 12⅝", clear glaze . . 165.00
Mugs
3", clear glaze, brown splotches. . . . 150.00
4¾", speckled cream glaze 185.00
5¼", black shiny glaze. 175.00
Pie Plates
7¼", clear glaze, 3 wavy lines of yel-
low slip 175.00
8¼", green speckled glaze, yellow slip
lattice dec 225.00
9½", clear glaze, minor wear 175.00
9¾, coggled edge, crow's feet and
dots in bright yellow slip 375.00
Pitchers
6", unglazed body, brushed brown
flowers and scallops, New Geneva,
PA 500.00
7¼", green spotted glaze, ribbed strap
handle, pinched in spout. 200.00
7¾", green and brown glaze, incised
bands 245.00
Plates
7", green and brown glaze on orange
ground, stylized tulip in yellow slip. 950.00
8", sponge dec 250.00
8", brown glaze on orange ground,
stylized tulip in yellow slip 900.00
8½", coggled edge, yellow slip
"C.B.". 300.00
10¼", notched rim, yellow slip
trailings 715.00
11½", clear glaze, stylized tulip in yel-
low slip, heightened with green . . . 1,000.00
Pot, 6¼", bulbous, vasiform, applied
tooled handles, coggle wheel dec

around neck, deep orange-glaze with
brushings of dark brown, front dec with
inscribed spread wing American eagle, attributed to Jacob Medinger,
Berks Co., PA, 1900-1930 . . . . 950.00
Puzzle Jug, 7¾", green glaze, amber
dec, incised "A.K. Pinka, North Western Pottery, Chicago" 225.00
Soap Dish, brown glaze, mkd John Bell,
Waynesboro 365.00
Sugar Bowl, brown glaze, lid with bird
finial. 950.00
Tray, 14½", rect, notched rim, green and
manganese glaze, yellow slip trailings,
center imp design of parrot sur-
rounded by grapevines 1,760.00
Turk's Head Molds
8½ x 3", 2 tone brown and clear
glaze. 100.00
8½ x 4", swirl design, clear glaze, ext.
with brown sponging, imp "John
Bell, Waynesboro" 275.00
8½" x 4¼", swirl design, clear glaze,
daubs of black on rim. 245.00
8¾", creamy amber glaze with brown
splotches 115.00
Whistle, 3", rooster on top, reddish
brown glaze 1,350.00

RELIGIOUS ITEMS

History: Objects for the worshipping or expression of man's belief in a superhuman power are
collected by many people for many reasons.

Icons are included since they are religious mo-
mentos, usually paintings with a brass encasement.
Collecting icons dates from the earliest period of
Christianity. Most available today were made in the
late 19th century.

Bibles
English, full leather binding, Philadel-
phia, 1801 . . . . 100.00
Russian, leather binding, gilt strap-
work dec, gilt metal clasps, c1760 . . 400.00
Bust, St. Francis, praying, gazing up-
ward, polychrome and giltwood, His-
panic, 23". 550.00
Crucifix, 12¾", polychrome boxwood,
finely carved, German, 17th C 1,500.00
Easter Egg, 4½", porcelain, painted,
Christ with crown of thorns, Russian,
19th C 300.00
Figures
Angel, dancing, playing violin, poly-
chrome and giltwood, Spanish, 8" 475.00
Christ Child, gilt ivory, ½". 350.00
Madonna, seated with book on lap,
polychrome and giltwood, Hispanic,
8½" 250.00

Painting and embroidery, 20¾ x 27″, possibly European, $350.00.

Mary Magdalene, standing, holding pot of ointment, wood, Gothic style, 20″.	125.00
Font, Holy water, Mandonna, 14″, Parian	175.00
Icons	
Greek, The Incredulity of Thomas, 18th C, 20 x 13⅝″	600.00
Russian, Presentation of Virgin in Temple, enamel, black and white, c1750. 6¾ x 3¾″.	385.00
Russian, St. Nicholas, wood, brilliant colors and gilt, 10 x 12½″	750.00
Last Rites Outfit, oak box, brass trim, int. fitted with crucifix and stand, salver, brush, holy water bottle, handled cup, silver mkd Homan Silverplate Co, Pat April 1897.	165.00
Lavabo, 4¾″ basin, 2 spouts, molded handle and hanging fixture, northern Renaissance style	190.00
Watch Stand, 12″, polychrome wood, pocket watch between 2 columns, stepped base, in front, reclining figure of Ceres holding basket of fruit, paper label, German	200.00

REVERSE PAINTING ON GLASS

History: The earliest examples of reverse painting on glass were produced in 13th century Italy. By the 17th century the technique had spread to Central and Eastern Europe. It spread westward as the glass industry center moved to Germany in the late 17th century.

The Alsace and Black Forest region developed a unique portraiture style. The half and three-quarter portraits often were titled below the portrait. Women tend to have general names. Most males are of famous men.

The English used a mezzotint method, rather than free-style, to create their reverse paintings. Landscapes and allegorical figures were popular. The Chinese began working in the medium in the 17th century, eventually favoring marine and patriotic scenes.

Reverse painting was done in America. Most were by folk artists, unsigned, who favored portraits, patriotic and mourning scenes, floral compositions, landscapes, and buildings. Known American artists include Benjamin Greenleaf, A. Cranfield, and Rowley Jacobs.

In the late 19th century commercially produced reverse paintings, often decorated with mother-of-pearl, became popular. Themes included the Statue of Liberty, the capitol in Washington, D.C., and various world fairs and expositions.

PORTRAITS

Chinese, Emperor, 22 x 16″	**150.00**
Chinese, young female painter in cartouche, framed, 22″ h	**225.00**
"Joseffina," young woman with red bow	

Jerome Napoleon, Baltimore, Maryland, 12¾ x 15¾″, $300.00.

in hair, low cut yellow dress, orig
frame, 9½ x 12″ **500.00**
Scottish lad, kilt and lyre, gilt frame,
8½ x 12″ **125.00**
"Spaniolin," young woman, blue bonnet,
green ribbon, salmon dress, orig
frame, 11¼ x 15″ **300.00**

SCENES

Basket of flowers, primitive, black
ground, multicolored flowers, framed,
6⅝ x 8½″.................... **60.00**
Battle scene, mounted warriors and foot
soldiers engaged in combat, Chinese,
Chinese Chippendale frame, early
19th C, 13½ x 19½″ **450.00**
Chinese, lady and gentleman of court,
seated at table on pavilion looking out
on garden, Chinese export, framed on
stand, 19th C, 18 x 28″ **750.00**
Courtship, 18th C gentleman presenting
rose to lady, handmaiden stands by,
nocturnal int., sgd Rottenberg, framed,
c1920, 13½ x 13⅞″............ **275.00**
Lady, leaning into mirror image on a
bamboo railing holding fan, deep blue
ground below green, red, and gilt curtains, 19th C, 13¼ x 19¼″....... **1,050.00**
Landscape, peasants resting by hay-
stack, farmhouse, church, well, sgd E.
Huber, c1920, 12½ x 15½″ **275.00**
Shepherd and shepherdess, multicolored, carved, molded giltwood frame,
Qunilong dynasty, Chinese export, 15
x 14¼″..................... **875.00**

RIDGWAY

History: Throughout the 19th century the Ridgway family, through a series of partnerships, held
a position of importance in Shelton and Hanley,
Staffordshire, England. The connection began with
two brothers, Job and George, and Job's two sons,
John and William. In 1830 John and William separated with John retaining the Cauldon Place factory and William the Bell Works. John no longer
was active by 1858. William and his heirs continued
at the Bell Works and the Church [Hanley] and
Bedford [Shelton] works until the end of the 19th
century.

Many early pieces are unmarked. Later marks
include the initials of the many partnerships.

Reference: G. A. Godden, Ridgway Porcelains,
1972.

Additional Listings: Staffordshire, Historical,
and Staffordshire, Romantic.

Bowl, 4″, scalloped edge, Pomerania,
floral border **35.00**

**Creamer and sugar, cov, white ground,
gray dec, gold trim, $85.00.**

Cup and Saucer, handleless, University,
light blue, c1840 .... **65.00**
Cup Plates
Chinese, Oriental building, c1835 ... **40.00**
Columbian Star, log cabin and figures,
star border, c1840 .... **50.00**
Dish, 8″, scalloped edge, deep blue, floral center, gilt, c1840–45......... **150.00**
Egg Cup, Catskill Moss, blue transfer,
1840–50.................... **125.00**
Mug, 5″, Coaching Days and Ways, silver
lustre trim................... **45.00**
Pitcher, tankard, 10″, Coaching Days
and Ways, Christmas Visitor....... **150.00**
Plates
9″, scalloped edge, India Temple, floral border, c1820 .... **65.00**
9½″, Albicon, c1835 .... **75.00**
9½″, Marcella **50.00**
12 sided, Doria, light blue **55.00**
Platters
7¾ x 10″, scalloped edge, Grecian,
river scene, urn, stone lions, bridge,
and gondolas................ **55.00**
8½ x 12″, octagonal, University, light
blue, c1841.................. **95.00**
10 x 16″, Amory, oriental scene **85.00**
Relish, Dish, oblong, British Flowers,
c1835...................... **35.00**
Syrup Pitcher, cov, Coaching Days and
Ways, blue transfer............ **55.00**
Teapot, cov, 5½″, Coaching Days and
Ways, black transfer, carmel ground,
silver lustre trim............... **95.00**

RING TREES

History: A ring tree is a small, generally saucer
shaped object made of glass, porcelain, metal, or
wood with a center post in the shape of a hand,
branches, or cylinder for hanging or storing finger
rings.

GLASS

Custard, Wing Scroll	100.00
Cut Glass, blue, 3½"	90.00
Milk, white tapering post, floral dec, 3"	25.00
Opaline, blue, gold dec, 2½"	55.00
Spatter, mottled, white and yellow, 2½"	40.00
Val St. Lambert, amber and clear	40.00

METAL

Iron, figural hand, sq base	18.00
Silver Plate, bear, standing with gun guarding tree, oval base, Pairpoint, 3¼ x 2⅛ x 3¼"	125.00
Sterling Silver, ornate design base, gadroon edge	45.00

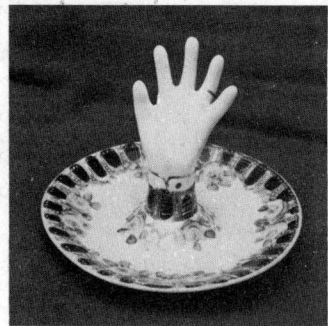

Porcelain, hand and dish, hp rose dec, gilting, mkd with maple leaf, and "Hand Painted," $45.00.

PORCELAIN

Austrian, white, pink flowers, gold trim	25.00
Flow Blue, figural hand, English	85.00
German, figural hand on round saucer, hp floral dec	35.00
Limoges, figural hand on round saucer, pansy dec	48.00
Limoges, white, blue flowers, artist sgd	25.00
Nippon, figural hand, floral dec, gold trim, green mark, 2 x 3½"	70.00
Noritake, gold figural hand on 3" sq base, blue mark	60.00
Parian, figural hand, molded base	45.00
Royal Worcester, beige satin, maroon, yellow flowers, gold trim, 1912 mark.	95.00

ROCKINGHAM AND ROCKINGHAM BROWN GLAZED WARES

History: Rockingham ware can be divided into two categories. The first consists of the fine china and porcelain pieces made between 1826 and 1842 by the Rockingham Company of Swinton, Yorkshire, England, and its predecessor firms: Swinton, Bingley, Don, Leeds, and Brameld. The Bramelds developed the cadogan, a lidless teapot. Between 1826 and 1842 a quality soft paste body with a warm, silken feel was developed by the Bramelds. Elaborate specialty pieces were made. By 1830 the company employed 600 workers and listed 400 designs for dessert sets and 1,000 designs for tea and coffee services in their catalog. Unable to meet its payroll, the company closed in 1842.

The second category of Rockingham ware is pieces produced in the famous Rockingham brown glaze, which was intense and vivid purple-brown when fired. It had a dark, tortoise shell mottled appearance. The glaze was copied by many English and American potteries. American manufacturers who used Rockingham glaze include D. & J. Henderson of Jersey City, New Jersey, United States Pottery in Bennington, Vermont, potteries in East Liverpool, Ohio, and several potteries in Indiana and Illinois.

Additional Listings: Bennington and Bennington-Type.

Baker, oval, 12½ x 9½", mottled	225.00
Bank, 4", figural, man with pitcher, "Money Taken in Here"	95.00
Basket, 1¼", miniature, bisque, white, purple flowers	90.00
Bowl, 10" d, 4½" h, mottled brown	90.00
Bottle, 5¾", figural, Landlord, colonial man holding up bottle, head is stopper, c1820	825.00
Creamer, 5½", figural cow, mottled	200.00
Cottage, 5" h, 4" l, 3 story, peaked roof, dormers, encrusted moss, flowers, and morning glories, c1820	600.00
Cuspidor, 8" d, 4½" h, mottled	30.00
Dish, 9" sq, rounded corners, emb rim, mottled	65.00
Figurine, swan, preening, white, gold highlights, c1820, 3¾"	375.00
Inkwell, 4", figural masks, mottled	65.00
Mug, 4", mottled	70.00
Pastille Burner, cottage, 5" h, 5" l, twin	

Toby jug, 6″, basketweave body, tricorn hat, $225.00.

peaked roof, dormer, orange double front doors and chimneys, large applied flowers	**450.00**
Pie Plate, 11¾″ d, 1⅜″ h, mottled	**175.00**
Pitchers	
6⅜″, emb, hunter and game, mottled	**65.00**
8¾″, emb, arm with hammer and "Protection to American Industry," "Everett" in emb label under spout	**225.00**
Plate, 7⅞″, scalloped rim, rayed center, mottled	**165.00**
Platter, 12¾″, octagonal, mottled	**125.00**
Shaving Mug, 4⅛″, emb, Toby figures on 2 sides, imp label E & W Bennett, Canton Avenue, Baltimore	**135.00**
Teapot, 8½″, emb scene, Rebeckah at the Well	**125.00**

ROCKWELL, NORMAN

History: Norman Rockwell (February 3, 1894–November, 1978) was a famous American artist. During the time he painted, from age 18 until his death, he created over 2,000 works.

His first professional efforts were illustrations for a children's book. He next worked for *Boy's Life*, the Boy Scout magazine. His most famous works were used by *Saturday Evening Post* for their cover illustrations.

Norman Rockwell painted everyday people in everyday situations, mixing a little humor with sentiment. His paintings and illustrations are treasured because of this sensitive approach. Rockwell painted people he knew and places with which he was familiar. New England landscapes are found in many of his illustrations.

Because of the popularity of his works, they have been reproduced on many objects. These new collectibles should not be confused with original artwork and illustrations. However, they do allow a collector more range in collecting interests and prices.

References: David P. Folds, Jr., *The Norman Rockwell Treasury, 1979*, Noroco, 1978; Carl F. Lucky, *Norman Rockwell Art and Collectibles*, Books Americana, Inc., 1981.

Museums: Corner House, Stockbridge, MA; Norman Rockwell Museum, Northbrook, IL.

Additional Listings: See *Warman's Americana & Collectibles* for more examples.

HISTORIC

Booklet, Jello	**30.00**
Calendar, Scout's Memories, 1931	**55.00**
Pen & Ink, 28½ x 30″, "Stockbridge at Christmas," framed, autographed "Sincerely, Norman Rockwell"	**350.00**
Postcards	
"Help the Fatherless Children of France," soldier and child, 1917	**50.00**
"Century of Progress Expo," Sandford's Ink ad, 1932	**45.00**

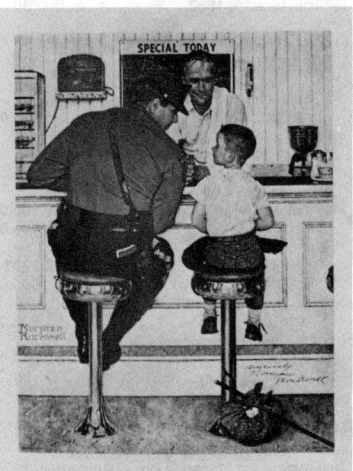

Print "The Runaway," Saturday Evening Post cover, Sept. 20, 1958, sgd, 11 x 14″, $350.00.

MODERN

Bells
Gorham, Snow Sculpture, 1976	50.00
Dave Grossman Designs, Drum For Tommy, 1976	25.00

Bottle, Charles Lindbergh, *Saturday Evening Post* cover, 1976 . . . . — **20.00**

Figurines
Gorham
Beguiling Buttercup	65.00
Circus, 5¼", 1975	80.00

Dave Grossman Designs
Discovery, 6", 1975	150.00
Drum for Tommy, 6¾", 1976.	65.00
Marble Players, 4½", 1973	500.00
Summertime, 5¾", 1976.	45.00

Rockwell Museum
Birthday Party	75.00
Washing Our Dog	80.00

Ingots & Medals
Franklin Mint, SS, set of 12, Spirit of Scouting, 1972.	275.00
Hamilton Mint, SS, Slumbering Santa, 1974.	25.00

Plates
Dave Grossman Designs
Can't Wait, Boy Scout annual, 1981	30.00
Leapfrog, bas relief, 1979.	40.00

Rockwell Society
Angel with black eye, 1975.	95.00
Toy Maker, 1977	220.00
The Tycoon, 1982	30.00

Prints
Harry Abrams, "Weighing In," Eddie Arcaro, 19 x 25", sgd	300.00

A-T-O Print Collection
"American LaFrance Is Here," firehouse, 24 x 24", sgd.	300.00
"You've Got To Be Kidding," hippie and construction workers on scaffolding, 24 x 28", sgd	275.00

Circle Gallery, Ltd
"Icabod Crane," 20 x 26", sgd, #.	2,100.00
"Settling In," 20 x 26, sgd, #	3,000.00

Eleanor Ettinger, Inc.
"April Fool," 24 x 26, sgd, #	3,200.00
"Boy on Stilts," 24 x 31", sgd, # .	800.00
"Young Spooners," 20 x 24", sgd, #.	1,200.00

Spoons, pewter, 6¾"
Back to School	30.00
Take Your Medicine	35.00

ROGERS & SIMILAR STATUARY

History: John Rogers, born in America in 1829, studied sculpturing in Europe and produced the first plaster-of-paris statue, "The Checker Players," in 1859. It was followed by "The Slave Auction" in 1860.

His works were popular parlor pieces of the Victorian era. He produced at least 80 different subjects and the total number of groups made from the originals is estimated to be over 100,000.

Casper Hennecke, one of Rogers' contemporaries, operated C. Hennecke & Company from 1881 until 1896 in Milwaukee, Wisconsin. His statuary often is confused with Rogers' work since both are very similiar.

It is difficult to find a statue in undamaged condition and with original paint. Use the following conversions: 10% minor flaking; 10% chips; 10–20% piece or pieces broken and reglued; 20% flaking; 50% repainting.

References: Paul and Meta Bieier, *John Rogers' Groups of Statuary*, privately printed, 1971; Betty C. Haverly, *Hennecke's Florentine Statuary*, privately printed, 1972; David H. Wallace, John Rogers: The People's Sculptor, Wesleyan Univ., 1976.

ROGERS

Charity Patient, 1866, 22", sgd "John Rogers New York"	500.00
Courtship in Sleepy Hollow, 14", sgd, parian.	1,000.00
Madam Your Mother Craves A Word, 8/3/1885, 20".	725.00
Mock Trial, 6/11/1877, 22".	650.00
Neighboring Pews, 1/29/1884, 18½". .	700.00
Peddler At The Fair, 12/10/1878, 21" .	1,000.00
Phrenology At The Fancy Ball, 8/3/1886, 19¾".	800.00
You Are A Spirit I Know, 11/3/1885, 18½"	450.00
Washington, 10/19/1875, 29"	500.00
Wounded Scout, 18½", sgd, parian . . .	1,200.00
Wrestlers, The, 9/20/1881, 27½"	950.00
Why Don't You Speak For Yourself, John?, John Alden and Priscilla, 2/10/1885, 22¼"	500.00

Rogers Type, "First Love," Hennecke, 13½" h, $200.00.

ROGERS TYPE

Beethoven, 20"	**200.00**
Croquet Player, 18"	**185.00**
Diver, 15"	**175.00**
Evening Devotion, 21"	**250.00**
Innocence Protected, 20½"	**150.00**
Red Riding Hood, 11½"	**350.00**
Tug of War, 7"	**175.00**
Welcome, 32", alabaster	**300.00**

ROOKWOOD POTTERY

History: Mrs. Marie Longworth Nicholas Storer, Cincinnati, Ohio, founded Rookwood Pottery in 1880. The name of this outstanding American art pottery came from her family estate "Rookwood," named for the rooks (crows) which inhabited the wooded grounds.

There are five elements to the Rookwood marking system—the clay or body mark, the size mark, the decorator mark, the date mark, and the factory mark. Rookwood art pottery can best be dated from factory marks.

In 1880–1882 the factory mark was the name "Rookwood" incised or painted on the base. Between 1881 and 1886 the firm name, address, and year appeared in an oval frame. Beginning in 1886, the impressed "RP" monogram appeared and a flame-mark was added for each year until 1900. After 1900 a Roman numeral, indicating the last two digits of the year of production, was added at the bottom of the "RP" flame-mark monogram. This last mark is the one most often found on Rookwood pottery today.

Though the Rookwood pottery filed for bankruptcy in 1941, it was soon reorganized under new management. Efforts at maintaining the pottery proved futile, and it again was sold in 1956 and in 1959. The pottery was moved to Starkville, Michigan, in conjunction with the Herschede Clock Co. It finally ceased operation in 1967.

Rookwood wares changed with the times. The variety is endless, in part because of the great variations in glazes and designs due to the creativity of the many talented artists.

Reference: Herbert Peck, *The Book of Rookwood Pottery*, Crown Publishers, Inc., 1968.

Collector's Club: American Art Pottery Association, P.O. Box 714, Silver Springs, MD 20901.

Ashtray, 4½ x 7" hi-glaze, owl on edge, dark green, 1952	**125.00**

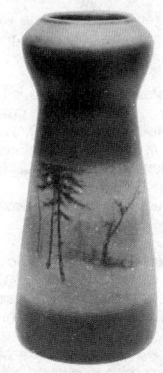

Vase, 9³⁄₁₆", winter scenic, blues and grays, matte finish, # 16590, 1911, artist sgd "F. Rothenbush," $1,200.00.

Ashtray and Matchholder, 5" w, 2" h, striker on one side, yellow clover dec, C Steinle, 1902	**200.00**
Bowls	
5" d, 8" h, V shape, porcelain glaze, floral dec, L. Epply, 1929	**225.00**
7½" d, 2¼", h, matte, yellow, reticulated fern design around top, K Shirayamadani, 1910	**140.00**
9½" d, 3" h, cameo glaze, peach and white, white flowers, large brown leaves, swirl sides, S Toohey, 1891	**625.00**
Boxes, covered	
3¼", round, vellum, green, dark green-blue top and bottom, red flowers on cov, K Van Horn, sgd R V, 1910	**700.00**
4" h, 6" d, candy, sq, handled, scarab knob, yellow floral sprays on base and cov, sgd, c1885	**575.00**
Creamer, 2½", brown glaze, orange berry dec, E Diers, 1899	**125.00**
Cup, 5" h, 6" d, 3 handled, carved matte floral dec, A Pons, 1907	**325.00**
Ewers	
4½", brown, high glaze, orange berry dec, W K, 1900	**150.00**
7¾", brown glaze, holly berry dec, L Lincoln, paper label, 1899	**320.00**
10½", standard glaze, silver overlay, floral dec, M Nourse, 1897	**1,000.00**
11¼", red clay, tiger eye glaze, one sharp handle, one very small modlded handle, large leaf and butterfly dec, Laura Fry, 1884	**875.00**
Figurine, donkey with baskets on back, 4", hi-glaze, green, 1935	**110.00**
Flower Frog, 5½", matte, white, nude girl seated with small frog,	**135.00**

Honey Jug, 5″, red clay, tan, white with black reeds and birds, gold high lights, M Rettig, kiln mark, 1883 . . . . **500.00**

Jardinieres

5½ x 5½″, brown glaze, 3 handles, blueberries, yellow and green leaves, F Rothenbrush, 1900 . . . . **500.00**

6 x 6″, vellum, yellow, blue flower, brown branches, 3 brown birds, blue int., P Conant, 1916 . . . . **650.00**

Jug, 8½″, bisque, gray, incised brown leaf and berry dec, A R V, 1884 . . . . **700.00**

Mugs

5½″, iris glaze, silver overlay, clover dec, silver, green, and blue, 1905 . **900.00**

6½″ h, 4″ d, standard brown glaze, portrait of cavalier, S Toohey, 1896 . . . . **575.00**

Nut Dish, 6″ l, 1⅝″ h, shaped like half nut shell, brown bisque outside, shell texture, int., high glaze, light brown, 4 flowers, A M Bookprinter, 1886 . . . . **140.00**

Paperweight, monkey, seated, 4″, high glaze, green, 1930. . . . . **160.00**

Pitchers

7¼″, high glaze, blue, white floral, A R V, 1887 . . . . **450.00**

10″, cov, high glaze, blue to white, pine cone dec, green, brown, and orange, A R V, 1887 . . . . **700.00**

Plaques

Birch Trees, 7⅛ x 11″ h, vellum, orig, frame, E Diers **1,400.00**

Moonlight, 6 x 8″ h, vellum, porcelain, dark blue, moon over lake, S E Coyne, 1922 . . . . **1,300.00**

Ramkin, 4½″ d, 1¼″ h, 2 handled, red clay, butterfly and marsh grass, gold glitter, M Rettig, 1883 . . . . **200.00**

Sign, 13 x 4¼″, scrollwork on each end, high glaze, cream, "Rookwood, Cincinnati" and trademark, dated 1947 . **625.00**

Teapot, 6″, dinnerware, white, blue sailing ship **150.00**

Tiles

6 x 6″, tea, parrots, 1924. . . . . **125.00**

10″, masted sailing ship. **200.00**

Vases

4″, sea-green glaze, 4 catfish, S Laurence, 1901 . . . . **2,000.00**

5½″, iris glaze, white, green, pink, and gray ground, pink and purple floral dec, C A Baker, 1910. . . . . **700.00**

5½″, pocket shape, iris glaze, yellow floral dec, Ed, Diers, 1903 . . . . . . **550.00**

5¾″, porcelain, white, birds and flowers, bright blue, K Levy, 1945 . . . . **500.00**

6½″, jewell porcelain, painted and sgraffito floral dec, E T Hurley, 1944 . . . . **400.00**

6½″, wax matte, purple to pink, purple flowers, K S, 1944 . . . . **430.00**

6½″ h, 6″ w, flared, porcelain, blue and white, white flowers with orange centers, K S, 1946 . . . . **425.00**

7¾″, porcelain, high glaze, white, 2 birds, blue and brown, L Epply, 1928 . . . . **400.00**

7¾″, vellum, scenic, multicolored, F Rothenbush, 1914 . . . . **800.00**

8″, vellum, yellow tinted over-glaze, floral dec, L Asbury, 1922. . . . . . . **500.00**

8⅜″, brown glaze, holly dec, M L P, 1896. . . . . **475.00**

8½″, wax matte, daffodil, K Shiraya-madani, 1932. . . . . **750.00**

8¾″, vellum, scenic, dark blue with blue bands top and bottom, Mc-Laughlin, 1914 . . . . **900.00**

10½″, brown glaze, yellow and dark brown top, dark green iris, A M Valentien, 1898 . . . . **1,250.00**

Wallpocket, 11½″, matte, blue, molded lily, 1920 . . . . **100.00**

ROSE BOWLS

History: A rose bowl, a decorative open bowl with a crimped, pinched, or petal top, held fragrant rose petals or potpourri which served as an air freshener in the late Victorian period. Practically every glass manufacturer made rose bowls in a variety of patterns and glass types, including fine art glass.

Additional Listings: See specific glass categories.

Satin glass, 4½″ d, yellow, white lining, molded petals, $65.00.

Burmese, 2½″ h, 2¾″ d, 8 crimp, acid finish, 5 petal flower decor with brown and green leaves **325.00**

Cameo, 3″ h, 3¼″ d, 3 petal top, mottled gold with tan, satin finish, acid cut brown trees along lake, enameled, sgd Daum Nancy. **600.00**

Cranberry, 3″ h, 3⅜″ d, 8 crimp top, blue and white enameled forget-me-nots, green leaves, 2 gold leaves **125.00**

Custard, Grape and Gothic Arches, ftd. **90.00**

Durand, 4⅞″, orange with blue hearts and vines, amber ftd **800.00**

Peachblow, 4½″, 8 crimp, floral decor . **140.00**

Satin glass
  4⅝″ h, 5″ d, shaded apple green, emb Shell and Seaweed **150.00**
  5″ h, 5½″ d, pink, white enamel flowers, maroon foliage **175.00**

Spangled Glass, 3¾″ h, 3¾″ d, 8 crimp, rose, white cased, silver mica in coral pattern **95.00**

Tiffany, 3″, gold with green hearts and vines, sgd. **625.00**

ROSE CANTON, ROSE MANDARIN, ROSE MEDALLION

History: The pink rose color has given its name to three related groups of Chinese export porcelain. Rose Mandarin was produced from the late 18th century to approximately 1840. Rose Canton began somewhat later extending through the first half of the 19th century. Rose Medallion originated in the early 19th century and was made through the early 20th century.

Rose Mandarin derives its name from the Mandarin figure(s) found in garden scenes with women and children. The women often feature gold decorations in their hair. Polychrome enamels and birds separate the scenes.

Rose Medallion has alternating panels of figures and birds and flowers. The elements are four in number, separated evenly around the center medallion. Peonies and foliage fill voids.

Rose Canton is similar to Rose Medallion except the figure panels are replaced by flowers. People are present only if the medallion partitions are absent. Some patterns have been named—Butterfly and Cabbage, Rooster, etc. The category actually is a catchall for all pink enamel ware not fitting into the first two groups.

Rose Medallion is still made, although the quality does not match the earlier examples.

ROSE CANTON

Bowl, 7½″, int. with large enameled flower, border with birds, butterflies, and floral motifs, ext. with continuous scene, c1830 . . . . **250.00**

Charger, 18″ d, hunters on horseback, florals sprays, wild geese around rim, 19th C **275.00**

Creamer, 4″, double twisted handle, gilt trim **200.00**

Cup and Saucer, demitasse, floral panels, c1860 . . . . **65.00**

Mug, 5″ h, seated figures, floral rim border, gilt trim, mid 19th c **375.00**

Plates
  7⅞″, scenic center with stags, birds, knarled trees and flowers, border of bamboo, flowers, birds, and butterflies, c1820 . . . . **145.00**
  9¼″, central scene with figures on terrace, border of fruit, flowers, birds, and butterflies, c1830 . . . . **125.00**
  9⅝″, central scene with 4 figures separated by 4 oriental objects, border of blue bats, flowers, birds, and butterflies, c1830 . . . . **95.00**
  10″, center dec of bouquet of flowers and berries, butterflies, and insects, iron red and gilt band, border of flowers and butterflies, c1820 . . . . **150.00**

Rice Bowl, 6¾″ d, 3½″ h **75.00**

Teapot, cov, brass handle, wicker basket with red lining **200.00**

Tureen, cov, 11″, lozenge shape, gilt floral ground, figural scenes in panels **300.00**

Umbrella Stand, 19″ h, 8″ d, cylindrical, sgd **475.00**

Vases
  7¾″, sq, figures in court scenes, bird among flowers, applied gilt demon face handles, early 19th C **175.00**
  8″, baluster shape, 2 cartouches in either side, bordered in gilt key design, white ground, enamel flowers, figures and objects, wide border bands atop bright gilt, c1830, pr **375.00**

Vegetable Dish, 8½″, oval, scalloped rim **150.00**

ROSE MANDARIN

Basin, 13¾″ d, 3½″ h, flared rim, 15 figures in center scene, fruit and floral

Rose Mandarin, plate, 9⅞″, $70.00.

dec, Ch'ing Dynasty, Ch'len Lung Period, 1736–1795 .... **895.00**
Bowl, 10″, figures at leisure in landscape, 18th C................. **750.00**
Cup and Saucer, scenic panels, butterfly and floral border **135.00**
Mug, 5½″, figures in court setting **245.00**
Plates
  9½″, late 19th C.............. **200.00**
  11″, 5 mandarins in center, butterfly border with ducks and goldfish ... **375.00**
Teapot, 6¼″, flower garlands, gilt border **320.00**

ROSE MEDALLION

Bough Pots, octagonal, flared, faceted sides with 2 figural reserves and 2 floral reserves, dense foliate ground, twisted rope handled, domed cov with painted fruit and flowers, c1860, pr................... **2,350.00**
Bowls
  7¾″, reserves of figural groups and flowers, 19th C **275.00**
  10½″, circular, shallow, floral center, alternating floral dec and scenes border, c1840 .... **125.00**
Chargers
  13¾″, 6 reserves, flowers and figural scenes, 19th C **300.00**
  16¾″, reserved panels of flowers, maidens, gold dec, 19th C **400.00**
Cup and Saucer, 3″ d cup, 5″ d saucer, floral reserves................ **75.00**
Dish, 9″, serving, floral panels with birds and butterflies, 19th C........... **225.00**
Gravy Boat, floral ground, scenic reserves.................... **125.00**
Fish Platter with drain, 18″ d **1,000.00**
Knife Rest, 4″ l, scroll shape, flat top.. **300.00**
Pitcher, water, 8¼″, ovoid, notched rim, bird, butterfly, and floral dec, c1840..................... **350.00**
Plates
  8″, scalloped edge, 19th C........ **250.00**
  8½″, octagonal, scenic reserves.... **175.00**
Platters
  12″, oval, mid 19th C........... **200.00**
  14¾″, butterflies and floral dec, c1810.................... **275.00**
Pomade Jar, cov, 2¼″ h, 1⅞″ d, mid 19th C.................... **75.00**
Punch Bowls
  11½″ d, early 19th C........... **750.00**
  15⅝″ d, early 19th C........... **1,700.00**
Saucer, 5½″, figural center, c1820.... **50.00**
Sugar, 5″, cov, medallions, twisted handle, 19th C **250.00**
Teapot with orig insulated basket, 5½″ **275.00**
Teapot and 2 cup in wicker basket, brass hardware, c1890 .... **375.00**

Tray, 3 shaped sides, figural and bird reserves, 19th C **225.00**
Tureen with undertray, cov, 14½″, gold gilt handles and knob, early 19th C.. **2,600.00**
Vases
  6¾″, bud, cylindrical, 2 cartouches, figures in first, birds and flowers in second, border of turquoise scallops, c1820 .... **175.00**
  9″, thin neck, flared rim, applied lion head and ring gilt handles, 2 large and 2 small cartouches on each side with oriental figures, c1830, pr...................... **600.00**
  24″, florals, dragons, and birds dec.. **300.00**
Vegetable Dishes
  9½″ l, 8″ w, oval, cov **350.00**
  10″, oval, shallow, 19th C **175.00**

MARKE

ROSENTHAL

History: Rosenthal Porcelain Manufactory began operating at Selb, Bavaria, in 1880. Specialties were tablewares and figurines. The firm is still in operation.

Biscuit Jar, 6½″ h, 6″ d, hp floral dec, gold edge and trim **75.00**
Bowls
  6″, "Lion D'Or" openwork edge, pale yellow ground, hp orange poppies and pale green leaves, gold outlining, heavy gold band, artist sdg Breidel **75.00**
  8″, white, cobalt blue border, center spray of wheat............. **50.00**
Butter Pat, rose dec, gilt edge, #58 .. **10.00**
Charger, 15″, delft blue, scenic **155.00**
Compote, 10″ d, 4″ h, hp floral center, fruit border **95.00**
Creamer and Sugar, rose dec, gold rims **40.00**
Cup and Saucer, cream ground, lavender and gold floral............. **25.00**
Dish, 8″, hp fruit, green leaves....... **95.00**
Figurines
  Bulldog, 7¼″, white and tan puppy, sgd T.H. Harthe.............. **325.00**
  Cat, 5¼″ l, reclining, black with yellow eyes, sgd Heidenreich **145.00**
  Dancer, 6″, enamel brocade full skirt, gold lustred **225.00**
  Nubian in white, playing mandolin, sgd Meisel................. **150.00**
  Nude, 9″, kneeling, sgd L. Friedrich-Gronau **150.00**
  Pelican, 3½ x 7½″, perched over diamond shaped tray with water lily dec **135.00**

Vase, 4⅝", oval, mallard flying, mkd "Germany Rosenthal/Kunstabteilung Selb/Handgemalt R. K.", $65.00.

Princess and the frog, 8½", princess bending over frog.	**235.00**
Russian Wolfhound, recumbent position, head raised, gray, black, and white.	**270.00**
Setter, 11½" l, gray and white German short hair.	**250.00**
Young child, 6½", holding flowers above shoulder while spotted fawn stands in front, sgd Lote.	**225.00**
Fish Set, set of six, 9" plates, fish swimming in water, scalloped gold rims	**175.00**
Hatpin Holder, hp violets, gold trim . . .	**40.00**
Mustard Jar, underplate, cov, 3½", Moss Rose pattern	**48.00**
Plates	
9½", portrait, classical lady, burgundy border, c1900	**65.00**
Dinner, set of 12, gilt rim, cobalt border, center spray of spring flowers.	**375.00**
Salt, ind, gold border	**12.00**
Vases	
9½", bulbous, hp multicolored floral dec.	**110.00**
Portait, buxomy girl, maroon ground, much gold, sgd R. Klein	**465.00**

ROSEVILLE POTTERY

History: In the late 1880s a group of investors purchased the J. B. Owens Pottery in Roseville, Ohio, and made utilitarian stoneware items. In 1892 the firm was incorporated and joined by George F. Young who became general manager. Four generations of Youngs controlled Roseville until the early 1950s.

A series of acquisitions began: Midland Pottery of Roseville in 1898, Clark Stoneware Plant in Zanesville (formerly used by Peters and Reed), and Muskingum Stoneware (Mosaic Tile Company) in Zanesville. In 1898 the offices also moved from Roseville to Zanesville.

In 1900 Roseville introduced its art pottery—Rozane. Rozane became a trade name to cover a large series of lines. The art lines were made in limited amounts after 1919.

The success of Roseville depended on its commercial lines, first developed by John J. Herald and Frederick Rhead in the first decades of the 1900s. In 1918 Frank Ferrell became art director and developed over 80 lines of pottery. The economic depression of the 1930s brought more lines, including Pine Cone.

In the 1940s a series of high gloss glazes were tried to revive certain lines. In 1952 Raymor dinnerware was produced. None of these changes brought economic success. In November 1954 Roseville was bought by the Mosaic Tile Company.

References: Sharon and Bob Huxford, *The Collectors Encyclopedia Of Roseville Pottery*, Collectors Books, 1976, fourth printing, 1980; Sharon and Bob Huxford, *The Collectors Encyclopedia Of Roseville Pottery, Second Series*, Collector Books, 1980.

Periodical: The Glaze, P. O. Box 4929, Springfield, MO 65804.

Collectors' Club: American Art Pottery Association, P. O. Box 714, Silver Springs, MD 20901.

Additional Listings: See *Warman's Americana & Collectibles* for more examples.

Ashtray, Pine Cone, 5" w, 2½" h	**75.00**
Baskets	
White Rose, pink, #364-12	**125.00**

Candlesticks, pr, 6¼" h, 4" w at base, Donatello, early R stamp and orig sticker, $260.00.

Zephyr Lily, hanging, rust, 8″ w, 5″ h **110.00**
Bookends, pairs
  Magnolia, brown, #13 .... **75.00**
  Zephyr Lily, green, #16 .... **75.00**
Bowl, Windsor, oval, rust, geometric design, 10½ x 7 x 3½″ w **185.00**
Candlesticks, pairs
  Donatello, 10″ **275.00**
  Morning Glory, green, orig seal, 4¾″ **250.00**
Cider Set, Peony, green, 7½″ pitcher with ice lip, 4 mugs **325.00**
Console Bowls
  Blackberry, oval, 13″ l, 3½″ h **185.00**
  Luffa, oval, rust to green, orig seal, #258, 14″ l, 3¾″ h **140.00**
Cookie Jar, cov, Clematis, blue **150.00**
Creamer, child's, duck in tall hat and untied shoes, green band, sgd Rv, 3½″ .. **55.00**
Ewer, Rozane, brown, floral trim, sgd, #829, RPC, 9½″ **225.00**
Flower Pot, Cherry Blossom, pink **130.00**
Jardinieres
  Dahlrose, 2 handles, orig seal, 9¼″ h, 12½″ w at center, 7″ base **190.00**
  Futura, rust, multicolored leaves, 10″ h, 15″ w, 8¼″ base **300.00**
Jardinieres and Pedestals
  Apple Blossom, blue, 30½″ **500.00**
  Donatelle, 27″ **575.00**
  Freesia, rust and brown, #669-8, 24½″ **475.00**
Jugs
  Blackberry, 5″ **150.00**
  Cherry Blossom, pink and blue, 6″ w, 4″ h **145.00**
Mug, Peony, blue-green, 3½″ **60.00**
Pitchers
  Donatello, 6½″ **155.00**
  Holland, 12″ **175.00**
  Pine Cone, green, #415, 9″ **120.00**
Planter, Futura, sq, light orange and blue, 7″ w, 5″ h **135.00**
Plate, baby's, seated dog, gray band, sgd Rv, 8″ **60.00**
Rose Bowl, Cherry Blossom, blue and pink, 2 handles, 1933, 5½″ d, 4″ h .. **135.00**
Tankard, Rozane Royal, brown, floral dec, seal, artist Myers, 15½″ h **575.00**
Tobacco Jar, cov, Dutch, decal of Dutch boy and girl with fish, 5½″ w, 5¾″ h **225.00**
Umbrella Stand, Donatella, 21″ **300.00**
Urn, Monticello, turquoise, #562 in crayon, 7½″ **120.00**
Vases
  Blackberry, 6½″ w, 4½″ h **155.00**
  Cherry Blossom, rust and cream, handled, 1933, 10½″ **200.00**
  Ferella, mottled red, handled, 4½″ w, 6½″ h **225.00**
  Morning Glory, white, 8″ **150.00**
  Topeo, red high glaze, 9½″ **275.00**
  Windsor, bulbous, rust, geometric design, 7″ w, 6¼″ h **185.00**

Wall Pocket, Fuschia, rust and brown, #1282-8 .... **200.00**
Window Box, Pine Cone, brown, #431-15 .... **110.00**

ROYAL BAYREUTH

History: In 1794 the Royal Bayreuth factory was founded in Tettau, Bavaria. Royal Bayreuth introduced their figural patterns in 1885. Designs of animals, people, fruits, and vegetables decorated a wide array of tablewares and inexpensive souvenir items.

Tapestry ware, rose and other patterns, was made in the late 19th century. The surface of the ware feels and looks like woven cloth. Tapestry ware was made by covering the porcelain with a piece of fabric tightly stretched over the surface, decorating the fabric, glazing the piece, and firing.

The Royal Beyreuth crest mark varied in design and color. Many wares were unmarked. It is difficult to verify the chronological years of production due to the lack of records.

Royal Bayreuth still manufactures dinnerware. It has not maintained production of earlier wares, particularly the figural items.

Additional Listings: Sunbonnet Babies.

Corinthian
  Ashtray **75.00**
  Creamer & Sugar **70.00**
  Pitcher, 8″, white figures on black, salmon throat **130.00**
  Vase **50.00**
Devil and Cards
  Ashtray, red devil **115.00**
  Creamer **120.00**
  Pitchers
    5¾″ d, 5¼″ h, green mark, mkd Bermuda **200.00**
    8″, water **250.00**
Elk
  Ashtray **125.00**
  Creamer **100.00**
  Salt Shaker **75.00**
  Toothpick **110.00**
Grape Cluster
  Bowl, pearlized **185.00**
  Mustards
    MOP, pink **125.00**

Vase, 8½″ h, white roses, ivory ground, blue mark, imp "Deponnert", $200.00.

Yellow	125.00
White, irid	75.00
Pitcher, water	275.00
Lobster	
Ashtray, 6¼″ l	50.00
Celery, 12¾″ l	130.00
Creamer & Sugar	120.00
Mustard	50.00
Sauce	70.00
Miscellaneous Patterns	
Basket, Oyster and Pearl, figural, irid, 4¾″ w, 4¾″ h	225.00
Candleholder, 5″ h, attached handle, saucer, yellow ground, black and white wading birds	140.00
Card Box, cov, pink roses	95.00
Celery, 12½″ l, white, heavy gold trim, gold mark	25.00
Cheese Dish, slanted top, miniature, blue mark	110.00
Creamers	
Apple	75.00
Black Cat	120.00
Coachman	175.00
Cockatoo	140.00
Melon	165.00
Oak Leaf	75.00
Poodle, gray	135.00
Shell, spiky, irid	60.00
Water Buffalo, black and red	100.00
Decanter, liquor, 7″, handles, musician scene	125.00
Hair Receiver, delicate white roses, gold scroll work on lid rim	85.00
Humidor, riders and dogs	200.00
Jar, Strawberry, cov, figural	225.00

Jewel Box, cov, Ivory Rose, blue mark	85.00
Match Holder, green, white storks	75.00
Mustard, cov, Strawberry, figural, 3¾″ h	75.00
Nappy, Cabbage Leaf, 4¼″ d	35.00
Nut Set, almond shape, master bowl, 6 cups	175.00
Pin Box, cov, 2½″ sq, pink, white flowers	65.00
Planter, men's tan oxfords, laces, matched, sgd	350.00
Plate, 7″, Cabbage	35.00
Relish, two musicians	60.00
Saucer, demitasse, Rose	35.00
Salt, sheep in bowl, ftd	60.00
Salt and Pepper Shakers, Conch Shell, irid blue, white and orange	75.00
Tootpicks	
Oyster and Pearl, 3 handles	200.00
Portrait of girl, dog, 2 handles, ftd	100.00
Vases	
3½″, Babes In Woods	100.00
4½″, Musicians	40.00
6″, Sheep scene, bulbous	85.00
Wall Pocket, two men in boat fishing	75.00
Nursery Rhyme	
Candlestick, 4″, Little Bo Peep	110.00
Pitcher, Little Boy Blue	85.00
Plate, 6″, Little Bo Peep	70.00
Set, 6 milk mugs, 1⅞″ h, 6 cereal dishes, 4¼″ d, 3 handled creamer and cov sugar, sgd	700.00
Pansy	
Creamer	175.00
Plate, 6″, satin, blue mark	40.00
Sugar, cov	175.00
Teapot	110.00
Poppy	
Creamer, lustre, yellow-green	125.00
Mustard, spoon, red	65.00
Salt, open, red	25.00
Sugar, cov, purple	65.00
Sandbabies	
Creamer	65.00
Wall Pocket	80.00
Snow Babies	
Creamer and Sugar	185.00
Posy Pot	80.00
Tea Tile	175.00
Sunbonnet Babies	
Bell, babies washing and hanging clothes	325.00
Bowl, 7½″, babies cleaning	325.00
Cake Plate, open handles, babies washing and ironing	250.00
Candlestick, handle, hood, babies cleaning	325.00
Mush Set, 3 pc, child's, babies cleaning and hanging clothes	325.00
Nappy, babies sweeping	145.00

Pin Box, cov, oval, babies sweeping	190.00
Pitcher, milk, bulbous, babies washing and ironing	210.00
Salt, pedestal	200.00
Sauce, 5½″ d	195.00
Tomato	
Creamer, 3½″	40.00
Mustard, cov, 4½″ d, lettuce leaf underplate	45.00
Sugar, cov	50.00
Teapot	75.00

ROSE TAPESTRY

Basket, 5½″, handled, 3 color roses	245.00
Bowl, 4¾″	250.00
Box, cov, kidney shape, 3 color roses	300.00
Cake Plate, 10″, handled	175.00
Creamer, 4″ h, pinched spout, gold rim and handle, 3 color roses	240.00
Dish, trefoil, ring handle	140.00
Frame, picture, oval, 6 x 8″ opening	300.00

Rose Tapestry, tray, 8 x 11¼″, white and blue ground, roses, blue mark, $375.00.

Hat Pin Holder, yellow roses	400.00
Hair Receiver, 3 gold feet, 3 color roses, 4″ d	200.00
Pin Boxes	
Pinched in sides, pink roses	155.00
Round, pink roses	165.00
Pitcher, 5¾″, gold handle	265.00
Planter, 3¼″ d, 2¾″ h, 2 gold handles at base, fluted rim, 3 color roses	165.00
Relish, blue mark	145.00
Ring Box, 2¼″ sq, 1¼″ h, pink roses	175.00
Salt and Pepper Shakers, 3 color roses, pr	325.00
Sugar, cov, 3 color roses	225.00
Wall Pocket, 3 color roses	425.00

TAPESTRY MISCELLANEOUS

Baskets	
Castle scene, 6″, ruffles, handle	175.00

Lady with geese	275.00
Bowl, man and woman, scenic	75.00
Creamers	
Cows, green ground	75.00
Scenic	195.00
Hat Pin Holder, scenic	300.00
Nappy, 4″, clover shape, handle, Arab on horse	165.00
Pin Box, cov, lilac dec, green mark	175.00
Pitchers	
Cavalier, pinched spout	225.00
Goats, pinched spout	225.00
Pheasant in meadow scene, pinched lip, blue mark, 4½″ h	150.00
Portrait of lady, 2¾″	215.00
Powder Box, colonial couple on cov, 3¼″ h	155.00
Tankard, miniature, stag with hounds	225.00
Toothpick, castle scenic	125.00
Tumbler, scenic	225.00
Vases	
4″, handled, 4 gold feet, scenic, deer and Grecian temple	200.00
7¼″, man hunting	275.00
Watering Can, swan scene	275.00

ROYAL BONN   *Bonn*

History: Clemers August established a porcelain factory at Bonn in 1755. It received royal endorsement and became identified as "Royal Bonn."

The majority of the Royal Bonn pieces in today's market are from the late 19th century and usually are marked with "Mehlem," a castle, or the initials "FM."

Biscuit Jars	
6″ h, 5⅜″ d, cream satin ground, pastel pink, blue, lavender and cream flowers, green leaves, heavy raised gold, mkd	125.00
6½″ h, 5⅝″ d, beige satin finish, pink and lavender flowers, green foliage, heavy raised gold trim, SP top, rim and handle	100.00
Bowl, 9½″ d, cream ground, floral dec, multicolored, metal rim, c1760	200.00
Cheese Dish, white, multicolored floral dec, gold trim, castle mark	95.00
Clock, cupids and raised floral dec, multicolored	165.00

Cup and Saucer, wild roses, blue and white	**30.00**
Ewer, 14″, Persian style, multicolored. .	**200.00**
Plates	
6½″, cream ground, purple and white water lilies, pink rim	**40.00**
9″, flowers with gold outlining.	**55.00**
11″, floral sprays, artist sgd, castle mark	**45.00**

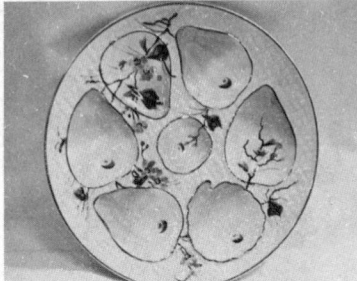

Oyster Plate, 8¾″, white ground, red floral motif, imp "Franz A. Mehlem", $100.00.

Tankard, 12″, yellow ground, scenic, boy and girl with sled, gold trim	**130.00**
Urns, covered	
8″, berries, foliage, gold trim and handles	**130.00**
14″, shaded green ground, multicolored floral dec, gold pedestal foot, 2 gold handles, artist sgd	**250.00**
Vases	
6″, portrait of cavalier, thin neck, 2 tiny handles	**150.00**
6½″, 3″ d, green ground, rooster, hen and chicks, mkd Royal Bonn.	**145.00**
8″, 4″ d, grass green ground, white and pink orchid, blue bands, heavy gold, gold trim, mkd, pr.	**225.00**
8″, 5″ d, brown and yellow ground, gold and orange flowers, mkd	**90.00**
8″, hp, scenic cartouche	**300.00**
16″, Victorian woman, child, pastel pink, blue and gold, 2 handles . . .	**800.00**
16¾″, maiden in orchid glade, banded by gold vines, painted by Bohme, printed and painted marks	**200.00**
42″, cov, portrait, Jane, Countess of Harrington, Lord Viscount Petersham and the Honorable Lincoln Stanhope, reserved on brilliant pink ground, gilt details, artist sgd, Dingendorf, imp mark for Franz A. Mehlem, mid 19th C.	**4,500.00**

ROYAL COPENHAGEN

History: Franz Mueller established a porcelain factory at Copenhagen in 1773. When bankruptcy threatened in 1779, the Danish king acquired ownership, appointing Mueller manager and adopting the name "Royal Copenhagen." The crown sold its interest in 1867; and, the company remains privately owned today.

Blue Fluted, Royal Copenhagen's most famous pattern, was created in 1780. It is of Chinese origin and comes in three styles: smooth edge, closed lace edge, and perforated lace edge (full lace). Many other factories copied it. Flora Danica, named for a famous botanical work was introduced in 1789 and remained exclusive to Royal Copenhagen. Botanical illustrations were done free hand; all edges and perforations were cut by hand.

Royal Copenhagen porcelain is marked with three wavy lines which signify ancient waterways and a crown, the latter added in 1889. Stoneware does not have the crown mark.

Additional Listings: Limited Edition Collectors' Plates.

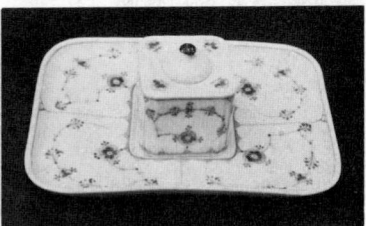

Inkwell with tray, 6″ w, 8½″ l, blue dec, fluted edges, $110.00.

Basket, underplate, 10½″ d plate, oval, reticulated, Flora Danica	**1,100.00**
Bottle, Kronburg Castle dec, blue and white	**85.00**
Bowl, 9″, Blue Fluted, half lace	**80.00**
Cache Pot, 4⅞″, Flora Danica	**375.00**
Candlesticks, pr, 6½″, sq base, Flora Danica	**425.00**
Chocolate Pot, Blue Fluted, half lace . .	**195.00**
Creamer and Sugar, Blue Fluted, full lace	**185.00**

Cup and Saucer, tea, Flora Danica . . .	300.00
Dish, 9¾", leaf shape, handle, Flora Danica	250.00

Figurines

Boxer, standing, fawn color, 5½" h, 5½" l	185.00
Fox, sitting, head held high, 5½" . . .	135.00
Mink, blue and gray, 7¼" l.	75.00
Owl, horned, sitting, 5½"	135.00
Penguin, 2½"	125.00
Pig, sitting on haunches, legs splayed, #914, 6½" l, 9¼" h.	280.00
Gravy Boat, underplate, white ground, blue morning glories	85.00
Mustard Pot, Cov, underplate, triangular, handle, Flora Danica	225.00
Plaque, 3¼" miniature, Langelinie, blue and white harbor scene with nude maiden on rock.	15.00

Plates

8", Lombardy, heavy gold fluted edge, turquoise dots	50.00
10", pierced, Flora Danica	425.00
Platter, 12", Blue Fluted, full lace.	250.00
Punch Bowl, 13" l, oval, saw tooth edge, Flora Danica.	1,225.00
Salt Cellar, pr, oval, Flora Danica.	300.00
Sauceboat, attached underplate, Flora Danica	375.00
Soup Bowl, underplate, 6½" bowl over handle, 6¾" saucer, Flora Danica. . .	325.00
Teapot, 5", Blue Fluted, half lace.	175.00
Tray, 11" l, 8" w, rectangular, hp beach scene, docked dorry and boathouse, artist sgd Harold Henriksen	120.00
Tureen, cov, 14¾" l over handles, Flora Danica	2,600.00
Tureen, underplate, Onion pattern, blue and white	175.00

Vases

2½", morning glory dec	30.00
8½", ovoid, trailing flowers, blue and white.	125.00
12" h, 7¼" d, crackle, gold fish and ship dec	350.00
Vegetable Dish, cov, 9", Blue Fluted, half lace	250.00

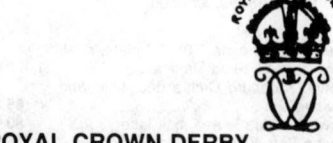

ROYAL CROWN DERBY

History: Derby Crown Porcelain Co., established in 1875 in Derby, England, had no connection with earlier Derby factories which operated in the late 18th and early 19th centuries. In 1890 the company

was appointed "Manufacturers of Porcelain to Her Majesty" (Queen Victoria) and from that date has been known as "Royal Crown Derby".

Derby porcelains from 1878 to 1890 carry only the standard crown printed mark. After 1891 the mark carries the "Royal Crown Derby" wording; and, in the 20th century "Made in England" and "English Bone China" were added to the mark.

A majority of these porcelains, both tableware and figures, were hand decorated. A variety of printing processes were used for additional adornment. Today, Royal Crown Derby is a part of Royal Doulton Tableware, Ltd.

Plate, 7⅛", Pattern 2451, $50.00.

Bowl, 4 ftd, chinoiserie dec	100.00
Coffee Pot, 2 pint, Imari pattern.	400.00
Creamer and Sugar, cov, Dublin shape, Imari pattern.	295.00

Cups and Saucers

Coffee, Imari pattern, 1921.	68.00
Cream ground, floral garlands, gold trim, c1820	90.00
Tea, Imari pattern, 1887.	75.00
Dinner Service, 42 pcs, vine pattern. . .	475.00
Ewer, 7½", reticulated neck and handle with raised gold dec on cobalt ground, body with enameled flowers on gold ground	650.00
Lamp Base, 7¼", factory drilled, seascape, blue and white, artist sgd, W. E. Dean, dated 1937	125.00

Plates

6", Imari pattern	40.00
8¾" scalloped, turquoise and encrusted gold jeweled border, scenic center, view of Tissington Spires, Dovedale, artist, E. Troswell	200.00
9", luncheon, Japanese pattern, blue, iron red and gilt, set of 12	450.00
10½", service, circular shaped edge enclosing swag border, plain center, set of 12.	400.00

Toby Pitcher, 4¼″, man taking snuff,
polychromed enamel, black hat and
shoes, flowered vest, striped pants,
late 19th C **300.00**
Vases
   4¼″, yellow, gold leaves, 1890 . . . . . **150.00**
   9″, buff ground, paisley design, multicolored enamel jewels **435.00**
   10″, pink ground, single hp blossom **425.00**
   12¾″, gourd shape, white and gold reticulated handles, green-blue
   ground, raised gold trim, enameled
   multicolored leaf dec, c1880 . . . . . **750.00**
Vegetable Dish, 10″ l, 7½″ w, Imari
style **95.00**

ROYAL
DOULTON
FLAMBE

ROYAL DOULTON

History: Doulton pottery began in 1815 under
the direction of John Doulton at the Doulton &
Watts pottery in Lambeth, England. Early output
was limited to salt-glazed industrial stoneware.
John Watts retired in 1854. The firm became Doulton and Company and production was expanded
to include hand decorated stoneware such as figurines, vases, dinnerware, and flasks. In 1872 the
firm began marking their ware "Royal Doulton."

In 1878, John's son, Sir Henry Doulton, purchased Pinder Bourne & Co. in Burslem and the
companies became Doulton & Co., Ltd. in 1882.
Decorated porcelain was added to Doulton's earthenware production in 1884. The Royal Doulton
mark was used on both wares.

Most Doulton figurines were produced at the Burslem plants from 1890 until 1978, when they were
discontinued. A new line of Doulton figurines was
introduced in 1979.

Beginning in 1913, an "HN" number was assigned to each new Doulton figurine design. The
"HN" numbers refers to Harry Nixon, a Doulton
artist. "HN" numbers were chronological until 1940,
after which blocks of numbers were assigned to
each modeler. From 1928 until 1954, a small number appeared to the right of the crown mark; this
number added to 1927 gives the year of manufacture of the figurines.

Dickens ware, in eathenware and porcelain, was
introduced in 1908. The ware decorated with characters from Dicken's novels. The line was with-
drawn in the 1940s, except for plates which continued until 1974.

Character jugs, a 20th century revival of early
Toby models, were designed by Charles J. Noke
for Doulton in the 1930s. They come in 4 major

sizes and feature fictional characters from Dick-
en's, Shakespeare and other English and American
novelists, and historical heros.

Doulton's Rouge Flambee (also Veined Sung) is
a highly glazed, strong colored ware noted most
for the fine modeling and exquisite colorings, especially in the animal items. The process used to
produce the vibrant colors in this ware is a Doulton
secret.

Production of stoneware at Lambeth ceased in
1956; production of porcelain continues today at
Burslem.

Reference: Ralph and Terry Kovel, *The Kovel's
Illustrated Price Guide to Royal Doulton*, Crown,
1980.

Animal Models
   Bull Terrier, HN 1132 . . . . **180.00**
   Cocker Spaniel, HN 1078 . . . . **70.00**
   Peacock, HN 2577 . . . . **85.00**
   Pig, HN 2650 . . . . **45.00**
   Siamese Cat, standing, HN 2660 . . . **45.00**
   St. Bernard, K 19 . . . . **25.00**
Ashtray, Dick Turpin, dated 1937 . . . . . **125.00**
Bowls
   Bunnykins, small **30.00**
   Shakespeare series, large **95.00**
Busts, pr, miniature, Sam Weller & Sairey
   Gamp **150.00**
Cake Plate, Coaching Days & Ways . . . **55.00**
Candlesticks, pr, Battle of Hastings,
   8¾″ **190.00**
Character Jugs, 1¼″
   Cardinal **200.00**
   John Peel **220.00**
   Micawber **110.00**
   Mr. Pickwick **200.00**
   Sairey Gamp **75.00**
   Sam Weller **100.00**
Character Jugs, Miniature, 2¼″ to 2½″
   'Ard of 'Earing **925.00**
   Cardinal, A mark **50.00**
   Dick Turpin, A mark **50.00**
   Fat Boy, A mark **60.00**
   Mr. Micawber **50.00**
   Ophelia **75.00**
   Paddy **52.00**
   Robin Hood, A mark **60.00**
   Tony Weller **55.00**
   Town Crier **120.00**
   Viking **110.00**
Character Jugs, 3½″ to 4″
   'Arriet **65.00**
   'Arry **75.00**
   Cap'n Cuttle, A mark **80.00**
   Cavalier **60.00**
   Fat Boy **85.00**
   Gladiator **275.00**
   John Peel **65.00**
   Old Charley **45.00**
   Sam Johnson, A mark **165.00**
   Ugly Duchess **250.00**

Charactor Jugs, 5¼ to 7"
Apothecary 50.00
Auld Mac 95.00
Don Quixote 55.00
Falconer 55.00
Jockey, A mark 150.00
Long John Silver 55.00
Old Charley 50.00
Simon the Cellarer 125.00
Tam O'Shanter 85.00
Viking 145.00
Chop Plate, Treasure Island, 13" . . . 90.00
Coffee Set, Chelsea Rose, pot and 4
demitasse cups and saucers 125.00

**Vase, 12", cobalt blue base, tan top,
$165.00.**

Creamer and Sugar, Coaching Days &
Ways 75.00
Cup and Saucer, demitasse, Pied Piper,
brown, King's Ware 65.00
Dickens Ware
Bowls
Artful Dodger, 7" 70.00
Barkis, 6" 50.00
Mr. Pickwick, 8¾", sq. 85.00
Condiment set, Bill Sykes & Mr.
Pickwick 175.00
Creamer, Tony Weller, 4" 80.00
Cup and saucer, Tony Weller, ... 70.00
Jug, Bill Sykes, miniature, 2½" 80.00
Match holder, Mr. Squeers, 2" 70.00
Mug, Tony Weller, 4¼" 110.00
Pitchers
Barkis, 6" 85.00
Fagin, 7" 85.00
Plates
Alfred Jingle, 6" 45.00

Barkis, 7½ 55.00
Sam Weller, 8½" 65.00
Teapot, Bill Sykes, 6", rect. 225.00
Tray, Sergeant Buz Fuz, 18 x 8" 175.00
Vase, Sidney Carton, 6¾" h, 3½" d, 2
handled 135.00
Ewer, 9¼", floral dec, hp, relief molded,
Burslem 150.00
Figurines
Alice 160.00
Ballerina 190.00
Boy & Peacock 150.00
Carpet Seller 215.00
Cobbler 200.00
Curly Nob 355.00
Daphne 130.00
Easter Day 240.00
Elsie Maynard 550.00
Jennifer, #2392 . . . . 95.00
Lady Fayre 375.00
Lady with hat, 1920 . . . . 125.00
Master Sweep 600.00
Melanie 200.00
Mermaid 525.00
Newsboy 450.00
Polly Peachbum, #549 . . . . 215.00
Scribe, #305 . . . . 825.00
Sweet & 20, #1589 . . . . 165.00
Uriah Heep 250.00
Victorian Lady, #1245 . . . . 350.00
Wood Nymph, #2192 . . . . 215.00
Flambe
Animal Models
Frog, 2" 175.00
Monkey, 2" 200.00
Bowls
4", Bernard Moore 50.00
7", sgd Noke 110.00
Menu holder, rabbit 250.00
Plate, Laughing Cavalier, Sung,
10" 225.00
Vases
House on lake, 12" 160.00
Scenic, 13", artist sgd 700.00
Sung, fish dec, artist sgd 1,000.00
Flask, Mrs. Caudle, stoneware, buff and
brown, c1846 . . . . 800.00
Gibson Girl Plates
A Quiet Dinner with Dr. Bottles After
Which He Reads Aloud Miss Bab-
ble's Latest Work 80.00
Message From the Outside
World 80.00
Miss Babbles Brings a Copy of the
Morning Paper, and Expresses Her
Indignation and Sympathy Over a
Scurrilous Article, Meanwhile, Other
Friends Are Calling Upon the
Editor 75.00
She Becomes a Trained Nurse 85.00
She Contemplates the Cloister 85.00
She Finds Some Consolation in Her
Mirror 80.00

She Goes into Colors 80.00
She is Subject or More Hostile Criticism 75.00
Humidor, cov, Doc Berry 55.00
Jam Jar, cov, with attached underplate, Gaffers, 4″ 120.00
Jardiniere, Ophelia & Hamlet, 8⅝″ h, 10″ d 325.00
Jugs
Captain Cuttle, A mark, 3½″ 90.00
Fat Boy, 2¼″ 55.00
Mugs, Large
'Ard of 'Earing 800.00
Gondolier 475.00
Izaak Walton 60.00
Veteran Motorist 50.00
Pitchers
Goffers series, man smoking pipe, wearing smock and tall black hat, 5¾″ 100.00
Night Watchman, dated 1908, 6″ 95.00
Old London series, Garrick at St. John's Gate, 3 scenes, blue and white, sgd Nunn, 6¾″ 150.00
Parson Brown, King's Ware, 7″ 100.00
The Eglinton Tournament, 7½″ 150.00
Plaques
Babes in Woods, lady with child at edge of woods, flow blue, 14″ 275.00
Twelve Disciples, sgd, George Tinworth, 9″ 300.00
Plates
Portia, Shakespeare series, 10″ 70.00
The Diversions of Uncle Toby 45.00
Platter, Madras, flow blue, 16½ x 20″ 225.00
Teapot, Glamis Thistle 75.00
Tobacco Jars
Caviliers, Here's A Health Unto His Majesty, blue and white 100.00
Izaak Walton 150.00
Toby Jugs, Seated
Capt Ahab, D 6506, dated 1958, Doulton & Co, Ltd, 4″ 60.00
Old Charley, 6030, c1940, 8¾″ 145.00
Robin Hood, 3½″ 55.00
Toothpick, Izaak Walton 95.00
Tray, Barnaby Rudge, 4 x 5⅜″ 50.00
Vases
Corn flowers, blue, cream, gold leaves and trim, artist sgd, E. Wood, 5¾″ h, pr 265.00
Dutchman, King's Ware, 4″ 70.00
Flowers, emb, brown, blue-grey, artist sgd, Florence Roberts, dated 1885, 10 2/8 x 5⅛″ 200.00
Impressed Leaves, flared rim, ftd, 7½″ 100.00
Lovers in garden, white, Burslem, 3″ 45.00
Wall Pocket, blackbirds, dated 1937 .... 200.00
Wash Bowl and Pitcher, 10½″ pitcher, 16¼″ d, 4¾″ h bowl, 8 sides, lilacs, green leaves, black navy and gold trim 250.00

ROYAL DUX

History: Royal Dux porcelain was made in Dux, Bohemia (Czechoslovakia) by E. Eichler at the Duxer Porzellan-Manufaktur, established in 1860. Many items were exported to the United States. By the turn of the century Royal Dux figurines, vases, and accessories were captivating consumers, especially Art Nouveau designs.

A raised triangle with an acorn and the letter "E" plus Dux, Bohemia was used as a mark between 1900 and 1914.

Bookends, pr, 9½″, figures of Pierrot, blue and white, c1900 .... 325.00
Bowls
11 x 7½″, oval, ftd, white, gold dec, Art Nouveau woman's head on each end 225.00
13½ x 7″, oval, lady sits on side, flower in hand, lavender, green, and gold 660.00

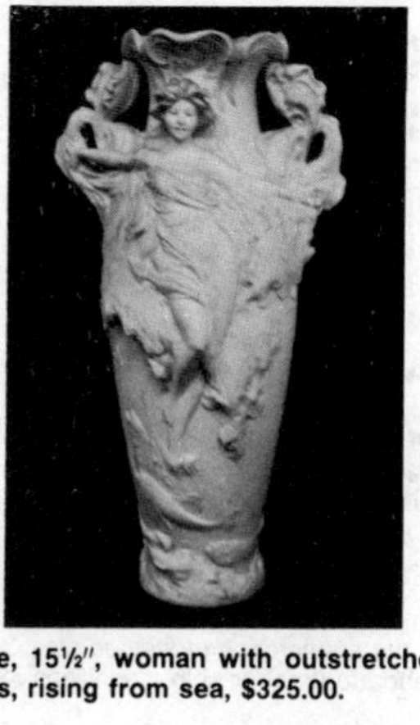

Vase, 15½″, woman with outstretched arms, rising from sea, $325.00.

Bust, young girl, iris blossoms in her long hair, blossom in low cut bodice, pale green, lavender and cream, imp mark, c1900 .... 1,050.00
Centerpieces
7½″ h, 9″ w, girl with basket and goose, flower bowl base, pink triangle mark 350.00

16½" 1, 2 draped females beside shell form bowl on swelling wave, flowers and leafage, green, pink, and beige, imp mark 725.00

Ewer, 10", multicolored applied fruit and flowers 195.00

Figurines

Cherub holding seashell, 9" 225.00

Fawn, cautious stance, oak foliage, imp artist sgd, pink triangle mark, 11½" 1, 8" h 110.00

Girl with cow, bucket in hand, white . 450.00

Lady and Gentleman, pr, lady with long pink dress, plumed hat, gentleman, green frock coat, holding hat in one hand and rose in the other, 22½" 750.00

Lady holding fan, pink, mkd Royal Dux, Bohemia, 9" 275.00

Peasants, pr, man and woman, pink, green, and gold, mkd Royal Dux, Bohemia, 11½" h, 4" d, ... 550.00

Stallions, one galloping, the other in rearing prance, flowing manes, imp artist sgd, pink triangle, 15" 1, 11½" h 125.00

Planter, 17 x 11 x 5½", shell on sides, scroll handles 385.00

Tray, 14" 1, 8" w, boy and girl in center, flower in relief at edges 395.00

Vases

5", applied flowers and fruit, orange and brown 95.00

11½", gray, 2 maidens sitting on each side of reticulated rim, pink triangle mark 285.00

15", green, applied orange poppies, mkd 100.00

17", Art Nouveau, full figures of young ladies 650.00

ROYAL FLEMISH

History: Royal Flemish was produced by the Mt. Washington Glass Co., New Bedford, Massachusetts. The process was patented by Albert Steffin in 1894.

Royal Flemish has heavy raised gold enamel lines on frosted transparent glass that separates areas into sections, often colored in russet tones. It gives the appearance of stained glass windows with elaborate floral or coin medallions in the design.

Advisors: Clarence and Betty Maier.

Biscuit Jar, 8" h, cylindrical shape, pale red roses and gold leaves over typical lines of raised gold which create panels in shades of tan, emb SP lid and bail, sgd 1,200.00

Cologne, 5½" h, clear, frosted, body with enamel dec of beautiful butterfly and daisies, heavy gold tracery on dark maroon enamel neck and lid, frosted clear glass finial 4,000.00

Ewer, 12", shield and lion on front, cross on reverse, applied handle which has cooling check 1,000.00

Vase, 6" d, Roman heads within medallions, sgd, orig label, $2,750.00.

Lamp, 11" h, vase with five large and five small GUBA ducks flying past a setting sun, years ago (perhaps at the factory) the base was drilled and a lamp conversion done 1,500.00

Pitcher, 7¼" h, 7¼" max d, typical panels in shades of tan over which are blossoms and foliage in silver, each of five blossoms has applied berry-like centers, clear glass handle, unsigned 2,250.00

Rose Jar, 9" h, round with beautiful enamel roses, small round collar at top with small ball-shaped lid, lid with jewel which replaced the original finial 2,250.00

Vases

5¾" h, 7¼" d, squatty shape, pastel colored pansies dec, unsigned . . . 1,750.00

9½", glass bead covered with gold enamel simulate berries hanging from the raised gold vines that encircle vase, panels in tones of tan and brown, top with gold tracery dec, two scroll handles, unsigned . 1,450.00

14", baluster shape with slender neck flaring to a fold-in tricorn top, panels of soft blue color with dec of mythical figures and florals in gold, sgd 3,100.00

14½", cylindrical with slight taper toward top, three snow geese in flight, blazing gold sun in background, over panels of soft blue, mauve, and green 3,500.00

GERMANY

RUDOLSTADT

ROYAL RUDOLSTADT

History: Johann Fredrich von Schwarzburg-Rudolstadt was the patron of a faience factory located in Rudolstadt, Thuringen, East Germany, from 1720 to c1790. The pottery's mark was a hayfork and later crossed two-prong hayforks in imitation of the Meissen mark.

In 1854 Ernst Bohne established a factory in Rudolstadt. His pieces are marked "EB."

Royal Rudolstadt has its name origin with wares imported by Lewis Straus and Sons (later Nathan Straus and Sons) of New York from the New York and Rudolstadt Pottery between 1187 and 1918. The factory's mark was a diamond enclosing the initials "RW" and which was surmounted by a crown. The factory manufactured several of the Rose O'Neill (Kewpie) items.

Bon Bon Dish, small, handled, white ground, pink rose dec	52.50
Bowl, 9", scalloped gold rim, hp roses and grapes, green leaves.	50.00
Biscuit Jar, 7½", hp blue and lavender violets, gold trim	175.00
Cake Plate, 10¼", hp white flower dec	40.00
Celery Tray, 13" l, handled, hp yellow roses, gold trim, artist sgd	92.50
Chocolate Set, pot, 6 cups and saucers, orchid dec on cream ground, heavy gold trim	250.00
Creamer, 4", white ground, red roses, green leaves, gold trim	65.00
Ewer, 7", ivory ground, multicolored raised floral sprays, gold trim, imp mark	75.00
Hair Receiver, 4¼", yellow ground, yellow roses, green leaves, gold trim . .	95.00
Hat Pin Holder, white ground, hp roses, green leaves.	50.00
Inkwell with attached saucer, 6" d, 3½" h, cream ground, multicolored flowers	60.00
Pitchers	
5½", cream ground, floral dec, gold trim.	45.00
8¾", white ground, hp multicolored floral dec.	80.00
Plates	
8", eight kewpies, hp foliage border, sgd.	120.00
8¼", green shaded to white, white	

and lavender pansies, gold design border.	75.00
8½", hp forget-me-nots	35.00
9⅝", purple floral dec, gold highlights.	62.50
Salt and Pepper, white ground, red rose dec.	55.00
Tray, 11½" l, 9" w, white ground, pink roses	75.00
Urn, 14", shaded blue ground, floral dec, gold handles and trim.	175.00
Vases	
8¾", purple violets dec, gold trim, handled.	75.00
10", cream to beige ground, multicolored pastel floral spray, reticulated gold neck and handles, blue mark.	160.00

Creamer and sugar, cov, cream ground with turquoise, pink and gold leaf dec, gold handles and finial, mkd, $75.00.

13½" cylindrical, ivory ground, orange and pink flowers, green and brown leaves, molded gold scroll and detail, blue mark #6230	125.00
14", cylindrical, shaded beige ground, multicolored floral sprays, molded gold scrolls	200.00

ROYAL VIENNA

History: Production of hard paste porcelain in Vienna began in 1720 with Claude Innocentius du Paquier, a runaway employee of the Meissen factory. In 1744 Empress Maria Theresa brought the factory under royal patronage; and, subsequently the ware became known as Royal Vienna. The firm went through many administrative changes until it closed in 1864. The quality of its workmanship always was maintained.

Many other Austrian and German firms copied the Royal Vienna products, including the use of the "Beehive" mark. Many of the pieces on today's market are from these firms.

Bowl, 10″, portrait, amber, rose, and deep burgundy, gold grape clusters . . 485.00

Chocolate Pot, 12″, cream ground, violets, much gold 165.00

Chocolate Set, pot, creamer, sugar, and tray, portrait of noble woman, gold gilt, maroon lined borders 155.00

Cups and Saucers
Coffee, ext. metallic green with gold, int. alpine village scene, beehive logo 165.00
Demitasse, yellow and gilt borders, scroll handle 25.00

Ewer, 10½″, beige to cream ground, violets, gold handle 400.00

Figurines
Cockatoos, white with turquoise and brown, beehive mark, c1900, 6″ h, pr 145.00
Young boy, vivid, enamels, imp beehive mark, #837, 7″ 285.00

Plates
9¼″, blue-green lustre border with raised arabesque motifs, center medallion "Maedchen mit Rosen," artist sgd Wagner 875.00

Urn, 9½″, **2 paintings, artist sgd "Homer," $1,200.00.**

9½″, hp medallion, girl in red dress with mandolin, shivering among snowflakes, platinum gray lustre border with raised gold arabesque dec, artist sgd Wagner, underglaze blue shield mark 950.00

9¾″, portrait, mother and daughter, floral border, gold stamped Royal Vienna in overglaze, ZS & Co./Bavaria in underglaze 150.00

10″, portrait, lady, cobalt blue, elabo-rate raised gold border, artist sgd H. Roldus, underglaze blue beehive 325.00

Platter, 14½″, 4 court ladies, much gold over deep reds, rainbow ground, 2 handles 150.00

Pokal, 13″, blue with gold dec, center panel with children in musical parade, artist sgd A. Ulich, beehive mark 350.00

Urns, covered
9½″, Diana and cupid in gilt cartouche, heavy gilt royal blue ground, c1910 . . . . 150.00
10½″, cobalt blue, hp mythological scene, after C. Keen, beehive mark, late 19th C. 110.00
Medallion with figures on top and bottom, much gold, 2 gold handles, blue beehive mark, orig paper label with Carlsbad 1904 . . . . . 450.00

Vases
10″, irid, ruby, raised gold flowers, portrait bust of lady with long brown hair, mkd 285.00
10¾″, portrait, full figure Victorian lady, elaborate gold dec, 2 handles, Königin Luise, beehive mark 800.00
12″, maroon, heavy gold beading, portrait, girl, red dress, long flowing hair, sgd Wagner 850.00

ROYAL WORCESTER

History: In 1751 the Worcester Porcelain Company, led by Dr. John Wall and William Davis, acquired the Bristol pottery of Benjamin Lund and moved it to Worcester. The first wares were painted blue under the glaze, followed closely by painting on the glaze in enamel colors. Among the most famous 18th century decorators were James Giles and Jeffreys Hamet O'Neale. Transfer-print decoration was developed by the 1760s.

A series of partnerships took over upon Davis's death in 1783: Flight (1783–93), Flight & Barr (1793–1807), Barr, Flight & Barr (1807–13), and Flight, Barr & Barr (1813–40). In 1840 the factory was moved to Chamberlain & Co. in Diglis. Decorative wares were discontinued. In 1852 W. H. Kerr and R. W. Binns formed a new company and revived the ornamental wares.

In 1862 the firm became the Royal Worcester Porcelain Co. Among the key modelers of the late 19th century were James Hadley and his three sons and George Owen, expert at pierced clay pieces. Royal Worcester absorbed the Grainger factory in 1889 and the James Hadley factory in 1905. Modern designers include Dorothy Boughty and Doris Lindner.

Museum: Charles William Dyson Perrins Museum, Worcester, England.

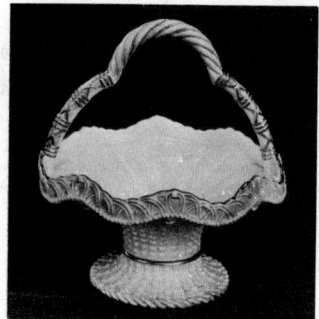

Basket, 5³/₄″ h, cane weave base, twisted reed handle, tan, gold highlights, purple mark, Reg. 26402/1080, c1891, $450.00.

Biscuit Jar, 6″ h, 4⁷/₈″ d, beige satin finish, multicolored pastel flowers, green leaves, date mark 1907 . . . . **275.00**

Bowls
    4 ⁵/₈″ h, 9″ d, beige, emb basketweave, large pink and green grape leaves, gold trim, c1896 . . . **350.00**
    7³/₄″, boat shape, pedestal base, gold handles, floral dec, gilt trim, date mark 1918 . . . . **380.00**

Candlesticks, pr, 10¹/₂″, blue, 4 ram's heads on each, date mark 1893 . . . . **275.00**

Compote, ftd, beaded wavy edge, wide gilt and cobalt dec band, center, painted fruit, early 19th C **150.00**

Creamer, 5¹/₂″, beige, floral dec, gold handle, rim, and base, sgd **150.00**

Creamer and Sugar, matte finish, ivory, gold emb pattern, c1886 . . . . **125.00**

Cup, 1³/₄″ h, 3 handles, beige, flowers, 1891 . . . . **90.00**

Dessert Service, 22 pcs, 8¹/₈″ vase, 9″ plates, cov sauce tureens, stands, oval and circular dishes, fruit centers, scrolled apricot borders, gilt motifs, sgd R. Sebright, dated 1914 or 1917. **4,730.00**

Dish, 9³/₄″, center, floral bouquet within gilt C-scroll and foliage, gilt dentril rim, c1770. . . . . **150.00**

Ewers
    6″, floral sprays, gold coiled handle, c1889 . . . . **135.00**
    11¹/₄″, bulbous, lizard handle, multicolored floral dec, 1884 . . . . **170.00**
    12″, fully reticulated, pale beige with gold trim and handle, Grainger, date mark 1898. . . . . **825.00**

Flask, 10″, moon shape, footed, handles, round panel with floral dec, date mark 1875 . . . . **475.00**

Figurines
    Bird, Scissor-tailed Flycatchers, modeled by Dorothy Doughty **550.00**
    Dog, Golden Retriever by Lindner #3309 Sandon **150.00**
    Frog, 3 ×2¹/₂ ts 1 ¹/₂″, white, sgd, c1890 . . . . **185.00**
    Goosie, Goosie, Gander, 5¹/₂″ **225.00**

Jardiniere, 18³/₄″ w, oval, lobed and fluted, pedestal base, floral dec, gilt trim, 1899 . . . . **800.00**

Jug, 6″ h, 7″ w, sq, Japanese tea ware, white with emb sprays and butterflies, bronze lizard handle, dated 1874 . . . **525.00**

Mug, 3¹/₈″ h, 3 ¹/₄″ d, beige satin, multicolored flowers, date mark 1903. . . . **140.00**

Pitchers
    3¹/₄″, high glaze, ivory ground, red bird, sgd, 1911 . . . . **135.00**
    4¹/₄″ h, 3″ d, beige satin, multicolored flowers, teal blue and gold handle, date mark 1899 . . . . **175.00**
    6¹/₂″, cream ground, gold mums outlined in red front and back, burnished gold trim, ornate handle, date mark 1888 . . . . **145.00**
    6¹/₂″, floral dec, elephant head handle, gilt band top and bottom **275.00**

Plates
    9″, flowers, leaves and pine cones . . **65.00**
    9¹/₄″, cabinet, center chrysanthemum on long stem, leaves and buds, gilt, blue and turquoise border with white enamel jeweling, c1885 . . . . **95.00**

Platter, 19″, oval, center blue flowers, 2″ blue flower border, date mark 1886 . . . . **200.00**

Potpourri Jars
    8″ h, 8″ d, reticulated top and cov, cream ground, multicolored floral sprays, 4 cameo jewels around top, 4 scroll feet, heavy gold, date mark 1890. . . . . **600.00**
    14″ h, 6¹/₂″ d, bulbous, ornate pierced top and inside cov, beige satin finish, yellow and rose flowers, small blue flowers outlined in gold, heavy gold trim, date mark 1919. . . . . . . **1,100.00**

Ring Tree, 2″ h, 3¹/₂″ d, beige satin finish, hp maroon and yellow florals, gold trim, 1912. . . . . **95.00**

Rose Jar, cov, floral dec **300.00**

Teapot, 5¹/₂″, bulbous, cream ground, floral and leaves dec, gold spout, handle, base and finial, date mark 1867 . . . . **300.00**

Toothpick Holder, cream bark with gold leaf dec, gold base and rim, sgd, #1049. . . . . **110.00**

Tureen, cov, 14¹/₂″, matte finish, brown ivy dec, brown and gold elephant head handles, crow's feet finial, matching 15″ ladle, c1880 . . . . **250.00**

Vases

5½″ h, 3¼″ d, basket shape, rope handle, satin finish, multicolored dec, date mark 1893 . . . . **225.00**

6½″ h, 4¼″ d, shell shape, pedestal base, beige, satin finish, gold trim, date mark 1903 . . . . **275.00**

7¼″, cornucopia on scroll base, beige satin finish, orchids, green leaves and gold trim, date mark 1898. **325.00**

8¼″ h, 3⅞″ d, bulbous, small neck, handles, beige satin finish, multicolored flowers, green foliage, gold trim, date mark 1902 . . . . **225.00**

8¾″ h, 6¾″ d, glossy finish, gold serpent handles, gold, silver and brown foliage with heron and butterfly in gold, c1882 . . . . **550.00**

8⅞″ h, 4½″ d, salamander handle, cream satin finish, blue flowers, tan foliage, gold outlining and trim. . . . **435.00**

8⅞″ h, 6½″ d, serpent handles, gold crane in flight, gold and silver florals, dark green and gold leaves and bamboo, gold trim, date mark 1880 . . . . **500.00**

23⅝″, reserve of 3 peacocks perched on gnarled tree in garden, blue matte ground, applied scroll griffin handles, molded griffin base, sgd E. Salter, date mark 1901 . . . . **1,100.00**

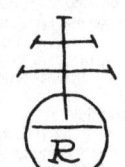

ROYCROFT

History: Earl Hubbard, founder of the Roycrofters in East Aurora, New York, during the turn of the 19th and 20th centuries, was considered a genius in his day. He was an author, lecturer, manufacturer, salesman, and philosopher.

Hubbard established a campus which included a printing plant where he published "*The Philistine*," "*The Fra*," and "*The Roycrofter*." His most famous book was "*A Message to Garcia*," published in 1899. His "community" also included a furniture manufacturing plant, a metal shop, and a leather shop.

References: Nancy Hubbard Brady, *The Book of The Roycrofters*, House of Hubbard, 1977; Nancy Hubbard Brady, *Roycroft Handmade Furniture*, House of Hubbard, 1973; Charles F. Hamilton, *Roycroft Collectibles*, A. S. Barnes & Company, Inc., 1980; Paul McKenna, *A New Pricing Guide For Materials Produced by The Roycroft Printing Shop*, Tona Graphics, 2nd edition, 1982.

Additional Listing: Copper.

Ashtray and Matchbox Holder, 3″ h, 3″ w, copper, stylized flower design, antique green accents, mkd. **50.00**

Book, 1897, *Sesame and Lilies*, John Ruskin, Roycroft publication **155.00**

Bookends, pr, 8½″ h, 5¾″ w, open frame style, hammered copper, design down sides, mkd **60.00**

Bud Vase Stand, 7¼″ h, sq base, handled, glass tube for flower, mkd **75.00**

Cigarette holder, 2¾″ h, 3″ d at top, c1919, $35.00.

Candlesticks, pr, thin stem, circular base, copper, hammered brass finish, style 420, mkd **200.00**

Chair, arm, oak, 24 x 22 x 26″, leather seat, mkd **225.00**

Chambersticks, pr, 2¼″ h, round, ftd, curved handles, copper, brass finish, some wear, style 415, mkd **45.00**

Chest, 44 x 20 x 47½″, 3 drawer, mkd **950.00**

Desk Organizer, 4″ h, 11½″ w, drawer, orig appointment calendar, mkd **80.00**

Frame, standing, 5″ h, 3″ w, smooth brass finish, mkd **45.00**

Inkwell, 1¾″ h, 3″ w, hinged cov, hammered copper, dark patina, no insert, style, 703, mkd **50.00**

Lamp, 18″ h, round base, slender midsection, helmet shade, hammered copper, mkd **420.00**

Tobacco Jar, cov, 6″ h, 8″ w, cylindrical, flange slotted, holds 6 pipes, smooth burnished copper finish, mkd **50.00**

Tray, 9¾″ d, octagonal, handled, copper, hammered brass finish, style 820, mkd **60.00**

Vases

4⅛″, squat, hammered copper, style 239, mkd. **245.00**

5″, cylindrical, hammered copper, banded design, style 236, mkd . . . **225.00**

6¼", 3" w, cylindrical, hammered copper, applied silvered band, style 203, mkd **465.00**
12¼", hammered copper, "American Beauty", style 210, mkd **330.00**
Wall Sconces, pr, 8¾" h, rect, copper, style 402, mkd **160.00**

RUBENA GLASS

History: Rubena crystal is a transparent blown glass which shades from clear to red. It also is found as the background for frosted and overshot glass. It was made in the late 1800s by several glass companies, including Northwood and Hobbs, Brockunier & Co. of Wheeling, West Virginia.

Rubena was used for several patterns of pattern glass including Royal Ivy and Royal Oak.

Atomizer, 6¾", incised floral dec **135.00**
Biscuit Jar, 7 x 9", melon ribbed body . **165.00**
Celery, IVT, ruffled rim **75.00**
Cologne Bottle, 6 x 2½, overshot, gold bands, fancy cut crystal stopper with gold trim **85.00**
Compote, 5½", wheel engraved floral dec **225.00**
Condiment Set, 5¾ x 4", 2 sq bottles, rect salt, rect mustard, SP holder, ring handle **165.00**
Creamer, Medallion Sprig, clear applied handle **150.00**
Cruets
  IVT, applied clear reeded handle, clear faceted cut stopper **150.00**
  Medallion Sprig, orig stopper **125.00**
Finger Bowl, underplate **75.00**
Mustard Jars
  Baby Thumbprint, enamel floral dec, SP lid **100.00**

Vase, 6", bud, enameled, $50.00.

IVT, blue and yellow flowers, green foliage **75.00**
Perfume Bottle, 5 x 2⅛", clear faceted cut stopper **65.00**
Pitcher, water, Royal Ivy **175.00**
Punch Cup, clear applied reeded handle **80.00**
Spooner, Royal Oak, frosted **100.00**
Toothpick, IVT, bulbous **65.00**
Tumbler, 3¼, enamel dec of crane and leaves **50.00**
Vases
  5", coralene dec, gold trim **275.00**
  11 x 5¼", Jack in the pulpit, ¾" vaseline applied edging **125.00**

RUBENA VERDE GLASS

History: Rubena Verde, a transparent glass that shades from red in the upper section to yellow-green in the lower, was made by Hobbs, Brockunier & Co., Wheeling, West Virginia, in the late 1880s. It often is found in the inverted thumbprint (IVT) pattern, termed "Polk Dot" by Hobbs.

Vase, 4" h, 2¼" d, webbed dec, $230.00

Bowl, 7½", sq, hobnail **100.00**
Butter Dish, 6", round, cov **300.00**
Celery Vase, 6¼", IVT **225.00**
Creamer, 5", bulbous, applied amber handle **200.00**
Cruet, IVT **250.00**
Finger Bowl, 4¼", ruffled rim, hobnail. . **65.00**
Lamp, peg, shell carriage base **175.00**
Pitchers
  7" h, 5½" d, bulbous, sq mouth, applied vaseline handle, IVT **200.00**
  8" h, 7" d, bulbous, sq mouth, applied vaseline handle, hobnail **250.00**
Sweetmeat Dish, 5¾" h, 5¾" d, octagonal top, fine notch cutting around edge, vaseline shell trim applied around center, SP basket frame **125.00**

Syrup, hobnail	**75.00**
Tumbler, 4″, hobnail	**160.00**

Vases
4¼″ IVT	**200.00**
6½″, cylindrical, hobnail	**275.00**
10″, ribbon, enamel floral dec	**90.00**
12¼″ h, 5¼″ d, cylindrical, ruffled rim, int panels, enameled white daisies, coral pink florals, green foliage	**175.00**

RUBY STAINED GLASS, SOUVENIR TYPE

History: Ruby stained glass was produced in the late 1880s and 1890s by several glass manufacturers, primarily in the area of Pittsburgh, Pennsylvania.

Ruby stained items were made from pressed clear glass which was stained with a ruby red material. Pieces often were etched with the name of a person, place, date, or event and sold as souvenirs at fairs and expositions.

In many cases one company produced the pressed glass blanks; and, a second company stained and etched them. Many patterns were used; but, the three most popular were Button Arches, Heart Band, and Thumbprint.

Salt shaker, Button Arches pattern, "A. B. Smith", $30.00.

Creamers
Button Arches, Aberdeen, SD	**20.00**
Heart Bank, Milwaukee, WI	**25.00**
Cruet, Beaded Swirl with Oval Lens, Chicago, IL	**85.00**
Cup, Belfast, ME	**30.00**
Decanter, Pentagon, etched	**60.00**

Goblet
Nail, Mother	**40.00**
Ring Band, Columbian Expo	**15.00**

Mugs
Atlantic City, 1907, 3″	**22.00**
Bernice, 1906, 2⅜″	**20.00**
Henry, 1900, 3″	**20.00**
Hotel Eastman, Hot Springs, AR, 1896, sunk honeycomb pattern, 3″	**45.00**
Pittsburgh, PA, Expo, 1902, 3″	**20.00**
Mustard Pot, World's Fair, 1893, thumbprint pattern, orig lid	**125.00**
Pitcher, 4″, Uncle Jim to Aunt May, 1907	**35.00**
Shot Glass, George, 1910	**25.00**

Toothpicks
Saugerties, NY	**20.00**
Shamrock, Providence, RI	**30.00**

Tumblers
Button Arches, frosted band, Mother-Christmas, 1905	**40.00**
Thumbprint, O. J. Elam, Brockton Fair, 1902	**35.00**

Vases, 6″
Grinnel	**25.00**
Mason City, IA	**30.00**

RUSSIAN ITEMS

History: During the late 19th and early 20th century Russia contained skilled craftsmen in lacquer, silver, and enamel wares. Located mainly in Moscow during the Czarist era, 1880–1917, were a group of master craftsmen, led by Faberge, who created exquisite enamel pieces. Faberge also had an establishment in St. Petersburg and enjoyed the patronage of the Russian Imperial family and the royalty and nobility from throughout Europe.

Almost all enameling was done on silver. Pieces are signed by the artist and the government assayer.

The Russian Revolution in 1917 brought an abrupt end to the century of Russian craftsmanship. The modern Soviet government has exported some inferior enamel and lacquer work, usually lacking in artistic merit. Modern pieces are not collectible.

Advisors: Barbara and Melvin Alpren.

ENAMELS

Beaker, wine, 3″ h, shaded enamel on gilded silver, stylized flowers, Nicholai Alekseev, Moscow, c1900	**800.00**
Bonbonniére, round box, 2″ d, shaded enamel allover design of flowers, foliage and geometric forms, on gilded silver, 6th Masters Artel, Moscow, 1910	**1,500.00**
Bowl, 3⅝″ d, multicolored flowers and foliage on lobed panels set with red hardstone cabochon jewels on gilded	

silver, Marie Semyenova, Moscow, c1900. . . . . **3,500.00**

Charka, lobed form cup with scroll handle, 3⅛" l, multicolored shaded pastel colors with exotic bird enameled inside cup, on gilded silver, maker's mark unclear, Moscow, 1900 . . . . . . **1,200.00**

Cigarette Case, 4¼" l, both sides with fantastic shaded enamel birds on floral multicolored scene on gilded silver, Pavel Ovchinnikov, Moscow, c1900 . **1,750.00**

Cup and Saucer, saucer 4½" d, multicolored stylized flowers and foliage borders of blue beads on gilded silver, Nicholai Zverev, Moscow, c1900 . . . **3,300.00**

Enamel, pill box, 1¾" d, $2,250.00.

Easter Egg, 3⅞" h with stand, enameled with scrolls and foliage, a star at each end on gilded silver, 11th Masters Artel, Moscow, c1900, fitted with stands for conversion to egg cups. **3,300.00**

Jewel Casket, 3" l, miniature trunk shape with knob top and four bun feet, plique-à-jour enamel on gilded filigree silver, makers mark A, assayed Viktor Savinkov, Moscow, 1865 . . . . **2,800.00**

Kovsh, 3½" l, boat shaped with pointed prow, hook handle with pastel flowers allover on gilded silver, 6th Masters Artel, Moscow, c1910 . . . . **1,450.00**

Napkin Ring, 1½" d, stylized enameling on lavender ground on gilded silver, 11th Masters Artel, Moscow, c1910. . . . . **700.00**

Salts

Open, 1¼", bombé form, enameled with flowers and blue beaded border on gilded silver, Ivan Saltykov, Moscow, c1895 . . . . **225.00**

Throne, 4¾" h, chair shape with lift-up seat enameled with stylized foliage and geometric forms and roosters on gilded silver, makers mark T. N. St. Petersburg, c1890, Cyrillic presentation inscription. **2,500.00**

Spoons

Berry, 7¼" l, large bowl with handle enameled in blue and red translucent colors, plique-à-jour enamel on gilded silver, Gustave Klingert, Moscow, c1900 . . . . **1,350.00**

Portrait, 5½" l, fig shaped bowl enameled with a young boyarina, En Plein enamel on gilded silver, Ivan Khlebnikov, Moscow, 1889 . . . . . . **1,400.00**

Sugar Sifter, 6½" l, spoon shape with large perforated bowl, enamel on gilded silver, Anton Kuzmichev, Moscow, 1880. . . . . **325.00**

Tea Caddy, 3¾" h, tapered form with top opening, enameled allover with birds and foliage on gilded silver, Fabergé, Moscow, c1900. . . . . **6,500.00**

SILVER

Beaker, 2⅞" d, engraved with strapwork, foliage, gilded upper border and int., mkd Kiev **275.00**

Bowl, 7¼" d, front nielloed with monogram within a rococo cartouche, Cyrillic inscription "Made in Tobolosk in the year 1773," surrounds with rococo scrolls, flowers, and foliage enclosing on both sides circular reserves, one enclosing two hands lighting tapers from a single flame, inscribed "Its Flame Is Harmless", second with two hands grasping a ring below the inscription "To Break Faith Is To Bring Dishonor", makers mark F. Ch. Assaymaster Lyev Vlasoc, Tobolosk, 1773 . . . . **2,500.00**

Casket, 13¾" l, rect, raised on 4 paw feet, sides chased with strapwork, stylized flowerheads on a pebbled ground, hinged cov with incurved step, chased border, top chased with flowerheads on a matted ground, flowerhead center, Cyrillic maker's marks V. S. S. (Potnikova Losseva #740), Assaymaster Anisim Kuzmin, Moscow, 1747 . . . . **8,500.00**

Cigar Box, 7⅛" l, rect, hinged cov, sides engraved with tax bands, ground chased to simulate wood grain, int. gilded with Cyrillic inscription, dated Jan. 13, 1876–1926, Khlebnikov, Moscow **2,750.00**

Key, 7⅝" l, Chamberlain's key of Czar Alexander II, top with Imperial eagle and cypher, fluted stem wrapped with oak leaves and openwork bit, makers mark J. U., St. Petersburg, 1855–64 . . . . **2,000.00**

Kovsh, 8" l, front monogrammed within oval foliate reserve, handle in shape of bird's head, Orest Kurylukov, Moscow, c1910 . . . . **850.00**

Salt, 5¼", form of boyarina holding a kovsh, Moscow, c1910 . . . . **1,200.00**

Salver, 11" d, octagonal, straight gardoon edge, border engraved, center engraved with Neptune driving through the waves, inscribed "He rules four continents", 3 bun supports, Assaymaster Kuzma Grigoriev, Moscow, 1745 . . . . **1,400.00**

Sugar, cov, 5¼" l, 2 handles, engraved with architectural views, flowers, foliage, strapwork, makers mark I. A. in script, Moscow, c1861 . . . . **250.00**

Tea Glass Holders, pr, 6¼" l, open work circular bases raised on 3 foliate feet, centers dec with swags of graduated beading, scroll handles, beaded borders, mkd Assaymaster Nikifor Moschalkin, St. Petersburg, c1794 . . . . . **1,500.00**

MISCELLANEOUS

Box, cov, 11" l, lacquerware, scenic lid **450.00**

Easter Egg, 4½" h, porcelain, front with St. Alexei, Metropolitan of Moscow, borders painted and gilded with Cross of Golgotta on brick red ground **1,200.00**

Humidor, 5" d, 4½" h, lacquerware, hp top, mkd inside with Russian coin mark, c1850 . . . . **400.00**

Icon, 12" h, wood, St. Nicholas, painted, brilliant colors, gilt **750.00**

Plates, 9¾", pr, porcelain, military scenes, first with mounted officer and four officers on foot; second with three officers on foot, one saluting, and 4th officer standing next to horse in background, gilded borders with ribbon tied branches on lilac ground, Black Russian Imperial Eagles within circular medallions, inscribed on back, mkd twice with Imperial cypher, once in green, once in blue **2,250.00**

Soup Tureen, cov, stand, 11½" h, porcelain, circular, twig form handles, white ground, caramel borders with gilding, Kuznetzov, c1900 . . . . **600.00**

Statue, bronze, 21½" h, mounted horseman with falcon perched on shoulder, Evgenie Alexandrovich, Lanceray, c1870 . . . . **5,000.00**

Vase, 21" h, porcelain, ovoid body, painted on one side with a scene of ships in a harbor, royal blue surrounds, gilded borders, 2 gilded foliate spiral handles, mkd with blue Imperial cypher, c1825 . . . . **5,000.00**

SABINO GLASS

History: Sabino glass, named for its creator Ernest Marius Sabino, originated in France in the 1920s and is an art glass which was produced in a wide range of decorative glassware: frosted, clear, opalescent, and colored glass. Both blown and pressed moldings were used. Hand sculpted wooden molds that were cast in iron were used and are still in use at the present time.

In 1960 the company introduced a line of figurines, one to eight inches high, plus other items in a fiery opalescent glass in the Art Deco style. Gold was added to the batch to attain the fiery glow. These pieces are the sabino that is most commonly found today. Sabino is marked with the name in the mold, an etched signature, or both.

Scent bottle, 6 nudes, inscribed Sabino, France, $100.00.

Ashtray, swallow, 3½"	40.00
Birds	
Baby	25.00
Baby on stump, 4"	55.00
Dove, head up	24.00
Fighting, 2 x 2¾"	25.00
Kingfisher on stump, 4½"	65.00
Mocking, 4½ x 6"	90.00
Nesting.	25.00
Shivering	55.00
Stork	150.00
Woodpecker	60.00
Bowls	
Beehive, 7" h, 7" d	165.00
Shell	150.00
Box, powder, Petailia	95.00
Butterfly, open or closed wings, 2¾" . .	30.00
Chick drinking, 3¾"	55.00

Dogs
German Shepherd	25.00
Pekinese, 2¾ x 3¾″	60.00
Dove, head up or down, 1¾″	22.00
Dragonfly, 5¼ x 6″	130.00
Elephant	22.00
Fish swimming, 4 x 4″	55.00
Gazelle	80.00
Isadora Duncan	910.00
Knife Rest, fish	22.00
Lady and Doves	300.00
Madonna, 5″	80.00
Mouse, 3″	55.00

Nudes
Kneeling, 6″	235.00
Silhouette, gold opalescent, 7″	140.00
Panthers, grouping, 5¾ x 7¾″	500.00

Perfume Bottles
Gaite	85.00
Petalia	100.00
Plate, sailing ship, sgd C. Harris, dated 1912, 8½″	225.00
Rabbit, 2″	20.00
Rooster, 7″	30.00
Snail, 1 x 3″	30.00
Snail Shell, 2 x 3″	60.00
Squirrel, 3″	28.00
Staute of woman, draped, 7¼″	400.00
Swan, 2″	20.00
Tray, birds on water	75.00
Turkey, 2″	30.00
Turtle, ¾ x 2″	20.00
Venus de Milo, 4½″	50.00

Vases
Beehive, bulbous, opalescent, blue, France	235.00
Bees on honeycomb	165.00
La Danse	975.00
Paradise	750.00

ℂ 𝒮 SALOPIAN

SALOPIAN WARE

History: Salopian ware was made at Caughley Pot Works, Salop, Stropshire, England, in the 18th century by Thomas Turner. The ware is polychrome on transfer. One time classified as Polychrome Transfer, it retains the more popular name of Salopian. Wares are marked with an "S" or "Salopian" impressed or painted under the glaze. Much of it was sold through Turner's Salopian warehouse in London.

Bowls
6¼″, Milkmaid and Cow, multicolored	125.00
6¾″, Oriental scene, black transfer	150.00
Charger, 11″, Bird on Branch, blue transfer	400.00

Creamer and Sugar, man and woman having tea in garden, black transfer	450.00
Cup Plate, 4½″, Double Deer	350.00

Cups and Saucers, Handleless
Bird on Branch, blue transfer	180.00
Castle ruins, black transfer, blue rim	100.00
Cottage scene, deer in foreground	120.00

Cup and saucer, handleless, 3⅝″ d cup, 5⅞″ d saucer, Cottage, $120.00.

Dish, 10″, oval, Milkmaid and Cow, scalloped edge, blue transfer	200.00

Mugs
2¼″, Cottage and Bird	450.00
2½″, Double Deer, five colors	400.00
Pitcher, 5½″, Oriental river scene, blue transfer, c1790	400.00
Plate, 8½″, Double Deer	250.00
Salt, master, ftd, Floral and Leaves	500.00
Saucer, 4⅝″, Oriental scene, brown transfer	125.00
Teapot, 4″ h, 8¼″ l, boy currying lamb, blue transfer	475.00
Toddy, 4½″, castle ruins, black transfer, blue rim	135.00
Waste Bowl, 6⅜″, 2¾″ h, Britannia, floral designs, brown transfer and polychrome enameling	100.00

SALT AND PEPPER SHAKERS

History: Collecting salt and pepper shakers, whether late 19th century glass forms or the contemporary figural and souvenir types, is becoming more and more popular. The supply and variety is practically unlimited; the price for most sets is within the budget of cost conscious, young collectors. Finally, their size offers an opportunity to assemble a large collection in a small amount of space.

One can specialize in types, forms, or makers. Great art glass artisans such as Joseph Locke, Nicholas Kopp, and others designed salt and pepper shakers in the normal course of their work.

Arthur Goodwin Peterson is the leading research scholar in the field. His *Glass Salt Shakers: 1,000 Patterns* provide the reference number given below. Peterson made a beginning; there are hundreds, perhaps thousands of patterns still to be catalogued.

The clear colored and colored opaque sets command the highest prices, clear and white sets the lowest. Although some shakers, e.g., the tomato or fig, have a special patented top and need it to hold value, it is not detrimental to the price to replace the top of a shaker.

The figural and souvenir type is often looked down upon by collectors. Sentiment and whimsy are prime collecting motivations. The large variety and current low prices indicate a potential for long term price growth.

Generally older shakers are priced by the piece, figural and souvenir types by the set. The pricing method is indicated at each division. All shakers are assumed to have original tops unless noted. Identification numbers are from Peterson's Book.

References: Helene Guarnaccia, *Salt & Pepper Shakers*, Collector Books, 1984; Mildred and Ralph Lechner, *The World of Salt Shakers*, Collector Books, 1976; Arthur G. Peterson, *Glass Salt Shakers: 1000 Patterns*, Wallace-Homestead, 1970.

Additional Listings: See *Warman's Americana & Collectibles* for more examples.

Advisor: Bea Morgan.

Pillar Rib, satin glass hp floral dec, two piece pewter top, Mt. Washington, P-1680, $85.00

ART GLASS (Priced individually)

Amberina, reverse, IVT, pewter top . . .	165.00
Barrel, ribbed, Mt. Washington, Burmese, floral motif, satin finish, 2 pc pewter top with finial, Peterson 154-A.	200.00
Egg, flat side, satin finish, 2½″ l, pewter top, 28-B; Mt. Washington made Co-	

lumbian Exposition souvenir set in this form for Libby	55.00
Fig, Mt. Washington, white, pansey and leaf dec, 2½″, pr	100.00
Hen, sitting, Mt. Washington, red body with florals, SP top in shape of chicken's head	365.00
Lalique Intaglic, frosted, cut.	75.00
Moser, unsigned, intaglio cut crystal, 9 panelled, sterling top with crystal insert, 3″	75.00
Pineapple, mold blown cased glass, pink, 3¼″, 35-N.	35.00
Rib and Scroll, Consolidated Lamp and Glass Co., opaque cased glass, pink, 3″, 170-A	45.00
Royal Ivy, Northwood Glass Co., frosted and clear shaded colors, tin top, 2¾″, 38-F	50.00
Wave Crest, yellow, swirl, enamel florals, pr.	125.00

FIGURAL AND SOUVENIR TYPES (Priced by set)

Black Cooks, man in white hat, lady in white apron and turban, pottery, red and white underglaze paint, large size for stove.	20.00
Bottles, miniature, Old Export Beer . . .	20.00
Candles, SS, mkd La Pierre Sterling, 3½″	35.00
Chefs, Little, set of 5, one holds fish, another knife, etc., white hats and aprons, hp, Germany	55.00
Cowboy Boots with spurs, china, brown.	4.50
Donald Duck, china	20.00
Flamingoes, china, pink, souvenir of Florida, 3″	8.00
Grapes, bunches, two clusters hanging from footed holder, silver electroplated metal	5.00
Owls, Shawnee	7.00
Pennsylvania Dutch Boy and Girl, cast metal, Amish costumes, 3″.	8.00
Punty Band, ruby stained etched "Reading Fair 1907", Heisey, tintop, 36 D .	60.00
Puss N Boots, gold trim	18.00
Seashells, quality china, shaded white to green, 3½″	8.00
Strawberries, china, hp	10.00
Windmill, china, blue and white, Occupied Japan	6.00

OPALESCENT GLASS (Priced Individually)

Circle, Double, Jefferson No. 231, green, brass top, 3″, c1900, 156.	50.00
Circled Scroll, Northwood, blue, tin top, 5″, 156-S	65.00
Chrysanthemum, Base Swirl, Northwood, blue, brass top, 2⅜″ h, 24-U .	50.00

Everglades, Northwood, white, gold
  highlights, pewter top, 160-K **60.00**
Jewel and Flower, Northwood, blue, re-
  placed top, 164-J **35.00**
Pillar Sixteen, Hobbs, cranberry, white
  lines, pewter top, 35-L **48.00**
Reverse Swirl, cranberry **35.00**
Seaweed, Hobbs, blown molded, cran-
  berry **40.00**
Spanish Lace, Northwood, blue, tin top,
  39-S **50.00**
Windows, Hobbs, blue, pewter top **45.00**

OPAQUE GLASS (Priced individually, unless noted)

Acorn, Hobbs, later Beaumont Glass,
  shaded pink to white, tin top, 3″, 21-
  A, found in black, (scarce) **44.00**
Argonaut Shell, custard **175.00**
Bavarian, hp, pink roses **25.00**
Beehive, Bryce, Higbee, white beehive,
  bees in relief, tin top, 22-R. **30.00**
Blue Willow, 6″. **25.00**
Bulging Panel, white, hp, brass top, 3″,
  23-Q **20.00**
Corn with Husk, white, painted husks, tin
  top, celluloid center **30.00**
Cosmos Band, blue, squatty, raised ring
  of flowers around bottom, brass top,
  25-T **35.00**
Cone, Consolidated Lamp and Glass
  Co., variety of colors, cased, 3″, 25-K.   **26.00**
Flower Bouquet, raised pattern, brass
  top, 3″, 29-J **24.00**
Grape and Leaf, green, brass top, 3¼″,
  30-C, also found cased **38.00**
Guttate, Consolidated Lamp and Glass
  Co., variety of colors, also cased,
  3¼″ **40.00**
Hen and Rabbit, egg shape, white, red
  or green paint overlaid with gold, hen
  one side, rabbit other, egg shape tin
  top, 3⅝″, 163-E **46.00**
Leaf Base, red, green leaf base to re-
  semble tomato, top with celluloid cen-
  ter, 32-F, pr **45.00**
Leaning, hues of blue, white, pink, and
  green, brass top, 3¼″, 32-T **50.00**
Melon, beaded, blue, pedestal base,
  2½″ **25.00**
Paneled Shell, light green, 3″, tin dome
  top, 35-A **25.00**
Pineapple, apple green, tiny feet, raised
  design, narrow neck, brass top, 35-N   **35.00**
Scroll with Pansies, white, 3⅜″ **30.00**
Sunset, Dithridge, white and variety of
  colors, 3″, 40-U. **28.00**
Winged Scroll, custard **100.00**

PATTERN GLASS (Priced individually, unless noted)

Actress, pewter top **40.00**

Adonis, deep blue. **20.00**
Button Arches, clear, pr **50.00**
Crystolite, crystal, Heisey, pr **30.00**
Daisy and Button, blue **15.00**
Diamond Pyramids, Fostoria Glass Co, pr   **25.00**
Double Prism (Heck), Model Flint Glass,
  heavy clear pattern, pewter top, 2¾″,
  30-Q **18.00**
Hobnail, pointed, clear **18.00**
Jeweled Heart, green, Northwood Glass
  Co **20.00**
Ladder with Diamonds, Duncan Miller,
  clear, 320 . . . .   **13.50**
Loop with Dewdrops, clear, U. S. Glass
  Co **20.00**
Nestor, clear amethyst, undecorated, or-
  nate top **32.00**
Pennsylvania, U. S. Glass Co., pewter
  top, 3″ **55.00**
Roman Rosette, clear, tin top, U. S.
  Glass Co, 3½″ **35.00**
Sawtooth, bulbous, dark amber clear
  squat shape, tin top, 2½″, 171-N . . .   **32.00**
Sunken Teardrop, clear, small ears on
  side, pedestal base, moon and star
  top, 3½″, 40-T **16.00**
Thousand Eye, clear, tin top, U. S. Glass
  Co, 3″, 42-B **20.00**
Whirligig, U. S. Glass Co., clear, tin top,
  3½″, 177-A. **12.00**

SALTGLAZED WARES

History: Saltglazed wares have a distinctive "pitted" surface texture, made by throwing salt into the
hot kiln during the final firing process. The salt vapors produced sodium oxide and hydrochioric acid
which react on the glaze.

Many Staffordshire potters produced large quantities of this type of ware during the 18th and 19th
centuries. A relatively small quantity was produced
in the United States. Saltglazed wares still are
made today.

Basket, 13″ l, lozenge shape, white,
  pierced with scrolling and geometric
  foliage, 2 handles, Staffordshire,
  c1765. . . . .   **500.00**
Bottle, 8½″, globular, flared neck incised
  with allover engine turn waves and
  dots, Staffordshire, c1760 . . . .   **450.00**
Cheese Dome, blue-gray ground, white
  relief floral and leaves **550.00**
Coffee Cup, 2½″, flared, white relief
  panels with vines and swags, Staf-
  fordshire, c1750 . . . .   **225.00**
Cup and Saucer, molded scenic panels,
  cup with strap handle, Staffordshire,
  c1755. . . . .   **500.00**
Dish, 6⅜″, oval, enameled, Chinaman
  holding gilt perch with 3 green parrots,
  Staffordshire, c1750 . . . .   **600.00**

Syrup, 7" h, pewter lid, celadon hue, classical dec, $225.00.

Jugs

6¾" h, 5¼" w, hexagonal, gray, raised white cupids and leaves, imp Oriental on base	**120.00**
9", figural bear, Nottingham, c1745. .	**625.00**
9⅞" h, 4¼", d, white, emb pastel pink and yellow roses	**100.00**
Mug, man on donkey with 2 Satyrs in relief, grape clusters and leaves background and handle	**200.00**
Pickle Dish, 5", triangular, press molded, trailing grapevine dec	**125.00**

Pitchers

5", scenic, hunter, horses, hounds, and stag, handle is twisted serpent which goes around both sides to serpent's head, open mouth is spout	**125.00**
6¾", white, medium blue applied classical figures of musicians and dancers	**80.00**
9¾", bulbous, high relief, entitled "Gypsy", Jones & Walley, dated 1842	**115.00**
Plate, 10", basketweave center, trellis and flowerhead border, Staffordshire, c1760	**375.00**
Platter, 14½", oval, rice molded, basketwork, scalloped rim	**325.00**
Tea Caddy, 3¾", bell shape, sprigged floral dec, c1740	**175.00**
Teapot, 3¾", child's, hinged pewter lid, basketweave pattern on bottom half, thistle and flower pattern on upper half, registry mark 1883	**150.00**

SALTS, OPEN

History: When salt was first mined, the supply was limited and expensive. The necessity for a receptacle in which to serve the salt resulted in the first open salt, a crude, hand-carved, wooden trencher.

As time passed salt receptacles were refined in style and materials. In the 1500s both master and individual salts existed. By the 1700s firms such as Meissen, Waterford, and Wedgwood were making glass, china, and porcelain salts. Leading manufacturers in the 1800s included Libbey Glass Co., Mt. Washington, New England Glass Company, Smith Bros., Vallerysthal, Wavecrest, Webb, and many outstanding silversmiths in England, France, and Germany.

Open salts were used as the only means of serving salt until the appearance of the shaker in the late 1800s. The ease of procuring salt from a shaker greatly reduced the use and need for the open salts.

References: L. W. and D. B. Neal, *Pressed Glass Dishes Of The Lacy Period 1825–1850*, privately printed, 1962; Allan B. and Helen B. Smith have authored ten books on open salts beginning with *One Thousand Individual Open Salts Illustrated* (1972) and ending with *1,334 Open Salts Illustrated: The Tenth Book* (1984). All are privately printed. Daniel Snyder did the master salt sections in Volumes 8 and 9.

Note: The numbers in parenthesis refer to plate numbers in the Smith's publications.

Advisors: Allan B. and Helen B. Smith.

CONDIMENT SETS WITH OPEN SALTS

China

Boat set, inscribed "A Present from Cleethorpes" on one side (461)	**50.00**
Viking Ship; gold dec, "Czechoslovakian" (461)	**30.00**
Metal	
Coolie pulling ricksaw, contains salt, pepper and mustard dishes, blown glass liners, Oriental (461)	**45.00**
Silver Plated, 3 pcs, emb pattern around bowls, Oriental (461)	**40.00**
Porcelain	
Bavarian, light pink with gold trim on leaf shaped holder, mkd "Made In Bavaria" (388)	**40.00**
Limoges, double salt and mustard, sgd "JM Limoges" (388)	**45.00**
Pottery, Quimper, double salt and mustard, white with blue and green floral dec, sgd "Quimper" (388)	**50.00**

INDIVIDUALS

China

Austria, tub shape, floral dec, sgd "Brothers" and "O & EG Royal Austria" (441)	**20.00**
Chinese export, c1750–1770 (434)	**600.00**
Dresden Saxony, lily dec on one side (434)	**45.00**
Germany, pedestal salts sgd "RS"	

(Reinhold Schlegelmilch) and
"Germany" **15.00**
Majolica, shaped like flower with overlapping leaves, mkd "No. 35" (439). **50.00**
Noritake, oval, int. dec in blue and gold
(382). **15.00**
Unknown, Viking ship complete pli-
que-a-jour in blue, red, and vaseline,
very unusual (455) **1,000.00**

Colored Glass

Amber, pedestal, Dragon, Cambridge
(468). **15.00**
Blue, basketweave, colorless rigaree
(378). **70.00**
Blue, pedestal, heavy base, French,
c1810 (386). **50.00**
Blue, stretch glass, unmarked (485) . **55.00**
Cobalt Blue, pedestal, gold bands, ap-
plied flowers, sgd "Moser" (380). . **180.00**
Cobalt Blue, pedestal, sgd "Steuben"
(485). **125.00**
Cranberry, cut back to clear (446) . . **60.00**
Cranberry, ruffled salt held by rigaree
in whire holder, unmarked (373) . . **95.00**
Frosted, oval, scenic dec, unsigned,
attributed to Daum Nancy (446) . . **265.00**
Green, wide lacy border (378) **25.00**
Lavender, pedestal, frosted (373) . . . **45.00**
Pink, Double Thumbprint with Rosette,
1920 (479) **10.00**
Ruby, blown, white lace trim (447) . . **70.00**
Ruby, dolphin (451) **30.00**

**Individual, pedestal, Chippendale han-
dles, scalloped rim, octagonal base,
Williamsburg pattern, by U.S. Glass,
G2X-642, $14.00.**

Cut Glass

Eight curved sides, polished cut bot-
tom (470) **6.00**
Hexagonal, 12 point star in bottom,
sgd "Libbey" (464). **35.00**
Pedestal, Diamond Point and Honey-
comb, sgd "Kosta" (469) **35.00**
Pedestal, Diamond Point circles
around bowl (468) **20.00**
Rectangular with wreath dec around
salt, sgd "Sinclaire" (464). **45.00**
Round with alternating zippered and
starred panels 361) **15.00**

Triangular, Star and Diamond, sgd
"Hawkes" (466). **55.00**
Tub, tab handles, Diamond and Fan
(361). **30.00**

Double Salts

China

Birds, gold rims, bug shown on in-
side bottom (460) **75.00**
Bowls, boat shaped, anchor handle
of floral dec (392). **30.00**
Meissen, floral dec inside and out,
crossed swords and crown mark
(460) **45.00**
Shells, maiden sitting between
them, French (392) **65.00**
Shells, yellow and white, seahorse
handle, sgd "Sant Ucci Peruto"
(392) **45.00**

Glass

Baccarat, pedestal, paneled sides,
one salt frosted panels sgd
(395) **65.00**
Blue, silver frames, 4 ribbed paw
feet (460). **65.00**
Clear, octagonal, Thumbprint, attrib-
uted to Sandwich (394) **35.00**
Vaseline, ten paneled, tall handle
(460) **40.00**
Milk Glass, turquoise, sgd "Vallerys-
tahl" and "Made In France" (460) **20.00**
Pottery, blue with pink and white flowers around bowls, French, Longwy,
c1900 (392). **60.00**

In Metal Frames

Clear, 4 ftd SS holder with 4 peacocks
around outside, mkd "Sterling"
(411). **25.00**
Cobalt blue liner, basket, pierced rib-
bon handles, mkd "E.P.N.S."
(413). **30.00**
Cobalt blue liner, round SS, hall-
marked, mkd "Made in Dublin, Ire-
land 1795" (412) **50.00**
Cobalt blue, round SS holder, mkd
"Webster Co." hallmark and "Ster-
ling" (411). **20.00**
Cobalt blue liner, white metal holder
on four small legs (414) **10.00**
Cranberry, dark, blown glass in baroque gold washed frame, mkd
"Whiting 3582" and "Gorham "G"
(412). **100.00**

Metals

Copper, heavy, pedestal, deep ma-
roon enamel (414) **18.00**
German Silver, dolphin feet, German,
c1890–1910 (333) **20.00**
Pewter, cov, blue liner, mkd "Hanle
Distinctive American Pewter" (414). **15.00**
Pewter, round, "Hampshire Pewter"
hallmark, new (415) **20.00**
Silver plated, pot, hallmarked "Wilcox
Silver Plate Co." (414) **15.00**

Sterling Silver, cov, handle, three feet, ornately dec bowl, hole in cover for spoon, mkd "L.P.G." and "No. 90" (353) 55.00

Pressed Glass

American, Fostoria, round, gold rim, rayed bottom (465). 20.00

Beaded Raindrop (464) 15.00

Dolphin, hollow base, French (469). . 30.00

Elliptical, round, rayed bottom (362) . 10.00

Hawaiian Lei, Higbee (477) 15.00

Heart-shaped, ridged top border and 16 point star in bottom (465). 20.00

Heisey, octagonal paneled salt on sloping octagonal base, mkd with Heisey "H" in diamond (475) 60.00

Thumbprint, pedestal, double round base, wide top rim, round thumbprints around bowl (362). 20.00

Vernon, rounded rim, 12 panels on lower sides above ring of indented diamonds which merge with rayed bottom (477) 10.00

FIGURALS

Donkey, painted, pulling colorful painted cart (458) 15.00

Goat, hauling green milk glass cart, sgd "Baccarat," 6" l (458) 200.00

Peacock, glass, amethyst wings, green base (462) 30.00

Seahorse, brilliant turquoise, white base, supports shell salt, mkd with first Belleck black mark (458) 500.00

Sleigh drawn by Griffon, Continental silver, c1860 (352) 300.00

Sleigh with Cupid driving reindeer, SS, made in Germany (352). 600.00

INTAGLIOS

Lady, amber, 4 ftd lacy brass stone studded frame (423) 60.00

Scene of Niagara Falls (368). 10.00

Tree, 2 blue intaglios, woman smoking (423) 75.00

Tree, 6 intaglios showing Venus and Cupid (423). 300.00

MASTERS

China

Germany, pedestal, girl sitting on grass, mkd "Printemps, Monbijou, Germany" (387) 20.00

Unknown Maker, round, subtly ribbed, floral dec, gold and green border (384). 35.00

Unknown maker, three curved feet, sprays of orange flowers and green leaves inside bowl (387) 20.00

Colored Glass

Amber, Staghorn, lacy, Sandwich, rare, Neal SNIC (384). 250.00

Blue, opalescent, silver rim, Registry number "176566" (384) 75.00

Blue, translucent, Leaf, Bakewell Pears, c1860 (457). 65.00

Blue-Green, rect, Gothic Arch, Sandwich, Neal GA 1, very rare (457). . 165.00

Cased, end of day, scalloped, five clear shell feet (447) 30.00

Cranberry, geometrically cut to clear (384). 85.00

Green, blown glass with threaded texture, clear base (449). 75.00

Green, light, dark green ruffled top, open pontil (449) 40.00

Pink, threaded glass, clear applied feet (384) 45.00

Raspberry, heavy, sq, Pairpoint (444) 32.00

Master, heavy diamond pedestal base, sawtooth top edge with fans at intervals, wide band in diamond pattern around bowl, $40.00.

Cut Glass

Daisy chain around bowl (409) 50.00

Heart shape, alternating diamond and fan pattern (404) 30.00

Octagon shape, six wide panels (409). 20.00

Round, diamond pattern on top of bowl, ribbed base (404) 25.00

Tub, sgd "J. Hoare Company" (397) 50.00

Metal

Silver plated, ruby glass, holder with two medallions for monogramming (359). 50.00

Sterling Silver

Boy with bow and arrow holding salt on his head, blue glass insert, mkd "800" Germany (355) 60.00

Four footed holder, mkd "Sterling 72," oval cranberry liner (411) . .	**75.00**
Oval, pedestal, floral chasing, Gorham hallmark, "Sterling" "T & Co." (359)	**150.00**
Pedestal, 4 medallion profiles, monogrammed S.C.W., made in 1865, mkd with Gorham hallmark and number 520 (358)	**115.00**
Pedestal, gold wash bowl with tassel handles (355)	**45.00**
Perforated beaded holder with ruby liner, mkd "Sterling" "8322" (411)	**50.00**

Pressed Glass

Arched Panel, octagonal, round rim (410)	**20.00**
Basketweave, sleigh (397)	**50.00**
Bubble glass, shell shaped (405) . . .	**20.00**
Bull's Eye variant, small rect, leaf, Sandwich, Neal GA 4a, rare (410)	**75.00**
Chandelier (409)	**25.00**
Diamond, shoe shape, Nova Scotia (397)	**35.00**
Grasshopper, early, no insert (404). .	**30.00**
Hobnail, round (407)	**25.00**
Lacy, oblong, pedestal, Neal OP 3, Boston & Sandwich Co. (407). . . .	**150.00**
Lacy, oblong, scalloped rim, 4 heavy feet, ribbed base 410)	**25.00**
Lacy, rect, Neal GA 4a, Boston & Sandwich (410)	**75.00**
Lacy, rect, Neal NE 4, New England Glass Co. (410)	**90.00**
Lacy, round, plain base, similar to Neal RD 12 (404)	**125.00**
Palmette (471)	**40.00**
Plaid, open (404).	**25.00**
Thousand Eye variant, sq (402)	**15.00**
Toboggan salt (397)	**40.00**

SAMPLERS

History: Samplers served many purposes. For a young child they were a practice exercise and permanent reminder of stitches and patterns. For a young woman they demonstrated her skills in a "gentle" art and preserved key elements of family genealogy. For the mature woman they were a useful occupation and functioned as gifts or remembrances, e.g., mourning pieces.

Schools for young ladies of the early 19th century prided themselves on the needlework skills they taught. The Westtown School in Chester County, Pennsylvania, and the Young Ladies Seminary in Bethlehem, Pennsylvania, are two examples. These schools changed their teaching as styles changed. Berlin work was introduced by the mid-19th century.

Examples of samplers date back to the 1700s. The earliest ones were long and narrow, usually done only with the alphabet and numerals. Later examples were square. At the end of the 19th century the shape tended to be rectangular.

The same motifs were used throughout the country. The name is a key element in determining the region. Samplers are assumed to be on linen unless otherwise indicated.

Dated 1862, cross stitch on homespun linen, 16 x 30½", $550.00.

1802, 19¾ x 26½", Betsy Ingalls, olive green homespun, alphabets, pious verse, stylized bird and flowers, vining borders.	**1,850.00**
1802, 21¼ x 26¼", Maria Alligood, alphabet, 2 pious verses, landscape, urns with flowers, floral border	**2,450.00**
1806, 23 x 24" , Mary Snowden, Phila., landscape under large weeping willow and cherry tree, stylized bud border, green, yellow, blue, and brown.	**1,450.00**
1808, 16¼ x 19¼", Harriet Thomas, Scituate, MA, alphabets, 14 lines of pious verse, 3 gold vases of flowers, floral and sawtooth border	**1,250.00**
1810, 9½ x 8", Claramond Winslow Greenwich, alphabets, numbers, house, trees and young ladies, green, gold, blue and white	**1,225.00**
1812, 20 x 24", Elizabeth Warburton, scenic, house, farm building, sheep, shepherd, and maiden, floral vining border	**675.00**
1817, 10½ x 15", Mary Childs, alphabets, house, flower and vines, faded	**225.00**
1817, 11 x 15", Clarinda Fuller, alphabet, numerals, pious verse, colonial house and basket of flowers	**450.00**
1820, 15 x 15¾", Elvira Beal, MA, alphabet above landscape scene, broad floral and leaf border, green, white, blue, and yellow	**3,300.00**
1822, 24 x 20½", Mary Faith Chatham, alphabets, numbers, pious verse, multisections containing farming vignettes, central vase of flowers, sawtooth and floral border.	**1,900.00**

1827, 17¾ x 13¾", Abigail Moore Alexander, Tunbridge, VT, alphabet, numerals, pious verse, landscape. **950.00**

1827, 33 x 29½", Elizabeth Taylor, PA, pious verse, family record, pots of flowers, bird, meandering floral vines **1,000.00**

1829, 23¼ x 26¼", Ann Winram, poem "The Day of Life," scenic, deer, trees, bird, vining floral border with sawtooth edge, gold, brown, red, blue, and green **1,350.00**

1830, 17" sq, Lucy Ann Williams, Charlestown, MA, alphabets, numerals, interlaced hearts with names and birthdates, pious verse, family record, green, blue, yellow and white **1,450.00**

1833, 16¾ x 17", Mary S. Little, RI, alphabet, numerals, pious verse, landscape scene, floral vining border, green, yellow, blue, and pink **1,100.00**

1837, 11¾ x 16½", Ester Jesse Paris, English, pious verse, trees, birds and baskets of fruit, floral border **275.00**

1837, 16 x 18", Matilda Forster, Reesorville, PA, bands of alphabets, numbers, flowers, trees, green, yellow, pink, and brown **500.00**

184–, 21 x 17", Hannah Trout, Chester County, PA, pious verse above farm scene, large basket of berries, large basket of flowers, floral vine border, red, yellow, blue and green **2,100.00**

SANDWICH GLASS

History: In 1818 Deming Jarvis was listed in the Boston Directory as a glass factor. The same year he was appointed general manager of the newly formed New England Glass Company. In 1824 Jarvis toured the glass-making factories in Pittsburgh, left New England Glass Company, and founded a glass factory in Sandwich.

Originally called the Sandwich Manufacturing Company, it was incorporated in April 1826 as the Boston & Sandwich Glass Company. From 1826 to 1858 Jarvis served as general manager. The Boston & Sandwich Glass Company produced a wide variety and quality of wares. The factory used the free-blown, blown three-mold, and pressed glass manufacturing techniques. Clear and colored glass both were used.

Competition in the American glass industry in the mid-1850s forced a lowering of quality of the glass wares. Jarvis left in 1858, founded the Cape Cod Glass Company, and tried to maintain the high quality of the earlier glass. At the Boston & Sandwich Glass Company emphasis was placed on mass production. The development of a lime glass (non-flint) led to lower costs for pressed glass. Some freeblown and blown-and-molded pieces, mostly in color, were made. Most of this Victorian era glass was enameled, painted, or acid etched.

By the 1880s the Boston & Sandwich Glass Company was operating at a loss. Labor difficulties finally resulted in the factory closing on January 1, 1888.

References: Raymond E. Barlow and Joan E. Kaiser, *The Glass Industry In Sandwich*, Vol. 4, privately printed, 1983; George S. and Helen McKearin, *American Glass*, Crown Publishers, Inc., 1941 and 1948; Ruth Webb Lee, *Sandwich Glass. The History Of The Sandwich Glass Company*, privately printed, 1966, 10th printing; Ruth Webb Lee, *Sandwich Glass Handbook*, privately printed, 1966, 9th printing; L. W. and D. B. Neal, *Pressed Glass Dishes Of The Lacy Period 1825–1850*, privately printed, 1962; Catherine M. V. Thuro, *Oil Lamps II: Glass Kerosene Lamps*, Wallace-Homestead, 1983.

Periodical: *The Sandwich Collector*, McCue Publications, P. O. Box 340, East Sandwich, MA 02537. Subscription: $12.00.

Museum: Sandwich Glass Museum, Sandwich, MA.

Additional Listings: Blown Three Mold and Cup Plates.

Bottles
  Cologne
    4¾", cobalt blue, 12 sided, Lee 243-1 through 12 . . . . **150.00**
    5¾", canary yellow, Ellipse, c1840–50s, minute rim roughage and slight chemical deposit **275.00**
    6¾", opaque jade green, Star and Punty, orig stopper, shallow chip on one point of foot, minor chips on stopper **2,800.00**
  Vinegar, 6¾", cobalt blue, blown three mold, period stopper, McKearin G-I-7, type 2 . . . . **300.00**
Bowls
  6¼", 5" h, clear, lacy, Peacock, ftd, cov, grape border, some roughage, chip on finial **550.00**
  6⅜", clear, lacy, Industry, few very small rim nicks, Lee 89-2 . . . . **200.00**
  7½", clear, lacy, Princess Feather, minimal roughage, Lee 135. . . . . . **75.00**
  9¼", clear, lacy, Oak Leaf, minimal roughage. **175.00**
  14¼", clear, lacy, Peacock, 8¼ x 3" section broken out and repaired by 5 rivets, few small edge chips, largest piece of lacy glass known. . . . **6,000.00**
Candlesticks
  6¾", brilliant deep amethyst, Loop and Petal, 2 minute under rim chips, slight roughage around ring foot, McKearin 200-35 . . . . **275.00**
  6¾", smoky electric blue, Loop and Petal, large heat crack **150.00**
  6⅞", powder blue, Loop and Petal, one minor nick on one petal, mold underfill. **525.00**

7″, opaque blue and white, Loop and Petal, white top, powder blue translucent base, c1835–40, slight under rim roughage to petals 250.00
9¼″, opaque blue and white, Acanthus Leaf, blue top, white stem and base, slight roughage on base . . . 400.00
9¾″, white Dolphin and base, powder blue top, c1840s, one small chip under petal, McKearin 204-66. . . . . . 450.00
10″, deep amber, Crucifix, c1840s, heavy annealing lines and some imperfections. 350.00
10¼″, opaque white Dolphin and sq base, yellow-green jade top, c1840s, slight roughage under petals, McKearin 204-66 . . . . 1,250.00

Candlesticks, pr
7″, canary yellow, Loop and Petal, c1840s, Lee 182-4. . . . . 300.00
7⅝″, opaque blue and white, Acanthus, faint heat or annealing crack in socket, Lee 187-4 . . . . 450.00
8¼″, opaque blue and white, blue top half, white lower half, McKearin 200-33. . . . . 650.00

Cup Plate, #465-I, 3½″, $30.00.

Compotes
6½″ d, 3″ h, clear, lacy, Princess Feather, c1830s, 2 scallops missing from rim, small shallow chip on edge of base, Lee 149-top 150.00
7¾″ d, 5⅞″ h, amethyst, Loop, same loop base used on Sandwich Loop and Petal candlesticks 1,900.00
8⅜″ d, 6″ h, canary yellow, paneled, hexagonal base, c1840s. 1,500.00

Creamers
4¼″, clear, lacy, Gothic Arch and Peacock, several small chips, firing check in foot ring. 125.00
6½″, opaque white, Sawtooth, applied handle. 175.00
Fiery opalescent, Gothic Arch and Palm, c1830s, slight roughage around pouring spout and rim, small to medium chips in foot ring 450.00

Dishes
5¼″, amber, lacy, Roman Rosette . . 300.00
5½″, amethyst, lacy, Roman Rosette, one rim chip, several small flakes. 200.00
5½″, cobalt blue, Tulip and Acanthus Leaf, c1830s, 3 shallow upper rim flakes, Lee 131-2. . . . . 175.00
6″, smoky amethyst, Ribbon, flint glass. 750.00
6⅝″, fiery opalescent, Rosette, small rim chips 125.00
7⅜″, oval, lacy, Rayed Peacock, light rim roughage 200.00
8⅛″, oblong, deep, clear, lacy, "Pipes Of Pan," Lee 166-top. 350.00
10¼ x 8″, oblong, clear, lacy, Hairpin, minimal roughage, some heavy annealing lines, Lee 96-2 . . . . 300.00

Door Knobs, hexagonal, blue, pewter mountings, pr 250.00
Egg Cup, 3⅜″, clear, lacy, 2 small rim chips, Lee 150-4. . . . . 200.00
Epergne, 10″ h, opaque jade-green, 2 parts, vase with gauffered rim, vase has 3 tiny chips in rim 300.00
Goblet, 4⅞″, emerald green, Vine, slight traces of gold dec on rim. 450.00

Lamps
8″, clear, pear-shaped Peacock font, c1840–50s, brass collar and stem mounted on sq base 100.00
9″, fluid, Punty and Ring, c1840s, brass collar and stem, mounted on sq marble base 150.00
11″, opalescent triple Dolphin base, goblet-shaped blue and white spiral font, possibly Nicholas Lutz 7,250.00
11¼″, emerald green, Loop base, plain rim, marble base 450.00
11½″, opaque blue, Acanthus Leaf top, whale oil burner, white base, Lee 193-center 450.00
11¾″, opaque blue, Onion, Thuro II (pg 17) 4,000.00
13″, Onion, citrine color base, strong jade font 5,000.00

Lamp, miniature, 4″, fluid, opalescent dark blue base, clear font, Smith 11. 400.00

Miniatures
Bowl, opalescent, lacy, 2 chips in upper rim, slight roughage around font ring, Lee 80-6 . . . . 275.00
Candlestick, clear, low. 350.00
Chamber Set (pitcher and bowl), deep cobalt blue, paneled, a few minute nicks on pitcher. 950.00
Creamer, clear, lacy, one shallow inner rim flake in spout, Lee 80-4 . . 120.00
Cup and Saucer, clear, lacy, slight nick in foot ring, larger than Lee 180 . . 200.00

Flatiron, clear, small flakes around bottom edge **150.00**

Salt, clear, lacy, oval, minor edge roughage, Lee 81-3 . . . .   **175.00**

Tureen, clear, lacy, lid and undertray, slight under rim flakes on cov **250.00**

Mustard Cup, 2¾", clear, lacy, Peacock, chip on underside of cov, Lee 114 . .   **425.00**

Newel Posts, 8", blue and white, transluscent Hobnail, orig brass mountings **375.00**

Plates

5", clambroth-purple-blue, checkerboard design in center, several scallops lightly flaked **180.00**

5⅞", medium blue, Peacock Feather, 4 scallops flaked **145.00**

6⅛", fiery opalescent, Basket of Flowers border, small unseen chip **235.00**

7", clear, lacy, 12 sided, one scallop with rim chip, light roughage, Lee 112-upper right **100.00**

7", fiery opalescent, Acorn and Oak Leaf **170.00**

9½", fiery opalescent, Roman Rosette, overall rim roughness, 2 small chips. **450.00**

Pomade Jars

3½" h, "The Little Cavalier," translucent blue, mkd on bottom "E.T.S. & Co. N.Y.," small chip in bottom of rim, large chip in front of cavalier's hat brim **550.00**

Opaque blue, clambroth lid, 2 chips in rim hidden by lid, Lee 207-bottom, lower left. **250.00**

Relish Dish, 8⅝", oval, clear, lacy, Hairpin, Lee 96-upper left **240.00**

Sauces

5", clear, Diamond, rope edge, 2 minor flat edge chips, unrecorded. **45.00**

5½", clear, lacy, Hairpin, slight rim chips, Lee 96-lower right **70.00**

Smoke Bell, 9¼" h, 5½" d, opaque white, opaque blue ring hanger, open bubble on bottom, may have been used with a matching hall lantern **100.00**

Spill Holders

Cable, opaque green-jade, gold presentation dec, large inner chip removed part of one fan, large chip under rim of one foot, McKearin 205-5 . . . .   **400.00**

Star, clambroth, slight blue-gray tint, slight rim roughage, wear to points of hexagonal base **250.00**

Star, electric blue, slight wear. **700.00**

Sugar Bowls, covered

Gothic, clambroth, bowl with slight shallow flakes, very good cov **225.00**

Gothic, fiery opalescent, outstanding

base, 3 chips in cov, McKearin 163-7 and 9. . . . .   **275.00**

Gothic Arches, emerald green, Lee 158-4 . . . .   **300.00**

Roman Rosette, clear, 5⅞" h, 5" d, small chip on foot **235.00**

Sugars, open

Acanthus, purple-blue, dark, c1830s, small crack in one side, McKearin 154-5 . . . .   **175.00**

Gothic Arch, electric blue, lacy, c1830s, small rim chip and very light rim roughage . . . . . ·. **125.00**

Toddy Plate, 4⅝", bright yellow-green [chartruese], Sunburst center, mold roughness. **50.00**

Trays

7", clear, lacy, Butterfly, slight rim roughage. **100.00**

7¾", clear, lacy, Butterfly variant, slight rim roughage, Lee 95-upper right **175.00**

Undertray, 12" d, clear, lacy, small sliver out of rim where two annealing lines meet **260.00**

Vases

7¼", amethyst, Bull's-eye and Ellipse, gauffered rim, c1840-50s **300.00**

9", light violet-blue, Bull's-eye and Ellipse, gauffered rim, c1840-50s, open bubble in one point of hexagonal font, heavy annealing lines in base **400.00**

9⅛", emerald green, 3 printic, gauffered rim, c1840-50s, McKearin 201-42 . . . .   **450.00**

9⅜", cobalt blue, 3 printic, gauffered rim, c1840-50s, light roughage to points and edges of foot, McKearin 201-42 . . . .   **300.00**

9¾", amethyst, Tulip, c1840s, McKearin 201-40 . . . .   **550.00**

10¾", deep cobalt blue, Loop, slight ground at factory for mold overflow **350.00**

Purple-blue, pale, hexagonal stepped foot, faceted bowl, gauffered rim, Lee 198-3 . . . .   **900.00**

Vegetable Dish, 10½", clear, lacy, pattern copied from old Meissen porcelain pattern, very small rim chips and light roughage, Lee 151-bottom left .   **400.00**

Whiskey Tasters

Clambroth, small chip and roughage in footing, Lee 150-5 and 7. . . . . .   **50.00**

Canary Yellow, lacy, Lee 150-5 and 7 . . . .   **100.00**

Emerald green, lacy, scalloped foot, one scallop partially chipped, other two scallops with minor chips, Lee 150-5 and 7. . . . .   **150.00**

Opalescent, fiery, lacy, large chip in ring foot **75.00**

SARREGUE MINES
SARREGUEMINES CHINA

History: Sarreguemines ware is a faience porcelain, i.e., tin-glazed eartherware. The factory was established in Lorraine, France, in 1770, under the supervision of Utzcheider and Fabry. The factory was regarded as one of the three most prominent manufacturers of French Faience. Most of the wares found today were made in the 19th century. Later wares are impressed Sarreguemines and Germany due to a change of boundaries and location of the factory.

Box, heart shape, floral dec, ormolu
mount, c1760 . . . . **95.00**
Compote, 8½" d, 5" h, ivory ground, floral dec, yellow, blue, and pink **40.00**
Dish, cov, 8½", majolica, molded basket weave, green-tan, applied handles, white egg finial **135.00**
Ewer, 10", tan ground, gold butterflies and flowers. **65.00**
Oyster Plate, majolica, gray, peach, and white **50.00**
Pitchers
Children climbing trees, relief **85.00**
Hound, sitting on haunches, baying, muted shades **120.00**
Plates
6½", castle scenes, floral border, artist sgd, set of 8 . . . . **105.00**
7½", small scalloped edge, beige, emb cherries and leaves **35.00**
7¾", majolica, scalloped green edge, yellow ground, 15 panels around

cluster of grapes, leaves, and tendrils, French, set of 8 . . . . **200.00**
8½", boy and girl in doorway **35.00**
Rose Bowl, 4" h, 4" d, majolica, multicolored dec **85.00**
Shell Dish, 10⅜", majolica, molded, salmon shading to pale pink, brown handle, imp mark, c1880 . . . . **75.00**
Tobacco Jar, cov, brown with yellow trim masks in relief **65.00**
Vases, pr, castle scenes, enameled in natural colors, scrolled handles, pedestal bases, sgd L. Langlois, printed mark, late 19th C **625.00**

SARSAPARILLA BOTTLES

History: Sarsaparilla refers to a number of tropical American, spiny, woody vines of the lily family whose roots are fragrant. An extract was obtained from these dried roots and used for medicinal purposes. The first appearance in bottle form dates from the 1840s. The earliest bottles were stoneware, later followed by glass.

Carbonated water often was added to sarsaparilla to make a soft drink or to make consuming it more pleasurable. For this reason, sarsaparilla and soda became synonymous even though they were two different entities.

References: Hugh Cleveland, *Bottle Pricing Guide*, Collector Books, 1980; Ralph & Terry Kovel, *The Kovel's Bottle Price List*, Crown Publishers, 1982, 6th ed.; Carlo & Dot Sellari, *The Illustrated Price Guide To Antique Bottles*, Country Beautiful Corp., 1975.

Periodicals: *Antique Bottle World*, 5003 West Berwyn, Chicago, IL 60630; *Old Bottle Magazine*, P. O. Box 243, Bend, OR 97701. Subscription: $10.00.

Additional Listings: See *Warman's Americana & Collectibles* for a list of soda bottles.

Ayer's, open pontil **50.00**
Belding's, Dr., Wild Cherry, aqua, 9¼" . **50.00**
Bristol Extract, Buffalo, open pontil, aqua, 5½" **65.00**
Burr & Water, Buffalo, NY, pottery, gray salt glaze **100.00**
Emerson's Sarsaparilla **40.00**
Extract of John Bull, Louisville, KY, green. **40.00**
Foley's Sarsaparilla. **20.00**
Gooch's Sarsaparilla, blue. **45.00**
Guysott's, Dr., Yellow Dock Sarsaparilla. **10.00**
Joy, Edwin W., Co., San Fransisco. . . . **15.00**
Kelley, J. L. & Co., open pontil, aqua . . **275.00**
Rusha, E. M., reverse Dr. De Andrews, amber, 10" **35.00**
Sand's Geniune, NY, rect, qt, 10" **75.00**
Townsend's, Dr., Albany, NY, No. 1, light yellow. **125.00**
Wetherill's, Exeter, aqua **40.00**

Character jug, lawyer, $110.00.

SATIN GLASS

History: Satin glass, produced in the late 19th century, is an opaque art glass with a velvety matte (satin) finish, achieved through treatment with hydrofluoric acid. A large majority of the pieces were cased or had a white lining.

While working at the Phoenix Glass Company, Beaver, Pennsylvania, Joseph Webb perfected Mother-of-Pearl (MOP) satin glass in 1885. Similar to plain satin glass in respect to casing, MOP satin glass has a distinctive surface finish and an integral or indented design, the most common being diamond quilted (DQ).

The most common colors are yellow, rose, or blue. Rainbow coloring is considered choice. Satin glass, both plain and MOP, has been widely reproduced.

Additional Listings: Cruets, Fairy Lamps, Miniature Lamps, and Rose Bowls.

Basket, 8", white, rose casing, scalloped camphor edges, camphor crossed branch handles **275.00**

Biscuit Jars

  6", blue, swirl ribbed, SP collar, cov, and bail. **155.00**

  6½" h, 4¾" d, lemon yellow, heavy gold prunus and branches, dragonfly in flight, cream lining, SP bail, ivory knob, Webb **495.00**

Bowls

  8" d, 5¾" h, sq, ruffled, frosted edging, peach interior, shaded apricot, MOP, ormulu foot. **600.00**

  8⅞" d, 6⅝" h, ruffled, frosted edge, shaded rose, SP pedestal foot . . . **135.00**

Carafe, 7½", pink, MOP, DQ, SP top . . **100.00**

Biscuit Jar, 10″ h, SP lid and bail, white, $265.00.

Celery Container, blue, MOP, raindrop, black, pink, and gold leaves, gold butterfly **95.00**

Condiment Set, Florette pat, pale blue, 3 pcs **150.00**

Cruets

  7" h, 3½" d, bulbous, 3 petal top, shaded yellow, DQ, MOP, applied frosted reeded handle, clear cut faceted stopper **275.00**

  Butterscotch, DQ. **130.00**

Ewers

  6", blue, DQ **100.00**

  7¾" h, 3¾" d, ruffled, shaded blue, herringbone, MOP, cased white, frosted applied handle **195.00**

  10", rainbow, MOP, herringbone, blue, yellow, and pink, mkd patent on bottom **950.00**

  12½" h, 4½" d, shaded pink, DQ, MOP, white lining, tricorn ruffled top, frosted thorn applied handle **425.00**

Finger Bowl, 4½", shaded yellow, DQ, MOP, white cased. **195.00**

Jam Dish, 4½" d, 3½" h, shaded pink, frosted shell applied ruffle top, bird among berries and leaves etched in black decor, SP holder **175.00**

Lamps

  17" h, 6" d, peg, emb yellow swirl overlay, in holders, pr **1,250.00**

  19" h, 5½" d, peg, melon sectioning, lemon yellow, emb designs, white lining, ruffled top, clear chimney, orig brass burner and ring. **595.00**

  24½", Gone With the Wind, deep raspberry, brass handles and pedestal base **450.00**

Pitchers, water

  7½" h, 7" d, rose, Florette pat, camphor applied handle **200.00**

  Blue, ruffle top, enamel floral decor . **250.00**

Rose Bowls

  3" d, 2½" h, 8 crimp top, lime green, swirl, MOP, frosted wafer foot, white lining. **285.00**

  5¾" d, 4¼" h, 4 crimp top, shaded rose to pink, cream morning glory decor with green foliage, white cased, frosted petal feet. **145.00**

Scent Bottle, 2½" h, 2¼" d, blue ribbon, MOP, gold prunus blossoms, hallmarked SS screw on top **325.00**

Sugar Shaker, green, acid finish, diamond block. **75.00**

Sweetmeat Jars

  3⅛" h, 4¾" d, rose, DQ, MOP, emb ribbed, white cased, SP top, rim, and handle **365.00**

  4" h, 4⅛" d, pink, emb ribbed, white cased, SP top, rim, and handle . . . **155.00**

  5¼" h, 3⅜" d, pink, DQ, MOP, white cased, SP top, rim, and handle . . . **300.00**

Tumblers
    3⅝", shaded blue to white, raindrop
      design, MOP, white cased **110.00**
    4¼", shaded pink, enameled blue and
      white flowers, green and yellow
      leaves, white cased **125.00**
Vases
    4½" h, 6" d, blue, ribbon, MOP, white
      cased, pinched in neck **495.00**
    5½" h, 3¾" d, sq, folded over top
      edge, shaded rose, hobnail, MOP,
      white cased **575.00**
    5¾" h, 4¼" d, bulbous, melon sec-
      tioned, shaded pink, white enamel
      flowers, gold foliage, frosted applied
      handles, white cased, pr **225.00**
    6" h, 4½" d, tricorn top, Flower and
      Acorn pat, deep rose, MOP, white
      cased **395.00**
    8" h, 4" d, shaded apricot, DQ, MOP,
      ruffled, frosted edge, frosted ap-
      plied thorn handles, pedestal foot,
      white cased **250.00**
    11¾" h, 4½" d, ruffled, frosted edge,
      shaded pink swirl, MOP, reeded
      frosted applied handles, pedestal
      foot, white cased **295.00**
    12", pie crust rim, rose shaded to gray-
      blue base **250.00**
Whimsey, 3½", fluted top with 2 sides
    folded over, green-white, rose striped,
    MOP **185.00**

SATSUMA

History: Satsuma, named for a war lord who
brought skilled Korean potters to Japan in the early
1600s, was a hand-crafted Japanese faience
glazed pottery. It is finely crackled, has a cream,
yellow-cream, or gray-cream color and is decorated
with raised enamels in floral geometric and figural
motifs.

Figural satsuma was made specifically for export
in the 19th century. Later satsuma, referred to as
satsuma-style ware, is Japanese porcelain also
hand decorated in raised enamels. From 1912 to
the present, satsuma-style ware has been mass
produced. Much of the ware on today's market is
of this later period.

Reference: Sandra Andacht, *Treasury of Satsuma,* Wallace-Homestead, 1981.

Belt Buckle, cobalt blue ground, iris,
    enameled, lavender and blue, green
    foliage, gilt outlining, SS mounting,
    c1905 . . . . **200.00**
Biscuit Jar, cov, 6½", geisha girl motif,
    dragon handles and finial, c1920 . . . **120.00**
Bottles
    5", bulbous, scenic, feudal lords, gilt
      jeweling, c1890 . . . . **125.00**

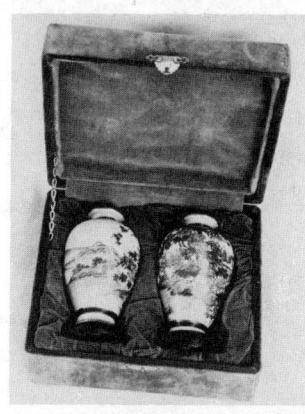

**Vases, pr, 4¾" h, Meiji Period (1869–
1912), mountain, river, foliage, and
peasant scene, wooden bases, orig velvet lined box, $650.00.**

    5", bulbous, waisted, gold on white,
      floral design **475.00**
Bowls
    4¼" d, 2" h, diapered ground, butterfly
      dec, wooden stand, c1870 . . . . . . **350.00**
    4¾", octagonal, int. scene of geishas,
      ext. figural reserves, ornate border,
      c1870 . . . . **275.00**
    12" d, 2¼", h, diaper border, 3 War
      Lords, enameled, gold trim, c1885. **250.00**
    12", dragon int. with flying cranes, ext.
      scenic with pagodas and water, sgd,
      early 19th C **275.00**
Box, cov, 5" d, hexagonal, floral sprays
    and butterflies, c1810 . . . . **275.00**
Brush Pot, 3½", white ground, water
    plants and foliage, sprinkled with gold
    dust, c1865. . . . . **150.00**
Cigarette Box, 4¾" l, 4" w, 1¾" h, mil-
    lefleur pattern, gilt ground, c1935 . . . **60.00**
Coffee Pot, 6½", flowers, phoenix bird in
    flight, turquoise, red, black, and gilt on
    white ground, c1865 . . . . **375.00**
Compote, 7½" d, 4¾" h, pedestal base,
    scenic with scholars and dragons in
    relief **175.00**
Creamer and Sugar, both cov, multi-flo-
    ral pattern. **350.00**
Cups and Saucers
    Demitasse, eggshell, floral motif,
      c1935 . . . . **35.00**
    Scalloped rims, enameled Samurai
      warriors and dragons, c1860 . . . . . **185.00**
Dish, 6⅛", fluted, figural scenes within
    fan and butterfly reserves **120.00**

Figurines

Boy, seated, playing with pug dog, boy has ball in one hand, other hand on dog, 11½" **850.00**

Warrior, seated, holding model of temple, gilt and enameled robes with floral and foliate dec, 3½" h **475.00**

Incense Burners (Koro)

3¾" h, 4" w, round, 3 ftd, scroll handles, courtesans on one side, mandarins on other, c1875 . . . . **2,400.00**

4¼" h, 4¾" d, scalloped, 4 ftd, reticulated SS top, raised gold and enamel work, 4 panels (one with fighting Samurai, two with ladies, one with haloed figures), Imperial Satsuma mark, 19th C. **950.00**

Jar, cov, 9", bulbous, pedestal base, handled, figural, 19th C **275.00**

Pin Tray, multi-floral pattern, sgd, c1930. . . . . **30.00**

Pitchers

4½", scenic, diapering on neck and handle, c1938 . . . . **150.00**

8" h, 6¾" d, tankard, Nishikide diapering and enameling, War Lords on one side, scholars on other, encrusted gold, sgd, c1885 . . . . **155.00**

Plate, 7", floral dec, diaper border and motifs, gilt, c1860 . . . . **550.00**

Powder Box, 4¾", round, scenic, geisha, gilt diaper border, c1905 . . . . **220.00**

Rice Bowl, 5" d, scalloped edge, flowering branches and robins, late 19th C. . **85.00**

Saki Bottle, cylindrical, hexagonal, white, gold dragon, red flames, c1935. . . . . **30.00**

Saki Pot, squat, multi-floral pattern, wrapped overhead handle, c1934. . . **80.00**

Salt and Pepper, floral dec, rust and blue, gold tops **22.00**

Tea Bowl, 2½", int. multi-floral pattern, ext. multi-floral pattern with circular and fan shape scenic reserves, sgd . **500.00**

Tea Caddy, 5", Nishikide diapering and enamel, two figural panels of children, encrusted gold, artist sgd, c1885. . . . . **115.00**

Tea Sets

4½", pot, cov sugar, creamer, flying cranes dec, bamboo finial and handles, c1885 . . . . **125.00**

Pot, sugar and creamer, 6 cups and saucers, dragon motif, dragon spouts and finials, orange and green, c1935. . . . . **200.00**

Teapots

3" h, 4¼" w, miniature, children playing ball in garden, floral dec around top and cov, sgd **725.00**

4½", peony blossoms, c1800 . . . . . . **225.00**

Toothpick Holder, 4½", figural, bird on log, c1900 . . . . **125.00**

Urn, enamel, raised peacocks, ducks, flowers, gold encrusted, gold Foo dog handles, rosewood base, sgd, c1840. . . . . **1,250.00**

Vases

4½", bud, urn shape, cobalt blue, figural reserves, gilt borders, late 19th C **275.00**

5", cobalt blue panel scene, geisha and lord, lake and mountain scene, gold flowers. **85.00**

6¼" h, elephant in seated position with large baluster shape gold and floral enamel vase on his back, 19th C **865.00**

6½", scenic, palaces, pagodas, religious procession crossing bridge, raised gold and enamel, black and gold mark **950.00**

7¼" h, 4" w, cobalt blue collar and base with lavender flowers and gold trim, body has garden of blue flowers, 2 pheasants in orange and lavender, trees, stream and hills, mkd **325.00**

9", cobalt blue, two panels, obverse with 15 women in garden scene, reverse with 12 holy men sitting by large Goddess Kawan Yen figure **250.00**

15", Japanese war lords and gods, multicolored and gold tracery, c1920 . . . . **195.00**

16", baluster shape, scroll handles, family and military scenes, late 19th C **650.00**

SCALES

History: Prior to 1900 the simple balance scale commonly was used for measuring weights. Since then scales have become more sophisticated in design and more accurate. A variety of styles and types include beam, platform, postal, and pharmaceutical.

Apothecary, balance, French Empire, no weights, base 23¾ x 11½ x 4", 23½" h scale on base **485.00**

Balance

Analytical, Wm. Ainsworth & Sons, Denver, metal case, no weights, 19½" h **80.00**

Spring, Excelsior, 50 pound capacity, brass **18.00**

Spring, "Warranted & Made by Thomas Marton, NY, 1871" on brass front plate, 8" plus hooks . . **20.00**

Candy Store

Toledo Model #405 A, 2 pound, brass scoop **125.00**

Toledo Model #415 T, 3 pound. . . . **85.00**

Fairbanks, mkd "lz 8″, 15½″ l, 8¾″ h, 50% orig paint, $50.00.

Counter
American Cutlery Co, red paint, 10″
balance arm, weight, brass pan. . . 175.00
Chatillion No. 2, Cl, brass bar. 55.00
The Standard Computing Scale Co.,
Detroit, gilt metal, c1890, 33″ h. . . 175.00
Egg, Acme Egg Grading Scale, Specialty
Mfg. Co, pat'd June 24, 1924, alumi-
num, 10″ l, 4″ h 20.00
Hanging
Detecto, galvanized basket 35.00
Wrought iron, tapered arm with
shaped hinge, link chain, bulbous
weight, 14½″ l, 4″ h. 250.00
Ice, spring balance, iron, brass face,
c1900. . . . . 25.00
Jewelers, balance, brass pans, wood
box base with drawer, ... 55.00
Platform type, Cl and brass, red painted
base, 1 & 2 pound weights, brass
hopper 75.00
Postage, Pelouse Mfg. Co. Chicago,
brass and Cl, brass hopper, gilt-
painted, 13½″ l. 35.00
Store
Dodge Micrometer Scale 250.00
John Catillon & Sons 2016, round
dial. 95.00
Nat'l Store Spec, 10″ fancy base . . . 300.00
Tobacco, advertisement, Speckled
Beauty & Early Bird. 40.00

SCHLEGELMILCH PORCELAINS

History: Erdmann Schlegelmilch founded his procelain factory in Suhl in the Thuringia region in 1861. Reinhold, his brother, established a porcelain factory at Tillowitz in Upper Silesia in 1869. In the 1860s Prussia controlled Thuringia and Upper Silesia, both rich in the natural ingredients needed for porcelain.

By the late 19th century an active export business was conducted with the United States and Canada due to a large supply of porcelain at rea-

sonable costs achieved through industrialization and cheap labor. Both brothers marked their pieces with the RSP mark, a designation honoring Rudolph Schlegelmilch, their father. Over 30 mark variations have been discovered.

The Suhl factory ceased production in 1920, unable to recover from the effects of World War I. The Tillowitz plant, located in an area of changing international boundaries, finally came under Polish socialist government control in 1956.

Note: Many "fake" Schlegelmilch pieces are appearing on the market. These reproductions have new decal marks, transfers, or recently hand painted animals on old, authentic R.S. Prussia pieces.

References: Mary Frank Gaston, *The Collector's Encyclopedia Of R.S. Prussia and Other R.S. and E.S. Porcelain*, Collector Books, 1982; George W. Terrell, Jr., *Collecting R.S. Prussia Identification and Values*, Books Americana, 1982; Clifford S. Schlegelmilch, *Handbook Of Erdmann And Reinhold Schlegelmilch, Prussia-Germany And Oscar Schlegelmilch, Germany*, privately printed, 1973, 3rd edition.

R.S. GERMANY

Berry Set, 10″ bowl, six 5″ bowls, light
green ground, white roses, green
mark 425.00
Biscuit Jar, 5½″, green and white
ground, white calla lily dec. 150.00
Bowls
7½″, hp, molded, light green to white,
pink and white floral center,
sgd. 175.00
9″, dark green to cream ground, or-
ange flowers 75.00
Cake Plate, pierced handles, lily of the
valley dec. 50.00

R.S. Germany, bowl, 10″ d, hexagonal relief petal border, gray tones in border, four red roses and buds, gold edge, light green mark, $50.00.

Cake Set, 9½" open handled plate, four 6½" serving plates, portraits of ladies in park scenes, pink flowers, green mark **235.00**

Candy Dishes

  5", soft beige, large pink and white poppies, gold outlining, 2 handles, ball feet with trailing gold leaf dec, green mark **55.00**

  7", sq, wide scalloped rim, gray-green ground, orange roses, green mark **50.00**

Celery Set, tray with 6 matching salts, cream ground, pink roses. **125.00**

Charger, 12", off white ground, cotton plant dec, gold trim and edge. **95.00**

Cheese and Cracker Plate, 2 tiered, 9½", tulips dec, blue mark **125.00**

Chocolate Pot, 9¾", white to green ground, white flowers, blue mark . . . **150.00**

Coffee Pot, demitasse, 7", blue and mint green ground, tea roses, large leaves, relief yellow and gold flowers, double handles, flower finial **125.00**

Compote, white shaded to blue, hp tulips, blue mark **90.00**

Creamer, brown ground, large pink roses **55.00**

Cups and Saucers

  Demitasse, soft beige, floral dec. . . . **35.00**

  Relief mold, ruffled rim, white dogwood blossoms, gold enamel centers and stems, light brown dec, blue mark **55.00**

  White shaded to brown, white roses, satin finish, blue mark. **50.00**

Hatpin Holders

  Calla lily dec. **70.00**

  Roses, large pink, smaller yellow, 4 molded feet, green mark. **55.00**

  Roses, shaded pink, gold trim, ftd base, green mark. **50.00**

Inkwell, off white, pink roses, blue mark **75.00**

Mayonnaise Bowl, gold clover, pink roses **55.00**

Mustards, covered and spoons

  Cream ground, brown pine cones . . . **50.00**

  White, pink, and yellow roses. **60.00**

Nappy, triangular shape, soft green, white hydrangeas, wide gold rim, gold handle, blue mark **50.00**

Nut Cups, set of 6, plain white, gold trim **100.00**

Pin Box, white ground, orange poppy. . **32.00**

Pin Tray, 8", oblong, open handles, yellow and pink roses, green mark **30.00**

Plates

  8¼", scenic, house by the lake, sailboat. **140.00**

  8½", green holly, red berries, white rose **55.00**

  10", open handles, orange to white ground, 4 large nasturtuims, pink, orange and yellow, green mark . . . **50.00**

  10½", open handles, deep welled, lavander leaves, gold outlining around edge, multicolored floralcenter . . . **95.00**

Powder Box, green ground, white flowers with long stems. **60.00**

Relish Tray, beige ground, yellow roses **55.00**

Sugar, brown ground, large pink roses **55.00**

Vases

  6", 2 handles, white shaded to blue, pink roses, blue mark. **35.00**

  10¾" h, 4½" d, scenic, Nightwatch. . **300.00**

R.S. Poland, sauce dish, 4½ x 4⅛", chamfered corners, multicolor floral band, gold line highlights, red and green mark, $30.00.

R.S. POLAND

Berry Set, 10¼" bowl, six 4½" bowls, carnation dec, red mark. **500.00**

Bowl, fruit, 10½" d, 2¾" h, scalloped edge, beige, tan and green ground, salmon pink roses, gold trim, red mark **120.00**

Hair Receiver, 2½", dome top, white ground, floral dec **110.00**

Hatpin Holder, 4½", off white, pink roses **125.00**

Sugar, cov, white ground, shaded pink roses, red and blue marks **100.00**

Vase, 13", green to tan ground, pheasants dec. **500.00**

R. S. PRUSSIA

Berry Set, 10" bowl, five 5" bowls, pale green-white ground, shaded green leaves, red star mark. **200.00**

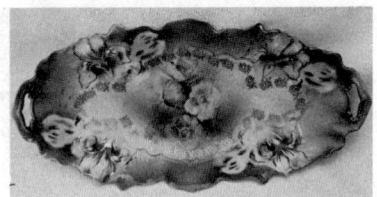

R.S. Prussia, relish, 9½″ l, 4½″ w, red floral center, iris on border, pink and lavender with gold trim, $75.00.

Biscuit Jar, pearlized with shells forming rim and feet, lily of the valley dec, red mark 150.00

Bowls

10″, 8 molded 3″ tan panels around rim with florals, shaded green ground, pink peonies 180.00

10″, portrait, Diana the Huntress, daisy mold 900.00

10½″, iris mold, relief pink poppies, green border, cream center, gold trim, red mark 300.00

10½″, bowl within a bowl, stippled floral edge mold, magenta to white, center, pink poppies, red mark 225.00

11″, carnation mold, pearlized floral dec, pink to rose, gold trim 185.00

Box, 5″, cov, molded edge, pink windflowers, green tints, red mark 65.00

Bread Tray, 12¼ x 6″, open handles, relief iris and roses, green and red, red mark 165.00

Cake Plates

9½″, relief head of girl, relief flowers at edge 165.00

10½″, open handles, scallop and fan mold, green ground, pink roses, gold trim, red star mark 95.00

11½″, pierced handles, fleur-de-lis mold, shaded green, multicolored roses, red mark 125.00

Celery Trays

11¼ x 5½″, iris variation mold, pink roses, heavy gold border 195.00

12″, stippled floral mold, pink roses, brown leaves, artist sgd, red mark 125.00

12¼ x 6¼″, swan scene, satin finish, red mark 290.00

Chocolate Pot, 9″, scalloped edge with raised daisies and gold trim, center with pink roses and white daisies reflected in water, red mark 400.00

Chocolate Set, 7 pcs, 9″ pot, 4 scallop mold, white ground, calla lilies, red mark 850.00

Chop Plate, 10½″, yellow center, swans border, gold trim, red mark 300.00

Coffee Pot, 10″, point and clover mold, shaded white to blue, pink and white rose sprays, floral finial 550.00

Creamer, ftd, scenic, village. 225.00

Creamer and Sugar, 4 scallop edge mold, satin finish, shaded blue to orange, pink and yellow roses, ring finial, red mark 300.00

Cups and Saucers

Cupid and cherubs in medallion inside cup, pedestal base, red mark 65.00

Floral dec, green shading, gold trim, red mark 95.00

Dish, 12 x 6¼″, white ground, shades of green, white flowers, rose centers, gold trim, red mark 125.00

Dresser Tray, 12 x 8″, point and clover mold, turquoise and gold border, yellow roses, red mark. 240.00

Hair Receiver, 4½″, ftd, light blue, pink roses 125.00

Hatpin Holder, 5″, scalloped top, ftd, multicolored floral spray, high gloss finish, red mark 160.00

Mustard Pot with Spoon, 3½″, white to light blue, pink wild roses, red mark 125.00

Pitcher, 4″, four red diamonds and gold beading around top, pearlized finish, red mark. 100.00

Plates

7″, dessert, scalloped ruffled edge mold, ¼″ w gold rim, gold stenciling, 2 large pink and white primroses, leaf garlands 85.00

8½″, six point and flower mold, yellow with gold flower parts, light pink medallion area, center yellow and white roses, red mark. 135.00

10½″, ornate leaf tendrils and scroll mold, lavender, lilac, and purple ground, poppies, florals in white pedestal urn, satin finish, red mark 325.00

Relish Trays

4 circle and medallion mold, pink roses, white lilies of the valley, beaded rim, gold outlining, red mark. 125.00

Reflecting water lilies, gold beaded trim, red mark 225.00

Salt and Pepper, 3″, 4 scallop mold, pink and white roses, satin finish 95.00

Sauce Pitcher and Underplate, white ground, shaded white dogwood 125.00

Scuttle Mug with Mirror, 4″, dark green and cream ground, pink roses, red mark 325.00

Shaving Mug, 4″, icicle mold, white ground, pink roses, red mark 200.00

Sugar Shaker, 4½″, white shaded to green, pink and white roses 160.00

Talcum Shaker, 5″, handles, rose dec, molded scalloped base, pearlized finish, red mark. **225.00**

Tankard, 13″, carnation mold, pink to cream ground, red roses, red mark. .   **675.00**

Teapot, 7″, hexagonal, cream ground, shaded yellow roses, gold garlands, red mark.   **325.00**

Toothpick Holders

  2¼″, scalloped top, 3 handles, shaded green, floral, red mark **275.00**

  2½″, 2 handles, red roses, red mark   **235.00**

Vases

  4½″, bottle shape, scenic, castle, shaded green ground **300.00**

  6¾″, bulbous, dark green and cream ground, pink roses, red mark. **150.00**

  7″, portrait, Summer, red mark **800.00**

  9″, flared neck, 2 curved handles, white to blue ground, shaded pink rose clusters, scalloped foot, red mark **550.00**

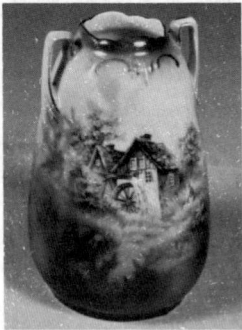

Vase, mill scene, $615.00.

R.S. SUHL

Bowl, 10″, pierced scalloped border, gold rim, white ground, pink and red roses **135.00**

Candy Dish, 7¾ x 4¾″, oval slipper shape, portrait, 4 women from mythological series **425.00**

Cup and Saucer, ftd, shaded pink roses, gold rim and handle, ...   **50.00**

Dish, 8″ l, 4⅝″ w, oval, pierced handle, scenic, classical ladies, white, pink and yellow, light green ground **475.00**

Plate, 8½″, portrait, Gibson girl, large pink floral hat **375.00**

Vase, 7½″ scenic, Nightwatch, shaded medium to dark brown, sgd Rembrandt in script, red mark. **400.00**

Relish, 7⅞″ l, 4″ w, 2″ h, green ground, white flowers, gold trim, mkd "R. S. Tillowitz, Silesia, hand painted", $35.00.

R.S. TILLOWITZ

Berry Set, 10″ master bowl, six 5¼″ bowls, poinsettia transfer **185.00**

Bowl, 7¾″, slant sides, open handles, 4 leaf shape feet, matte finish, pale green ground, roses and violets, gold flowered trim on rim, mkd **95.00**

Cheese and Cracker Plate, tiered, 8½″ d, 2½″ h, pink rose dec, blue mark. .   **45.00**

Mustard Pot with ladle, blue forget-me-nots, gold handle and finial **50.00**

Plate, 7″, open handles, 2 hp parrots, yellow ground **45.00**

Vase, 10″, pheasants, brown and yellow, 2 curved handles **110.00**

SCHNEIDER GLASS

History: Brothers Ernest and Charles Schneider, founded a glassworks at Epiney-sur-Seine, France, in 1913. Charles, the artistic designer, previously had worked for Daum and Galle.

Although Schneider art glass is best known, the firm also made table glass, stained glass, and lighting fixtures. The art glass exhibits simplicity of design; bubbles and streaking often are found in larger pieces. Other wares include cameo cut and hydrofluoric acid etched designs.

Schneider signed their pieces with a variety of script and block signatures, "Le Verre Francais," or "Charder."

Robert, son of Charles, assumed art direction in 1948. Schneider moved to Loris in 1962.

Bowl, 4½″ d, 2½″ h, mottled blue and orange, sgd **100.00**

Compotes

  7″, amethyst base, white stem, orange mottled center. **200.00**

Vase, 7½″ h, 7″ d, flated, light amber, sgd, $135.00.

8¾″, orange to blue int., striped glass stem, 3 glass cherries in orange and green glass encased in wrought iron with leaves extending from the fruit, sgd 450.00
Pitcher, 6¼″ h, mottled pink, dark maroon handle, orig paper label, sgd .. 375.00
Plate, 4″, mottled rose 80.00
Tray, 16″ d, amethyst to mottled pink, sgd 275.00
Vases
   5½″, blue, black and clear, cased orange int., blown into ftd wrought iron base, sgd, mkd France, c1925 ... 275.00
   8″ h, 10″ d, flaring, trimmed rim, egg whites motif with rust design, polished pontil, sgd 125.00
   8½″, mottled orange, purple, cream and yellow, sgd 285.00
   10″
      Brown, green and orange, satin finish 185.00
      Cylindrical neck, bulbous base, deep lavendar streaked with blue, 2 orange handles on neck, inscribed Schneider/France 400.00
   16″, sq, blues, yellow shading to pink and white in lower body, acid stamped Schneider, inscribed France on bottom 650.00

SCHOENHUT TOYS

History: Albert Schoenhut, son of a toymaker, was born in Germany in 1849. In 1866 he ventured to America to work as a repairman of toy pianos

for Wanamaker's, Philadelphia, Pennsylvania. Finding the glass sounding bars inadequate, he perfected a toy piano with metal sounding bars. His piano was an instant success, and the A. Schoenhut Company had its beginning.

From that point, toys seemed to flow out of the factory. Each of his six sons entered the business. The business prospered until 1934 when misfortune forced the company into bankruptcy. In 1935 Otto and George Schoenhut contracted to produce the Pinn Family Dolls.

At the same time, the Schoenhut Manufacturing Company was formed by two other Schoenhuts. Both companies operated under a partnership agreement that eventually led to O. Schoenhut, Inc., which continues today.

Some dates of interest: 1872-toy piano invented; 1903-Humpty and Dumpty and Circus patented; 1911–1924-wooden doll production; 1928–1934-composition dolls.

African Safari, man, 8″, carved wood, painted dark brown, orig cotton shorts and sash 275.00
Animals
   Alligator, painted eyes, 12″ 350.00
   Bear, brown painted eyes 125.00
   Buffalo, glass eyes 225.00
   Bulldog, brown painted eyes 225.00
   Camel, glass eyes, on hump, 9½″ .. 200.00
   Camel, painted eyes, two humps, 8″. 175.00
   Cat, glass eyes, 7″, leather ears, tail. 215.00
   Deer, glass eyes 275.00
   Donkey, large, glass eyes 100.00

Dandy Duddles, 9¾″ h, wood, painted, yellow neck, blue jacket, red bottom black feet, orange bill, $265.00.

Elephant, glass eyes	**135.00**
Gazelle, glass eyes, c1910.	**500.00**
Giraffe, 11″ high, painted eyes	**240.00**
Goat, painted eyes, leather goatee, 7″.	**100.00**
Gorilla, painted eyes, leather ears, beaded teeth, 8″	**850.00**
Hippopotamus, glass eyes	**250.00**
Horse, circus rider saddle	**110.00**
Kangaroo, painted eyes, leather ears, 2 short front legs, 11½″	**200.00**
Leopard, glass eyes	**225.00**
Lion, glass eyes, 9″.	**160.00**
Monkey, painted eyes, 8″.	**225.00**
Ostrich, painted eyes, 9″	**250.00**
Pig, glass eyes, twisted rope tail, 7″.	**150.00**
Poodle, painted eyes	**115.00**
Reindeer	**125.00**
Rhinocerous, painted eyes, leather ears, rope tail, carved wooden tusk, 10″.	**150.00**
Tiger, glass eyes.	**185.00**
Wolf, brown, painted eyes, 9″.	**250.00**
Zebra, glass eyes	**225.00**
Blocks, wooden, "ABC"	**85.00**
Book, *Toy Book of Humpty Dumpty Circus,* copyright 1918	**75.00**
Circus, 22 pcs, tent, 2 donkeys, 1 horse, 1 elephant, 2 clowns, 1 acrobat, 3 ladders, 4 chairs, 1 flag banner, 4 barrels, 1 platform, 1 acrobat swing	**1,500.00**

Circus Accessories

Barrel.	**18.00**
Chair	**20.00**
Platform	**15.00**
Tent, 25 x 35″.	**350.00**

Circus Performers

Acrobat, woman, 8″, bisque head, painted facial features, orig costume	**225.00**
Bareback Rider, woman, 8″, bisque head, wooden articulated body, orig costume	**225.00**
Man, 6″, carved wood head and body, oversized ears and feet, wide grin, orig cotton and felt costume	**125.00**

Ringmasters

6″, carved wooden head and body, painted facial features, orig costume, c1923	**225.00**
8″, bisque head, wooden body, orig costume.	**225.00**
Woman, 6″, carved wooden head and body, painted blue eyes, marcelled wig, orig cotton and felt costume. .	**125.00**
Dirigible, 13″, orig box, c1929	**85.00**

Dolls

13″, baby, carved wooden socket head, painted facial features, sea green eyes, orig blonde mohair wig, wooden jointed bent limb baby body, mkd "HE Schoenhut" in circle on head, "Schoenhut Doll Pat. Jan.

17, 1911, USA" on paper label on torso.	**400.00**
14″, toddler, carved wooden socket head, painted facial features, blue-green eyes, pouty expression, blonde bobbed mohair wig, orig paper headband, wooden carved and spring jointed toddler body, yellow romper suit, mkd "Schoenhut Doll, Pat. Jan. 17, 1911"	**400.00**
19″, girl, carved wooden socket head, painted facial features, deeply carved intaglio brown eyes, brunette human hair wig, wooden carved spring jointed body, pink ribbed Greenaway style dress with smocking, mkd "Schoenhut Doll, Pat. Jan. 17, 1911"	**575.00**
20″, adult man, carved wooden socket, deeply sculptured, painted facial features, intaglio brown eyes, brunette human hair wig, adult carved body, swivel waist, orig underwear, silk shirt, black wool suit, black leather shoes, c1912.	**2,340.00**

Farm Characters

Farmer, 8″, carved wooden swivel head, painted facial features, wooden articulated body, blue cotton plaid shirt, green linen trousers	**225.00**
Goat, painted eyes	**100.00**
Goose, painted eyes	**200.00**
Horse, painted eyes, 10″	**150.00**
Milkmaid and cow, 8″ woman, carved wood, painted facial features, orig cotton plaid dress, pinafore, cotton mobcap, wooden milk pail in clothespin hand, 9″ carved wooden painted cow, round glass eyes, leather horn, carved udder, leather harness with bell, rope tail	**400.00**
Jolly Jogger, 11″, papier mache head, molded blonde hair, painted facial features, carved wooden block torso, loosely jointed wooden arms and legs	**250.00**

Personalities

Barney Google and Sparkplug, paper label "Copyright 1922 by King Features Syndicate, Inc.".	**475.00**
Felix, 4″, ball jointed, 7 pc body, mkd "Patent June 23, 1925"	**200.00**
Hobo	**125.00**
Maggie and Jiggs, rolling pin and pail.	**660.00**
Teddy Roosevelt, ammunition belt, hat, 8″	**450.00**

Pianos

Baby Grand, 12 keys, 13 x 9″	**160.00**
Upright, 18 keys, wooden, stool, 19½ x 20 x 10″.	**155.00**
Rolly Dolly, 5″, papier mache, mustached chubby man, molded dunce	

cap, painted facial features, mkd "Schoenhut Rolly Dolly, Patent Dec. 15, 1908".................... **100.00**

SCIENTIFIC INSTRUMENTS

History: Chemists, doctors, geologists, navigators, and surveyors used precision instruments as tools of their trade. Such objects are well designed and beautifully crafted. The principal medium is brass. Fancy hardwood cases also are common.

Reference: Crystal Payton, *Scientific Collectibles Identification & Price Guide*, privately printed, 1978.

Advisor: Ben Weber.

Calipers, cooper's, sliding type, 31½" l, c1850...................... **125.00**
Chronometer, marine, 2 day, W. Brocking, Hamburg, #1360, mahogany 2 tier box, German.............. **1,000.00**
Drawing Instruments, brass, ivory handles, rosewood veneer case, lift out tray, c1870.................. **75.00**
Hydrometer, Baume, orig box **80.00**
Microscropes
   Bausch & Lomb, 12", brass and iron, horseshoe base, 3 lens-turret, case, c1905.................... **125.00**
   R & J Beck Binocular, 18", folding, brass, orig finish, all accessories, orig mahogany case, c1865 ..... **850.00**
   Martin Drum, 11", extended by slide tube, brass, all accessories, orig mahogany case.............. **425.00**
   James W. Queen & Co, Philadelphia, 14" h, brass, 3 cornered base, extra lenses, orig walnut case........ **600.00**
Octant, Spencer & Co, London, 13" l, triangular ebony frame, bone degree scale, 2 mirrors, set of colored filters, wood case, 19th C **50U.00**

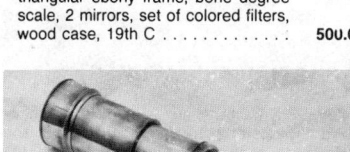
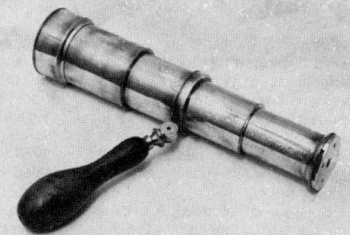

Telescope, hand held, two drawer, mkd "Plöss in Wien", 9", $275.00.

Sextant, Spencer Browning & Co, London, brass, orig mahogany case.... **675.00**
Surveyor's Instruments
   Chain, 66' l, 100 links, steel, brass handles.................... **90.00**
   Chronometer, 2 day, 24 hour dial, Robert Molyneux, 30 Southhampton Rd, London, #2389, mahogany case with 2 keys and leather strap, c1840.................... **2,800.00**
   Dump level, Cooke, Troughton & Simms................... **300.00**
   Theodolite with box, Stanley, 19th C. **1,450.00**
   Transit level, Garley Engineering Instruments, Troy, NY, 19½" l, wooden tripod base, brass instrument, dovetailed case, worn black finish.................... **350.00**
Telescope, Dolland, day and night, c1870.................... **250.00**

SCRIMSHAW

History: Norman Flayderman defined scrimshaw as "the art of carving or otherwise fashioning useful or decorative articles as practiced primarily by whalemen, sailors, or others associated with nautical pursuits." Many collectors expand this to include the work of French POWs during the War of 1812 and Eskimos.

Collecting scrimshaw was popularized during the presidency of John F. Kennedy. The biggest problem in the field is fakes. A very hot needle will penetrate the common plastics used in reproductions. Ivory will not generate static electricity when rubbed, plastic will. Patina is not a good indicator; it has been faked with tea, tobacco juice, burying in raw rabbit hide, and other ingenious ways. Usually an old design will not be of consistant depth of cut as the ship rocked and tools dulled; however, skilled forgers have even copied this.

Sotheby's offered the Barbara Johnson whaling collection in four recent sales, the fourth being held in December 1983. The fame of the collection and the understandable desire to own a part of it led to very high prices. These prices may not be sustained when some material is later resold, unless provenance to the collection is provided.

References: E. Norman Flayderman, *Scrimshaw, Scrimshanders, Whales And Whalemen,* N. Flayderman & Co., 1972, out-of-print; Richard C. Malley, *Graven By The Fishermen Themselves,* Mystic Seaport Museum, Inc., 1983.

Museums: Cold Spring Harbor Museum, Long Island, NY; Kendall Whaling Museum, Sharon, MA; Mystic Seaport Museum, Mystic, CT; National Maritime Museum, San Francisco, CA; Old Dartmouth Historical Society, New Bedford, MA; Whaling Museum, Nantucket, MA.

Advisor: Bill Wheeler.

Busk, corset stay, 12¾" l, light colored bone, age crack to center, engraved on both sides with ships, whales, and ladies (possibly from Godey's), colored. **500.00**

Cane, walking, bone shaft and ivoryhandle, part twist and part octagonal whale bone shaft terminates with a wood palm on turned ivory handle, 35" l. **325.00**

Dipper, coconut shell bowl, pewter connector, fine carved walrus tusk handle terminating in a carved walrus head, 12" l. **325.00**

Ditty Box, oval, c1840, top and bottomare baleen (very flexible dark colored material from the mouth of "sieve" whales) veneer nailed and riveted to pine, engraved with a garland of leaves round the top, trees and a mansion shown front and rear on respective sides of box, good detail [Johnson Collection] **3,575.00**

Eskimo Work

Awl on thong, carved bone awl,good even patina, nicely madecordage thong, awl 4½" l, thong 18" l. **50.00**

Sled Runner fragment, old bone, 4½" x ± 2½" at wide end of triangle, finished bottom edge, ragged at break **50.00**

Fid, spike-like tool (bone, wood, or metal) used to open or untwist the strands of cordage in splicing or doing fancy work, bone, nice patina, light yellow-gray, no cracks or chips, 7½" l **200.00**

Model, uncased, sailor made bone ship model of full rigged ship, all whalebone (probably pan bone), 7" l, 5¼" h, sound cond, some rigging slack. . . **900.00**

Pie Crimper, Jagging Wheel, entirely of-whale ivory with nice open work wheel in star form, c mid-19th C, 6¼" l, no broken parts of cracks . . . **450.00**

P.O.W. Bone Model, British 3 decker, *Sovereign,* 24" l, 18¾" h including stand, French P.O.W.s in War of 1812 in British prison, rigging slightly loose, few minor restorations needed, (Note: Be careful in buying "POW" bone models; they are being faked in great numbers and even offered in British catalogs) **1,100.00**

Seam Rubber, a sail maker's tool (shaped like a small chisel with a wide blade) to smooth seams, 4½" l, ebony separator between whale bone handle and blade, fine even patina, wear signs at the blade only **225.00**

Swift, barrel shaped clamp to hold it to table, engraved whale on center shaft, each outer arm has several engraved designs including rope and vines, 20¾" h, made entirely of whalebone **700.00**

Toothpick, ivory carved in form of woman, 4" l, exc. cond, no chips or cracks, even honey patina **300.00**

Whale Stamp, used like rubber stamp in log book, bone and ebony with small whale's tooth handle, impression of head of sperm whale, indicates one struck that got away, pricked in letters on handle "ERG," 2" h **260.00**

Whale Tooth

3½" h, half figure portrait of young boy, no cracks, good cond. **250.00**

6¾", red, blue, and black design on both sides, Prince of Servia on front, Princess with 2 natives, sailing ship, flowers, begging dog, etc., on back, no cracks **550.00**

Ship model, 8½"l, 7"h, baleen waterline, ivory cradle, port and starboard lights, helm well, lifeboat, professionally restored to museum standards, $1,200.00.

SEBASTIAN MINIATURES

History: Sebastians are hand painted, lightly glazed figurines of characters from literature and history. They range in size from 3 to 4 inches. Each figurine is made in limited numbers. Other series include children and scenes from family life.

Prescott W. Baston, the originator and designer of sebastian figures, began production in 1938 in Marblehead, MA. Sebastian Studios are located in Hudson, MA.

Each year a Sebastian Auction is held in Boxborough, Massachusetts, at the Sebastian Collector's Society meeting. Prices are determined from this source plus the work of the Sebastian Exchange Board which develops a price list that is the standard reference for the field.

Reference: Dr. Glenn S. Johnson, *Sebastian Miniature Collectors Guide*, privately printed, 1982; **Periodical:** *The Sebastian Exchange*, P. O. Box 4905, Lancaster, PA 17604. Subscription: $16.00. **Collectors' Club:** Sebastian Collector's Society, 321 Central Street, Hudson, MA 01749. Dues: $10.00. *Sebastian Miniature News* (quarterly). **Advisor:** Paul Sebastian.

Lobsterman, Marblehead paper label, $45.00.

	Low	High
17 - Indian Warrior	125.00	150.00
21 - Dan'l Boone	150.00	175.00
27 - John Smith	125.00	150.00
33 - James Monroe	125.00	150.00
55-A - Bob Cratchet & Tiny Tim	75.00	95.00
73 - Henry VIII	150.00	175.00
75 - Falstaff	125.00	150.00
88 - Prince Philip	175.00	225.00
121 - John Hancock	175.00	200.00
123 - Santa Claus	75.00	95.00
125 - Patrick Henry	125.00	150.00
130 - Emmett Kelly	200.00	250.00
156 - Cleopatra (ver.1)	200.00	250.00
176 - Christopher Columbus	200.00	250.00
180 - Caroline Cabot	225.00	275.00
185 - Chiquita Banana (ver. 1)	300.00	350.00
192 - Chief Pontiac	350.00	400.00
195 - Weighing the Baby	150.00	200.00
197 - Benjamin Franklin	75.00	95.00
204 - Tabasco Sauce	250.00	300.00
212 - Old Powder House	200.00	275.00
233 - The Nativity	165.00	185.00
237 - Campfire Girl	300.00	400.00
290 - Mt. Vernon	275.00	350.00
315 - Mark Twain	75.00	95.00
322 - The Infantryman	350.00	400.00

SEVRES

History: The principal patron of the French porcelain industry in early 18th century France was Jeanne Antonette Poisson, Marquise de Pompadour. She supported the Vincennes factory of Gilles and Robert Dubois and their successors in its attempt to make soft paste porcelain in the 1740s. In 1753 she moved the porcelain operations to Sevres, near her home, Chateau de Bellevue.

The Sevres soft paste formula used sand from Fontainbleau, salt and saltpeter, soda of alicante, powdered alabaster, clay, and soap. Louis XV allowed the firm to use the "double L's." Many famous colors were developed, including a cobalt blue. The great scenic designs on the ware were painted by such famous decorators as Watteau, La Tour, and Boucher. In the 18th century Sevres porcelain was the world's foremost diplomatic gift.

In 1769 kaolin was discovered in France; and, a hard paste formula developed. The baroque gave way to rococo, a style favored by Jeanne du Barry, Louis XV's next mistress. Louis XVI took little interest in Sevres. Many factories began to turn out counterfeit copies. In 1876 the factory was moved to St. Cloud and was eventually nationalized.

Biscuit Jar, 7" h, 4⅜" d, purple and cream ground, acid cut purple iris, gold trim, engraved sgr and Sevres		450.00
Cups and Saucers		
Coffee, cylindrical, cobalt blue, painted fish mongers, cobalt rims reserved with raised gilt floral and foliate designs, painter Fontaine, purple and blue interlaced L's, date mk 1775		700.00
Green, hp portrait of Pauline Bonaparte, gold ornate handle, sgd NAY, "M Imple de Sevres" in red cartouche, c1894		95.00
Dresser Box, 9" l, 6½" w, oval, hinged dome lid, maroon with floral bouquets, scroll work and gilt metal trim, floral decor inside lid and base, mkd		265.00
Figures, pr, 8¼", white, unglazed, boy with hands clasped standing beside basket of fruit, girl holds up skirt containing fruit, sgd L Tne, c1760		1,500.00
Jardinieres, pr, 8", fruit and flower sprays, blue and gilt scroll handles,		

Ewer, 12″, urn body, courting scene, couple walking, pastel, sgd with artist's initials, metal handles, rim and base mkd, $285.00.

blue line rim with gilt foliage, painter Micared, blue interlaced L mk, date letter 1767 . . . . **1,900.00**
Jewelry Case, 6″ l, 7″ w, cobalt blue and gold, lift off lid with gilt scroll cartouche of man and woman fishing, Victorian dress, sgd Dana **500.00**
Necessaire, cov, 3″ h, white, polychrome floral swags and wreaths, silver gilt mounted hinge with French hallmarks, velvet lining, contains 2 perfume bottles, needles, ivory needle case and chatellaine **2,600.00**
Plates
9¼″, center with radiating star-shaped rosettes in gilt, multicolored border with animals in scrolling flowering foliage divided by fruit panels and crowned initials LP for Louis Philippe, blue printed Sevres interlaced LP, date letter 1846, set of 10. **1,350.00**
10″, birds in landscape and on branches, molded border of feuillede-choux in blue and gilt with painted trailing flowers, blue interlaced L enclosing date letter for 1756. . . . . **250.00**
Sugar Bowl, cov, 3½″ h, gilt scroll cartouches with exotic birds on branches and flowering foliage, reserved on bleu-celeste ground, flowering branch finial, gilt dentil rims, blue

interlaced L enclosing date letter for 1771 . . . . **725.00**
Tray, 15½″, yellow, painted, blue portrait medallions **200.00**
Tureen, cov, and stand, circular, multicolored bouquets, scattered flower sprays, gilt scroll handles and artichoke finial, 18″ d, oval stand, gilt shell and scroll molded handles, blue crowned interlaced L, date letter for 1774 . . . . **650.00**
Urn, 16½″, full figure lady and angel, heavy gold top, sgd I Deniere. **400.00**
Vase, 30″, urn shape, pedestal foot, cobalt blue and gold, 2 ladies and gentleman in garden, applied metal handles with rings, sgd Adonis **750.00**

SEWING ITEMS

History: As late as 50 years ago, a wide variety of sewing items were found in almost every home in America. Women, of every economic and social status, were skilled in sewing and dress making.

Even the most elegant ladies practiced the art of embroidery with the aid of jeweled gold and silver thimbles. Sewing birds, an interesting convenience item, were used to hold cloth (in the bird's beak) while sewing. Made of iron or brass, they could be attached to table or shelf with a screw-type fixture. Later models featured a pincushion.

References: Pamela Clabburn, *The Needlework Dictionary*, Susan Burrow Swan, *Plain & Fancy*.

Museums: Fabric Hall, Historic Deerfield, Deerfield, MA; Museum of American History, Smithsonian Institution, Washington, D.C.; Shelbourne Museum, Shelburne, VT.

Additional Listings: See *Warman's Americana & Collectibles* for more examples.

Basket, open, splint handles, base and trim, Shaker, 12″. **45.00**
Bodkin, whalebone, carved hand at top, c1850–60, 4⅞″ **120.00**
Boxes
Mahogany veneer on pine, flame grain veneer on beveled edge lid, fitted tray, orig blue and white printed paper lining, Shaker, Sabbothday Lake, Maine, c1890, 3½ x 7¾ x 11″. **50.00**
Walnut, maple, and cherry, two tiered, drawer in lower tier, top compartment for spools with eight ivory eyelets, pincushion on turned base, 5¼ x 7″ **65.00**
Wood, inlaid geometric design on lid, int. orig blue paper lining, mirror, and fitted tray, Shaker, Maine, 3¾ x 7⅞ x 11″. **75.00**

Wood, turned tree on top with wire rods for spools, pincushion top, nailed drawer in base, 13½″ h . . . 110.00

Cabinet, spool, brass handle, folding legs, two doors, ten spool holders, 19th C, 14 x 4¼ x 17″ h 200.00

Chair, simple construction, one slat back, old natural finish, woven cane seat, Shaker, 27″ seat height 325.00

Chatelain, chains with round pincushion, pick, pencil, ring loop top, SS 175.00

Darning Egg, ebony, SS embossed floral handle, 6½″ 35.00

Embroidery Hoop with table clamp, cherry and walnut, Shaker, 6¼″ d . . . 115.00

Hem Gauge, SS emb, circular slide . . . 25.00

Knife, 4 blades, silver inlays of anchor, heart, cross, club, star, and crescent, 3 blades have inlaid copper circle . . . 150.00

Knitting Machine, CI, hand crank, orig black paint, red and yellow striping, emb metal label "Franz & Pope Knitting Machine Co, Patented 1872, Bucyrus, Ohio" 10″ l 25.00

Knitting Needles, dark wood, acorn turned whale ivory top, mid 19th C, 13½″ 200.00

Needle Case, tole, black ground, red and yellow dec, 9¾″ l 75.00

Pincushion, shoe, pewter, red velvet cushion 40.00

Scissors
Embroidery, SS, c1900, 4¼″ 50.00
Stork, SP, 3″ 30.00
Tailor, iron, mid 19th C, 7½″ 50.00

Sewing Birds, brass
2 pin cushions, dated Sept. 15, 1853 175.00
Emb, table clamp, pincushion, 5″ l . . 100.00

Shuttle, tatting, SS 25.00

Sleeve Board, cherry wood, 24½″ l . . . 45.00

Spinning Wheel, hickory and ash,

chipped carved detail on block and pine bobbin box, old refinishing, 30¾″ wheel, 42″ h overall 200.00

Spool Holders
Scrimshaw ivory, 3 graduated tiers, wood star center, early 19th C, 6¼″ h 1,000.00

Walnut, 3 round graduated tiers, 4 drawers in base with turned whalebone knobs, pincushion top, 29 whalebone pegs to hold spools, c1860–70, 14″ h 550.00

Swift, scrimshaw, star inlaid clamp, c1850–70, 23″ h 850.00

Tape Measures, figural
Book, gold tooled, mkd Austria, 1¾″ 25.00
Dog, standing, stuffed black velour, red plastic collar, tongue is tape, tail holds aluminum thimble, 4¾ x 4¾″ 25.00
Dog's head, metal, wearing hat, kerchief, tongue is red tape 25.00
Horse, celluloid, red saddle, Japan . . 18.00

Thimbles
Gold, size 8, wide engraved band with ornate design 200.00
Gold, size 10, wide plain band with a grooved base, 14K, F.S. Hoffman . 150.00
Silver, amethyst glass top, engraved rectangle and X design band set with 3 small rubies 125.00
Silver, size 7, alternating plain and ornate panels, H. Muke Sons 30.00
Silver, size 10, ornate band divided into medallions, each set with either turquoise or diamond, Simons 250.00

Thimble Holders
Alpine boy, surrounded by 6 thimbles, brass, round base, 4″ 85.00
Cat, setting on 3″ oval base with thimble and thread holders, SP 65.00
Wooden, 7 hooks, pincushion, match pocket, advertising, Geneva, Iowa 20.00

Yarn Winder, turned legs, chamfered block base, turned column, drum top with top mounted clock hand counter, brown patina, Shaker, 25½″ d, 46″ h 145.00

Tape, Westminster Abby, spring return, plastic or celluloid, 1½ x 1⅝ x 1⅞″, c1910, $135.00.

SHAKER

History: The Shakers, so named because of a dance used in worship, are one of the oldest communal organizations in the United States. This religious group was founded by Mother Ann Lee who emigrated from England and established the first Shaker community near Albany, New York, in 1784. The Shakers reached their peak in 1850 with 6,000 members. Less than ten Shakers are living today.

Shakers lived celibate and self-sufficient lives. Their philosophy stressed cleanliness, order, simplicity, and economy. Highly inventive and motivated, the Shakers created many utilitarian household forms and objects. Their furniture reflects their striving for quality and purity in design.

In the early 19th century, the Shakers produced many items for commercial purposes. Chairmaking and the packaged herb and seed business thrived. In every endeavor and enterprise, the members followed Mother Ann's advice: "Put your hands to work and give your heart to God."

Reference: Milton C. and Emily Mason Rose, *A Shaker Reader*, Main Street Press, Universe Books

Arm Chair, child's, simple turnings, mushroom cap arms, dark finish, burlap seat, red and black woven tape back, label on back leg, Mt. Lebanon, NY, #1	**425.00**
Barber's Brush	**40.00**
Baskets	
Gathering, woven splint, 10¾ x 14¾"	**90.00**
Miniature, woven splint, gray weathered finish, 5¼ x 4" h plus wood handle	**130.00**
Boxes, Covered	
Set of 3, finger construction, copper tacks in 2 smaller boxes, natural finish, ink inscriptions on 2 smaller boxes, "Nutmeg" and "Cayenne Pepper", 6", 5½", 4¾"	**435.00**
Utility, oval, dark green paint, 6"	**200.00**
Bucket, 13½ x 13½", wooden stave construction, blue paint	**135.00**
Candlestand, pine, red finish, mortised	

Butter churn, strap hinges old red paint, $365.00.

crossed member foot, rect column post with chamfered corners, one board round top, New Lebanon, NY, 30½" h, 16" d	**200.00**
Carrier, five finger construction, copper tacks, bentwood handle, "Sage" stenciled on lid and both ends, 11 x 14¼ x 6⅝" plus handle	**350.00**
Commode, butternut, cut out legs, paneled doors, Watervliet, NY, 29" w, 16¾" d, 29" h	**350.00**
Gout Stool, folding, made from different size dowels, 12½ x 21"	**50.00**
Hand Mirror, double string inlay around oval glass, MOP inlay in handle, 12" l	**175.00**
Pegboard, poplar, 5 walnut hooks, old dark finish, 39¾" h	**145.00**
Pie Lifter, wire prongs, turned wooden handle, 14¼" l	**35.00**
Rake, wood, pale blue paint, 67" l	**145.00**
Rocker, ladderback, orig dark finish, old upholstry seat, orig label on back of bottom slat, Mt Lebannon, NY #6 . .	**425.00**
Saw Frame, wood, Mt Lebannon, 37" l	**75.00**
Sheet, wool, homespun, 2 piece, hand sewn hems, embroidered "2" from house #2, Pleasant Hill, KY, 68 x 79"	**160.00**
Sieve, bentwood, horsehair, 6½" d, 4¾" h	**130.00**
Spinning Wheel, stamped J. A. for John Anderson, Alfred, Maine 1751–1829, c1790, 61" h, 45" d	**275.00**
Stand, pine with hardwood posts, one board shelf and top, refinished with red stain, 20¼ x 20½, 31" h	**425.00**
Swift, umbrella style, walnut with pine standard	**145.00**
Table, cherry, turned legs, bulbous feet, H stretcher with rope carved detail at widest part, 2 board top, old finish, Pembroke, 18 x 35½ with 8¼" leaves, 26¾" h	**700.00**
Towel Bar, cherry, removeable bar for continuous towel, 21¾" l	**125.00**
Warming Shelf, tin, 3 round shelves clamp to stove pipe, each 9½" d . . .	**220.00**
Washstand, pine and poplar, simple turnings, one dovetailed drawer in base, red-brown finish, 20¼ x 17¾ x 29" plus gallery	**300.00**

SHAVING MUGS

History: Between 1870 and 1920, American men used decorated shaving mugs to demonstrate individualism and pride in their occupation or social organization. Sanitary laws of that time required separate cups in the barber shops. The owner's name painted on the cup insured individuality. Additional gold filigree, colored flowers, scenes, fraternal symbols, and occupational motifs increased sales appeal. European porcelain blanks were decorated by American barber supply houses for a modest fifty cents to two dollars.

Shaving mugs are found in all degrees of workmanship and materials: tin, silver, glass, and pottery. Unusual occupationals and fraternal symbols are the most desired collectibles, but not necessarily the most attractive or skillfully done. Look for skilled art work and sound condition. Occupational mugs with persons performing work or unusual or obsolete occupations are most prized.

One popular collectible is the scuttle, so called because of its "coal scuttle" shape, with separate compartments for water and soap. Made in both Europe and America, scuttles usually are decorated with elaborate decals or transfer designs of flowers, scenes, or portraits. Animal forms are found occasionally.

References: B. Handelsman, "Shaving Mugs," *The Encyclopedia Of Collectibles*, Time-Life Books, 1980; R. B. Powell, *Antique Shaving Mugs Of The United States*, privately printed, 1972, 1st ed.; R. B. Powell, *Occupational & Fraternal Shaving Mugs Of The United States*, privately printed, 1st ed.

Collectors' Club: Shaving Mug Collectors of America, R. D. #6, Box 176, Bedford, PA 15522. Dues: $10.00. *Newsletter* (quarterly).

Museums: Atwater-Kent Museum, Philadelphia, PA; The New York Historical Society, New York, NY; Shelburne Museum, Shelburne, VT; Texas Cultural Studies Museum, San Antonio, TX.

Note: Prices are for pieces in very good condition unless otherwise indicated.

Advisor: Donald Brown.

BARBER SHOP: FRATERNAL

B.P.O.E.	175.00
Foresters Of America	105.00
I.O.O.F., links, bible, and sword, good	70.00
I.O.O.F., links and eye, good	125.00
Jr. O.U.A.M.	100.00
L.O.O.M.	125.00

BARBER SHOP: OCCUPATIONAL

Barber Shop, customers	200.00
Bartender, no customers, flowers	70.00
Bartender, two customers, excellent motif, handle cracked	45.00
Bartender, three customers, excellent motif, handle cracked	70.00
Bike Racer, two wheeler, excellent, chip	100.00
Blacksmith, works at anvil, excellent	190.00
Butcher killing steer, excellent	210.00
Butcher, tools, steer's head, good	115.00
Electrician, installing bell, excellent	320.00
Express Wagon, horses, excellent	265.00
Garden Tools, intertwined	275.00

Fraternal, I.O.O.F., P.H. Zink, $35.00.

Grocery Store, front, good	90.00
Grocery Store, int., customer, excellent	165.00
Hearse, horses	245.00
Horse Breeder, excellent	330.00
Ice Wagon, horses, good	145.00
Jockey, horse's head and shoe, fair	70.00
Milk Wagon, horses, excellent	145.00
Painter, bucket and brush, excellent	190.00
Paperhanger, man pasting paper	225.00
Pawn Broker, symbol on flag, good	70.00
Pharmacist, morter and books, crack	80.00
Prize Fighter, gloves	210.00
Railroad	
Caboose, good	145.00
Caboose, good, mkd B & M, crack	215.00
Engine, excellent	165.00
Shoe Salesman, boots and shoes, excellent	335.00
Stationary Steam Engine, excellent	300.00
Steamboat, *Daniel Drew*, on Hudson River	225.00
Telephone Lineman on pole, excellent	330.00
Trolleys	
Two man city car, excellent	345.00
Two open ends, I.O.O.F. symbol, crack	215.00
Wood and Coal Wagon, horses, excellent	300.00

BARBER SHOP: OTHER

Comic, frog smoking, excellent	105.00
Florals	
Blue panel, doctor's name	30.00
Drapes and tassels	45.00
Green panel, good	35.00
Horsehead, no name, good	45.00
Name, gold, excellent	15.00
Numbered, small	20.00
Panels	
Black, gold name, good	30.00

Scuttle, china, white ground, (ed and pink roses, gold trim, mkd "Germany", 3¾ x 6½", $75.00.

Cream, bird nest, eggs, and flowers, excellent	**65.00**
Lavender, flowers on rim, excellent. .	**65.00**
Scenic, elaborate, excellent.	**240.00**
Sports	
Dog chasing rabbit out of horn	**255.00**
Fishing Boat, rods, fish, excellent . . .	**200.00**
Hunting Dogs, two (2), green panel. .	**200.00**

SCUTTLES

Florals	
Basic motif	**22.00**
Blue Leaves	**18.00**
Crinkled surface	**15.00**
Fancy decoration	**40.00**
Lots of red and yellow.	**15.00**
Pink ground	**15.00**
Shaded colors.	**18.00**
Small designs	**20.00**
Panels, color	**30.00**
Souvenir, map of Maine	**15.00**

SHAWNEE POTTERY

History: The Shawnee Pottery Co. was founded in 1937 in Zanesville, Ohio. The company acquired a 650,000 square foot plant that formerly housed the American Encaustic Tiling Company and where it produced as many as 100,000 pieces of pottery per day until 1961, when the plant closed.

Shawnee limited its chief production to kitchenware, decorative art pottery, and dinnerware. Distribution was primarily through jobbers and chainstores.

Shawnee can be marked "Shawnee," "Shawnee U.S.A." "USA #---," "Kenwood," or with character names, e.g., "Pat. Smiley," "Pat. Winnie," etc.

Reference: Mark Supnick, *Collecting Shawnee Pottery: A Pictorial Reference And Price Guide,* privately printed, 1983, 1st edition.

Advisor: Mark Supnick.

Bank, Winnie or Smiley cookie jar	**120.00**
Cookie Jars	
Puss 'N Boots, mkd "Pat. Puss 'N Boots"	**45.00**
Smiley, mkd "Pat. Smiley" or "USA"	**60.00**
Winnie, mkd "Pat. Winnie" or "USA"	**70.00**
Corn King Items	
Casserole, individual, #73	**32.00**
Cup and Saucer Set, #90–91	**25.00**
Mug, #69.	**25.00**
Plate, 10", #68	**22.00**
Relish Tray, #79	**16.00**
Teapot, large, #75	**40.00**
Pitchers	
Bo Peep	
Large, mkd "Pat. Bo Peep"	**45.00**
Small, mkd "Shawnee #47"	**35.00**
Little Boy Blue, mkd "Shawnee #46"	**35.00**
Smiley Pig, mkd "Pat. Smiley"	**45.00**
Planters	
Grist Mill, mkd "Shawnee #769" . . .	**12.00**
Polynesian Girl, mkd "Shawnee #896"	**16.00**
Train Set, 4 pieces, mkd "#550, 551, 552, and 553" or "USA"	**90.00**

Teapot, 7" h, 8" w, Tom The Piper's Son, pink pig spout, light blue handle, yellow hat, $37.50.

Teapots	
Granny Ann	
Hand decorated with gold trim and decals	**110.00**
Plain, mkd "USA" or "Pat Granny Ann"	**45.00**
Tom The Pipers Son, mkd "Tom The Pipers Son"	**35.00**

SILHOUETTES

History: Silhouettes (shades) are shadow profiles, produced by hollow cutting, mechanical tracing, or painting. They were popular in the 18th and 19th centuries.

The name came from Etienne de Silhouette, a French Minister of Finance, who tended to be tight with money and cut "shades" as a pastime. In America the Peale family was one of the leading silhouette makers. An impressed stamp marked "PEALE" or "Peale Museum" identifies their work.

Silhouette portraiture lost popularity with the introduction of the daguerreotype prior to the Civil War. In the 1920s and 30s a brief revival occurred when tourists to Atlantic City and Paris had their profiles cut as souvenirs.

Children
4¼ x 5″, girl, hollow cut, gilted highlights, red coral necklace, penciled lace ruffle, gilted black lacquer frame **350.00**
5⅜ x 6⅝″, bust of boy in military uniform, gilted highlights, black lacquer frame **125.00**
Gentlemen
2¾ x 4″, bust, hollow cut, inscribed

Andrew Jackson, 6½ x 10″, $145.00.

Joshua Baily, age 37, dated November 20, 1835 .... **450.00**
6½ x 3½″, George Washington, bust, miniature, details of coiffure in gray wash, sgd S. Folwell, Pinxt 1791, framed **775.00**
8½ x 12″, full length, hollow cut, lithograph ground, Aug. Edouart, fecit 1846, Saratoga **400.00**
Groups
14¾ x 13″, family group, 5 figures, brown, black, and white watercolor ground, sgd Sam'l Metford, New Haven, 1840 .... **1,800.00**
18¾ x 15½″, two men and woman, seated on chairs, pen, ink, and pencil room int., birdseye veneer frame, sgd Aug. Edouart. fecit 1840................... **695.00**
Ladies
2¾ x 3½″, hollow cut profile, wearing turtoise shell comb, costume printed and colored with brown watercolor, reposse metal frame, c1840 .... **675.00**
3 x 3¾″, hollow cut, watercolored, black dress, carrying tiny green umbrella and blue reticule, c1840 ... **375.00**
3¼ x 4¼″, hollow cut, wearing yellow dress, black and gold oval glass mat, c1835 .... **450.00**

SILVER

History: The natural beauty of silver lends itself to the designs of the artist and craftsman. It has been mined and worked into an endless variety of useful and decorative items. Pure silver is too soft to be fashioned into strong, durable, and serviceable utensils. Therefore, a way was found to give silver the required degree of hardness by adding alloys of copper and nickel.

Silversmithing in America goes back to the early 17th century in Boston and New York. It began in the early 18th century in Philadelphia. Boston was influenced by the English styles, New York by the Dutch.

References: Judith Banister (ed.), *English Silver Hall-Marks*, Wallace-Homestead, 1970; Louise Bilden, *Marks Of American Silversmiths In the Ineson-Bissell Collection*, Univ. of VA Press, 1980; Donald L. Fennimore, *Silver & Pewter*, Alfred A. Knopf [Knopf Collector's Guides To American Antiques], 1984; Dorothy Robinson, *The Official Price Guide To American Silver and Silver Plate*, House of Collectibles, 1980; Seymour B. Wyler, *The Book Of Old Silver, English, American, Foreign*, Crown Publishers, Inc., 1937.

Additional Listings: See Silver Flatware in *Warman's Americana & Collectibles* for more examples in this area.

SILVER, AMERICAN, COIN

Coin silver is slightly less pure than sterling silver. Coin silver has 900 parts silver to 100 parts alloy. Sterling silver has 925 parts silver. American silversmiths followed the coin standards. Coin silver also is called Pure Coin, Dollar, Standard, or Premium.

Tablespoon, 9¾" l, J. Brenise, York County, PA, $45.00.

Beaker, William Moulton, Newburyport, MN, c1810, cylindrical, engraved sets of initials, 3 oz, 10 dwts, 3½" h **450.00**

Bowl, Henry B. Stanwood, Boston, c1850, circular, spreading foot, floral swags, monogram, 5¾" d **275.00**

Butter Spreader, Asa Blanchard, Lexington, Kentucky, 6" l.............. **650.00**

Cake Basket, Balwin Gardiner, NY, c1820, circular, flared sides, beaded rims, pierced and chased border with scrolling foliage and berries, pedestal foot, swing handle, 12¼"......... **1,900.00**

Canns, pr, Joseph Lownes, Philadelphia, c1800, slightly tapered, cylindrical, horizontal bands of lobes, engraved monogram, angled scroll handles, 31 oz, 10 dwts, 4¾"............... **4,500.00**

Christening Cup, Lincoln & Reed, Boston, tapered, rolled foot, scroll handle, 3⅝"........................ **225.00**

Coffee Pots
  John Ewan, Charleston, SC, c1825, baluster form, chased, leaves and flowerheads, borders of running thistles, swan neck spout, bud finial, 38 oz, 10 dwts, 11½" h **1,450.00**

  Ward and Bartholomew, Hartford, CT, c1825, shaped spherical form, pedestal base, body chased with leaves, foliate dec, bird's head spout, 4 paw feet, domed cov, bird finial **700.00**

Creamer and Sugar, cov, Churchill & Treadwell, Boston, c1815, oblong,

monogrammed, ball feet, roses stamped on collars, urn finial, 23 oz, 10 dwts, 5¼" h creamer **550.00**

Creamers
  Beggs and Smith, Cincinnati, OH, c1850, octagonal, monogram in cartouche, repousse, floral and scroll dec, scroll handle, 7 Oz, 6⅛" h.... **600.00**

  Gorham Mfg. Co, Providence, RI, vase form, circular foot, engine turned dec on body, leaf capped scroll handle, 5⅞" h................. **225.00**

  Cup, Wood & Hughes, NY, c1850, circular bulbous body, beaded lip, foot bands, repousse chased center scroll, hollow cast double scroll handle with thumb piece, gilt int., 3⅝" h.................... **225.00**

Julep Cups
  Garner & Winchester, Lexington, KY, 3½ oz, 3½" h, 3" d **575.00**

  William Kendrick, Louisville, KY, 1860–70, monogrammed, 3½ oz, 3¾" h, 3⅛" d **375.00**

  William Sharrord, Richmond, KY, 3½ oz, 3⅜" h, 3" d **750.00**

Ladles
  Cream, Asa Blanchard, Lexington, KY, monogrammed, 5¾".......... **350.00**

  Clark and Pelletreau, NY, c1830, fiddle pattern, single struck shell terminal..................... **200.00**

  Joseph Lownes, Philadelphia, c1815, fiddle pattern, contemporary folitate engraving, 14"............... **275.00**

  William A Poindexter, Lexington, KY, engraved script initials, 5 oz **400.00**

  Franklin Richmond, Providence, RI, c1830, fiddle pattern, engraved... **150.00**

Pap Boat, Hugh Wishart, NY, c1800, oval, two sets of foliate initials **1,000.00**

Pill Box, oval, stylized lion, high relief, 2" l, ¾" d................. **75.00**

Pitchers, water
  Baldwin Gardiner, New York, c1825, baluster form, narrow leaf tip borders, scroll handle, spreading base, 40 oz, 10 dwts, 10⅝"......... **1,400.00**

  Unmarked, 1826, lobed lower body, pedestal foot with band of scrolling foliate, grapevine band on shoulder, rim band of shells, engraved initials and date, 27 oz, 11¼" h........ **425.00**

  Wood & Hughes, NY, vase shaped, repousse chased scrolls, flowers and foliage at neck, leaf capped scroll handle, 4 shell supports, 11¾" **950.00**

Porringer
  John W. Forbes, New York, c1830, round, keyhole handle with engraved monograms, 7 oz, 10 dwts, 5⅜" d.................. **600.00**

Daniel Henchman, Boston, c1760, round, keyhole handle, engraved, 8 oz, 5″ d **2,500.00**

Serving Spoons, pr, S. E. Young, Laconia, NH, c1840, monogrammed . . . **40.00**

Sugar Spoon, Stephen D. Choate, Cincinnati, OH and Louisville, KY, c1830–40, "St. Charles" on handle **85.00**

Tea Set, 3 pcs, William Thompson, NY, c1815, rect baluster form, pedestal foot, straight gadrooned border, foliate motif **1,100.00**

Teapot, Geradus Boyce, NY, c1825, panel baluster form, flat chased, land seascape motif, rococo leaf dec, "S" scroll handle, 4 leaf and scroll feet, 8″ **400.00**

Teaspoons, set of 5, Holmes & Tuttle Mfg. Co, Bristol, CT, up curved fiddle handle, engraved initials **80.00**

Vase, cov, Robert Swan, Philadelphia, c1795, urn shape, pedestal base, 4 beaded ball feet, pierced gallery at shoulder, reed form cov, urn finial, engraved monogram, 17 oz, 8 dwts, 11″ h **3,600.00**

Waiter, Cooper and Fisher, NY, c1850, circular form, engine turned dec, egg and dart border, 8″ **125.00**

Wine Pitcher, John Ketts, Louisville, KY, urn shape, pedestal base, engraved monogram, 14 oz, 9¼″ h **850.00**

SILVER, AMERICAN, STERLING

There are two possible sources for the origin of the word sterling. The first is that it is a corruption of the name Easterling. Easterlings were German silversmiths who came to England in the Middle Ages. The second is that it is named for the starling (little star) used to mark much of the early English silver.

Sterling silver has 925/1000 parts pure silver. Copper comprises most of the remaining alloy. American manufacturers began to switch to the sterling standard about the time of the Civil War.

Basin, Gorham & Co, 1895, circular, swirling lobed sides, beaded rim, 66 oz, 17⅛″ d **900.00**

Bowl, Tiffany & Co, NY, c1925, hemispherical, rim foot, 23 oz, 19 dwts, 9⅛″ **400.00**

Bread Tray, unmarked, boat shape, chased with band of fluting, 6.5 oz, 11″ **100.00**

Cake Basket, Frank M. Whiting Co, North Attleboro, MA, 20th C, oval shape on pedestal foot, Georgian style, engraved foliage band below rim, monogrammed swing handle, 33 oz, 15″ l **550.00**

Chambersticks, pr, Dominick & Haff,

Cigarette case, 3 x 2″, raised floral motif, mkd "Pat. Dec. 4, 1888", $100.00.

Newark & New York, 1879, sq cylindrical sconces with detachable circular nozzles, flying loop handles, chased, flowers and foliage, matted ground, 4 ball and claw feet, 16 oz, 10 dwts, 5″ w **775.00**

Charger, Caldwell, Philadelphia, circular, reticulated floral and scroll border, chased with floral and foliate designs, conjoined monogram in center, 51 oz, 16″ d **950.00**

Compote, W. Gale & Son, New York, 1862, circular shallow bowl, pierced sides, ram's mask with pendant ring handles, sq stem, speading base with Greek key rim, 20 oz, 8¾″ d **275.00**

Creamer, Sugar, cov, and Waste Bowl, S. Kirk & Son, Baltimore, MD, c1850 and c1865, repousse and chased, buildings, fences, and rocks, flowering foliage, sugar bowl with lion's mask and ring handles, flower finial, 42 oz, 7⅜″ h creamer **825.00**

Dish, cov, entree, Stieff Co, 1925, oval, ornately chased, repousse with flora, 25 oz, 92″ l **550.00**

Epergne, Tiffany & Co, NY, c1870, openwork stand, 3 legs, 3 round frosted sweetmeat dishes with raised centers, tendril handles, center finial, 33 oz, 10¼″ h **1,100.00**

Ewer, S. Kirk & Son Co, 1903–24, vase shape, round pedestal foot, chased and repouse with 2 architectural vignettes and scrolls, foliage and lovebirds between, chased bracket handle with ram's head thumbpiece, 46 oz, 15" h **1,350.00**

Mirror Plateau, Gorham Mfg Co, Providence, c1870, rect, sloping sides, stamped marine frieze of dolphins and putti riding sea horse, bracket feet, wood base, 14¼" l **550.00**

Mug, Wood & Hughes, 19th C, foliate bands at base & rim, chased foliate cartouche with monograms, bracket handle, 4.3 oz, 3½" h **125.00**

Platter, Bailey, Banks & Biddle, Philadelphia, c1900, foliate rim, wide border with vacant foliate scroll cartouches, 42 oz, 15⅛" d. **525.00**

Salver, S, Kirk & Son, Baltimore, c1850, oval, applied entwined rope rim, engraved wrigglework border, band of leaves on surface rim, armorials in center, 4 panel supports, 48 oz, 10" l. **900.00**

Sauce Boat, S. Kirk & Son, Baltimore, 1880–90, chased with flowers and foliage, matted ground, monogrammed, scroll handle, beaded rim, 3 hoof feet, 10 oz, 6⅞" l **325.00**

Vegetable Dish, cov, Shreve, Crump & Low, oval, plated liner, engraved scrolling foliage, corners and stand with turned bone handles, 60 oz, 19" l. **875.00**

SILVER, CONTINENTAL

Continental silver does not have a strong following in the United States. The strong feeling of German silver cannot compete with the lightness of the English examples. In Canada, Russian silver finds a strong market.

Austrian

Inkstand, maker's mark, F A D, Vienna, 1792, oval, beaded rim, pierced foliage, leaf chased panel feet, 2 cylindrical bottle holders with silver mounted bottles, taper stick with cylindrical seal box, 11⅜" l .. **700.00**

Tray, tea, Vienna, 1815, oval, plain surface, pierced gallery, 2 paneled feet, loop handles raising from leaves, wood base, 19⅝" l **725.00**

Dutch

Tea Caddy, Johannes Feddema, Leeuwarden, 1779, quadrangular, sliding base, slip on cap chased with flower head, sides chased with figures, floral sprays and birds, 4 oz, 10 dwts, 4⅞" h **900.00**

Tea Service, 1882, teapot, cov creamer, cov sugar bowl, and tea caddy, Friesland style, fluted, chased scrolling foliage, figural finial, 31 oz, teapot, 7¼" h **950.00**

French

Bowl, cov, maker's mark, J V M, Paris, 1819–38, circular, molded borders, 2 handles rising from duck heads, slightly domed cov with leaf tip rim, engraved monogram, butterfly finial on acorns, 16 oz, 5¼" d at rim ... **675.00**

Candlesticks, pr, Louis XVI, maker's mark, G F, Paris, 1789, circular bases, fluted stems and scones, leaves and berry dec, laurel and gadroon borders, detachable nozzles, 17 oz, 10 dwts, 11" h **1,000.00**

Wine Taster, Louis XV, Jean Berard, Saumur (Juridicition D'Angers), 1728–33, plain shallow circular shape, name stamped at rim, twin serpent handle, 1 oz, 10 dwts, 3" D **1,800.00**

German

Beaker, Gottfried Ihme, Breslau, 1721–27, tapered cylindrical shape, chased with scrolling foliage, crowned heart shape cartouches, matted ground, 2 oz, 3¾" h **600.00**

Bowl, c1900, oval, cartouche shape, paneled sides with fluted cornucopia flanking oval cartouches, center chased with five frolicking putti, 22 oz, 8 dwts, 14⅞" l **500.00**

Candlesticks, pr, maker's mark, G S, Nuremberg, c1825, circular bases with triform center, slender vase shape stems supported by 3 scrolls and applied with oval plaques cast with birds and grapevines, detachable nozzles, beaded bases, 10½" h **775.00**

Centerpiece, Mudra & Stiller, c1900, oval, 2 handled, ribbon bows and berried leaves, 28 oz excluding liner, 18⅝" over handles. **675.00**

Italian, candlesticks, pr, Antonio Cappelletti, Rome, c1810, fluted circular bases, beaded borders, vase shape stems chased with drapery swags, fixed nozzles, loaded bases, 11¼" h **1,000.00**

Portugese, tea and coffee service, maker's mark, J P L (Vidal no 1274), Oporto, c1855, teapot, coffee pot, cov creamer, cov sugar bowl, and waste bowl, chased with bands of rococo ornament on matted ground, shell and foliate borders, 137 oz, coffee pot 10½" h **2,750.00**

Russian

Cigarette Case, S Nazarov, Moscow, 1893–95, rect, applied gold and enamel crests on cov, match and tinder cord compartments, 5 oz, 4" l **300.00**

Vodka Cup, assaymaster Stepan Belkin, alderman Fyodor Petrov, Moscow, 1780–83, scroll handle,

lobed and engraved with shellwork,
1 oz, 10 dwts, 2¼"............. **400.00**

SILVER, ENGLISH

From the seventeenth century to the mid-19th century, English silversmiths set the styles which American silversmiths copied. The work from this period
exhibits the highest degree of craftsmanship. Active collection of English silver takes place in the
American antiques marketplace.

William III, caudle cup, John Sutton, London, 1698, circular, chased, spiral fluting and band of rope twist, punched
alternating sprigs and acorns, 2
reeded scroll handles, 12 oz, 5½" h **1,000.00**
George I
  Basting Spoon, John Holland I, London, 1725, ribbed Hanovarian stem,
  engraved initials, rattail bowl, 5.5 oz,
  13½" l **450.00**
  Tankard, Thomas Tearle, London,
  1729–30, cylindrical, plain, domed
  cov, scrolling thumbpiece, 22½ oz, 7" **1,000.00**
George II
  Coffee Pot, William Williams I, London,
  c1745, tapered, cylindrical with
  tucked in base, molded foot, leaf
  dec spout, urn finial, 24 oz, 9½" h **1,000.00**
  Cruet Set, Samuel Wood, London,
  1756, three joined circles on scroll
  and shield supports, rococo cartouche engraved with armorials,
  scroll handle, 3 cut glass bottles, 2
  with silver necks, hinged cov and
  scroll handles, other with silver
  mount and cov, 12 oz **500.00**
  Marrow Scoop, London, 1754, engraved initials, 1.5 oz, 8½" **125.00**
  Salts, pr, open, David Hennell I, London, 1749, circular, gadroon rims, 3
  shell headed hoof feet, 4 oz **325.00**
  Salver, London, 1740, round, shell and
  scroll border, engraved shells,
  scrolling foliage and fruit filled baskets, center crest, 4 scrolled paw
  feet, 77 oz, 17¼" d **2,750.00**
George III
  Caudle Cup, W & J Priest, London,
  1769, chased with lobes and flutes,
  floral cartouche and cable girdle,
  stamped with leaves, engraved initials, leaf capped scroll handles, 9
  oz, 15 dwts, 4" h............. **600.00**
  Coffee Pot, Ker & Dempter, Edenburgh, 1763, baluster shape, short
  leaf and shell spout, chased with rococo ornament, swags of fruit and
  flowers, bird finial, 36 oz, 11½" h . **1,400.00**
  Cruet Set, William Kingdon, London,
  1812, rect, gadroon rim with shells
  and leaves at the angles, lion mask

and grapevine supports, frame with
oak leaf and acorn border, central
ring handle, 6 cut glass bottles and
2 jars, 36 oz, 7⅛" h........... **800.00**
Inkstand, John Enes, London, 1803,
rect, reeded borders, dec panel
feet, 3 cut glass receptacles with
silver rims and taper stick, fully mkd,
29 oz, 10 dwts, 11" l **700.00**
Plates, dinner, set of 12, William
Holmes, London, 1768, beaded rim
with flowerhead and scrolls, chased
rococo borders, engraved armorials
in rococo cartouche, 206 oz, 10
dwts, 9½" d................ **6,000.00**
Salts, set of 4, Thomas Wallis, London, 1800, boat shape, reeded rims,
pedestal feet, 9 oz excluding clear
glass liners, 3¾" l **525.00**
Sauce Pan, cov, William Bennett, London, 1809, baluster shape, spreading bse, beaded rim, short spout, silver and turned wooden handle with
heart shaped terminal, flat domed
cov, wood finial, engraved, 9 oz,
5⅜" h.................... **800.00**
Tea Urn, London, 1768, ovoid, engraved armorials and trailing flowers, spreading sq base with pierced
foliate scroll apron, gadroon borders, beaded leafy twig handles,
flame finial, 85 oz, 10 dwts,
20½" h................... **2,500.00**
Teapot and Stand, Peter & Ann Bate-
man, London, 1791, octagonal,
paneled, bright cut borders with formal foliage, vacant shield on drapery mantle, conforming domed
cov, tapered spout, 4 fluted supports on stand, 21 oz, 10 dwts, teapot 7½" h................. **850.00**
George IV
  Beakers, nesting pr, Thomas Bur-
  wash, London, 1822, tapered cylindrical shape, engraved armorials in
  rococo cartouches, gilt int., 9 oz, 10
  dwts, 3⅛ and 8" h........... **950.00**
  Cake Basket, James McKay, Edin-
  burg, 1826, rect, gadroon rim with
  shells and foliage, matching swing
  handle, rim foot, 39 oz, 14¼" l ... **1,400.00**
  Decanter Set, Thomas & John Settle,
  Sheffield, 1821, trefoil shape, paw
  foot with laurel panels, central
  chased foliate handle, 3 baluster
  shape cut glass decanters, mushroom stoppers, 31 oz, 10 dwts,
  12¼" h................... **900.00**
  Salts, pr, maker's mark, I W, London,
  1825, circular, shaped gadroon
  rims, chased with flowers, shell feet
  with Chinese masks, 22 oz, 10 dwts,
  3¼" d.................... **200.00**

William IV

Candle Snuffers, pr, Barnard Bros, London, 1836, applied foliate scrolls and paterae, 7″ l 150.00

Vinaigrette, Thomas Spicer, Birmingham, 1834, oblong, engraved foliage scrolling vacant cartouche, pendant ring, hinged gilt grill cast and pierced with scrolls, 1″. 200.00

Victorian

Flagon, Charles Fox, London, 1840, baluster shape, scroll handle, flower finial, fully mkd, 26 oz, 9⅞″. 525.00

Punch Bowl, E. Hutton, London, 1893, round, lobed and fluted body, pedestal foot, 41 oz, 11⅝″ d 900.00

Salver, Martin & Hall, Sheffield, 1870, ropework rim, pierced border, 3 matching feet, engraved presentation inscription in foliate band, 28 oz, 2¼″ 550.00

Smoker's Compendium, E B A, London, 1896, rect, hinged cov, compartments, match holder, and cigar lighter, 10½″ h. 300.00

Toasting Fork, S W Smith, Birmingham, 1876, telescopic, chased with spiral bands of foliate scrolling, ring handle, 4 oz, 24″ l extended. 100.00

Edwardian

Cup, Crichton Bros, London, 1910, bell shape, Georgian style, reeded molded girdle, leaf capped scroll handles, 15 oz, 5½″. 200.00

Punch Bowl, Hamilton & Inches, Edenburgh, 1904, circular, 2 angular loop handles, pedestal base, 68 oz, 10″ h 1,500.00

SILVER, ENGLISH, SHEFFIELD

Sheffield Silver, or Old Sheffield Plate, was made by a fusion method of silver plating used from the mid-18th century until the mid-1880s when the silver electroplating process was introduced.

Sheffield plate was discovered in 1743 when Thomas Boulsover of Sheffield, England, accidently fused silver and copper. The process consisted of sandwiching a heavy sheet of copper between two thin sheets of silver. The result was a plated sheet of silver which could be pressed or rolled to a desired thickness. All Sheffield plate articles were worked from these plated sheets.

Most of the silver plated items found today marked "Sheffield" are not early Sheffield plate. They are later wares made in Sheffield, England.

Cake Basket, early 19th C, oblong, scrolling handles, wire work mid band, swing handle, 13½″ l. 475.00

Candelabras, pr, 3-light, c1815, quadrangular shape, gadroon and shell

Vase, 8½″, opalescent fluted top, $100.00.

borders, recurving arms centered by balls, detachable nozzles, 19″ h. . . . 700.00

Cheese Dish, cov, c1790, oval, beaded rim, slight dome cov, engraved crest, fruitwood knop, fruitwood removable handle, hot water base, 14¼″ 250.00

Cruet, 4 bottles, sq tray, gadroon border, 4 panel supports, 5½″. 175.00

Epergne, T & J Creswick, c1820, stepped round base, 3 paw feet headed by acanthus, 4 acanthus draped reeded arms with 4 small cut glass dishes, central cut glass dish on central waisted acanthus scroll stem 1,325.00

Inkstand, c1810, rect, gadroon rim, paw feet, 9½″ 350.00

Salver, c1820, shaped circular rim with shell, flowers and angled scrolls, 3 winged paw feet, 17½″ d 600.00

Sauce Tureen, cov, c1825, oval bombe form, gadroon rim, foliate scroll handles and finial, 4 scroll feet headed by scroll and shellwork, 8″ l 300.00

Soup Tureen, cov, c1825, oval, gadroon rim with alternating foliate shells and anthemia, reeded, and foliate handles, domed cov with lobed and scroll dec,

flowerhead finial, 4 leaf capped scroll
feet, 15" over handles **1,200.00**
Teapot, cov, c1800, spherical, 4 paw
feet, 8¼" h **400.00**
Tray, tea, Mathew Boulton Co, c1820,
raised gadroon rim with shells and
leaves, matching handles, engraved
armorials, 4 palm and acanthus feet,
only one sunburst, 26½" over han-
dles **800.00**
Vegetables Dishes, cov, pr, c1825,
round, scrolling foliage borders, flat
domed cov, detachable handles,
12⅛" d **650.00**
Vension Dish, oval, gadroon rim with
birds, shells, and scrolls, 4 lion's leg
feet with shells and grapevines,
matching handles, screw-on plug in
patera form to fill with hot water,
24¼" l **600.00**
Wine Coasters, pr, c1840, round, bombe
sides, egg and dart rims, crested
bases, centering wooden bases,
5¾" d **200.00**
Wine Cooler, c1840, urn shape, ribbed,
spreading scroll and leaf base, 2 foliate handles, detachable liner,
10⅛" h **475.00**

Syrup, 7½" h, floral relief and incising, made by Samson, Hall, Miller & Co., monogram, $75.00.

SILVER, PLATED

Plated silver production by an electrolytic method
is credited to G. R. and H. Elkington, England, in
1838.

In electroplating silver, the article is completely
shaped and formed from a base metal and then
coated with a thin layer of silver. In the late 19th
century, the base metal was Britannia, an alloy of
tin, copper, and antimony. Other bases are copper
and brass. Today the base is nickel silver.

In 1847 the electroplating process was introduced in America by Rogers Bros., Hartford, Connecticut. By 1855 a number of firms were using the
method to mass produce silver plated items in large
quantities.

The quality of the plating is important. Extensive
use or polishing can cause the base metal to show
through. The prices for plated silver items are low,
making it a popular item with younger collectors.

Basket, Middletown, medallion pattern,
int. engraved dec, figural feet, swing
handle **75.00**
Butter Dish, cov, Rockford Silver Plate
Co, circular, die rolled scroll borders,
flat handles, triangular finial, 4 paneled
feet, 6½" d **65.00**
Center Basket, unmarked, oval, diaper
pattern sides, applied scroll and floral
rims, foliate bracket handles, crested,
17¼" l **300.00**
Center Bowl, International, round, shal-
low, raised cast base, emb fruiting
vines, 16¼" d **175.00**
Coffee Pot on Lamp Stand, Elkington &
Co, pyriform, hand chased floral dec,
reticulated tripod lamp stand,
14½" h **200.00**
Cup and Saucer, Victor, beaded rims,
monogram **75.00**
Egg Frame, Homan Mfg Company,
round tray with 6 cups, central cast
handle, grapes and vine dec, 9" h . . **90.00**
Humidor, Derby Silver, 1887, round,
lined, 8" **200.00**
Knife Rests, pr, unmarked, figural cro-
quet mallets and balls **175.00**
Pitcher, ice water, Roger, Smith & Co,
ovoid, polar bear finial on handle,
12¾" h **100.00**
Platter, meat, Ellis Barker, England, oval,
shell and gadroon border, 22½" l . . . **150.00**
Shaving Mug, Hartford Silver Plate **60.00**
Soup Tureen, Rogers & Bros, boat
shape, half fluted, emb and chased
flowers and scrolls, angular handles,
4 hoof feet, domed cov with ladle
notch, 13¼" l **250.00**
Syrup, Barbour Bros, tavern scene, reed
wrapped handle **35.00**
Tea and Coffee Set, E G Webster & Son,
coffee pot, teapot, cov sugar, creamer, and waste bowl, fluted, tapered
oval forms, chased with formal scroll
patterns, coffee pot 9½" h **125.00**
Trays
James Dixon & Co, c1848, shaped
grapevine rim, 2 acanthus handles,
lightly chased flowers and leaves,

center monogram, 3³/₈″ over handles **650.00**
E G Webster & Son, rect, bracket handles, gadroon borders, hand chased with copper mounts, 27″ l. **250.00**
Trophy Cup, Wilcox Silver Plate Co, waisted circular shape, scroll trimmed cov base, 3 applied horn handles with bud finials, 8³/₄″ **100.00**
Wine Cooler, 19th C, fluted body, shaped edge, band of cast grape leaves at bottom, everted base, separate liner, 12″ **650.00**

SILVER DEPOSIT GLASS

History: Silver deposit glass, consisting of a thin coating of silver actually deposited on the glass by an electrical process, was popular at the turn of the century. The process was simple. The glass and a piece of silver were placed in a solution. An electric current was introduced which caused the silver to decompose, pass through the solution, and remain on those parts of the glass on which a pattern had been outlined.

Basket, 10″, grape leaf and vine dec . . **95.00**
Biscuit Jar, cov, black, floral and foliage dec **75.00**

Vase, 16″, green with silver dec, c1920, $95.00.

Candy Jar, cov, scroll band top and cov **55.00**
Creamer and Sugar, cov, 4″, chrysanthemun design, silver rim and handles **65.00**
Ewer, 15″, tapered body, crystal, scrolls, urns with flowers, silver collar, hinged cov and handle **425.00**
Perfume Bottle, 8″, bulbous, heavy crystal, mushroom stopper **75.00**
Pitcher, 10″, large peonies **60.00**
Powder Box, cov, ftd, ruby, scroll dec top and bottom, New Martinville **75.00**
Salt, individual, 3″ d, grape leaf and vine dec **25.00**
Sherbert, underplate, clear, scroll dec . **27.50**
Tumbler, clear, webb and scroll **30.00**
Whiskey Set, tilted decanter, 4 ftd shot glasses, ruby, poppies, Paden City . . **70.00**

SILVER OVERLAY

History: Silver overlay is silver applied directly to a finished glass or porcelain object. The overlay is cut and decorated, usually by engraving, prior to being molded around the object.

Glass usually is of high quality, either crystal or colored. Lenox used silver overlay on some porcelain pieces. The majority of design motifs are from the Art Nouveau and Art Deco periods.

Bar Bottle, Scotch, 12½″, deep amber, heavy engraved leaves and thistles, SS neck, orig SS cork stopper **165.00**

Decanter, 10½″, cranberry glass, floral motif, hexagonal stopper, $685.00.

Cologne Bottle, 7³⁄₄″, slight corset shape, flares to 3³⁄₄″ d base, scrolls, flowers, leaves, engraved detail, orig stopper, mkd Gorham **135.00**

Cruet, 11″, green, florals, leaves, matching stopper, cut bottom **350.00**

Decanter, 11¹⁄₂″, emerald green, vines and flowers, presentation piece, dated Aug. 12, 1898, sgd Alvin Silversmiths **600.00**

Match Holder, 2 handled **22.00**

Perfume Bottles, pr, 3¹⁄₂″ h, 3¹⁄₄″ d, heavy Art Nouveau floral with engraving, orig stoppers, mkd Alvin **190.00**

Pitcher, 8¹⁄₄″, clear, floral decor **290.00**

Sherbert, 2¹⁄₂″, underplate, 4¹⁄₄″, clear . **30.00**

Tumbler, 5″, grapes, vines, leaves **65.00**

Vases

6³⁄₄″ h, 2¹⁄₂″ d, stick shape, disc base, poinsettias on swirled stems **200.00**

14″ h, 5¹⁄₄″, heavy Art Nouveau engraved floral and leaf, ftd bulbous base, mkd Gorham **300.00**

SILVER RESIST

History: Silver resist ware was first produced about 1805. It is similar to silver lustre in respect to the silvering process and differs in that the pattern appears on the surface.

The outline of the pattern was drawn or stenciled on the ware's body. A glue or sugar-glycern adhesive was brushed over the part not to be lustred, causing it to "resist" the lustering solution which was applied and allowed to dry. The glue or adhesive was washed off. When fired in the kiln, the lustre glaze covered the entire surface except for the pattern.

Bough Pot, 9″ l, "D" shape, 3 arched panels of bird with prey and floral clusters, molded border outlined in iron red enamel, cov with foliate border and urn knop, 3 knop feet, Leeds, c1810 **400.00**

Creamer, 4³⁄₄″, huntsman and 2 hounds in wooded landscape, barn in distance, floral border, Staffordshire, c1815 . . . . **475.00**

Flower Pot, underplate, 4¹⁄₄″, pink lustre, wide floral borders, satyr's mask and ring handles, Leeds, 1810–27 . . . . . **325.00**

Jugs or Pitchers

6³⁄₈″, robin on branch in roundel, oval with figures, sheep, and house, floral sprays, Staffordshire, c1815 . . . **725.00**

6¹⁄₂″, pink, wrigglework pattern, bands of lozenges and zig-zags, iron red enamel rim, Leeds, c1815 . . . . **500.00**

7¹⁄₂″, purple-pink, strawberry vine dec, Leeds, c1815 . . . . **525.00**

Cup and saucer, cup 2¹⁄₂″ h, saucer 5¹⁄₂″ d, Greek key dec, $85.00

Loving Cup, 5¹⁄₈″, stylized floral spray, foliate border foot, Staffordshire, 1810–1815 . . . . **185.00**

Mug, 3¹⁄₄″, peacock on branch, flowering shrubbery, foliate vine border, Staffordshire, 1815 . . . . **300.00**

Vase, 7³⁄₈″, ovoid, flowerhead within roundel reserved on wrigglework ground, guilloche border, feathered neck, rim, and foot, rect base, Leeds, 1810 . . . . **310.00**

Wine Goblet, 4¹⁄₄″, wheat and tendrils border **95.00**

SMITH BROS. GLASS

History: After establishing a decorating department at the Mt. Washington Glass Works in 1871, Alfred and Harry Smith struck out on their own in 1875. Their New Bedford, Massachusetts, firm soon became known worldwide for its fine opalescent decorated wares, similar in style to those of Mt. Washington.

Their glass often is marked on the base with a red shield enclosing a rampant lion and the word "Trademark."

Advisor: Ralph U. Saarinen.

Atomizer, 6¹⁄₂″, melon shape, pansy motif, sgd **120.00**

Sweetmeat, 5¼″ d, melon body, white ground, green and orange leaf dec, SP cov, frame, and bail, Rampart lion in shield-mark, $360.00.

Biscuit Jars
    6½″, melon shape, satin cream ground, floral decor, SP lid, sgd .. 340.00
    8″, sq swirl, beige ground, florals, pink, rust, and green, rampant lion mk 695.00
Bowls
    5½″ d, 3″ h, melon ribbed, beige ground, pale blue and violet pansies, beaded rim, rampant lion mk. 275.00
    5½″, melon ribbed, cream ground, pink and blue mums, gold band, sgd...................... 250.00
Planter, 8″ l, 4″ h, melon ribbed, satin finish, cream ground, tan and brown floral decor, SP insert, rampant lion mk....................... 260.00
Rose Bowl, 5½″, melon ribbed, pansy decor, sgd 250.00
Salt, melon ribbed, gold prunus blossoms, gold beaded rim, rampant lion mk....................... 125.00
Sugar Shaker, ribbed, green leaves, dainty blue flowers 100.00
Sweetmeat, melon ribbed, satin finish, carnation decor, sgd 450.00
Vase, 3¾″, beaded top, enamel daisies motif, brass bottom and feet 180.00

SNOW BABIES

History: Snow babies, small bisque figurines spattered with glitter sand, were made originally in Germany and marketed in the early 1900s. There are several theories about their origin. One is that German doll makers copied the designs from their traditional Christmas candies. Another theory, the most accepted, is that they were made to honor Admiral Peary's daughter who was born in Greenland in 1893 and was called the "Snow Baby" by the Eskimos.

Babies
    Asleep in igloo, Santa about to climb down chimney 95.00
    Carolers, two, holding lantern, 3½″.. 75.00
    Holding ball, mkd Germany, 2″..... 95.00
    Holding hoop, 1¾″ 80.00
    Holding wooden broom, 4″........ 225.00
    Lying on tummy, 3″ 100.00
    Playing accordian, 2″ h, 2½″ w 80.00
    Reclining, arms oustretched, 1½″ h, 2½″ w................... 60.00
    Seated
        One arm extended............ 40.00
        One leg tucked under, c1930 .... 25.00
    Sledding
        Girl on sled, 7 colors, 1¾″ 45.00
        One on sled, another pulling, 1½″ h, 2½″ w................. 95.00
        Pulling penquins on sled........ 150.00
        Sitting, arms outstretched....... 50.00
        Sitting on red sled, mkd Germany, 1⅜″..................... 80.00
        Standing on sled 55.00
        Three on sled, 5″ w........... 200.00
        Two on sled, pebbled garments .. 95.00
Figurines
    Bear, 2¼″................... 60.00
    Bear on skies, 2″ 50.00
    Sheep, 2″.................... 45.00
    Santa on polar bear, mkd Germany, 1¾″ 150.00
    Snowman.................... 55.00
Planter, baby lying on tummy, red, brown, c1920, 4″ w............. 140.00

Sitting, 1⅛″ h, $45.00.

SNUFF BOTTLES

History: Tobacco usage spread from America to Europe to China during the 17th century. Europeans and Chinese preferred to grind the dried leaves into a powder and sniff it into their nostrils. The elegant Europeans carried their snuff in boxes and took a pinch with their finger tips. The Chinese upperclass, because of their lengthy fingernails, found this inconvenient and devised a bottle with a fitted stopper and attached spoon.

In the Chinese manner, these utilitarian objects soon became objects d'art. Snuff bottles were fashioned from precious and semi-precious stones, glass, porcelain and pottery, wood, metals, and ivory. Glass and transparent stone bottles often were enhanced further with delicate hand paintings, some done on the interior of the bottle.

Cinnabar, red, Lapis Lazal, top, late 19th C, 2¾" h, $300.00.

Agate

Banded, 2½", low relief carving of a horse, good hollowing, 20th C. **150.00**

Gray, 2½", large area of white with carving, single cylindrical drilling, 20th C **110.00**

Honey, 3", carving of a Foo lion and bat, reverse has small bat near base, well hollowed, mid 19th C . . **425.00**

Soochow Carved, 2⅝", monkeys playing under willow and rock work, sgd with 3 calligraphic characters, reverse has carving of birds, branches and willows, late 18th to 19th C . . **600.00**

Amethyst, 2⅝", carved foot in form of a flower, well hollowed, matching stopper, late 18th C. **225.00**

Carnelian, 2⅞", medium high relief carving with open work under vines on

each side, matching stopper, last half 19th C **550.00**

Chalcedony, 3⅛", blue, carved in high relief, baskets of flowers, crane and deer, indented foot, matching carved stopper, late 19th C. **400.00**

Chrysoprase, 2¾", uncarved, indented foot, well hollowed, matching stopper, 20th C **200.00**

Cinnabar, 3", red over black, carved to show diapered ground, metal mounted stone stopper, lacquer dec on neck ring **500.00**

Cloisonne, 2⅝", repousse, greens, blues, and red on gold ground, seal under foot, matching stopper, late 19th C **275.00**

Enamel on Metal, 2¾", flowers and berries springing from rock work, early 20th C **350.00**

Hair Crystal, 2½", sparse hairs in 4 legged frog, well hollowed, lapis stopper, mid 19th C. **200.00**

Hawk's Eye, 2⅞", carving of pagodas, huts, and mountain scene, well hollowed, 20th C **200.00**

Ivory, 3", geisha being served tea on a terrace, geometrical designs on sides and top, Japanese, sgd **350.00**

Jade

White, 2¾", floral carving, flat foot, mid 19th C **150.00**

Yellow, 2½", basket weave design, good hollowing, late 18th C **850.00**

Malachite

2⅜", nice markings, poor hollowing, 20th C **200.00**

2½", figural of man kneeling on one knee, poor hollowing, matching stopper forms hat, 20th C. **250.00**

Peking Glass, 3", imitation of agate mottling, flat foot, late 19th C **200.00**

Porcelain

2½", emb figures of Foo dogs, enameled in rouge de fer, metal stopper, early 19th C **300.00**

3", overall polychrome pattern of raised human figures, reddish seal signature on bottom, 19th C **200.00**

3⅛", kneeling maiden at worship with her servant standing in background, collared coral stopper, sgd with seal of Emperor Ch'ien Lung **425.00**

3½", blue and iron red underglaze, dragons cavorting through clouds, seal of Yung Cheng under foot, metal mounted coral stopper, mid 19th C **185.00**

Puddingstone, 1⅞", good hollowing, jade stopper, 20th C **80.00**

Rhodonite, 2⅝", indented foot, medium hollowing, matching stopper, early 20th C **150.00**

Rock Crystal, 2½", 4 columns of calligraphy, rounded ovate bottom, mask handles, crystal stopper, 19th C **250.00**

Serpentine, 2⅞", gray and brown stone, incised calligraphic characters on both sides, well hollowed, matching wood stopper, 19th C **145.00**

Tiger Eye, 2⅜", carved in low relief on one side only, early 20th C **125.00**

Yi-Hsing, 2¾", shoulders and sides enameled in deep blue, front inset panel dec with enameled design of a bird and flowers, reverse with inset panel in natural color with 11 character inscription in calligraphy, silver mounted jade stopper, late 18th C **800.00**

SOAPSTONE

History: The mineral steatite, used in producing all sorts of soapstone wares, has a greasy feel, and has been utilized for carved figural groups and other designs by the Chinese and others. Utilitarian pieces also were made. Soapstone pieces were very popular during the Victorian era.

Bookends, pr, 5", carnelian, carved bird, flowers, and urn **50.00**

Box, 1¾", rect, reeded sides, carved low relief dragons on top, 18th C **600.00**

Bust, woman, carved, wearing lacy mantilla, flowers on her bodice, inscribed Caldrini 91, turned marble socle, Italian, c1891, 28½" **450.00**

Candlestick, 7", carved crane and floral dec, pierced base **95.00**

Vase, 2½", tan and brown, carved rodent, $85.00.

Figurines

Fruitpicker, woman, peasant costume, kerchief over hair, holding basket of fruit in left arm, inscribed E. Battiglia, Italian, late 19th C, 29½" **900.00**

Group, Buddhistic lioness seated on hind legs with pair of cubs, mutton fat tone with some gray inclusions, late 18th C, 2½" **400.00**

Nude woman, classical, seated with drapery over legs, flowers on base, late 19th C, 25" l **575.00**

Griddle, iron frame and handle **45.00**

Lamp, carved, Oriental woman with black lacquered hair, Ching dynasty . **300.00**

Seals, pr, 8" h, carved, guard dog tops, engraved bases, Chinese, 19th C ... **95.00**

Toothpick Holder, 3 carved monkeys .. **35.00**

Urns, pr, 6" h, pedestal bases, carved florals, reddish tones, mkd China ... **80.00**

Vases

5", carved, scrolls and florals, tan and brown **80.00**

7" h, 10" w, carved, peacock and florals **150.00**

Wall Pocket, 4 chimneys, carved crow dec **35.00**

SOUVENIR AND COMMEMORATIVE CHINA AND GLASS

History: Souvenir, commemorative, and historical china and glass includes those items produced to celebrate special events, places, and people.

Among the china plates those by Rowland and Marcellus and Wedgwood are most eagerly sought. Rowland and Marcellus, Staffordshire, England, made a series of blue and white historic plates with a wide rolled edge depicting scences beginning with the Philadelphia Centennial in 1876 and continuing to the 1939 New York World's Fair. Wedgwood collaborated in 1910 with Jones, McDuffee and Stratton to produce a series of historic dessert sized plates depicting scenes throughout the United States.

Many localities issued plates, mugs, glasses, etc., for anniversary celebrations or to honor a local historical event. These items seem to have greater value when sold in the region from which they originated.

Commemorative glass includes several patterns of pressed glass which celebrate persons or events. Historical glass includes campaign and memorial items.

Reference: Bessie M. Lindsey, *American Historical Glass,* Charles E. Tuttle Company, Inc., 1967.

Additional Listings: Cup Plates, Pressed Glass, Political Items, and Staffordshire, Historical. Also see *Warman's Americana & Collectibles* for more examples.

CHINA

Chocolate Pot, Johnson City, TN, Soldier's Home, 9″.	115.00
Creamer, St. Lawrence	175.00
Pitcher, Piney Woods Inn, sepia, 7³/₄″, Hampshire Pottery.	95.00
Plates	
Buffalo Pottery, Wanamakers Store, 1911, 4½″.	65.00
Johnson Bros, View of Boston, MA, sepia, oak leaf and acorn border, 11½″	30.00
Rowland & Marcellus, rolled and flat rims	
Albany, NY, capitol.	40.00
Bunker Hill Monument, 10″.	45.00
Emma Willard School, Troy, NY . .	45.00
Hartford, CT, capitol.	35.00
Landing of Hendrick Hudson, 10″ .	40.00
Leavenworth, S	35.00
Mohawk Trail thru Berkshires, 9¼″	40.00
Royal Ponciana, FL, 10″.	30.00
Thousand Islands.	40.00
Washington's Prayers at Valley Forge, 10½″.	50.00
Worcester, MA, City Hall.	40.00
Wallis Gimson & Co., octagonal, Governor General's Ottawa Residence and Boston City Hall, flowers, butterfly, ivory ground, c1895.	20.00
Wedgwood, blue, 9¼″	
Boston Statehouse.	40.00
Bunker Hill Monument	30.00
Capture Vincennes.	45.00
Grand Union Hotel, Saratoga, NY .	45.00

Plate, 10″, Gettysburg, General Meade's Headquarters, F. Winkle & Co, blue and white, $50.00.

Green Dragon Tavern, Boston . . .	40.00
Homestead Fairbanks Family	45.00
Landing of Pilgrims.	35.00
Longfellow's Early Home	30.00
Mt. Vernon	30.00
Old Boston Theater	40.00
Old Feather Store, Boston	45.00
Old Man of the Mountain	40.00
Old South Church, Boston	40.00
Pearl of Orrs Island	45.00
Santa Barbara Mission	40.00
United Women's Effort, Lynn, MA.	45.00

GLASS

Bottles	
Cleveland, figural, frosted and clear, Cleveland embossed in base, 10″ h	110.00
Douglas MacArthur, aqua.	55.00
Butter, cov, Actress	75.00
Compote, Jenny Lind, 8½″, milk glass, open, scalloped top.	175.00
Creamer, Emblem pattern	95.00
Dishes, cov	
Stage Coach.	150.00
Uncle Sam	75.00
Goblets	
Emblem, Centennial	65.00
Grand Army of the Republic.	95.00
Lamp, Coolidge Drape, 8″	165.00
Match Holder, Indian Chief, pedestal, milk glass, 3½″.	50.00
Mugs	
Bryan, cov, emb bust, "The Peoples Money".	75.00
Independence Hall, clear	45.00
Our Country's Martyrs, emb busts of Lincoln and Garfield.	50.00
Springfield, MA, irid yellow, picture of library, applied gold piglet hanging over rim, Germany.	20.00
Mustard, cov, Tecumseh, log cabin shape, 3 ³/₄″, 2″, clear	65.00
Paperweights	
Lincoln	225.00
Plymouth Rock	95.00
Pickle Dish	
Actress.	45.00
Emblem	60.00
Pitcher, milk, Garfield Drape	75.00
Plates	
Actress, Frieda Hempel	35.00
Garfield Drape, "We Mourn"	50.00
Garfield Memorial	25.00
Garfield Star, clear, frosted busts . .	35.00
Grant Peace, green.	75.00
McKinley, "Protection and Plenty" .	35.00
Platters	
Grand Army of the Republic.	100.00
Nellie Bly	165.00
Rock of Ages, milk glass center. . .	75.00
Symbolic, clear	120.00

Three Presidents, clear, frosted busts.	145.00
Washington Centennial	
George Washington	90.00
Independence Hall	95.00
Salt, Liberty Bell	35.00
Ships, set of 5, milk glass, Battleship *Maine*, and *Olympia, Wheeling, Oregon*, and *Newark*,	275.00
Toothpicks	
Emmetsburg, IA, custard glass	30.00
Lane, SD, purple amethyst	25.00
Tray, Blaine & Logan, clear, frosted busts	250.00
Tumblers	
Ashburton, flint, bar, emb Civil War patroitic emblems, laurel wreath, and "Union".	225.00
Lord's Prayer	35.00
Louisiana Purchase, milk glass	20.00
McKinley "Protection and Plenty".	35.00

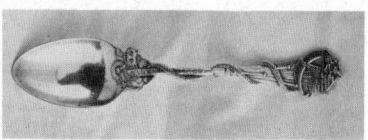

Salem, 1692, Daniel Low, Sterling, $145.00.

SOUVENIR AND COMMEMORATIVE SPOONS

History: Souvenir and commemorative spoons have been issued for hundreds of years. Early American silversmiths engraved presentation spoons to honor historical personages or mark key events.

In 1881 Myron Kinsley patented a Niagara Falls spoon; and, in 1884 Michael Gibney patented a new flatware design. M. W. Galt, Washington, D.C., issued commemorative spoons for George and Martha Washington in 1889. From these beginnings a collecting craze for souvenir and commemorative spoons developed in the late 19th and first quarter of the 20th century.

Reference: Dorothy T. Rainwater and Donna H. Fegler, *American Spoons, Souvenir and Historical,* Everybodys Press, Inc., 1977.

Collectors' Club: The Scoop Club, 84 Oak Avenue, Shelton, CT 06484. *Spoony Scoop Newsletter.* Dues: $8.00

Additional Listings: See *Warman's Americana & Collectibles* for more examples.

Allentown, PA, Allentown Grocery Co. building in bowl, demitasse.	15.00
Aztec Calendar, round bowl, Aztec design emb on handle, demitasse	30.00
California Oranges	20.00
Cape May, NY, branch shaped handle with sea shell	55.00
Catalina, buffalo in bowl, teaspoon.	20.00
Central High School, Detroit, gold washed	25.00
Chapultepec, Mexico, emb view, Mexico, state seal on handle	32.00
Chicago World's Fair, view of Woman's Building in bowl, handle of woman	

holding globe, profile of Bertha Palmer, reverse, dec, demitasse	50.00
Colorado, Look Out Mountain, 5″.	17.50
D.A.R., teaspoon	65.00
Denver, mule handle, ss	15.00
English crest, twisted handle, plain bowl, demitasse.	35.00
Georgia, black boy on handle, state seal, demitasse.	22.00
Glasgow, brass, thistle handle	20.00
Indianapolis, state seal on handle, view of Soldiers & Sailors Monument emb on bowl, demitasse	30.00
John Harvard	20.00
King Cotton	30.00
Lancaster, PA	20.00
Lion of Lucerne, twisted handle, plain gilted bowl	50.00
Livingston, Montana, Indian motif, SS.	20.00
Matador, full figure bowl, emb view of Monterey, Mexico	55.00
Montreal, Canada, demitasse	15.00
Mt. Vernon, emb in bowl, handle of George Washington's Masonic sword, reverse dec, demitasse	55.00
New York, skyline handle, Statue of Liberty in bowl, teaspoon	85.00
Niagara Falls, emb waves in bowl, teaspoon	48.00
Panama-Pacific Exposition, San Francisco, 1915.	50.00
Percy's London Silver Vaults, England, SS, demitasse.	15.00
Queen Mary, R.M.S., silver on copper	25.00
Rabbit's Foot, coffee	15.00
Roger Williams, demitasse	30.00
St. Augustine, FL, Old City Gates, emb handle, reverse dec, orange spoon.	40.00
San Francisco Fire, 1906, cut handle.	150.00
Santa Maria.	35.00
Skagway, Alaska, copper	15.00
Southern Pines, NC, Indian, full figure with arms upraised	45.00
Statue of Liberty, emb round bowl, Gorham, SS.	45.00
Tacoma, Old Church, emb flowers on handle, teaspoon	24.00
Williamsport, emb shield, knight's head on handle, teaspoon	35.00
Yarmouth, enamel on handle.	15.00

SPANGLED GLASS

History: Spangled glass is a blown or blown molded variegated art glass, similar to spatter glass, with the addition of flakes of mica or metallic aventurine. Many pieces are cased with a white or clear layer of glass. Spangled glass was developed in the late 19th century and still is being manufactured.

Originally spangled glass was attributed only to the Vasa Murrhina Art Glass Company of Hartford, Connecticut, who distributed the glass for Dr. Flower of the Cape Cod Glassworks, Sandwich, Massachusetts. However, research has shown that many companies in Europe, England, and the United States made spangled glass and attributing a piece to a specific source is very difficult.

Berry Bowl, leaf mold pattern, cased, cranberry, Hobbs and later Northwood, c1890, $38.00.

Baskets
6″, scalloped top, looped handle, pink, silver mica, white cased 150.00
7″ h, 7″ d, fluted edge, twisted handle, rose with red, pale yellow, and ivory, silver mica. 200.00
Berry Set, leaf mold, cranberry spatter, mica flakes, white cased, Northwood   350.00
Bowl, 4″, multicolored, silver mica flakes. 175.00
Candlesticks, pairs
8″, green, maroon, gold mica, white cased 100.00
8¾″ h, 3⅞″ d, shaded deep to light pink, white spatter, green aventurine, white cased 120.00
Chamberstick, 5¼″ h, 3½″ d, clear applied ruffled base and handle, maroon, gold, and white, green aventurine, white cased 60.00
Creamer, leaf mold, cranberry, silver mica flakes, white cased, Northwood   160.00
Creamer and Sugar, cov, creamer: 3½″ h, 3¼″ d, sugar: 5½″ h, 3½″ d, blue, gold flakes 225.00
Ewer, 7½″ h, 2⅞″ d, blue spatter, silver

mica, white cased, clear applied thorn handle 120.00
Pitchers
6¾″ h, 4¾″ d, cobalt blue, gold flakes, applied amber handle with flakes 225.00
8″, pink, silver mica, clear cased, clear reeded handle 165.00
8″ h, 4¾″ d, green, maroon, and white spatter, silver mica flakes 120.00
Rose Bowl, 3¼″ h, 3⅝″ d, octagonal crimp top, blue and white spatter, mica flakes. 90.00
Syrup, 6″, pewter lid, cranberry spatter, silver mica, clear applied, handle . . .   165.00
Tumblers
3⅝″ h, 2⅝″ d, IVT, cranberry with cream spatter, mica flakes 55.00
4″, pink on white, splashes of yellow and blue, silver mica, white cased   80.00
Vases
6″, flat sided, 2 handles, green, gold flakes 90.00
7½″ h, 4½″ d, crystal edging around ruffle top, pink, blue, and maroon spatter, mica flakes, white cased. .   120.00
9″ h, 4⅝″ d, clear ruffle edge, pink and blue with maroon spatter, mica flakes, white cased 100.00
Whiskey Taster, 2¼″, blue and white, silver mica. 70.00

SPATTER GLASS

History: Spatter glass is a variegated blown or blown molded art glass. It originally was called "End-of-Day" glass, based on the assumption that it was made from leftover batches of glass at the end of the day. However, spatter glass was found to be a standard production item for many glass factories.

Spatter glass was developed at the end of the 19th century and still is being produced. It was made in the United States and Europe. Many modern examples come from Czechoslovakia.

Basket, 6″ h, 5″ d, maroon, green, and yellow, white cased, clear applied thorn handle 175.00
Berry Bowl, master, Leaf Umbrella pattern, cranberry spatter 200.00
Box, 7½″ h, 4½″ d, egg shape, hinged cov, yellow, blue bell shaped florals, white leaves and branches, cased, 3 applied clear gold dec feet. 250.00
Darning Eggs
Adult size, handled, red, yellow and green 115.00
Child size, ball with handle, dark colors 45.00

Syrup, cranberry, clear, and white, ring neck, clear handle, SP top, $155.00.

Jars, covered
  6¼″ h, 3½″ d, small blue forget-me-
    nots dec, applied clear finial 65.00
  6½″ h, 3¾″ d, maroon, white, yellow,
    and green, white cased, clear ap-
    plied feet and finial. 75.00
Pitchers
  5¼″ h, 4⅛″ d, bulbous, 3 petal top,
    clear reeded applied handle, yellow
    and maroon with white spatter, emb
    spattering, yellow cased 85.00
  7⅞″ h, 5¼″ d, bulbous, 3 way ruffled
    top, pink and white, clear reeded ap-
    plied handle. 175.00
  8″ h, 5¾″ d, water, bulbous, round
    mouth, deep maroon and white,
    clear applied handle. 110.00
Rose Bowl, 3½″ h, 3½″ d, octagonal
  crimp top, rose, white cased 100.00
Salt, master, 1¾″ h, 3″ d, clear shell rigaree top, green and white, cased,
  clear petal feet 70.00
Sugar Shaker, 5¼″, ribbed, pink 45.00
Syrup, leaf mold, vaseline satin 325.00
Tumbler, 3¾″ h, 2¾″ d, green and white,
  emb swirl 45.00
Tumble-up, 2 pcs, bottle with clear ap-
  plied leaf feet, elongated thumbprint
  design, green, red, yellow, and pink,
  cased white 300.00
Vase, 9″, multicolored, pr 175.00

SPATTERWARE

History: Spatterware is made of common earthenware, although occasionally creamware was
used. The earliest English examples were made

about 1780. The peak period of production was
1810-1840. Marked pieces are rare. Firms known
to have made spatterware are Adams, Barlow, and
Harvey and Cotton.

  The amount of spatter decoration varies from
piece to piece. Some objects simply have decorated borders. These often are decorated with a
brush, requiring several hundred touches per
square inch to achieve the spatter effect. Other
pieces have the entire surface covered with spatter.
Aesthetics of the final product is a key to value.

  Collectors today focus on the patterns–Cannon,
Castle, Fort, Peafowl, Rainbow, Rose, Thistle,
Schoolhouse, etc. On flat ware the decoration is in
the center. On hollow pieces it occurs on both
sides.

  Color of spatter is another price key. Blue and
red are most common. Green, purple, and brown
are in a middle group. Black and yellow are scarce.

  Like any soft paste, spatterware was easily broken or chipped. Prices are for pieces in very good
to mint condition.

Bowls
  Peafowl, set of 6, 5″, red, blue, and
    green, green spatter. 1,500.00
  Schoolhouse, 5½″, red spatter. 425.00
Coffee Pot, cov, 10″, octagonal, grape
  finial, blue spatter 825.00
Creamers
  Morning Glory, 4″, blue, green, and
    black, red spatter. 435.00
  Rainbow
    Blue and pale lavender spatter,
      5⅜″. 350.00
    Green and black, 4¼″ 335.00
  Vine & Berry, 3½″, red and yellow,
    green spatter. 525.00

**Plate, 8½″, Tulip, yellow rim, knife
marked and crazed, $215.00.**

Cup Plates
Peafowl, 4⅜", yellow spatter 325.00
Schoolhouse, 4⅜", red spatter 275.00
Cups and Saucers, handleless
Beehive in green, yellow, and black,
    blue spatter 950.00
Bud & Berries, red, blue, green, and
    black, red spatter 265.00
Peafowl, red, blue, green, and black,
    red spatter 325.00
Queen's Rose, black and brown spat-
    ter, Davenport dark 150.00
Rooster, blue spatter 825.00
Schoolhouse, red, ochre, green, and
    brown, blue spatter 575.00
Thistle, red and yellow rainbow
    spatter 255.00
Miniatures
Cups
    Peafowl, childlike, red, blue, ochre,
        and black, green spatter 450.00
    Tree, green and black, brown
        spatter 375.00
Cup and Saucer, blue spatter 315.00
Mugs
Blue spatter, 3⅞" 175.00
Stick spatter, gaudy floral design, rab-
    bit borders, 5⅜" 345.00
Mustard, 2¼", vining dec in red, green,
    and black, purple spatter 245.00
Pitchers
Peafowl, 6", red, blue, green, narrow
    band of red spatter on rim, handle,
    and foot 375.00
Rainbow, 7¾", red, blue and green. . 565.00
Thistle, 8½", yellow spatter 3,250.00
Plates
Acorn, 8½", two shades of green,
    ochre, and black, purple spatter . . 375.00
Bull's eye
    8¼", yellow and red rainbow
        spatter 825.00
    9½", red and green concentric cir-
        cles form center, red and green
        alternating bars of spatter 250.00
Dahlia, 8⅜", red, blue, green, and
    black, purple spatter 275.00
Morning Glory, 8¾", blue, black, and
    green, yellow spatter 225.00
Peafowl
    8¼", red, green and mustard, blue
        spatter 250.00
    8¼", green spatter 350.00
    9¼", blue spatter 325.00
    9½", red spatter 350.00
    9½", yellow spatter 3,000.00
Primrose, 8⅝", purple, green, black,
    and ochre, red spatter 200.00
Rainbow Loop, 8¼", green, purple,
    yellow, and black 775.00
Rose, 9¾", red, green, and black, red
    and blue spatter, imp "Cotton &
    Barlow" 250.00

Schoolhouse
8¼", green, red, and black, green
    spatter 625.00
9¾", red, brown, and green, blue
    spatter 550.00
Star, 6½", 6 pointed star in 13 point
    sunburst border, red, blue, and
    green, red spatter 200.00
Thistle, 8½", red and green, red
    spatter 285.00
Tulip, 8½", blue, red, green, and black,
    black and purple rainbow border . . 475.00
Platters
Peafowl in tree, 13½", red, green,
    blue, and black, blue spatter 2,500.00
Stripes, vertical, 14⅝", red, blue, and
    green spatter 345.00
Salt, Rainbow, 3", red and green
    spatter 325.00
Soup Plate, stick design, 9½", red, blue,
    and green 130.00
Sugar Shaker, Rainbow, 4⅞", blue and
    purple 450.00
Sugars, cov
Peafowl, 4¾", red, yellow, and blue,
    blue spatter 450.00
Rainbow, 5⅜", red, yellow, green, and
    black 300.00
Rose, 4⅞", red, green, and black, red
    and blue spatter 250.00
Teapots
Rainbow
    5¼", red and yellow 850.00
    8¾", octagonal, red and blue spat-
        ter, blue spatter on handle 425.00
Thistle, 7¼", red and green, yellow
    spatter 925.00
Toddy Plate, Acorn, 5⅛", two shades of
    green, yellow, and black, purple
    spatter 500.00
Wash Bowl, 13⅝" x 4½", blue spatter . . 200.00

SPONGEWARE

History: Spongeware is a specific type of decoration, not a type of pottery or glaze. The decoration was not applied with a sponge as is commonly believed.

Spongeware decoration is found on many types
of pottery bodies—ironstone, redware, stoneware,
yellow ware, etc. It was made in both England and
the United States. Marked pieces indicate a starting
date of 1815, with manufacturing extending to the
1880s.

Decoration is varied. In some pieces the sponging is minimal with the white underglaze dominant.
Other pieces appear to be sponged solidly on both
sides. Pieces from 1840-1860 have sponging which
appears in either a circular movement or a streaked
horizontal technique.

Examples are found in blue and white, the most common color. Other prevalent colors are browns, greens, ochres, and greenish-blue. The greenish-blue results from blue sponging which has been overglazed in a pale yellow. A red overglaze produces a black or navy color.

Other colors are blue and red (found on English creamware and American earthenware of the 1880s), gray, grayish-green, red, dark green on stark white, dark green on mellow yellow, and purple.

Pitcher, 8″ h, fluted top, Cobalt and tan sponge, $175.00.

Baking Dishes, covered
7½″, yellow ground, brown and green sponging	75.00
8½″, cream ground, red, brown, and blue sponging	125.00
Bank, 6″ h, pig, white clay, brown and blue sponging	75.00
Bean Pot, blue and white, 4 qt	225.00

Bowls
5″, set of 6, yellow ware, brown	100.00
6⅛ x 2⅞″, yellow ware, brown and green	75.00
7¼ x 3⅛″, cream, brown	35.00
7⅜ x 3⅝″, white, blue, lion and unicorn mark with imp "B.B"	180.00
9½ x 5¼″, cream ground, brown and blue	120.00
Butter Crock, cov, blue and white	115.00
Casserole, cov, 8¼ x 4½″, yellow ware, green and brown, flowers form cov in 10 panel mold	110.00
Creamer, 4½″, yellow ware, brown and green	75.00

Crock, cov, 13 x 10¼″, blue with green and amber glaze	285.00
Dish, 7½ x 4⅜″, yellow ware, blue, rim spout, wire bale handle	65.00

Jugs
4″, blue-green	65.00
5½″, baluster, blue and white	150.00
Mug, 4″, cream, brown	115.00

Pitchers
6½″, green and white	95.00
6¾″, cream with white glaze, blue sponging	100.00
8¾″, blue and white	95.00
8⅞″, blue and white, blue flowers	235.00
11⅛″, blue and white, blue band	160.00

Plates
6¾″, cobalt blue, scalloped rim	85.00
10½″, blue and white, dec on both sides	125.00
Platter, 12½″, oval, blue and white	195.00
Soap Dish, red and blue on white	200.00
Soup Plate, 10″, blue and white	145.00
Sugar, cov, blue and white	180.00
Toddy Plate, 4¾″, blue and white, mkd "Burford Bros"	40.00
Wash Bowl and Pitcher, blue and white, blue stripes	500.00

STAFFORDSHIRE ITEMS

History: A wide variety of ornamental pottery items originated in England's Staffordshire district, beginning in the 17th century and extending to today. The height of production was from 1820 to 1890.

These naive pieces are considered folk art by many collectors. Most items were not made carefully; some were even made and decorated by children.

The types of objects are varied, e.g., animals, cottages, and figurines (chimney ornaments). The key to price is age and condition. The older the piece, the higher the price is a general rule.

Advisors: Barbara and Melvin Alpern.

Animals
Bull Mastiffs, pr, recumbent, 5″ l, c1840	400.00
Cow, standing, pearlware, bocage ground, 7″ l, c1830	475.00
Dalmation, on hind legs, 5″ h, c1850	250.00
Greyhounds, pr, sitting, 4″ h, c1850	300.00
Lamb, recumbent, bocage ground, 5½″ h, c1830	225.00
Poodle with young, green base with gold tassels, 3″ l, c1830	325.00

Poodles, pr
1¾″ h, standing, one with basket in its mouth, other with hat, c1830	300.00
3½″ h, with young, c1855	300.00

Cow and milk maiden, 6¾" h, 7" l, dark brown hair, orange shoes, $250.00.

Ram, standing, spill vase, 5" h, c1855	200.00
Swan, group, spill vase, 5" h, c1845.	200.00
Whippet, recumbent, quill holder, 4½" l, c1850.	150.00
Zebras, pr, standing, 4½" l, c1880 . .	300.00
Cottages	
Flat Back	
4" l, two story house, money box, gray with black trim, c1890	225.00
5" h, two story house, two turrets, c1890	300.00
Money Box, Wesleyan Chapel, name on front, 4½" l, c1890	400.00
Pastille Burners	
3", multicolored moss on roof and in front, c1820	325.00
3½", white porcelain, umbrella shaped roof, multicolored flowers, c1840	325.00
3½", yellow, with dog and cat in front, c1840	300.00
4½", thatch roof, brown base with grass front, c1830.	500.00
5", castle form, lavender, 2 pcs, white moss trim all over, c1835.	900.00
5", pillars in front, orange and blue flowers on roof and in front of cottage, c1830	325.00
5¼", octagonal, salmon colored, white roof, c1835	500.00
Pastille Burner and Inkwell, 2 pcs, salmon colored, 3" tall, c1835. . . .	400.00

Figurines

Boy, young, astride donkey crossing bridge, 6" h, c1875	175.00
Girl, young, astride goat, 6" l, c1875	150.00
Group, man, lady, and dog, flowered base, bocage ground, mkd "Tenderness," 6¾" h, c1900.	350.00
Lady, on horse, inscribed "The Princess," 7" l, c1875	225.00
Sailor, full uniform, 7" h, c1875	150.00

STAFFORDSHIRE, HISTORICAL

History: The Staffordshire district of England is the center of the English pottery industry. There were eighty different potteries operating there in 1786, with the number increasing to 179 by 1802. The district includes Burselm, Cobridge, Eturia, Fenton, Foley, Hanley, Lane Delph, Lane End, Longport, Shelton, Stoke, and Tunstall. Among the many famous potters were Adams, Davenport, Spode, Stevenson, Wedgwood, and Wood.

In historical Staffordshire the view is the most critical element. American collectors pay much less for non-American views. Dark blue pieces are favored. Light views have lost popularity during the past five years and, in many cases, have dropped in value. Among the forms, soup tureens have shown the highest price increases.

A recent development in historical Staffordshire is the mail auctions of David Arman of Woodstock, Connecticut, who is following a trend which he and other dealers have established for a number of specific antiques categories.

References: David and Linda Arman, *Historical Staffordshire: An Illustrated Check List*, privately printed, 1974, out-of-print; David and Linda Arman, *First Supplement, Historical Staffordshire: An Illustrated Check List*, privately printed, 1977, out-of-print; Ada Walker Camehl, *The Blue China Book*, Dover, reprint; A.W. Coysh and R. K. Henrywood, *The Dictionary Of Blue And White Printed Pottery, 1780–1880*, Antique Collectors' Club, 1982; Ellouise Larsen, *American Historical Views On Staffordshire China*, Dover, reprint.

Notes: Prices are for proof examples. Adjust prices by 20% for an unseen chip, a faint hairline, or an unseen professional repair; by 35% for knife marks through the glaze and a visible professional repair; by 50% for worn glaze and major repairs.

The numbers in parenthesis refer to the books by Linda and David Arman, which constitute the most detailed list of American historical views and their forms.

Advisors: David and Linda Arman.

W. ADAMS & SONS   ADAMS
ADAMS

The Adams family has been associated with ceramics from the mid-17th century. In 1802 William

Adams of Stoke-upon-Trent produced American views.

In 1819 a fourth William Adams, son of William of Stoke, became a partner with his father and was later joined by his three brothers. The firm became William Adams & Sons. The father died in 1829 and William, the eldest son, became manager.

The company operated four potteries at Stoke and one at Tunstall. American views were produced at Tunstall in black, light blue, sepia, pink, and green in the 1830–40 period. William Adams died in 1865. All operations were moved to Tunstall. The firm continues today under the name of Wm. Adams & Sons, Ltd.

CLEWS

From sketchy historical accounts that are available, James Clews took over the closed plant of A. Stevenson in 1819. His brother Ralph entered the business later. The firm continued until about 1836 when James Clews came to America to enter the pottery business at Troy, Indiana. The venture was a failure because of the lack of skilled workmen and the proper type of clay. He returned to England but did not re-enter the pottery business.

Adams plate, 10″, Mitchell & Freemans China & Glass Warehouse, Chatham Street, Boston, dark blue, c1804–1840, $450.00.

Cities Series, dark and medium blue
Albany, 10″ plate (16)	325.00
Baltimore, vegetable dish (17)	2,500.00
Chillicothe, 10½″ platter (20)	2,500.00
Philadelphia, 5½″ plate (26)	350.00
Quebec, 9″ plate (28)	275.00
Washington, 7¾″ plate (30)	250.00

Doctor Syntax, dark blue
Doctor Syntax setting out on his first tour, 12″ covered dish (35)	650.00
*Doctor Syntax Disputing his bill with landlady, 10″ plate (38)	165.00
*Doctor Syntax mistakes a Gentleman's house for an inn, 10″ soup (42).	175.00
Doctor Syntax with the dairy maid, 3⅞″ cup plate (46).	400.00
Doctor Syntax and the gypsies, soup tureen (51)	1,500.00

Hudson River Series
Fort Edwards, Hudson River, pink, 5¼″ plate (460)	65.00
View Near Sandy Hill, Hudson River, pink, 4″ cup plate (461)	75.00

Log Cabin, medallions of Gen. Harrison on border (458)
Teapot, pink	255.00
Waste Bowl, brown	225.00
Seal of United States, dark blue, pitcher, 7½″ (443).	850.00

U.S. Views
Lake George, U.S., brown, vegetable dish (448)	175.00
Shannondale Springs, Virginia, U.S., pink, 8″ plate (451)	75.00

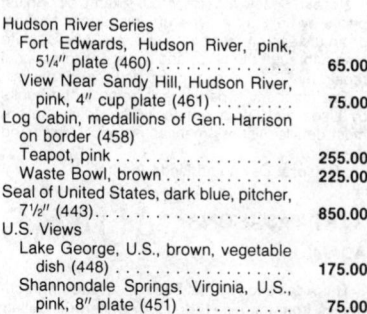

Clews, plate, 8¾″, States Plate, $275.00.

Doctor Syntax turned nurse, 7¾" plate (56) ... **175.00**

Doctor Syntax, advertisement for a wife, 16" platter (64) ... **650.00**

Don Quixote Series, dark blue

Don Quixote's Library, vegetable dish (68) ... **600.00**

Don Quixote, repose in woods, 6" plate (71) ... **175.00**

Sancho Panza and the priest and barber, 7½" plate (75) ... **165.00**

Sancho Panza's debate with Teresa, 9" plate (78) ... **150.00**

Landing of Lafayette at Castle Garden, dark blue (1)

Cup Plate, 3½", oval medallion ... **450.00**

Pitcher, 5½" ... **750.00**

Pitcher, 8" ... **875.00**

Plate, 7½" ... **275.00**

Plate, 10" ... **275.00**

Platter, 15" ... **750.00**

Platter, 21¾", well and tree ... **1,100.00**

Soup, 9" ... **275.00**

Teapot ... **850.00**

Vegetable Dish, 10", square ... **750.00**

Picturesque Views Series

Bakers Falls, Hudson River, pink, 9" plate (101) ... **75.00**

Fort Edward, Hudson River, light blue 4⅛" cup plate (102) ... **100.00**

Hudson, Hudson River, black, gravy tureen (107) ... **300.00**

Hudson, Hudson River, brown, 10½" soup (107) ... **85.00**

Near Hudson, Hudson River, brown, 7" plate (113) ... **75.00**

Penitentiary in Allegheny, near Pittsburgh, pink, 15½" tray (117) ... **450.00**

Troy From Mount Ida, light blue, 6" pitcher (120) ... **225.00**

Peace and Plenty, dark blue (34)

Cup Plate, 4½" ... **600.00**

Plate, 10" ... **275.00**

Platter, 17" ... **750.00**

Pittsfield Elm, dark blue (33)

Plate, 8" ... **245.00**

Platter, 15" ... **800.00**

Soup, 10½" ... **275.00**

States or America and Independence Series, dark blue

Building, Deer on Lawn, 10½" plate (2) ... **275.00**

Dock, large building and ships, 19½" platter (4) ... **1,900.00**

Mansion, circular drive, vegetable dish (14) ... **750.00**

Mansion, small boat with flag in foreground, 13½" bowl (12) ... **1,250.00**

works formerly were owned by the Wedgwood family. The firm produced transfer scenes in a variety of colors, such as black, light blue, pink, sepia, green, maroon, and mulberry. Over 40 different American views of Conn., Mass., Pa., N.Y., and Ohio were issued. The firm is believed to have closed about 1844.

J. & J. Jackson, plate, "The Race Bridge, Philadelphia," American Scenery Series, $100.00.

American Scenery Series, all colors

Albany, N.Y., 20" platter (462) ... **375.00**

At Richmond, Va., 7" plate (465) ... **85.00**

Bunker Hill Monument, 6½" plate (468) ... **175.00**

Deaf & Dumb Asylum, Phila., 7" plate (471) ... **85.00**

Fort Ticonderoga, NY gravy tureen with cover (473) ... **300.00**

Hartford, Conn., 10" soup (476) ... **85.00**

Iron Works at Saugerties, 12" platter (478) ... **250.00**

State House, Boston, 10½" plate (484) ... **85.00**

View of the Canal, Little Falls, Mohawk River, 10½" plate (490) ... **140.00**

Water Works, Phila., 9" plate (487) ... **75.00**

Yale College, deep dish (493) ... **175.00**

Miscellaneous

New York, Select Sketches series, 17" platter (496) ... **600.00**

Schenectady on Mohawk River, 8" pitcher (494) ... **275.00**

J. & J. JACKSON   J&J. JACKSON

Job and John Jackson began operations at the Churchyard Works, Burslem, about 1830. The

THOMAS MAYER

In 1829, Thomas Meyer and his brothers, John and Joshua, purchased Stubbs' Dale Hall Works of

Burselm. They continued to produce a superior grade of ceramics.

Mayer, platter, 11¾″, Arms of the American States series, Georgia, $2,750.00.

Arms of the American States, dark blue

CT, gravy tureen (498)	**3,000.00**
DE, 17″ platter (499)	**2,500.00**
GA, 11¾″ vegetable dish (500)	**2,750.00**
MA, 9½″ platter (502)	**2,500.00**
PA 21″ platter (506)	**10,000.00**

Lafayette at Franklin's Tomb, dark blue,
sugar bowl (510) **650.00**
Lafayette at Washington's Tomb, dark
blue, sugar bowl (511) **650.00**
Lafayette at Franklin's Tomb, dark blue,
waste bowl (512) **650.00**

CHARLES MEIGH

Job Meigh began the Meigh pottery in the Old Hall Pottery, Hanley, in 1780. Later his sons and grandsons entered the business. The firm's name is recorded as Job Meigh & Sons, 1823; J. Meigh & Sons, 1829; Charles Meigh, 1843.

The American Cities and Scenery series was produced by Charles Meigh between 1840 and 1850. The colors are light blue, brown, gray, and purple. Sometimes the colors appear in combination.

Albany, 7½″ Pitcher (544)	**225.00**
Baltimore, washbowl (546)	**175.00**
Capitol at Washington, tureen, round, cover (550)	**500.00**
City Hall, NY, 10¼″ plate (551)	**62.50**
Hudson City, 10¼″ soup (552)	**55.00**
Utica, cup plate (556)	**100.00**
Village of Little Falls, 8¼″ plate (558). .	**65.00**
Yale College, New Haven, 9½″ plate (560)	**75.00**

MELLOR, VENABLES & CO.

Little information is recorded on Mellor, Venables & Co. except that they were listed as potters in Burselm in 1843. Their Scenic Views series with

the Arms of the States border does include the arms for New Hampshire. This state is missing from the Mayer series. However, the view was known in England and collectors search for a Mayer example.

Arms of States, white body, light color
transfers (529)

MD, teapot	**375.00**
PA, sugar bowl	**275.00**

Scenic Views, Arms of States Border,
light blue, pink, brown, purple
Albany, 15″ platter (516) **275.00**
The President's House from the River,
14″ pitcher (520) **250.00**
Tomb of Washington, Mt. Vernon,
7½″ plate (521) **85.00**
View of Capitol at Washington, 11″,
vegetable dish (526). **225.00**

W. RIDGWAY

J.W.R.

Stone China

J. & W. RIDGWAY AND WILLIAM RIDGWAY & CO.

John and William Ridgway, sons of Job Ridgway and nephews of George Ridgway who owned Bell Bank Works and Cauldon Place Works, produced the popular Beauties of America series at the Cauldon plant. The partnership between the two brothers was dissolved in 1830. John remained at Cauldon.

William managed the Bell Bank works until 1854. Two additional series were produced based upon the etchings of Bartlett's *American Scenery*. The first series had various borders including narrow lace. The second series is known as Catskill Moss.

Beauties of America is in dark blue. The other series are found in the light transfer colors of light blue, pink, brown, black, and green.

American Scenery
Albany, washbowl (279) **275.00**
Columbia Bridge on the Susquehanna,
pitcher (281) **275.00**
Columbia Bridge on the Susquehanna,
soup tureen (281) **550.00**
Peekskill Landing, Hudson River, tea-
pot (287) **250.00**
Peekskill Landing, Hudson River, veg-
etable dish (287) **225.00**
Valley of the Shenandoah from Jef-
ferson's Rock, 7″ plate (289) **80.00**
Wilkes-Barre, Vale of Wyoming, coffee
pot (294) **325.00**
Beauties of America, dark blue
Almshouse, Boston, soup tureen
(254) **1,800.00**

Ridgway, plate, 7″, Catskill Moss series, The Narrows From Fort Hamilton, $75.00.

Almshouse, New York, 16″ platter (255)	700.00
Bank, Savannah, gravy tureen (257).	1,000.00
City-Hall, New York, 10″ plate (260).	125.00
Exchange, Baltimore, cup plate (264)	400.00
Exchange, Charleston, vegetable dish (265)	650.00
Library, Phila., 8″ plate (268)	225.00
Octagon Church, Boston, 10″ soup (271)	225.00
Catskill Moss	
Anthony's Nose, 6″ plate (295)	85.00
Caldwell, Lake George, 5″ sauce dish (298)	50.00
Kosciusko's Tomb, 10″ plate (305) . .	85.00
Kosciusko's Tomb, 10″ soup (305) . .	75.00
Meredith, 9½″ plate (307)	85.00
President's House, tray (311)	125.00
Valley of Wyoming, cup (317)	35.00
Columbia Star, Harrison's Log Cabin	
End View, plate (276)	100.00
End View, soup (276)	110.00
Side View, cup with handles (277) . .	55.00
Side View, sugar bowl (277)	275.00
Side View, plowing, 10¼″ plate (277)	125.00

ROGERS

ROGERS

John Rogers and his brother George established a pottery near Longport in 1782. After George's death in 1815, Spencer, John's son, became a partner; the firm operated under the name of John Rogers & Sons. John died in 1816. His son continued the use of the name until he dissolved the pottery in 1842.

Boston Harbor, dark blue (441)	
Cup plate	600.00
Cup and Saucer	375.00
Sugar Bowl	650.00
Waste Bowl	450.00
Boston State House, dark blue (442)	
Creamer	375.00
Plate, 10″	150.00
Platter, 14″	450.00
Platter, 19″	700.00
Soup Tureen	1,200.00

R.S.W.

STEVENSON

As early as the 17th century the name Stevenson has been associated with the pottery industry. Andrew Stevenson of Cobridge introduced American scenes with the flower and scroll border. Ralph Stevenson, also of Cobridge, used a vine and leaf border on his dark blue historical views and a lace border on his series in light transfers.

The initials R. S. & W. indicate Ralph Stevenson and Williams are associated with the acorn and leaf border. It has been reported that Williams was Ralph's New York agent and the wares were produced by Ralph alone.

Stevenson, plate, 8½″, Harvard College, Acorn and Oak Leaves Border series, $385.00.

Acorn and Oak Leaves Border, dark blue	
Baltimore Exchange, 5½″ plate (348)	650.00
Columbia College, N.Y., 7½″ plate (350)	425.00
Harvard College, 10″ soup (352)	250.00

Octagon Church, Boston, 4½" cup
plate (356). **600.00**
Park Theater, N.Y., 10" plate (357). . **150.00**
State House, Boston, 5" plate (360). **450.00**
Water Works, Phila., 10" soup (363). **350.00**
Floral and Scroll Border, dark blue
Almshouse, New York, 10" plate
(394). **900.00**
Catholic Cathedral, New York, 7½"
plate (395). **1,150.00**
City Hall, New York, 7" plate (397). . **800.00**
Columbia College, New York, 6½"
soup (398). **800.00**
Troy from Mt. Ida, 9¾" platter (402). **2,250.00**
View of New York From Weehawk,
soup tureen (404) **7,500.00**
Lace Border
Erie Canal at Buffalo, 10" soup (386). **125.00**
New Orleans, cup and saucer (387) . **125.00**
New Orleans, sugar bowl (387) **275.00**
New Orleans, teapot (387). **300.00**
Riceborough, Ga., washbowl (388) . . **750.00**
Vine Border
Almshouse, Boston, 14" platter (365) **650.00**
Almshouse, New York, 7" pitcher
(366). **850.00**
Battery, New York, 7¾" plate (367) . **450.00**
Capitol, Washington, 10" soup (370). **350.00**
Columbia College, NY, 8" plate (372) **450.00**
Hospital, Boston, 9" plate (378) **250.00**
Pennsylvania Hospital, Phila., soup
tureen (383). **4500.00**

**Stubbs, plate, 10¼", blue, Fairmount
Near Philadelphia, $425.00.**

STUBBS

In 1790 Stubbs established a pottery works at
Burselm, England. He operated it until 1829 when
he retired and sold the pottery to the Mayer brothers. He probably produced his American views
about 1825. Many of his scenes were from Boston,
New York, New Jersey, and Philadelphia.

Rose Border, dark blue
Boston State House, 7" pitcher
(335). **550.00**
City Hall, New York, 6" plate (336) . . **400.00**
City Hall, New York, teapot (336) . . . **600.00**
City Hall, sugar bowl (336) **375.00**

Spread Eagle Border, dark and medium
blue
City Hall, New York, 6½" plate (323). **275.00**
Fair Mount Near Phila., 10" soup
(324). **150.00**
Fair Mount Near Phila., 22" platter
(324). **900.00**
Highlands, North River, 10" plate
(325). **900.00**
Hoboken in New Jersey, salt shaker
(326). **450.00**
Mendenhall Ferry, 4½" cup plate
(327). **375.00**
State House, Boston, 14½" platter
(331). **600.00**
Upper Ferry Bridge over the River
Schuylkill (332)
Dish, round **350.00**
Plate, 8¾". **185.00**
Platter, 19" **650.00**
Vegetable Dish **500.00**
Wash Pitcher. **500.00**

S. TAMS & CO.

The firm operated at Longton, England. The exact date of its beginning is not known, but believed
to be about 1810–1815. The company produced
several dark blue American views. About 1830 the
name became Tams, Anderson, and Tams.

Capitol, Washington, deep bowl (514) . **900.00**
Capitol, Washington, wash pitcher
(514). **950.00**
United States Hotel, Phila., 10" plate
(515) **550.00**
United States Hotel, Phila., 10" soup
(515) **550.00**

WOOD

Enoch Wood, sometimes referred to as the Father of English Pottery, began operating a pottery at Fountain Place, Burselm, in 1783. A cousin Ralph Wood was associated with him. In 1790 James Caldwell became a partner and the firm was known as Wood and Caldwell. In 1819 Wood and his sons took full control.

Enoch died in 1840. His sons continued under the name of Enoch Wood & Sons. The American views were first made in the mid-1820s and continued through the 1840s.

It is reported that the pottery produced more signed historical views than any other Staffordshire firm. Many of the views attributed to unknown makers probably came from the Woods.

Marks vary, although always with the name Wood. The establishment was sold to Messrs. Pinder, Bourne & Hope in 1846.

Wood, custard cup, "Wadsworth Towers," shell border, $450.00.

Celtic China, light transfer colors
Buffalo on Lake Erie, vegetable dish (236).........................	225.00
Columbus, Ga., 3⅞" cup plate (238)	400.00
Harvard College, 10" plate (240) ...	125.00
Natural Bridge, Va., 9¼" plate (244).	95.00
Pass in the Catskill Mountains, 7" plate (247).....................	85.00
Shipping Port on the Ohio, KY, 12" platter (249)...................	650.00
Transylvania University, Lexington, KY, 10" soup (250)	130.00
Trenton Falls, 8" plate (251)	85.00

West Point, Military Academy, open-work dish (252)	400.00

Floral Border, irregular, dark blue
Commodore MacDonnough's Victory (154)	
Coffee Pot...................	1,500.00
Cup and Saucer.............	350.00
Plate, 9"	375.00
Entrance of the Erie Canal into the Hudson at Albany (156)	
Plate, 6"..................	750.00
Soup, 10"	825.00
Erie Canal, Aqueduct Bridge at Rochester, pitcher, with first canal view, 5½" (157)	900.00
Erie Canal, View of the Aqueduct Bridge at Little Falls (158)	
Pitcher, with one of the views, 7" .	900.00
Pitcher, wash..............	1,000.00
Wadsworth Tower, sugar bowl (155).	450.00

Four Medallion, Floral Border Series, light transfers
Castle Garden, 8" plate (225)......	95.00
Monte Video, 7½" plate (229)	85.00
Race Bridge, Phila., gravy tureen (233)......................	350.00

General Jackson (224)
Cup Plate...................	650.00
Pitcher, lustre, 4"	900.00
Plate, 7"....................	850.00

Shell Border, circular center, dark blue
Belleville on the Passaic River soup tureen (159).................	2,500.00
Castle Garden Battery, New York, 18½" platter (160)	1,100.00
Catskill Mountains, Hudson River, custard cup with handle (162)	450.00
City of Albany, State of New York, 10" plate (163)...................	350.00
Highland, Hudson River, vegetable dish (167)	750.00
Mount Vernon, 5¾" plate (173)	400.00
Mount Vernon, 7½" plate (173)	300.00
Railroad, Baltimore and Ohio, level, 10" plate (183)	600.00
Railroad, Baltimore and Ohio, incline 9" plate (182)	600.00
West Point Military Academy, 12" platter (188)	850.00
White House, Washington, cup plate (189)......................	750.00

Shell Border, irregular center, dark blue
Cadmus, 10" soup (125)	425.00
Commodore MacDonnough's Victory (130)	
Coffee Pot...................	1,500.00
Plate, 9"	375.00
Teapot	850.00
Constitution and Guerriere, 10" plate (131)......................	900.00
Erith on the Thames, vegetable dish (136)......................	650.00
Union Line, 9¼" plate (144).......	375.00

Union Line, 10″ soup (144)	375.00
Wadsworth Tower (147)	
Coffee Pot	1,400.00
Cup and Saucer	350.00
Pitcher, 4½″	600.00
Waste Bowl	400.00
Washington's Tomb, dark blue (190B)	
Creamer	600.00
Soup, 10″	850.00
Sugar Bowl	650.00
Teapot	750.00

UNKNOWN MAKERS

Anti-Slavery, light blue, 9¼″ plate (608)	150.00
Erie Canal Inscription (597)	
Cup Plate, 3¾″	1,200.00
Pitcher, 5¼″	900.00
Plate, 10″	450.00

Unknown, mug, 2⅜″, child's "Aqueduct Bridge At Little Falls," white ground, black transfer,

Famous Naval Heroes, 7; pitcher (604)	800.00
Famous Naval Heroes, washbowl (604)	1,100.00
Franklin Flying a Kite, light blue, 3¾″ platter, miniature (603)	125.00
Great Fire, City of New York, series, plates, each (605–607)	125.00
Mount Vernon, Washington's Seat, 8″ pitcher (600)	800.00

STAFFORDSHIRE ROMANTIC

History: The Staffordshire district of England produced dinnerware between 1830 and 1860 with romantic scenes. A large number of potters were involved and over 800 patterns have been identified.

The dinner services came in a variety of colors with light blue and pink perhaps the most popular. Usually the pattern is identified on the back of the piece. It was not uncommon for two potters to issue pieces with the same design. Therefore, check the pattern name as well as the maker's name.

It would be impossible to list all patterns. A representative selection follows. Some price ranges to keep in mind are: cups and saucers (handleless) $35–50; cup plates $40–75; plates, 9–10″, $5–50; platters $25–75.00.

Reference: Petra Williams, *Staffordshire: Romantic Transfer Patterns,* Fountain House East, 1978.

Abbey Ruins, Thomas Mayer, 1836–38	
Cup and Saucer, handless, red	40.00
Cup Plate	45.00
Platter	65.00
Soup Plate, 10½″	35.00
Amoy, Wm Ridgway, 1830–34	
Bowl	40.00
Creamer	65.00
Cup and Saucer	60.00
Plate	50.00
Platter, 12 x 15″	150.00
Beehive, Wm Adams, 1810–25	
Creamer and Sugar, cov, pr, red	100.00
Cup and Saucer, handleless	45.00
Plate	40.00
Bird Pattern, Job & John Jackson, 1831–35	
Cup and Saucer, handleless	80.00
Plate	65.00
Bombay, John Maddock, cake set, oval platter with molded handles, 12 x 9½″, six 7″ plates, floral borders	50.00
Canova, Thomas Mayer, 1826–35	
Cup Plate	40.00
Plate, 7½″, red and green	20.00
Platter, 10″	50.00
Soup Plate	35.00

Cup and saucer, Venus by Podmore, Walker & Co, pink, $45.00.

Canton Views, Elkin Knight, Bridgewood,
plate, 8½" 30.00
Corinth, James Edwards, 1842–51
  Cup Plate 40.00
  Plate, 8½", pink 40.00
Excelsior, George Wooliscroft, 1851–53
  Cup and Saucer, handleless, pink... 40.00
  Cup Plate, 12 sided 35.00
  Plate, 9½", lavender 40.00
Grecian Scenery, Enoch Wood and
Sons, 1814–36, plate 90.00
Italian Scenery, John Meir & Son,
1837–97
  Bowl 35.00
  Cup and Saucer, handleless 40.00
  Plate 30.00
Jenny Lind, Charles Meigh & Son,
1851–61
  Cup and Saucer, handleless, pink... 40.00
  Cup Plate 45.00
  Plate 50.00
Oriental Scenery, John Hall & Sons,
1885, cup plate 45.00
Oriental Scenery, Thomas Mayer,
1826–35
  Cup Plate, purple 40.00
  Plate, 10½" 30.00
  Platter 75.00
  Sauce Boat, 8" 90.00
  Toothbrush holder, 4½" 25.00
Palestine, Wm Adams, 1836–64
  Plate, 9½", red 40.00
  Soup Plate, 10¾", purple 40.00
Pastoral Courtship, Andrew Stevenson,
1816–30
  Pitcher, milk 225.00
  Plate, 8½" 65.00
  Platter 125.00
Peruvian Horsehunt, Anthony Shaw,
1853, plate, 10", brown 40.00
Priory, Edward Challinor, 1853–62
  Cup and Saucer, handleless 35.00
  Plate, 9½", octagonal 50.00
  Soup Plate 55.00
Rhine, Booth & Meigh, 1826–37
  Creamer 75.00
  Cup and Saucer, handleless 65.00
  Plate 50.00
  Sauce Tureen 100.00
  Vegetable Dish, cov, octagonal 110.00
Sicilian, maker unknown
  Bowl, 11½" 75.00
  Cup Plate 50.00
  Plates
    Dinner 50.00
    Salad 45.00
  Sauce Tureen, underplate, ladle,
    brown 150.00
Tuscan Rose, John & William Ridgway,
1814–37
  Cup Plate 40.00
  Plate 35.00
  Platter, 19½" 45.00

Views of Mesopotamia, maker unknown,
Dessert Service, 13 pcs, 10 plates, 2
shell dishes, one lozenge shape, black
transfer 200.00
Vista, Frances Morely, 1845–58
  Cup Plate 40.00
  Plate, 8 sided 85.00
Woodsman, Joseph Heath & Co.
1828–41
  Bowl 35.00
  Cup and Saucer, handleless 45.00
  Plate 50.00

STAINED AND/OR LEADED GLASS PANELS

History: American architects in the second half of the 19th century and the early 20th century used stained and leaded glass panels as a chief decorative element. Skilled glass craftsmen assembled the designs, the best known being Louis C. Tiffany.

The panels are held together with soft lead cames or copper wraps. When purchasing a panel, check the lead and have any repairs made to protect your investment.

Collectors' Club: Stained Glass Association of America, 1125 Wilmington, Ave., St. Louis, MO 63111. Stained Glass Magazine quarterly publication.

47 x 22½", green border, red sq, custard, wood frame, cartouche center, multicolored, $250.00.

Folding Door, 50 x 88", 4 panels, designed by Orland Giannini, executed by Giannini & Hilgart for Brunsmaid House, Des Moines, IA, 1902, each section with arrow motif in mottled green glass flanked by opal white glass tiles, pale yellow border, stained wood frame 9,350.00
Windows
  15 x 20", leaded, attributed to Tiffany
  Studios, mottled purple wisteria and
  other blossoms, green leaves,
  brown vines, and mottled blue and
  yellow ground 1,100.00

29½ x 9″, attributed to Bigelow Kennard & Co., early 20th C, depicting cherry-red hollyhocks and deep blue iris above white lotus blossoms, floating on pastel blue water, framed **5,000.00**
30 x 62″, railroad station type **425.00**
39 x 24¼″, crest of blue shield with faceted yellow circular center, surrounded by floral vines, flanked by elongated pointed panels with triangle motif between points, light pink reserve, orig frame **300.00**
48 x 23¾″, Louis IX wearing embroidered flowing robe, holding crown of thorns, blue and brown lozenge pattern ground, framed **1,100.00**
75 x 105½″, lunette form, executed by Duffner & Kimberly for Auburn Academic High School, Auburn, NY, c1907, 3 panels, continuous forest landscape, large central tree, brilliant colors, inscription "HODIE NON CRAS" **8,250.00**
144 x 48″, Tiffany Studios for Kingston Presbyterian Church, Kingston, PA, 1916, landscape of 2 banks, lake inlet, elegant fir trees, purple mountains, above geometric panel inscribed with 23rd Psalm and dedication **23,100.00**

STANGL POTTERY BIRDS

History: Stangl birds were produced in ceramics from 1940 until the Stangl factory closed in 1972. The birds were produced at Stangl's Trenton plant and shipped to their Flemington, New Jersey, plant for hand painting.

During World War II the demand for these birds and Stangl pottery was so great that 40 to 60 decorators could not keep up with the demand. Orders were contracted out to private homes. These orders then were returned for firing and finishing. Colors used to decorate these birds vary according to the artist.

As many as ten different trademarks were used. Almost every bird is numbered; many are artist signed. However, the signatures are used only for dating purposes and add very little to the value of the birds.

Several birds were reissued between 1972 and 1977. These reissues are dated on the bottom and valued at approximately one half of the older birds.

References: Joan Dworkin and Martha Horman, *A Guide To Stangl Pottery Birds,* Willow Pond Books, Inc., 1973; Norma Rehl, *The Collectors Handbook of Stangl Pottery,* Democrat Press, 1982.

Additional Listings: See Stangl pottery in the American Dinnerware category in *Warman's Americana & Collectibles* for more examples.
Advisor: Robert Berman.

Cardinal, #3444, $45.00.

3250A	Duck, 2½″	**45.00**
3250C	Duck, 2″, antique gold finish	**20.00**
3273	Rooster, 5¾″	**125.00**
3276D	Bluebirds, pr, 8½″	**100.00**
3408	Bird of Paradise, 5½″.	**75.00**
3445	Rooster, 9″.	**125.00**
3448	Blue Headed Vireo, 4¼″ . . .	**45.00**
3449	Parrot, 5½″.	**85.00**
3451	Willow Ptarmigan, 11 x 12″ . .	**400.00**
3455	Shoveler Duck, 12¼ x 14″. .	**650.00**
3457	Pheasant, 7 x 16″	**375.00**
3459	Falcon, 10½ x 9½″	**650.00**
3580	Cockatoo, 8⅛″	**100.00**
3581	Chickadees, group, 5½ x 8½″	**140.00**
3589	Indigo Bunting, 3¼″	**35.00**
3595	Bobolink, 4¾″	**80.00**
3599A	Hummingbirds, pr, 8 x 10½″	**275.00**
3626	Broadtail Hummingbird, 6″ . .	**100.00**
3529	Broadbill Hummingbird, 4½″	**100.00**
3634	Allen Hummingbird, 3½″ . . .	**40.00**
3722	European Finch, 4½″	**90.00**
3758	Magpie Jay, 10¾″	**350.00**
3849	Goldfinch, 4″.	**50.00**
3923	Vermillion Flycatcher, 6 x 6″	**200.00**

STATUES

History: Beginning with primitive cultures, man produced statues in the shape of people and animals. During the Middle Ages most works were religious and symbolic in character and form. The Renaissance rediscovered the human and secular forms.

During the 18th and 19th century it was fashionable to have statues in the home. Many famous works were copied for popular consumption.

Statuette or figurine denotes smaller statues, one-fourth life size or smaller.

Additional Listings: Bronzes and Busts.

Bronze
  Bacchus and Bacchanti, pr, standing with weight on one foot, arm raised, beckoning to each other, molded and stepped white marble plinth with gilt bronze panels depicting playful putti, late Louis 24½" h   **3,250.00**
  David, standing, cast from a model by Louis Moreau, gilt bronze, socle base, applied strapwork tette cartouch, incised signature, 31¼" h .   **1,500.00**
  Joan of Arc, after J. Berthoz, 33" h .   **475.00**
  Satin, c1500. 12" h **700.00**
Giltwood, Christ Child, nude, standing, arms out stretched, glass eyes, polychrome, waisted wood base with bands of acanthus, 13½" h **275.00**
Ivory, Emperor Constantine, crowned figure holding orb and sword, his cloak opening to reveal scenes from his life, Diepper, 8¾" h **750.00**

Pot metal, 18", girl with hoop, girl with book, pr, $200.00.

Marble, Venus, white powdered, metal base, 10" h **65.00**
Porcelain
  Cupid, draped, holding marriage contract in right hand, slipper behind his back, quiver and arrows by his feet, circular base, Meissen, crossed swords mark, c1860, 11" h **575.00**

Julia and Pantalone, pr, after models by Franz Anton Bustelli, she in green dress, 8¼" h, he with cloak, 7¼" h, Nymphenburg, imp mark **700.00**
Man and lady, pr, he holding sheaf of wheat, bird with lamb at his feet, she holding rose, lamb at her feet, molded rocaille bases, German, 8¼" h **365.00**
Pottery, man astride piebald horse, brown cap, blue coat, yellow britches, raised rect mottled base, Whieldontype, late 18th C, 8¾" h **1,350.00**
Wax, Holy Family, oval ebony wooden base, ball feet, glass dome cov, 18th C, 14¾" h **275.00**
Wood, Hunter and Stag, stag beneath tree stump, hunter waving his hat aloft, Austrian, 31" h **875.00**

STEIFF

History: Margarete Steiff, GmbH, established in Germany in 1880, is known for very fine quality stuffed animals and dolls as well as other beautifully made collectible toys. It is still in business today, and its products are highly respected.

The company's first products were wool-felt elephants made by Margaret Steiff. In a few years the elephant line was expanded to include a donkey, horse, pig, and camel.

By 1903 the company also was producing a mohair jointed Teddy Bear, whose production dramatically increased to over 970,000 units in 1907. Margarete's nephews took over the company at this point. The bear's head became the symbol for its label, and the famous "Button in the Ear" round, metal trademark was added.

Newly designed animals were added: Molly and Bully, the dogs, and Fluffy, the cat. Pull toys and kites also were produced, as well as larger animals on which children could ride or play.

Become familiar with genuine Steiff products before purchasing an antique stuffed animal. Plush in old Steiff animals was mohair; trimmings usually were felt or velvet. Unscrupulous individuals have attached the familiar Steiff metal button to animals that are not Steiff.

References: Peggy and Alan Bialosky, *The Teddy Bear Catalog*, Workman Publishing, 1984, revised edition; Shirley Conway and Jean Wilson, *100 Years of Steiff, 1880–1980*, Berlin Printing, 1980; Shirley Conway and Jean Wilson, *Steiff Teddy Bears, Dolls, and Toys With Prices*, Wallace-Homestead, 1984; Margaret Fox Mandel, *Teddy Bears And Steiff Animals*, Collector Books, 1984.

Additional Listings: Teddy Bears. See Stuffed Toys in *Warman's Americana & Collectibles* for more examples.

Advisors: Peggy and Alan Bialosky.

Alligator, "Gaty," 14" l, mohair, open mouth **85.00**

Cow, "Bessey," 5" h, mohair, felt horns, metal bell, red leather collar....... **75.00**

Dinosaurs

"Brosus," 14" l, mohair, open mouth **100.00**

"Tysus," 8" h, mohair, jointed arms, open mouth................. **100.00**

Doll, girl, 15", jointed felt body, glass eyes, seam down middle of face, mohair wig, orig felt clothers......... **500.00**

Duck, early, 3" h, yellow mohair, orange felt elongated bill, legs, and feet.... **45.00**

Fish, 11" l, mohair, large fish eyes, open felt mouth.................... **85.00**

Monkey, "Coco," 5" h, mohair, felt face, ears, and feet.................. **75.00**

Owl, 5½" h, mohair, felt wing tips and feet, jointed head, green eyes which glow in dark **70.00**

Pigeon, 9" h, white plush felt wings and tail, $100.00.

Pony, 6½" h, mohair, white with tan markings, black hooves, red leather bridle and reins............... **75.00**

Rabbit, 16" h, mohair, open mouth, jointed red plush body, removable felt cap and scarf **125.00**

Terrier, wire haired, 7½" h, mohair, white with black and tan markings....... **75.00**

Zebra, 9" h, mohair **125.00**

STEINS

History: A stein is a mug especially made to hold beer or ale, ranging in size from the smaller ³/₁₀ liters and ¼ liters to the larger 1, 1½, 2, 3, 4, and 5 liters, and in rare cases to 8 liters. (A liter is 1.05 liquid quarts.)

Master steins or pouring steins hold 3 to 5 liters and are called krugs. Most steins are fitted with a metal hinged lid with thumblift. The earthenware character-type steins usually are German in origin.

Reference: Major John L. Hairell, Ret, *Regimental Steins*, privately printed, 1984; Dr. Eugene Manusov, *Encyclopedia of Character Steins*, Wallace Homestead, 1976; Mike Wald, *HR Steins*, SCI Publications, 1980.

Collectors' Club: Stein Collectors International, P.O. Box 463, Kingston, NJ 08528. Dues: $20.00 *Prosit* (quarterly).

Advisor: Ron Fox

Bisque, ¼ L, character, Indian, mkd Bohne **350.00**

Glass, ½ L

Blown and cut, Munich maid on porcelain inlay lid **125.00**

Enameled, Prussian eagle **150.00**

Pressed, relief, goat on front, prism lid and dwarf thumblift **250.00**

Lithophane, ½ L, Alpine couple **125.00**

Pewter, ²/₁₀ L, relief, scenes of Nurnberg, mkd "F. & M.N.".............. **85.00**

Porcelain

Character Type, ½ L

Cat with hangover, mkd Musterschutz **500.00**

Four men under pewter umbrella lid **1,000.00**

Frog, mkd "St. Augustine" in gold letters, mkd Mustershutz **800.00**

Owl, mkd "Merkelbach & Wirk"... **250.00**

Uncle Sam, mkd "Musterschutz".. **2,000.00**

HR, ½ L

Etched frog band with dwarfs drinking, mkd #419............. **250.00**

Relief blacksmith scene, mkd #461 .... **175.00**

Regimentals

½ L

5 Inft. Regt., Bamberg 1911-13, 4 maneuver scenes, roster **300.00**

German, ½ liter, hunters and stag theme, pewter top with ceramic center, mkd "1635," $300.00.

11 Inft. Regt., Regeusberg 1904-
06, 2 maneuver scenes, rear
roster **300.00**
1½ L, 10 Train Reg., Hannover
1898–1900, 2 maneuver scenes,
front roster **500.00**
Pottery
Print over glaze
½ L, Zither player **125.00**
1 L, City of Ingolstadt **100.00**
Relief
¼ L, Munich Child, mkd #895 . . . **200.00**
1 L, monks drinking, "Empire Theatre the Conquerors," mkd
"Whites Pottery, Utica, NY". . . . **115.00**
Silver Plated, 17″ h, relief, cherub with
mandolin and goblet finial, 3 female
nudes, raised feet **1,225.00**
Stoneware
¼ L, relief, Gambrinus on front with
American shield and flags on sides,
c1865 . . . . **100.00**
½ L
Applied relief eagle and florals, mkd
"Bunzlow," c1750. . . . . **1,200.00**
Clock tower **150.00**
Wood, ½ L, barrel with copper bands. . **75.00**

STEUBEN GLASS

History: The Steuben Glass Works began in 1904 with Frederic Carder, an Englishman, and Thomas G. Hawkes of Corning, New York. In 1918 the Corning Glass Co. purchased the Steuben Works. Carder remained with the company and designed many of the pieces bearing the Steuben mark. Probably the most widely recognized wares are "Aurene," "Verre De Soie," and "Rosaline," but many other types were produced.

The firm continues operating, producing glass of exceptional quality.

References: Paul Gardner, *The Glass of Frederick Carder*, Crown Publishers, 1971; Paul Perrot, Paul Gardner, and James S. Plaut, *Steuben: Seventy Years Of American Glassmaking*, Praeger Publishers, 1974.

Museums: The Corning Museum of Glass, Corning, NY.

A.C.B. (ACID CUT-BACK)

Bowls
5¾″, plum jade, cut with Roman heads
in circles **1,700.00**
6″ d, 3⅜″ h, tapered, plum jade, med-
allions with Greek head and floral
dec urns **1,850.00**

8″ d, 7½″ h, plum jade, 3 layer. **1,850.00**
Cat, 7″, black jade over alabaster, Nedra
design, # 6078. . . . . **1,700.00**
Lamp, table, plum jade, oriental village
scene, floral cutting base and top. . . **2,000.00**
Vases
10″, classical shape, homogenous
green jade, acanthus leaf design,
sgd in Cameo **775.00**
10″, drilled for lamp base, yellow jade,
3 geese in flight, brown trees, black
band at top **2,700.00**
12″, green jade to alabaster, double
etched, butterfly and flower design **1,800.00**

AURENE

AURENE

Basket, 6½″ gold, rosettes at handle
base, sgd, # 433 . . . . **550.00**
Bowls
7″, blue, sgd, # 2687 . . . . **600.00**
8″, irid gold, sgd Frederick Carder,
1852. . . . . **450.00**
12 ″ d, 4¾″ h, irid, flaring rim, sgd,
2861. . . . . **650.00**
Bon bon Dish, gold, ruffled stretch bor-
der, sgd, # 138 . . . . **150.00**
Candleholder, 10″, twisted stem, blue,
sgd # 686. . . . . **350.00**
Candlesticks, pr, 3½″ h, 3⅞″ base, sgd,
domed foot with prunts on each stem,
rolled over top, sgd F. Carder,
6384 . . . . **650.00**
Centerpiece Bowl, 9″, gold, turned down
rim, unsigned **250.00**
Cologne Bottle, 6½″, gold, pink petal
flower finial and black jade stopper,
sgd, # 3245. . . . . **500.00**
Creamer and Sugar, 3¼″ creamer, gold,
2½″ sugar, gold, 2 handles, sgd,
756 . . . . **700.00**
Cup and Saucer, irid gold, sgd. **325.00**
Ink Bottle, 4½″, blue, melon rib, 3 reeded
and scrolled feet, orig label **875.00**
Jelly Compote, 6″ h, gold, sgd,
2642 . . . . **250.00**
Lamp Base, 12¾″ h base to neck, bal-
uster, irid blue drippings above jade
yellow ground, acid etched with graduated circles, silver metal figural
mounts, c1920 . . . . **920.00**
Nut Dish, 4″, gold, ftd, sgd, #139 . . . . **240.00**
Perfume Bottles, pr, 4½″, blue, melon
rib, pointed and ribbed stopper,
1414 . . . . **1,200.00**
Puff Box, 6″ d, 4½″ h, gold, pagoda
shaped cov, sgd Steuben Aurene
6237 . . . . **750.00**

Vase, 11½", bulbous base, straight cylinder neck, outward floral top, spiral, rose, fleur-de-lis signature, $225.00.

Sherbert, underplate, blue, calcite on
    ext. bowl, stem, and foot **450.00**
Tazza, 8", blue-gold, stretch ruffled bor-
    der, twisted stem, sgd, # 367 . . . . . **400.00**
Urn, 2½", miniature, blue, sgd **500.00**
Vases
    2½", gold, sgd, # 2648. . . . . **350.00**
    5⅛", gold paneled flower form, orig
      silver and black label **550.00**
    6", blue, ribbed, flared top, sgd **400.00**
    8¾", fan shape, irid blue, inlaid veining
      and leaves in irid ivory, sgd,
      # 6897. . . . . **1,100.00**

CALCITE

Bowl, 4" d, 7" h, gold, partial paper
    label. **400.00**
Compote, 7", int. gold, stretch border. . **675.00**
Tray, 6", round, gold. **300.00**
Vases
    8", gold, flower form, # 346 . . . . . . **450.00**
    8", gold, trumpet shape, orig label . . **275.00**

CLUTHRA

Bowl, 10½", classical form, purple **775.00**
Cologne Bottle, 7" h, pink to white. . . . **400.00**
Vases
    6¼", blue, sgd in script **700.00**
    8", dark pink, sgd, shape # 2683 . . **850.00**
    10½" , white. **550.00**
    11" h, 10½" d, amethyst, sgd. **1,400.00**

IVORINE

Bowls
    7", white. **225.00**
    9" d, 5" h, ftd **400.00**
    10" d, 4" h, gold aurene rim. **300.00**
    Grotesque, sgd, shape # 7535 . . . . **450.00**
Candlesticks, pr, 4½" **160.00**
Center Bowl, 13½" **400.00**
Nut Dish, 3¾", ftd **90.00**
Vases
    5½" h, 5¾" d, sgd **200.00**
    6", fan shape, sgd. **225.00**

JADE

Bowls
    7" d, 4" h, green, diagonal rib pulled
      into 6 sided shape, alabaster ped-
      astal foot, shape # 6241 . . . . **165.00**
    12", fruit, low, ftd, dark blue, wafer
      pontil **650.00**
Cologne Bottle, 7¼", yellow, # 1988. . **450.00**
Darner, black **100.00**
Flower Pot, 6½", green with 3 calcite
    bands on top **325.00**
Lamp Base, 16½" h base to neck, dou-
    ble gourd shape, plum, acid etched
    floral festoon, gilt metal mounts,
    c1920. . . . . **800.00**
Plate, 8", green **90.00**
Sherbert, underplate, blue, alabaster
    foot and stem **400.00**
Vase, 10¾", green, alabaster handles,
    # 2939 . . . . **600.00**
Wine Glasses
    6", green, alabaster base and stem,
      mkd **75.00**
    6¼", apricot, white opaline stem. . . . **65.00**

MISCELLANEOUS

Centerbowl, 10" d, 5½" h, aquamarine
    top and bottom, hollow yellow swirled
    stem, sgd **125.00**
Candleholders, pr, 7", gold-purple **280.00**
Compote, 7" d, 5" h, air trapped, bristol
    yellow-silverina, mica flecked, shape
    # 6637 . . . . **650.00**
Cordial, clear, blue threading, mkd **60.00**
Creamer and Sugar, 5½", clear, bright
    gold handle and pedestal feet, helmet
    design **100.00**
Elephant, 5½" h, 7" l, crystal, standing
    with trunk raised above head **425.00**
Goblet, 9", Art Deco, black and crystal,
    long stem, sgd **125.00**
Lamp Base, 13" h base to neck, balus-
    ter, transparent amber with swirls of
    moss green, salmon, and brown, gilt-
    bronze mounts, c1923 . . . . **925.00**
Mug, 6", mat-su-noke, crystal, applied
    green dec, green rim and handle . . . **225.00**

Plate, 8½", selenuim red 250.00
Tazza, 8" d, amethyst, ribbed, sgd F.
  Carder 375.00
Vases
  7", bud, ivory, black glass ring above
    base, sgd F. Carder Steuben 225.00
  8¼", swirled trumpet shape, pale
    green, sgd 200.00
  9¾", clear, applied blue threading, sgd
    F. Carder Steuben 165.00
  11", fan shape, amber, green foot,
    sgd 190.00
  14", amber, paneled, ring handles,
    sgd 250.00

ORIENTAL POPPY

Dessert, small, ftd 350.00
Goblet, ftd 325.00
Plate, 8½" 350.00
Puff Box, 3⅝" h, 5" d, glossy, flower
  finial 900.00
Sherbert, ftd 400.00

ROSALINE

Basket, white jade handle 450.00
Bowl, 10", sgd 225.00
Candlesticks, pr, 12", alabaster wafer. . 600.00
Candy Dish, cov, alabaster finial 325.00
Compote, 10" d, 5" h, alabaster base . 400.00
Cruet, alabaster neck and stopper 200.00
Pitcher, 6" , alabaster handle 250.00
Plates
  6½", copper wheel etched. 160.00
  9" 250.00
Puff Box, 5" d, 5½" h, alabaster knob . 300.00
Salt 190.00
Sherbert, underplate, alabaster foot and
  stem 250.00
Vases
  8" , trumpet shape, pedestal base . . 200.00
  10", bud, acid cutback, rosaline to al-
    abaster, flowers, leaves, swag dec 400.00
Wine Glass, 5½ 250.00

VERRE DE SOIE

Basket, 4½" d, 4½" h, raspberry prunts
  on handle 125.00
Bowls
  8", 3 ftd, sgd 200.00
  12", inverted bell shape, applied pink
    glass dec 300.00
Candlesticks, pr, 10", rosaline edges . . 400.00
Centerpiece Bowl, 19", melon rib, ap-
  plied rosaline rim. 350.00
Compote, 7" d, 5¼" h, engraved floral
  and leaf 275.00
Fingerbowl, underplate, etched 150.00
Goblet, pink banded top, sgd Steuben
  with fleur-de-lis 150.00

Nut Dishes, 6 individual size, 1 large,
  etched 260.00
Pitcher, 9¾" 250.00
Plate, 7", acid etched garland dec, sgd
  Hawkes 175.00
Rose Bowl, 3½", sgd 140.00
Sherbert, underplate 75.00
Vases
  5¼" h, 5" d, top is pulled into 4 sep-
    arate openings, sgd F. Carder Verre
    De Soie, shape # 2762 . . . . 125.00
  8", gauffered rim, F. Carder 210.00
  12½", diamond design around top . . 375.00
Vinegar Bottle, SS top, sgd Hawkes. . . 175.00
Wine Glass, 6", turquoise prunts and
  reeding. 95.00

STEVENGRAPHS

History: Thomas Stevens of Coventry, England, first manufactured woven silk designs in 1854. His first bookmark was produced in 1862, followed by the first Stevengraphs, perhaps in 1874, but definitely in 1879 at the York Exhibition. The first "portrait" Stevengraphs (of Disraeli and Gladstone) were produced in 1886, and the first postcards incorporating the silk woven panels in 1903. Stevens offered many other items with silk panels, including valentines, fans, pin cushions, needle cases, etc.

Stevengraphs are miniature silk pictures, matted in cardboard, and usually having a trade announcement, or "label," affixed to the reverse. Thomas Stevens' name appears on the mat of the early Stevengraphs directly under the silk panel. Many of the later "portraits" and the larger silks (produced initially for calendars) have no identification on the front of the mat other than the phrase "woven in pure silk" and have no label on the back. Other companies, notably W. H. Grant of Coventry, copied this technique. Their efforts should not be confused with Stevengraphs.

American collectors favor the Stevengraphs of American interest, such as "Signing of the Declaration of Independence," "Columbus Leaving Spain," "Landing of Columbus." Sports related Stevengraphs such as "The First Innings" (baseball), and "The First Set" (tennis) are also popular, as well as portraits of Buffalo Bill, President and Mrs. Cleveland, George Washington, and President Harrison.

The bookmarks are longer than they are wide, have mitred corners at the bottom, and are finished with a tassel. Originally, Stevens' name was woven into the fold-over at the top of the silk, but soon the identification was woven into the fold-under mitred corners. Almost every Stevens' bookmark has such identification, except the ones woven at the World's Columbian Exposition in Chicago, 1892–93.

Postcards with the very fancy embossing around the aperture in the mount almost always have Stevens' name printed on them. Embossed cards from the "Ships" and "Hands Across The Sea" series generally are not printed with Stevens' name. The most popular postcard series in the United States are "Ships" and "Hands Across the Sea," the latter incorporated two crossed flags and two hands shaking. Seventeen flag combinations have been found, but only seven are common. Stevens produced silks that were used in the "Alpha" publishing Co. cards. Many times the silks were the top or bottom half of regular bookmarks.

References: Geoffrey A. Godden, *Stevengraphs and Other Victorian Silk Pictures,* Associated University Presses, Inc., 1971; Chris Radley, *The Woven Silk Postcard,* privately printed, 1978; Austin Sprake, *The Price Guide to Stevengraphs,* The Antique Collectors' Club, Baron Publishing, 1972.

Collectors' Club: Stevengraph Collectors' Association, P. O. Box 57, Irvington-on-Hudson, New York, NY 10533. Dues: $10.00. Newsletter (quarterly).

Museum: Coventry, England.

Advisor: John High.

Postcard, Kenilworth Castle, $50.00.

BOOKMARKS

A Wish/I wish that/Happiness	**75.00**
Centennial/1776–1876/Philadelphia/ USA/George/Washington/The first in peace.	**125.00**
Chapel Street/Old Chapel/Blackburn . .	**50.00**
Friendship/From A True Friend/How sweet the/Bonds.	**50.00**
God is Good/Morn amid the/ Mountains.	**35.00**
Jackson, Stonewall, The Late General.	**150.00**
Souvenir/of the/Independence/of/ America, orig backing, no identification.	**100.00**
To My/Daughter/At dawn of morn . . . , orig backing	**50.00**

POSTCARDS

Crystal Palace Interior.	**135.00**
Hands Across The Sea	
R.M.S. Cedric (US/Irish flags)	**60.00**

R.M.S. Franconia (US/Swedish flags)	**35.00**
R.M.S. Regina (Union Jack/US flags), faded	**15.00**
S.S. Caledonia (US/Scottish Royal Standard flags)	**45.00**
His Majesty King Edward VII	**100.00**
Ships	
R.M.S. Calgarian	**75.00**
R.M.S. Titanic.	**55.00**
S.S. Columbia.	**80.00**
T.S.S. California	**50.00**

STEVENGRAPHS

Burns, Robert.	**140.00**
Clifton Suspension Bridge	**435.00**
Columbus Leaving Spain.	**250.00**
First Innings, The	**360.00**
For Life or Death, Heroism on Land. . .	**100.00**
God Speed the Plough	**175.00**
International Exhibition, Glasgow	**150.00**
Mersey Tunnel Railway.	**550.00**

STEVENS AND WILLIAMS

History: In 1824 Joseph Silvers and Joseph Stevens leased the Moor Lane Glass House at "Briar Lea Hill" (Brierly Hill), England, from the Honeyborne family. In 1847 William Stevens and Samuel Cox Williams took over, giving the firm its present name. In 1870 the firm moved to its Stourbridge plant. In the 1880s the firm employed such renowned glass artisans as Frederick C. Carder, John Northwood, other Northwood family members, James Hill, and Joshua Hodgetts.

Stevens and Williams made cameo glass. Hodgets developed a more commercial version using thinner-walled blanks, acid etching, and the engraving wheel. Hodgetts, an amateur botanist, was noted for his brilliant floral designs.

Other glass products and designs manufactured by Stevens and Williams include intaglio ware, Peach Bloom (a form of peachblow), moss agate, threaded ware, jewell ware, tapestry ware, and Silveria. Stevens and Williams made glass pieces covering the full range of late Victorian fashion.

After WWI the firm concentrated on refining the production of lead crystal and achieving new glass colors. In 1932 Keith Murray came to Stevens and Williams as a designer. His work stressed the pure nature of the glass form. Murray stayed with Stevens and Williams until WWII and later followed a career in architecture.

References: R. S. Williams-Thomas. *The Crystal Years,* Stevens and Williams Limited, England, Boerum Hill Books, 1983.

Additional Listings: Cameo Glass.

Biscuit Jar, 6³⁄₈" h, 5¹⁄₄" d, golden amber, applied green ribs, eye trim around center, SP top and bail **195.00**

Bride's Bowl, 10" d, 9" h, milky blue transparent glass, Hobs & Ruffle top bowl, SP stand **350.00**

Compote, 5⅜" d, 6¾" h, rose bowl with turned over rim, alabaster balustrade stem and base, sgd. **125.00**

Vase, 7½", bulbous, crimped tricorn, white ground, pink interior, applied white flowers, clear green leaves and vines, $400.00.

Creamer; 2½" h, 2⅝" d, white, pink lining, applied blue flower and green leaves, applied amber handle, scissor cut top edge **195.00**

Ewer, 6½", clear, DQ, cased opal shading up to apricot neck and ruffle top, floral and gold enamel, clear handle **235.00**

Finger Bowl with matching underplate, pink **50.00**

Perfume Bottle, swirled red and green, swirl SS top **320.00**

Sweetmeat Jar, 4¼" h, 4⅛" d, pink and white opaque swirl striped, emb ribbed pattern, SP top, rim and handle **145.00**

Vases
  5½" h, 4⅞" d, cream outside with vaseline and green ruffled leaf applique, cranberry center, pink inside, 3 petal top, green edging **160.00**
  7½" h, 5½" d, bulbous bases, MOP, lavender and rose ribbon swirl, sgd, pr **900.00**
  10¼" h, 5¼" d, ruffled, blue inside, amber edging, outside opaque white, amber branches, pink and amber leaves, amber acorns, pr . . **450.00**

STICKLEYS

History: There were several Stickley brothers: Albert, Gustav, Leopold, George, and John George. Gustav often is credited with creating the Mission style, a variant of the Arts and Crafts style. Gustav headed Craftsman Furniture, a firm located in New York with much of its actual production taking place near Syracuse. A characteristic of Gustav's furniture is exposed tenon ends. Gustav published *The Craftsman*, a magazine supporting his anti-machine points of view.

Originally Leopold and Gustav worked together. In 1902 Leopold and John George formed the L. and J. G. Stickley Furniture Company. This firm made Mission style furniture and cherry and maple early American style pieces.

George and Albert organized the Stickley Brothers Company, located in Grand Rapids, Michigan.

Reference: David M. Cathers, *Furniture Of The American Arts and Crafts Movement*, New American Library, 1981.

Bed, 58 x 82½ x 44½, stained oak, head and footboard consisting of 13 wide slats, early 20th C **2,000.00**

Bedspread, double, linen, white zinnias, orig label **500.00**

Bookcase, 48 x 54½", stained oak, glass paneled doors, 3 shelves, hammered metal escutcheons, early 20th C . . . **1,210.00**

Catalog, "Handcraft Furniture, L. & J. G. Stickley, Inc." **275.00**

Chairs
  Arm, oak, upholstered seat, copper and black label mkd "The Work of L. & J. G. Stickley,". reupholstered **100.00**
  Morris, pr, stained oak, adjustable 4 slat back, flat arms, orange vinyl upholstery, mkd "L. & J. G. Stickley," c1915 . . . . **900.00**
  Side, pr, ladder back, 36" h **250.00**

Chest of Drawers, 62", oak, 2 doors over 8 drawers, red decal **7,000.00**

Dressing Table, 48 x 48½", stained oak, 5 short drawers, mirror, red decal mark, early 20th C. **1,450.00**

Footstool, oak, reupholstered seat, applied label "The Work of L. & J. G. Stickley" **150.00**

Lantern, hand wrought copper, amber glass **2,700.00**

Mirror, table, 26", oak, gently arching crest, rect frame, swiveling between rect support on 2 trestle form feet, red decal mark, c1915. . . . . **330.00**

Night Stand, 16 x 27", stained oak. . . . **200.00**

Rug, India, 72 x 80", brown and green **1,000.00**

Table, 36 x 30 ⅛", stained oak, rect top, drawer, 4 sq legs, shelf, paper label inscribed "656," red decal mark, c1910. . . . . **600.00**

Wastebasket, 12″ h, oak slats banded together with wrought iron, branded mark, paper "Craftsman" label **1,000.00**

STIEGEL TYPE GLASS

History: Baron Henry Stiegel founded America's first flint glass factory at Manheim, Pennsylvania, in the 1760s. Although clear glass was the most common color made, amethyst, blue (cobalt), and fiery opalescent are found. Products included bottles, creamers, flasks, flips, perfumes, salts, tumblers, and whiskeys. Prosperity was short lived. Stiegel's extravagant living forced the factory to close.

It is very difficult to identify a Stiegel made item. As a result the term "Stiegel type" is used to identify glass made at that time period in the same shapes and colors.

Enamel decorated ware also is attributed to Stiegel. True Stiegel pieces are rare. An overwhelming majority is of European origin.

Beware of modern reproductions, especially in enamel wares.

Reference: Frederick W. Hunter, *Stiegel Glass*, 1950, available in Dover reprint.

Advisors: David and Linda Arman.

ENAMELED

Bride's Bottles
5½″, clear, lovebirds on one side, 5 lines of German calligraphy on other, pewter collar missing, 2 chips on rim **300.00**
7½″, clear cobalt blue, yellow urn of flowers on each side, pewter collar, cap missing **700.00**
Cordial, 3½″, clear, bucket shaped, ring turning on standard, dome pedestal base, thick band of roses and leaves **80.00**
Flips
3⅞″, clear, flowers and birds, small area of wear in paint **250.00**
4⅛″, clear, lovebirds and flowers, minor flaking **350.00**

ENGRAVED

Bottles, case
8¼″, clear, qt, tulip dec, flared neck **85.00**
8½″, clear, engraved on each side with a hillside scene of spruce trees and a split rail fence (heart replaces fence rail on one side), side panels dec with floral engraving **235.00**
Chalice, 7¾″, clear, large knop stem, teardrop air trap in stem, engraved heart and flower with German script around its bowl **225.00**

Creamer, 3½″, ftd, expanded diamond pattern, fiery opalescent, $800.00.

Flips
5½″ h, 4⅜″ d, clear, knotted bow dec **50.00**
8″, clear, engraved with a large potted tulip on one side, single flower on opposite side **125.00**
12½″ h, cov, clear, copper wheel engraved rayed medallion with heart and lovebirds, applied flame finial, ex-collection Jim and Eileen Courtney **1,000.00**
Mug, 5″, clear, applied strap handle, etched dec of tree from which hang 2 birdcages with birds **175.00**
Tumbler, 4¼″ h, 3⅝″ d, clear, 16 flute pattern, staggered sizes, floral and tendril dec **100.00**

OTHER

Bottles
Castor, 6″, cobalt blue, 20 rib mold, flanged mount, pontil base, orig tam-ó-shanter stopper, Am., early 19th C **275.00**
Chestnut, 4¾″, amethyst, expanded diamond daisy pattern, vertical ribs in base, shallow flakes on lip, attr. to Stiegel, illus. *Antiques* (June 1967, pg 744), ex-collection Jim and Eileen Courtney **1,750.00**
Chestnut, 5¾″, amethyst, expanded diamond with vertical ribs on base, minor int. sickness and ext. wear, attr. to Stiegel, illus. *Antiques* (June 1967, pg 744), ex-collection George McKearin and Jim and Eileen Courtney **1,900.00**

Scent or smelling, 3⅛", cobalt blue, fiddle body, swirled ribs **90.00**
Creamer, 3¼", cobalt blue, expanded diamond, applied handle **500.00**
Flask, 4½", clear, expanded diamond, 24 diamonds, pitkin neck **75.00**
Flip, 5⅜" h, 4¼" d, clear, 12 flute pattern **55.00**
Mug, qt, clear, applied strap handle . . . **90.00**
Salts, Master
  Cobalt blue, 20 vertical ribs, small amount of slag around circumference **175.00**
  Medium purple-blue, 3⅛", 16 rib mold, applied foot, Midwestern, probably Ohio, c1835. . . . . **300.00**
Sugar Bowls, covered
  5¾", cobalt blue, eleven diamond motif, applied foot, flame finial with swirled ribbing, attr. to Stiegel, illus. *Antiques* (June 1967, pg 744), ex-collection Jim and Eileen Courtney **1,700.00**
  6¾", cobalt blue, plain, applied foot, flame finial, attr. to Stiegel, similar to #28 in Hunter's *Stiegel Glass*, ex-collection Jim and Eileen Courtney **475.00**

STONEWARE

History: Made from dense kaolin clay and commonly salt-glazed, stonewares were hand-thrown and high fired to produce a simple, bold vitreous pottery. Stoneware crocks, jugs, and jars were produced for storage and utility purposes. This use dictated shape and design—solid, thick-walled forms with heavy rims, necks, and handles with little or no embellishment. When decorated, the designs were simple: brushed cobalt oxide, incised, slip trailed, stamped, or tooled.

Stoneware has been made for centuries. Early American settlers imported stoneware items at first. As English and European potteries refined their earthenware, colonists began to produce their own wares. Two major North America traditions emerged based only on the location or type of clay. North Jersey and parts of New York were the first area; the second was eastern Pennsylvania spreading westward and into Maryland, Virginia, and West Virginia. These two distinct locations, style of decoration, and shape are discernible factors in classifying and dating early stoneware.

By the late 18th century, stoneware was manufactured in all sections of the country. During the 19th century, this vigorous industry flourished until glass "fruit jars" appeared and the wide spread use of refrigeration. By 1910, commercial production of salt-glazed stoneware came to an end.

Advisors Kip and Linda Jones.

Batter Jugs
  White, N., & Co., Binghamton, NY, blue at spout and ears, lid missing **185.00**

Unknown maker, Albany slip, wire bail handle, 1½ gallon **75.00**
Bird House, brick molded, conical roof, 2 holes. **175.00**
Bottles
  Cowden & Wilcox, 9¼" h, 1 qt, c1860 . . . . **70.00**
  Unknown maker, doughnut shape, 7", flowers at ring and spout **750.00**
Bowls
  Hermann, P., Baltimore, milk, 10", blue leaf motif. **215.00**
  Unknown maker, 12", milk, four 3-petal flowers, pouring spout **200.00**
Butter Crocks, unknown makers
  5", ½ gallon, imp "½", 5 slip trailed curly-cues, brown/gray body, c1860 . . . . **165.00**
  10", feather motif, matching lid. **300.00**
Canning Jars
  Hamilton, James, Greensboro, PA, stenciled label, 9" **75.00**
  Unknown maker, 9", tulip motif. **180.00**

Crock, Richard C Remmey, Philadelphia, 2 gallon feather dec, $425.00.

Churns
  Read, T., New Philadelphia, OH, 20½", brushed cobalt blue tulips and vines, 6 gallon, c1850 . . . . . . **325.00**
  Webster, M.C., & Son/Hartford/2, 13½", 2 gallon, dark blue over imp mark and handle ends, c1840, flake on left ear. **145.00**
Coolers
  Satterlee & Mory/Fort Edward/4, 13¼" h, 4 gallon, bird design 12" w, bright brushed blue design, c1861. **900.00**
  Unknown maker, 11" h, 2 gallon, inscribed 2/Ice Water, c1890, electric

blue inscription and two bands around body, handles, bright brass spigot **225.00**

Crocks

Ballard, O. L. & A. K./Burlington, VT/3, 11½″ h, 3 gallon, pear shape, delicate pale blue brushed flower, bright glaze, c1856. . . . . **145.00**

Caire, Adam/Pokeepsie[sic] NY/5, 12½″, 5 gallon, graceful brushed frond, c1878 . . . . **135.00**

Goodale, D/Hartford, 10½″, 1½ gallon, ovoid, undecorated, mark and handle ends in pale blue wash, cinnamon beige ground, c1818 . . . . . **125.00**

Haxstun Ottman & Co/Fort Edward, NY, 2 gallon, stylized cobalt blue flower **135.00**

Porter/Pleasantville, 10″, 1 gallon, semi-ovoid, imp, design on both sides, well glazed, c1845 . . . . **350.00**

Ryan Brothers/Ellenville, NY/2, 9¼″, 2 gallon, imp, simple brushed blue flower, c1875. . . . . **115.00**

Sipe, Nicholas & Co/Williamsport, PA, 9″, 1½ gallon, imp, brushed blue design on light gray ground, c1875 . . **185.00**

Thomas, W. H./Huntingdon PA/3, 11½″, 3 gallon, semi-ovoid, vine like design, mixed brown/gray ground, c1871 . . . . **225.00**

Tyler, M/Albany/Manufacturer/1, 8½″, 1 gallon, ovoid, imp, mark with deep royal blue under shiny glaze, c1843 . . . . **120.00**

Whites, Utica, NY/6, 14″, 6 gallon, large floral design, c1865 . . . . **425.00**

Whittemore, A. O./Havana, NY, 7½″, 1½ gallon, floral design, c1869 . . . **140.00**

Unknown maker, 9½″, 2 gallon, ovoid, dark blue brushed floral and vine design, dark gray ground **180.00**

Jars, Preserving

Ballard & Bros/Burlington, VT, 2 gallon, brown Albany slip, lid **135.00**

Cortland/2, 11″, 2 gallon, imp name, strong blue slip trail design covering most of front, amber toned body . . **225.00**

Goodale/Stedman/Hartford, 10″, 1 gallon, imp mark washed in dark inky blue **115.00**

Goodwin/&/Webster/Hartford, 14″, 2 gallon, ovoid, bright blue at handle ends and on mark **265.00**

Harrington, T/Lyons, 11¼″, 2 gallon, stylized tree or vine design in blue. **475.00**

Whites, Utica/2, 12½″, 2 gallon, running bird design in strong blue . . . **385.00**

Unknown makers

12″, 2 gallon, strong blue stylized flower design **115.00**

14¼″, 3 gallon, ovoid, bow like design on front and back, blue on

handle ends, body varying from greenish gray to reddish on reverse, c1830 . . . . **350.00**

17½″, small floral dec in blue, cov **185.00**

Jugs

Adams, W. R., imp "Microbe Killer Co," salt glazed **20.00**

Albany/NY/2, 13½″ h, 2 gallon, bright blue stylized filigree design **145.00**

Cowden & Wilcox/Harrisburg, PA, 12½″, 2 gallon, dark, thickly applied blue flower on amber body, blue at handle ends, c1860 . . . . **300.00**

Crafts, T & Co/Whately, 11″, 1 gallon, ovoid, maker's name filled in with dark blue, alligator-skin glaze **130.00**

Graves, D. W./West Moreland, 11½″, 1 gallon, primitive 3 finger design in blue, shallow flakes at mouth, body discolored **185.00**

Lyons, 16″, 3 gallon, tapered, brushed flower on amber-tan body **165.00**

Macumber & Van Arsdale/Ithaca, NY, 18¼″ h, 5 gallon, double handle, cobalt blue scrolling flower, gray body, c1864, chips at base and spout . . **175.00**

Schenfelder, D.R./Reading, PA, 13″, 2 gallon, floral design under light even glaze, elliptical mark with imp rosette in center, c1869 . . . . **165.00**

Somerset/Potters' Works, 11½″, 1 gallon, star like flower design in strong blue under bright glaze, very minor nick on mouth, minor bubbling on highlights of design **235.00**

Unknown makers

11″, 1 gallon, filigree design, attributed to St. Johnsbury pottery . . . **85.00**

13½″, advertising, imp "2/Pure Fruit Juice/From Brooklawn Farm/Esopus on Hudson," bright blue lettering, 2 gallon. **55.00**

14″, 2 gallon, ovoid, imp "2/Brandy," attributed to Morgan & Van Wickle pottery, shoulder encircled by narrow imp bands of vines and birds, washed in pale blue, small chips. **400.00**

Pitchers

Purdy, H., double flower, 4 gallon . . . **500.00**

Wright, F. T, & Son/Stoneware/Taunton, 10½″ h, 1 gallon, c1850. . . . . **100.00**

Unknown maker, 10¾″, double tulip. **325.00**

Pot, 8¼″, ¾ gallon, ovoid, handleless, trilobal cobalt leaf design, small base nicks, 3″ vertical hairline on back . . . **80.00**

Spittoon, 8″ d, leaf and floral motif. . . . **175.00**

STONEWARE, BLUE AND WHITE

History: Blue and white stoneware refers to molded, saltglazed, domestic, utilitarian earthenware with a blue glaze produced in the late 19th and early 20th centuries. Earlier stoneware was usually handthrown and either undecorated, hand decorated in Spencerian script floral and other motifs, or stenciled. The stoneware of the blue and white period is molded with a design impressed, embossed, stenciled, or printed.

Although known as blue and white, the base color is generally grayish in tone. The blue cobalt glaze may coat the entire piece, appear as a series of bands, or accent the decorative elements.

All types of household products were available in blue and white stoneware. Bowls, crocks, jars, pitchers, mugs, and salts are just a few examples. The ware reached its height between 1870 and 1890. The advent of glass jars, tin containers, and chilled transportation brought its end. The last blue and white stoneware was manufactured in the 1920s.

Reference: Kathryn McNerney, *Blue & White Stoneware,* Collector Books, 1981.

Collectors' Club: Blue & White Pottery Club, P. O. Box 297, Center Point, IA 52213.

Dues: $10.00

Crock, cov, 7¾″ d, grape pattern, glazed interior, mkd "Robinson Clay, Akron, OH," $195.00.

Bowls

Currant & Diamond	**90.00**
Flying Bird	**145.00**
Wildflower, 10″	**55.00**
Butter Crocks, cov	
Blue Bands	**85.00**
Daisy, wooden lid	**75.00**
Wildflower	**85.00**
Canisters, wooden lids	
Coffee, Wildflower	**85.00**
Sugar, Blue Bands	**110.00**
Casserole, cov, Windmill	**135.00**
Jug, 7½″ h, adv, "Merry Christmas from J. Thoner, Wines & Liquors, Wheeling, West Virginia"	**300.00**
Keg, stag deer decor, bale handle, "Bardwell's Root Beer"	**225.00**

Mugs

Bluebird	**100.00**
Felko, adv	**115.00**
Pitchers	
Apricot	**110.00**
Beaded Rose	**110.00**
Cherry & Leaves, 6″	**275.00**
Deer & Fawn	**165.00**
Indian in headdress	**250.00**
Poinsettia	**205.00**
Rose Trellis	**175.00**
Rolling pin, Wildflower	**155.00**
Salts	
Apricot	**115.00**
Daisy	**115.00**
Peacock	**295.00**
Swastika, wooden lid	**75.00**
Soap Dishes	
Beaded Rose	**90.00**
Triple Roses	**95.00**
Spittoon, Rose & Bead Panel	**125.00**
Toothpick, swan	**75.00**
Wash Bowl & Pitcher, soap, toothbrush, slop jars, mug, Bowtie & Roses decor, 6 pcs	**475.00**
Water Cooler, 14″ h, 9½″ d, elk and polar bear decor, spigot	**495.00**

STRETCH GLASS

History: Stretch glass was produced by many glass manufacturers in the United States from the early 1900s through the 1920s. The most prominent makers were Cambridge, Fenton (who probably manufactured more stretch glass than any of the others), Imperial, Northwood, and even Steuben. Stretch glass can be identified by its iridescent, onionskin-like effect. Look for mold marks. Imported pieces are blown and show a pontil mark.

Bowls

10¾″ rolled edge, vaseline	**32.00**
12″, white, Fenton	**40.00**
Candlesticks, pr, 8″, irid blue, Imperial	**85.00**

Bowl, 9¾″ d, 3¼″ h, fluted body, vaseline, flat rim with applied gold band of pheasants in medallions and floral motif, $45.00.

Candy Dish, 6½" d, sq, irid blue, Imperial	**75.00**
Cologne Bottle, cov, irid blue	**25.00**
Compotes	
7¾", blue, Northwood, N in circle	**58.00**
8" d compote, 13" d underplate, blue	**35.00**
Console Set, 11" d flaring bowl, pr 10" h candlesticks, yellow, Fenton	**50.00**
Plates	
8", irid blue, pedestal base	**45.00**
8", yellow, engraved flowers	**40.00**
Powder Jar, irid green	**15.00**
Punch Bowl, 12" d, 5½" h, flared, Amberina	**200.00**
Sherbert, 4", ribbed, blue	**35.00**
Tumble-up, irid blue	**40.00**
Vases	
6", fan shape, ribbed, green	**30.00**
8½", cylindrical, green	**35.00**
10", blue, vertical cut	**45.00**

Hanging, 4¼" h, spherical, old black paint, white, yellow, and green flowers	**45.00**
Ceramic	
Counter Top, three Victorian ladies, all wearing large bonnets, long curls, skirts join at waist, each facing different direction	**45.00**
Wall, Cocker Spaniel, face, place for scissors behind one ear	**65.00**
Chalkware, wall	
Apple, red, green leaves	**20.00**
Boy, top hat and pipe	**35.00**
Strawberry, face	**25.00**
Glass, Counter Top	
Beehive, 4½", flint, dome shape, tin. closure	**45.00**
Cranberry overlay, white coinspot design, dome	**75.00**
Thousand Eye, amber	**65.00**
Pottery, wall, Bellhop (black) face, mkd Fredericksburg Art Pottery	**75.00**

STRING HOLDERS

History: The string holder developed as a utilitarian tool to assist the merchant or manufacturer who needed tangle-free string or twine to tie packages. The early holders were made of cast iron, some patents dating to the 1860s.

When the string holder moved to the household, lighter and more attractive forms developed. The string holder remained a key kitchen element until the early 1950s.

Beehive, 6½" d, 4½" h, cast iron, $20.00.

Cast Iron
  Counter Top

6½" h, reticulated sphere on triangular base, old black repaint	**25.00**
8½" h, dome, reticulated, to hold cone	**35.00**

SUGAR SHAKERS

History: Sugar shakers, sugar castors, or muffineers all served the same purpose: to "sugar" muffins, scones, or toast. They are larger than salt and pepper shakers, were produced in a variety of materials, and were in vogue in the late Victorian era.

Amberina, 5¼", DQ, MOP, pewter top	**650.00**
Bohemian, green, cut	**135.00**
Cranberry	
5", baby IVT, 9 panels, nickel top	**85.00**
Ribbed opal, lattice	**95.00**
Crown Milano, ribbed, wild rose dec	**475.00**
Cut Glass	
Alhamber pattern, Greek key, SS top	**275.00**
Block and Fan, 3 ¾" h, 3" d, stars, rayed base, SS chased top and rim	**175.00**
Duncan Miller, Diamond Point and Quartered Block pattern, blown, clear, SP top, pontil mk	**35.00**
Findlay, 5", pale blue, ribbed top, floral design base	**450.00**
Libby Maize, amber leaf dec	**70.00**
Milk Glass	
Green, rose dec	**70.00**
White, 5 ⅞" h, 2 ¾" d, yellow bands, pastel flowers, nickel plated brass top	**40.00**
Mt. Washington, egg shape	
Green enamel dec, 4½"	**125.00**
Yellow, Crown Milano dec	**250.00**
Opalescent, blue, swirl	**60.00**
Pattern Glass, Banded Portland	**45.00**
Peachblow, Wheeling, shiny	**500.00**
Pickard, 4½", poppies, sgd, c1910	**235.00**

Opalescent, Reverse Swirl, cranberry, Buckeye Glass, $200.00.

Rubena Glass, 5¼″ h, 3″ d, IVT, blue, yellow, and white daisies, green foliage, SP top **125.00**
Rubena Verde, enamel dec **180.00**
Satin Glass
  3¼″ h, 4″ d, Fleurette pattern, squat, pink, brass top **125.00**
  3½″, Cone pattern, nickle plated top **75.00**
Smith Bros., 6″, opaque white, floral dec, SP top **70.00**
Spangle Glass, ruby, silver mica **55.00**
Spatter, ribbed, pink and white **85.00**
Wedgwood, blue, classical figures **45.00**

SWANSEA

History: This superb pottery and porcelain was made at Swansea (Glamorganshire, Wales) as early as the 1760s with production continuing until 1870.

Marks on Swansea vary. The earliest marks were SWANSEA impressed under glaze and DILLWAN under glaze after 1805. CAMBRIAN POTTERY was stamped in red under glaze from 1803-1805. Many fine examples, including the Botanical series in pearlware, are not marked, but may have the botanical name stamped under glaze.

Fine examples of Swansea often may show imperfections, such as firing cracks. These pieces are considered mint because they left the factory in this condition.

Center Dish, 9¾″, exotic bird on branch in landscape, scroll and floral molded border, flared foot, red script mark, c1820 .... **325.00**

Cottage, 3½″ h, 4′ l, bisque, white, applied roses, clematis, and moss climbing walls, c1820 .... **1,500.00**
Creamer, pottery, 7¼″ l, figural cow, white with clover shape spots, c1810 .... **325.00**
Cup and Saucer, 3⅝″ cup, 6″ saucer, floral dec, c1815 .... **120.00**
Dessert Service, 17 pcs, tazza, oval, handled, 12¾″ w, 2 saucers, 9¼″, 2 sq dishes, 9″, 12 plates, 8¼″, pheasants and floral centers, puce and gilt trellis border, 2nd border of lotus, chrysanthemum, and vines, shaped gilt rims, red printed and imp marks, c1815 .... **4,200.00**

Plate, 8½″, floral, sgd under glaze, c1812, $115.00.

Goblet, 5⅛″, copper lustre, black transfer, Oriental figures in garden by pagodas, 1820 .... **50.00**
Plate, 8½″, creamware, botanical, Borkea Tea Tree, multicolored, brown rim, c1800 .... **200.00**

SWORDS

History: The first swords in America came from Europe. The chief cities for sword manufacturing were Solingen in Germany, Klingenthal in France, and Hounslow and Shotley Bridge in England. Among the American importers of these foreign blades was "Horstmann" whose mark is found on many military weapons.

New England and Philadelphia were the early centers for American sword manufacturing. By the Franco-Prussian War, the Ames Manufacturing Company was exporting American swords to Europe.

Sword collectors concentrate on a variety of styles-commission vs. non-commission officers' swords, presentation swords, naval weapons, and swords from a specific military branch such as cavalry or infantry. The type of sword helped identify a person's military rank and, depending on how he had it customized, his personality as well.

Following the invention of repeating firearms in the mid-19th century, the sword lost its functional importance as a combat weapon and became a military dress accessory. Condition is a key criteria determining value.

Reference: Harold L. Peterson, *The American Sword 1775–1945*, Ray Riling Arms Books Co, 1965.

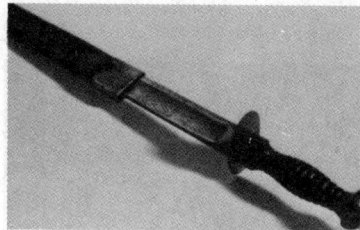

Dutch, engraved "1793, crossed anchors, and A.A.," 23″ l, orig scabbard, $425.00.

AMERICAN

Artillery, Light, Saber, 1840, 38″, brass hilt, wood grip with brass wire wrap and leather.................... 300.00

Militia Infantry Officer, 1830–1850, 34¼″, brass hilt, pistol grip ivory pommel, military motif cast in knuckle guard, gilded blade, brass scabbard . 575.00

Musicans, 1840, 34″, brass hilt, leather scabbard 175.00

Naval Cutlass, 1845, Roman design grip, inspector's mark "JL", "RC" on quillons..................... 275.00

Naval Cutlass, slightly curved, blade mkd "USN 1863" and "25 M/432", wire wrap grip, leather scabbard frog.... 375.00

Revolutionary, 38½″, 32¾″ blade, ivory grip, unmarked steel blade with 3 fullers starting 6½″ from top of blade, brass hilt, geometric design, sword knot....................... 625.00

Revolutionary, 39½″, 33″ blade, unmarked iron blade, single fuller starting at hilt, spiral carved hardwood grip, brass pommel and guard......... 650.00

EUROPEAN

English
Artillery, George V Royal, 34″ blade, plated hilt, wire wrapped black fishskin cov grip, leather dress knot, leather cov field service scabbard. 165.00

Grenadier Guards Sergeant's, Herbert & Co, London, c1850, 28″, slightly curved, single edge 200.00

Hunting, 25¼″, iron blade with running wolf stamp on both sides, silver quillons and pommel cap, spiral carved wood grip with silver wrapping. ... 450.00

Infantry, 1742, 31½″, slightly curved blade, brass hilt, brass grip with spiral pattern 150.00

Royal Engineer's, officers', 1897, 32¾″ Wilkinson blade, Victorian pattern, etched, crowned VR, Royal Engineers, thunderbolt scrolls and owner's crest, engraved pierced brass hilt, steel scabbard 150.00

French
Cavalry, officers' sabre, 32½″, 27¾″ blade, slightly curved, checkered ivory handles, unmarked iron blade, 3 fullers starting at hilt 200.00

Cavalry, officers' sabre, Napoleonic era, c1800, 33½″, curved watered steel, pipe backed, clipped back blade 600.00

Cavalry, trooper's, model AN 11, 38¾″, round backed bi-fullered single edged blade, regulation triple bar brass guard, ribbed pommel, wire wrap leather cov grip, steel scabbard.................. 250.00

German
Duelling, mid 19th C, iron basket hilt, "Solingen", iron scabbard....... 175.00

Imperial German, WW II, etched, "1 Thuringen Feld art, Regt. No. 19", reverse, battle scene, red and silver sword knot, scabbard 160.00

Scottish, 32″ blade, 37¾″ overall, iron pommel, iron basket hilt with heart cutout, sharkskin wrapped grip, etched blade with vines, crown over entwined initials, X III beneath, "London/Worland/Jermyn St/St Jame's/London, reverse, etched 6 point star.................. 375.00

ORIENTAL

Chinese, Imperial Officer's, 29½″, double edge, down-drooping gilt cross guard fishskin cov grip, gilt pommel . 300.00

Japanese, Samuri Sword, WW II, 37″, 27″ manufactured blade, typical WW II military hilt, black lacquered wood scabbard 175.00

TEA CADDIES

History: Tea once was a precious commodity. Special boxes or caddies were used as containers to accommodate different teas, including a special cup of blending.

Around 1700 silver caddies appeared in England. Other materials, such as Sheffield plate, tin, wood, china, and pottery, also were used. Some tea caddies became very ornate.

Creamware, 4½″, rect, tortoise shell pattern, late 18th C	175.00
Meissen, 5⅝″, pear shape, turquoise ground, Watteau subjects, reserved sprigs of flowers, gilt borders, silver cov, lion finial, mkd, c1745	1,400.00
Pearlware, 5½″, round, chocolate ground, blue dec with heart shape reserves	150.00
Rosewood, 12 x 6 x 6½″, oblong hinged top, paneled incurvate sides, ball feet, George III	225.00
Silver, 4½″, lift of lid, classical figures in relief, English, Sheffield type	150.00
Staffordshire, 5¾″, rect shape, tapering shoulders, molded Apollo, foliage, dated 1779	900.00
Tortoise Shell, 7 x 4¼ x 5½″, oblong, stepped hinged lid, bun feet, William IV	400.00
Walnut, 9 x 5 x 5¼″, rect, coved and molded hinged top with brass bail handle, pierced brass panel corners, brass scallop feet, George III, c1775	450.00

Rose wood, 4⅛ x 4⅝ x 5″, brass hinges, dome top, inlaid fruitwood on all four sides, $500.00.

TEA LEAF LUSTRE

History: Tea leaf lustre is a type of gold lustre decoration on ironstone china, which resembles a stylized form of the oriental tea leaf. It also was known as "Lustre Band with Sprig." The ware was produced by a number of English and American potteries. Principal English potters were J. and G. Meakin, Wedgwood, Shaw, Clementson, and Mayer and Grindley.

Recently some reproductions have appeared. They can be spotted by their poor coloration, by uneven copper lustre decoration, and by weight. The original ironstone pieces are much heavier than the newer ceramic pieces.

Reference: Annise Doring Heaivilin, *Grandma's Tea Leaf Ironstone*, Wallace-Homestead, 1981.

Collectors' Club: Tea Leaf Club International, P. O. Box 904, Mount Prospect, IL 60056. Dues: $10.00. *Tea Leaf Readings* (bimonthly).

Museums: Lincoln Home, Springfield, IL; Sherwood Davidson House, Newark, OH; and, Ox Barn Museum, Aurora, OR.

Additional Listings: See *Warman's Americana & Collectibles* for more examples.

Bacon Rasher, J & G Meakin	30.00
Bone Dish, Mellor-Taylor	60.00
Bowl, 8″ sq, Meakin	35.00

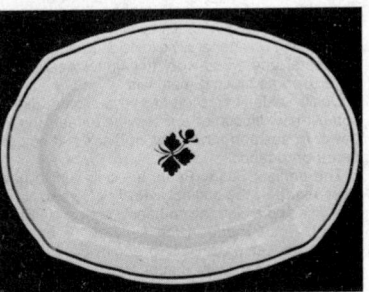

Platter, 12½″, oval, shaped edges, mkd "Royal Ironstone China, Alfred Meakin, England," $45.00.

Butter Dish, cov, drainer, oval, H. Burgess	125.00
Butter Pat, sq, Wedgwood	11.00
Casserole, cov, 10″ l, 8″ h, oval, pine cone knob, A. Shaw	150.00
Compote, 11″ d, 5″ h, pedestal base, Wilkinson	310.00
Creamer, 5″ h, oblong, A. Shaw	125.00
Cups and Saucers	
Bamboo, Meakin	50.00
Demitasse, Meakin	95.00
Mugs	
Child's, 2½″	85.00
Shaving, 3½″, A. Shaw	120.00
Mush Bowl, Meakin	30.00
Pitchers	
7½″, Powell & Bishop	100.00
9″, bamboo, Meakin	250.00
Plate, 9¾″, lily-of-the-valley, A. Shaw	30.00
Platter, oval, 14 x 10″, Meakin	40.00
Soap Dish and Drain Insert, Meakin	75.00
Soup Tureen, 13½ x 9″, H. Burgess	325.00

Sugar Bowl, Alfred Meakin	75.00
Teapots, covered	
9½", Henry Burgess	100.00
10", Wilkinson.	150.00
Toothbrush Holder, A. Shaw	150.00
Vegetable Dish, cov, ftd, 6 sides,	
A. Shaw.	100.00
Wash Bowl and Pitcher, A. J.	
Wilkinson	300.00

TEDDY BEARS

History: Originally thought of as "Teddy's Bears," the name comes from President Theodore Roosevelt. These stuffed toys are believed to have originated in Germany and in the United States during the 1902–03 period.

Most of the earliest Teddy Bears had humps on their backs, elongated muzzles, and jointed limbs. The fabric used was usually mohair; the eyes were either glass with pin backs or black shoe buttons. The stuffing was generally excelsior. Kapok (for softer bears) and wood-wool (for firmer bears) also were used as stuffing materials.

Quality older bears often had elongated limbs, sometimes with curved arms, oversize feet, and felt paws. Noses and mouths were black and embroidered onto fabric.

The earliest Teddy Bears are believed to have been made by the original Ideal Toy Corporation in America and a German company, Margarete Steiff, GmbH. Bears made in the early 1900s by other companies can be difficult to identify because they had a strong similarity in appearance and because most tags or labels were lost through childhood play.

Teddy Bears are rapidly increasing as collectibles and their prices are increasing proportionately. As in other fields, desirability should depend upon appeal, quality, uniqueness, and condition. One modern bear already has been firmly accepted as a valuable collectible among its antique counterparts: the Steiff Teddy put out in 1980 for the company's 100th anniversary. This is a reproduction of that company's first Teddy and has a special box, signed certificate, and numbered ear tag. Eleven thousand of these were sold worldwide.

References: Peggy and Alan Bialosky, *The Teddy Bear Catalog*, Workman Publishing, 1984, revised edition; Shirley Conway and Jean Wilson, *100 Years Of Steiff, 1880–1980*, Berlin Printing, 1980; Shirley Conway and Jean Wilson, *Steiff Teddy Bears, Dolls, and Toys With Prices*, Wallace-Homestead, 1984; Margaret Fox Mandel, *Teddy Bears and Steiff Animals*, Collector Books, 1984; Ted Menten, *The Teddy Bear Lovers Catalog*, Delilah Communications, Ltd., 1983; Patricia N. Schoolmaker, *A Collector's History Of the Teddy Bear*, Hobby House Press, Inc., 1981; Helen Sieverling (comp.) and Albert C. Revi (ed.), *The Teddy Bear And Friends Price Guide*, Hobby House Press, Inc., 1983.

Periodicals: *The Teddy Bear And Friends*, Hobby House Press, Inc., 900 Frederick Street, Cumberland, MD 21502. Subscription: $9.95; *The Teddy Bear News*, P. O. Box 8361, Prairie Village, KS 66208. Subscription: $15.00.

Collector's Clubs: Good Bears Of The World, P. O. Box 8236, Honolulu, HI 96815. Dues: $8.00. *Bear Tracks* (quarterly); Teddy Bear Boosters Club, P. O. Box 520, Stanton, CA 90680; Teddy Bear Collectors Club, P. O. Box 601, Harbor City, CA 90710.

Advisors: Peggy and Alan Bialosky.

BEARS

4¾", mohair, jointed limbs, tail moves head up and down and from side to side, c1950s	300.00
9", Steiff, mohair, felt paws, clown hat and collar, early 1900s	500.00

10", Steiff, plush heads and paws, felt bodies, open felt mouths, orig clothes, pr, $450.00.

13", early Steiff, mohair, hump, fully jointed, classic style	400.00
14", Commonwealth Toy & Novelty Co., mohair, metal mouth open to be "fed" crackers which can be removed through back zipper.	250.00
15", mohair, fully jointed, squeeze-action music box hidden in torso	500.00
17", Ideal, brown plush, cream paws and ears, molded muzzle, squeaker tail . .	50.00
18", mohair, fully jointed, unique metal-rimmed, sleep eyes	500.00
19", mohair head and paws, cloth "doll" body, glass eyes, cotton suit	200.00
20", Knickerbocker, mohair, fully jointed, velvet paws, firmly stuffed	300.00
22", English "Roddy" or German Schuco, mohair, fully jointed, tail moves heap up and down and from side to side.	1,000.00

23", mohair, jointed arms, orig light bulb eyes, leather collar	**400.00**
26", mohair, standing bear on wheels, pull-string growler	**700.00**

BEAR RELATED ITEMS

Book, Peggy and Alan Bialosky, *The First Teddy Bears: Pictures And Price Guidelines*, privately printed, 1980, first edition..	**20.00**
Dishes, doll, china, setting for four with teapot, creamer, and sugar bowl, bears and children painted on each piece	**150.00**
Photograph, child with teddy bear, early 1900s.	**15.00**
Rattle, baby, Victorian, SS bear on MOP handle, sculpted two-sided detail . . .	**175.00**

TELEPHONES

History: The deregulation of the nation's telephone industry and increasing interest in antique telephones has led to increasing values for old telephones and equipment.

Lover's telegraphs and other crude sound operated and unpatented telephones existed prior to Alexander Graham Bell's 1876 patent. However, it is generally accepted that Bell invented the telephone powered by electricity.

The most valuable antique telephones come from the pre-1895 period and must be marked, dated, or easily documented. Instruments also must be unaltered and have all major original parts. Telephones marked Charles Williams, Jr., a Boston manufacturer whose factory was the "birthplace" of the infant Bell Telephone Company, are among the most valued.

Post 1895 telephones have value if modified or converted to be compatable with today's modern phone network. Conversions should be done by an expert who will supply additional parts without removing any of the major components to accomplish conversion.

Refinishing also requires expert skills. Do not remove original circuitry. Restoring nickel and black baked enamel finishes is most desirous. Buffing original parts to expose the brass beneath will make it difficult to distinguish those parts from the many dated and old fashioned marked, solid brass fake parts and whole telephones which have been flooding the market for a decade. No mass produced telephone made in the United States prior to 1950 was offered with a shiny brass finish!

Advisor: Dan Golden.

Tombstone, Western Electric parts, $350.00.

Automatic Dialing Telephones

Couch, S.H., Autophone.	**250.00**
Globe Automatic, wall model	**950.00**
Lorimer Automatic, all models	**1,500.00**
Monson Automatic, wall model.	**1,200.00**
National Automatic, wall model.	**1,500.00**
Ness Automatic, wall model	**700.00**
Select-O-Phone.	**250.00**
Strowger Patent	
Pre-1898 models	**2,500.00**
Automatic Electric, candlestick model	**1,200.00**
Wall Model, large	**1,500.00**
Wall Model, small.	**650.00**
Double Box Telephones	
48" long, tandem, any manufacturer.	**550.00**
49 to 60" long, tandem 2 boxes	**750.00**
60 to 70" long, tandem 2 boxes	**1,200.00**
71" and longer	**1,500.00**
Oak, plain, Stromberg-Carlson type, c1899	**350.00**
Unusual in any way, any manufacturer	**450.00**
Fiddleback Telephones	
Gilliand, American Bell with Blake transmitter, or Charles Williams . . .	**1,000.00**
Vought Berger, Kellogg, Western Electric, Stromberg Carlson, Dean, Diamond, etc.	**275.00**
Pay Phones	
Common 1950s style.	**150.00**
Gray Pay Station	
Desk Model, wooden, slots for coins up to dollar, marked	**3,000.00**
Wall Phone, wood	**2,500.00**
Wall Phone, 72".	**3,000.00**

1920s style (Known as Laurel & Hardy style)	**400.00**
Pay Box, cast iron, small c1910	**150.00**

Single Box Wall Telephones, Wooden Picture Frame Front

1910–15	**225.00**
Cathedral Top, lightning arrestors at top	**300–400.00**
Plain Front, 1915–1920s	**200.00**
Unusual style	**450–600.00**

Stands

Gossip Benches, approx.	**70.00**
Ornate, carvings	**600.00**
1920s style, plain	**150.00**

Switchboards

Pre-1894, wall mounted, marked American Bell-Blake, Gilliand, Edison, National Bell, or Charles Williams	**2,000.00**
Pre-1910, wall mounted	**500.00**

Pre-1935

Light Bulbs	**250.00**
Transmitter boom.	**400.00**
1935 to Present	**Surplus Value**
Hotel Annunciators	**200–800.00**
Mansion Annunciators, depending on size and ornateness	**.75–450.00**

Telephone Booths

1890s, leaded glass	**2,000–3,500.00**
1910 to 1912, single door	**2,000.00**

1914 to 1940, folding door

Oak	**1,200.00**
Walnut	**1,100.00**

Triple Box

American Bell, Edison, Blake, Berliner on transmitter	**1,700.00**
American Electric, Kokomo	**1,200.00**
Bell Telephone	**1,200.00**
Chicago	**950.00**
Elliott	**1,200.00**
Gilliand.	**1,700.00**
Keystone	**900.00**
Mianus	**900.00**
Molecular	**1,400.00**

Note: If any of these sets are missing the 7″ long exposed terminal receiver, subtract $150.00

Upright Desk Stands (Candlestick Phones)

Hour Glass or Potbelly shape	**750.00**
Oil Can shape.	**500.00**

Straight Pipe, regular style

Dial type	**185.00**
No dial	**95.00**
With magneto box	**160.00**

Notes: Extremely unusual candlestick phones made of wood or in an outrageous style may be worth in excess of $1,000.00. All phones mass produced from the WWI to 1950 were made in black. The Western Electric model is now being reproduced in solid shiny brass.

TEPLITZ CHINA

History: Around 1900 twenty-six ceramic manufacturers were located in Teplitz, a town in the Bohemian province of Czechosolvakia. Other potteries were located in the nearby town of Turn. Wares from these factories were molded, cast, and hand decorated. Most are in the Art Nouveau and Art Deco styles. Most pieces do not carry a specific manufacturer's mark. They are simply marked "Teplitz," "Turn-Teplitz," and "Turn."

Basket, 6½″, floral dec, mkd Teplitz	**95.00**
Centerpiece, 11″ l, 6½″ h, scrolled cornacopia shape, young girl and cupid, shades of ecru, beige, and pink, mkd 6207/58	**300.00**

Ewers

11¼″, off white ground, yellow flowers outlined in gold, green leaves, gold band at top, gold handle, pierced design	**200.00**
17″, matte green ground, gold and pink dragonfly in relief, mkd Turn-Teplitz, Bohemia, RS&K Austria	**120.00**

Figurines

Lady, Art Nouveau, gold-bronze skin, long hair with applied grape wreath, green gown with applied fruit, holding grapes, artist sgd Doebrieh, mkd Teplitz 15,"	**650.00**
Lady and gentleman, dressed in Empire style, mkd Turn-Teplitz, 15″	**250.00**
Pitcher, 6½″, The Goose Girl, open handles, Stellmacher mark	**70.00**
Tobacco Jar, cov, Arab on horse	**165.00**

Vase, 6½″ h, 11″ w, ecru shading to beige and pink, mkd "6207/58," $300.00.

Vases

7″, butterfly dec, multicolored **225.00**

7″, 4 handles, poppies, blue and lavender, gold relief beading, mkd Turn-Teplitz, pr **180.00**

8¼″, 3 handles, gray ground, polychrome figure of cavalier, Stellmacker mark **100.00**

9½″, Art Nouveau, aqua, girl's face in relief, long hair **165.00**

9½″, ftd, handle, gold floral dec with web and spider **125.00**

13″, 2 handled, gray to green ground, white enameled floral and leaf dec   **150.00**

14¼″, free form baluster shape, ochre and green matte glaze, imp marks   **175.00**

18″, baluster shape, olive-green, molded at shoulder with pendant blossoming wisteria, green, blue, and rose, imp marks **685.00**

18¾″, 6¼″ d, gold figural mermaid sitting on neck, satin green and gold top and base, wide brown band around center with white flowers, mkd **600.00**

Window Box, 14¼ x 5 x 4¾″, yellow ground, iris dec, purple and lavender, Egyptian fan mark **225.00**

TERRA COTTA WARE

History: Terra cotta is wares mades of a hard, semi-fired ceramic clay. The color of the pottery ranges from a light orange-brown to a deep brownish red. It is usually unglazed, but some pieces can be found partially glazed or decorated with slip designs, incised, or carved. Examples include utilitarian objects as well as statuettes and large architectural pieces. Fine early Chinese terra cotta pieces recently have brought substantial prices.

Brazier, 16″, baluster shape container, removable cov, wood and iron handles, sponged glazed cream ground, aubergine and pale turquoise, Italian, late 19th C **325.00**

Cup and Saucer, glazed, undecorated .   **60.00**

Figures

Horse and Rider, 9″ l, rider raising his crop, horse rearing, black paint, imp Made in/Austria/252, early 20th C   **750.00**

Victorian lady, seated on painted column form base, 51″ **450.00**

Match Holder, 9¼″, figural, colonial man seated, tricorn hat, polychrome blue vest, white shirt, brown pants, holding bucket, another at his feet, c1800 . .   **450.00**

Plaque, 13¼″ d, raised figures of man and woman in wine cellar, mkd Musterschutz **225.00**

Stein, applied cane ware iris, 1800–10   **75.00**

Syrup, 8″, Egyptian design, Sheffield pewter lid **100.00**

Tobacco Jar, 10″, figural man in long tailed coat, white vest, and skull cap   **150.00**

Vase, 13″, gourd shape, black dragon in relief, 2 handles, mkd **85.00**

Nodder, 3¾″ h, pink vest with high glaze, $145.00.

TEXTILES

History: Textiles are cloth or fabric items, especially anything woven or knitted. Those that survive usually represent the best since these were the objects that were used carefully and stored by the housewife.

Textiles are collected for many reasons—to study fabrics, understand the elegance of an historical period, and for decorative and modern use. The renewed interest in clothing has sparked a revived interest in textiles of all forms.

Reference: William C. Ketchum, Jr., *The Knopf Collectors' Guides to American Antiques, Quilts,* Alfred A. Knopf, Inc., 1982.

Collectors' Club: Costume Society of America, 330 West 42nd Street, Suite 1702, New York, NY 10036.

Additional Listings: Clothing, Quilts and Samplers. See *Warman's Americana & Collectibles* for a listing of crochet work.

Bedspread, 88 x 72″, cotton, candlewick, all white, central panel of large circle embellished with leaves, sprigs, 4 peacocks, 2 large urns, corners of stylized pine trees, border of scallops and pendant hearts, cotton fringe, sgd "Susan Wilkin 1822, Sussex, NJ" **1,450.00**

Coverlet, jacquard, J. Lutz/E. Hempfield Township/For/Rebecca Hershey/1839, 99 x 77″, 4½″ fringe, $650.00.

Bed Ticks

    41 x 76″, linen, blue and onion skin dyed gold, tape tie, red embroidered "E" **225.00**

    61 x 72″, cotton homespun, indigo, white, and red with white homespun backing, hand sewn, handloomed tapes **450.00**

Bolster Cover, 18 x 72″, homespun linen, white embroidered initial "P," embroidered floral wreath **50.00**

Coverlets

  Jacquard

    Two color (blue and white), double weave, field of snowflake roundels, tulip buds and flowers, and stars and polka dots, borders of paired birds beneath willow trees, compotes with flowers and pendant sprays, corners of spread eagles and shields, mkd "Mary Dibble/Delhi/1841," Delaware County, NY, 100 x 80″ **660.00**

    Two color (blue and white), single weave, 2 pc, oval reserves in center, bird corners, corners mkd "J. & S./Slaybaugh/Bucyrus/Crawford/County/Ohio 1846," 66 x 80″ **425.00**

    Two color (tan and natural white), single weave, 2 pc, floral medallions, eagle borders, corners mkd

"Emily Covert/J.M./Davidson/Fancy/Weaver/Lodi 1837," 70 x 96″ **300.00**

    Four color (red, blue, green, and white), single weave, central medallion, corners mkd "Made by/J. Haag/Inemaus/For/J.O./1850," orig fringe, 76 x 96″ **455.00**

  Overshot

    Two color (green and white), 2 pc, 60 x 78″. **200.00**

    Three color (indigo blue, onion skin brown, and natural), 3 pc, intricate optical pattern, 88 x 98″ **275.00**

Hooked Rag Rugs

    25 x 42½″, running horse in shades of brown, dark blue ground, scalloped and polka dot border in red, black, white, blue, teal, and red wool edging. **1,250.00**

    29 x 68″, reclining lion, serpent at right, scrolling borders, red, black, brown, and green, late 19th C **675.00**

    31½ x 37½″, central flying bird in olive with red and magenta wings, background design of hearts, leaves, and geometrics in blue, white, green, red, black, and brown. **625.00**

    34 x 64″, floral, cornucopia, meandering vine border, red, blue, green, yellow, beige, and black, 19th C **825.00**

    39½ x 61″, farm scene with barn, farm house, flowers and trees, in beige, maroon, blue, green, and yellow, c1930. **1,450.00**

    73 x 108″, tall ship mkd "Kate Young 1865," fully rigged, border of blossoms and leaves, beige, green, yellow, rose, and lavender, c1930 . . . **900.00**

Pictures, Needlework

    19¾ x 20″, young lady standing in wooded landscape, painted face and hands, oval reserve bordered by embroidered buds and blossoms, executed in white, green, red, yellow, and pink silk threads on white satin ground, sgd "Miss Mary Hoyt, M.E. & A. Sketchley's School, Poughkeepsie", early 19th C, framed **3,000.00**

    16¼ x 20¼″, tent stitch, lady seated at pond fishing, courtier at right, tree with large red and gold pears, large white house in background, executed in brown, rose, white, blue, and green wool threads on canvas, MA, c1750. . . . . **3,850.00**

Pillow Cover, Trapunto, 24 x 32″, cotton, white, basket of flowers with feather quilted wreath and initials "C.M.L.". . **400.00**

Rag Carpeting, 37½ x 144″ strips, set of 3, (makes 9 x 12′ rug), white with light green bands, dark green stripes, PA **435.00**

Sheet, 78 x 88", homespun linen, olive embroidered initials "E.P. 1800".... **75.00**

Show Towel, 16¾ x 63", homespun, embroidered inscription at top in pink, brown, and blue, cut and drawn work, knotted fringe, dated "1811 Lancaster Caunty (sic)".................. **175.00**

Towel, 19½ x 32", blue and white, woven floral band with butterflies, knotted fringe..................... **70.00**

THREADED GLASS

History: Threaded glass is glass decorated with applied threads of glass. Before the English invention of a glass threading machine in 1876, threads were applied by hand. After this invention, threaded glass was produced in quantity by practically every major glass factory.

Threaded glass was revived by the art glass manufacturers, such as Durand and Steuben, and continues to be made today.

Atomizer, blue threads on red ground. . **75.00**

Bowl, white threads on clear, polished pontil...................... **25.00**

Candlesticks, pr, 12", green threads, sgd "Steuben" in block letters **200.00**

Compote, 9 x 6½", cranberry threads on clear **500.00**

Finger Bowl, 5", fluted edge, chartreuse threads..................... **65.00**

Jam Jar, pink threads on clear, SP lid and handle.................. **100.00**

Pefume Bottle, 5½", blown, machine applied threads, Lutz type **250.00**

Plate, 8¾", cranberry threads on clear, polished pontil............... **45.00**

Compote, 8⅛" d, 7" h, light green, controlled bubbles, unsigned, possibly Steuben, $130.00.

Rose Bowl, 5 x 6¾", cranberry threads on clear **45.00**

Sugar Castor, pink threads on clear... **75.00**

Syrup, cranberry threads on clear **165.00**

Toothpick, 3", cranberry threads on green ground, clear rigaree top **100.00**

Tumbler, 4¼", aqua threads on clear.. **225.00**

Vase, 6", gold threads on irid blue ground **300.00**

TIFFANY

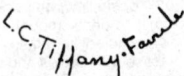

History: Louis Comfort Tiffany (1849–1934) established a glass house in 1878 primarily to make stained glass windows. There he developed a unique type of colored iridescent glass called Favrile. His Favrile glass differed from other art glass in manufacture as it was a composition of colored glass worked together while hot. The essential characteristic is that ornamentation is found within the glass. Favrile was never further decorated. Different effects were achieved by varying the amount and position of colors which project movement in form and shape.

In 1890, in order to utilize surplus materials at the plant, Tiffany began to design and produce "small glass" such as iridescent glass lamp shades, vases, and stemware and tableware in the Art Nouveau manner.

Commercial production began in 1896. Most Tiffany wares are signed with the name L. C. Tiffany or the initials L.C.T. Some pieces also carry the word "Favrile" as well as a number. A number of other marks can be found, e.g., Tiffany Studios and Louis C. Tiffany Furnaces.

Louis Tiffany and the artists in his studio also are well known for the fine work in other area areas—bronzes, pottery, jewelry, silver and enamels.

References: Victor Arwas, *Glass, Art Nouveau and Art Deco,* Rizzoli International Publications, Inc., 1977; Robert Koch, *Louis C. Tiffany, Rebel In Glass,* Crown Publishers, Inc., 1966.

Note: All glass is of the Favrile type unless otherwise noted.

Bench, 81 x 15 x 19¼", rect top set with multicolored tesserae in geometric pattern, bronze frame draped at front with reticulated screens of colored glass tiles, early 20th C **11,550.00**

Bookends, gilt bronze, cast with 2 columns surmounted by peacocks and spanned by a leafy arch, foliate and bird border, imp "Tiffany Studios/New York/1614", 1899-1920 .... **300.00**

Bowls

2½" h, enamel on copper, squared sides with incurvate lip cast and enameled on 4 corners with shaded sapphire blue peacocks of green, coral, and blue, sapphire-blue ground, int. in aubergine enamel, inscribed "L.C.T./EL/85" **3,850.00**

7" h, bulbous, short ft, cobalt blue glaze, monogram "LCT," inscribed "L. C. Tiffany Favrile Pottery P953" **350.00**

8" d, deep amber irid, ribbed sides, inscribed "L. C. T. Favrile," 1892-1928 . . . . **345.00**

9½" d, shallow, amber irid, flaring lip, gilt bronze mount, loop handle, enameled in red, pink, and dusty rose with circles and rectangles, inscribed "L. C. Tiffany Inc. Favrile," 1920 . . . . **725.00**

Boxes, cov, enamel on copper

2", round, bulging sides cast and enameled with cherry laden leafy branches, flattend circular cov with button knop, shades of cherry-red, lavender, and brown against a ground shading from midnight blue to amber and green, int. of lime green enamel, inscribed "L.C.T./SC 161/42444," 1904-14 . . . . **1,210.00**

3", elongated spherical body, flattened cov, body enameled with spray of pale pink and white cherry blossoms, green leaves against deep purple irid ground, inscribed "Louis C. Tiffany/E.L. 71," 1904-14 . . . . **3,425.00**

Brandy Snifter, bluish gold, lily pad and threaded dec, sgd "L. C. Tiffany Favrile" **300.00**

Candlesticks, pr, 17", Favrile and bronze, circular base and slender rod standard supporting a waisted candlecup of green glass, bobeches, imp "Tiffany Studios/NY/21100," 1900 . . **1,000.00**

Centerpiece, 19¾" h, Favrile and gilt bronze, cylindrical amber irid vase, green stylized feathering, classical support cast with female masks, flattened dish cast with acanthus leaves and scrollwork, vase inscribed "L.C.T," base imp "Tiffany Studios/NY," 1899–1920 . . . . **525.00**

Champagne, irid gold, sgd "L.C.T. U9785" **120.00**

Chandelier, 24", Favrile and bronze, domical shade of radiating mottled green tiles above a lower drop border of vertical amber glass tiles, orig ceiling cap and chain, imp "Tiffany Studios, NY, 1515-38," 1899–1920 . . . . **7,200.00**

Cocktail, irid gold, sgd "L. C. T. Favrile" **110.00**

Compotes

4⅝" d, 1¾" h, low standard, ftd, irid gold, sgd "L.C.T. Q5294" **150.00**

4¾", floriform, deep silvery blue irid, wide ruffled rim and hemispherical bowl raised on short standard, circular ft, inscribed "L.C. Tiffany Favrile 1529–7426L," 1917 . . . . **700.00**

Desk Set, 7 pc, gilt bronze, Zodiac pattern, lamp with rect gilt bronze pivoting shade, pr of blotter ends, cov inkwell, rect pen tray, cov stamp box, calendar, imp "Tiffany Studios/NY," 1899– 1920 . . . . **1,000.00**

Figure, bronze, cat playing with miniature paperweight ball, sgd **225.00**

Fingerbowls with underplates

5⅞", Queen pattern, amber irid, inscribed "L.C.T.," 1892–1928 . . . . . **200.00**

7¼", paperweight type, waisted wide mouth bowl, dec with stylized deep dusty rose, amber, and green lotus blossoms and leaves, inscribed "1654F and L. C. T. Favrile V796," 1892-1928 . . . . **2,200.00**

Flower Bowl and Frog, 11" d, shallow amber irid bowl dec with green trails and intaglio carved leaves, flower frog of 2 tiers of loops, inscribed "L.C. Tiffany Favrile 8525L," 1917 . . . . **900.00**

Humidor, 7¾", paneled straight caramel sides dec with 2 bands of silvery blue and amber irid lappets, circular gilt bronze domed cov, inner cap cast with Arabesques, inscribed "L.C.T.," inner cap imp "FG81," 1892-1928 . . . . . . **2,000.00**

Inkwells, covered

2½" h, Favrile and bronze, sloping sides, domed cov cast with undulating scrollwork, obverse with rect panel of amber irid mosaic tile, bronze cast cov with amber irid bead, imp "25903," 1900-20 . . . . . **2,000.00**

4½", Doré bronze, Bookmark pattern, octagon shape **400.00**

4¾", bronze, Chinese pattern, hinged cov, imp "Tiffany Studios/NY/1753" **450.00**

8½" l, bronze, crab with hinged back opening to small compartment, holding bucket with hinged shell mounted lid, opening to inkwell fitted with glass liner, imp "Tiffany Studios/NY/29233" and monogramed "Tiffany Glass and Decorating Co." **2,100.00**

Lamps

Aladdin, 14" h, conical shade, baluster base in cased pale lemon yellow glass dec with concentric rows of green scallops and amber irid vertebrate devices, 3 amber irid prunts, inscribed "L.C.T." and "L.C. Tiffany-Favrile," 1899–1920 . . . . **2,200.00**

Bridge, 52½" h, 10" d, domical shade in cased caramel glass dec with radiating bands of amber irid wavy feathers, pivoting between a harp shaped support on slender cylindrical standard, raised on 3 legs ending in spade feet, shade inscribed "L.C.T. Favrile," base imp "Tiffany Studios/NY" **2,100.00**

Floor, 64″ h, 22½″ d, domical leaded glass shade of field of golden tulips against mottled blue-green ground, cylindrical standard of gilt bronze cast with coiling tendrils, dished leaf molded base, 4 petal form feet, finial, shade imp "Tiffany Studios/NY/1548," base imp "Tiffany Studios/NY/379" **23,100.00**

Table

23″ h, 16″ d shade, helmet form shade with allover pattern of nasturtium blossoms on a trellis in mottled shades of yellow, amber, crimson, and salmon, white trellis, mottled green leaves against mottled blue ground, adjustable bronze cast base with 4 gardrooned legs ending in pad feet, shaped quatrefoil foot, bronze finial, shade imp "Tiffany Studios/NY," base imp "Tiffany Studios/NY/S230," 1900–20 . . . . **18,800.00**

26″ h, 18″ d shade, domical shade with drop lower border of radiating panels of mottled green tiles with medial border of mottled amber and green oak leaves and acorns, bronze base with urn form standard cast with leaves, trumpet form lower section continuing to circular foot cast with leaves, bronze finial, shade imp "Tiffany Studios New York 1467," base imp "Tiffany Studios/NY/368," 1900–20. . . . . **10,000.00**

Mirror, 15⅝″, circular, set with irid peacock eyes, pivoting between 2 scrolling supports on shaped integral base, bronze case peacock feathers, set with blue, green, and striated irid camel glass eyes, imp "Tiffany Studios/NY," 1899–1920 . . . . **13,200.00**

Paperweight, 4½″, Favrile, scarab shape, pale amber-blue irid, 1892–1928 . . . . **900.00**

Perfume Vial, 4¾″, bulbous body, expanded cylindrical neck, dec with chocolate brown and lime green stripes, silver lip and attached cap, inscribed "L.C.T. 6111N," 1919 . . . . . **1,100.00**

Pin Tray, 7⅞″, Favrile and bronze, rect, rounded corners, whiplash motifs reserved against amber irid mosaic ground, reeded whiplash borders, imp 23303, imp "L.C.T.," 1900–20 . . . . . **2,530.00**

Plate, 6¼″, pale green glass, 5 evenly spaced peacock eyes, feathers, amber, blue, green, and brown irid, inscribed "L.C.T. Favrile F2770," 1896 **2,550.00**

Punch Cup, 2½″ h, applied handle, brilliant gold, dark green heart shaped leaves, vines. **300.00**

Rose Bowl, 2½″, gold, dec with green leaves, vines, sgd "L.C.Tiffany, Favrile, 4770G" **775.00**

Salt, irid gold, ftd, sgd "L.C.T." **110.00**

Sherbets

3½″ h, Vintage pattern, irid gold, intaglio cut leaves and grapes, inscribed "L.C.T." **225.00**

3¾″, opal, dusty rose outer edges, inscribed "L.C.T. Favrile," 1920. . . . **275.00**

4¾″ d, irid gold, intaglio cutting of grape and leaves band, inscribed "L.C. Tiffany Favrile" **200.00**

Table Screen, 9¾″ h, 16⅝″ l, Favrile and bronze, 4 panels set with leaves of irid blue-green and amber Cypriote glass, pale yellow mottled glass ground, lower striated green geometric panels, early 20th C **2,200.00**

Trivet, 7″, round, set with irid glass with 2 graduated circles, 12 interlocking loops, midnight blue ground, imp "Tiffany Studios/NY/22261," 1892–1928 . . . . **1,450.00**

Vases

2¾″, pyriform, opal body dec at short neck with amber irid striated feathers, edged in lime green, inscribed "L.C.T. Favrile," 1892–1928 . . . . . **1,210.00**

5¼″, Favrile Agate, ovoid, slanting shoulder, thick walled clear glass sides, pale streaked avocado and

Vase, 5½″ h, 6″ d top, conical, white opaque body with white streaks, white opaque base with blue rim, flat top with yellow stretched effect, mkd "1546 L.C. Tiffany, Favrille," orig paper label, $1,125.00.

ochre trailings, cut to clear at waist with band of roundels, int. washed with pale irid, inscribed "L.C.Tiffany Favrile 7006D," 1909 . . . . **7,700.00**
6⅜", pottery, waisted cylindrical, mustard sides molded in medium relief with pendant milkpods, int. glazed in green with ochre drippings, inscribed "LCT," 1904-14 . . . . **330.00**
6¾", enamel on copper, spherical, sides enameled in shades of amber, lavender, and sapphire with allover stylized pattern of poppies and leaves, int. enameled in dusty rose and ochre, inscribed "Louis C. Tiffany/X100" **1,650.00**
7¾", Cypriote glass, double conical form, lobed neck, pitted amber irid sides dec with golden amber irid threading, inscribed "L.C.T. K2460," 1899 . . . . **950.00**
9", irid gold with pink and lavender highlights, large green maple leaf and vine dec, sgd "L. C. Tiffany, Favrile". **1,500.00**
10", bud, trumpet, opal sides dec with amber irid striated feathers, raised circular foot, inscribed "L.C. Tiffany Favrile 5080J". **385.00**
14¼", floriform, ruffled lip, onion form bowl, green striated feathers on opal ground, slender rod standard with medial knop, raised amber irid circular domed foot, amber irid int., inscribed "L.C.T. W5555". **6,100.00**
19¼", floriform, three sided neck, expanded waist, tapering elongated body, pearly opal shading to clear, opal vertical stringing, green feathering, short standard, circular domed foot, inscribed "L.C.T. W7183," 1905. . . . . **3,575.00**

TIFFIN GLASS

History: A. J. Beatty & Sons built a glass manufacturing plant in Tiffin, Ohio, in 1888. On January 1, 1892, the firm joined the U. S. Glass Co. and was known as factory "R". Quality and production at this factory were very high and resulted in fine depression era glass. Beginning in 1916 wares were marked with a paper label. From 1923 to 1936, Tiffin produced a line of black glassware, called Black Satin. The company discontinued operation in 1980.

Reference: Fred Bickenheuser, *Tiffin Glassmasters, Book I,* Glassmasters Publications, 1979; *Tiffin Glassmasters, Book II,* Glassmasters Publications, 1981.

Vase, 5", bulbous, black, red painted poppies and green leaves, $40.00.

Ashtray, 6", picture of Carnegie National Bank, 1902–1928	30.00
Basket, Black Satin	40.00
Candy Dish, cov, 8", pink, floral etching, orig label	35.00
Compotes	
Amberina, satin finish	35.00
Black Satin, 10", hp red poppies on inside	70.00
Lemon, satin finish, 6½" h, ftd	45.00
Tangerine, sq top	40.00
Console Bowl, Amberina	70.00
Finger Bowl, underplate, June Night	22.50
Perfume, 6" h, Black Satin, hp florals, tong applicator	65.00
Plates	
8", June Night	15.00
11", 2 handles, Black Forest	35.00
Rose Bowl, Black Satin, coralene poppies, label "Peacock Products,Minneapolis"	165.00
Stemware	
Champagne, Persian Pheasant	25.00
Cocktail, Flying Nun, green stem, crystal bowl	22.00
Goblet, Canterbury, amber	13.50
Iced Tea, Melissa	17.50
Juice, Rambler Rose	10.00
Liqueur, Athlone	13.50
Parfait, Persian Pheasant	22.00
Wine, June Night	22.50
Tumbler, ftd 6½", Fuchsia, crystal	12.00
Vases	
7", Tangerine, satin finish, pr	65.00
7½", car flower holder, cobalt blue, orig metal holder	175.00
8", Black Satin, coralene poppy dec	50.00
10", Cherokee Rose, bud	20.00

TILES

History: The use of decorated tiles peaked during the latter part of the 19th century. Over one hundred companies in England alone were producing tiles about 1880. By 1890 companies had opened in Belgium, France, Australia, Germany, and the United States.

Tiles were not limited to adorning fireplaces. Many were installed into furniture, such as washstands, hall stands, and folding screens. Since tiles were easily cleaned and, hence, hygenic, they readily were used on the floors and walls of entry halls, hospitals, butcher shops, or any place where sanitation was a concern. Many public buildings and subways also employed tiles to add interest and beauty.

Condition is an important fact in determining price. A cracked, badly scuffed and scratched, or heavily chipped tile has very little value. Slight chipping around the outer edges of a tile is, at times, considered acceptable by collectors, especially if these chips can be covered by a frame.

It is not uncommon for the highly glazed surface of some tiles to have become crazed. Crazing is not considered a deterent as long as it does not detract from the overall appearance of the tile.

References: J. & B. Austwick, *The Decorated Tile*, Pitman House Ltd., 1980; Julian Barnard, *Victorian Ceramic Tiles*, N. Y. Graphic Society Ltd., 1972; Terence A. Lockett, *Collecting Victorian Tiles*, Antique Collectors Club, 1979.

Collectors' Club: Tile & Architectural Ceramics Society, c/o Ironbridge Gorge Museu, Ironbridge, Telford, Shropshire, England TF8 7AW.

Advisor: Pamela A. Luttig.

Newburgh, NY, geometric with central rosette, brown over yellow, 3″ sq, $25.00.

American Encaustic Tile Company, Zanesville, OH

Bat flying across quarter moon, 6″ sq, emb, root beer brown	75.00
Elephant on Drum, 4″ sq, imp, multicolored	45.00
"Fortune And The Boy," 6″ sq, transfer printed, polychrome	75.00
Geometric design, 6″ sq, slightly emb, blue, cream, and mauve	10.00
Head, classical, 4″ sq, emb, banner reading "Dedication of A. E. Tile, April 19, 1892," pale blue	35.00
Heads, pr, classical man and woman, 6″ sq, emb, amber	180.00
"The Lion In Love," 6″ sq, transfer printed, polychrome	85.00
Medieval Man, three tile panel, framed, 6 x 18″, emb, root beer brown	180.00
Rose and Bud, 6″ sq, emb, pale mauve	15.00
Ships and Windmills, delft-style, 6″ sq, transfer printed, blue on white	25.00

Art Nouveau

Floral, 6″ sq, molded, white and yellow on dark green, unmarked	30.00
Flower, stylized leaves, 6″ sq, molded, turquoise and green, cream ground, unmarked	25.00
Flowers, three stylized, 6″ sq, molded, dark green, unmarked	25.00
Flowers, yellow, 6″ sq, molded, interweaving with green leaves on cream ground, artist: Lewis Day, mkd "Pilkington"	50.00
Leaves and Flowers, tube-lined stylized, 6″ sq, orange and green, blue ground, mkd "England"	40.00

J. & J. G. Low, Chelsea, MA

Flowers, 6″ sq, highly emb, deep green	35.00
Head, old man's, 6″ sq, emb, amber	85.00
"President Grant," 6 x 8″, emb, amber	125.00

Mettlach [Villeroy & Boch]

Children, scene, 6″ sq, multicolored transfer	50.00
Dutch scene, four tile panel, orig frame, 6 x 24″, blue on white	200.00

Minton China Works

"Alfred," 6″ sq, transfer printed, black on white, from "Early English History" series by J. Moyrs Smith	45.00
Chinese scene, 6″ sq, transfer printed, blue on white	35.00
"Elfin" on toad stool, 6″ sq, transfer printed, brown on white, from "Early English History" series by J. Moyr Smith	60.00
"Elijah And Samuel," 6″ sq, blue on white, from "Old Testament" series by J. Moyr Smith	30.00

Farmyard scene with sheep, 6″ sq,
transfer printed, brown on white,
sgd W. WISE, dated 1879. . . . . . . 75.00

Lady playing harp, classical, 8″ sq,
transfer printed, blue, yellow, and
brown on white, sgd J. MOYR
SMITH 90.00

Peasant with bag on back, 6″ sq,
transfer printed, brown and cream 85.00

Miscellaneous

Blue Willow, 6″ sq, transfer printed,
blue on white. 45.00

Compass points, four, 6″ sq, depicted
with flowers, woman in center, aesthetic movement design, transfer
printed, brown on cream,
. . . . 35.00

Detroit Skyline, round, emb, brown on
blue, Pewabic, Detroit, MI 65.00

Floral spray, 6″ sq, transfer printed,
polychrome, unmarked 15.00

Flower, tapestry-like design, 6″ sq, polychrome, mkd "Doulton" 125.00

Head, man's, classical, 6″ sq, emb,
amber, sgd Isaac Broome, Trent
Tile Company, Trenton, NJ 150.00

Hedge Hog, 6″ sq, ruby lustre, artist:
Wm. DeMorgan 400.00

Poppy, 8″ sq, hp polychrome, artist
sgd, mkd "Doulton" 200.00

"Spring," 6″ sq, girl surrounded by four
panels of flowers, artist: Kate
Greenaway, transfer printed, brown
on cream, R. T. Boote 55.00

Wild Rose, 6″ sq, transfer printed, polychrome and brown, unmarked 15.00

Mosaic Tile Company, Zanesville, OH

Abraham Lincoln, head, paperweight,
hexagonal, emb, white on blue . . . 20.00

Betsy Ross sewing flag, 6″ sq,
polychrome 20.00

"Where Are You Going My Pretty
Maid?" 6″ sq, transfer printed,
polychrome 85.00

Owens Pottery, Zanesville, OH

Girl feeding chickens, 6″ sq, hp
polychrome 85.00

Girl with hoop, 6″ sq, hp polychrome 85.00

U. S. Encaustic Tile Works, Indianapolis,
IN

"Dawn," panel, 6 x 18″, depicts
woman, emb, green 175.00

Flowers, 6″ sq, emb, beige 8.00

Girl with bundle of sticks, 6″ sq, emb,
amber 85.00

Wedgwood

Calendar, 1908, brown on white 45.00

Dog's face, 6″ sq, transfer printed,
black on white 70.00

"March," 6″ sq, boy and girl against
the wind, transfer printed, poly-
chrome 125.00

"May," 6″ sq, lady and girl, artist: Kate

Greenaway, transfer printed, blue
on white 85.00

"November," 8″ sq, boy by seashore,
transfer printed, brown on white . . 125.00

TINWARE

History: Beginning in the 1700s many utilitarian household objects were made of tin. Tin is nontoxic, so it can be used for storing food, rust resistant, and fairly durable. It often was plated to iron to provide strength. Because it was cheap, tinware and tin plated wares were in the price range of most people.

An early center of tinware manufacture in the United States was Berlin, Connecticut. Almost every small town and hamlet has its own tinsmith, tinner, or whitesmith. Tinsmiths used patterns from which to make items. They cut out the pieces, hammered and shaped them, and soldered the parts. If a piece was used with heat, a copper bottom was added because of the low melting point of tin. The Industrial Revolution brought about machine made, mass produced tinware pieces. The hand made era ended by the late 19th century.

This category is a catchall for tin objects which do not fit into other categories in our book.

Additional Listings: Advertising, Kitchen Collectibles, Lanterns, Lamps and Lighting, and Tinware: Decorated.

Batter Bucket, 12″, capped spout 35.00

Bird Cage, 29″ h, cylindrical shape, cylindrical bars 135.00

Dipper, 12½″ l, 6″ d, bowl, $38.00.

Boxes, covered

8½" l, 5½" h, rect, black paint, hinged lid, hasp, c1880	**125.00**
9" l, 5½" h, hanging type, crimped and molded edge on black plate	**135.00**
10½" l, 6½" h, oval, strap handle. . .	**60.00**
11½" l, 5½" h, oval, oak graining, hinged lid, hasp	**55.00**
Breadboard, 22½ x 24", tin covered wood, orig paper labels	**60.00**
Broiling Rack, for small game, 9½ x 12", 6 wire hooks, drip pan with handle on back.	**85.00**
Bucket, cov, 6" h, 4" d, bail handle . . .	**12.00**
Burglar Lamp, 7½", black paint, clear lens, font and kerosene burner.	**35.00**
Cake Pan, 9½ x 11", heart shape	**45.00**
Candle Box, hanging, 10½", cylindrical, hinged lid, shield shape back	**275.00**
Candle Lantern, 14" glass on 3 sides, punched leaf design on 4th side, hinged door below ear handle	**140.00**

Candle Molds

4-tube, 10⅝" h	**90.00**
6-tube, 10", with handle.	**60.00**
8-tube, 10½", handle at top	**65.00**
10-tube, 10¾".	**85.00**
Candle Sconce, 14" h, high reflector back with crimped inverted circles on top.	**165.00**
Candle Snuffer, 2¼" h, conical	**15.00**
Candlestick, 4¼", hogscraper	**85.00**
Coffee Pot, cov, 12", side spout	**55.00**
Collander, 14¾" d	**20.00**
Comb Case, 9" h, 8¾" w, emb design, diamond shape mirror, "Comb & Brush"	**30.00**
Creamer, cov, 3¾" side spout	**15.00**
Grater, 14" l, primitive, wood frame . . .	**90.00**
Lunch Box, 22" l, oval, cylindrical, compartments, tin cup on end	**42.00**
Matchbox, hanging, 4¾" l, green paint	**22.00**
Pie Dough Cutter, 10" d, scalloped edge, mkd Kreamer	**35.00**
Pitcher, water, 9" h, wide spout, strap handle and bail handle	**85.00**
Sconce, 9" h, 6½" w, 2 brass burners with tublular spouts and snuffer caps, built in font, shadowbox reflector with crimp hood	**125.00**
Scoop, 12¼" l, turned wooden handle	**45.00**
Tinder Box, 4½" d, 2" h, candle socket on top, c1890	**275.00**
Torch, hanging, 9½" h plus hanging bale, 6 spouts around cylindrical font	**75.00**

TINWARE: DECORATED

History: Decorating sheet iron, tin, and tin coated sheet iron dates back to the mid-18th century. The Welsh called the practice pontipool, the French To'le Peinte. In America the center for tin decorated ware in the late 1700s was Berlin, Connecticut.

Several styles of decorating techniques were used: painting, japanning, and stenciling. Designs were done by both professionals and itinerants. English and Oriental motifs strongly influenced both form and designs.

A special type of decoration was the punch work on unpainted tin practiced by the Pennsylvania tinsmiths. Forms included cookie cutters, coffee pots, spice boxes, grease lamps, and ash covers.

Document Box, 4 x 3 x 4½", dome lid, blackground, white band trim with red flowers and green leaves, $195.00.

Bread Tray, 12¾", rect, flaring sides, dark brown, flowers and leaves, yellow, red, and green, 19th C	**450.00**
Cache Pot, 5½", decoupage dec	**200.00**
Candle Box, hanging, 14" l, cylindrical, dark brown, hinged cov, 2 attached hanging brackets, early 19th C	**325.00**
Coffee Pot, 12", tapering shape on domed foot, hinged lid, brass finial, strap handle, flowers in repousse dec, 19th C	**725.00**
Cup, 2⅞" d, 1¾" h, pink, stenciled hearts and flowers design, "My Girl".	**45.00**
Deed Box, 6⅞", small, dome top, brown japanning, floral dec, red, yellow, and green	**85.00**
Document Box, 8½" l, 4½", h, dome hinged lid, dark brown, bands of fruit and leaves, red, yellow, and green, 19th C	**275.00**
Food Warmer, 8¼", brown japanning, yellow striping, orig whale oil burner and font	**90.00**
Inkwell, 3⅛" d, 1⅞" h, brass trim, white porcelain insert, red with polychrome floral dec, French	**75.00**
Lard Lamps, pr, 14¾" h, 24½" w, red paint, gilded roses and floral dec, removeable front with double arms of burners made to accept flat wicks, reservoir bases have long tubular trough to catch drips	**400.00**

Letter Set, 5 pcs, floral and bird dec . . **300.00**
Snuff Box, 2⅜" d, 1¾" h, round, black, cov has landscape scene with boy fishing **75.00**
Sugar Shaker, 3¼", brown japanning, yellow and green dec **85.00**
Tea Caddy, 5" h, red, yellow banding, black striping, primitive portrait of woman, green dress, white collar, beads in hair, holding yellow bird, black pine tree **200.00**
Teapot, 8¾", brown, floral dec on both sides, red, yellow, and green **325.00**
Tobacco Box, 5", brown japanning, stenciled yellow label, "Famous Cake Box Mixture" **65.00**
Trays
  8¾", octagonal, black, crystallized gold center, white border with red and green leaves **400.00**
  24½" l, rect, black, painted masted schooner with American flags, multicolored, stenciled oak leaves and fruit **475.00**
Urns, cov, pr, 12¾", oval, black, gilt chinoiserie scenes, lion mask and ring handles, spire cov, acorn finial, raised oval bases, mid 19th C **200.00**
Vases, pr, 8½", rect, flared, Empire style, red, transfer printed, black with neoromantic frieze, paw feet, platform bases, 19th C **550.00**

TOBACCO CUTTERS

History: Before pre-packaging, tobacco was delivered to merchants in bulk form. Tobacco cutters were used to cut the tobacco into desired sizes.

Brass Gear, Cl, mkd, c1880, 12 x 6 x 7¾" **200.00**
Climax Plug, Cl **55.00**
Drummond Tobacco Co **70.00**
Little Imp **50.00**
Lorillard's Chew Climax Plug, red tin tag, brass cut piece, made by Penn Hardware Co, Reading, PA, 17¼" l **100.00**
Mule, R. J. B. Tobacco Co **50.00**
S. A. Pace Grocery Co, Corsican, TX . . **130.00**

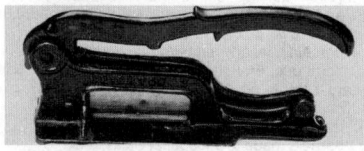

Brighton, cast iron, $35.00.

Shield Shape, wrought iron, wood base, 14" l **50.00**
Standard **55.00**
Superior **50.00**
Wood Base, Cl cutter, 6¼ x 7¼ x 10 ½" **45.00**
Wood Base and Handle, brass ferrule, swivel shredder, hand forged blade . **35.00**

TOBACCO JARS

History: A tobacco jar is a container for storing tobacco. Tobacco humidors were made of various materials and in many shapes, including figurals. The earliest jars date to the early 17th century. However, most examples in today's market were made in the late 19th or early 20th century.

Dog's head, 5⅝" h, terrier, matte finish, mkd "N588," stamped blue "R" in diamond, $150.00.

Bisque
  4¾" h, 4" d, figural, devil, smiling, red, black, and yellow **120.00**
  4⅞" h, 3½" d, Negro lady's head, white, cream, and green bandana tied around head **90.00**
Brass, 5½", cylindrical, button finial, tin int., early 19th C **45.00**
Chalkware, 12", figural, Negro sitting on stump **150.00**
Lead, 6", octagonal, Negro's head finial, c1820 . . . . **75.00**
Lenox, 6½", blue, emb, shoulder outlined in silver, green wreath mark . . . **115.00**
Majolica
  8", head of bearded seaman, Cape Cod hat on lid, duffle bag and robe in lower half **160.00**

Monk, bust, smiling, cigarette in mouth, smoke curling, pink and blue, Art Nouveau, German. **100.00**

Pewter, 6½″, cylindrical, button finial, c1760. . . . . **75.00**

Porcelain, 5½″, figural, baby's head, bonnet, pacifier in mouth **95.00**

Pottery

5¾″ h, 4″ d, Negro lady's head, blue turbin, imp B.R. & # on base **120.00**

8″ h, 7⅜″ d, brown tree trunk, branch handles, branch finial, cream trim and panel, "A Pipe Let's Take for Old Times' Sake", L.F.C. 1920 . . . **125.00**

Roseville, Dutch boy and girl, Compliments of Hotel Olympia, Boston, MA. **200.00**

TOBY JUGS

History: A toby jug is a drinking vessel usually depicting a full-figured, robust, genial drinking man. They originated in England in the late 18th century. The term "Toby" probably related to the character Uncle Toby from *Tristam Shandy* by Laurence Sterne.

Within the last 100 years or more, tobies have been reproduced copiously by many potteries in the United States and England.

Additional Listings: Royal Doulton.

Chelsea, 4″, seated, wart on nose, gray coat, blue breeches. **150.00**

Copeland & Spode, 8½″, Winston Churchill, white glaze. **110.00**

Earthenware, 11½″, seated, brown hat, olive coat, blue waistcoat, ochre breeches, late 18th C **325.00**

English

3½″, Nevil Chamberlain, umbrella forms handle, imp Chamberlain, black stamp "Handpainted, made in England, English Ware, Lancaster Ltd" **45.00**

11¾″, seated on trunk, blue suit, flowered waistcoat, late 18th C **175.00**

Faience

10¼″, standing, plum hat, long blue coat, early 19th C **225.00**

15″, standing, brown coat, yellow waistcoat, purple trousers and tie, late 18th C **190.00**

Lenox, 10″, George Washington **325.00**

Rockingham Glaze, 8¾″, Ale Drinker . . **190.00**

Royal Worcester, 4½″, miniature, full figure, girl clutching black umbrella in one hand, yellow basket in other, black bonnet, blue dress, red and white poka-dot apron, mkd, c1930 . . **80.00**

Staffordshire

9″, King of Clubs, white and gilt **135.00**

10″, spotted face, brown frock coat,

Old Staffo Toby, Shorter & Son, Ltd., Staffordshire, 5⅜″, $35.00.

black hat, holding jug and clay pipe, early 19th C **125.00**

Wedgwood, 7″ h, 10″ d, full figure, mustache, light brown coat, brown hat, holds lantern aloft, mkd Wedgwood & Co. Ltd./England. **60.00**

Whieldon, 9¾″, creamware, seated, holding foaming jug, brown streaked brown tricorn and shoes, mottled brown coat, cream breeches, green waistcoat, c1780. . . . . **935.00**

Yorkshire, 10″, seated, holding jug and goblet, blue coat, copper lustre on hat, waistcoat and breeches, c1830 . . . . **360.00**

TOOLS

History: Before the advent of assembly line and mass production, practically everything required for living was handmade at home or by a local tradesman or craftsman. The cooper, the blacksmith, the cabinet maker, and the carpenter all had their special tools.

Early examples of these hand tools are collected for their workmanship, ingenuity, place of manufacture, or design. Modern day craftsman often search out old hand tools to use to authentically recreate the manufacture of an object.

References: Kathryn McNerney, *Antique Tools, Our American Heritage,* Collector Books, 1979; R. A. Salaman, *Dictionary of Tools,* Charles Schribner's Sons, 1974.

Collectors' Club: Early American Industries Association, P. O. Box 2128, Empire State Plaza Station, Albany, NY 12220. *The Chronicle* (monthly).

Museum: Shelburne Museum, Shelburne, VT

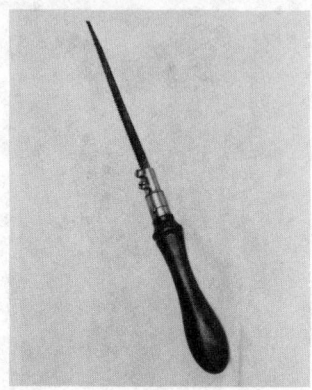

Pad saw (keyhole), saw tip tooth, British 15½″ l, $30.00.

Anvil, mkd "Fisher, Trenton"	**100.00**
Bench Vise, harness maker's, foot treadle, leather strap, 38″ h	**175.00**
Braces	
Chairmaker's	**160.00**
Ultimatium, mkd "William M. Marples"	**475.00**
Broadaxe, PA, orig handle	**100.00**
Calipers, double, wrought iron, twisted handle, 17″ l	**75.00**
Caulking Hammer, shipwright, 13 x 13″	**45.00**
Chisel, corner, 2 cutting edges, 18th C	**75.00**
Draw Gauge, leather, mkd "Francis & Ward"	**75.00**
Drill, brass, eggbeater type	**250.00**
Engraver's circle cutter, mkd "Mulbeck"	**250.00**
Hammer, brass head	**75.00**
Jack, Connestoga wagon, wrought iron, simple tooling, mkd "#592", dated 1802, 21″ h	**165.00**
Jigsaw, mounted on wooden base, mkd "Shipman & Binder"	**95.00**
Level, spirit, mkd "Daniel M. Lyon, Newark," mid 1800s	**35.00**
Molder, complex, mkd "J. Searing" . . .	**45.00**
Mortise Gauge, rosewood and brass, mkd "Daniel M. Lyon, Newark"	**40.00**
Planes	
Pill box	**450.00**
Plow	
Cast iron, scissor type fence, mkd "Morris," patented	**700.00**
Wooden, 2 turned handles, primitive relief carving of foliage scrolls, chip carved edge, scene of building, trees, dated 1831, 11″ l . . .	**185.00**

Rule, wooden, folding, brass trim, sliding brass caliper, mkd "Stanley", 12″ . . .	**20.00**
Saws	
Buck, mortised wooden frame, 15½″ l	**40.00**
Fret, wooden frame, brass trim, iron fittings, 13″ l, 6″ blade	**75.00**
Scythe, hay cutting, mortised wooden rack, orig yellow paint, 46″ l	**65.00**
Wheel measure, cast iron, mkd "Wiley & Russell Mfg Co., Greenfield, MA", 12″ l	**35.00**

TOOTHPICK HOLDERS

History: Toothpick holders, indispensible table accessories of the Victorian era, are small containers used to hold toothpicks.

They were made in a wide range of materials: china (bisque and porcelain), glass (art, blown, cut, opalescent, pattern, etc.), and metals, especially silver plate. Makers include both American and European firms.

Toothpick holders were used as souvenir items by applying decals or transfers. The same blank may contain several different location labels.

References: William Heacock, *Encyclopedia Of Victorian Colored Pattern Glass, Book I, Toothpick Holders From A To Z,* Antique Publications, 1981; William Heacock, *1,000 Toothpick Holders: A Collector's Guide,* Antique Publications, 1977.

Collectors' Club: National Toothpick Collector's Society, P. O. Box 246, Sawyer, MI 49125. Subscription: $8.00.

Additional Listings: See *Warman's Americana & Collectibles* for more examples.

Advisor: Judy Knauer.

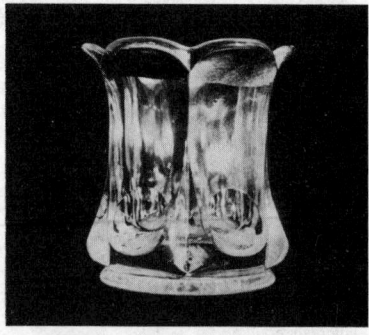

Placid Thumbprint, New Martinsville, clear with gold band, $34.00.

China
  Germany, swirled, wide base, pink
    roses 22.00
  Nippon, pedestal, floral design, green
    M in wreath mark. 25.00
  Royal Bayreuth, rose tapestry, 2 han-
    dled, ftd 275.00
Glass
  Burmese
    Fig mold, crimped top, satin finish,
      blue enameled flowers 400.00
    Tricorn, DQ, glossy finish 375.00
  Consolidated Lamp & Glass, Guttate
    Blue Opaque 85.00
    Pink Opaque 65.00
  Cut, sq, large uncut sq base 55.00
  Duncan, Zipper Slash
    Amber stained 38.00
    Ruby stained 30.00
  Fostoria, Carmen, clear 40.00
  Heisey
    Fancy Loop, clear 55.00
    Prince of Wales Plumes
      Clear, gold 150.00
      Clear, ruby stained 225.00
    Winged Scroll, ivorina verde (cus-
      tard), good dec. 175.00
  Milk
    Georgia Gem, green, opaque 55.00
    Parrot and Top Hat, worn point . . . 30.00
    Ribbed Base, painted design. 25.00
    Serpent, coiling, painted grass . . . 30.00
  New Martinsville, Placid Thumbprint,
    clear, gold highlights 34.00
  Opalescent
    Diamond Spearpoint, light blue . . . 75.00
    Jeweled Heart, light blue 220.00
  Pattern
    Duchess
      Clear, gold 70.00
      Green, gold 135.00
    Jefferson Optic (Tiny Optic), ame-
      thyst, enameled design 45.00
    Kansas, clear. 40.00
    Paneled 44, pedestal, handled,
      clear, silver trim 40.00
    Twisted Hobnail, clear 20.00
    York Herringbone (Scalloped Swirl),
      ruby stained, no souvenir mes-
      sage 45.00
  Pomona, second grind, crimped top,
    applied rigaree. 150.00
  Saddle Over Barrel, clear, blue, or
    amber 35.00
  Silver Plated, Crying Baby, Tufts, ped-
    estal. 125.00

TORTOISE SHELL ITEMS

History: For many years amber and mottled colored tortoise shell has been used in the manufacture of small items such as boxes, combs, dresser
sets, and trinkets.

Note: Anyone dealing in the sale of tortoise shell
objects should be familiar with the Endangered
Species Act and Amendment in its entirety. As of
November, 1978, antique tortoise shell objects can
be legally imported and sold with some restrictions.

Pin, 1½" l, $20.00.

Boxes, covered
  2", pearl and ivory dec, SS hinges and
    catch 60.00
  3" d, 1½" h, heart shape, SS trim. . . 300.00
  3" d, ivory portrait on cov, lady in red
    fur-trimmed dress, gold plated
    frame 175.00
Bracelet, 3" d, silver inlay 28.00
Card Cases
  4 x 2¾", nacreous shell inlay design
    of tulips, flowers, and butterfly, plate
    with initials "GEP," red velvet lining,
    19th C 175.00
  4 x 3", MOP floral design. 50.00
Cigarette Case, 4½" l, 2¾" w, enamel
  dec 300.00
Frame, 7½ x 6½" brass inlay dec 175.00
Mantilla Comb, large, hand carved. . . . 100.00
Moustache Comb, 4", SS case 50.00
Planter, 6" h 75.00
Tea Caddy, 7½", hinged top with ivory
  dec, divided int., flat bun feet, George
  III, c 1800. 600.00
Watch Chain, 14" l, fob and locket,
  c1840–60 . . . . 170.00

TOYS

History: In America the first cast iron toys began
to appear shortly after the Civil War. Leading 19th
century manufacturers include Hubley, Dent, Kenton, and Schoenhut. In the first decades of the 20th
century, Arcade, Buddy L, Marx, and Tootsietoy
joined the earlier firms. Wooden toys were made
by George Brown and other manufacturers who did
not sign or label their work.

In Europe, Nürnberg, Germany, was the center
for the toy industry from the late 18th through the
mid 20th century. Companies such as Lehman and
Marklin produced high quality toys.

Several auction houses, including Lloyd Ralston Toys and Phillips, have speciality auctions consisting entirely of toys. Christie's 1984 auction of the Raggedy Ann Antique Doll and Toy Museum of Flemington, New Jersey, was a landmark sale.

Every toy is collectible. The key is the condition and working order if mechanical. Examples listed are considered to be in good to very good condition to mint condition unless otherwise specified.

References: Jurgen and Marianne Cieslik, *Lehmann Toys*, New Cavendish Books, 1982; Ernest & Ida Long, *Dictionary of Toys Sold in America*, privately printed, two volumes; David Longest, *Character Toys and Collectibles*, Collector Books, 1984; Albert W. McCollough, *The Complete Book of Buddy "L" Toys: A Greenberg Guide*, I. Greenberg Publishing Co., 1982; Richard O'Brien, *Collecting Toys: A Collectors Identification and Value Guide*, Books Americana, 1984, 4th edition; Martyn L. Schorr, *The Guide To Mechanical Toy Collecting*, Performance Media, 1979; James Wieland and Dr. Edward Force, *Tootsie Toys, World's First Die Cast Models*, Motorbooks International, 1980; Blair Whitton, *The Knopf Collector's Guide to Amerian Toys*, Alfred A. Knopf, 1984.

Periodicals: *The Antique Toy World*, 3941 Belle Plaine, Chicago, IL 60618. Subscription: $15.00; *Professor Pug Frog's Newsletter*, 3 Hillside Avenue, Peabody, MA 01960.

Museums: American Museum of Automobile Miniatures, Andover, MA; Museum of the City of New York, New York, NY; Perelman Antique Toy Museum, Philadelphia, PA; Smithsonian Institution, Washington, D.C.; Margaret Woodbury Strong Museum, Rochester, NY; Toy Museum of Atlanta, Atlanta, GA.

Additional Listings: Disneyana and Schoenhut. Also see *Warman's Americana & Collectibles* for more examples.

Arcade, Freeport, IL, 1893–1946
Andy Gump In His 348 Auto, painted, nickel plated Cl, 17"..........	**325.00**
Avery Tractor, 4¾", c1920.........	**150.00**
Caterpillar Tractor, steel tracks, diesel, 8"........................	**325.00**
City Ambulance, 6", c1920........	**165.00**
Coupe, painted Cl, red, rumble seat, 5"...........................	**85.00**
Fire Apparatus Truck, Mack, 21" ...	**400.00**
Ford Coupe, rumble seat, No. 116 ..	**100.00**
Greyhound Lines GMC, sightseeing bus, painted Cl, 10"...........	**80.00**
Ice Truck, 6½"...................	**175.00**
International Harvester dump truck, c1929....................	**245.00**
Model A, painted Cl, gray and black, 8½"......................	**400.00**
Sedan, 2 door, painted Cl, green, 4".	**75.00**

Bing
Garage, 2 car, litho tin, 2 clockwork cars, 8"...................	**250.00**
Ocean Liner, mechanical, litho tin, 8"	**175.00**
Touring Car, litho tin clockwork, blue-gray, 2 seater with driver, 12½", c1915................	**825.00**

Bliss, Rhode Island, c1900
Ocean Liner, *Uncle Sam*, litho on cardboard, 31" l..............	**1,800.00**
Piano, upright, mahogany stained, 12 keys, gilt painted columnar legs, litho scene above keyboard, 14 x 10"......................	**375.00**

Browers, American, 1873; Automatic Dancer, carved wood, black man dancing in front of litho paper wood cabin, clockwork, patented Sept. 23, 1873, 9"................. **2,550.00**

Brown, George, American, c1870
Equestrienne Balancing, painted tin, lady and horse attached to counter weight, 15".................	**6,000.00**
Fire Pumper, "Atlantic," painted, stenciled tin, Cl, restored, 7¼"......	**350.00**
Spring Wagon, painted tin, Cl wheels, horses and wagon, 9"..........	**850.00**

Buddy L, steam shovel, $265.00.

Buddy L, American, 1921–Present
Cement Mixer, painted pressed steel	**325.00**
Coupe..........................	**750.00**
Greyhound Bus.................	**100.00**
Model T dump truck, painted pressed steel, orig labels, 11"...........	**600.00**
Pickup Truck...................	**750.00**
Pile Driver, painted pressed steel, repainted, 18½" l..............	**450.00**
Station Wagon, #371...........	**325.00**
Van, deluxe trailer, #366.........	**350.00**
Wrigley's Truck, painted pressed steel, orig decal, 23½".........	**625.00**

Carette, German, c1910
Landaulette, litho tin clockwork, cream, blue trim, blue roof, 9"....	**1,550.00**
Limo, #51, 4 figures...........	**3,500.00**
Sedan, 14"....................	**2,200.00**
Steam Launch, painted tin, white and red hull, tin canopy over steam engine, 3 blade propeller, anchor,	

composition figure, tin flag, 14″ l,
c1911 .... **1,000.00**

Chein, J., Harrison, NJ, c1930
Clown with punching bag, litho tin, cel-
luloid, windup, 8″ **100.00**
Dump Truck, litho tin, mechanical,
8½″ **90.00**
Roller Coaster, litho tin windup, 20″ . **100.00**
Ski Boy, litho tin windup, orig. box,
5½″ **75.00**
Skier, litho tin windup, 6″ **75.00**

Cuzner, J., American, trotter, painted tin
clockwork, man seated in 4 wheeled
cart, beige painted horse, 7″ l, patent
March 7, 1871 .... **3,300.00**

Distler, German
Firehouse and ladder truck, litho tin
clockwork, 11¾″ **725.00**
Roadster, painted tin clockwork, orange fenders, cream chasis, 9½″,
c1940 .... **250.00**

Fleischmann, German
Ocean Liner, painted tin clockwork, 3
blade propeller, black and red hull,
white superstructure, 2 flags, 2 lifeboats, detachable mask, orig box,
13½″ **775.00**
Ocean Liner, painted tin, key wound,
white, blue, and red, deck details include twin smokestacks, life boats
on upper deck, 16″ **675.00**
Sausage Grinder, litho tin, steam attachment, plastic figure, MIB, 5″ . . **75.00**

Gendron Wheel Co., Toledo, Ohio
Fire Truck, ladder wagon, rubber
tipped metal wheels, wooden lad-
ders, red paint, black and yellow
trim, labeled "Gendron", 60″ l. . . . **950.00**
Pedal Cars
"Flyer-Toledo," sheet metal and
wood, orig red paint, black and
yellow trim, 40″ l, steering needs
work **325.00**
"Gendron," sheet metal and wood,
orig blue paint, yellow striping,
orig decal, 40″ l **1,100.00**

Gong Bell Co., American
Clown holding hoop for jumping dog,
No. 44, 12½″............... **3,100.00**
Clown riding fish, Cl, 6½″ **1,400.00**
Two Coons, black man entering hol-
low log, raccoon entering other end,
9″ l, c1880 .... **3,300.00**
Wild Mule Jack, Cl, 8″ **400.00**

Gunthermann, Bonzo on tricycle, litho tin
clockwork, 6¾″ **400.00**

Hitt, Oscar, "Hiway Henry," litho tin, key
wind, jalopy, red, yellow, and brown,
shinged dog house forms engine,
clothesline suspended from roof, old
man and woman seated, c1920 . . . . **850.00**

Hubley, Lancaster, Pennsylvania, 1894–
1965.

Bell Telephone Truck, painted Cl,
white rubber tires, 8″ **200.00**
Brougham, Cl and chrome, horse and
driver, 16″.................. **500.00**
Car Transport, painted Cl, red, 2 cars,
10″...................... **200.00**
Coal Dump Truck, Cl, 16″ **1,000.00**
Eagle Milk Wagon, 12″ **300.00**
Plantation Wagon, painted Cl, re-
painted, 14½″ **100.00**
Pumper, painted, Cl, 15″ **175.00**
Sleigh, 2 horse, painted and nickel
plated Cl, 15″ **425.00**
Trotter, Cl, horse and driver, 8¾″,
c1900..................... **250.00**
Yellow Cab, painted and nickel plated
Cl, rubber tires, 7½″........... **150.00**

Ives, Bridgeport, CT
Chinaman, mechanical walking man,
wood, pot metal, hair, cloth dressed, clockwork, Hotchkiss Pat.
1870..................... **2,400.00**
General Butler, mechanical walking
man, wood, pot metal, hair, cloth
dressed, clockwork, Hotchkiss
Patent.................... **2,500.00**
Hippodrome Chariot, painted tin and
brass, Cl, cloth dressed wooden
body, painted brass molded face,
clockwork, 16″............... **17,000.00**
Horse and Buggy, dressed driver, mechanical, painted tin with painted
floral dec, Cl wheels, brass hands,
molded brass face, cloth dressed,
clockwork, 1 iron leg missing,
17″ l..................... **6,000.00**
Pull Toy, walking horse, mounted on
3 wheels, orig straw tail, 6½″ l . . . **1,100.00**
Uncle Tom, mechanical walking man,
wood, pot metal, hair, cloth dressed,
clockwork, Hotchkiss patent, orig
box...................... **3,500.00**

Kenton, Kenton, OH
Chariot, Cl, 3 horses, lady driver, 10″. **450.00**
City Truck, Cl and tin, 20″ **1,000.00**
Ice Wagon, painted Cl, no driver,
11″...................... **200.00**
Jaeger Cement Mixer, painted Cl and
nickel plated Cl, 6½″ l **125.00**
Milk Wagon, horse drawn, painted Cl,
12½″ **85.00**
Overland Circus Bandwagon, painted
Cl, 15½″.................. **350.00**
Overland Circus Wagon, painted Cl,
pressed steel, polar bear, 14″. . . . **450.00**
Ox Cart, painted Cl, 11″........... **450.00**
Pumper, horse drawn, painted Cl,
13″...................... **100.00**

Kingsbury, Keene, NH
Chrysler Airflow, painted pressed steel
clockwork, 14″............... **175.00**
Hudson Telephone, 13½″ **275.00**
New York Greyhound Bus, 18″..... **225.00**

Rumble Seat Roadster, electric lights,
12½″ 250.00

Lehmann, Nürnberg, Germany
Anxious Bride Nanni, litho tin clock-
work, orig clothing and handker-
chief, 9″, c1910 . . . . 1,450.00
Auto Bus, tin windup, 8″ 500.00
Balking Mule, litho tin clockwork,
5½″ 175.00
Beetle, litho tin windup, 4″ 100.00
Berolina Touring Car, litho tin, orig
cloth convertible top, 6½″, c1914 . 1,550.00
Bucking Broncho, No. 625, litho tin
base, painted clockwork, 7″,
c1910 . . . . 400.00
Dancing Sailor, No. 535, painted tin,
orig clothing and box, 7½″, c1910 775.00
Express, mechanical, litho tin, 6″ . . . 200.00
New Century Cycle, painted tin litho
clockwork, 5″. 345.00
Nina The Cat, chasing mouse, painted
tin clockwork, 10½″ 525.00
Quack-Quack, duck and cart, tin
windup, 7½″ 250.00
Zulu, ostrish cart with driver, tin
windup, 7¼″ 350.00

Marklin, German
Battleship, *Kurfrust Friedrick Wilhelm*
type, tin, hull painted gray and brick
red, decks complete outfitted,
clockwork, repainted, 34½″, c1904 6,750.00
Cruiser, *Brooklyn*, painted tin, hull
painted gray and black with red
keel, deck outfitted, orig wheeled
base, 28″ l, c1904 . . . . 10,000.00
Doll Carriage, painted tin, cream and
gold, 9¼″, c1910 . . . . 725.00
Doll Stroller, painted tin, cream and
yellow, 6″, c1910 . . . . 825.00
Ocean Liner, *Lusitania*, painted tin,
electric, hull painted black and brick
red, decks outfitted, red flag with
rampant lion, orig wheeled base, 2
lead seamen and passengers,
stamped mark on rudder, 37½″ l,
c1908 . . . . 28,600.00
Ocean Liner, painted tin, red, black,
and white, deck with 4 lifeboats,
bridge, 3 deck houses, masts and
funnels, clockwork, mkd on rudder,
15″ l, c1910. . . . . 1,540.00

Marx, American, 1921–Present
Amos & Andy Fresh Air Taxi, painted
tin, key wound, 8″ 425.00
Busy Bridge, litho tin windup 24″ . . . 250.00
Charlie McCarthy Car, litho tin windup,
8″. 350.00
Dogwood The Driver, litho tin windup,
orig box, 8″ 800.00
Donald Duck Duet, litho tin windup,
orig box, 10¼″. 350.00
Joe Penner & His Duck Goo-Goo, litho
tin windup, orig box, 8″. 275.00

**Buffalo Toys, American, Silver Dash, sil-
ver body, red wheels, 2 yellow figures,
black hats, litho tin windup, Pat 1-20-25,
12″ l, $235.00.**

Moon Mullins & Kayo Handcar, litho
tin windup, orig box, 6″. 500.00
Mortimer Snerd Car, litho tin windup,
8″. 300.00
Popeye The Pilot, litho tin windup, 8″
wingspan. 165.00
Porky Pig, litho tin windup, 8″. 165.00
Tricky Taxi, litho tin windup, 4½″ . . . 100.00
Uncle Wiggily's Car, litho tin windup,
orig box, 8″ 350.00
Mignot, France, firefighting set, painted
tin, horse drawn pumper, ladder, barrel
cart and firemen, orig box, c1900 . . . 1,250.00
Pratt & Letchworth, American
Dray, painted Cl and wood, no driver,
one wheel replaced, 10″. 100.00
Hanson Cab, Cl, yellow and black,
brown horse, 12″, c1880 . . . . 360.00
Sulky, Cl, orange, blue, black, horse
and driver, 12″, c1880 . . . . 950.00
Surrey, painted Cl and pressed steel,
wheel under horse missing, re-
painted, 15″. 250.00
Schuco, Germany
Boy Scout playing violin, tin windup . 95.00
Clown violinist, tin and cloth, 4½″. . . 75.00
Clown with suitcase, litho tin and cloth
windup, 4½″ 80.00
Donald Duck, litho tin windup, orig blue
felt sailor shirt and hat, 6″ 400.00
Strauss, Ferdinand, Corp, New York City,
20th C
Bus, double decker, litho tin windup . 355.00
Ham & Sam, The Minstrel Team, litho
tin windup, 5½″ 300.00
Mailplane, painted tin windup, red and
blue, 12″. 125.00
Play Golf, litho tin, 12″. 125.00
Santee (sic.) Claus, litho tin windup,
11″. 425.00
Tootsie Toys, American
Auto Transport, 4 Buicks, 1922 . . . . 150.00
Bluebird I, Daytona record car, 1927 35.00

Buick Coupe	30.00
Cadillac Sedan, 1926	45.00
Graham Wrecker, 1932	40.00
Grocery Delivery Van, 1921	65.00
Laundry Delivery Van, 1921	45.00
Mack Searchlight Truck, 1922	40.00
Oldsmobile Roadster	40.00
Steamroller, c1931	50.00

Unique Art

Bombo, litho tin windup, orig box, 9½″	50.00
GI Joe & His K-9 Pups, litho tin windup, orig box, 9″	145.00
Kiddy Cyclist, litho tin, 9″	90.00
Lincoln Tunnel, litho tin windup, 24″	100.00
Rodoe Joe, litho tin windup, 8″	125.00
Yipee-I-Aaay, litho tin windup, orig box, 7½″	100.00

Unknown Makers

Cat wheeling mouse in stroller, painted tin clockwork, orig box, 6½″, c1910, Japanese	825.00
Doll's swimming pool, hand enameled circular pool, central clockwork mechanism driving concealed paddles, rect base with pay booth, changing rooms, steps to entrance, drain hole to one side, 17½″ l, c1900, German	900.00
Ferris Wheel, painted tin clockwork, 6 gondolas, litho tin passengers, 14½″, c1915, German	200.00
Keg, wooden, alphabet scroll printed on blue cloth tape, red key with black trim, 3¼″, American	200.00
Louis Armstrong, litho tin clockwork, holding plastic trumpet, 10″, Japanese	175.00
Omnibus, litho tin, cream and green, orig box, mkd "J de P", 10¼″, c1930, French	550.00
Phaeton, open, horsedrawn, tin, simulated lattice dec, detailed decal carpet, slender spoke wheels, central front lamp, 28″ l, c1890, German	3,000.00

Wilkins, Keene, NH, late 19th C and early 20th C

Chief's Wagon, painted CI and pressed steel, repainted, 12″	80.00
Consolidated Streetcar, painted CI, 13″	900.00
Covered Dray, painted CI and pressed steel, repainted, 15″	150.00
Goat Cart, painted CI, 10″	300.00
Hook and Ladder, painted CI, wooden ladders, 24″	550.00
Landau, painted CI	350.00
Surrey, painted CI, 13½″	350.00

Wyandotte, American

Sedan and house trailer, 25½″	145.00
Toytown Estate Wagon, litho tin windup, 20″	125.00

TRAINS, TOY

History: Railroading has always been an important part of childhood, largely in part because of the romance associated with the railroad and the emphasis on toy trains.

The first toy trains were cast iron and tin; windup motors added movement. The Golden Age of toy trains was 1920–1955 when electric powered units were available and names such as Ives, American Flyer, and Lionel were household words. The construction of the rolling stock was of high quality. The advent of plastic in the late 1950s lessened this quality considerably.

Toy trains were designated by a model scale or gauge. The most popular are HO, N, O and standard. Narrow gauge was a response to the modern capacity to miniaturize. Its popularity has lessened in the last few years.

Condition of trains is critical. Items in fair condition (scratched, chipped, dented, rusted or warped) and below generally have little value to a collector. Restoration is accepted, provided it is done accurately. It may enhance the price one or two grades. Prices listed below are for very good to mint condition unless noted.

References: Bruce Greenberg, *Greenberg's Price Guide to American Flyer S Gauge, Pocket Edition*, Greenberg Publishing Co., 1980; Bruce Greenberg, *Greenberg's Price Guide To Lionel Trains: 1901–1942*, Greenberg Publishing Co., 3rd Edition, 1983; Bruce Greenberg, *Greenberg's Price Guide To Lionel Trains: 1945–1983*, Greenberg Publishing Co., 1982; Bruce C. and Linda F. Greenberg, *Greenberg's Price Guide To Lionel Trains, Prewar and Postwar, 1901–42 & 1945–83, Pocket Edition*, Greenberg Publishing Co., 1983; Bruce Greenberg, *Greenberg's Price Guide to Lionel Trains, Postwar O and O-27 Trains*, Greenberg Publishing Co., 3rd Edition, 1982.

Collector's Clubs: Lionel Collector's Club, P.O. Box 11851, Lexington, KY 40578; The National Model Railroad Association, P.O. Box 2186, Indianapolis, IN 46206; The Toy Train Operating Society, Inc., 25 West Walnut Street, Suite 305, Pasadena, CA 91103; The Train Collector's Association, P.O. Box 248, Strasburg, PA 17579.

Additional Listings: See *Warman's Americana & Collectibles* for more examples.

AMERICAN FLYER

Cars

631 T & P, dark gray	75.00
807 Rio Grande, box car, door opens	450.00
900 Northern Pacific, passenger car	125.00
979 Caboose	25.00
24319 Pennsylvania salt	245.00
24572 U.S. Navy flat car	90.00

Locomotives

263 Steam	425.00
346 Steam	200.00

375 GM American Flyer GP-7	**450.00**
499 New Haven, GE Electric	**175.00**
4667 Std gauge	**200.00**
21918 Seaboard, Baldwin	**300.00**

Sets

4637 locomotive, Shasta set, 4 Pocahontas coaches, std gauge	**1,500.00**
4644 locomotive, 3 coaches, std gauge	**400.00**

Lionel, No. 10, Standard Gauge, #332 bag car; #339 pullman; #341 observation, Peacock, illuminated cars, c1930, $400.00.

LIONEL

Cars

60 Trolley, O gauge, orig box	**300.00**
69 Maintenance Car, motorized	**250.00**
3360 Burro Crane, O gauge, orig box	**200.00**
6517 Erie Caboose, O gauge	**350.00**

Locomotives

255 Locomotive and tender, O gauge	**450.00**
262 Locomotive and tender, O gauge	**150.00**
381E Locomotive, Std gauge	**2,500.00**
400 Locomotive and tender, Std gauge, repainted	**2,000.00**
2321 Lackawanna, AB diesel, O gauge	**350.00**
2338 Milwaukee, diesel, O gauge . . .	**525.00**
2341 Jersey Central, AB diesel, O gauge	**500.00**

Sets

385 Locomotive and tender, #1766, 1767, 1768, Std gauge	**2,500.00**
700E scale Hudson and tender, 714 box car, 715 tank car, 716 hopper, 717 caboose, O gauge	**4,150.00**

TRAMP ART

History: Tramp art was prevalent in the United States from 1875 to the 1930s. Items were made by itinerant artists, who left no record of their identity. They used old cigar boxes and fruit and vegetable crates. The edges of items were chip-carved and layered, creating the "Tramp Art" effect. Finished items usually were given an overall stain. Today they are collected primarily as folk art.

Boxes

6½", cloth tape hinge, int. has old cigar box label	**45.00**
8" w, 15" h, hanging, chip-carved heart and circles	**85.00**
9½", inside lid has old printed Havana Cigars label	**70.00**
14 x 17 x 7¼", velvet panels and top	**75.00**

Frames

7 x 9", cathedral arches	**40.00**
10 x 12¾", chip-carved, ornate	**75.00**
Jewel Box, 10" l, 3 drawers, hinged lid	**90.00**
Matchbox, hanging, 7¼" h, ...	**40.00**
Planter, hanging, white porcelain knobs	**95.00**

Cosmetic Box, 10½" x 6 x 4", mirror inside red lining, $85.00.

Sewing Box, 7" w, 5½" h, chamfered corners, pin cushion top with spool spindles, 1 drawer.	**90.00**
Shaving Mirror, 15¼" w, 32¾" h, drawer in base, back and front covered with applied chip-carved designs	**300.00**
Table, 22½" h, figural log cabin attached to top.	**75.00**

TRUNKS

History: Trunks are portable containers that clasp shut for the storage or transportation of personal possessions. Normally "trunk" means the ribbed, flat, or dome top models of the second half of the 19th Century. Unrestored they sell between $50 and $150. Refinished and relined the price rises to $200 to $400, with decorators being a principal market.

Early trunks frequently were painted, stenciled, grained, or covered with wallpaper. These are collected for their folk art qualities and as such experience high prices.

References: Martin and Maryann Labuda, *Price & Identification Guide to Antique Trunks*, privately printed, 1980.

Dome Top, leather covered, 26½ x 15 x 12½", initaled with nail heads, iron hardware and rivets, $175.00.

DOME TOP

Leather cov, brass studs, fancy tooled dec, dated 1870, 20" l.	225.00
Leather cov, brass studs, initials "G R", dated 1774, 39½" l.	725.00
Pine, black ground, strawberries, flowers with gold and green leaves, gold initials "D S", lined with newspaper dated November 1835, 28" l	700.00
Pine, red paint, black brush graining, dovetailed, iron bandings, hinges, and bear trap lock, 36 x 15 x 13" h.	140.00

FLAT TOP

Leather, brown, int., one small basket above larger basket, Louis Vuitton, sq, 26 x 25 x 25"	550.00
Pine, red and black paint, dovetailed, wrought iron strap hinges and side handles, green int., 26½ x 21¾ x 18½" h.	75.00

TUCKER CHINA

History: William Ellis Tucker (1800–1832) was the son of a Philadelphia schoolmaster who had a small shop on Market Street, where he sold china which he imported from France. William helped in the shop and became interested in the manufacture of china.

In 1820 a supply of the white-clay kaolin was discovered from a Chester County, Pennsylvania, farm. Kaolin is the prime ingredient for translucence in porcelain. William Tucker organized a pottery. The business prospered, but not without many trials and financial difficulties. Tucker had many partners. The marks found on Tucker china include: "William Ellis Tucker," "Tucker and Hulme," and "Joseph Hemphill". Workmen's incised initials sometimes are found.

The business operated between 1825 and 1838, when Thomas Tucker, William's brother, was forced by business conditions to close the firm.

Museum: William Penn Memorial Museum, Harrisburg, PA.

Coffee Pot, cov, white translucent porcelain, bands of coin gold, polychrome naturalistic flowers in bright colors, domed dec cov with polychrome flowers and foliate knob, vine dec on neck.	650.00
Cup and Saucer, 2¾ x 5", sepia monochrome of Italinate landscape, gilt rim on saucer, chipped	175.00
Pitcher, 9¾", vase shape, dec in gilding, fruiting grapevine border between band borders, repeated dec around rims and on handle	475.00
Saucer, 5½", pink roses, blue blossoms, green leaves, alternating with gilt floral sprigs, center radiating gilt lines, gilt border rim.	150.00
Soup Plate, 8¾", gilded floral border with rim edge band, molder's mark "V" for Vivian.	175.00

Pitcher, 9¼", florals in rose, iron-red, blue, green, purple, and yellow, gilt bands, $975.00.

Tea and Coffee Service, 27 pcs, cov coffee pot, cov sugar bowl, nine tea cups, four saucers, two 8⅝" plates, ten cake plates, each piece painted with building in landscape, gilt band rim borders, spout, handles, finials with gilting, 8 pc incised moulder's letters, 3 saucers mkd "H" for William Hand, 5 cake plates mkd "V" for Vivian **2,550.00**

Tureen, cov, 11½", circular body, angular handles, domed cov with foliate molded knob, incised molder letter "U" or "N", undecorated white translucent porcelain. **3,200.00**

VAL SAINT-LAMBERT

History: Val Saint-Lambert, a twelfth century Cistercian abbey, was located during different historical periods in France, Netherlands, and Belgium (1930 to present). In 1822 Francois Kemlin and Auguste Lelievre, along with a group of financiers, bought the abbey and opened a glassworks. In 1846 Val Saint-Lambert merged with the Société Anonyme des Manufactures de Glaces, Verres à Vitre, Cristaux et Gobeletaries. The company bought many other glassworks.

Val Saint-Lambert developed a reputation for technological progress in the glass industry. In 1879 Val Saint-Lambert became an independent company; it employed 4,000 workers. Val Saint-Lambert concentrated on the export market making table glass, cut, engraved, etched, and molded pieces, and chandeliers. Some pieces were finished in other countries, e.g., silver mounts added in the United States.

Val Saint-Lambert executed many special commissions for the artists of the Art Nouveau and Art Deco period. The company also made cameo-etched vases, covered boxes, and bowls. Famous artists continued to work at Val Saint-Lambert throughout the 20th century. The firm celebrated its 150th anniversary in 1975.

Bowl, 8¼ x 5", 4" h, Belgian cameo glass, clear matted ground, purple morning glories, unsigned **375.00**
Drink Mixer with pouring spout, 7", cutting around center, heavy base, sgd **75.00**
Perfume Bottle, stopper, 6", pink, cut to clear. **210.00**
Pitcher, 8", cylindrical, flaring, Imperial pattern **80.00**
Powder Box, 6½" d, 4" h, Art Deco, frosted **48.00**
Tray, 6", crystal, gold trim **100.00**

Vase, 13¾", pink with purple floral dec, sgd, $440.00.

Vases
8", white, irid, streaked with blue pads and pulls, artist initialed S.J.H., inscribed **165.00**
11", cylindrical, cut crystal overlay, clear and ruby swirls flanked by diamond cuts, mkd. **215.00**

VALENTINES

History: Valentines date back to 279 A.D. The first written valentine appeared in a letter dated 1477. In 1842 Thomas Strong of New York produced the first major American valentines which were romantic or comic in theme.

In 1848 Esther Howland of Worcester, Massachusetts, began making fine lacy valentines, considered the most beautiful paper creations of the 19th century. They had a small "H" stamped in red in the corner. In the early 1870s her company became the New England Valentine Company and used the mark, N.E.V.CO. George C. Whitney Company bought the firm shortly thereafter.

Valentines are collected by artist &/or type. Some collectible artists are Brundage, Dobb, Greenaway, Howland, Meek, Strong, Tucker, and Whitney. Collectible types are Civil War, comic, cutout, fold-out, folk art, handmade, lacy, lithographed, mechanical, Penny Dreadfuls, and sailor's. The price range for early valentines is wide, from a few dollars to hundreds of dollars, and varies according to artist, composition, condition, size, and type.

Sailors, 4¾″ w, 5¾″ h, mirrored, shell encrusted, $95.00.

Cut-out, 12¼″ d, round, scalloped border
  enclosing initials M.A.B., int., hearts
  and stars, mounted over red, yellow,
  and green paper, PA, 19th C **1,000.00**
Fold-over, 10½ x 10½″, sq, paper folded
  into squares, many outlined with gilt
  paper cut-outs and watercolor floral
  sprays, inscriptions in both English
  and German, PA, 19th C **550.00**
Penny Dreadful, Rose Co., fat man,
  c1907. . . . . **6.00**
Pop-up, die cut, beehive, bees, florals,
  German script, Schanaer, Germany . **50.00**
Sailor's, double, 9″ across both, 2 octagonal cases, heart in center of one,
  star in other center **600.00**
Shadowbox, 4 x 4½″, cardboard, emb
  gilded paper, basket of paper flowers
  with "I Love Thee," wavy glass cov-
  ering **45.00**
Tuck, Raphael, 7″, Scottish highlander,
  glass eyes, head moves **12.00**
Winsch, miniature book, verse inside,
  front dated 1913 . . . . **10.00**

VALLERYSTAHL GLASS

History: Vallerystahl (Lorraine), France, has
been a glass producing center for centuries. In
1872 two major factories, Vallerystahl glassworks
and Portieux glassworks, merged and produced art
glass until 1898. Later pressed glass covered animal dishes were introduced. The factory continues
operation today.

Additional Listings: Animal Dishes, Covered.

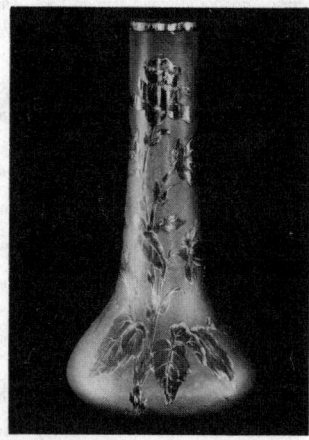

**Vase, 12″, amberina ground, gold daf-
fodils, $3,500.00.**

Animal Dishes, covered
  Duck, blue milk glass. **45.00**
  Hen, cobalt glass **35.00**
  Setter Dog, 4½″, white milk glass. . . **60.00**
  Swan, blue milk glass **40.00**
Candlesticks, pr, figural Joseph and
  Mary, sgd **200.00**
Candy Dish, 4⅛″ d, white milk glass,
  basketweave design, rope handles,
  basketweave design on cov, rope
  finial. **85.00**
Compote, sq, 6″, lacy dec, blue milk
  glass **150.00**
Dish, cov, 4 x 5″ figural walnut with grass-
  hopper finial, chocolate, sgd. **150.00**
Ice Cream Dish, matching underplate,
  petal shape, aqua **25.00**
Plate, 7½″, blue, floral dec **30.00**
Vases
  8″, DQ, multicolored enamel thistle
    dec, sgd **275.00**
  9½″, cameo, budding branches, en-
    ameled insects against frosted
    ground, gilt highlights, c1900, sgd **600.00**

VAN BRIGGLE POTTERY

History: Artus Van Briggle, born in 1869, was a talented Ohio artist who studied in Paris for three years while working at Rookwood. In 1899 he moved to Colorado for his health and established his own pottery in Colorado Springs in 1901.

Van Briggle's work was influenced heavily by the Art Nouveau "school" he saw in France. He produced a great variety of matte glazed wares in this style. Colors varied.

The "AA" mark, a date, and "Van Briggle" were incised on all pieces prior to 1907 and sometimes into the 1910s and 20s. Dated pieces are the most desirable.

Artus died in 1904. Anne Van Briggle continued the pottery until 1912.

Van Briggle pottery still is made today. These modern pieces often are confused for older examples. Among the glazes used are Moonglo (off white), Turquoise Ming, Russet, and Midnight (black).

Reference: Barbara Arnest (ed.), *Van Briggle Pottery: The Early Years*, The Colorado Springs Fine Art Center, 1975.

Collectors' Club: American Art Pottery Association, 270 Spangler Mill Road, New Cumberland, PA 17070. Dues: $12.00.

Museum: Pioneer Museum, Colorado Springs, CO.

Advisor: Scott H. Nelson.

1901–1920

Bowls
4½", yellowish green, 1902, pattern 41	**350.00**
5½", light blue, 1905, pattern 327	**225.00**

Bowl, 6¾" d, 3½" h, turquoise matte with mottled brown glaze around rim, Design 268, unknown designer, mkd, 1906, $575.00.

5½", light pink, 1907–12, pattern 638	**210.00**
8", maroon, 1916, pattern 849	**65.00**
Bookends, 5", maroon, owls, 1910s	**110.00**
Plates	
8", blue, green, and brown, 1903, pattern 20	**400.00**
8", maroon, grapes and leaves, 1907–12, pattern 15	**185.00**
Tiles, 6" sq	
Floral, three colors, 1907–12, unmarked	**125.00**
Landscape, four colors, 1907–12	**125.00**
Vases	
3½", yellow, 1903, pattern 193	**650.00**
5", gray-green, 1907, pattern 451	**260.00**
7", curdled brown, 1907–12, pattern 636	**385.00**
6", turquoise, 1915, pattern 858	**45.00**

1921–1968

Bowls	
3", plain, maroon, sgd A.S.	**75.00**
5", turquoise, dark blue, floral	**35.00**
Conch Shell, 12", blue	**55.00**
Figurine, 6", elephant, blue	**40.00**
Lamp Base, Damsel at Damascus, butterfly shade, maroon	**125.00**
Vases	
3½", dragonflies, brown with green, pattern 684	**30.00**
5", rect, rose with blue flower	**30.00**
7", dark blue, cream drip, high glaze, sgd Anne Van Briggle	**20.00**
12", three headed Indian, maroon and dark blue	**110.00**

VASART

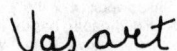

History: Vasart is a contemporary art glass made in Scotland by the Streathearn Glass Co. The colors are mottled, and sometimes shade from one hue to another. It is readily identified by an engraved signature on the base.

Basket 5" h, 8¼" l, mottled green shading to pink	**85.00**
Bowls	
2", scalloped rim, mottled green	**30.00**
5¾" d, 2½" h, fold over rim, mottled gray, sgd	**95.00**
6", mottled pink to green	**50.00**
Hat, mottled green to clambroth, sgd	**65.00**
Lamp, 10¼" h, 5½" d, flower form, 5 piked rims, bubble glass, pink top, blue middle, white bottom, pink and white pulled swirls	**300.00**
Tray, 12 x 4", oval, mottled blue shading to green	**75.00**

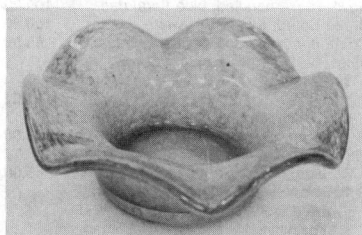

Ashtray, mottled light blue, 4½″ d, sgd, $50.00.

Tumbler, blue shading to orange stripes **50.00**
Vase, 6″, pink and blue flared top, multicolored spatters **90.00**

VENETIAN GLASS

History: Venetian glass has been made on the island of Morano, near Venice, since the 13th century. Most of the wares are thin walled. Many types of decoration have been used: embedded gold dust, lace work, and applied fruits or flowers. Venetian glass continues to be made today.

Basket, 7½″ h, 6½″ d, flared notched rim, purple to clear, controlled bubbles, gold flecked handle **55.00**

Vase, 10¾″, lettering, white on clear with gold dust, 2 handles, $225.00.

Bottle, lavendar, floral dec, goldstone.. **95.00**
Bowl, 9″, flared rim, blue........... **25.00**
Candlesticks
  10″, pr, figural, yellow dragon stems **250.00**
  11¼″, 5¼″ d base, brass fittings, canary, opalescent ribbon twist stem **135.00**
Champagne Glass, cranberry, clear dolphin stem **50.00**
Compote, 10″, cobalt blue, gold overlay **185.00**
Cruet, 8″, vertical latticino bands, blue, pink, and yellow **95.00**
Decanter and 3 shot glasses, ruby, white enameled violets, pale green leaves, raised gold scroll work........... **145.00**
Goblets, pr, wheel engraved, geese fighting and the victory **105.00**
Juice Glass, 3¾″, clear, multicolored twisted spirals, 19th C........... **40.00**
Perfume Bottle, stopper with long dauber, clear with gold spatter **400.00**
Rose Bowl, ruffled, ftd, pink, gold flecks..................... **90.00**
Salt, figural swan, green **25.00**
Tumbler, 6¾″, old fisherman, multicolored..................... **40.00**
Vases
  8¼″, millefori inlay.............. **110.00**
  12″, bud, clear, heavy gold border top and bottom, sawtooth edges, raised clover leaf and flowers **95.00**
  13″, pr, ovoid, long flaring necks, pink swirl with deep pink ruffled rim, pink rimmed pedestal base, applied spangle prunts on sides **100.00**
Wine Decanter, 11″, crystal **150.00**
Wine Glass, blown, pale blue, pink wafer middle **25.00**

VERYLS GLASS

History: Veryls glass is an art glass originally made in France after 1930. For a period of a few months, Heisey Glass Co., Newark, Ohio, produced the identical glass, having obtained the rights and formula from the French factory.

The French produced glass can be distinguished from the American product by the signature. The French is mold marked; the American is etched script signed.

Ashtray, 4½ x 3½″, lovebirds, frosted, script sgd **45.00**
Bowls
  6½″, pine cone, frosted, mold sgd .. **75.00**

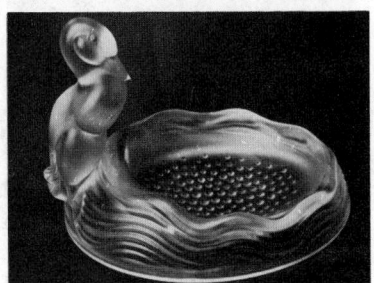

Ashtray, 6″ oval, sgd, $45.00.

11¼″, 3½″ h, waves, frosted and clear, Verlys France	325.00
11¾″, tassel, frosted	110.00
13½″, flying geese and fish, frosted to clear, mold sgd	125.00
Opalescent, thistle, sgd twice	230.00
Box, cov, 5¼″ d, topaz, chrysanthemum on lift off lid	315.00
Charger, 12″, clear, American birds and bees, sgd	160.00

Figurines

Elephants, pr, topaz	325.00
Pigeon, 4¼″, frosted	285.00
Planter, 10⅛″, clear, chrysanthemums	80.00
Plate, 6¼″, pine cones, mold sgd	60.00
Salad Bowl, 13½″, poppies	125.00
Soap Dish, 5⅝″ l, 4″ h, figural, fish, frosted	65.00
Vase, 9″, amber, large floral design, sgd	225.00

VILLEROY & BOCH

History: Pierre Joseph Boch established a pottery near Luxemburg, Germany, in 1767. Jean Francis, his son, introduced the first coal-fired kiln in Europe and perfected a water-power-driven potter's wheel. Pierre's grandson, Eugene Boch, managed a pottery at Mettlach; Nicholas Villeroy also had a pottery nearby.

In 1841 the three potteries were merged into the firm of Villeroy & Boch. Early production included a hard paste earthenware comparable to English ironstone. The factory continues to use this hard paste formula for its modern tablewares.

Additional Listings: Mettlach.

Bowl, 10½″, handled, blue floral dec	100.00
Bread Board, 5½ x 8½″, white	100.00
Cruet, 8½″, blue and white	65.00

Mugs

3½″, tan, leaf and twig dec, twig handle	45.00
6″, cream, raised blue lines, figural leaves, twig handle	65.00

Pitchers

3″, blue, cherries and leaves	45.00
10⅝″ h, 4¾″ d, 6 sided, gray, dark gray raised scrolls, leaves, pods, and birds, white lining, beige crest mark with V & B	250.00
Plaque, 16″, Swiss chalet, mountains, underglaze, #1044	375.00

Plaque, 13¾″ d, blue inner circle, profile of woman in white, four masks, four love-birds on ochre outer edge, trimmed in brown, imp #879, c1885, $415.00.

Plate, 9″, white, black hunting scene	90.00
Platter, 15¼ x 11″, Onion dec	65.00
Ramkin, underplate, blue and white	40.00

Steins

³⁄₁₀ l, 5⅝″ h, pewter top, cream, girl carrying tankard and tray with peacock	100.00
½ l, 6½″, blue ground, 5 white figures, #171, Mercury mark	225.00
Teapot, 6¼″, white, blue dec	125.00

Vases

7″, yellow, white floral design in relief	90.00
7½″, tan, beige figure in relief, silver lustre trim	250.00
12″, bottle shape, Dresden, sgraffitto geometric	90.00
15″, incised, 4 seasons, #1537, sgd C. Gorig	250.00

WARWICK

WARWICK CHINA

History: Warwick China Manufacturing Co., Wheeling, West Virginia, was incorporated in 1887 and continued until 1951. The company was one of the first manufacturers of vitreous glazed wares in the United States. Production was extensive and included tableware, garden ornaments, and decorative and utilitarian items.

Pieces were hand painted or decorated by decals. Collectors seek portrait items and fraternal pieces for groups such as the Elks, Eagles, and Knights of Pythias.

Some experimental, eggshell-type porcelain was made before 1887. A few examples are in the market.

Basket, cavalier portrait, 2 handles . . .	**60.00**
Bone Dish, flow blue, scenic, mkd	**45.00**
Bowl, red currants, leaves, gold trim. . .	**45.00**
Butter Pat, white ground, brown flowers	**5.00**
Chocolate Pot, cov, 10½", twig handle with thumbrest, brown to creamy yellow and ivory, branches of orange thornapples, mkd Warwick China . . .	**175.00**
Creamer and Sugar, brown, floral dec .	**50.00**
Mug, 5", monk portrait, red habit, skull cap, brown ground	**45.00**
Pitchers	
Cider, 7", bearded sea captain smoking clay pipe	**155.00**
Tankard, 13", monk at his dinner, brown to yellow	**200.00**

Pitcher, 10½", brown with rose motif, "IOGA," $100.00.

Water, 10½", ice lip, ivory, floral dec	**85.00**
Plates	
10¼", bulldog dec	**85.00**
12½", chop, scalloped rim, yellow to brown ground, berry dec	**75.00**
Soup Bowl, flow blue, mkd	**50.00**
Syrup, metal cov, underplate, 4", berry dec	**65.00**
Vases	
10", shaded brown, florals, IOGA . . .	**50.00**
10½", portrait, profile of lady holding rose, dark brown to tan, IOGA mark	**245.00**
10½", stork portrait, white ground, twig handle, IOGA	**150.00**
13¼", brown to tan, coral columbines	**200.00**

WATCHES

History: The market in all types of watches is brisk. They can be found from flea markets to the specialized jewelry sales at Butterfield's, Phillip's, and Sotheby's. Condition of movement is first priority; design and detailing of case is second.

In pocket watches, listing aids are size (18/0 to 20), number of jewels in movement, open or closed (hunter) face, and whether the case is gold, gold filled, or some other metal. The movement is the critical element since cases often were switched. However, an elaborate case, especially of gold, adds significantly to value.

Pocket watches designed to railroad specifications are desirable. They are 16 to 18 in size, have a minimum of 17 jewels, adjust to at least five positions, and conform to many other specifications. All are openfaced.

Study the field thoroughly before buying. The literature is vast including books and newsletters from clubs and collectors. Abbreviations: S = size; gf = gold filled; yg = yellow gold; j = jewels.

References: Roy Ehrhardt, *Foreign and American Pocket Watch: Identification and Price Guide, Book 3*, Heart of America Press, 1976; Cooksey Shugart and Tom Engle, *The Complete Guide To American Pocket Watches: 1982*, Overstreet Publications, 1982.

Collectors Club: National Association of Watch & Clock Collectors, 514 Poplar Street, Box 33, Columbia, PA 17512. Dues: $20.00. *Bulletin* (bimonthly) and *Mart* (bi-monthly).

Museums: American Clock & Watch Museum Inc. Bristol, CT; Hoffman Clock Museum, Newark, NY; National Association of Watch and Clock Collectors Museum, Columbia, PA; The Time Museum, Rockford, IL.

Character
Dan Dare, pocket, scenic dial, monster and Dan Dare in spacesuit, Ingersall Ltd, London **150.00**

Hunter, 6 size, Illinois, 14K solid gold case, 15 jewel $275.00.

Daniel Boone, wristwatch, beige dial, plain silver hands, Swiss Made, orig strap, c1952 . . . .   50.00
Dick Tracy, wristwatch, orig strap, 1951. . . . .   125.00
Lucy, wristwatch with second hand, orig strap, c1952 . . . .   45.00
Pendant
  Swiss, Vacheron & Constantin, Geneva, no. 356721, c1910, hunter, lever movement, 18K gold matte case, chased on front with border of foliage and ribbon swag set with rose diamonds, 32mm 750.00
  Unmarked, enamel and diamond, c1890, hunter, gilt cylinder oval movement, enamel dial with lilac chapter ring and centered by a lilac patera, 18K gold oval case, front lid with applied butterfly set with rose diamonds, black enamel ground, openwork trefoil-form bow, 38mm.   900.00
  Unmarked, enamel and pearl, c1900, openface, gilt cylinder movement, enamel dial in 18th C style, 18K gold case, polychrome enamel putti at play, split pearl-set bezels, 25mm .   500.00
Pocket
  American
    Elgin, National Watch Co, #1155973, c1882, openface, 16S, 15j, nickel lever movement, 18K gold case, box hinge, monogrammed, 50mm. 900.00
    Elgin, National Watch Co,

#6995672, c1896, hunter, 12S, 21j, nickel lever movement, porcelain dial, 18K gold case, engraved hunter scene on front, reverse, engraved schooner, 55mm 700.00
Hamilton Watch Co, #1440310, model 940, c1915, openface, 18S, 21j, motor barrel, adjusted 5 positions, double roller, double sunk enamel dial, gf case, 50mm 300.00
E. Howard & Co, Boston, #215701, c1875, hunter, 18S, nickel lever half plate movement, highly jeweled, enamel dial, 14K gold engine turned case, stamped EH & Co, gold chain composed of bars set with striated agate, 55mm . . 1,200.00
E. Howard & Co, #304500, c1880, openface, 18S, 17j, three quarter plate, gilt lever movement, 14K gold case, monogrammed cartouche, 51mm 600.00
Illinois, Railroad King, openface railroad, 18S, 17j, full plate design movement, nickel plate case . . .   500.00
International Watch Co, c1910, openface, nickel lever movement, enamel dial, 14K gold case, 51mm 700.00
Longines, c1905, hunter, chronograph with register, nickel lever movement, enamel dial, subsidiary dials at three o'clock for recorded minutes, nine o'clock for seconds, 18K gold case with applied and engraved horse race scene, monogrammed back, 54mm 1,000.00
Henry Randel, Marion, NJ, #21679, c1885, hunter, nickel movement, enamel dial, 18K gold case with butterfly cut out, engraved flower bouquet, 54mm 900.00
Waltham Riverside Maximus, #10552700, c1901, hunter, 16S, 23j, lever movement, damascened nickel movement plates, 14K gold engine turned case, 54mm 900.00
Danish, Jules Jurgensen, Copenhagen, #12380, c1880, hunter, lady's, nickel lever movement, enamel dial, patented bow setting, 18K gold engine turned case, 42mm 1,400.00
English, Dent, 33 Cockspur Lane, London, #26969, 1871, hunter, eccentric seconds, gilt three quarter plate lever movement, enamel dial, subsidiary seconds at 9 o'clock, 18K gold engine turned case, 50mm . . 1,300.00

French

Cartier, Paris, #6198, c1920, hunter, lever movement, silver dial engine turned in rayed design, 18K gold ultra thin case, white enamel monogram, 14K gold chain and pen knife overlaid with black enamel, 50mm **2,800.00**

La Maisonette, c1900, hunter, chronometer, gilt pivoted detent movement, helical hairspring, enamel dial, 14K gold engine turned case, 58mm **700.00**

German, George Karp, Darmstadt, c1900, hunter, gilt lever movement, double sunk enamel dial, 14K gold case, monogrammed, 55mm **1,100.00**

Swiss

L. Audemars, #14207, Brassus & Geneva, c1890, openface, minute repeating, highly jeweled nickel lever movement, jewels in gold screwed settings, enamel dial, 18K gold case, 48mm **2,500.00**

Patek Philippe & Co, #36404, c1870, openface, lever movement, gold dial, 18K gold engine turned case, 50mm **1,050.00**

Vacheron & Constantin, Geneva, Chronometre Royal, #348090, c1900, openface, wolf's tooth wind, large ruby palets, 18K gold engine turned case monogrammed, 57mm. **1,400.00**

Unmarked, openface

c1840, gild verge movement, bridge pierced and engraved with scrolls, enamel dial, SS engine turned case, 61mm **1,200.00**

c1880, quarter repeating, nickel lever movement, highly jeweled, slide repeat, enamel dial, gold foliate hands, 18K gold polished case, 50mm **700.00**

Wristwatch, Lady's

French, Boucheron, Paris, c1950, 18K gold engine turned dial, matching pink gold rectangular case and bracelet strap **2,100.00**

Swiss

Patek Phillippe & Co, Geneva, #181510, Fabrique pour Beyer Zurich, c1915, lever movement, circular 18K gold hinged case, 9K gold flexible link bracelet **700.00**

Rolex Oyster Perpetual, c1945, self winding, sweep second hand, waterproof, 18K gold tonneau case with florentine finish **650.00**

Wristwatch, Man's

American, Hamilton Watch Co, model 979-F, #2931668, c1940, 19j, 14K gold and enamel case **650.00**

Swiss

Patek Phillipe & Co, Geneve, #953128, c1946. lever movement, heavy molded sq 18K gold case, faceted lobed lugs **1,400.00**

Ulysee Nardin, Locle & Geneve, #17194, c1910, chronograph with 30 minute register and constant seconds, nickel lever movement, 18K gold case. **900.00**

WATERFORD

History: Waterford crystal is quality flint glass commonly decorated with cuttings. The original factory was established at Waterford, Ireland, in 1729. Glass made before 1830 is darker than the brilliantly clear glass of later production. The factory closed in 1852. After 100 years it reopened and continues in production.

Compote, 4¼″ h, 4⅞″ d, $150.00.

Bowl, 9″, diamond cut, triple sprig chain border, star cut base	90.00
Cruet, 9″, diamond cut, faceted stopper, applied handle	125.00
Decanters	
10″, ribbed, diamond cut, star cut base, spherical star and diamond cut stopper	125.00
13″, ovoid, flaring base, fluting at base and neck, flared lip, diamond cut, faceted conical stopper	130.00
Fruit Bowl, 5¾″ d, 5¾″ h, turned down rim, diamond cut, sq pedestal base .	275.00
Jar, cov, 6″, diamond cut, triple sprig chain bordering thumb cut rim and star cut lid, faceted knob	120.00
Pitchers	
8″, diamond cut, applied handle	150.00

10½″, ribbed, applied handle **200.00**
Plate, 8″, center diamond cut **85.00**
Tumbler, allover cut **75.00**
Vases
  5½″, fluted neck, flaring rim, hobnail
    cut, bands of triple sprig chain on
    star cut base **50.00**
  6″, hobnail cut, triple sprig chain
    around waist, star cut base **75.00**

WAVE CREST

WAVE CREST WARE

History: The C. F. Monroe Company of Meriden, Connecticut, produced the opal glassware known as wave crest from 1898 until World War 1. The company bought the opaque, blown molded glass blanks for decoration from the Pairpoint Manufacturing Co. of New Bedford, Massachusetts, and other glass makers including European factories. Florals were the most common decorative motif. Trade names used were "Wave Crest Ware," "Kelva," and "Nakara."

Reference: Elsa H. Grimmer, *Wave Crest Ware,* Wallace-Homestead, 1979.

Biscuit Jar, 7″, white and powder blue
  ground, moon and stars pattern in light
  pink and blue, white beading **500.00**
Boxes
  3¼″, sq, hinged, relief dec, blue en-
    amel flowers, red banner mark . . . **250.00**
  4½″, hinged, blownout pansy on lid,
    bronze shading to yellow, sgd **375.00**

Biscuit jar, barrel shape, rococo cartouche, pastel floral design, SP top, $250.00.

5½″, oval, hinged, light blue, emb,
  lined, black mark **325.00**
6½″ d, 3″ h, round, moss green, pink
  flowers top and sides, beaded enamel trim, orig lining, sgd Nakara . **750.00**
Broom Holder, emb blank, ornate or-
  molu, sgd **875.00**
Candleholder, green, cherub, ormolu
  top, mkd Nakara **175.00**
Creamer and Sugar, cov with SP bail
  handle, 3½″ h, 4″ d, blownout and
  swirled enameled pale pink flowers,
  small gold dots over all, emb SP frame
  holder **360.00**
Ewer, 14″, SP top, winged cherub on
  handle and spout, beige, florals and
  leaves with enamel work **175.00**
Humidor, cov, 5½″ h, round, brass fittings, rose, white floral spray dec, CI-
  GAR on front in gold, mkd Nakara . . **525.00**
Jewel Stand, 3¼″ h, 4″ d, ormolu stem,
  feet, and handled rim, pink apple blos-
  som dec **245.00**
Jewel Tray, 5¾″ l, 3½″ w, oval, ormolu
  handles and feet, emb medallions,
  raised dots and florals, orig satin lining, red banner mark **325.00**
Letter Holder, 4 x 5½ x 3″, puffy, blue
  floral with white beading, brass ormolu
  rim **265.00**
Paperweight, gilded metal angels with
  cymbals on top **300.00**
Photo Holder, puffy, blue with flowers . **450.00**
Pin Tray, 4½″, emb rococo, handled, red
  banner mark **125.00**
Sugar Shaker, 3″, yellow ground, Erie
  twist, pink, gold, gray, and white dec **125.00**
Sweetmeat, pansy dec, SP rim and cov,
  double twisted handle, red banner
  mark **400.00**
Toothpick Holder, transfer, cat looking
  through branches, ormolu base and
  rim **185.00**
Vases
  6″, bud, 2 handled, urn ftd, blue
    ground, pink floral dec, blownout,
    sgd **300.00**
  8¼″, pale pink, blue reserve with pink
    and rust daisies, white enamel dots,
    sgd Kelva **375.00**
  15¾″, 2 panels with 4 ducks flying
    over stalks of cat o'nine tails blown-
    out in between, sgd **950.00**

WEATHERVANES

History: A weather vane indicates wind direction. The earliest known examples were found on late 17th century structures in the Boston area. The vanes were handcrafted of wood, copper, or tin. By the last half of the 19th century, weathervanes adorned farms and houses throughout the nation. Mass produced vanes of cast iron, copper, and sheet metal were sold through the mail order catalogs or at country stores.

The champion vane is the rooster. In fact, the name weathercock is synonymous with weathervane. The styles and patterns are endless. Weathering can affect the same vane differently. For this reason, patina is a critical element in collecting vanes.

Whirligigs are a variation of the weathervane. Constructed of wood and metal, often by unskilled craftsmen, whirligigs not only indicate the direction of the wind and its velocity, but their unique movements served as entertainment for children, neighbors, and passersby.

Note: Reproduction of early models exist, are being aged, and sold as originals.

Cast iron, 32″ l, flat, MA, c1830, $1,275.00.

VANES

Arrow, pine, directional arrow, 15½″ h, 15¼″ l 125.00
Cow, molded copper, full bodied, horns, American, 19th C, 25″ h, 23″ l 1,250.00
Eagle perched on orb, molded and gilded copper, 19th C, 29″ h, 47″ wingspan 1,050.00
Fish, carved, painted wood, flattened, relief, 19th C, 41½″ l 1,700.00
Grasshopper, crouching, molded copper body, wings and upper legs, CI lower legs, applied CI antennae, mounted on round metal rod, late 19th C, 9½″ h, 37″ l 1,760.00
Horse, running, molded copper, full bodied, flattened form, molded head and tail, mounted on rod standard in wood base, yellow paint and gilt, 19th C, 22″ h, 37″ l 900.00
Horse, standing, CI, full bodied, cut sheet metal tail, painted, American, mid 19th C, 34¾″ h, 25¼″ l 13,500.00

Hunter With Gun, wood, cut out directionals, arrow has figure of hunter with gun, painted orange, white and black, pine post, 50″ h 650.00
Indian Warrior on Horseback, carved and painted wood, horse at full gallop, Indian brandishing spear, NE, c1875, 24″ h, 22½″ l 20,000.00
Locomotive, figural, sheet metal, orig polychrome paint, c1860, 13″ h, 24″ l. . 450.00
Rooster, running, CI, cast in 2 parts, sheet iron tail, mounted on rod on wooden base, late 19th C, 21½″ h, 24″ l 1,050.00
Soldier, folk art, wood, movable arms, carved features, brass tack buttons, tin plume in hat, black, red and yellow paint, turned wooden base, 21⅜″ h . 3,500.00
Stag, leaping, molded gilt copper, mounted on iron rod, CI directionals above molded sphere, 19th C, 19½″ h, 31½″ l 2,000.00

WHIRLIGIGS

Ferris Wheel, wooden vanes provide animation to 2 articulated wooden figures that turn crank powering sheet metal ferris wheel, each bucket has 2 wooden heads with painted features, red, yellow, green, and orange, 30″ h, 34″ l 675.00
Man with Hat, primitive, wood, orig yellow paint, black detail, turned finial base, early 20th C, 23½″ 225.00
Negro Minstrel Dancer, wood, painted, c1900, 12″ h, 6″ w 250.00
Uncle Sam, wood, painted red, white, blue, and black, 10″ h 375.00

WEBB, THOMAS & SONS

History: Thomas Webb & Sons was established in 1837 in Stourbridge, England. The company probably is best known for its very beautiful English cameo glass. However, many other types of colored glass were produced including enameled glass, iridescent glass, pieces with heavy glass ornamentation, cased glass, and other art glass besides cameo.

Additional Listings: Burmese, Cameo, and Peach Blow.

Biscuit Jar, 7″, creamy ivory, enamel blossoms, leaves, and butterfly, ornate brass ftd holder and cov 850.00
Bowls
  5″, butterscotch, gold dec, 2 handles 150.00
  5½″, beige satin, gold butterfly and prunus blossoms 850.00

Cameo, vase, 6″, blue ground, white dec, etched banner label "Thomas Webb & Sons," $3,000.00.

8″, ribbed, chartreuse and white, MOP, DQ, berry pontil	**275.00**
17″, cobalt blue overlay, cut to clear, sgd	**300.00**
Box, cov, 4½″, yellow satin, gold floral and butterfly dec	**425.00**
Bride's Basket Bowl, 10½″, ruffled edge, pink and white, enameled floral dec	**400.00**
Ewer, 9″, pink, gold floral and butterfly dec	**250.00**
Jar, 5½″, pale yellow, honeycomb, SP bail and cov	**325.00**
Perfume Bottle, 4″, ball shape, blue satin, white floral and leaf dec, SS screw-on top	**950.00**
Rose Bowls	
3¼″ d, 3″ h, caffet-au-lait, applied gold floral and vine dec	**550.00**
3½″ d, blue satin, applied gold prunus blossoms, white lining	**450.00**
Tumbler, 4½″, blue satin, MOP	**150.00**
Vases	
7½″, tapered, yellow, gold florals, leaves, and butterfly	**375.00**
8½″, red and white morning glory dec, butterfly on reverse side, sgd Thomas Webb	**1,650.00**
10½″, shaded apricot to beige, white enamel dec	**350.00**
12″, pr, bluebirds flying, flowers, and dragonflies, propeller mark	**650.00**
17″, stick, wine with gold bird and leaf dec, propeller mark	**275.00**

WEDGWOOD

WEDGWOOD

History: In 1754 Josiah Wedgwood entered into a partnership with Thomas Whieldon of Fenton Vivian, Staffordshire, England. Products included marbled, agate, tortoise shell, green glaze, and Egyptian black wares. In 1759 Wedgwood opened his own pottery at the Ivy House works, Burslem. In 1764 he moved to the Brick House (Bell works) at Burslem. The pottery concentrated on utilitarian pieces.

Between 1766 and 1769 Wedgwood built the famous works at Etruria. Among the most renowned products of this plant were the Empress Catherina of Russia dinner service (1774) and the Portland Vase (1790s). Product lines were cane ware, unglazed earthenwares (drabwares), piecrust wares, variegated and marbled wares, black basalt (developed in 1768), Queen's or cream ware, Jasper ware (perfected in 1774), and others.

Bone china was produced under the direction of Josiah Wedgwood II between 1812 and 1822 and revived in 1878. A moonlight lustre was made from 1805 to 1815. Fairyland lustre began in 1920. All lustre production ended in 1932.

A museum was established at the Etruria pottery in 1906. When Wedgwood moved to its modern plant at Barlaston, North Staffordshire, the museum was continued and expanded.

References: Harry M. Buten, *Wedgwood ABC, But Not Middle E*, Buten Museum of Wedgwood, 1964, available in reprint; David Buten and Jane Clancy, *Eighteenth-Century Wedgwood: A Guide For Collectors And Connoisseurs*, Main Street Press, 1980; Robin Reilly, *Dictionary Of Wedgwood*, Antique Collectors Club, 1980.

Museum: Buten Museum, Merion, PA.

BASALT

Biscuit Jar, 6″, classic figures in relief, SP mountings and cov, ball feet, mkd Wedgwood	**150.00**
Bough Pot, 9⅝″, 3 Muses, trees, flowering plants, and fruit, pierced cov, 19th C	**325.00**
Busts	
Mercury, 18½″, sgd	**875.00**
Shakespeare, 12″	**1,100.00**
Venus, 14⅜″ h, 7⅝″ d, mkd Wedgwood only	**900.00**
Candlesticks, 5″ h, 6″ d, figural Sphinx, mkd Wedgwood only, pr	**1,550.00**
Centerpiece Bowl, 12″ d, raised grapevine border, mkd Wedgwood/Made in England	**90.00**

Coffee Pot, 8″, Strawberry, strawberry
finial on cov, ftd **575.00**
Creamer, 4″, Capri, enameled florals,
c1860. . . . . **175.00**
Cup and Saucer, octagonal, bronzed and
gilt classical figures in ovals, musical
trophy suspended from ribbons, foli-
age swags, imp mark, c1840 . . . . . . **545.00**
Figurines
Eros and Euphrosyne, 16½″ h, 4⅞″ d,
Eros perched on woman's shoulder,
mkd Wedgwood only **900.00**
Lion, 3″ h, 6″ l, stalking **600.00**
Raven, 4½″ h, 5¼″ l, glass eyes, mkd
Wedgwood, c1916 . . . . **425.00**
Medallion, 2″, oval, bust portrait of Thu-
cyd, imp Wedgwood & Bently, c1780 . **130.00**
Jug, 10⅞″ h, 5½″ d, mkd Wedgwood
only, late 18th C **500.00**
Plaques
Erato, 6¾″, oval **750.00**
Mother and child, 4½″, round, sgd
Mayer **300.00**
Venus and Cupid, 6¾″, oval. **750.00**
Sucrier, 5¼″, seated woman finial **350.00**
Tea Set, 5¾″ pot, 4¼″ sugar, 4½″ crea-
mer, Strawberry. **450.00**
Urn, 11″, pedestal, sq base, cov, swags,
acanthus leaves at base and cov,
c1860. . . . . **1,700.00**
Vases
5″, bottle shape, relief, Grecian fig-
ures **110.00**
5″ spill, Goddess of Music **100.00**
9¾″, flaring, applied trailing vines, formal leaves, flaring foot with fruiting
vines, imp marks, 19th C **300.00**
20¾″, ovoid shape, applied Apollo
and the Muses, cov with vase shape
finial, 2 plain loop handles, imp
Wedgwood, 19th C **1,875.00**

**Dish, game, Caneware, unglazed, oval,
8½ x 6½″, $200.00.**

CANEWARE

Coffee Pot, 9″, engine turned bamboo
dec, glazed, imp, late 18th C **225.00**
Creamer, 3″ h, glazed int., c1860. . . . . **100.00**
Cup and Saucer, coffee, assembled, en-
gine turned bamboo dec, imp Wedg-
wood, c1780. . . . . **300.00**
Game Dish, 8½ x 6¼″, oval, unglazed **180.00**
Pie Dish, 8″ d, c1805 . . . . **675.00**
Plate, 8″, c1810 . . . . **150.00**
Sugar, cov, 6″, prunus blossoms,
c1800. . . . . **290.00**
Teapot, 4″ h, 6″ d, Wicker, cov with sheaf
of wheat finial. **450.00**
Vase, 6″, cupid as The Four Seasons,
floral arabesques, ribbed circular ped-
estal foot, imp Wedgwood, c1815. . . **250.00**

CREAMWARE

Basket and Stand, 8″ h, 10¼′ l, reticulated, twisted rope handle, oak leaf
and acorn dec, c1790 . . . . **650.00**
Bough Pot, 8″ h, 7″ d, c1820 . . . . **500.00**
Bowl with Ladle, 4¾″, grape and leaf
dec **275.00**
Cup and Saucer, vintage dec, sage
green relief, c1820 . . . . **350.00**
Dish, pierced border, imp Wedgwood,
c1830. . . . . **100.00**
Figurines
Bulldog, glass eyes, naturalistically
molded, imp mark, late 19th C . . . **320.00**
Polar Bear, seated, 10 x 4⅛ x 7″ l, sgd
Skeaping, mkd Wedgwood, c1927 **400.00**
Jug, 6½″, leaf dec **190.00**
Plate, 9½″, ribbon edge, gilted, c1790 . **100.00**
Platter, 10″ l, Melton, setter dog and
quails, sepia transfer **55.00**
Tea Caddy, 4¼″, molded fruiting
branches in cartouches, brown, green,
and yellow, Wedgwood-Whieldon,
c1770. . . . . **200.00**
Tureen, attached underplate, cov, hp . . **275.00**
Vase, 5½″, cylindrical, Wedgwood only,
c1880. . . . . **250.00**
Wine Pot, mkd, 18th C **450.00**

DRABWARE

Bowl, 7½″ d, 3¼″ h, Arabesque
pattern **175.00**
Butter Dish, cov, blue leaves **200.00**
Creamer **100.00**
Jug, 8″ h, 5¾″ d, panels with emb clas-
sical ladies, mkd Wedgwood only,
c1820. . . . . **2,250.00**
Plaque, 4½″, blue raised figures, mkd
Wedgwood only **300.00**

Pitcher, 4¾", blue classical figures. . . . **325.00**
Sugar, 7", glazed, gilded bands **175.00**
Teapot, 6½", blue band of flowers in
relief **125.00**
Vase, 5", urn shape, lilac acanthus
leaves and bellflowers in relief **300.00**

JASPERWARE

Biscuit Jars
5½" h, 4¾" d, tricolor, lavender bands
top and bottom, sage green center,
white classical ladies and cupids,
SP bail, mkd Wedgwood only **750.00**
6½" h, 5¾" d, gold, black garlands,
lion's heads, classical figures and
grapevine around base, mkd Wedg-
wood only **575.00**
7" h, 4¾" d, deep blue, classical
ladies, mkd Wedgwood only **135.00**
Bough Pot on holder, 5¾", ovoid body
on tripod base, blue, alternate stiff
white leaves and palmettes, lion's
heads and ring capitals, flat cov,
seven pierced openings, 19th C **575.00**
Bowl, 4⅞" d, 2⅜" h, light blue, small
classical figures, raised leaves and
bands, mkd Wedgwood only, c1862 **245.00**
Box, 6" d, 4½" h, blue, emb scrolls all
over, top with cherubs and 2 love
birds, scroll feet **125.00**
Breakfast Set, 6 pcs, coffee pot, sugar,
creamer, cup and plate with dome cov,
ivory ground, lilac and sage green lily-
of-the-valley and fern. **675.00**
Cheese Dish, dome cov, 9¼" d, 4½" h,
medium green classical figures, garlands of grapevine, mkd Wedgwood,
c1890. . . . . **150.00**
Clock, 12¼" h, 3½" d, deep green, clas-
sical women and cupid, floral bands,
mkd Wedgwood England **600.00**
Condiment Set, 4¾", dark blue, classical
figures, SP handle and cov, mkd
Wedgwood Made in England **110.00**
Creamer and Sugar, cov, 4¾", dark blue,
woman and children, band of grapes
near top, mkd Wedgwood only, Eng-
land **170.00**
Cups and Saucers
2⅛" h, 3" d cup, twisted rope handle,
5½" saucer, deep blue, classical
ladies **165.00**
2½" cup, 3⅛" saucer, light blue, small
classical figures, mkd Wedgwood
only, c1762 . . . . **245.00**
Dish, 5¾" l, 3½" w, diamond shape,
deep blue, classical lady with harp, floral leaf border, mkd Wedgwood only **50.00**
Ewer, 9", deep blue, mythological figures, geometric band top and bottom,
white leaf dec on handle, late 19th C. **385.00**

Flower Holder, underplate, 5", dark blue,
white classical figures, trees, c1850 . **190.00**
Hair Receiver, heart shape, medium
blue, angel and cherub, numbered . . **250.00**
Jam Jar, 4" h, 3¼" d, gold, black grapes
and leaves garlands, lion's heads, SP
top, mkd Wegwood only **175.00**
Jardiniere, 5¼" h, 6" d, dark blue, clas-
sical figures, garlands connected with
lion's heads and rings, white int., mkd
Wedgwood, c1890. . . . . **125.00**
Jug, 5¼" h, 3⅞" d, deep blue, classical
ladies and cupids, 2 fretwork bands . **125.00**
Mug, 5¼", green, classical figures, mkd
Wedgwood England. **120.00**
Pitcher, 6¼", tankard shape, blue, clas-
sical figures, grapeleaf border, mkd
Wedgwood England, c1900 . . . . **110.00**
Plaque, 7¼", oval, medium green, clas-
sical man holding mask in left hand,
long walking stick in right hand, mkd
Wedgwood only **300.00**
Platter, 9¼" oval, medium blue, classical
figures, sgd Wedgwood **125.00**
Salt, 3½", blue, white Dancing Hours . . **200.00**
Sugar, cov, 3⅛" h, 3⅞" d, red, classical
figure **400.00**
Syrup Jug, 8", thumb lift cov, dark blue,
white acanthus leaves, c1865. . . . . . **300.00**
Tankard, 6¼", 3⅞", deep blue, classical
figures, grapes and vines, mkd Wedg-
wood only. **145.00**
Tea Caddy, cov, 7" h, light green, white
figure and trees, pointed knob **375.00**
Tea Kettle, 7½" h, 6¼" d, deep blue,
wicker covered, metal handle, white
alternating leaves and flowers, mkd
Wedgwood only, 1820 . . . . **650.00**
Teapot, 4½", 8" handle to spout, dark
blue, white trees, figures, band of
leaves around lid, mkd Wedgwood
only, England **120.00**
Tobacco Jar, 6½", dark blue, classical
figures, trees, acanthus leaves on cov,
acorn knob, mkd Wedgwood Made in
England **110.00**
Trophy Cup, 5" d, 3 handled, light green,
classical figures under arches **390.00**
Vases
5½" h, 3" d, gold, black garland of
black grapes and vines, white
bands, mkd Wedgwood only **300.00**
10¼" h, 4¼" d, pedestal foot, black,
white classical ladies with musical
instruments, bolted base, mkd
Wedgwood only **475.00**
12¼", cov, tricolor, blue ground, white
swags, ribboned acanthus leaves
centering 2 green medallions of
Thalia and Calliope flanked by mar-
tial trophies, rim and cov with floral
designs, sq foot with palmetto bor-
der, 18th C **2,250.00**

LUSTRES

Butterfly
Bowls
    3⅝″ d, 2⅛″ h, ext. with mottled brown and gold butterflies, int. with MOP luster with green stainings. Oriental motif, mkd Wedgwood Butterfly Lustre **150.00**
    8¼″ d, 3¾″ h, white MOP, lacy silver Lightning pattern, int. with mottled flame, gold butterfly center, mkd **450.00**
  Melba Cup, 3″, mottled blue, brown and orange, scroll and diaper border, int. with large multicolored butterfly, mkd Portland Vase, Wedgewood England, c1915. . . . .   **285.00**

Dragon
Bowls
    3½″, octagonal, mottled blue, gold dragons, int. with light green . . .   **275.00**
    8½″ d, 4″ h, octagonal, flame, mottled, large gold dragon, int. with mottled blue, gold dragons, mkd Wedgwood Dragon Lustre **425.00**
  Compote, 10¾″ d, 6¼″ h, pedastal base, blue, brown Wedgwood Portland vase mark **450.00**
  Ginger Jar, 11″, light blue, gilded . . .   **700.00**
Vases
    8″, trumpet shape, blue, brown Wedgwood Portland vase mark .   **300.00**
    8¾″ h, 5⅞″ d, pedestal base, mottled powder blue, maroon and gold dragons, gold trim, int. with MOP, fancy trim, mkd Wedgwood Dragon Lustre **500.00**

Fairyland
Bowls
    4½″, Mizami **650.00**
    8″ d, 5⅝″ h, Garden of Paradise, int. with peach melba, Jumping Faun, mkd Wedgwood Fairy land Lustre, Z4968. . . . .   **2,000.00**
    8⅞″ d, 3¾″ h, poplar trees, int. with elves and bell branch **1,800.00**
  Cup, 4¼″ d, 3½″ h, peach melba, leapfrogging elves and fairies, gold stars, Portland vase mark, Z4968 . . . .   **800.00**
  Punch Bowl, 11″ d, Chinese garden, int. with elves and birds, Z4968/11, c1920.   **2,600.00**
  Sherbert Dish, 4″ d, 3″ h, mottled blue-green, flying cranes and temple dog. **550.00**
Vases
    8″ h, 3¼″ d, The Jewelled Tree with Feng Hwang and bridge panels, black tree, pink sky, mkd Wedgwood Fairyland Lustre, Z4968 . .   **1,400.00**
    8″ h, 4″ d, red ground, firbolgs . . .   **1,390.00**

Hummingbird
  Box, cov, 2¼″ h, 4½″ d, sq, mottled blue, gold birds, int. with flame . . .   **450.00**
  Jar, cov, 9½″, mottled green **725.00**
Vases
    6⅛″ h, 3″ d, mottled blue, colored hummingbirds outlined in gold, gold trim, int. with flame with gold trim, mkd Wedgwood Hummingbird Lustre **210.00**
    11¾″ h, 5¾″ d, trumpet shape, mottled blue, colored hummingbirds, gold trim, int. with mottled flame, mkd Wedgwood Hummingbird Lustre, Z5294. . . . .   **475.00**

Moonlight
  Candlesticks, pr, 6″, sq base, splashed pink with orange and gray, imp Wedgwood, c1810. . . . .   **350.00**
  Cup and Saucer, tea, splashed pink with orange and gray **350.00**
  Dish, 12¼″, shell form, splashed pink with orange and gray, imp Wedgwood, c1810 . . . .   **175.00**
  Sauce Tureen, cov, 7¼″, mottled pink, orange and gray, imp Wedgwood, c1810 . . . .   **475.00**

MAJOLICA

Biscuit Jar, 7⅝″ h, 8⅜″ d, mottled green and brown, SP cov with sphinx finial, SP base and mounts, c1875 . . . . . .   **275.00**
Bowls
    9″ d, 4⅛″, h, white and brown, emb white seashells, rose and gold seaweed, turquoise int., SP rim band, mkd. **125.00**
    10¾″, scalloped, turquoise ground, red lobsters in blue panels, alternating with vegetables in gray panels, ochre rim, imp Wedgwood D2916/D, dated 1865 . . . .   **450.00**
Butter Pat, 3″, Shell and Seaweed, imp Wedgwood **25.00**
Compote, 8½″ d, 4½″ h, brown ground, grape leaves, flowers and grapes, imp Wedgwood **225.00**
Dish, 8½″, shell shape, mottled green .   **50.00**
Jug, centennial, 8⅛″, oval, cobalt blue ground, turquoise portraits of Washington and Lincoln on each side, green foliate decor, imp Wedgwood, dated 1895 . . . .   **450.00**
Pitcher, 10″, Bird and Fan, fan spout, twig handle, turquoise int., imp Wedgwood **475.00**
Plates
    8½″, white ground, brown branch and leaves, crimson prunus with yellow centers, imp Wedgwood, dated 1880. . . . .   **45.00**

9″, mottled center, basket weave border, imp Wedgwood	**70.00**
Platter, 13″ l, oval, Oriental, white ground.	**125.00**
Teapot, 7″, Shell and Seaweed, white ground, snail shell finial	**350.00**

MISCELLANEOUS

Candlesticks, pr, Victorian Ware, 8⅛″, urn shape.	**1,500.00**
Condiment Set, mustard, salt and pepper, bamboo lattice design, green, white and yellow, SP holder	**450.00**
Dinner Service for 12, Napoleon Ivy, yellow border, gray leaves	**650.00**
Ewer, 8½″, pear shape, ribbed handle, satry's mask, c1800.	**350.00**
Flower Holder, 5½″ h, 3¾″ d, pierced top, pedestal base, salt glaze, light gray, blue flowers and leaves, mkd Wedgwood only	**275.00**
Plates	
9″, hunting dogs center, mottled deep blue ground, gold trim, mkd Wedgwood England, Portland vase	**145.00**
9″, Strawflower pattern, c1825	**130.00**
Sweetmeat, cov, 5½″, pedestal base, pink ground, gold filigree medallion portrait of man's head, blue Wedgwood mark	**65.00**
Tea Caddy, 8″, octagonal, Imari type dec, brown Wedgwood mark	**60.00**
Teapot, 6½″, ivory ground, pink and gold floral dec, gold handle and knob, brown Wedgwood mark	**125.00**

PEARLWARE

Bough Pot, pierced cov, 8½″, urn shape, mottled brown, stiff leaves at pedestal base, mkd	**1,000.00**
Box, 9″, oblong, brown print and enamel birds, butterflies and floral sprigs, gilt band at rims, imp Wedgwood, c1869.	**150.00**
Cups and Saucers	
Coffee, blue floral dec, c1815.	**100.00**
Demitasse	**175.00**
Fruit Stand, 12⅞″, center floral spray, gilt wigglework border, molded foliate rim, imp Wedgwood, c1845. . . .	**150.00**
Jardiniere, 5⅞″, round tapered body, dark brown ovals dec, dark brown band border with flower heads, imp Wedgwood, early 19th C	**100.00**
Leaf Plate, 8⅜″, green enamel ground, veining, gilt edged rim, imp Wedgwood, c1825.	**150.00**
Pitcher, 3⅛″, Chrysanthemum, imp Wedgwood, c1810.	**150.00**
Plates	
8⅝″, shell shape, shaded pink, imp Wedgwood, c1871	**55.00**

9½″, Water Nymph, water lilies and leaves, imp Wedgwood Pearl, c1840	**50.00**
Platter, 10½″, Chrysanthemum, iron red floral border, imp Wedgwood, c1810	**175.00**
Soup Tureen, cov and ladle, blue dahlias, green foliage, black rope dec edge	**400.00**
Sweetmeat Dish, 5¼″, shell shape, scalloped edge, c1875	**35.00**
Vase, cov, 6⅝″, tan slip engine turned gadroons, relief beadwork and swags, imp Wedgwood, late 18th C	**425.00**

QUEENSWARE

Bough Pot, 10″, emb, pierced top, c1845.	**375.00**
Chocolate Pot, 4″, green leaf dec	**125.00**
Condiment Set, 8½″	**150.00**
Pitcher, 5″, white, pink dec	**60.00**
Platter, oval, reticulated, mkd Wedgwood	**450.00**
Sauce Tureen, cov, 8¾″ l, enamel floral attached stand, Wedgwood	**90.00**

TERRA COTTA WARE

Ashtray, 4½″, scenic, laurel border . . .	**50.00**
Candlesticks, pr, 7¾″, circular, enamel flower dec, imp Wedgwood, c1840 . .	**300.00**
Cup and Saucer	**85.00**
Pitcher, 4½″, c1820	**150.00**
Sugar, cov, classical relief, acanthus leaves on cov, 1850	**175.00**
Teapot, cov, 6″, plain	**200.00**
Tobacco Jar, cov, round, classical figures, Wedgwood Made in England, 20th C	**190.00**

WELLER POTTERY

History: In 1872 Samuel A. Weller opened a small factory in Fultonham, near Zanesville, Ohio, to produce utilitarian stoneware, such as milk pans and sewer tile. In 1882 he moved his facilities to Zanesville. In 1890 Weller built a new plant in the Putnam section of Zanesville along the tracks of the Cincinnati and Miskingum Railway. Additions followed in 1892 and 1894.

In 1894 Weller entered into an agreement with William A. Long to purchase the Lonhuda Faience Company, which had developed an art pottery line under the guidance of Laura A. Fry, formerly of Rookwood. Long left in 1895, but Weller continued to produce Lonhuda under a new name, Louwelsa. Replacing Long as art director was Charles Babcock Upjohn. He, along with Jacques Sicard, Frederick Hurten Rhead, and Gazo Fudji, developed Weller's art pottery lines.

At the end of World War I, many prestige lines were discontinued; and, Weller concentrated on commercial wares. Rudolph Lorber joined the staff and designed lines such as Roma, Forest, and Knifewood. In 1920 Weller purchased the plant of the Zanesville Art Pottery. Weller claimed to be the largest pottery in the country.

Art pottery enjoyed a revival when the Hudson Line was introduced in the early 1920s. The 1930s saw Coopertone and Graystone Garden ware added. However, the depression forced the closing of the Putnam plant and one on Marietta Street in Zanesville. After World War II, cheap Japanese imports took over Weller's market. In 1947 Essex Wire Company of Detroit bought the controlling stock. Early in 1948 operations ceased.

References: Sharon and Bob Huxford, *The Collectors Encyclopedia Of Weller Pottery*, Collector Books, 1979.

Periodical: *The Glaze*, P. O. Box 4929, Springfield, MO 65804.

Collectors' Club: American Art Pottery Association, P. O. Box 714, Silver Springs, MD 20901.

Additional Listings: See *Warman's Americana & Collectibles* for more examples.

Vase, 6¾″, Hudson, white ground, dec, imp mark, $245.00.

Ashtrays
Coppertone, 4½″, figural frog, ink
stamp 60.00
Roma, 3″, ivory, floral dec 55.00
Baskets
Silvertone, 13″, molded grapes, ink
stamp 200.00
Warwick, 9″, twisted handle, molded
brown and green leaves, ink
stamp 175.00
Bowls
Bonito, 10½″, round, 4¾″ flower frog,
sgd, artist NC 120.00
Kenova, 4½″, molded lily 125.00
Candlesticks, pr
Coopertone, 3½″, round, mkd "Weller
Pottery" 120.00
Glendale, 5½″, bird dec 150.00
Console Set, 4 pc, Silvertone, round
bowl, 12″ w, 3½″ h, pr candlesticks,
5¾″ w, 2¼″ h, flower frog, 4½″ w,
sgd 250.00
Ewers
Floretta, 10½″, bisque ground, incised
pears 375.00
Louwelsa, 7″, brown glaze, yellow daffodil, artist sgd, half circle 200.00
Figurals
Frog, Coppertone, 5½″ h, sgd, symbol 200.00

Squirrel, standing, Woodcraft, 7½″ . . 350.00
Woodpecker on tree stump, Brighton,
6½″ h, imp block 275.00
Inkwell, 7 x 3¼″, turtle with pottery insert
and lid, frog handle 325.00
Jardineres
Dickensware, 1st line, 8½″, brown, floral dec, half circle 350.00
Forest, 8½″, trees 250.00
Louwelsa, 8 x 9½″, brown, pansy dec,
sgd 250.00
Jardineres with Pedestals
Flemish, 29½″, floral dec 550.00
Ivory, 31½″, cream and brown daisies,
black trim 750.00
Lamp, oil, Dickensware, 12″ h to top of
wick, 11″ d base, brown, tulips in red
and yellow 275.00
Mugs
Dickensware, 4½″, brown, molded
white lily of the valley 350.00
Louwelsa, 6⅛″, brown glaze, Indian
portrait, sgd "L. J. Burgess" 900.00
Pitcher, Forest, 5½″, glazed, #14 . . . . 135.00
Planters
Forest, 6½ x 3½″, small 70.00
Souevo, hanging, 6½″, pointed base,
geometric design 165.00
Woodcraft, 7¼ x 6″, 3 foxes imp
block 175.00
Plaque, McKinley profile, 4½″ w, gray,
imp block 50.00
Tankards
Etna, 14″, shaded gray, grapes 350.00
Louwelsa, 11″, blackberries, artist sgd
HH 255.00

Tobacco Jars, cov

    Dickensware, 6½", light green to blue, incised leprachon smoking pipe, cream and brown............ **375.00**

    Knifewood, 6½", bird dogs, ducks, leaves, treets, block letters...... **400.00**

Umbrella Stand, Louwelsa, 22½", brown, yellow chrysanthemums **325.00**

Urn, Hudson, 14", blue, dogwood, 2 handles, sgd, symbols............. **850.00**

Vases

    Aurelian, 6 x 7½", ftd, dark brown, yellow tiger lily, green leaves, artist sgd F, #587................... **485.00**

    Baldin, 9½ x 9½", fruit, shades of green and brown, 2 handles, imp block sgd **225.00**

    Floretta, 7½", light and dark brown glaze, molded grapes.......... **175.00**

    Forest, 8", oval................ **150.00**

    Glendale, double, 7 x 7¾", bird on nest with 4 blue eggs.......... **185.00**

    Hudson, 8½", green, blue morning glories, artist sgd "Pillsbury", imp block.................... **400.00**

    Hudson, floor, 15", pink and light green ground, iris, blue, yellow, green leaves, artist sgd "Timberlake", imp block.............. **1,350.00**

    Louwelsa, 7½ x 8", pillow shape, portrait of man's head, sgd, # **950.00**

    Silvertone, 8½", floral dec, 2 handles, sgd, symbol.................. **135.00**

    Woodcraft, 16" h, owl perched on lime by knothole, imp block......... **575.00**

Wall Pockets

    Glendale, 7 x 7¼", double bud, yellow bird and nest................ **225.00**

    Woodcraft

        Owl in circle, 10"............. **150.00**

        Squirrel, 9½"................. **150.00**

Window Box, Forest, 5¼ x 14½" l, imp mark **200.00**

WHALING

History: Whaling items are a specialized part of nautical collecting. Provenance is of prime importance since whaling collectors want assurances that their pieces are from a whaling voyage. Since ship's equipment seldom carries a ship's identification, some individuals have falsely attributed a whaling provenance to general nautical items. Know the dealer, auction house, or collector from whom you buy.

Special tools, e.g., knives, harpoons, lances, spades, etc., do not overlap the general nautical line. Maker's marks and condition determine value for these items.

Sotheby's offered the Barbara Johnson whaling collection in four recent sales, the fourth being held in December 1983. The fame of the collection and the understandable desire to own a part of it led to very high prices. These prices may not be sustained when some material is later resold, unless provenance to the collection is provided.

Richard Bourne, Hyannis, Massachusetts, and Chuck DeLuca, York, Maine, regularly hold auctions featuring whaling material.

Reference: Thomas G. Lytle, *Harpoons And Other Whalecraft*, Old Dartmouth Historical Society, 1984.

Museums: Cold Spring Harbor Museum, Long Island, NY; Kendall Whaling Museum, Sharon, MA; Mystic Seaport Museum, Mystic, CT; National Maritime Museum, San Francisco, CA; Old Dartmouth Historical Society, New Bedford, MA; Whaling Museum, Nantucket, MA.

Additional Listings: Nautical Items and Scrimshaw.

Advisor: Bill Wheeler.

Apothecary Chest, complete medicine chest with bottles of medicine and some implements, brass side handles, ivory maker's label on top, good cond, evidence of old repairs **500.00**

Articles, contact between the various members of the crew and the ship setting forth each man's job and pay together with the rules of the voyage, *Ontario*, Captain Hyram Prior, Boston to North Atlantic, Dec. 1846, sgd by Collector of Customs, Boston, framed, 24½ x 19¾"................... **250.00**

Bag, cloth, paper label for "Whale Smoking Tobacco," picture of whale and ship in background, good cond..... **100.00**

Bill of Sale for ship's hardware, e.g., cable anchors, rigging, chain, etc., 12½ x 8" folded, 3 pgs, c30 items listed, Brown Lennox in Columbia, 1835, bought by Capt. Welch and owners, name *Elisa Warwick* penciled in **25.00**

Block, massive lignum vitae whaleship's double cutting-in block, used to hoist blubber aboard, one wooden and one iron sheeve mkd on one side "s" as a line guide, sold with a whaleship's flat block, wooden sheeve, iron strap **675.00**

Block, whalebone, 3⅓" l, Nantucket, c1870, carved from one piece of whalebone, whalebone sheeve held in place with a whale ivory pin which has a steel core **360.00**

Blubber Fork, used to pitch cut up pieces of blubber into the boiling pot (tryworks), head only, 18" l, unmarked.................... **325.00**

Blubber Spade, used to cut blubber on deck, initial "K" carved on handle .. **200.00**

Bottle, glass, paper label "Ideal Sperm Sewing Machine Oil," Providence, RI, bottle retains about half its contents, good cond **150.00**

Branding Iron, burns name of owner on casks of whale oil, brass head, 8½ x 1″, "E. S. Mitchell" on iron shaft **65.00**

Broadside, Kehew's Navigation Store, New Bedford, 7 x 9″, framed, printed on green paper advertising "charts of all parts of the world visited by whalemen" **675.00**

Chart, M. E. Maury, pub. by Harper and Brothers, 1868, showing "the present states of our knowledge to the drift of the ocean . . . ," together with a printed map of the harbor of New Bedford, c1850, 11½ x 15″, framed, some water stains **450.00**

Cooper's Scribe, c1820, Greenport N.Y. Whaling cooperage, used by cooper to mark the howell or recess in the head of the barrel, all wood including the keeper screw **85.00**

Crows Nest Glasses, c1850, copper binoculars, orig sailcloth stitched and labeled bag with spliced lanyard, glasses 6¼″ l **1,100.00**

Dipper, whale oil, used to dip oil from the trypot to the cooling cask, copper bucket ±2 gallons, wooden shaft, 6′ l, mkd on handle "Ship Eagle 1890" **200.00**

Door, cabin, captain's, Whaleship *Admiral Blake*, Capt. William C. Hathaway, dated 1860, off square, paneled, vented, sliding door made to accomodate the shape of the hull, old stencils on the face with ship and captain's name, cedar, painted and combed wood grain, iron lock **1,000.00**

Flags, two ship's flags from Whaleship *William S. Henry*, Capt. D. B. Greene, c1860, first an American flag with 37

stars, 139½ x 76½″, second a flag with blue field and 30 stars, each mkd in old hand "D. B. Greene" **1,000.00**

Hangings, Captain's Cabin Macrame (fancy work), from *Wanderer*, 1924, curtains and valance in geometric intricate knot work designs, twists, and geometrics, 82″ l **900.00**

Harpoon Iron, single toggle type, sgd "JDD" for maker James D. Driggs, used, bent, and straightened **300.00**

Lance, killing head, device with which the whale was killed after catching him with the harpoon, 52″ l, unsigned, surface rust and pitting, split cone mount **150.00**

Lithograph, "*HMS AGAMEMNON*" laying the Atlantic cable in 1858. A whale crosses the line," hand colored, stern view of cable ship with whale crossing cable where it enters water, 11¾ x 14¾″, framed **135.00**

Log Book, whale stamps, Whaleship *Adeline Gibbs*, Fairhaven, voyage to the Pacific, commences October 10, 1843, 5 or 6 entries per page, 40 whale stamp impressions **2,400.00**

Polar Bear Rug, bear captured c1895, estate of Capt. Albert C. Sherman, New Bedford, who was master of several steam whalers in the 1890s, especially active in Herschel Island area of western artic, some minor yellowing **2,250.00**

Painting, ship, Steam Whaler *Beluga*, San Francisco, with sails furled and trying out oil in artic waters, framed with documents including the captain's instructions on back, 27½ x 36¼″ **6,000.00**

Sailcloth bags, like duffle bags, two macrame cloth and fancy work sailors' clothing bags **150.00**

Sea Letter, Whaleship *John Coggeshall*, New Bedford, John C. Norton, master, dated Oct. 23, 1852, four languages, sgd Millard Fillmore as President and Daniel Webster as Sec. of State **1,200.00**

Seaman's Protection Papers, printed document sgd and filled in by official in port of issue, identifies an Am. seaman, includes his name, description, place of birth, and certifies he is Am. citizen and entitled to protections thereof, issued to Martin Baker by Lemuel Williams, collector of New Bedford **355.00**

Street Sign, "Whalers Lane," 34½″ l, painted pine, Nantucket, c1925, weathered paint in black on white. . . **250.00**

Trypot, kettle in which blubber was boiled down to provide the whale oil,

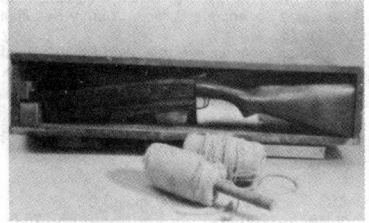

Bridger harpoon gun, 30¼″ l gun, 14″ barrel, fitted wooden case 32½″ l, 7″ w, 8½″ h, case painted gray, black lettering reads "Bridger Shoulder Line Gun Naval, Co." complete with ammunition, tools, instructions, $300.00.

32" h, 41" d, iron, 19th C [Johnson collection]. **1,000.00**

WHIELDON

WHIELDON

History: The Staffordshire potter, Thomas Whieldon, established his shop in 1740. He is best known for his mottled ware, molded in forms of vegetables, fruits and leaves. Josiah Spode and Josiah Wedgwood, in different capacities, had connections with Whieldon.

Whieldon ware is a generic term. His wares were never marked; other potters made similar items. Whieldon ware is agate-tortoise shell earthenware, in limited shades of green, brown, blue and yellow. Most pieces are utilitarian items, e.g., dinner ware and plates; but, figurines and other decorative pieces are found.

Bowl, waste, Cauliflower, molded green
   overlapping leaves with white florettes
   border, white int., Wedgwood-Whiel-
   don, c1755. . . . . **675.00**
Cradle, 3¾", 3 mottled colors, c1770. . **375.00**
Figurine, 3¼", pug dog, seated,
   streaked, ochre, brown and gravy. . . **450.00**
Leaf Dish, 7" 3 overlapping leaves
   molded with veins, stalk handle with
   pendent flowers, green and yellow,
   c1755. . . . . **225.00**
Plates
   9¼", octagonal, rope twist rim, tor-
     toise shell glaze, manganese,
     ochre, blue and green, reverse in
     speckled gray **250.00**

Plate, 8½", octagonal, $500.00.

9½", feather edge, tortoise shell
   glaze. **300.00**
Tea Caddy, 4¾", stippled ground, glazed
   vertical bands of green and yellow,
   Wedgwood-Whieldon, c1780 . . . . . . **325.00**
Teapot, 4", Grape. **1,100.00**

WHISKEY BOTTLES, EARLY

History: The earliest whiskey bottles made in America were blown by pioneer glass makers in the 18th century. The Biningers (1820–1880s) were the first bottles specifically designed for whiskey. After the 1860s distillers favored the cylindrical 'fifth' form.

The first embossed brand name bottle was the amber E. G. Booz Old Cabin Whiskey bottle which was issued in 1860. Many stories have been told about this classic bottle. Unfortunately, most are not true. Research has proved that "booze" was a corruption of the words "bouse" and "boosy" from the 16th and 17th centuries. It was only a coincidence that the Philadelphia distributor also was named Booz. This bottle has been reproduced extensively.

Prohibition (1920–1933) brought the legal whiskey industry to a standstill. Whiskey was marked "medicinal purposes only" and distributed by private distillers in unmarked or paper label bottles.

The size and shape of whiskey bottles is standard. Colors are limited to amber, amethyst, clear, green, and cobalt blue (rare). Corks were the common closure in the early period, with the inside screw top being used in the 1880–1910 period.

Bottles made prior to 1880 are the most desirable. In purchasing a bottle with a label, condition is a critical factor. In the 1950s distillers began to issue collectors' special edition bottles to help increase sales.

References: Hugh Cleveland, *Bottle Pricing Guide,* Collector Books, 1980; Ralph & Terry Kovel, *The Kovels' Bottle Price List,* Crown Publishers, 1982, 6th ed.; Carlo & Dot Sellari, *The Illustrated Price Guide To Antique Bottles,* Country Beautiful Corp., 1975.

Periodicals: *Antique Bottle World,* 5003 West Berwin, Chicago, IL 60630; *Old Bottle Magazine,* P. O. Box 243, Bend, OR 97701. Subscription: $19.00.

Additional Listings: See *Warman's Americana & Collectibles* for a listing of Collectors' Special Editions Whiskey Bottles.

Bell/Of Anderson, rect, milk glass, 8",
   qt, 1870–1900 . . . . **75.00**
Bininger's Regulator, clock, golden am-
   ber, 6", 1850–1860. . . . . **200.00**
E. G. Booz's/Old Cabin/Whiskey, G V
   11-4, Whitney Glass Works, Glass-
   boro, New Jersey, golden amber,
   6¾" 1860–1880 . . . . **350.00**

Hodico, Hollenbach, Dietrien & Co, Reading, PA, lgt, amber, 11⅛″ h, $40.00.

Brown Thompson & Co/Louisville, Ky, amber, 1860–1890	**15.00**
Casper's Whiskey/Made By Honset/ North/Carolina People, cobalt blue, 11⅞″, 1870–1890.	**225.00**
Chambers & Brown, amber, c1865. . . .	**20.00**
Chapin & Gore, amber, 10¼″, 1870– 1890	**15.00**
Chestnut/Grove/G. Wharton, golden amber, vertically ribbed, 9½″, 1860– 1880	**250.00**
Cleve, Joseph, amber, 1870–1890 . . .	**15.00**
R. B. Cutter's/Pure/Bourbon, handled, gray-puce, smoky green handle, 8¼″, ¾ qt, 1845–1860	**600.00**
Duffy Malt Whiskey Company/Balti- more, Md, aqua, 11¼″, 1870–1890 .	**15.00**
Flora Temple, green, 8⅜″, pt, 1860– 1880	**275.00**
Jas. H. Gibson/St. Louis, Mo, amber, 12¼″, 1860–1890	**25.00**
Ginter/Co/Importers, deep yellow- green, 11″, 1860–1880	**60.00**
J. T. & Co/Walnut St/Philada, amber, 9½″, 1860–1880	**60.00**
Michaelus & Lindeman/New York, am- ber, 11″, 1860–1880.	**30.00**
E. P. Middleton & Bro/Phila/Wheat Whiskey, 12¼″, 1860–1880	**125.00**
G. W. Middleton/Philada. Wheat Whis- key/1825, amber, 9½″, 1860–1880.	**60.00**
The/Old Mill, handled, golden amber, applied emb medallion, 1⅛″, 1840– 1860	**270.00**
Edwd Quinlwan/St Louis/Mo, amber, 9½″, 1860–1880	**25.00**
Quirye/(Dog's Head)/Dr Koch/Berlin, milk glass, 8¼″, 1880–1900	**85.00**

Turner Brothers/New York, Buffalo, NY & San Francisco, Cal, sq, deep olive green, 9¾″, 1860–1800	**65.00**

WHITE PATTERNED IRONSTONE

History: White patterned ironstone is a heavy earthenware, first patented in 1813 by Charles Mason, Staffordshire, England, using the name "Patent Ironstone China." Other English potters soon began copying this opaque, feldspathic, white china.

All white ironstone dishes first became available in the American market in the early 1840s. The first patterns had simple Gothic lines similar to the shapes used in transfer wares. Pattern shapes were named New York, Union, and Atlantic, designed to appeal to the American housewife. Motifs, such as wheat, corn, oats, and poppies, were embossed on the forms as the American western prairie influenced design. Eventually over 200 shapes and patterns, with variations of finials and handles, were made.

White patterned ironstone is identified by shape names and pattern names. Many potters only named the shape in their catalogues. Pattern names usually refer to the decoration motif.

Reference: Jean Wetherbee, *A Look At White Ironstone,* Wallace-Homestead, 1980.

Baker, open, Atlantic shape, Boote, 1853	**30.00**
Bowls	
Fruit, pedestal, Elsmore Forster	**50.00**
Soup, Ribbed Raspberry with Bloom.	**20.00**
Butter, cov, Athens shape, Podmore Walker, 1857	**75.00**

Coffee Pot, Grape Medallion, $200.00.

Cake Plate, pedestal, Grenade, Boote .	65.00
Child's teapot and creamer, Ceres, Elsmore Forster.	160.00
Cookie Plate, pedestal, Alcock.	20.00

Creamers

Corn & Oats, Davenport & Wedgwood	30.00
Gothic shape, Alcock.	42.00
Grenade shape, Boote.	54.00
Memmon shape, Meir	52.00

Gravy Boats

Full Ribbed, Pankhurst.	35.00
Octagon shape, Shaw, 1851	35.00
Honey Dish, Laurel, Wedgwood	15.00
Hot Toddy, Wheat and Barley, Meakin	10.00
Pitcher, Milk, Prairie shape, Clementson.	55.00

Pitchers, Water

Full Ribbed, Pankhurst, 9¾" h	80.00
Hyacinth, Wedgwood.	40.00

Plates, luncheon

Budded Vine, Meakin.	15.00
Wheat, Meakin	25.00

Plates, dinner

President, Edwards	20.00
Sydenham shape, Boote	15.00
Trent shape, Alcock	20.00
Platter, Ribbed Raspberry with Bloom, Meakin.	20.00
Punch Bowl, handled, Gothic shape, J.F..	110.00
Relish, Shell, Pankhurst	25.00

Sauce Tureens, 3 pcs

Corn & Oats, Davenport & Wedgwood	75.00
Memmon shape, Meir, 1856.	90.00
Ribbed Chain, Pankhurst	110.00

Soup Tureens, 4 pcs

Atlantic shape, Boote, 1858	375.00
Canada shape, 1877	275.00
Twin Leaves, Edwards, 1851	270.00

Sugars, covered

Octagon shape, Boote, 1851	35.00
Tiny Oak & Acorns, Pankhurst	45.00
Teapot, cov, St. Louis shape, Edwards	95.00
Toothbrush Holder, Wheat & Blackberry, Meakin.	30.00

Vegetables, covered

Atlantic shape, Boote, 1858	85.00
Fuchsia, Meakin	45.00
Trent shape, Alcock	35.00
Wheat	50.00
Wash Bowl, pitcher, Wheat & Blackberry, Meakin	175.00

WILLOW PATTERN CHINA

History: Willow pattern china derives its name from a design in the Chinese tradition and its inspiration from early Canton ware brought to Europe from China in the 16th century. The willow pattern is attributed to Thomas Minton who was apprenticed in the 1780s to Thomas Turner at Caughley Pottery in England's Staffordshire district.

The first (1780) underglaze transfer design did not contain all the Chinese legend motifs found in the later "standard" willow pattern developed in 1810 by Josiah Spode. The standard pattern has several distinctive features - a willow tree, two pagodas, a rail fence with finials, two birds, and a three-arch bridge with three figures crossing it.

By the year 1830 there were over 200 makers of willow pattern china in England. By the 20th century its production had spread to Germany, France, Japan, Holland, Ireland, and the United States. English firms still producing the pattern are Booth's by Royal Doulton, Burleigh, Coalport, Johnson Brothers, Meakin, Sadler (teapot only), and Wedgwood.

The most common dinnerware color is blue. However, pieces also can be found in black, brown, green, pink, and yellow (mustard made by Royal Doulton), as well as in polychrome. The willow pattern extended beyond china dinnerware and can be found on fabrics, wallcoverings, plastic tumblers, snuff tins, candles, needlepoint, linen calendars, napkins, placemats, tea cosies, Toby jugs, tiny miniature sets, watches, stationary, and tinware.

References: Mary Frank Gaston, *Blue Willow: An Identification & Value Guide,* Collector Books, 1983; Veryl Marie Worth, *Willow Pattern China,* privately printed, 1979.

Collectors' Club: The Willow Society, 359 Davenport Road, Suite 6, Toronto, Ontario, Canada M5R 1K5. Dues: $10.00. *The Willow Transfer Quarterly.*

Additional Listings: Buffalo Pottery. See *Warman's Americana & Collectibles* for more examples.

Advisor: Lois K. Misiewicz.

Pitcher, 7", white ground, blue handle and spout, gold trim, $165.00.

Butter Dish, cov, 8″ d, Buffalo	75.00
Cake Stand, 12″ d, 3″ h, mkd Ironstone	125.00
Castor Set, china condiment holders, wooden lazy susan, Japan	100.00
Cheese Dish, slanted cov, unmarked	100.00
Compote, 9½″ d, 5″ h, Coalport	150.00
Cup and Saucer, plain edge, Allerton	20.00
Egg Cup, double, English	15.00
Gravy, liner, 9 x 5″, Allerton	60.00
Pitcher, Milk, 12″ h, polychrome, English, unmarked	100.00

Plates

6″, plain edge, Allerton	10.00
8½″, daisy pattern, floral border, Allerly	75.00
9″, plain edge, Allerton	17.50
10″, plain edge, Allerton	20.00

Platter

11¼ x 8½″, *old Burleigh Ware*	65.00
19 x 15½″, well and tree, scalloped footed base, mkd Semi-China	150.00
Pudding Mold, 4½″ d, English	25.00
Ship's Light, brass candle holder, Royal 6″ plate	50.00
Sugar and Creamer, plain edge, Allerton	65.00
Tea Caddy, 8″ h, mkd on base "Rington Ltd., The Merchants, Newcastle upon Tyne"	125.00
Teapot, plain edge, Allerton	85.00
Toaster, Pan Electric Mfg Co. of Cleveland, OH	200.00
Toby Jug, English, some mkd with Staffordshire knot	150.00
Toothpick, English	35.00
Wash Set, bowl, pitcher, chamber pot, toothbrush, tumbler, and 3-piece soap dish, flow blue, Doulton, English	600.00
Vegetable, cov, 9½″ d, 4″ h, Booth's	85.00

WITCH BALLS

History: A witch ball simply is a hollow sphere of colored or multicolored glass. There are various myths surrounding the origin and purpose of the witch ball. Some say they were displayed by the fireplace to catch demon spirits as they descended the chimney and then were taken outside for cleaning. Others contend they were used to store salt by the chimney to keep it dry.

In all probability a witch ball was a glassmaker's whimsey, used strictly for decorative purposes atop an unfilled flower vase.

Don't confuse witch balls with Christmas tree ornaments, target balls, floats, or early glass fire extinguishers. Witch balls come in a variety of sizes. They can not be attributed to one specific glass maker or company.

Amber Glass, 7¼″ h, vase, 11¼″ overall, blown, Saratoga, NY	450.00

Goblet and witch ball, lattice, (Lutz-type), pink, white, and gold design, 7″ h goblet, 4″ d ball, $385.00.

Cobalt Blue to sapphire, 2½″, ball only, blown in mold, clear	125.00

Nailsea Type

6″ ftd vase, 13″ overall, clear, white opaque loopings, scarred pontil mark, South Jersey glass, c1870	550.00
8¾″ ftd vase, 7½″ d ball, clear, white loopings, South Jersey	475.00
9″ ruffled rim vase, 16″ overall, pale aqua, white opaque loopings, polished pontil, South Jersey glass, c1875	775.00
9⅞″ ball and holder, blown holder, applied foot and stem, joined by wafers, clear ball with white, red, and blue loopings	850.00
Opalescent Glass, blue, 5″ h blown pitcher with applied handle, 4″ d, ball	250.00

WOODENWARES

History: Many utilitarian household objects and farm implements were made of wood. Although they were used heavily, these implements were made of the strongest woods and well taken care of by their owners. This category serves as a catch-all for wood objects which do not fit into other categories.

Additional Listings: See *Warman's Americana & Collectibles* for more examples.

Bee Carrier, 10″, sliding glass top, dovetailed, 3 compartments	50.00
Book Press, 14¼ x 6¾″ bed, 19″ h, iron	

Egg cup, Lehn ware, hp, pink ground, stem with leaves, applied rose decals, remnant of paper label, pedestal foot, 3½" h, $125.00.

screw, wooden handles, old red paint	350.00
Bowls	
7", heavy burled	110.00
11¾", oval, burled	225.00
25 x 15½", chopping, oval, solid maple, old natural finish	300.00
Boxes	
9½" l, 5" h, oval, bentwood pine, smaller box on lid, laced seams, wood spring catches, swivel lids, stylized floral relief carving	300.00
9½ x 5 x 5", sliding lid, walnut, dovetailed, base moulding	150.00
Bucket, sugar, 14½" d, 14½" h, all wooden stave construction, old gray paint	125.00
Butter Paddle, 9¼" l, 3½" w, 4 primitively carved compass stars	250.00
Butter Scoop, 9¼", ash, burl, figure and hook on end of handle	120.00
Compote, 10½" d, 8¼" h, turned, red paint	90.00
Cutting Board, 14¾ x 7½", oblong, primitive painting of man smoking clay pipe	65.00
Dipper, 6¼" l, 6¼" d, burled	225.00
Foot Warmer, 9¼" x 7½" x 7¾", chip carved, cast brass handle, reticulated opening in top, white clay dish with green glaze inside for coals, European	150.00
Funnel, cider	60.00
Grain Measure Set, 5 pcs, oak, copper nails, mkd Daniel Ceagin, manufacturer and seller, Wilton, NH	400.00

Jar, cov, 12¾" d, 9½" h, turned from 1 solid piece of fruitwood, button knob, bale handle, sgd "T P White Painsville, Ohio June 16th 1871"	1,200.00
Kraut Cutter, 20¾ x 8", walnut, dark finish, heart cut out top	135.00
Ladle, 9⅝", birch, curl in bowl, carved primitive dog head on end of handle	275.00
Mortar and Pestle, 7", turned maple mortar, lignum vitae pestle	165.00
Pastry Board, 38½ x 20", camelback top, red paint on side, hole for hanging	100.00
Pegboard, 46" l, poplar, 7 whittled hooks, old gray patina	90.00
Pipe Box, 10½", cherry, one drawer, scalloped top, old red paint	150.00
Rack, hanging, 21" h, 12½" w, walnut, hand carved griffin	85.00
Reel, 31" h, maple base, mortised pine top, orig dark green paint	250.00
Rolling Pin, maple	8.00
Salt, master, cov, 4", maple, 3 concentric rings, mid 18th C	125.00
Smoothing Board, 26½" l, relief carved with crown, monogram, chip carving, stylized horse handle, 1817	800.00
Spice Box, 9¾", round, bentwood, "Spice" stenciled on lid, tin corners, int. canisters with stenciled labels, stamped "Patent Package Co., Newark, New Jersey, Pat Aug 31, 1858"	150.00
Spoon, 6¾", fruitwood	45.00
Towel Rack, 31" h, 33¾" w, mortised pine, shoe feet, orig dark finish	300.00
Wall Pocket, 6", basket shape, ivy carving, orange and green paint	45.00

WORLD'S FAIRS AND EXPOSITIONS

History: The Great Exhibition of 1851 in London marked the beginning of the World's Fair and Exposition movement. The fairs generally feature exhibitions from nations around the world displaying the best of their industrial and scientific achievements.

Many important technological advances have been introduced at world's fairs. Examples include the airplane, telephone, and electric lights. The ice cream cone, hot dog, and iced tea were products of vendors at fairs. Art movements often were closely connected to fairs with the Paris Exhibition of 1900 generally considered to have assembled the best of the works of the Art Nouveau artists.

References: Kurt Krueger, *Meet Me In St. Louis—The Exomumia Of The 1904 World's Fair*, Krause Publications, 1979; Howard Rossen and John Kaduck, *Columbia World's Fair Collectibles*, Wallace-Homestead, 1976, revised price list 1982.

Collectors' Clubs: ECHO, 1436 Killarney, Los Angeles, CA 90065; World's Fair P. O. Box 339, Corte Madera, CA 94925.

Salt and pepper shakers, egg shape, (left) matte finish, blue letters; orig pewter top, $75.00; (right) glossy finish, orange letters and blue numbers, orig pewter top, $65.00.

1876, Philadelphia, United States International Centennial Exhibition, glass paperweight, scenes of exposition buildings.................... **75.00**

1893, Chicago, World's Columbian Exposition
Bell, 4½″, frosted, twisted handle, 5 point star................... **140.00**
Candle holder, 2 pcs, handled, 18 multicolored jewels and fancy filigree . **145.00**
Clock, frying pan.............. **200.00**
Salt, egg shape, sgd Libby........ **125.00**

1901, Buffalo, NY, Pan-American Exposition
Booklet, 8¾ x 6″, 80 pgs......... **20.00**
Napkin ring, SP.............. **20.00**
Paperweight, figural buffalo, ready to charge, 3⅝″ l, milk glass, green, hexagonal base, made for Greentown exhibit................ **500.00**

1904, St. Louis, Louisiana Purchase Exposition
Pocket match holder........... **25.00**
Ticket.................... **20.00**
Tip tray, pavillion with insets of Napoleon and Jefferson, American Can Co.................. **35.00**

1907, Hampton Roads, VA, Jamestown Ter-Centennial Exposition, bisque figure of Pocahontas next to tree with child on swing............... **75.00**

1933–34, Chicago, Century of Progress International Exposition
Ashtray, copper, "Sky Ride," 1934 Chicago Expo **8.00**
Marbles, 28, orig see-thru cheesecloth bag, unopened............... **45.00**
Plate, 7½″, Black Forest, mkd Pickard **18.00**

1935, San Diego, California-Pacific International Exposition, map, 22 x 33″ **20.00**

1939–40, New York City, New York World's Fair, Plate, American Potter **30.00**
1939–40, San Francisco, Golden Gate International Exposition, compact ... **15.00**
1962, Seattle, Century 21 Exposition, bowl, 8″, round, black plastic, logo, Needle, Monorail.............. **5.00**

YELLOW WARE

History: Yellow ware is a heavy earthenware of differing weight and strength which varies in color from a rich pumpkin to lighter shades which are more tan than yellow. Although plates, nappies, and custard cups are found, kitchen bowls and other cooking utensils are most prevalent.

The first American yellow ware was produced at Bennington, Vermont. English yellow ware has additional ingredients which make its body much harder. Derbyshire and Sharp's were foremost among the English manufacturers.

Baking Dish, 11″, oval............ **85.00**
Bowls
4⅜ x 1⅞″, brown sponging **120.00**
4½ x 2¾″, tan and blue sponging. .. **110.00**
7⅜ x 2¼, blue sponge spatter, ext. deep amber glaze over blue dec.. **145.00**
8″, large rim spout, white band, brown stripes, blue seaweed type dec... **180.00**
12½ x 3¼″, braided rim, imp shield, "Sharpes Warrented Fireproof"... **45.00**
Chamber Pot, 8 x 5¾″, white band, brown stripes, seawood type dec ... **160.00**
Crock, brown band.............. **75.00**
Desk Set, 4 pcs, basket, pitcher, inkwell, sander, tied sheaf of wheat pattern, sanded finish, English **150.00**
Jar, cov, 8 x 6½″, white band with brown stripes, green seawood type dec ... **100.00**
Molds, food
Corn, oval.................. **75.00**
Fish, 5¾ x 7½″, oval, brown, sponged Rockingham glaze **100.00**
Pineapple, 4⅞ x 7″, oval **85.00**

Bowl, 6¼″ d, 2¾″ h, brown bands, $25.00.

Mug, 4¾", blue striping, mkd "100%
Buckeye Pure" 35.00
Pie Plates
  9⅞", green and brown sponged dec,
    slightly misshaped 55.00
  10", finger crimped edge, purple
    glaze. 75.00
Pitcher, 7¾", brown and blue sponge
  spatter band, brown stripes 125.00
Rolling Pin, 15½" l 100.00
Salt Crock, cov, hanging, 6 x 4", emb
  peacocks, amber runny glaze. 175.00
Spittoon, rect, wide and deep convex ribbing, sponged green-gray and brown
  dec 135.00
Toby Jug, 5⅜", hand molded face, ap-
  plied dec, 2 tone brown and clear
  glaze 155.00

ZANE WARE
MADE IN U.S.A.

ZANE POTTERY

History: In 1921 Adam Reed and Harry Mc-
Clelland bought the Peters and Reed Pottery in
Zanesville, Ohio. The firm continued production of
garden wares and introduced several new art lines:
"Sheen," "Powder Blue," "Crystalline," and
"Drip." The factory was sold in 1941 to Lawton
Gonder.

Additonal Listings: Gonder and Peters and
Reed.

Jardinnere, 34" h, green matte glaze,
artist sgd "Frank Ferreu," $295.00.

Bowl, 5", Moss Aztec 38.00
Candlesticks, pr, 10" twisted, blue,
  mkd 75.00
Vases
  7", Moss Aztec, pansy dec, #412 . .   25.00
  10", Landsun, tan, 4 deep blue glaze
    stripes.   40.00
Wall Pocket, 8¼", Moss Aztec. 35.00

LA MORO

ZANESVILLE POTTERY

History: Zanesville Art Pottery, one of several
potteries located in Zanesville, Ohio, began production in 1900. A line of utilitarian products was
first produced. Art pottery was introduced shortly
thereafter. The major line was La Moro which was
hand painted and decorated under glaze. The impressed block print mark La Moro appears on the
high glazed and matte glazed decorated ware. The
firm was bought by S. A. Weller in 1920 and became
known as Weller Plant No. 3.

References: Louise and Evan Purviance and
Norris F. Schneider, *Zanesville Art Pottery In Color*,
Mid-America Book Company, 1968; Evan and
Louise Purviance, *Zanesville Art Tile In Color*, Wal-
lace-Homestead Book Co., 1972.

Teapot, 2¾" h, souvenir type, dark
green, mkd "Tyces Pottery/Zanesville/
Ohio," $35.00.

Ashtray, 4" d, ivory. 20.00
Bowl and Flower Frog, 7", matte glaze,
  dark blue 40.00
Crock, 7", gallon size, blue number . . .   20.00
Paperweight, 6¼" l, turtle, amber. 120.00
Tile, 6", sq, scenic, windmill, blue and
  white 30.00
Vases
  8¾", bulbous bottom, cone top and
    neck, 2 handles, mkd La Moro . . . 300.00
  9½", pansy dec, mkd La Moro 250.00

ZSOLNAY POTTERY

History: Wilmos Zsolnay (1828–1900) assumed control of his brother's factory in Pécs, Hungary, in the mid-19th century. In 1899 Miklos, Wilmos's son, became manager. The firm still produces ceramic ware.

The early wares are highly ornamental, glazed, and have a cream color ground. "Eosin" glaze, a deep rich play of colors reminiscent of Tiffany's iridescent wares, received a gold medal at the 1900 Paris exhibition. Zsolnay Art Nouveau pieces show great creativity.

Originally no trademark was used. Beginning in 1878 a blue mark depicting the five towers of the cathedral at Pécs was used. The initials "TJM" represent the names of Miklos's three children.

Zsolnay's recent series of iridescent glazed figurines, which initially were inexpensive, now are being sought by collectors and show a steady increase in value.

Vase, 7⅞″, purple irid, mottled, elongated leaf, separated ribbon bands extending to lip forming handles, mkd "Zsolnay, PECS," $365.00.

Bowls
4″ h, 8″ d, heart shape, high glaze, fish, flowers, red, blue, and green, small gold curls 425.00
7½″ h, 12″ l, shape of two horns coming up to meet each other, reticulated on all 4 sides, leaf and flower dec int., and ext. lined with gold 475.00
Box, cov, 4 x 5″, green. 70.00
Celery Tray, 13″ l, 7½″ w, large diagonal band of piercing pastel floral dec, heavy lustre finish 175.00
Dish, 8½″ l, 7½″ w, fan shape, fold cver reticulated border, beige, gold, and pink dec. 160.00
Ewer, 7½″, cream ground, yellow and beige dec, reticulated gold neck band and gold base, ornate handle. 100.00
Figures
Boxer, 5½″, green. 60.00
Eagle, 6½″, green. 75.00
Fox, 4½″, green 50.00
Retriever, 9″ l, 7″ w, green. 85.00
Jug, 13¼″, floriform, green and blue irid lustre, sgd with medallion mark in relief, #5517M 85.00
Pin Dish, figural, girl 25.00
Plate, 8″, blue ground, purple orchids. . 65.00
Puzzle Jug, 8″ h, 4″ d, handled, beige, reticulated roundels, multicolored flowers, aqua jewels, gold trim, steeple mark, artist sgd 375.00
Tumbler, 6½″, irid green-gold lustre, 4 molded maidens, castle mark. 140.00
Vases
5½″, ovoid, irid red, applied finish of irregular flagstone dec with crevices in between 95.00
11″, scalloped rim, vivid cobalt, dark red leaves in panel at base. 125.00
14½″, closed top, open on each side, open reticulation on applied designs on all sides, light blue with gold, red, and light green dec 575.00
17½″ baluster, peacock lustre, printed and impressed mark. 650.00

PHOTO CREDITS

We wish to thank those who permitted us to photograph objects in their possession. Unfortunately, we are unable to identify the sources for all of our pictures; nevertheless, we are deeply appreciative for all who contributed to this and past editions, and to the 1st edition of *Warman's Americana & Collectibles.*

Alabama: Birmingham, Ida A. Noser. **California**: Ross, Laurel House Antiques; San Diego, Bob Brown; San Francisco, Beaver Bros. Antiques, Lynn and Arnold Scher, Butterfields, Di Lelio's; San Marcos, Dan Golden; Santee, Glaser's Antiques. **Connecticut**: East Hartford, The Pine Bough, Shirley and Harold Olsen; Sandy Hook, Bea Morgan; South Windsor, Lee and Bob Greenberg; Stamford, Donal Markey; Torrington, Noble Peddler Antiques, Rick and Linda Ronalter; Woodstock, David and Linda Arman.

Delaware: Wilmington, Terrace Antiques. **Florida**: Cape Coral, Charles Peterson, Jr., Country Closet Antiques, Sandra Martz; Clearwater Beach, Bill Wheeler; Skodack, Laurie Crusie; Tamarae, Re Collections, Lee and Harold Berman. **Georgia**: Atlanta, Art Deco Atlanta, Jim Marin, Solomon's Mines; Dunwoody, The Hoepfingers; Jefferson, Cunningham's Collectibles. **Illinois**: Arlington Heights, T. Johnson; Northbrook, Al and Susan Bagdade; Peotone, Kathy Wojciechowski.

Indiana: Bourbon, Corky Morris; Gary, Carolyn Stahl; Highland, V and A Antiques; Indianapolis, J & B Antiques, Bill and Jo Ann Voorhies, Ruby Cochran. **Iowa**: Arnold's Park, Paul and Paula Brenner. **Maine**: Kennebunk, Richard W. Oliver Auction & Art Gallery; Topsham, Allan and Helen Smith. **Maryland**: Annapolis, Theriault's; Cantonsville, C. M. Geppi.

Massachusetts: Boston, Lee R. Piper; Hyannis Port, Richard A. Bourne Co. Inc.; Melrose, Alma Libby Antiques; Middleboro, Charles and Barbara Adams; South Weymouth, Minnah's, Edna K. Burns; Weston, Jones' Antiques; Winchester, Dad's Follies, Lorry and Bruce Hanes; Worcester, Ralph U. Saarinen. **Michigan**: Monroe, Herb and Joyce Krueger. **New Hampshire**: Peterborough, Lee and Rally Dennis; Salem, B & B Antiques & Collectibles.

New Jersey: Barnegat, Linda Kleinman; Bergenfield, R.A.G. Time; Bridgewater, Roy and Josephine Woodall; Cape May, Cape Island Antiques, Roger Crawford; Denville, Mike Reffie; Edgewater, Krosnick Studio; Morris Plains, Elyce Litts; Old Bridge, Mrs. Galinsky; Oradell, Elliott Thomson; Paterson, Edward W. Leach; Toms River, Shelley, Norman, Phyllis Galinkin; Woodbury, Daphne Majewski.

New York: Brooklyn, Ben Weber; Center Moriches, Cedarfield Antiques, Jim and Geri Strebel; Corning, Blake's Antiques; Endicott, Terry Scanlin; Fishkill, Robert Doyle, Glenn Kramer; Johnson City, The Epergne; Merrick, Philip Chasen; Middletown, Ralph and Shirley Hofheinz; New York, Eppelsheimer & Co., John High, Pascoe & Solomon, Inc.; Oneida, Jan & Marilyn Eckhard; Oswego, Deco Dave; Poughkeepsie, Ken Moore; Riverhead, Lyon's Den; Rochester, Robert Neroni Antiques, Miriam S. Rogachefsky; Saugerties, Pat Guargilia; Valley Stream, Craig Dinner. **Ohio**: Akron, Nance Darrow; Canfield, Thomas Parent; Newton Falls, Bob and Kathy Wujcik; Novelty, Peggy Bialosky; Worthington, Betty Powell. **Oregon**: The Dalles, Hilda and Hugh Creighton.

Pennsylvania: Adamstown, Helen Bereskie, Dottie Freeman, Allan Teal, Bonnie Hohl; Allentown, Jim Lo Antiques; Bath, Roy Repsher; Biglerville, Attic Antiques, Ron and Bea Dewees; Boyertown, Stone House Antiques, Thelma Cook, Joe Rath; Carlisle, Schwiebert's Antiques; Cogan Station, Munsell's, Roan Bros. Auction Gallery; Coopersburg, Neil and Clodogh Wotring; Emmaus, Little Lehigh Antique Shop; Ephrata, Historical Society of Cocalico Valley; Gap, Burgess Antiques; Harrisburg, Jerry Orris; Horsham, Eyecatchers, Beth H. DiTullio; Huntingdon Valley, Copper Eagle Antiques, Mary L. Purdy, Edna C. Smith; Kulpsville, Kay Adams; Kutztown, Windy Hill Antiques, Dot and Jake Makosky; Langhorne, The Abrahams; Macungie, Thomas Moore; Mars, Craig and Norma Krisher; Martinsburg, John Querry; Mercer, Phil and Karol Atkinson; Montgomeryville, Burmese Cruet, Clarence and Betty Maier; New Hope, Ted and Linda Freed; Northampton, Irons Antiques; Oley, Mrs. Lena Eyrich; Pittsburgh, Regis and Mary Ferson; Plymouth Meeting, Alexsandra's; Pottstown, Eye Of The Peacock, John and Susan Shuman; Reading, Jeremiah Beard; Schneckville, Joan and Bob Coad; Skippack, Peggy Regan; West Chester, Judy Knauer; Wexford, Wexford General Store; Williamsport, Mike's Antiques, Michael Rath; Yardley, Artiques, Ellie Archer; Zionsville, Charles Moore, Rinsland Americana Mail Auction.

Rhode Island: North Scituate, Woody's Antiques; Riverside, Suzanne Christie.

South Carolina: Greenville, H. Ray Davis. **Virginia**: Charlottesville, Rose Valley Antiques; Fairfax, Benjamin Rapaport. **Vermont**: Cavendish, Sigourney's Antiques.

West Virginia: Lewisburg, Vintage Furniture, Jerry Stevens. **Canada**: Montreal, Coach House Antiques.

PRICE LIST CREDITS

We wish to thank the following people who cooperated with us by sending us price lists and other useful information.

Arizona: Phoenix, Armellinos. **California**: Livermore, Charles May; Montclair, Albill. **Colorado**: Golden, The Foss Co.; Pueblo, Sheila Malouff, Colorado Estates, Inc. **Florida**: Ft. Lauderdale, Pat Regis. **Illinois**: Athens, Betty Tice; Evanston, Helen Reed; Chicago, The Bradford Exchange; Northbrook, Norman Rockwell Musuem; Rockford, Richard Irvin. **Indiana**: Kokomo, L. Winkleman; Michigan City, Pat Beale. **Iowa**: Ogden, Shirley Bakley. **Maryland**: Forest Hill, Teter. **Massachusetts**: North Adams, Marlow Antiques.

Michigan: Bay City, L. Butterfield; Burton, Plantation Galleries; Grosse Pointe, Charterhouse & Co.; Homer, N. Semora. **Minnesota**: Mabel, Kay Hyter. **Missouri**: Kansas City, Old World Antiques; Marshall, Brenda Roberts. **Mississippi**: Sebastopol, John Sharp. **New Jersey**: Teaneck, Judy Posner. **New York**: Guilderland, Veeder's Antiques; New York, Roscha; West Seneca, Sharon O'Reilly. **Ohio**: Canfield, Cricker Hill. **Pennsylvania**: Punxsutawney, Dennis Keck; Yardley, Artiques. **Virginia**: Richmond, Mrs. Edison C. Konkle, Jr. **Wisconsin**: Cedar Grove, Cedar Antiques.

PATTERN GLASS SURVEY CREDITS

We wish to thank the following dealers who participated in a survey of pattern glass dealers. We sincerely appreciate their fine cooperation.

Arizona: Phoenix, Crystal Cat Antiques. **California**: Calimesa, Don and Lois Bailey Antiques. **Connecticut**: Branford, C & R Antiques. **Delaware**: Harrington, Hill's Antiques. **Illinois**: Morton, P & L Vey's Antiques. **Indiana**: Chesterton, Salt Box Antiques. **Maryland**: Forest Hill, Teter. **Massachusetts**: Ayer, Dendara's Antiques; Buzzards Bay, The Old House; Northboro, Joseph P. Rice; Townsend Harbor, Peter Lukesch; Yarmouthport, Lil-Bud Antiques. **Michigan**: Redford, E & S Antiques; Saginaw, Bunny Shran. **Missouri**: St. Louis, Ken Dall Antiques.

New York: Crown Point, Dori Miles; Fairport, Franklin Badger; Millbrook, The Wicker's Antiques; Swormville, Dody Everett. **Ohio**: Cleveland Heights, Olin M. King; Strongsville, Mrs. Violette Schneider. **Pennsylvania**: Greencastle, Marcy's Antiques; Lancaster, The Ahlfelds; Lansdown, Harbach & Culver Antiques; Mt. Holly Springs, Fair Antiques; Pittsburgh, Joan Bierman's Antiques; Shippensburg, K & R Antiques; Wilke-Barre, Golden Webb Antiques. **Virginia**: Atlantic, Henry L. Derby. **Washington**: Marysville, Mike Anderton.

INDEX

Year After Year Collectors Ask:
"What does Warman's say?"

REMEMBER WHEN

. . . you traded bubble
gum cards

. . . sent away for a
radio premium

. . . bought your first
'Batman and Robin'
comic book.

All of these items and
thousands more are part
of the antiques market's
most thriving new field
—collectibles.

Warman's Americana & Collectibles documents under one cover the broad
aspects of this key antiques field. But it is more than a price guide:
- Collecting Hints for every category
- Histories
- References, periodicals and collectors clubs
- 27,000 items, 250 categories and 500 photographs

Available in leading book stores or use the convenient order form
in this book.

SEND ME THE FOLLOWING WARMAN PRICE GUIDES:

_____ **Warman's Antiques and Their Prices, 19th
edition,** $10.95 + $1.50 p/h (Total $12.45) $ _____

_____ **Warman's Americana & Collectibles, 1st edition,**
$12.95 + $1.50 p/h (Total $14.45) $ _____

_____ Add my name to your mailing list and notify
me of future editions.

☐ Check or money order enclosed. Sorry, No $ _____
charge or COD's. Pa. residents add 6% sales
tax per book.

NAME (Please print) _____

ADDRESS _____

CITY, STATE, ZIP _____

SEND TO: Warman Publishing Co., Dept. 19, P.O. Box 26742,
Elkins Park, PA 19117. Tele: (215) 657-1812.

SEND ME THE FOLLOWING WARMAN PRICE GUIDES:

_____ **Warman's Antiques and Their Prices, 19th
edition,** $10.95 + $1.50 p/h (Total $12.45) $ _____

_____ **Warman's Americana & Collectibles, 1st edition,**
$12.95 + $1.50 p/h (Total $14.45) $ _____

_____ Add my name to your mailing list and notify
me of future editions.

☐ Check or money order enclosed. Sorry, No $ _____
charge or COD's. Pa. residents add 6% sales
tax per book.

NAME (Please print) _____

ADDRESS _____

CITY, STATE, ZIP _____

SEND TO: Warman Publishing Co., Dept. 19, P.O. Box 26742,
Elkins Park, PA 19117. Tele: (215) 657-1812.

SEND ME THE FOLLOWING WARMAN PRICE GUIDES:

_____ **Warman's Antiques and Their Prices, 19th edition,** $10.95 + $1.50 p/h (Total $12.45) $ _____

_____ **Warman's Americana & Collectibles, 1st edition,** $12.95 + $1.50 p/h (Total $14.45) $ _____

_____ Add my name to your mailing list and notify me of future editions.

☐ Check or money order enclosed. Sorry, No $ _____
charge or COD's. Pa. residents add 6% sales tax per book.

NAME (Please print) _____

ADDRESS _____

CITY, STATE, ZIP _____

SEND TO: Warman Publishing Co., Dept. 19, P.O. Box 26742, Elkins Park, PA 19117. Tele: (215) 657-1812.

SEND ME THE FOLLOWING WARMAN PRICE GUIDES:

_____ **Warman's Antiques and Their Prices, 19th edition,** $10.95 + $1.50 p/h (Total $12.45) $ _____

_____ **Warman's Americana & Collectibles, 1st edition,** $12.95 + $1.50 p/h (Total $14.45) $ _____

_____ Add my name to your mailing list and notify me of future editions.

☐ Check or money order enclosed. Sorry, No $ _____
charge or COD's. Pa. residents add 6% sales tax per book.

NAME (Please print) _____

ADDRESS _____

CITY, STATE, ZIP _____

SEND TO: Warman Publishing Co., Dept. 19, P.O. Box 26742, Elkins Park, PA 19117. Tele: (215) 657-1812.